Psychiatric Dictionary

Psychiatric Dictionary

FOURTH EDITION

LELAND E. HINSIE, M.D.

and

ROBERT JEAN CAMPBELL, M.D.

Psychiatric Dictionary, fourth edition, is a continuing version
of the Dictionary by Leland E. Hinsie and Jacob Shatzky,
first published in 1940.

New York

OXFORD UNIVERSITY PRESS

London   1970   Toronto

Preface to the Fourth Edition

The concern about mental health issues that gripped the nation in the 1960's forced new perspectives in psychiatry that were not confined to the theorist. Clinician and program planner, educator and student, administrator and researcher—all were affected by an infusion of concepts and models derived from other branches of medicine and other fields of knowledge. Each of these often carried its own vocabulary, syntax, and grammar as it entered the arena of mental health, which is no longer the exclusive domain of psychiatry. Each of them, too, has tended to question the relevance and practicality of some of psychiatry's traditions and customs, and has thus engendered a reappraisal of theories which by age, rather than merit, had been transmuted into doctrine and dogma. The multidisciplinary approach, an important instance of which is the increasing collaboration between psychiatry and the social sciences, has underscored the futility of a 'nothing but' philosophy or a single-model approach to the understanding of human behavior. As a result, there has developed a general awareness that mental and emotional disorder reflects not only the biological and psychological organization of the patient himself, but is equally a reflection of processes in the society in which he lives. It is hoped by many that general system theory may provide the needed linkages between fields that ideally will supplement and enrich each other in their attempts to define the humanness of man. It must be admitted, however, that so far those linkages have been few, and it has not always been easy to distinguish between neologistic restatement and bona fide advancement of knowledge.

That advances have been made and that perspectives have shifted are undeniable. There have been enough advances to defy any simple grouping, but a listing of some of them may suffice to indicate the breadth and diversity of their range: the breaking of the genetic code and the understanding of many genetic and chromosomal abnormalities; new knowledge of protein chemistry and of enzyme action and immunity; ecology, community and social psychiatry, and transcultural psychiatry; development of a new nomenclature of mental disorder to conform to the International Classification of Diseases; the neurophysiology of sleep, dreaming, learning, and memory; differentiation of various types of mental retardation; rehabilitation and social therapy; primary prevention of mental disorder; drug dependency and drug abuse; developmental studies; crisis intervention, brief therapy, and behavior therapy; psychopharmacology, including tranquilizers, thymoleptics, and lithium (which is unique in that it may have a specific preventive effect on certain types of affective disorders).

It is hardly to be hoped that the manner in which these changes have been assimilated into the present edition of the *Psychiatric Dictionary* will fully satisfy the specialists who identify themselves with the various fields involved. Some of the fourteen hundred new listings have been defined extensively, while others have been defined in a single sentence or paragraph. The editor's decision to include, or exclude, any entry has been guided by several factors: clinical relevance, with the assumption that much detailed knowledge in any field is readily available in specialized texts; the frequency with which items recur in general texts and in psychiatric journals; and the degree to which a new concept or method appears to have received confirmation in subsequent investigations. Critical examination of the older definitions in the light of recent developments and advances has been responsible for the elimination of approximately five hundred entries, and for substantial modification or expansion of more than one thousand others.

The editor continues to be heavily indebted to Dr. Leland E. Hinsie for his encouragement and support, and for providing the foundation on which the present revision rests. I am also grateful to the authors and publishers who granted permission for quotation from their works, to Miss Kathleen Spengeman for her secretarial assistance, and to the staff of Oxford University Press for their co-operation.

New York
October 1969

R.J.C.

Preface to the First Edition

As the title of this Dictionary implies its material has been drawn mainly from the words and concepts current in the field of psychiatry— with definitions and illustrative quotations that aim to give these terms vital, clinical meaning. Though brevity was the ideal, in many instances, where needed, the articles are more or less encyclopedic in character.

The framework of the Dictionary is made up of psychiatric terms, but considerable attention has been devoted to terms in allied fields— clinical neurology, constitutional medicine, genetics and eugenics, mental deficiency, forensic psychiatry, social service, nursing and occupational therapy.

A liberal use of cross-references, including the familiar *q.v.* and *see also*, and double registration of compound expressions under the main idea and under the modifying part, should make the book more serviceable and search for desired information easier and more efficient. For instance, the impulse to buy is registered as *oniomania* and as *buy, impulse to;* excessive hunger is registered as *bulimia* and as *hunger, excessive.* Thus, a technical or scientific term which has escaped one's memory for the moment, may usually be found under its popular English equivalent: *automatic action* is listed as such and as *paraphonic state* and as *action, automatic.*

This Psychiatric Dictionary comprises all important terms and concepts used during the span of time approximately since Hippocrates up to our own days. The terms no longer in use are marked *obs.* (obsolete), while those which are losing currency have been designated as *obst.* (obsolescent). Accordingly, it is possible for the reader to gain an appreciation of the historical development of psychiatric nomenclature and to grasp more clearly the meaning of old and new scientific achievements in the field.

This volume contains approximately 7500 title-entries, including personal names most eminent in the field of psychiatric science. Each entry registers a phonetic transcription of its pronunciation (see p. ix for Key to Pronunciation used in the transliteration) and the philological derivation of the term.

Dr. Leland E. Hinsie is responsible for the definition of terms used in descriptive psychiatry, psycho-analysis, analytical psychology, psycho-biology, forensic psychiatry, mental deficiency, sexology, nursing and social work.

The philological part of the dictionary was done by Dr. Jacob Shatzky. The entire manuscript was prepared for the press by Mr. Judah A. Joffe, to whom the authors and their collaborators are sincerely grateful.

Miss Margaret Neubart did all the secretarial work connected with this volume, and has earned our deepest thanks for her efficiency and capability.

We wish to express our appreciation to the collaborators; to the many authors and publishers who permitted us to quote from their works; and last, but not least, we appreciate with deep gratification the close and cordial co-operation of the staff of the Oxford University Press.

September 1940   L.E.H.

                                                    J.S.

Key to Pronunciation

ā (bāke), ë (thēme), í (fíne), ō (slōpe), ū (tūbe)
a (back), e (them), i (fin), o (slop), u (tub)

å—shâre, fâir, beâr
ä—fär, fäther
à—àsk, brànch, bàth
aw—saw, caught, thought
ē—(plantar, her, first, motor, purpose;
voyeur; folie de persecution)
ô—(ôften, lông, dôg, sôft)
oi—(toil, boy, void)
ōō—sōōn, move (mōōv), rule (rōōl)
oo—foot, bush (boosh), wood, would
(wood), wool
ou—out, now, bough
b—as in back, bell, cupboard, raspberry
ch—as in church, itch, question (kwes'-
chun), nature, virtuous
d—as in do, bidden
f—as in for, effort, phonetic, cough
g—as in go, league, ghastly
gz—as in examine, example
h—as in how, h (a) emophilia, cajal
hw—as in what, nowhere
j—as in just, judge (juj), gist, gestation
k—as in cake (kāk), tick, eunuch, choir
(kwīr)
K—as in Loch Lomond, Bach (bäK)
ks—as in complex, experimental
kw—as in equal, quite, choir (kwīr)
l—as in let, lost, doll, Lloyd
m—as in made, more, immediate,
trimmed, dumb, tomb, solemn
n—as in no, never, innumerable, sinned
(sind), benign (bē-nīn'), knee

ñ—as in cañon
N—as in F. bon (bôN)
ng—as in sing-song, tongue, language
(lang'gwij), slink (slingk), finger
(fing'-gēr), puncture (pungk'chēr)
p—as in put, place, spot, stop, stopped
(stopt)
r—as in red, root, berry, rheumatism,
logorrh (o) ea
s—as in say, paste, miss, cent, concept,
patience, scissors, sciatica, schizm,
psyche
sh—as in shall, fashion, rash, chagrin,
machine, brioche, crustacea, pernicious, physician, schist, conscience,
nausea, tension, sugar, remission,
tissue, intention, differential
t—as in tin, but, mitt, doubt, looked,
stripped, thyme, ptotic
th—as in thick, bath, health, litho-
TH—as in their, father, bathe
ü—as in F. menu (mē-nü'), G. Wüllner
v—as in vase, reverse, save, of (ov)
w—as in will, question (kwes'chun),
suave, choir (kwīr)
y—as in year, million, pinion
z—as in zygote, gauze, raise, Times,
positive, possess, scissors (siz'ērz),
xenophobia
zh—as in seizure, glazier, abrasion, division, measure, garage
'—as in chasm (kàz'm), principle (prin'sip'l)

Psychiatric Dictionary

A

a In Rorschach scoring, animal response, increasing percentage of which indicates lack of imagination.

A.A. Abbreviation for (1) *achievement age* (q.v.); (2) *Alcoholics Anonymous* (q.v.).

Aobj Rorschach scoring symbol for a response derived from or connected with the body of an animal; such a response is more commonly scored as *a* (q.v.).

Abadie's sign (à-bà-dez′) (Jean Marie (Charles) Abadie, French ophthalmologist, 1842-1932.) An early sign in tabes in which there is loss of deep pain from pressure on the testes or tendo Achillis.

abalienation (ab-ā-lyen-ā′shun) *Obs.* Loss or failing of the senses or mental faculties.

abasia (à-bā′z(h)ē-à) Inability to walk. See *astasis-abasia*.

abbess A derisive term for the madam of a brothel. Her male counterpart is called an abbot, while the prostitutes are termed nuns or Sisters of Charity.

abbot See *abbess*.

abderite (ab′de-rīt) *Obs.* Stupid person. Abdera was 'a town in Thrace, the birthplace of Democritus and several remarkable men; its inhabitants, however, had the character of being more stupid than other people.' (Tuke, D.H. *A Dictionary of Psychological Medicine*, vols. 1-2, Blakiston, Philadelphia, 1892)

A.B.E.P.P. Abbreviation for American Board of Examiners in Professional Psychology.

aberration, mental Any morbid deviation from normal mental activity; when used today the term ordinarily does not relate to deviations in intelligence.

abient See *avoidant*.

abilities, primary mental See *test, PMA*.

abiotrophy (ab-i-ot′-rō-fi) Premature loss of vitality of cells or tissues. The longevity of the heart, for instance, may be appreciably shorter than that of other organs of the body, leading to early disturbance in function which upsets homeostasis or organ-equilibrium. Lewis has shown that, in schizophrenia, the heart is hypoplastic and hence functionally inadequate. He believes that the shut-in type of personality, so often found in patients with schizophrenia, is a secondary result of cardiovascular inadequacy.

The concept of abiotrophy was used by Gowers as an explanation of possible dementia, viz., that precocious aging of the central nervous system was due to limited viability of the nerve cells concerned. Such an explanation, however, exaggerates the similarities and overlooks the very marked differences between the different members of the organic dementia group.

ablation Removal or interruption of function of a bodily part of organ, especially by surgical means.

ablutomania (ab-lū-tō-mā′nē-à) Morbid impulse to wash or bathe, or incessant preoccupation with thoughts of washing or bathing; seen often in obsessive-compulsive psychoneurosis.

abnormal psychology That division of psychology devoted to the study of mental disorders and psychopathology.

aboiement (à-bwà-mäN′) *Obsnt.* Involuntary production of abnormal sounds. It is often observed in schizophrenic patients who not infrequently, in advanced stages, make many animalistic sounds. See *Gilles de la Tourette syndrome*.

abortion, therapeutic Surgical interruption of pregnancy for medical reasons. There are no statutes in the United States which legalize abortion on the basis of serious hereditary disorders, although the procedure in such cases may legally be justified on the basis of unendurable mental strain. Colorado, New Mexico, Maryland, and the District of Columbia have more liberalized statutes than the other states and permit abortion when the mother's health is seriously jeopardized. In New York state, abortion is permitted only as a life-saving measure; within the field of psychiatry, then, the only legally valid indication is the danger of suicide. Current psychiatric opinion in regard to therapeutic abortion tends to the conservative side, since it is well known that a psychosis which develops during or after one pregnancy is not a constant concomitant of all later pregnancies. Further, interruption of pregnancy may be more traumatic to the patient than pregnancy and delivery because of guilt feelings which commonly follow abortion.

aboulia (à-bōo'lē-à) *Abulia* (q.v.).

above and below When Adler uses this term, he implies the unconscious notion existing in every psyche, male or female, of femaleness as a degradation and maleness as an ideal. In other words, there is the conception of man as *above* and woman as *below*, femininity being a position of inferiority to be avoided while masculinity is a goal of superiority to be striven for.

ABPN Abbreviation of American Board of Psychiatry and Neurology, Inc., established in 1934 as the official agency to examine and certify physicians as specialists *(diplomates)* in psychiatry, child psychiatry, neurology, and neurology with special competence in child neurology.

Abraham, Karl (1877-1925) First psychoanalyst in Germany; manic-depressive psychosis, pregenital stages, character types, symbolism.

Abram man (Possibly connected with Abraham's receiving the beggar Lazarus into his bosom, Luke XVI, 22.) 'Another name for Tom o'Bedlam, so called from the Abraham ward in Bedlam, which had for its inmates begging lunatics, who used to array themselves "with party-colored ribbons, tape in their hats, a foxtail hanging down, a long stick with streamers," and beg alms; but "for all their seeming madness, they had wit enough to steal as they went along."' (Tuke, D.H. *A Dictionary of Psychological Medicine*, vols. 1-2, Blakiston, Philadelphia, 1892) *Obs.* in the United States.

abreaction The process of bringing to consciousness and, thus, to adequate expression, of material which has been unconscious (usually because of repression). Abreaction refers to the two aspects of a 'complex'—the intellectual representation and the accompanying affect—and includes not only the recollection of forgotten memories and experiences but also their reliving with appropriate emotional display and discharge of affect. The method used to bring the repressed material into consciousness is called *catharsis* (q.v.); the term abreaction technically refers to the end-result.

The term 'abreaction of emotion' refers to the discharge of emotion in the course of psychotherapy. This process is usually facilitated by the patient's gaining awareness of the causal relationship between the previously undischarged emotion and his symptoms. When such a discharge of emotion occurs during psychotherapy, it is often possible for the patient to see the link between his current irrational behavior and his demands toward his therapist, as well as the forgotten earlier counterpart from which the emotional attitude originated. The patient is thereby enabled to modify his anachronistic, immature, incongruous, and unreal emotional demands in favor of more adequate and appropriate behavior.

abreaction, motor The living-out of an unconscious impulse through muscular or motor expression.

abscess, brain Abscess of the brain (purulent encephalitis, encephalopyosis) is an inflammatory condition due to the invasion of pyogenic micro-organisms resulting in a circumscribed collection of pus in any part of the brain. In DSM-II, associated psychoses are coded 292.x, associated non-psychotic syndromes are coded 309.0.

absence 1. Loss of consciousness in an hysterical attack. 2. Petit mal. See *epilepsy.*

absent-mindedness A tendency to be occupied with one's own thoughts to such degree that only inadequate attention is given to events which occur in external reality; consequently, memory may seem to be faulty, especially for routine and relatively insignificant happenings. Absentmindedness, then, is habitual inattention, but without the implication of severe pathology such as is associated with autism and withdrawal.

absent state The vacant, transfixed, dream-like state characteristic of the patient with a temporal lobe seizure. Also characteristic of such seizures are hallucinations of smell or taste (the 'uncinate' seizure; see *fit, uncinate*), a feeling of dream-like detachment, and the experience of *panoramic memory*, in which the patient may feel that he is rapidly re-enacting long periods of his life.

absorption Engrossment with one object or idea with inattention to others.

abstinence The act or practice of voluntarily refraining from the use of something or from some action.' (The Century Dictionary) One of the important parts of the definition is the voluntary nature of abstinence. The term is used extensively in psychoanalysis, particularly with a sexual connotation. According to psychoanalysis, abstinence may be voluntary or involuntary. More frequently it is involuntary, being influenced largely by repressed complexes, such as a deeply rooted sense of guilt. While the fear of actual dangers (infection, legal forces, pregnancy) may be an impelling reason for abstinence, it is more than likely that forces within the personality contribute largely to it.

The term abstinence is also used in a non-sexual sense in the case of alcoholism and addictions, to refer to refraining from the addicting drug.

Abstinence is used with a slightly different meaning in relation to psychoanalytic treatment. Freud, noting that the analytic method had originally been developed for the treatment of conversion hysteria, recognized that certain modifications were necessary in other clinical conditions. In anxiety hysteria and obsessional neurosis, particularly, he advocated that analysis be carried out in a state of abstinence. But abstinence in this sense did not mean merely sexual abstinence, nor did it mean that the patient was to be denied any and every satisfaction. Rather, abstinence rules were directed at substitutions for symptoms, and in order to keep alive the element of frustration necessary for optimal treatment response. The analyst was enjoined to oppose those activities, interests, pleasures, and habits of the patient that drained off anxiety which was better handled during treatment sessions.

abstinence syndrome Withdrawal syndrome. See *addiction*.

abstract attitude Categorical attitude. Goldstein has noted that one characteristic of the patient with an organic brain disorder is his relative inability to assume the abstract attitude or to shift readily from the abstract to the *concrete* (where thinking is determined by and cannot proceed beyond some immediate experience) or vice versa. The *abstract* attitude includes the following abilities: assuming a mental set voluntarily; shifting voluntarily from one aspect of a situation to another; keeping in mind simultaneously various aspects of a situation; grasping the essentials of a whole, and breaking a whole into its parts, and isolating these voluntarily; abstracting common properties; planning ahead ideationally; assuming an attitude to the merely possible; thinking or performing symbolically; and detaching the ego from the outer world.

abstraction 'The drawing out or isolation of a content (e.g. a meaning or general character, etc.) from a connection, containing other elements, whose combination as a totality is something unique or individual, and therefore inaccessible to comparison.' (Jung, C.G. *Psychological Types*, Harcourt, Brace, 1923.) Abstraction is an activity which belongs to psychological functions in general, and Jung differentiates between abstracting thinking, abstracting feeling, abstracting sensation, and abstracting intuition. 'Abstracting-thinking brings into relief a content that is distinguished from other irrelevant elements by its intellectual, logical qualities. Abstracting-feeling does the same with a content characterized by feeling; similarly with sensation and intuition.' (ibid.)

abstractionism, systematic See *dissociation, semantic*.

absurdity In psychonanalysis, anything that is contradictory or incoherent or meaningless in a train of thought or a constellation of ideas.

abulia (à-bū'li-à) Absence of will-power or wish-power; the term implies that the individual has a desire to do something but the desire is without power or energy. Abulia itself is rare and with few exceptions occurs only in the schizophrenias. The more frequent disturbance in the will is a reduction or impairment (hypobulia) rather than a complete absence. Bleuler included abulia and hypobulia among the fundamental symptoms of the schizophrenias.

Social abulia means inactivity, focal or diffuse, of an individual toward the environment, due to inability to settle on a plan of action. There may be a desire to contact the environment, but the desire has no power of action.

abulic-akinetic syndrome See *syndrome, akinetic-abulic.*

acalculia (à-kal-kū'lē-a) A type of *aphasia* (q.v.) characterized by inability to perform arithmetic operations, seen most commonly with parietal lobe (retrolandic) lesions. Various groups of acalculia are recognized: (1) dyscalculia of the spatial type in which disturbance of spatial organization of numbers predominates and is often associated with spatial dyslexia, spatial agnosia, sensori-kinetic apraxia, somato-spatial apractognosia, and directional and vestibular oculomotor disorders; (2) predominance of alexia or agraphia for numbers and figures and (3) anarithmia, in which disturbances in the performance of arithmetic operations predominate. The second and third groups are often associated with speech disturbances and alterations in the process of verbalization.

acanthesthesia (à-kan-thes-thē'zhē-à) A type of paresthesia in which the patient experiences a sensation of pinpricks.

acarophobia (à-kar-o-fō'bē-à) A morbid dread of mites. The meaning of the term has been extended to include a wide variety of small things, animate (e.g. worms) or inanimate (e.g. pins, needles). The fear may be associated with the idea that insects or worms are crawling beneath the skin, a thought not uncommon in patients suffering from alcoholism or drug addiction. It is perhaps also associated with Lilliputian ideas.

acatalepsia (à-kat-à-lep'sē-à) Impairment of the reasoning faculty; abnormal inability to comprehend.

acatalepsy (à-kat'à-lep-sē) *Obs.* Formerly used synonymously with *dementia.*

acatamathesia (à-kat-à-mà-thē'zhē-à, -zē-à) *Obs.* Inability to understand language. (*Dictionary of Philosophy and Psychology*, ed. by Baldwin, J.M., Macmillan, New York, 1928) This is the perceptive (sensory) aspect of aphasia. See also *speech disorders.*

acataphasia (ā-kat-à-fā'zē-à) A form of disordered speech in which 'the patients either do not find the expression appropriate to their thoughts, but only produce something with a similar sound ("displacement paralogia"), or they let their speech fall into quite another channel ("derailment paralogia"). A patient said he was "wholly without head on the date" for "he did not know the date"; another complained he "lived under protected police" instead of "under the protection of police."' (Kraepelin, E. *Dementia Praecox and Paraphrenia*, tr. by Barclay, R.M., Livingstone, Edinburgh, 1919) See also *speech disorders.*

acathexis (à-kà-thek'sis) Lack of emotional charge or psychic energy with which an object would ordinarily be invested. Certain things, objective or subjective, hold no feelings or emotions for an individual; they are not infused with emotions; they are not charged or cathected. This idea has received special consideration in the field of psychoanalysis, with reference to the attachment of affects to ideas or thoughts. Some patients have an unusual capacity for separating affect from an idea that is highly significant to them. The affect may be transferred to an indifferent or inconsequential idea or it may attach itself to some unconscious material. Thus, one may express an idea or a series of ideas that seem to have no meaning or feeling for him. At times an entire complex may be utterly devoid of affect when it comes into consciousness.

acathisia (à-kath-i'zi-à) Also termed acathisia paraesthetica, acathisia psychasthenica, acathisia spastica. Inability to sit

down because of the intense anxiety provoked by the thought of doing so. In
acathisia spastica, the thought or act of
sitting provokes hysterical convulsions.

Haase first applied the term (in 1955)
to the inability to sit still and to other
irritative, hyperkinetic symptoms that
are sometimes seen as a complication of
phenothiazine or reserpine therapy.
See *akatizia*.

acceleration, developmental Precocious
growth in any area—motor, perceptual,
language, or social. An uneven growth
pattern is often found in schizophrenia,
with unusual sequences of retardation
and acceleration especially in postural
development. This has been interpreted
by some as a disorder of timing and integration of neurological maturation
(Fish, B. Archives of Neurology 2, 115-
121, 1960).

accessibility Receptivity to external
influences. Inaccessibility is characteristic of *withdrawal*.

accessory Additional, contributory, or secondary as opposed to fundamental or
primary. In psychiatry, the term is chiefly
used in reference to the symptomatology
of the schizophrenias, whose symptoms
were divided by Bleuler into (1) fundamental or primary symptoms and (2)
accessory or secondary symptoms.

accidental In psychoanalysis, accidental
refers to that which is adventitious or of
external origin, in contradistinction to
that which is endowed or of inherent
origin. Accidental experiences are of two
kinds: dispositional, when they occur
early in life and strongly influence character development; and definitive, when
they occur later and act as precipitating
or provocative agents.

accident, cerebrovascular Apoplexy;
stroke. Cerebrovascular accidents include
those conditions in which gross cerebral
damage, hemorrhage, or softening follow
a group of acute vascular disorders—cerebral thrombosis (82%), cerebral hemorrhage (15%), and cerebral embolism
(3%). In DSM-II, associated psychoses
are coded 293.x, non-psychotic syndromes
309.3.

Cerebral thrombosis is commonly a
manifestation of cerebral arteriosclerosis
and occurs in that age group, although
children with an acute infectious disease
and young syphilitic adults may also develop cerebral thrombosis.

Often the patient awakens in the morning completely paralyzed on one side of
the body, monoplegic or aphasic. Not infrequently, however, thrombosis occurs in
the daytime, especially when the patient
is inactive, but also during exertion. Most
cases recover with gradual recession of
the pathologic change.

Cerebral hemorrhage may occur suddenly, without warning, as a true 'stroke.'
It occurs most commonly as a result of
arteriosclerosis or hypertension, in the
middle and older age groups.

Children and young adults with congenital abnormalities of the cerebral vas-
culature, such as aneurysms, may likewise
be afflicted. Since hypertension of the
essential type is so frequently familial,
death from cerebral hemorrhage correspondingly runs in families. The exciting
causes are such acts as straining at stool,
coughing, retching, coitus, violent emotion, or heavy eating, all of which elevate
the blood pressure. Thus, hemorrhage
frequently occurs in the daytime during
periods of activity, although many cases
occur at night during periods of insomnia.
Unconsciousness occurs suddenly and the
patient topples over or falls to the ground.
Coma may gradually deepen and the
patient die in a few hours. Far more
common is a coma of several days' duration during which the patient may rouse
a little and then lapse back into deep
coma. Some patients gradually recover
consciousness and survive the attack.

Cerebral embolism creates the same
clinical picture as cerebral thrombosis;
but emboli are usually multiple and the
syndrome may be more bizarre. The commonest causes of emboli are: (1) diseases
of the heart—as with auricular fibrillation and coronary occlusion with mural
thrombi, which may break off and become
embolic to the brain; or as in bacterial
endocarditis, with valvular vegetations,
which may become dislodged and flow
to the brain; (2) pulmonary diseases,
with septic emboli lodging in a cerebral
vessel, damaging the wall of the vessel,
causing one or more brain abscesses and
sometimes meningitis. Cerebral embolism
comes on suddenly, without warning, and

severe general symptoms appear as in hemorrhages. There may be convulsions and coma. Death may occur in a few hours when the embolus has lodged in vital areas. The embolism may produce only softening, but most frequently hemorrhage also. It is the most frequent cause of sudden hemiplegia in childhood.

accident, intentional Huddleson stresses the consideration that accidents may be psychologically determined. 'If an outraged employee with no other means of retaliation is so preoccupied, worried, or angry that he "accidentally" thrusts his hand between gears and thus gains many weeks of compensation and care in lieu of employment and chagrin following the threat of imminent discharge, sociologic sympathy with his predicament ought not to obscure a psychologic estimate of his injury as virtually self-inflicted.' (Huddleson, J.H. *Accidents, N, uroses and Compensation,* Williams & Wilkins, Baltimore, 1932)

accident-proneness See *proneness, accident.*

accident, purposeful See *proneness, accident.*

accommodation Adjustment, especially of the eye for various distances. Absolute accommodation is the accommodation of either eye separately; binocular accommodation is like accommodation in both eyes in co-ordination with convergence (the accommodation reflex). Accommodation occurs on shift of far to near vision, which is followed by thickening of the lens, convergence of the eyes, and constriction of the pupils. The most widely accepted theory of the mechanism of accommodation is that of Helmholtz: contraction of the ciliary muscle reduces the tension of the zonular muscle, thus permitting the elastic capsule of the lens to shape the lens and to increase its convexity. Convergence is produced by the action of both internal rectus muscles (innervated by N. III); pupillary constriction is produced by the action of the sphincter muscle of the iris (innervated by the short ciliary nerves, the parasympathetic outflow from the Edinger-Westphal nucleus to the ciliary ganglion).
2. Nerve accommodation is the rise in

threshold during the passage of a constant, direct electric current because of which only the make and break of the current stimulates the nerve.
3. Social accommodation refers to the functional changes in habits and customs occurring in persons and groups in response to other persons and groups and in response to the common environment. Such accommodation is typically made for the sake of social harmony. The concept of accommodation is used in analyzing attitudes in situations of superordination and subordination, as those of slavery, caste, class, status, and leadership. The social heritage, culture, and social organization are accommodations which are transmitted from generation to generation.

accretion (à-krē'shun) Growth by simple addition of parts or coherence of elements. Used particularly in learning psychology to refer to the learning of responses through frequency of association rather than through any inherent relatedness.

acculturation Originally, a term of social anthropology: the transfer of one ethnical group's culture to another. By extension, the implanting in children of the customs, beliefs, and ideals held to be important by adults of the culture group: a process of cultural indoctrination of children, much of which is carried out by educators without a formal plan, as an unconscious attempt at disseminating their own beliefs.

accumulation See *soteria.*

accuracy compulsion A term used in Rorschach interpretation to refer to the tendency of the subject to be overly accurate in his responses to the cards; he makes many corrections and indicates dissatisfaction with his responses, but is unable to improve them.

acedia (à-sē'dē-à) *Obs.* A syndrome characterized by carelessness, listlessness, apathy, and melancholia.

acenesthesia (à-sen-es-thē'zhē-à) Absence of the feeling of physical existence, a common symptom in many psychiatric states.

acerophobia (à-sēr-ō-fō'bē-à) Fear of sourness.

acetylcholine (à-sēt-il-kol'ēn) A reversible acetic acid ester of choline, $CH_3 \cdot CO \cdot O \cdot CH_2 \cdot N(CH_3)_3 \cdot OH$. It is generally believed that acetylcholine, which is normally present in many parts of the body, is the sole mediator at autonomic synapses and in the transmission of the nerve impulse from motor nerve to skeletal muscle. It has been suggested that acetylcholine is also the sole mediator for central synaptic transmission, although there is no direct evidence for this. More recent work suggests that other substances (viz. serotonin and norepinephrine) are more likely the central synaptic neurohumors. For the theory of mechanism of action of acetylcholine in nerve impulse transmission, see *process, elementary.*

achievement age (A.A.) The term denotes the relationship between the chronological age and the age of achievement as established by standard achievement tests. The latter comprise a series of educational tests as distinguished from intelligence tests. Achievement age is synonymous with educational age and one speaks of educational or achievement quotient. When the latter is divided by the mental age (I.Q.) the result is expressed as accomplishment quotient (A.Q.).

Achilles reflex Ankle jerk. Tapping the tendo Achillis results in plantar flexion at the ankle due to contraction of the soleus and gastrocnemius muscles; the tibial nerve is both afferent and efferent for this reflex, and its center is S_{1-2}.

achluophobia (à-klū-ō-fō'bē-à) Fear of darkness.

achromatic color response A Rorschach scoring term for a response of black, gray, white, or mention of lack of color; also designated C'. See *ShR.*

achromatic response A Rorschach scoring term for a response of texture or of anything which is described as achromatic.

achromatopsia (à-krō-mà-top'sē-à) Total color blindness.

acme In psychoanalysis the term means the highest point of pleasure in sexual intercourse.

acmesthesia (ak-mes-thē'zhē-à) Perception of sharp points by touch rather than by pain; acuesthesia.

acoasm *Akoasm* (q.v.).

acolasia (à-ko-lā'zē-à) *Obs.* Morbid intemperance or lust.

aconuresis (à-kon-ū-rē'sis) See *enuresis.*

acoria (à-kō-'rē-à) 'With Hippocrates it meant moderation in eating; but in Aretaeus it is used in regard to drink in the sense of insatiable desire. Bulimia.' (Tuke, D.H. *A Dictionary of Psychological Medicine,* vols. 1-2, Blakiston, Philadelphia, 1892)

acousma (à-kōōz'mà) See *akoasm.*

acousticophobia (à-kōōs-ti-kō-fō'bē-à) Fear of sounds.

acquisitiveness *Hoarding* (q.v.).

acrai (ä'krī) *Obs.* An Arabian term, synonymous with nymphomania and satyriasis.

acrasia, acrasy (à-krā'zē-à, ak'rà-sē) Morbid intemperance in anything; at one time it was synonymous with *acratia,* debility, impotence, inefficiency.

acro- (ak'rō) Combining form meaning pertaining to *extremity* or *tip,* from Gr. *ákros,* highest, topmost.

acrocinesia, acrocinesis (-si-nē'sē-à, -nē'sis) Excessive movements, as those, for example, observed in the manic phase of manic-depressive psychosis.

acrocyanosis (-sī-à-nō'sis) Blueness of the extremities, extending usually to the wrists and ankles; in psychiatric patients, it is seen most frequently among schizophrenics, perhaps because in persons with an asthenic habitus the venous bed typically preponderates over the arterial.

acrodynia (-din'ē-à) Vegetative neurosis; trophodermatoneurosis; pink disease;

erythroedema polyneuritis. A disorder of the vegetative nervous system occurring in children between the ages of 4 months and 7 years and consisting of myelin degeneration in the peripheral nerves and chromatolysis of the anterior horn cells. The disease is most common in Australia and North America and occurs typically between the fall and early spring. Some believe the disorder is infective in origin, others regard it as a deficiency disease. Symptoms include irritability, photophobia, excessive sweating, an irritating and erythematous rash with slight swelling on the hands and feet, and symptoms of polyneuritis. The disease usually lasts for 3 to 12 months. Treatment is symptomatic.

acroesthesia (-es-thē′zhē-à) Increased sensivity to pain in the extremities.

acrohypothermy (-hī′pō-thēr-mē) Abnormal coldness of the extremities, seen often in patients with schizophrenia, in whom it is commonly associated with *acrocyanosis* (q.v.).

acromania (-mā′nē-à) *Obs.* Chronic incurable insanity.

acromegaly, acromegalia (-meg′à-li, -mē-gā′lē-à) Hyperpituitarism produced usually by an acidophilic adenoma of the anterior lobe (epithelial portion) of the hypophysis; acromegaly is sometimes seen in individuals with no adenoma whose hypophysis shows an increase in number of eosinophilic cells in an otherwise normal gland. The disorder was first clearly defined by Pierre Marie in 1886 and hence is sometimes called 'Marie's disease.' Acromegaly occurs in adults after the epiphysial lines have closed; acidophilic adenomas arising prior to closure of the epiphysial lines in adolescence produce gigantism. Acromegaly consists of a localized increase in size of various structures (head, hands, feet, lips, jaw) resulting in a peculiar bodily configuration seen in no other disorder. Associated with this is profuse, offensive perspiration; bitemporal or frontal headache, excessive growth of hair, impotence, sterility, increase in basal metabolic rate, and glycosuria are also seen frequently. Bitemporal hemianopia develops with progression of the disorder.

Schizophrenic and manic-depressive psychoses are said to be rare in acromegaly, although it is quite regularly accompanied by striking alterations of personality: impulsiveness (*c.* 90% of cases), moodiness and mood swings (60%), anger outbursts (50%), and often periodic or constant somnolence. In DSM-II, associated psychoses are coded 294.0, non-psychotic syndromes 309.5.

acromicria (-mik′rē-à) Term used in constitutional medicine, especially by Kretschmer, and Pende, for the physical condition characterized by selective smallness and shortness of one or more extremities.

Benda proposed the term 'congenital acromicria' to replace *mongolism* (q.v.) and to indicate his view that mongolism is a form of pituitary hypofunction which to some extent is the opposite of acromegaly.

acroparesthesia (-pàr-es-thē′zē-a) Numbness, tingling, and/or other abnormal sensations of the extremities; seen frequently in organic disorders, especially peripheral nerve lesions, but by some the term is used only to refer to such unpleasant sensations occurring without demonstrable organic basis. Still less commonly, the term refers to an extreme degree of paresthesia.

acrophobia Fear of high places.

ACT Atropine coma therapy. See *therapy, atropine coma.*

act, completion of See *ending, act.*

act ending See *ending, act.*

act-habit Any personality trait, habitual mode of response, etc., that is an outgrowth of cultural-environmental attitudes, such as 'minimal attention' or 'scientific' rearing, or 'oversolicitiousness,' 'over-warmth,' or 'over-protectiveness.'

act, purposeless See *act, symptomatic.*

act, reflex While discussing *The Psychology of the Dream Processes,* Freud emphasizes that 'all our psychic activities proceed from (inner or outer) stimuli and terminate in innervations.' There is a sensory and a motor end to the psychic apparatus. See *system.* He adds that 'the psychic apparatus must be constructed like a reflex apparatus. The reflex act remains the type of every psychic activity as well.' (Freud, S. *The Interpretation of Dreams*, 3rd ed., tr. by Brill, A.A., Macmillan, New York, 1933)

act, symptomatic A symptomatic act, like a symbol, is representative of some unconscious component. According to Freud, symptomatic acts must fulfill three conditions: (1) they must fall within normal limits, that is, they must not be morbid acts; (2) they must be temporary manifestations, subject to easy correction; and (3) if unrecognized by the individual committing them, when his attention is called to them, he should not understand the motivation, but ascribe to it inattention or accident.

Symptomatic acts constitute some of the peculiarities of everyday life. They are expressed as mannerisms, slips of the tongue *(lapsus linguae)* or of memory *(lapsus memoriae)* or of the pen *(lapsus calami)*, misprints, fake visual recognition, mislaying of objects, etc.

act, unintentional See *act, symptomatic*.

ACTH Adrenocorticotropic hormone; one of the anterior pituitary hormones. See *syndrome, general adaptation*.

acting in A type of *acting out* (q.v.) that occurs during the therapy session; the patient discharges drive tension through action rather than through words.

acting out, neurotic The partial discharge of drive tension that is achieved by responding to the present situation as if it were the situation that originally gave rise to the drive demand. Acting out is a displacement of behavioral response from one situation to another; not every displacement, however, results in acting out. As so defined, acting out includes the phenomenon of transference. The term transference is employed if the attitude or behavior is in response to certain definite persons; the mechanism is called acting out if something has to be done indiscriminately. Acting out is more than a mere feeling or thought, a mere mimic expression, or a mere single movement— it is a real acting. 'It is an acting which unconsciously relieves inner tension and brings a partial discharge to warded-off impulses (no matter whether these impulses express directly instinctual demands, or are reactions to original instinctual demands, e.g. guilt feelings); the present situation, somehow associatively connected with the repressed content, is used as an occasion for the discharge of repressed energies; the cathexis is displaced from the repressed memories to the present "derivative," and this displacement makes the discharge possible.' (Fenichel. 'Neurotic Acting Out,' *Psychoanalytic Review 32*, 197, 1945) Fenichel says further: 'It is true that there are also symptoms which involve a certain acting; but these symptoms could also be called "acting out." In general, compulsive acts, e.g., are not included in the conception of "acting out," because they are limited in their extent, and because they are experienced as strange and not as ego-syntonic. If certain rituals are rationalized to such an extent that the subject identifies himself with them, they certainly can be included in the conception of "acting out."'

In psychoanalysis, the patient may act out memories, instead of recalling them. An unmarried female patient, for example, imagined herself pregnant from a much older man during the course of her analysis. It later became apparent that the patient was acting out her infantile incestuous desires for her father, desires which, in the beginning, she was unable to verbalize under analysis.

But acting out does not occur only in psychoanalysis. The character structure of a person, for example, is a chronic and habitual pattern of reaction which develops as the result of conflict between instinctual demands and the frustrating outer world. Although such a behavior pattern originates in the family situation, he preserves this pattern throughout his life as his typical method of reacting to any frustration. This displacement also constitutes acting out.

action, automatic In discussing *suggested action*, P. Janet writes: 'these characteristics of the performance of suggested actions have often received specific names. Delboeuf proposed to speak of the state in which they were performed as a "paraphonic state." I myself have generally used the expression "automatic" actions or beliefs. These tendencies, these dispositions to the performance of an aggregate of co-ordinated movements, may remain in "latent condition," or may be "activated" more or less completely by passing through the stages of "erection," "desire," and "effort," in order to reach at length the stage of "completed action," or the stage of "triumph."' (Janet, P. *Psychological Healing*, vols. 1-2, tr. by Paul, E. and C., Macmillan, New York, 1925)

action, chance See *chance-action*.

action current Action potential; the regular sequence of small electrical deflections accompanying physiological activity of muscle or nerve. Such changes in electrical potential are commonly measured nowadays by the cathode ray oscillograph.

action, deferred This expression carries special meaning in psychoanalysis. Thus, when discussing the primal scene (in the case of the Wolf-man), Freud says that the patient observed his parents in the act of sexual intercourse, when the patient was 1½ years old. The impressions, however, were not understood by the child at the time; at a later period, though, certain experiences occurred that caused revival of the primal experience and gave significance to it. There was deferred action. Freud believes that *deferred action* often takes place with regard to castration threats.

action, faulty See *act, symptomatic*.

Action for Mental Health See *Joint Commission on Mental Illness and Health*.

action, ludic See *activity, ludic*.

action pattern See *instinct*.

action potential Action *current* (q.v.).

action potential, specific See *instinct*.

action, psychomotor Action resulting directly from an idea or perception.

action research See *research, action*.

action, social 'The term "social action" in its broadest sense implies any concerted movement by organized groups toward the achievement of desired objectives. It is thus opposed to or contrasted with

individual action.' (Fitch, J.A., in *Social Work Year Book 1939*, edited by Kurtz, R.H., Russell Sage Foundation, New York)

action, subconscious See *activity, ludic*.

action, symbolic Purposeless or symptomatic act. See *act, symptomatic*.

activated sleep See *dream*.

activating RNA See *chromosome*.

activation Stimulation of one organ-system by another; the term stimulation is generally reserved for external influences only.

active In psychoanalysis, often used to describe the goal of a sexual impulse, with *active* referring to masculine qualities, and *passive* referring to effeminacy. The term is also used to describe the analyst, who is *active* when he endeavors to influence the patient to produce material for analysis.

The term, *active technique*, can refer to anything that is not the classical 'expectant' technique (i.e. maintaining neutrality throughout the analysis without recourse at any time to suggestion, recommendations, prohibitions, etc.). But at the same time it is obvious that complete neutrality is probably impossible in the analytic situation, for there are few interpretations that do not imply and suggest to the patient that further material lies behind the associations he has given. For all practical purposes, active technique is used to describe more extensive interference on the part of the analyst than is usual in orthodox or classical technique; and such active techniques are particularly associated with the name of Ferenczi. Among the maneuvers utilized in active forms of therapy are positive injunctions or prohibitions, usually aimed at habits, phobias, obsessions, psychosexual habits, etc. (See *abstinence*.) A major objection to the use of active techniques is that they encourage re-enactment rather than memory-work in analytic sessions, and this in turn encourages 'anchoring' to a present-day situation. 'We must admit frankly that active therapy is different in principle from the customary therapy. It is simply analytically guided interference. In playing the part of the super-ego by issuing positive injunctions and negative prohibitions we are behaving in the same way as the non-analytical therapeutist who pins his faith on exhortation, persuasion, guidance or therapeutic pedagogy. The question to which we *must* sooner or later find an unequivocal answer is whether the results of expectant analysis are so unsatisfactory in certain cases as to justify non-analytical empirical approaches. This is a question that cannot be settled until analysts are ready to subject their immediate results and after-histories to accurate statistical investigation, a readiness which will depend in turn on the degree of frankness with which they are prepared to confess their failures.' (Glover, E. *The Technique of Psycho-Analysis*, International Universities Press, New York, 1955)

activities, graded In occupational therapy, those occupations and handicrafts which have been classified according to the degree of mental and physical effort 'required for accomplishment. By means of this classification it is possible to increase the complexity of the work as the capacity of the patient increases.

activity In occupational therapy, any occupation or interest wherein participation requires exertion of energy. See also *passivity.*

activity, concealed antisocial The antisocial nature of certain types of behavior is sometimes concealed by the fact of its arising out of socially approved motivation. Kardiner refers to this as *concealed antisocial activity.* For example, he writes: 'competitiveness must be regarded in our society as a normal manifestation of self-assertion, when it is governed by the super-ego system. But there are neurotic and criminal forms of self-assertion. A neurotic self-assertion is an attempt to deny by force a deep feeling of inferiority or insecurity. There are some types of self-assertion that are injurious in intent, but that escape being criminal by a technicality. A good trader may misrepresent by omission, but not by commission. If he misrepresents by omitting damaging details, he is merely a sharp trader and is both condemned and applauded; if he deliberately misrepresents, he is lying and

is therefore only condemned. It is by this route that much concealed antisocial activity passes for normal.' (Kardiner, A. *The Psychological Frontiers of Society*, Columbia University Press, New York, 1945)

activity, group In occupational therapy an activity in which several patients participate. Its chief value is its socializing effect upon the mentally ill patients who are asocial.

activity, immobilizing Slavson suggests this term in relation to activity group psychotherapy as a form of *libido-binding* activities. By this he means activities that tie one down to a specific interest or occupation: to attain this he has devised a special environment for group psychotherapy, which is in contrast to *stimulating* or libido-activating activities. (Slavson, S.R. *An Introduction to Group Therapy*, The Commonwealth Fund, Oxford University Press, New York, 1943) See *psychotherapy, group.*

activity, libido-binding See *activity, immobilizing.*

activity, ludic Automatic action is as a rule insufficient, in that it 'cannot produce the appropriate outward effects, since there is a more or less complete suppression of those perfectionments of the action which would render it psychologically real. This is the stage of "quasi-action" (Baldwin), or of "ludic action." If the insufficiency relates especially to the outward characteristics of the action, to its objective consequences, we have to do with "play" properly so called. If, on the other hand, the insufficiency relates especially to the subjective modifications of the individual, to the adaptations of his own personality to the action, then we have to do with "automatic action." When the alterations of individual sentiment are pushed to an extreme, and when automatic actions are performed by one who does not remember what he has done and is unaware of what he is doing at the time, we term such actions "subconscious actions."' (Janet, P. *Psychological Healing*, vols. 1-2, tr. by Paul, E. and C., Macmillan, New York, 1925)

It has been established that higher animals have a quantity of energy left after performing all the movements required by their physiological life-processes. This excess energy must be expended (without purpose) in some way, most usually in play-activity, called *ludic activity.*

activity quotient The ratio of the total number of verbs in a subject's speech or writing to the total number of adjectives; the activity quotient is said to be a measure of the subject's emotionality.

activity, socializing In therapy groups, this term denotes the activity that brings an individual into interaction with other members of the group.

activity, stimulating The opposite of immobilizing activity. See *activity, immobilizing.*

actograph An apparatus designed to record the movements of the sleeper, usually by means of connection with the spring mattress.

actual neurosis See *neurosis, actual.*

actual self See *self.*

acuesthesia (à-kū-es-thē′zhē-à) See *acmesthesia.*

aculalia (à-kū-lā′lē-à) Nonsensical or jargon speech, such as is seen with Wernicke's type of aphasia associated with lesions of the left angular gyrus (and usually also the base of the first and second temporal convolutions) in right-handed persons. The affected subject shows marked intellectual impairment, an inability to comprehend spoken or written language, and although the patient can speak he is likely to talk nonsense. This corresponds to Head's 'syntactical aphasia.'

acusia (-àkū′z[h]ē-à) Combining form meaning hearing.

acute affective reflex Kretschmer's term for the earliest indications of emotional discharge (usually, tremors) in response to great stress.

acute brain disorders In DSM-I, various psychiatric syndromes due to temporary, reversible, diffuse impairment of brain tissue function. These disorders are part of the group formerly designated 'organic psychoses'; the term acute, as used in the revised nomenclature, refers primarily to the reversibility of the process, and an acute brain disorder is one from which the patient will ordinarily recover. See *brain disorder; symptomatic; syndrome, organic.*

acute confusional state See *confusional state, acute.*

adaptability, cultural This term, according to Freud, indicates man's personal capacity to transform the egoistic impulses into social drives.

adaptability, heterogeneous See *adaptability, homogeneous.*

adaptability, homogeneous The capacity to adapt that is uniformly possessed by all members of the species, such as the adaptation to intensity of light entering the eye by means of the pupillary reflex. Homogeneous adaptability is differentiated from heterogeneous adaptability, which refers to genetic variability within the species or within a population (i.e. differences between individuals) in the capacity to adapt.

adaptation Fitting or conforming to the environment, usually with the implication that advantageous change has taken place. Adaptation is typically achieved through a combination of alloplastic maneuvers (which involve alteration of the external environment) and autoplastic maneuvers (which involve a change in the self). The end result of successful adaptation is *adjustment;* unsuccessful attempts at adaptation are termed *maladjustment.*

In occupational therapy this term means modification or alteration of an occupation to suit the specific need or disability of a patient.

In neurophysiology, adaptation refers to the diminished rate of discharge shown by an end-organ subjected over a period of time to a constant stimulus. Adaptation in this sense is comparable to the term tolerance when the latter is used in reference to a drug.

adaptation, alloplastic See *psychodynamics, adaptational.*

adaptation, autoplastic See *psychodynamics, adaptational.*

adaptation, ontogenetic See *psychodynamics, adaptational.*

adaptation syndrome See *syndrome, general adaptation.*

adaptedness The state which results from appropriate adjustments to conditions, as distinguished from adaptation, which strictly speaking refers only to the process whereby the adjustments are brought about. In common usage, the term adaptation has both meanings.

adaptiveness, social 'From the point of view of mental deficiency, the most important group is that concerned with social adaptation, and in view of the ambiguity and various meanings attached to the term "intelligence," it might perhaps be advisable to apply the term "common sense" to the quality which is characteristic of this group. In any case, whether we call it social adaptiveness, social intelligence, common sense, *nous,* or the more popular "gumption," the ability is clearly a composite one and made up of many different processes, such as comprehension, discrimination, reasoning, prevision and planning.' (Tredgold, A.F. *A Text-Book of Mental Deficiency,* 6th ed., Wood, Baltimore, 1937)

He further writes: 'It is seen . . . that the psychological basis of mental deficiency consists essentially in the imperfect, and often irregular, development of that group of intellectual factors of mind which combine to form what we may designate *social adaptiveness.*' (ibid.)

addephagia Variant of *adephagia.* (q.v.). See also *bulimia.*

addict, object A term used to describe the behavior of certain schizophrenic patients who, to prove that they maintain some contact with the objective world, seek out and cling to objects and ideas and on the basis of this develop obsessions, monomania, elaborate inventions, etc.

addiction Strong dependence, both physiologic and emotional, upon alcohol or some other drug. True addiction is characterized by the appearance of an *abstinence syndrome* of organic origin

when the drug is withdrawn. It appears that in the addicted person the presence in the body of the addicting drug becomes necessary to maintain normal cellular functions, and when the drug is withdrawn, distortion of physiological processes ensues and abstinence symptoms are provoked. An addict, in other words, is a person who, whatever the apparent reason, has become physically and emotionally dependent upon a drug, substance or compound, so that he must maintain a certain level of intake of that substance. Often, in addition, the craving for the substance has a compulsive, overpowering quality, and there is often the tendency to use the substance in ever-increasing amounts.

Addiction is considered to be a state of periodic or chronic intoxication, detrimental to the user and to society, produced by the repeated consumption of a natural or synthetic drug. The user has lost the power of self-control, at least in relation to the drug, and his behavior comes to be determined to a considerable extent by the use of chemical agents.

Because addiction usually implies physical dependence, it is gradually being replaced by the term drug dependency, (304.x). See *dependency, drug.*

addiction, cyclic A syndrome originally described by Wulff which occurs most commonly in women and consists of periods of depression, feelings of ugliness, and overeating or overdrinking alternating with periods of normal or elated mood, feelings of beauty, and ascetic behavior. These patients show a preoedipal mother conflict with unconscious hatred of the mother and of feminity. Their urge to eat is an attempt to incorporate something to counteract femininity — milk, penis, child and/or narcissistic supplies which soothe the anxieties. Although described as a psychoneurosis by Wulff, cases of cyclic addiction are often found to fall nosologically within the schizophrenic group.

addiction, enema The frequent and habitual taking of enemas to gratify deep, hidden, unconscious character needs, but usually rationalized 'for health.'

addiction, polysurgical A phenomenon not infrequently met with in psychiatric patients who are addicted to surgical operations: they solicit or, through multiple symptoms, manage to have many operations though as a rule 'the necessity for an operation seems more psychological than physical.' (Menninger, K.A. *Man against Himself*, Harcourt, Brace, New York, 1938) See *syndrome, Munchausen.*

Addisonian syndrome (Thomas Addison, English physician, 1793-1860). Addison's disease; melasma suprarenale; adrenocortical insufficieny, due usually to atrophy or destructive inflammatory lesions. Symptoms include: weakness, anorexia, hypotension, cutaneous pigmentary changes (bronzed skin), hyponatremia, hyperkalemia, vomiting, diarrhea, irritability, periodic hypoglycemia, and decreased or absent excretion of α-ketosteroids and 11-oxysteroids. In some cases, paranoid reactions are seen (294.0). Treatment consists of replacement therapy with desoxycorticosterone acetate and supplementary sodium chloride or aldosterone.

additive W A Rorschach scoring term for a response in which the subject reports details but finally combines these into a whole response.

ademonia (à-dē-mō'nē-à) Agitated depression.

ademosyne (à-dē-mos'i-nē, -moz'inē) *Obs.* Nostalgia.

adenoid See *type, adenoid.*

adenoma, basophil(e) Tumor of the anterior lobe of the pituitary gland, characterized by a pluriglandular symptom complex *(Cushing's syndrome).* The symptoms are adiposity of the body and face but sparing the limbs, amenorrhea and hypertrichosis in women, acrocyanosis with cutis marmorata, hypertension, purple striae distensae, at times polycythemia and peculiar softening of bones, and frequently hyperglycemia.

Young adults are more commonly affected and duration of life is about five years following appearance of symptoms. Psychoses (in DSM-II, coded 293.3) develop in approximately 25 per cent of cases; they are commonly of the manic, melancholic, or anxious-agitated

variety. In another 35 per cent of cases, there are marked personality changes (in DSM-II, coded 309.7), usually in the direction of apathy.

adephagia (à-dē-fā'jē-à) *Obs.* A morbidly voracious appetite, synonymous with *bulimia.*

adiadochokinesis (à-dī-ad-ō-kō-ki-nē'sis) Loss of power to perform rapid alternating movements. This symptom is indicative of disorder of the cerebellum or its tracts.

adient Positively oriented or moving-toward. The adient drive or behavior or response is a situation which results in behavior acting toward the stimulus, increasing and perpetuating its action; it is the opposite of the avoidant drive.

Adie's syndrome A syndrome of unknown etiology characterized by enlarged pupil which shows the tonic pupillary reaction (when the patient is directed to gaze at a near object, the affected pupil slowly contracts to a size even smaller than the normal pupil) and by diminution or loss of tendon reflexes. The disorder occurs almost exclusively in females and usually has its onset in the third decade. It is a benign condition and unrelated to syphilis; also known as pseudo-Argyll Robertson pupil and pupillotonic pseudotabes.

adiposogenital dystrophia (ad-i-pō-sō-jen'i-tal dis-tro'fē-à) See *Frohlich's syndrome* and *Laurence-Moon-Biedl syndrome.*

adjustment See *adaptation.*

adjustment reaction In the 1952 revision of psychiatric nomenclature, this term was used to refer to certain *transient situational personality disorders* (q.v.) occurring in various periods of life.

adjustment, social Adaptation of the person to his social environment, in the field of social problems referring 'to the relations of the person to his family, community, political state or economic order in reference to some assumed standard or norm.' (Young, K. *Encyclopaedia of the Social Sciences,* vol. 1, Macmillan, New

York, 1930, p. 438) Adjustment may take place by adapting one's self to the environment or by changing the environment.

Adler, Alfred (1870 - 1937) Austrian psychiatrist, founder of the school of Individual Psychology; inferiority complex; overcompensation.

admission, first A person admitted for the first time to an institution of a given class (e.g. mental hospital or institution for the retarded).

adolescence The state or period of growth from puberty to maturity. In normal subjects its beginning is marked by the appearance of secondary sexual characteristics, commonly at about age 12; its termination is at about age 20. Adolescence is the period in which sexual maturity is achieved in that for the first time both the sexual and reproductive instincts attain full maturity and unite into a single striving; it can further be considered the age of final establishment of a dominant positive ego identity, the age in which 'tu-ism' replaces narcissism, the age in which sexual development dovetails into the development of object relationships leading to the mature, adult stage of impersonal object love (alloerotism) and unhampered orgastic heterosexuality.

Adrenalin A proprietary brand of *epinephrine* (q.v.)

adrenergic A term used for all nerves which release sympathin at their terminals; viz. the postganglionic sympathetic fibers, excluding those to the sweat glands and certain blood vessels. It is believed that central sympathetic nervous system fibers may also be adrenergic.

adrenochrome See *psychotomimetic.*

adrenocortical insufficiency *Addison's disease* (q.v.).

adrenocorticotropic hormone ACTH; one of the anterior pituitary hormones. See *syndrome, general adaptation.*

adulthood Maturity; see *developmental levels.*

adultomorphism Interpretation of the behavior of children in terms of adult behavior. See also *anthropomorph.*

advantage by illness See *illness, advantage by.*

adventurousness The condition characterizing the child in the preschool period in which there is an urge to rough-and-tumble freedom and curiosity. This involves the need of using the larger muscles rather than the smaller ones. Activities such as climbing, running, tricycle riding, ball playing, the use of big toys, the need to touch and handle everything within reach, and wandering away in search of new adventures characterize this period. The short span of attention required produces a rapid shifting from one activity to another. See *wanderlust.*

Adx A Rorschach scoring symbol for a response of a part or a detail of an animal where most subjects would see the whole animal; also known as an oligophrenic response. See *Do.*

adynamia (ad-i-nā'mē-à) Weakness; asthenia; a common symptom among psychiatric patients.

aedoeomania (ē-dē-ō-mā'nē-à) *Obs.* Nymphomania.

aelurophobia (ā-lūr-ō-fō'bē-à) *Ailurophobia* (q.v.)

aero- (ā-ēr-ō-) combining form meaning *air*, from Greek, *aér*, air.

aero-acrophobia (-ak-rō-fō'bē-à) Fear of open, high spaces: the morbid dread of being at a great height such as occurs when one is in an airplane. This malady should not be confused with air-sickness, which is a disturbance of vertigo-type.

aëroasthenia (-as-thē'nē-à) See *aëroneurosis.*

aëroneurosis (-nū-rō'sis) A form of psychoneurosis, perhaps an actual neurosis, said to occur among aviators; the symptoms are anxiety, restlessness, and varying physical phenomena.

aerophagia (-fä′jē-à) Swallowing of air, usually in such quantity as to produce abdominal distention and symptoms of hyperventilation (see *syndrome, hyperventilation*). The symptom is often based on unconscious wishes or conflicts, such as pregnancy wishes or cannibalistic impulses.

aërophobia Morbid dread of air, often ascribed to allegedly deleterious airborne influences; sometimes it also includes fear of one's own body odors.

aerumna (ē-room′nà) *Obs.* Melancholia associated with a physical ailment.

aeschromythesis (es-krō-mi-thē′sis) *Obs.* 'A term used by Hippocrates for the obscene language uttered by the delirious or maniacal, especially in puerperal mania.' (Tuke, D.H. *A Dictionary of Psychological Medicine*, vols. 1-2, Blakiston, Philadelphia, 1892)

affect (ä′fekt) The feeling-tone accompaniment of an idea or mental representation. The affects are the most direct psychic derivatives of the instincts and are psychic representatives of the various bodily changes by means of which the drives manifest themselves. The affects regularly attach themselves to ideas and other psychic formations to which they did not originally belong, and as a result their origin and meaning remain hidden from consciousness. If an affect is completely suppressed, it may appear not as an emotion but rather as physical changes of innervations, such as perspiration, tachycardia, paresthesia, etc. In other cases, especially in catatonic and manic states, the affects may appear without disguise.

The term affect is also used, more loosely, as a class name for feeling, emotion, or mood.

In Burrow's phylobiology: symbolically biased feeling that contrasts with the organism's primary total feeling—the distorted composite resulting when the organism's total pattern of motivation is overtly intercepted and superseded by the symbolic or partitive pattern of behavior. Affect always implies the partitive (personal, projective, symbolic) type of attention that results from the artificial linkage of feeling and symbol. This (affect-symbol) linkage represents a principle of motivation that is now rooted in the behavior of man as a neuro-social mechanism. Synonyms: image-feeling, projective feeling, partitive reaction. (Burrow, T. *The Biology of Human Conflict*, Macmillan, New York, 1937, pp. 165-6)

affect-block See *block, affect.*

affect, blunted See *affectivity, disturbances of.*

affect, charge of '. . . that part of the instinct which has become detached from the idea, and finds proportionate expression, according to its quantity, in processes which become observable to perception as affects.' (Freud, S. *Collected Papers*, Vol. 4, Leonard and Virginia Woolf and The Institute of Psychoanalysis, London, 1925.) See *cathexis.*

affect, cooling of See *affectivity, disturbances of.*

affect, detached This is a term used by Freud to explain the psychological theory of obsessions and phobias. An idea which is unbearable to the ego may have its associated affect separated from it, and this affect persists in the psychical sphere. The unbearable idea is thus weakened and remains present in consciousness, detached from all associations. Its affect, now freed from the unbearable idea, attaches itself to other ideas, which are not in themselves unbearable, but which through this 'false connection' grow to be obsessions. The detachment of its affect from an unbearable idea is undertaken as a defense against this idea.

affect, discharge of This term, employed by Freud, indicates an energetic reaction to an affective experience. This energetic reaction includes the whole range of voluntary and involuntary reflexes, by which, according to experience, the emotions—from weeping up to a clear act of revenge—are habitually worked off.

affect, dislocated See *affect, transposition of.*

affect, displacement of See *affect, transposition of.*

affect-energy The energy that comes from the excitement engendered by applying a psychic stimulus to the whole human organism, with all its individual systems. Also called *affective energy.*

affect-hunger See *hunger, affect.*

affect, inversion of *Counter-affect; reversal of affect;* transformation of an affect into its opposite. 'If I am conversing with a person to whom I must show consideration while I should like to address him as an enemy, it is almost more important that I should conceal the expression of my affect from him than that I should modify the verbal expression of my thoughts.' (Freud, S. *The Interpretation of Dreams,* 3rd ed., tr. by Brill, A.A., Macmillan, New York, 1933)

affect, organ localization of An affect, especially anxiety, can be felt in any organ of the body, but particularly in the organs that are directly supplied by the autonomic nervous system, such as the heart, lungs, stomach, intestines, etc.

affect-phantasy Jung's term for any phantasy that is strongly imbued with feelings.

affect, retention of See *affect, strangulated.*

affect, strangulated An affect that is repressed along with its attached mental content; it is retained in the unconscious and together with its psychic component produces morbid symptoms.

affect, transformation of in dreams In psychoanalytic interpretation it is often found that the feelings that one may really have masquerade in dreams as their exact opposites. The emotion of joy turns up as sorrow. Love is found disguised as the feeling of hatred. Sobs are discovered to be concealed by laughter. This process, usually referred to as the *transformation of an affect (feeling) into its opposite,* is one of the many processes by which the dream obscures its true meaning. If the psychic material out of which the dream is constructed contains an affect that has been repressed, this affect can gain representation in the dream by inversion into an opposite affect.

affect, transposition of Displacement of the affective component of an unconscious idea onto an unrelated and harmless idea,

seen typically in obsessive-compulsive and depressive patients.

affectability *Obs.* The state of being able to express emotion or feeling. The expression is seldom employed in psychiatry, although inquiry is frequently made into the emotional susceptibility of the individual.

affectate *Obs.* To arouse feeling or emotion.

affectation Artificiality of manner or behavior. Affectation is a form of simulation in that there is a crudely disguised effort to act as someone else, usually for purposes of gaining esteem.

affected, germinally This genetic term (equivalent to the German *keimkrank*) qualifies an individual (1) as being heterozygous for some *recessive* morbid character and thus carrying the predisposition for this trait in its genotype without manifesting it phenotypically, or (2) as a homozygote for any kind of hereditary character with *inhibited* manifestation.

affectio hypochondriaca (ȧf-fek′tē-ō hü-pō-Kôn-drē′ȧ-kȧ) *Obs.* Hypochondriasis.

affection A general term, implying feeling and emotion, as distinguished from cognition and volition. Baldwin (*Dictionary of Philosophy and Psychology,* vols. 1-2, Macmillan, New York, 1928, p. 23) defines it as 'any states of pronounced feeling. In English usage, the term applies both to the more permanent sentiments (Ger. *Gefühle*), and to passing emotional states (Ger. *Affente*). The best writers distinguish it from passion, as having less vehemence, and as less distinctly, if at all connected with a sensuous basis.'

affection, masked By this term Stekel describes the kind actions and tender behavior adopted by certain individuals in order to disguise their real inner sentiment of hatred for the person toward whom they act so kindly. It is as if they wore a mask of love to cover the real face of hate. See also *reaction-formation.*

affection, partial Suggested by Hirschfeld as synonym for *fetishism* (q.v.).

affective Pertaining to affect.

affective-cathexis (-kȧ-thek′sis) See *cathexis.*

affective psychoses In DSM-II coding, this group includes those psychoses characterized by a primary, severe disorder of mood and secondary disturbances in thinking and behavior which are in consonance with the affect, viz., involutional melancholia (296.0) and manic-depressive disorder in its various forms (296.1 —296.3). Psychotic depressive reaction is listed under Other Psychoses and coded 298.0. See *nomenclature, 1968 revision.*

affective-sensation See *feeling-sensation.*

affectivity Susceptibility to affective stimuli. Bleuler says that 'every psychism can be divided into two parts, an intellectual and an affective.' He then adds that 'under the term affectivity we comprise the affects, the emotions and the feelings of pleasure and pain.' (Bleuler, E. *Textbook of Psychiatry,* tr. by Brill, A.A., Macmillan, New York, 1930)

affectivity, disturbances of One of Bleuler's fundamental symptoms of the schizophrenias. Typical disturbances include indifference, blunted affect, and shallowness, flatness, and constriction of the affects. Early in the course of the disorder there may be oversensitivity, overlability or sanguineness. Mood is often inconsistent or exaggerated, with a lack of adaptability and of capacity for appropriate modulation of mood-tone. Parathymia, paramimia, disharmony of mood, dissociation of affect and intellect, and contradictoriness of emotional expression are also among the schizophrenic disturbances of affectivity.

It is probably the incongruity between the affect displayed and the verbal productions of the patient that is more characteristic of schizophrenia than any other change in affect; for lability of affect is seen in many organic brain disorders, and blunting or cooling of affect is particularly frequent in the pre-senile and senile brain disorders.

affectomotor Characterized by intense mental excitement and muscular movements. The combination, seldom seen alone, is usually found in conjunction with other symptoms and is a part of many psychiatric conditions. The term has been used loosely to refer to the manic phase of manic-depressive disorder, much in the same way that the expression 'affective psychosis' has been employed.

affecto-symbolic Burrow's term for the type of behavior that is distorted by emotional bias, associated with the undue attachment of man's feeling processes to symbolic constructs. Contrasted with organismic, orthopathic. Synonym: partitive.

affectus animi (af-fek′toos ȧ′ne-me) *Obs.* (L. 'disposition of mind') A general term for any type of mental disorder.

afferent (af′er-ent) Moving towards; in neurophysiology, concerned with transmission of nerve impulse into the central nervous system, in contrast to *efferent,* concerned with transmission of nerve impulse away from the central nervous system. See *reflex.*

affinal (a-fi′nal) Related by marriage.

affinity A marriage-partner's relationship contracted with the other partner's (blood-)kindred, by the act of marrying. See *kinship.*

affusion A form of hydrotherapy. 'The patient sits or stands in a bathtub. A sheet is placed around the body under the arms, and water at a temperature of 50° to 60°F. is poured from a pitcher from fifteen to twenty seconds. The patient is then rubbed with coarse towels until reaction is obtained.' (Bailey, H. *Nursing Mental Diseases,* 3rd ed., Macmillan, New York, 1935)

aftercare Continuing treatment and rehabilitation services provided to a patient within the community to which he has gone following in-patient hospitalization.

after-contraction An involuntary movement occurring as a continuation of an original willed, voluntary movement; often utilized as a demonstration of suggestibility in the pre-induction period of hypnosis by directing subject to abduct his arm against a wall and after a few seconds telling him to step away from the wall. In many subjects, the previously abducted arm will then float upwards involuntarily; this latter is termed after-contraction.

after-discharge Continuation of nerve impulse after cessation of the stimulus.

after-expulsion Secondary repression; see *repression.*

after sensation Continuation of sense impression after stimulation of the sense organ has ceased; after-image.

agapaxia Emotional hypersensitivity and hyperactivity to stimuli, such as is seen particularly in psychically superior individuals.

agapism The doctrine exalting the value of love, especially in its general, nonsexual sense.

agastroneuria (à-gas-trō-nū'rē-à) Neurasthenia of the stomach.

AGCT Army General Classification Test of intelligence, used during World War II and after. It is designed for use with literate adults.

age, basal In psychometrics, the highest age level of testing at which the subject passes all the subtests. See *scattering.*

âge critique (äzh krē-tēk') (F. 'critical age') The menopausal or climacteric period.

âge de retour (äzh dē rē-tōor') (F. 'age of return') The period of old age or senility, when vital powers begin to be or are diminished.

agency-centered consultation See *consultant.*

agenesis, agenisia (à-jen'e-sis, aj-ē-nē'sē-à) See *aplasia.*

agenetic Showing defective, or absense of, development of some part or parts of the body.

agent, catalytic In group psychotherapy, a patient who activates catharsis in other patients.

agent provocateur (à-zhäN' prô-vô-kà-tēr') (F. 'instigating agent') Precipitating cause.

ager naturae (à'ger nä-tōo'rī) (L. 'the field of nature') The uterus.

agerasia (aj-ē-rā'sē-à) A youthful appearance in an old person.

ageusia, ageustia (à-gū'sē-à, à-gūs'tē-à) Absence or impairment of the sense of taste; it may be due to disorder in the gustatory apparatus (i.e. the taste buds). It is also seen in psychiatric conditions, particularly in depressions; patients frequently refer to the fact that foodstuffs are tasteless. Ageusia is sometimes a part of depersonalization syndromes, such as occur in hysteria and the schizophrenias.

agglutination Condensation of more than one word-root or word into a single word. See *neologism; contamination.*

agglutinations, image Kretschmer says that in dreams and twilight states mental activity appears in the form of sensory images. He says: 'What was thought of during the day in words, at night passes before us in dreams, in a visible series of images. These images sometimes maintain a scenic arrangement, but, with deeper clouding of consciousness, they fall to pieces into fragments of pictures which apparently go on without rules or regulations, and, under the influence of affects, again conglomerate into peculiar image groups, the *image agglutinations.* The faces of several persons, several objects of similar emotional value, in the dreams are seen as one, and are conglomerated into unity; this we call, with Freud, "condensation."' (Kretschmer, E. *Hysteria,* tr. by Boltz, O., Nervous & Mental Disease Publishing Company, New York and Washington, 1926)

aggregation Summation; integration; synthesis. Bernard has subdivided evolution into five periods, each of which is a result of aggregation such as occurred when unicellular organisms first colonized to produce multicellular organisms (physical aggregation). In the fifth period, in which man emerges, the aggregation is psychical, occurring through the instinct of gregariousness and leading to the emergence of a 'super-mind.'

aggression, aggressiveness, aggressivity In psychiatry, the term refers to one or more different concepts: (1) destrudo, the energy of the death drive or death instinct, as contrasted with libido; see *instinct, death;* (2) ideas and/or behavior which are angry, hateful, or destructive; (3) activity or action, especially when carried out in a forceful way. While the terms 'rage' and 'hate' are often used interchangeably to describe manifestations of the aggressive drive, some would differentiate between them, using 'rage' to describe a primitive reaction that occurs before the formation of stable object representations, and 'hate' or 'hatred' to describe a type of object-directed representation of aggression.

aggression panic See *homosexual panic.*

aggressive instinct See *instinct, death.*

agitation A tension state in which anxiety is manifested in the psychomotor area with hyperactivity (such as handwringing or pacing) and general perturbation.

agitolalia (aj-i-tō-lā′lē-à) Agitophasia.

agitophasia (aj-i-tō-fā′zhē-à) Cluttered speech due to excessive rapidity under stress of excitement.

agnosia (ag-nō′sē-à) Loss of ability to comprehend the meaning or to recognize the importance of various types of stimulation. The term agnosia is usually confined to loss of recognition of symbols in the non-language field, for auditory and visual agnosias in the language field are essentially aphasias. The most common agnosias are: astereognosis (tactile agnosia; loss of power to perceive the shape and nature of an object and inability to identify it by superficial contact alone); anosognosia (ignorance of the existence of disease, especially hemiplegia or depersonalization in regard to paralyzed parts of the body); autotopagnosia or somatotopagnosia (impairment in ability to identify or orient the body or the relation of its individual parts); ideational or sensory apraxia is also essentially an agnosia. Finger agnosia, the inability to tell which finger has been touched by the examiner, has been reported to occur in many childhood schizophrenics and in children with minimal brain dysfunction.

In psychiatry, agnosia refers to the loss or disuse of knowledge of objects, when the knowledge appears to have been altered by emotional circumstances. In some schizophrenics, for example, the desire not to know their families produces a special kind of agnosia in that they will maintain that they have no knowledge whatsoever of the parents or siblings who stand before them. Such agnosia is seen also in hysterics, in depressed patients, and in epileptics, and it can be reproduced under hypnosis.

agnosia, social Wilhelm Reich's term for the inability of the psychopath to achieve satisfaction in living.

agnosia, tactile Inability to recognize objects, such as paper, glass, soap, cotton, metals, etc. by touching them. See *tactile sensation, double simultaneous.*

agnosia, visual-spatial A syndrome described by Paterson and Zangwill consisting of failure to analyse spatial relationships and inability to perform simple constructional tasks under visual control. This syndrome is usually associated with lesions of the posterior portions (occipito-parietal) of the right cerebral hemisphere in right-handed patients.

agoraphobia (ag-ō-rà-fō′bē-à) The dread of open spaces. The patient becomes panic-stricken, sometimes at the thought of, but more often at the impending visit to an open space. As a reaction against such an eventuality he generally remains indoors and prefers to be at home, near the mother or someone possessing a kind, helpful, guiding influence.

agrammaphasia (à-gram-à-fā′zhē-à) Ungrammatical, incoherent speech.

agrammatism (à-gram′à-tiz′m) Ungrammatical speech; a form of *aphasia* (q.v.), in which the patient forms his words into a sentence without regard for grammatical rules of declension, conjugation, comparison of adjectives and adverbs, auxiliary verbs, prepositions, conjunctions, articles, etc. Agrammatism is seen most frequently in *Alzheimer's disease* and in *Pick's disease* (qq.v.). With some authors, the term is synonymous with *syntactic aphasia;* see also *speech disorders.*

agraphia (à-graf′ē-à) Loss of the power, or the inability, to communicate (ideas) in *writing,* and thus a subdivision of *aphasia* (q.v.). This is the motor (or expressive) aspect of the ailment of which the sensory (or perceptive) counterpart is *alexia* (q.v.). The inability may involve individual letters, or syllables or words or phrases, as in varieties of aphasia, and is usually attributed to cerebral disorders.

When *agraphia* is not a physiological ailment, but due to psychic or emotional factors and is merely voluntary, it is the graphic counterpart of *mutism* (q.v.). A patient who acknowledged organic ability to write was entirely unable to write a letter or a word, lest, as she thought, it would result in serious harm; she possessed excellent intelligence and manual dexterity. Patients with involutional melancholia are often inhibited emotionally from writing, but the inhibition in this respect is only representative of more or less categorical inhibition. See also *speech disorders; acalculia.*

agraphia, acquired 'Loss of a previous ability to write resulting from brain injury or brain disease' (Orton, S.T. *Reading, Writing and Speech Problems in Children*, Norton, New York, 1937)

agraphia, congenital 'Unusual difficulty in learning to write which is out of harmony with the other intellectual accomplishments and manual skills of the individual.' (Orton, S.T. *Reading, Writing and Speech Problems in Children*, Norton, New York, 1937)

agriothymia (ag-rē-ō-thim'ē-à) Insane ferocity. *Obs.* 'Maniacal furor'; at one time synonymous with 'homicidal insanity.'

agriothymia ambitiosa (àm-bē-tē-ō'za) The desire to destroy nations.

agriothymia hydrophobica (hē-drô-fō'bē-kà) Irresistible impulse to bite.

agriothymia religiosa (re-lē-gē-ō'zà) 'The irrepressible desire to uproot and destroy other religions and those cultivating them —Mohammedism.' (Tuke, D.H. *A Dictionary of Psychological Medicine*, vols. 1-2, Blakiston, Philadelphia, 1892)

agromania (ag-rō-mā'nē-à) Morbid impulse to live in the open country or in solitude, not infrequently a symptom of schizophrenia.

agrypnia (à-grip'nē-à) *Obs.* Insomnia.

agrypnia excitata (eks-kē-tä'tà) Insomnia associated with mental excitement and listlessness as to surroundings.

agrypnia pertaesa (per-tī'zà) Insomnia due to physical disorder.

agrypnia senilis (se-nē'lēs) Sleeplessness of old age.

agrypnocoma (à-grip-nō-kō'mà) Coma vigil.

agrypnotic (ag-rip-not'ik) Inducing wakefulness; somnifugous; relating to or characterized by insomnia.

ague, leaping (ā'gū) Dancing mania. See *choreomania.*

agyiophobia (à-ji-yō-fō'bē-à) Fear of streets; approximately equivalent to *agoraphobia* (q.v.).

aha, ah-hah A term used to refer to a type of experience in which there is sudden insight into or solution of a problem; at a particular moment, the features of the problem suddenly fit together in a unitary pattern.

ahypnia (ā-hip'nē-à) Insomnia.

Aichhorn, August (1879 -) Psychoanalyst; the first to apply psychodynamic principles to antisocial behavior ('Wayward Youth,' 1935).

aichmophobia (āk-mō-fō'bē-à) Fear or dread of pointed objects, such as knives, usually associated with the thought of using the feared object as an offensive weapon against someone, even though there is no conscious reason for doing so. The symptom often leads to peculiar eating habits, such as eating alone and without silverware, or to the selection of occupations in which dangerous implements or their symbolic equivalents are not likely to be encountered.

A.I.D. Acronym for *acute infectious diseases* (usually of childhood); also, more recently, acronym for *artificial insemination by donor*, or for *autoimmune diseases.* See *autoimmunity.*

aidoiomania (ī-dō-yō-mā'ne-à) *Erotomania* (q.v.).

ailment, functional A mild transitory episodic symptom, usually the result of disturbed physiological functioning (pathophysiology). Such disturbed functionings are the visceral components of emotion, or the visceral expression of emotion or emotional conflicts. See *neurosis, vegatative.*

ailurphobia (ī-lū-rō-fō'bē-à) Fear of cats. The term is synonymous with galeophobia and gatophobia. The fear of cats has the same psychical significance as the fear of animals in general. It is a fear of being injured by them; usually, upon careful inquiry, it is found that there is dread of injury to a particular part of the body, namely, the genital area or its psychical equivalent.

aim The activity in which an impulse or drive manifests itself and, more specifically, the activity by which the drive or impulse achieves gratification or discharge.

'What distinguishes the instincts from one another and furnishes them with specific attributes is their relation to their somatic *sources* and to their *aims.* The source of the instinct is an exciting process in an organ, and the immediate aim of the impulse lies in the release of this organ stimulus.' (Freud, S. *The Basic Writings of Sigmund Freud,* tr. by Brill, A.A., Random House, New York, 1938)

The modes of pleasure during the so-termed infancy period, that is, up to the latency period, chiefly center around the several erotogenic zones (oral, anal, dermal, muscular, etc.). During the latency period much of the energy and pleasure formerly identified with these zones is deflected into sublimations. The relinquishment of energy from the pre-genital areas is called 'aim-inhibited.' At puberty there is reanimation to a greater or lesser extent of the aim-inhibited tendencies and their somatic manifestations.

aim-inhibited See *aim.*

aim-transference The transfer of a person's objectives from one life situation to another. The development of aim-transference is encouraged particularly in short-term psychotherapy, when conditions do not permit the development and subsequent solution of the transference neurosis, as defined by psychoanalysts.

Aim-transference is illustrated by the case of an 18-year-old schizophrenic male whose mother allowed him no independence. She had dressed and fed the patient throughout his life. The patient himself desired to be independent and in fact wanted to become strong and dominant, like his father. These aims were encouraged in therapy and by the strong male personality of the psychiatrist, who arranged special situations that enabled the patient to become the active leader of a small group. This transfer of early aims to the therapeutic situation constitutes the aim-transference. In the situation described, aim-transference was reinforced by aim-experience, when the therapist maneuvered the environment so that the patient was able to achieve his goals.

AIP Acute intermittent porphyria; See *porphyria, acute intermittent.*

akataphasia (à-kat-à-fā'zhē-à) See *acataphasia.*

akatizia (à-ke-tē'zhē-à) *Acathisia* (q.v.); motor restlessness and, specifically, a feeling of muscular quivering; one of the possible complications of treatment with the phenothiazines. Often, the symptom is of such intensity that it becomes impossible for the patients to sit still day or night, and which is decribed by them as more difficult to endure than any of the symptoms for which they had been originally treated. Acquaintance with this symptom of akatizia, which often persists for a considerable time after the drug has been withdrawn, is important because it is sometimes mistaken for an agitated depression and wrongly treated with ECT. (Kalinowsky, L. *American Journal of Psychiatry, 115:* 294-298, 1958)

Akerfeldt test See *ceruloplasmin.*

akinesia, akinesis (ak-i-nē'sē-à, ak-i-nē'sis) Absence or diminution of voluntary motion; when seen as a part of psychiatric syndromes, it may range from moderate inactivity to almost complete immobility. Ordinarily, akinesia or hypokinesia is accompanied by a parallel reduction in mental activity. In the stuporous phase of catatonic schizophrenia, for example, there is almost complete physical and mental immobility.

Akinesia may be circumscribed in the

sense that the patient becomes immobile only in a given setting or while under the influence of a particular trend of thought; this is sometimes termed *selective akinesia*.

akinesia algera (à-kē-nā'sē-à al'ge-rà) A clinical syndrome characterized by general painfulness associated with any kind of movements. Moebius restricted the use of the term to those conditions arising on a psychogenic basis; to him it was a manifestation of hysteria.

akinetic-abulic syndrome See *syndrome, akinetic-abulic*.

akinetic epilepsy A type of petit mal epilepsy. See *epilepsy*.

akoasm (ak'ō-az'm) An elementary auditory hallucination. 'Such would be simple sounds, as buzzing, crackling, ringing, and the like. The more complicated hallucinations which are conceived by the patient to be "voices"—verbal auditory hallucinations—are known as *phonemes*.' (White, W.A. *Outlines of Psychiatry*, 12th ed., Nervous & Mental Disease Publishing Company, Washington, D.C., 1929)

akoluthia (à-ko-lū'thē-à) Semon's term for a phase of engraphy corresponding to what others have termed 'primary memory' or 'memory in the making.'
'The fact is, we cannot observe mental events in the happening; what we really do is to observe them in retrospect. And yet it is not the kind of retrospect that is usually associated with past events of some time ago; it is more the observing of a point of time intermediate between the present and the past. . . . What we are observing in this case is not the present, nor is it such a past as involves the functioning of memory . . .' (Nicole, J.E. *Psychopathology*, 4th ed. Bailliere, Tindall & Cox, 1947.)

alalia (à-lā'lē-à) Speechlessness; loss of ability to talk. It was used in the eighteenth and later into the nineteenth century for what is now generally denoted by *aphasia*. At present the *-lalia* frequently used in compositions like *echolalia, bradylalia*, etc., connotes *talking* rather than *'speaking—saying,'* i.e. the exercise of the power of talking as contrasted with the

faculty for significant or meaningful speech. See *speech disorders*.

alarm reaction See *reaction, alarm*.

Albright's disease A syndrome consisting of multiple pseudocysts in the skeleton, segmental pigment disorders of the skin and pubertas praecox; the disease is due to hypothalamic-hypophysial dysfunction.

alcohol-antabuse reaction See *antabuse*.

alcoholic paranoid state Alcoholic paranoia (in DSM-II, 291.3); a chronic condition, presumed to be primarily of organic origin, consisting of persisting infidelity or jealousy delusions, that appears mainly in male alcoholics.

alcoholic psychoses See *alcoholism*.

Alcoholics Anonymous (A.A.) An organization formed in 1935 by an Akron physician and a New York broker, both former alcoholics, for the purpose of rehabilitating chronic alcoholics. Since its founding, Alcoholics Anonymous has expanded into an international movement. Its principles include: (1) a belief in God or natural law; (2) frank self-appraisal; (3) a willingness to admit and correct wrongs done to others; (4) a trust in mankind, and (5) dedication to the rescue of those who sincerely desire to conquer alcoholism by making them members of the organization as successful abstainers.

alcoholism Alcohol poisoning; the effects of excess intake of alcohol. The various disorders associated with excessive alcohol intake are more extensively described under separate listings, as indicated (numbers refer to DSM-II coding):
  1. acute intoxication—309.13 (see *intoxication, alcoholic*).
  2. chronic alcoholism—303.x (see *alcoholism, chronic*).
  3. pathologic intoxication, or mania a potu—291.6 (see *intoxication, alcoholic*).
  4. *delirium tremens* (q.v.)—291.0
  5. alcoholic hallucinosis—291.2 (see *hallucinosis, alcoholic*).
  6. *Korsakov psychosis* (q.v.)—291.1
  7. alcoholic deterioration—291.5 (see *dementia, alcoholic*).
  8. alcoholic pseudoparesis—291.9 (see *pseudoparesis, alcoholic*).

9. alcoholic epilepsy—291.9 (see *epilepsy, alcoholic*).

10. *Wernicke's encephalopathy* (q.v.) —291.9

11. *alcoholic paranoid state* (q.v.)— 291.3

alcoholism, chronic Addiction to alcohol; in DSM-II, this is considered as one of the personality disturbances. A patient is considered to suffer from chronic alcoholism if (1) his use of alcohol is of such extent as to interfere with successful physical, personality, and/or social functioning and (2) he is either unable to recognize the deleterious effects of his habit or, recognizing them, he is nonetheless unable to curtail his alcohol consumption and continues in an almost compulsive way to drink heavily. This definition thus differentiates the chronic alcoholic from the excessive or 'problem' drinker, who may use alcohol to excess and while under its influence behave pathologically, but who is able to control his drinking once he becomes aware of the possible disastrous effects of his habit. Under 'Alcoholism' in DSM-II, the following are differentiated: episodic excessive drinking (303.0; the patient becomes intoxicated as frequently as four times a year); habitual excessive drinking (303.1; intoxicated more than 12 times a year); and alcohol addiction (303.2).

Jellinek has divided alcoholism into the following types: (1) Alpha Alcoholism: excessive and inappropriate drinking without any loss of control or the inability to abstain; (2) Beta Alcoholism: excessive and inappropriate drinking complicated by physical diseases such as cirrhosis, gastritis, and neuritis, but no clearcut evidence of psychological or physical dependence; (3) Gamma Alcoholism: malignant alcoholism, characterized by a progressive course, physical dependence, often acquired tolerance and, invariably, psychologic dependence with inability to control drinking; (4) Delta Alcoholism: inability to abstain, acquired tolerance, withdrawal symptoms, but the quantity of alcohol ingested can be controlled; this form is seen particularly in wine-drinking countries; and (5) Epsilon Alcoholism: dipsomania, spree-drinking, convention drinking, etc.

It has been estimated that there are approximately four and a half million chronic alcoholics in the United States; that the incidence of chronic alcoholism of all degrees is 4390 per 100,000; that the incidence of chronic alcoholism with complications is 1097 per 100,000. While it has been said that 85 per cent of all chronic alcoholics are male, it is generally agreed that the female is beginning to account for a greater percentage of chronic alcoholism than formerly. About 80 per cent of patients fall within the 35 to 50 years age group; those who appear superficially to be chronic alcoholics at an earlier age are likely to be in the psychopathic or schizophrenic groups, and those who are older more commonly have involutional reactions.

Although the psychodynamics of alcoholism are only poorly understood, it is believed that most chronic alcoholics are characterized by a (? constitutional) increase in orality and that the attitudes of their parents are typically such as to frustrate these oral needs. Resultant disappointment and rage must be turned away from those on whom the individual is dependent, leading to tense depression, guilt, and masochism, with a turning to alcohol which (1) physiologically reduces the strength of the drives, particularly the aggressive drives; (2) minimizes the effects of stress, and (3) affords a symbolic substitute for the desired gratification, thus giving a temporary pleasure and elation and allowing a retreat to the original infantile megalomania. Eventually, a pattern is established: frustration brings anxiety and rage, alcohol brings relief, but this is only temporary and does not bring a solution and more alcohol is required, leading to secondary frustration, to anxiety and rage, to more alcohol, etc.

More recently, Williams has postulated that chronic alcoholism is a genetotrophic disease; this may be a more accurate description of what has been described as the constitutional increase in orality. See *disease, genetotrophic.*

alcoholomania (al-ko-hôl-ō-mā'nē-à) *Rare.* A morbid craving for alcoholic beverages.

alcoholophilia (-fil'ē-à) *Rare.* Morbid craving for alcohol.

aldosteronism (al-dàs'têr-ō-nis'm) *Conn's syndrome,* consisting of severe metabolic and electrolytic changes due to hyperplasia or tumor of the adrenal cortex. Symptoms and signs include: headache, muscular weakness, polydipsia, polyuria, low serum potassium, high serum sodium and alkalosis.

alector (à-lek'tēr) A person who is unable to sleep.

alerting system See *formation, reticular.*

Alexander, Franz (1891 - 1964) Hungarian psychoanalyst; trained with Sachs and Abraham in Berlin; in 1929 appointed the first (and to date the only) Professor of Psychoanalysis at the University of Chicago; chief contributions have been in the area of brief analytic therapy and psychosomatic medicine.

Alexanderism (from Alexander the Great) *Agriothymia ambitiosa* (q.v.).

alexia (à-lek'sē-à) Loss of the power to grasp the meaning of written or printed words; word-blindness; visual aphasia. See *lobe, occipital; reading, disabilities of; speech disorders; acalculia.*

alexia, acquired 'Loss of a previous skill in reading which follows disease or damage to certain parts of the brain.' (Orton, S.T. *Reading, Writing and Speech Problems in Children,* Norton, New York, 1937)

alexia, congenital (cf. *agraphia, congenital.*) 'Inability to learn to read with the rapidity and skill which would be expected from the individual's mental age and achievements in other subjects.' (Orton, S.T. *Reading, Writing and Speech Problems in Children,* Norton, New York, 1937)

algedonic (al-jē-don'ik) Characterized by or relating to pleasure and pain, or the agreeable and the disagreeable.

-algesia (-al-jē'zē-à) Combining element meaning pain, from Gr. *álgésis,* sense of pain.

algesimeter (al-je-sim'ē-tēr) Same as *algometer* (q.v.).

algolagnia (al-gō-lag'nē-à) Schrenck-Notzing coined the term algolagnia to cover both sadism and masochism. Sadism thus came to be known as active algolagnia, while masochism was called passive algolagnia. (*Zeitschrift für Hypnotismus,* vol. IX, pt. 2, 1899)

algometer (al-gom'ē-tēr) An instrument which purports to measure sensitiveness to pain in terms of amount of pressure exerted upon the skin by a blunt instrument. It is sometimes called *algesimeter.*

algophily (al-gof'i-li) *Rare.* A term coined by Fere (*L'Instinct Sexuel,* p. 138), synonymous with masochism.

algophobia (al-gō-fō'bē-à) Morbid fear of pain.

algopsychalia (al-gō-sī-kā'lē-à) See *psychalgia.*

alienatio mentis (à-lē-ā-nä'tē-ō men'tēs) (L. 'alienation of the mind') Insanity.

alienation 1. A general term, now largely restricted to forensic psychiatry, indicating mental or psychiatric illness or insanity; when used in this way, alienation is ordinarily qualified by the adjective, mental. 2. The repression, inhibition, blocking, or dissociation of one's own feelings so that they no longer seem effective, familiar, or convincing to the patient. Such alienation of one's own feelings is characteristic of obsessive-compulsive psychoneurosis. It may also be seen in the schizophrenias, but in the latter certain organs, body areas, or even the whole body are often perceived as if they did not belong to the person or as if they were different from the usual. The result is estrangement and depersonalization.

alienist *Obs.* Just as the term alienation in a psychiatric sense has been gradually restricted to the field of medical jurisprudence, so also the expression alienist refers to the specialist in psychiatry from the standpoint of law.

alienus (à-lē-ā'noos) *Obs.* Delirious, maniacal.

all-or-none The principle that, regardless of the intensity of the stimulus, a single neuron reacts either with maximal intensity or not at all.

allachesthesia (à-làk-es-thē'-zhē-à) Referral of a tactile sensation to a point remote from the point of stimulation; allesthesia. Usually, the displacement of sensation is symmetrical; it suggests a temporal lobe lesion.

allachesthesia, visual A rare phenomenon, indicative of parietal lobe lesion, consisting of referral or transposition of visual images to an opposite point in space.

allele (a-lēl'), **allelomorph** (a-lē'lō-mawrf) In genetics these interchangeable terms mean either of two genes which go to different mature germ cells: each gene is an *allele* of, or is *allelic* to, the other.

The two conditions of a character which are developed by allelic genes are usually called 'alleles' too. Brown and blue eyes in man are alleles of each other, as is red and white color in snapdragons. The separation of such allelic genes to different cells is explained by the fact that they occupy the same locus in their respective chromosomes and come together side by side, when the *homologous* chromosomes unite to form a pair (see *homologue*). Obviously alleles must arise by unlike mutations of originally homologous genes located at the same position in a chromosome pair.

Three or more genes occupying the same locus in homologous chromosomes in a species are called *multiple alleles*. The best known instance of multiple alleles in man is the blood groups.

allelic, allelomorphic Pertaining to or having the nature of an *allele* or *allelomorph*.

allesthesia (al-es-thē'sē-à) See *allachesthesia*.

allo- (al'ō-) A combining form, meaning different, other.

alloch(e)iria (al-ō-kī'rē-à) A condition, apparently of neural origin, in which the location of touch or pain sensations is transferred to a corresponding place on the part of the body opposite to that stimulated.

allocortex (al-ō-kor'teks) Rhinencephalon; a part of the olfactory and allied systems of the cerebral cortex. The term is used primarily in speaking of the cytoarchitecture, or microscopic structure, of the cortex, in which case the allocortex is contrasted to the isocortex (or neocortex).

alloerotic (al-ō-e-rot'ik) Of or pertaining to the extension of erotism or libido upon other individuals.

alloerotism, alloeroticism The final phase in the development of object relationships, marked by a stable integration or fusion of the drives and their deflection into appropriate channels; also known as the phase of impersonal socialization, adult sexuality, and mature genitality. It includes not only the ability to discharge libidinal impulses on a heterosexual object (as was achieved in the heteroerotic phase), but it also includes the ability to enter into a love relationship with the sexual object, a loving of the object more than a being loved by the object. See *ontogeny, psychic; stage, postambivalent.*

alloesthesia *Allachesthesia* (q.v.).

allolalia (al-oō-lā'lē-à) Any unusual or abnormal state of speech or utterance.

allophasis (al-of'à-zis) *Obs.* Incoherent speech.

alloplasty (al'ō-plas-tē) Adaptation by means of altering the external environment; contrasted with *autoplasty* (q.v.).

'Catalepsy and mimicry therefore would be regressions to a much earlier primitive method of adaptation of the organism, an autoplastic adaptation (adaptation by means of alteration in the organism itself), while flight and defense aim at an alteration in the environment (alloplastic adaptation).' (Ferenczi, S. *Further Contributions to the Theory and Technique of Psycho-Analysis,* tr. by Suttie, J.I., Leonard and Virginia Woolf and the Institute of Psychoanalysis, London, 1926)

allopsyche (al-ō-sī'kē) The mind or psyche of another.

allotriogeusia (a-lot-rē-ō-gū'sē-à) Perversion of the sense of taste.

allotriogeustia (a-lot-rē-ō-gūs'tē-à) 1. Perversion of the sense of taste. 2. Abnormal appetite.

allotriophagy (a-lot-rē-of'a-jē) Morbid impulse to eat unnatural foodstuffs.

allotropy (a-lot'rō-pi) Adolf Meyer's term for *allopsyche.*

Allport, Gordon Willard (1897 - 1967) U.S. psychologist and educator; developed a holistic psychology of human behavior, the core concepts of which are the *proprium* (the nuclear self or self concept, consisting of those habits, attitudes, and values which are deeply ego-involved) and the *personal disposition* (the hierarchy of perceptual-motivational-behavioral unities that characterize a person). 'Allport would certainly agree that, in many individuals, the Freudian framework labels for us the propriate strivings and the central dispositions. But he would equally assert that many therapeutic failures occur because the therapist keeps doggedly probing for infantile motivations in a personality where the propriate dispositions are organized around roles and conflicts of the adult situations.' (Stagner, R. in *Handbook of Clinical Psychology*, edited by Wolman, B.B., McGraw-Hill, New York, 1965)

alogia (à-lō′jē-à) Speechlessness usually due to intellectual deficiency or confusion. See *speech disorders*.

alogous (al′ō-gus) *Obs.* Unreasonable, irrational.

aloneness, autistic Kanner's term for the lack of desire for human contact that is a leading symptom of early infantile autism. See *autism, early infantile*.

Alpers's disease See *poliodystrophy, progressive infantile cerebral*.

alpha-arc A term suggested by Frost to refer to the sequence of a stimulus leading to motor behavior via a simple sensori-motor path. Beta-arc refers to arousal of higher cortical paths by the functioning of an alpha-arc (thus leading to a 'sensation' rather than simple 'awareness'), and not by an outside stimulus directly. The term alpha-arc is approximately equivalent to 'immediate response' in Watson's behavioristic psychology, while the term beta-arc is roughly equivalent to Watson's 'delayed response' or 'implicit behavior.'

alpha index An index devised by Piotrowski for the diagnosis of schizophrenia on the basis of response to the Rorschach test. The index consists of the following criteria: the number of whole responses is no greater than 6; the sum of the light

shading responses is greater than the sum of the color responses; the presence of "dark shock"; a fall in sharply conceived forms below 70%. Accuracy of diagnosis is said to be 83-91%.

alpha rhythm, alpha wave See *electroencephalogram*.

alpinism A non-specific term referring to neuropsychiatric syndromes appearing in relation to low atmospheric pressure, such as the asthenia syndrome of persons living in high altitudes.

alter The other; Parson's term for the person in any social interaction with whom one interacts. See *ego*.

alter-egoism An altruistic feeling for only those individuals who are in the same situation as oneself.

alternating psychosis The circular form of manic-depressive psychosis. See *psychosis, manic-depressive*.

altrigenderism (al-tri-jen′dēr-iz′m) The state of being of or attracted to, the other gender. Beginning in the late infantile period the child takes an interest, to a greater or lesser extent, in members of the other *gender*, i.e. of the opposite sex. This term *altrigenderism* is suggested for these natural, wholesome activities between members of the two genders. When the interests become amorous, though not overtly sexual, *heteroerotism* is the proper term. When the sexual element (without sexual congress) enters into these relations, the condition is called *heterosexuality*, while *heterogenitality* as a term is limited to sexual intercourse.

altruism Regard for the interests and needs of others; a term coined by the French philosopher, Auguste Comte (1798-1857), who maintained that the chief problem of existence is 'vivre pour autrui' (to live for the sake of others). In psychiatric literature altruism and morality seem to be closely related, if not identical. Bleuler equates altruism with ethics.

'Freud says that the development from egotism to altruism is brought about through the formation of libidinal ties which inevitably limit narcism. This, according to him, is the only basis for the development of community interest.' (Healy, W. Bronner, A.F. and Bowers, A.M. *The Structure and Meaning of Psychoanalysis,* Knopf, New York, 1930)

alucinatio (à-lōō-kē-nä'tē-ō) *Obs.* Hallucination.

alusia (àlū'sē-à) *Obs.* Insanity; hallucination.

alusia hypochondriaca (hē-pô-kôn-drē'à-kà) *Obs.* Hypochondriasis.

alysm (al'iz'm) Restlessness exhibited by a sick person.

alysmus (al-iz'mus) *Obs.* Anxiety and dejection accompanying disease.

alysosis (à-lē-sō'sis) Boredome, sometimes appearing as a central phenomenon in the simple form of schizophrenia. It is also known as *otiumosis.* (Bergler, E. *Psychiatric Quarterly 19,* 38, 1945)

Alzheimer's disease (Alois Alzheimer, German neurologist, 1864-1915) Presenile dementia; a progressive dementia with apraxia and speech disturbances; in DSM-II, coded 290.1 or, if non-psychotic, 309.6. Symptoms include memory loss, loss of interest, and carelessness which progress until disorientation, epileptiform attacks and, finally, spastic contractures are evident. Family history often reveals some degree of hereditary tainting.

The disease occurs more often in women than in men (in a ratio of 2½ to 1) and begins insidiously between the ages of 40 and 60 (average age at onset, 55 years). At first, there is loss of interest, difficulty in concentration, increased muscle tone, and difficulty in walking; later, suspiciousness and ideas of reference appear. Eventually there is complete disorientation for time, place, and person, and there is marked emotional and intellectual regression. Speech deteriorates progressively from paraphasic talkativeness to isolated words and phrases (logoclonia).

The pathology consists of generalized brain atrophy, most marked in the frontal lobes; microscopically, neurofibrillary tangles are seen to replace the nerve cells and are typically arranged in the form of whorls or baskets. Senile argentophile plaques are also present.

Alzheimer's disease may last anywhere from several months to over 10 years, but the average duration of life once symptoms are discovered is 6½ years. There is no known treatment.

amathophobia (à-math-ō-fō'bē-à) Fear of dust.

amaurosis (am-aw-rō'-sis) Complete blindness.

amaurotic family idiocy *Cerebromacular degeneration; Tay-Sachs's disease;* a familial disease of lipoid metabolism, caused by a single recessive autosomal gene, characterized by progressive degeneration of cerebral neurons, and resulting in blindness, muscular wasting and enfeeblement, and mental retardation (in DSM-II, 31x.2).

Four forms are recognized: (1) *infantile form,* orginally found mainly among Polish Jews, the symptoms appearing as early as the third month; (2) *late infantile form,* appearing between the second and fifth years; (3) *juvenile form,* appearing in older children between the sixth and twelfth years was described by Spielmeyer. It resembles the infantile type, shows gradual mental impairment and terminates in blindness and death within two years. Although optic atrophy occurs, there are no changes in the macula lutea; (4) *adult form,* occurring after puberty, though usually not beyond the third decade. Some writers refer to the infantile form only as Tay-Sachs's disease, to the late infantile form as Bielschowsky's disease, to the juvenile form as Vogt-Spielmeyer's disease, and to the adult or tardive form as Kuf's disease.

amaxophobia (à-mak-sō-fō'bē-à) Fear of being in a vehicle.

ambi- Combining form meaning *both.*

ambilevous (am-bi-le'vus) 'Poor in manual dexterity with both hands; "doubly left-handed."' (Orton, S.T. *Reading, Writing and Speech Problems in Children,* Norton, New York, 1937)

ambisexuality Ferenczi proposed that, from the standpoint of the psyche, the term ambisexuality be used instead of bisexuality. In their earliest manifestations emotions should not be regarded as masculine or feminine; rather they are qualities that have the capacity for association with either masculinity or effeminacy or with both.

ambitendency Although some authors use the term ambitendency in the same sense that they use ambivalency, others seem to imply that an ambitendency is ambivalency in action. Bleuler equates ambivalence of the will with ambitendency. See *ambivalence.*

ambition Psychodynamically, ambition represents a fight against *shame* (q.v.) by proving that there is no need to be ashamed any more.

ambition, negative Reik's term used to describe the behavior of the masochistic individual who evades every possibility of achieving his goal: he seems to follow the line of greatest resistance against himself, instead of that of greatest advantage for himself. The negative ambition is a grim reversal of an originally strong and positive ambition, in such a way that every opportunity is missed, every chance of success is turned into failure, every competition is avoided. The individual is 'so excellent a loser that it is to be suspected that he is not a good loser at all.' (Reik, T. *Masochism in Modern Man,* Farrar and Rinehart, New York, 1941)

ambit, partial Burrow's term for the sphere of the organism's partial, false, conditioned mergents. It represents a system of reflexly conditioned habituations which unites or separates clusters of individuals on a partitive or symbolic basis. Contrasted with total ambit.

ambit, total Burrow's term for the sphere of the organism's total or true mergents. It embodies such reaction-patterns as are expressive of an inherent principle of phyloorganismic equilibrium. Contrasted with partial ambit.

ambivalence (am-biv′à-lens), **ambivalency** Bipolarity; the co-existence of antithetic emotions, attitudes, ideas, or wishes toward a given object or situation. The term was coined by Bleuler, who differentiated between affective or emotional ambivalence, intellectual ambivalence, and ambivalence of the will. In current usage, the term ambivalence without further qualification ordinarily refers to affective ambivalence.

Ambivalence is characteristic of the unconscious and of children. Its overt appearance in the adult implies the presence of definite pathology, such as obsessive-compulsive psychoneurosis, manic-depressive psychosis, or schizophrenia.

Ambivalence is one of the fundamental symptoms of schizophrenia (Bleuler), and here it may appear in any one or more of its three forms. In affective ambivalence, the very same concept is accompanied simultaneously by pleasant and unpleasant feelings; thus a patient suffers the most intense anxiety that 'they' will shoot her and yet constantly begs the doctor to shoot her. Another patient professes great love for her nurse and seems, in fact, to be very positively disposed toward the nurse, but in almost the same breath she asks how she can kill her. In ambivalence of the will, the desire to do a certain thing is accompanied by a desire not to do that thing. Thus a patient wants to eat and does not want to eat; or he demands work only to become furious when something is given him to do. In ambivalence of the intellect, an idea appears simultaneously with the counter-idea. One schizophrenic patient, for example, complained that he had no face and yet asked for a razor to shave the beard off his face; another answered, 'Definitely not' when asked directly if he heard voices and when then asked what they said replied, 'Oh, all sorts of things.' Ambivalence of the will and intellect are often at the basis of what is considered to be obsessive doubting in schizophrenic patients.

Affective ambivalence was noted by Abraham to be characteristic also of manic-depressive psychosis, and he described these patients as having a 'constitutional ambivalence of the object cathexis.' Among the psychoneuroses, the obsessive-compulsive group most characteristically shows ambivalence of severe degree. The ambivalence seen in the schizophrenias is often distinguishable from that seen in the manic-depressive and in the obsessive-compulsive groups in that schizophrenic ambivalence tends to be of severer degree, more widespread throughout all the object relationships of the patient, more overtly expressed, and often fully conscious to the patient.

Ambivalence persists normally to some degree throughout life, but even in late childhood it is markedly reduced in comparison to the age period of 2 to 5 years, and in the adult it typically appears in one part in consciousness while the antithetic feeling or idea or goal remains unconscious. Ambivalence first makes its appearance in the oral sadistic stage, when introjection and incorporation are the important methods of forming object relationships. The object relationships of this stage represent the earliest and most extreme form of ambivalence, from which are later derived love and hate.

ambivalent Relating to the co-existence of antithetic emotions.

ambiversion The balance of the two traits, introversion and extraversion. The two main temperamental or personality organizations denoting the person's general attitude to the environment, namely, introversion and extraversion, are present at birth and believed to be constitutional. When, in certain individuals, extraversion and introversion are combined in about equal amounts their personality organization is more properly to be called ambiversion. (Hinsie, L.E. *Understandable Psychiatry,* New York, 1948)

amblynoia simplex et catatonica (amblē-noi'à) Evenson's term for dementia praecox (the schizophrenias).

amblyopia (am-blē-ō'pē-à) Dimness or partial loss of vision without discoverable lesion in eye structures or optic nerve; often, it appears to develop as a result of intoxication with drugs, including tobacco.

ambulatory insulin treatment See *treatment, ambulatory insulin.*

ambulatory schizophrenia See *schizophrenia, ambulatory.*

amelectic (am-ē-lek'tik) *Rare.* Indifferent, careless, apathetic.

ameleia (am-el'ē-yà) Indifference.

amenomania (à-men-ō-mā'nē-a) A term introduced by B. Rush to denote a form of monomania, the equivalent of what modern psychiatrists call the manic phase of manic-depressive psychosis.

ament (ā'ment) One afflicted with mental deficiency.

ament, facile See *deficiency, mental.*

amentia (à-men'shē-à) Subnormal development of the mind, with particular reference to intellectual capacities. A.F. Tredgold defined amentia as 'a state of restricted potentiality for, or arrest of, cerebral development, in consequence of which the person affected is incapable at maturity of so adapting himself to his environment or to the requirements of the community as to maintain existence independently of external support.' Its synonyms are: feeblemindedness, mental retardation, intellectual inadequacy, hypophrenia, oligophrenia and oligergasia.

In DSM-II, mental retardation refers to subnormal general intellectual functioning that originates during the developmental period and is associated with impairment of learning and social adjustment and/or maturation. It is coded according to degree, as follows: 310—borderline (I.Q. 68-83); 311—mild (I.Q. 52-67); 312—moderate (I.Q. 36-51); 313—severe (I.Q. 20-35); 314—profound (I.Q. under 20).

Amentia implies intellectual incapacity prevalent from birth or from the early months of life. Dementia has a wider meaning, being used to designate disorder in the intellectual, ideational, and emotional spheres. When the term dementia is used, there is ordinarily the implication that the subject at one time possessed healthy and relatively intact mental faculties, from which he subsequently regressed. Amentia, however, carries the inference that the intellectual defects have been in evidence since birth or a short time thereafter. The term amentia is more widely used in England than in the United States.

Some authorities use the term amentia as a diagnosis for acute hallucinatory confusion with a toxic-infective-exhaustive etiology. Such use of the word, originating in the Viennese school, has not been generally accepted in the United States.

Tredgold classified the amentias as follows:

A. *Primary or congenital amentia,* based on numerical deficiency, irregular arrangement, and imperfect development of cortical neurones.
   1. simple 2. microcephalic 3. mongolian
B. *Secondary or acquired amentia,* based on arrested development of cortical neurones

I. due to gross cerebral lesions 4. syphilitic 5. amaurotic 6. hydrocephalic 7. porencephalic 8. sclerotic 9. paralytic 10. other toxic, inflammatory and vascular

II. due to defective cerebral nutrition 11. epileptic 12. cretinous 13. nutritional 14. isolationary or sense deprivative

amentia, acquired See *amentia, secondary.*

amentia, congenital See *amentia, primary.*

amentia, degree of In England, where 'the legal concept of mental deficiency is that of social incapacity' (Tredgold), three terms are used to designate the degree of mental deficiency: *idiocy, imbecility,* and *feeblemindedness.* Each of these three grades is subdivided again into *high-, medium-,* and *low-grade.*

In England idiots are defined as 'persons in whose case there exists mental defectiveness of such a degree that they are unable to guard themselves against common physical dangers.' Individuals with an intelligence quotient (I.Q.) of less than 25 are idiots.

Imbeciles are defined as 'persons in whose case there exists mental defectiveness, which, though not amounting to idiocy, is yet so pronounced that they are incapable of managing themselves or their affairs, or, in the case of children, of being taught to do so.' An imbecile possesses an I.Q. of between 25 and 50.

The feeble-minded are legally defined in England as 'persons in whose case there exists mental defectiveness which, though not amounting to imbecility, is yet so pronounced that they require care, supervision, and control for their own protection or for the protection of others, or, in the case of children, so that they appear to be permanently incapable by reason of such defectiveness of receiving proper benefit from the instruction in ordinary schools.' The general range from the standpoint of I.Q. is from 50 to 90. In America the term *moron* corresponds closely to the English *feeble-minded,* though the I.Q. is usually stated to range from 50 to 75. (Tredgold, A.F. *A Text-Book of Mental Deficiency,* 6th ed., Wood, Baltimore, 1937)

amentia, deprivative Mental retardation (amentia) due to the lack of some constituent of the environment which is necessary for complete development of the brain. Among the several deprivative factors, three are well recognized. First, involvement of the endocrine glands, particularly the thyroid, associated with cretinism (in DSM-II, coded 31x.2); second, malnutrition ('*nutritional amentia,*' 31x.2); third, lack of sensory stimuli ('*amentia due to sense deprivation,*' '*isolation amentia,*' 31x.8).

amentia, developmental Mental retardation that appears to be occasioned in part by germinal and in part by environmental factors, and particularly retardation with psychos-social (environmental) deprivation (in DSM-II coded 31x.8).

amentia, eclampsic *Obs.* Formerly applied to cases of mental retardation who manifested epileptiform convulsions for a short period only, in early infancy.

amentia, exhaustive See *amentia; delirium, collapse.*

amentia, hydrocephalic (hī-drō-sē-fal'ik) Mental deficiency associated with hydrocephalus, that is, excessive cerebro-spinal fluid within the ventricles (internal hydrocephalus) or in the subarachnoid space (external hydrocephalus). In DSM-II, coded 31x.4.

amentia, infective Mental retardation due to arrest of development following some form of cerebral infection (in DSM-II, 31x.0). Three forms are usually recognized: meningitic, encephalitic, and hydrocephalic.

amentia, inflammatory See *amentia, infective.*

amentia, isolation See *amentia, deprivative.*

amentia, microcephalic (mī-krō-se-fal'ik) Mental retardation associated with microcephaly; ordinarily the greatest circumference of the skull is 17 inches. The majority of retardates with microcephaly are of severe or profound degree and would thus be classified as 313.4 or 314.4 in DSM-II.

amentia, mongolian See *mongolism.*

amentia, nevoid (nē'void) Mental deficiency associated with a venous angioma.

amentia, phenylpyruvic (fē-nil-pī-rōō'vik) Mental deficiency (usually idiocy) associated with abnormal quantities of phenylpyruvic acid in the urine; in DSM-II, 31x.2. See *phenylketonuria*.

amentia, primary When mental deficiency exists at birth and is 'due to inheritance and to some intrinsic peculiarity of the germ cell, it is called *primary amentia*.' (Tredgold, A.F. *A Text-Book of Mental Deficiency*, 6th ed., Wood, Baltimore, 1937). It used to be known as congenital amentia.

amentia, sclerotic (skle-rot'ik) Mental deficiency associated with cerebral sclerosis or overgrowth of neuroglial tissue; in DSM-II, coded 31x.3.

amentia, secondary When 'there is no abnormal inheritance and no germ peculiarity, but the full development of the brain has been prevented by adverse factors of the environment,' the resulting mental deficiency is called secondary amentia; it corresponds with the older expression acquired amentia. (Tredgold, A.F. *A Text-Book of Mental Deficiency*, 6th ed., Wood, Baltimore, 1937)

amentia, sub-cultural Tredgold says that 'from the psychological aspect, many defectives appear to differ quantitatively rather than qualitatively from their non-defective fellows; indeed, they are often regarded as merely the tail end of a normal variation, and have been termed *sub-cultural* defectives by Dr. Lewis.'

amentia, syphilitic Mental retardation due to central nervous system syphilis (in DSM-II, coded 31x.0).

amentia, traumatic Mental retardation secondary to cerebral injury (in DSM-II, coded 31x.1).

ametropia (à-me-trō'pē-à) Any error of refraction as a result of which parallel rays are focussed not on the retina itself but in front of it *(myopia)*, or behind it *(hyperopia)*.

amimia (à-mim'ē-à) A disorder of language, characterized by the inability to use gestures appropriately to conform with the idea to be expressed. The individual may also be unable to imitate or re-produce by motion the facial expressions and gestures of others. He may likewise make the inappropriate or wrong gestures in endeavoring to convey his thoughts or feelings, e.g. shaking his head sidewise when saying yes, and nodding his head in disapproval. This is the motor (or expressive) aspect of amimia. Its counterpart is sensory (or perceptive) amimia when the patient does not understand or assigns a wrong meaning to another's gesture, taking that a sidewise shake of the head means consent, and the other person's nod means disapproval.

amine An organic substance containing the radical group NH_2. Of particular interest in experimental psychiatry and neurochemistry at the present time are the *biogenic amines* because of their possible role in brain functioning. The biogenic amines are subdivided into the *catecholamines* (among which are epinephrine, mescaline, amphetamine, dopamine, and DMPEA) and the *indoles* (among which are tryptophan, serotonin, hydroxy-indolacetic acid, and bufotenine). See *epinephrine*; *ergotropic*; *serotonin*.

amine oxidase *Monoamine oxidase* (q.v.).

amixia (à-mik'sē-à) Restriction of marriage to one race, caste, etc., to prevent miscegenation.

amnemonic (am-nē-mon'ik) Relating to loss of memory.

amnesia (am-nē'zē-à) Inability to recall past experiences. Onset is often acute, following a physical or psychic trauma, but it may develop subacutely (as sometimes occurs in idiopathic epilepsy) or chronically (as in schizophrenia). Amnesia is more often feigned than any other mental anomaly; 'the first thing to decide in such a case is the presence or absence of those disorders which experience suggests may be associated with some degree of amnesia: alcoholism, epilepsy, hysteria, melancholia, mania, confusional insanity, dementia praecox, dementia paralytica, senile dementia, and amentia.' (East, W.N. *An Introduction to Forensic Psychiatry in the Criminal Courts*, Wood, Baltimore, 1927, p. 354)

When the loss of memory is associated with physical injury, in a person who prior to the injury had not exhibited any essential psychopathology, the extent of the amnesia in time is generally limited to the more recent and immediate experiences relating to the injury; furthermore, the amnesia is ordinarily complete for all experiences covering the time in question.

When the loss of memory is related to psychic trauma (e.g. loss of a loved one), it is generally restricted to loss of memory of experiences directly and remotely connected with the cause of the amnesia, and it may show a peculiarly selective quality. A hysterical mother was unable to recall any part of her life with her husband or child, although her memory was excellent for other experiences extending over the period of time corresponding to her selective or systematized amnesia.

The terms 'retroactive' or 'retrograde amnesia' are used to designate loss of memory for events prior to the trauma. The patient, while unable to recall those experiences, may still possess good memory for experiences more recent than the trauma itself.

amnesia, anterograde See *amnesia, retrograde.*

amnesia, autohypnotic *Repression* (q.v.), as opposed to normal forgetting.

amnesia, catathymic (kat-à-thī'mik) Circumscribed loss of memory which is limited to a single experience. For example, a patient with clear memory for all other events had no memory for circumstances connected with her pregnancy.

amnesia, circumscribed See *amnesia, retrograde.*

amnesia, continuous Anterograde amnesia. 'In continuous or anterograde amnesia the subject forgets every experience nearly as fast as it happens.' (Prince, M. *The Unconscious,* Macmillan, New York, 1916)

amnesia, episodic M. Prince says that 'in the first two types [episodic and epochal] the experiences which are forgotten may have occurred during the previous normal condition. In the episodic the particular episode which is forgotten may have been, strangely enough, one which from the

very important part it played in the life of the subject and its peculiar impressiveness and significance we should expect would be necessarily remembered, especially as memory in other respects is normal.' (*The Unconscious,* Macmillan, New York, 1916)

amnesia, epochal 'In the epochal type of amnesia a person, perhaps after a shock, suddenly loses all memory for lost *epochs;* it may be for days and even for years of his preceding life. In the classical case of Mr. Hanna, studied by Boris Sidis, the amnesia was for his whole previous life, so that the subject was like a new-born child.' (Prince, M. *The Unconscious,* Macmillan, New York, 1916)

amnesia, infantile Amnesia for the period of infancy and early childhood, i.e. from birth to the end of the fifth year of life. Memory for this period of our lives is practically nil and even those few isolated fragments which some people believe they can remember 'as clearly as though it were yesterday' are seldom wholly accurate.

amnesia, negativistic A condition in which the delusion is held that memory and orientation are lost.

amnesia, post-hypnotic Loss of memory for events transpiring during the hypnotic stage.

amnesia, retrograde Amnesia extending backward, to include material antedating the onset of amnesia proper. When the amnesia encompasses material subsequent to the onset of amnesia it is termed *anterograde amnesia.*

amnesia visualis verbalis (vis-ū-à'lis ver-bàl'is) Witmer's term (1907) for a type of *reading disability* (q.v.).

amnestia (am-nest'i-à) *Obs.* Older term for *amnesia* (q.v.).

amnestic aphasia See *aphasia, amnestic.*

amnestic apraxia See *apraxia, amnestic.*

amniotic (am-ni-ot'ik) Equivalent of *intra-uterine.*

amok See *amuck.*

amoker One who runs amok.

amoralia (à-mō-ral'ē-à) *Obs.* Moral imbecility; *psychopathic personality* (q.v.).

amor lesbicus (à'môr les'bi-koos) Sapphism; see *homosexuality, female.*

amorphosynthesis Faulty perception of the form of objects; one type of amorphosynthesis is *metamorphopsia* (q.v.).

amphetamine (am-fet'à-mēn) Benzedrine; phenylisopropylamine; a sympathomimetic amine similar to ephedrine but with a greater ability to stimulate the higher centers, particularly the cortex. See *benzedrine dependency; dependency, drug.*

amphierotism (am-fē-er'ō-tiz'm) A term coined by Ferenczi to indicate the condition in which a person is able to conceive of himself as a male or female or both simultaneously.

amphigenesis (am-fi-jen'ē-sis) A form of sexual inversion in which a person, predominantly homosexual, is able also to have sexual relations with members of the opposite sex. Thus one speaks of amphigenic inversion in contradistinction to absolute inversion, in which sexuality is restricted to the members of the same sex only.

amphimixis (am-fi-mik'sis) 1. A term used to indicate the fact that both parents contribute to the inheritance of their offspring. 2. Ferenczi's term for the union and integration of the component instincts (oral, anal, and urethral) into the genital function. The genitals attain their specific importance only when the earlier phases have been more or less surmounted and the genitals become the leading sexual zone and the central organ for discharging the entire libido. After puberty, the residues of the earlier developmental phases find expression in preparatory activities (forepleasure) and serve merely to stimulate the genital strivings.

Amsterdam retardation See *syndrome, De Lange.*

amuck Bleuler says that 'on the basis of two clear-cut cases Kraepelin would like to class with epilepsy the *running amok*

of the Malays, in which the patients run through the streets with drawn daggers, cut people down at random until they collapse, or, which is more frequent, are shot down or made harmless in some other way.' (Bleuler, E. *Textbook of Psychiatry*, tr. by Brill, A.A., Macmillan, New York, 1930)

amusia (à-mū'zē-à) Musical inability, whether for perception or (re)-production of musical (or vocal) sounds.

amychophobia (à-mi-kō-fō'bē-à) Morbid fear of being scratched.

amygdala (à-mig'dà-là), **amygdaloid nucleus** A part of the basal ganglion complex; the amygdala is a small, discrete, nuclear mass situated on the roof of the temporal horn of the lateral ventricle at the inferior end of the caudate nucleus. It projects directly to the hypothalamus, and interruption of these connections gives rise to sham rage. See *rhinencephalon.*

amygdaloidectomy (a-mig-dà-loid-ek'tō-mē) Ablation of the amygdaloid nucleus; this psychosurgical procedure has been used particularly in hallucinating patients, in the belief that the amygdaloid nucleus is a mechanism for transforming thought processes into temporally patterned motor movements, either of the vocal musculature as in subjective auditory experiences, or of the still vaguer projections or representations experienced through vision, smell, taste or touch.

amyostasia (à-mi-ō-sta'zhē-à) Muscle tremor.

amyosthenia (à-mi-os-thē'nē-à) See *aphoria.*

amyotony (à-mī-ot'ō-nē) See *aphoria.*

amytal interview (am'i-tal) See *narcotherapy.*

An Rorschach scoring symbol for anatomy response.

anabolic (an-à-bol'ik) Pertaining to or characterized by anabolism. In constitutional medicine the term is more specific, applying to the theories of Pende, who believes 'that it is becoming more and more possible to place the entire analysis and interpretation of human individuality upon the fundamental principle of rhythm and anabolic-catabolic balance of material metabolism.' (Pende, N. *Constitutional Inadequacies,* tr. by Naccarati, S., Lea & Febiger, Philadelphia, 1928)

The anabolic biotype is the fundamental underlying biotype to which the more superficial characterizations of the types called *megalosplanchnic, brachymorphic* and *parasympathicotonic* (q.v.) are related. See *type, pyknic; pyknic.*

anabolism Biochemical changes by which food is converted into living materials within a cell or the combination of cells forming an organism.

anachoresis See *atelesis.*

anaclinic (an-a-klin'ik) See *anaclitic.*

anaclisis (à-nàk'li-sis) A reclining. The infant is dependent upon its mother or a substitute for its well-being and sustenance. Such dependence is called anaclitic. Some individuals continue throughout life to depend upon others for physical and emotional support. The term is used in psychiatry almost exclusively from the emotional point of view. Individuals who lean emotionally on others are anaclitic. The term would be applied, for instance, to the passive, effeminate husband whose feelings, actions and thoughts are largely regulated by a dominant wife.

According to Jones, anaclisis is the process of a sexual drive becoming attached to and exploiting various non-sexual self-preservative trends such as eating and defecation.

anaclitic (an-à-klit'ik), **anaclinic** (-klin'ik) Relating to or characterized by anaclisis or dependence upon another or others; characterized by dependence of libido on another instinct, e.g. hunger. See *depression, anaclitic.*

'If we could speak of "object choice" in this early stage of infancy, we would say that the first object choice is an anaclitic one, in which the individual leans on another object for gratification of hunger, bodily needs, for protection, and the like.' (Nunberg, H. *Principles of Psychoanalysis,* International Universities Press, 195.)

anacusia (à-nà-kū'sē-à) Total deafness.

anaesthesia See *anesthesia.*

anagogy, anagoge (an-a-gō'jē) Psychic material that is expressive of ideals. Silberer believes that dreams are susceptible of two different interpretations. One of the interpretations is that usually ascribed by psychoanalysts, namely, infantile sexual interpretation. The other is related to the spiritual, idealistic, nonsexual forces of the unconscious; hence, the expression anagogic interpretation. The latter is of the kind stressed by Jung in his understanding of deeply lying forces in the unconscious.

anal-erotic Relating to libidinal phenomena of the anal zone.

anal-erotism Localization or concentration of libido in the anal zone. According to psychoanalytic formulations, during the infancy period, libido spreads diffusely over the body, but certain areas, known as erotogenic zones, take up a large quantity of libido. Three such zones merit special consideration: the oral, anal, and genital. The earliest concentration of libido is in the oral zone; with further development most of the oral libido shifts to the anal region, which in turn gives up a fair portion of its libido to the third or genital area.

The libido which is originally connected with the anal zone subsequently goes over into other services. Part of it, for instance, becomes attached to the habits and disciplines identified with anal training (regularity of stool, etc.); hence, regularity of action later becomes incorporated in the personality without conscious recognition of its original manifestation. Regularity, punctuality and allied character traits are therefore also called anal-erotic. Another part of anal libido shifts over to the genital zone, or, as it is called during the infancy period, the phallic zone. A third part remains in more or less original form, in the anal zone.

Psychoanalysts place great stress not only on the function of the anal structure but also on the results (feces) of anal activity. 'Thus the interest in feces is carried on partly as interest in money, partly as a wish for a child, in which latter an anal-erotic and a genital impulse ("penis-envy") coincide.' (Freud, S. *Collected Papers,* vol. 2, tr. by Riviere, J., Leonard and Virginia Woolf and the

Institute of Psychoanalysis, London, 1924-5, p. 169) See *character, anal; defense, character.*

anal-sadism See *sadism, anal.*

anal-sadistic Relating to anal-sadism or the aggressive instinctual quality identified with the anal region and its functions.

anal triad See *triad, anal.*

analeptic (an-à-lep'tik) A stimulating or restorative drug, such as caffeine or amphetamine. More specific antidepressant drugs (e.g. mono-amine oxidase inhibitors and tricyclic compounds, such as imipramine) are generally termed *psychoanaleptics.*

analfabetia partialis (à-nal-fa-bet'ē-à pàr-tē-à'lis) Wolff's term (1916) for a type of *reading disability* (q.v.).

analgesia, analgia (an-al-jē'sē-à, à-nal'jē-à) Loss or absence of the sense of pain. Analgesia may be of somatic or psychic origin; the psychiatric conditions in which it is most frequently seen are schizophrenia, conversion hysteria, and hypnotic states.

anality A general term referring to the anal components of sexuality, to manifestations of instinctual conflict centering about the anal stage of sexual development, to manifestations of anal erogeneity which indicate fixation at the anal stage of development. Anality is prominent in obsessive-compulsive neurosis, hypochondriasis, and masochism. See *anal erotism.*

analogue, libido This is an expression introduced by Jung (analytical psychology) to refer to 'the symbol which converts energy.' He adds that 'by this I define a representation that is suited to express the libido equivalent, by virtue of which the libido is led over into a form different from the original one. Mythology offers innumerable images of this sort, ranging from sacred objects like *churingas,* fetishes, etc., up to figures of gods. The rites with which the sacred objects are surrounded often disclose very plainly their character as transformers of energy. Thus, for example, the primitive rubs his *churinga* rhythmically and thereby takes into himself the magic power of the fe-

tish, at the same time imparting a fresh "charge" to the fetish.' (Jung, C.G. *Contributions to Analytical Psychology,* tr. by Baynes, H.G. and C.F., Kegan Paul, Trench, Trubner, London, 1928)

analysand (à-nal'i-zand) The one who is being analyzed.

analysis A word of widespread use in psychiatry and psychoanalysis: (1) alone in the more specific sense of psychoanalysis; (2) in combination with various modifying adjectives or phrases; (3) in its root, to form other derivative words.

analysis, active A method of dream interpretation used in a technique in which the analyst does not confine himself to the mere passive elucidation of the patient's free associations but intervenes directly and actively, making revelations and giving advice suggested to him mainly by the manifest content of the dream. This method, introduced by Stekel, is also called 'active analytical psychotherapy.' It constitutes a departure from the passive method of free association, and it is, indeed, 'an interpretation which lays more stress upon the manifest content of the dream' than on any other factor. Critics of this method emphasize the fact that it constitutes an 'intuitive' technique and that this 'intuitive power' cannot be taught to other analysts. Stekel admits that the 'imaginative insight into the workings of the dreamer's mind' is an essential factor. In the active analytical method the psychiatrist is concerned with 'interpretation that he has enucleated as much as possible from the symbolical wrappings without any aid from the patient.' (Stekel, W. *The Interpretation of Dreams,* Liveright, New York, 1943)

analysis, anamnestic (an-am-nes'tik) Investigations of the mental history of an individual, partly derived from the subject himself, partly from his associates, constitute what is called anamnestic or mental analysis. The expression is used by Jung to distinguish his methods from those of Freud. Jung says: 'The third method of anamnestic analysis is of greater importance, both as a method of investigation and of therapeutics. It practically consists in a careful anamnesis, or reconstruction of the historical development of a neurosis.' (Jung, C.G. *Contribu-*

tions to Analytical Psychology, tr. by Baynes, H.G. and C.F., Kegan Paul, Trench, Trubner, London, 1928)

Strictly speaking, all mental analyses are anamnestic; they are simply given other names to indicate special points of view.

analysis, blind In Rorschach interpretation and perceptanalysis, inferring personality traits solely from the responses to the ink blots without knowledge of the subject, his symptoms, or his history other than age and sex.

analysis, character Psychoanalytic treatment of a character disorder. See *defense, character.*

analysis, child Psychonanlytic treatment of children.

The technique carried out in children is quite different in many respects from that carried out in adults. For example, Anna Freud says of the analyst that 'he must analyze and he must educate, must in one breath permit and forbid, loosen and hold in check again.' Melanie Klein has done extensive experimental work under the heading of play technique.

analysis, content Interpretation of a subject's production on the basis of what is said, rather than on the basis of how it is said. The interpretation of symbols in a patient's dream, for example, is content analysis. Lindner advocated the use of content analysis as a supplemental tech- to the more formal analytical procedures in interpretation of the Rorschach test. He isolated 43 responses which were said to be characteristic of specific diagnostic groupings and/or to indicate essential motivants and dynamisms.

analysis, control Psychoanalytic treatment of a patient by a trainee in analysis whose therapeutic methods are under the close supervision of (i.e. are being 'controlled' by) an experienced analyst.

analysis didactic See *analysis, orthodox; analysis, tuitional.*

analysis, direct Direct analysis, or direct analytic therapy (as Federn termed it), is a method advocated by Rosen for treatment of schizophrenics. The method consists essentially of the therapist's entering into the patient's delusional reality and making direct interpretations of the patient's unconscious based upon the therapist's guess as to what the important and significant psychodynamics might be. The unparalleled success claimed originally for the technique has not been substantiated or verified by independent investigators.

analysis, directed See *analysis, focussed.*

analysis, discontinuous Interrupted or staggered analysis, especially a reduction in the frequency of sessions as part of gradual and planned termination of psychoanalytic treatment. So far as can be determined, only a minority of 'classical' analysts favors discontinuous analysis; it seems that most would agree with E. Glover when he says: 'Without being too dogmatic on the subject, it may be said that whereas an adequate analysis can be carried out using a five-session week of fifty minutes' duration, any further reductions should be viewed with suspicion.' (*The Technique of Psycho-Analysis,* International Universities Press, New York, 1955).

analysis, distributive This is an expression used in objective psychobiology. The analysis of information gained about the patient 'is distributed by the physician along the various lines which are indicated by the patient's complaints and symptoms, by the problems which the physician himself can recognize, by the patient's imaginations concerning the present and the past as well as by actual situations, attitude to the future and outstanding features of his personality.' (Diethelm, O. *Treatment in Psychiatry,* Macmillan, New York, 1936)

analysis, ego In psychoanalytic treatment, the uncovering and interpreting of the ego's (and superego's) defenses against impulses. Libido-analysis and ego-analysis go hand in hand in treatment: libido-analysis, for example, discovers *what* it is that has been repressed, while ego-analysis discovers *why* the infantile ego found it necessary to repress the impulse in the first place.

analysis, existential See *existentialism.*

analysis, expectant See *analysis, focussed.*

analysis, focussed Selective analysis; directed analysis; a modification of the orthodox psychoanalytic technique (which is termed by Glover *expectant analysis* because the analyst waits and follows the spontaneous unfolding of the patient's psyche with leisurely, free-floating, analytical attention). In the focussed or selective analysis, interpretations are purposively geared to a particular aspect of the patient's pathology—particular defenses, particular shades of transference, particular types of conflict, and particular stages of instinctual needs that seem to be of paramount importance.

analysis, fractional A technique employed by Alexander as one of his brief therapy methods. In fractional analysis, psychotherapy is suspended for calculated intervals, while the patient works through insights already attained and prepares himself for gaining more.

analysis, group Analytic group psychotherapy. See *psychotherapy, group.*

In Burrow's phyloanalysis, the term refers to the investigation of the impairment of co-ordinate group function.

analysis, minor This term describes a psychotherapeutic method in which the analysis of psychic material is rather minor: it attempts neither an exhaustive study of (as does Freudian analysis in general) nor deeper delving into the subconscious conflicts of the individual, but confines itself only to the elucidation of the salient details considered of primary importance in relation to the neurosis and the individual's personality conflict. In minor analysis the method employed is, of course, of shorter duration than in the so-called orthodox, or Freudian, psychoanalysis, with the analyst's intuition and perspicacity playing a leading role in this technique. Through the interpretation of the most conspicuous of the psychic materials the analyst arrives at conclusions, makes revelations, and gives suggestions with the aim of enabling the patient to gain a quick insight into his troubles. (Stekel, W. *The Interpretation of Dreams,* Liveright, New York, 1943)

analysis, orthodox The strictly Freudian analysis, better known as psychoanalysis, and constituting the science of the function of the unconscious. It uses primarily the technique of free association, interpretation of dreams, and elucidation of everyday mistakes in order to unmask the patient's unconscious motivations. The psychic material obtained in this manner is then made available to the patient, in order to prompt the emotional acceptance rather than the intellectual knowledge of his conflicts. It must be emphasized that the patient gains very little from the intellectual knowledge of his conflicts; what really counts and helps is the release of tension through emotional acceptance. 'It is not so important that the patient knows as that he *feels* the forgotten wish or experience.' Psychoanalytical education is conducted in various centers and institutes and is based on the training of students in Freudian theories and techniques, with a prerequisite that every student undergo a complete analysis himself, which is called 'didactic analysis.'

analysis, passive Stekel uses this expression to describe the feature of Freudian psychoanalysis which calls upon the psychiatrist to wait patiently for the production of free associations by the individual and subsequently to interpret them without active intervention. Departing from this technique, Stekel has introduced his own method of active psychoanalytical therapy, in which the analyst arrives at conclusions without the help of the patient's associations, simply by resorting to the study of the manifest content of dreams. Stekel asserts that if 'we follow the plan of waiting for free associations, the patient will take advantage of our inactivity in order to circumvent us.' In a general sense, Stekel and his disciples employ the term passive analysis as synonymous with Freudian *orthodox psychoanalysis.* See *analysis, orthodox.* (Stekel, W. *The Interpretation of Dreams,* Liveright, New York, 1943)

analysis, Schicksal Szondian depth analysis, an eclectic system that borrows heavily from Freudian and Jungian psychology and further emphasizes the 'familial unconscious,' or hereditary tendencies. See *test, Szondi.*

analysis, selective Pseudo-psychoanalytic treatment in which the material (e.g. defense mechanisms, levels of development, etc.) chosen for interpretation is a function of the interests (and problems) of the therapist rather than a reflection of the psychic structure and function of the patient. To some extent, such selection is operative in all types of psychotherapy, including psychoanalysis, and is probably responsible at least in part for the effects the actual character and personality of the therapist have on his techniques and results. See *analysis, focussed.*

analysis, self The analysis of oneself, that is, of one's psychic components. According to the most acceptable doctrines today, self-analysis cannot be expected to be successful save in the understanding of the most superficial aspects of oneself. It has psychotherapeutic value only in this meager way and is regarded by psychiatrists as merely an adjunctive procedure.

analysis, structural A type of psychotherapy described by E. Berne (*American Journal of Psychotherapy 11:* 293 -309, 1957), based on the belief that psychiatric disorders arise from pathological relationships between the various ego states: exteropsychic (Parent), neopsychic (Adult) and archaeopsychic (Child). Structural analysis aims at strengthening the boundaries between these states so that the Adult can become the effective executive of a healthy way of living.

analysis, training See *analysis, tuitional; analysis, orthodox.*

analysis, tuitional A term used by Ferenczi to refer to character analysis carried out for purposes of training the individual in the concepts and problems of psychoanalysis (Freudian) through personal analysis of the individual. The analysand is in the position of a student who pays tuition for his instruction.

analysis, vector Alexander's term for the process of determining the degree of participation of the organism's basic tendencies—reception, elimination, and retention—in the genesis and development of neurosis.

analyst One who analyzes, that is, resolves a whole into its parts. In psychiatry today there are four main classes of analysts of the psyche, according to the schools they represent. While the term psychoanalyst has its generic meaning, it is understood today to refer to those who adhere to the

formulations of the psychoanalysis of Freud. Analysts who follow Jung's concepts are called analytical psychologists; those who use the concepts of Meyer are psychobiologists; those following Adler are individual psychologists.

analyst, lay See *psychiatrist.*

analytic group psychotherapy See *psychotherapy, group.*

analytic psychology Jung's system of psychology, which, compared with Freudian psychoanalysis, minimizes the role of sexuality in emotional disorders. Jung regards the mind as something much more than the result of past experiences; for him it also is a preparation for the future, with aims and goals which it tries to realize within itself. The reminiscences of personal experience become unconscious and then join with fundamental ideas and trends of all mankind ('collective unconscious') which act as the background of all human thought and emotion. Jung stresses a mystical, religious factor in the unconscious.

analytical Relating to analysis or to the resolution of something into its parts.

analyzer Pavlov's term for the functional neural unit that provides the basis for differential sensitivity; the analyzer consists of receptor, afferent nerves and their central connections.

anamnesia (an-am-nē′zhē-à) *Rare.* The recollection of phenomena which immediately precede an illness.

anamnesis (an-am-nē′sis) The term literally means recollection. In medicine it commonly refers to the historical account of a patient's illness antedating the period of illness. It is distinguished from catamnesis, which refers to the history of the patient following an illness.

anamnesis, associative A type of psychiatric history-taking developed by Deutsch which attempts to elicit the causal relationship between the patient's somatic symptoms and his psychic structure. Of consequence in the anamnesis are not only the factual details but how they are said and when they are said in the interview. The patient is stimulated to give information by having him describe his organic complaints without making him aware of a psychological background. He is allowed to give a detailed account of his complaints and his ideas about the illness. Then he stops and waits to be questioned by the interviewer. When it is clear that the patient will not continue spontaneously, the examiner repeats one of the points of the patient's last sentence in interrogative form, using the same words the patient used insofar as possible. The patient then gives new information about his symptoms and is stimulated to further associations. Reference to others in his environment, present or past, then appear. The person who appears first in the case history is usually the relevant person from a psychosomatic point of view. Somatic and emotional symptoms with reference to this person are used as word stimuli for further associations. Then the patient himself usually correlates his organic illness with his emotional life. During the associative anamnesis, the examiner is on the lookout for three essential points in establishing the psychosomatic unity of the patient's complaints: the old conflict, the recent conflict, and the time factors involved. The associative anamnesis is used to greatest advantage with psychosomatic disorders. The anamnesis is taken in one sitting, which lasts from one to two hours. (*Psychoanalytic Quarterly 8*, 353, 1939)

anancasm (à-nang'kaz'm) Any form of repetitious, recurrent, orderly, sterotyped behavior or thinking which if left unperformed will lead to an increase in anxiety and tension. Though including obsessive and compulsive traits, the term does not apply to repeated fulfillment of recurrent physiologically determined needs such as sleep and sex. Dr. Helen G. Richter believes that phobias are also anancasms, because they may drive the individual to seek protection through compulsions or obsessions. ('Some Observations on Anancasm,' *American Journal of Psychiatry 96*, 1459-67, 1939-40)

anancastia (à-nang-kas'tē-à) E. Kahn's term for the compulsive, obsessive type of personality.

anandria (an-an'drē-à) Absence of masculinity.

anaphase (an'à-fāz) The biological term *anaphase* signifies the third state of the division of a cell by mitosis, characterized by polar migration of the chromosomes.

anaphia (an-à'fē-à) Absence of sense of touch; commonly used to refer to a relative rather than an absolute loss of tactile sensibility.

anaphrodisia (an-af-rō-diz'ē-à) Absence of sexual feeling.

anaphylaxis, psychic Reactivation of earlier symptoms by an event similar to the one that initially produced the symptoms. As in physical anaphylaxis, the initial event may be called the sensitizing agent, the later event the activating agent. A patient with severe asthma demonstrated psychic anaphylaxis; through psychoanalysis his symptoms were discovered to be derived from an early childhood experience of near-drowning. The asthma itself was an anxiety equivalent related to his fear of loss of love and his mother's scream for help. The sensitizing agent in this case was the early trauma of near-drowning; the activating agent was his fear of loss of love when his wife threatened to leave him. It is noteworthy that in psychic anaphylaxis, at least, the reaction is specific and is a response to the sensitizing agent rather than to the activating agent.

anarithmia A type of *acalculia* (q.v.).

anarthria (an-är'thrē-à) Complete inarticulateness. In 1876 Leyden proposed this term for *aphasia* (q.v.). See also *speech disorders*.

anasarca hystericum (à-nà-sär'kà hē-ster'ē-koom) A transient swelling, generally of the abdominal parietes, in a hysterical person; phantom tumor.

anathymiasis (à-na-thim-ī-à-sis) *Obs.* An old term for hysterical flatus or 'the vapors,' used by the old Greek philosophers to describe the soul; an exhalation.

anaudia (an-aw'dē-à) Aphonia.

androgyneity (an-drō-ji-nē'i-ti) Bipolar potentiality in sex, until the individual, in certain primitive societies, is turned into one of definite sex upon the performance of a rigidly prescribed ritual. Androgyn(eit)y is an anthropological term referring to this ritual and does not in any way connote the biological facts of hermaphroditism—the actual manifestation of the characters of both sexes in a single individual. [In Yiddish an *andrigines* means a namby-pamby creature, neither fish nor flesh.] (*Psychoanalytic Review* 16, 280, 1929)

androgynism, psychic (an-droj'i-niz'm) Bisexuality in the mental sphere. Dualism produced by the co-existence of masculine and feminine traits.

androgynous, androgynal, androgynoid, androgynic (an-droj'i-nus, -nal, -in-oid, -drō-jin'ik) Exhibiting the state or condition of, or the resemblance to a combination of male and female characteristics in one individual. Sometimes, used in a more specialized sense, indicating, in contrast to *gynandrous,* the predominance of *masculine* features in a hermaphrodite with certain female characteristics.

andromania (an-drō-mā'ni-ȧ) *Nymphomania,* (q.v.).

andromonoecism (an-drō-mō-nē'siz'm) See *hermaphroditism.*

androphobia Morbid fear of men.

androphonia *Obs.* An old term for homicide.

androphonomania *Obs.* Homicidal insanity.

anemia, cerebral An inexact, descriptive term for reduced blood flow to the brain. The diminished blood supply may be in the brain as a whole (generalized cerebral anemia) or it may be limited to one or more specific areas of the brain (local cerebral anemia). Generalized cerebral anemia may be acute, as in cardiac failure or in psychological or physiological shock, or it may be chronic, as in pernicious anemia, leukemia, other blood dyscrasias, repeated blood loss, cerebral arteriosclerosis, cachexia, etc. Symptoms of acute cerebral anemia include: roaring in the ears, spots before the eyes, swaying, weakness, apathy, somnolence, unconsciousness, pro-fuse sweating, and cold, pale skin. Symptoms of chronic cerebral anemia include: headaches, feeling of pressure in the head, roaring in the ears, dizziness, insomnia, or drowsiness, and in many cases progression to an organic reaction with memory disturbances, delusions, and hallucinations.

Local cerebral anemia is seen in cerebral arteriosclerosis, intracranial tumor, vasospasm, hypertensive encephalopathy, etc. Symptoms include fleeting pareses, transient aphasias, temporary sensory disturbances, hemianopsia, and focal convulsive twitches.

anemophobia (an-ē-mō-fō'bē-a) Fear of wind.

aneos (a'nē-os) 'Struck with the loss of voice and reason.' (Motherby, G. *A New Medical Dictionary,* 5th ed., for J. Johnson, St. Paul's Church-Yard, etc., London, 1801)

anergasia (an-ēr-gas'ē-ȧ) Loss of functional activity. When a clinical psychiatric syndrome is associated with structural pathology of the brain, it is classified by Adolf Meyer as an anergasia. The organic psychoses are called anergastic reaction-types.

anergia, anergy (an-ēr'ji-ȧ, an'ēr-ji) Lack of energy; passivity.

anerotism (an-er'ō-tiz'm) See *negativism, sexual.*

anesthesia, anaesthesia (an-es-thē'zē-ȧ) Absence of sensation.

anesthesia, glove A disorder in the sensory field in which the patient has no sense of feeling in an area roughly corresponding to that covered by a glove; this anesthesia is usually psychogenic.

anesthesia, sexual *Frigidity* (q.v.).

anesthesia, spiritual The total loss of moral sensibility, which Stekel characterizes as the cocaine of the soul ('das seelische Kokain'): practically a flight into moral irresponsibility. Certain neurotic patients use this mental mechanism in order to avoid making painful decisions.

anethopath (ȧ-neth'ō-path) An ethically or morally uninhibited person.

anethopathy (an-e-thop'à-thē) Also, less properly, *anetopathy*. Absence of moral inhibitions; unethicalness; Karpman's term for primary, essential, genuine, idiopathic psychopathy or *psychopathic personality* (q.v.). This is the group from which so-called habitual criminals come. In such cases, usually, no deep-seated psychic motivations can be elicited, and patients appear to be 'disease fast'—no matter what is done for them in terms of psychotherapy, their patterns of reaction continue unchanged. The conspicuous trait in their mental makeup is complete egocentricity, which is also reflected in their narcissistic sexual behavior. (Karpman, B. *Journal of Clinical Psychopathology 10*, 160-194, 1949)

aneuthanasia (an-ū-thà-nā'zē-à) Painful death.

anginophobia (an-jī-nō-fō'bē-à) Fear of choking.

angiogram (an'jē-ō-gram) An X-ray of the blood vessels of an area following injection of an artery supplying the area with a suitable contrast medium (usually Diodrast ®). In neurology, internal carotid angiography is used to study the arterial vessels of the cerebral hemispheres; vertebral angiography (arteriography) is used to study the circulation of the posterior fossa and the posterior portions of the cerebral hemispheres. Angiography is useful in demonstrating intracranial aneurysms, vascular malformations, and tumors.

angiomatosis, tregeminal cerebral *Sturge-Weber-Dimitri's disease;* hemangioma over the meninges of the parietal and occipital lobes and underlying maldevelopment of the brain resulting in mental retardation (31x.3). Patients usually also show a cutaneous angioma ('port wine stain') along the distribution of the trigeminal nerve.

angioneurotic edema See *edema, angioneurotic.*

anhedonia (an-hē-dō'nē-à) Absence of pleasure in acts that are normally pleasurable. It is seen often in schizophrenic patients and may be one of the earliest signs in the pseudoneurotic variety described by Hoch and Polatin.

anhidrosis (an-hi-drō'sis) Deficiency or absence of perspiration.

aniconia (à-ne-kō'nē-à) Absence of mental imagery.

anilingus Application of the tongue and lips to the anal zone, usually as a part of sexual foreplay.

animastic (an-i-mas'tik) Of or pertaining to the soul; psychic.

animatism (an'i-mà-tiz'm) The ascription of psychic qualities to inanimate as well as animate objects is called animatism. The condition is vividly exemplified, for example, in schizophrenic subjects, who often personify the whole of the inanimate world, as if the latter possessed the same mental qualities as human beings do. The same process occurs in primitive cultures.

animi agitatio (à'nē-mē à-gē-tä'tē-ō) Mental agitation.

animism (an'i-miz'm) The theory that all things in nature, both animate and inanimate, contain the so-called spirit or soul. See *animatism.*

animus See *anima.*

anisocoria (an-ī-sō-kē'rē-à) Inequality of the pupils in size.

ankle-jerk *Achilles reflex* (q.v.).

anlage (àn'là-gē) A particular genetic factor predisposing to a given trait or the entire *genotypical* structure of an individual. The term is an abbreviation of *Erbanlage* or *hereditary predisposition,* and this is the sense in which it is used in American genetics (see *predisposition*).

annihilation, Milligan method See *Milligan annihilation method.*

anniversary hypothesis This hypothesis asserts the following: if a person has lost a parent by death in childhood, and that person subsequently marries and has children, and is later hospitalized for the first time for mental illness, such first hospitalization is likely to occur when the eldest child of that person is within one year of his own age when his parent died.

annulment A mental mechanism by which the patient annuls, i.e. renders 'nonexistent,' certain specific events or ideas which are painful or disagreeable to him. In certain respects, this mechanism resembles repression, but it is basically of an entirely different nature. 'The fundamental difference lies in the fact that in annulment painful experiences are shifted into daydreams, while in repression painful experiences may be eliminated from consciousness and pushed into the unconscious, after which they may reappear in dreams or symptoms.'

Annulment can be compared with hysterical amnesia, with the following differences: (1) in annulment specific events or specific ideas are rendered 'nonexistent'; (2) the patient's amnesia is not general, but concerns individual factors; and (3) the knowledge of these facts at no time leaves the realm of the patient's consciousness. 'The patient behaves as if the event in question never existed.' (Stekel, W. *Compulsion and Doubt*, Liveright, New York, 1949)

annulment, marriage See *marriage, psychiatric aspects of.*

annulus fibrosus (an'ū-lus fi-brō'sus) See *disk, herniated lumbar intervertebral.*

anoesia (an-ō-ē'sē-à) *Obs.* Mental deficiency.

anoesis (-ē'sis) Absence of cognition or knowledge; a state of sheer feeling, having no reference to objects; non-cognitive consciousness.

anoia (à-noi'à) *Obs.* Insanity; roughly comparable to *vesania* (q.v.).

anomalous Relating to deviations from the average, but excluding the deviations due to disease processes.

anomaly A deviation from the average. In medicine anomalies are distinguished from disease processes, although the clinical signs and symptoms may be similar

in both. For example, an underdeveloped heart may be anomalous; it may be too small, organically and functionally, for the body in which it is located. The anomaly may be relative or absolute.

Personality may also be anomalous. The so-called 'character neuroses' are of that order, in that the personalities are in the periphery of the normal or average personality circle. Schizoidism and cycloidism are also regarded as anomalies.

anomaly, constitutional See *inadequacy, constitutional.*

anomia (an-ō'mē-à) Benjamin Rush used this term to mean congenital defect of the moral sense. In neurology, anomia is a type of aphasia with a disturbed capacity to name objects.

anorexia (an-ō-rek'sē-à) Loss of appetite.

anorexia, elective Conscious restriction of the quantity of food eaten to the extent of incurring a morbid reaction to foodstuffs. (Déjérine and Gauckler)

anorexia, mental *Obs. Anorexia nervosa* (q.v.).

anorexia nervosa (nâr-vō'sa) A psychiatric syndrome first described by Sir William Gull (1868) as apepsia hysterica; Gull proposed the term anorexia nervosa in 1874. The chief symptoms are inability to eat, weight loss, and amenorrhea. There is usually an accompanying mood change of depression and often also complaints referable to the lower gastrointestinal tract, the most common of which is constipation. It is worthy of emphasis that although the clinical picture is termed anorexia, there need not be a true loss of appetite; the important feature is that, for some reason, food is not taken in. Patients offer various rationalizations for this, ranging from disgust reactions to specific foods to fear of choking on food and to fear of vomiting after eating. In DSM-II, anorexia nervosa is classified as a special symptom, feeding disturbance (306.5), unless it is a symptom of other recognizable organic illness or defect or mental disorder.

Anorexia nervosa occurs typically in females between the ages of 12 and 21; it has been reported also, however, in older women and in men (in which case impotence rather than amenorrhea seems to be a cardinal feature). Anorexia nervosa is not a specific disorder and there is no neurosis or psychosis which is specific to this syndrome. Many authors stress the frequent occurrence of schizophrenia in such cases; others have grouped it with the obsessive-compulsive or hysterical disorders.

Differentiation should be made between anorexia nervosa, as described above, and pituitary cachexia (Simmond's disease). The latter tends to occur in middle age, is usually precipitated by physical illness, and weight loss occurs later in the course of the illness. In Simmond's disease, amenorrhea is seen only in approximately 50 per cent of cases, despite such other indications of endocrine dysfunction as premature aging, wrinkling of the skin, loss of sexual desire, and atrophy of the sexual organs. Lassitude and weakness are conspicuous in Simmond's disease but are surprisingly infrequent in anorexia nervosa despite severe weight loss. The 17-ketosteroids are reduced in Simmond's disease but normal in anorexia nervosa.

anorexia, primary mental See *anorexia, secondary mental.*

anorexia, secondary mental Déjérine and Gauckler describe as secondary mental anorexia those cases where the taking of food has been restricted with the idea of relieving some former digestive trouble. 'We shall give the name primary mental anorexia to those cares in which originally, and often voluntarily, the amount of food taken by the individual had, for some cause or other, been diminished. The common characteristic of all these patients is that, when their affection has reached a certain stage, they get to the point where *if they should want to eat they would not be able to,* for they no longer have any feeling of hunger.' (Déjérine, J. and Gauckler, E. *The Psychoneurosis and Their Treatment by Psychotherapy,* 2nd ed., tr. by Jelliffe, S.E., Lippincott, Philadelphia and London, 1915)

anorexia, social This is an expression used by Déjérine and Gauckler to refer to the anorexia 'of poor people, who are obliged by the necessities of life to deprive themselves [of food] to such a degree that,

when the illness or lack of employment which has caused these privations has disappeared, they find it impossible to take food again.' (Déjérine, J. and Gauckler, E. *The Psychoneuroses and Their Treatment by Psychotherapy,* 2nd ed., tr. by Jelliffe, S.E., Lippincott, Philadelphia and London, 1915)

anorgasmy (à-nawr′gaz-mi) Lack of sexual pleasure.

anosmia (an-oz′mē-à) Absence of sense of smell.

anosognosia (à-nos-ō-gnō′zhē-à) Unawareness of physical illness.

anosphresia (an-os-phrē′sē-à) *Anosmia* (q.v.).

ANS *Autonomic nervous system* (q.v.).

answers, syndrome of approximate An individual's tendency to answer questions with relevance to the general topic, but with glaring disregard of details—the so-called 'syndrome of approximate answers,' also known in psychiatric literature as the *Ganser syndrome* (q.v.), the condition having been first described by Ganser.

For instance, when shown a 25-cent piece the patient calls it a dollar or a dime. He writes three when asked to write two, raises the left arm when asked to raise the right, calls a match a cigarette; a comb is a brush or something to use for the hair. This syndrome usually occurs in persons facing criminal responsibility and may be an attempt to avoid trial and punishment. (Hinsie, L.E. *Understandable Psychiatry,* Macmillan, New York, 1948)

Antabuse A drug used in the treatment of chronic alcoholism; known also as disulfiram and tetraethylthiuram disulfide. It appears that Antabuse interferes with the enzyme systems which normally break down alcohol in the organism. As a result, when alcohol is ingested by a subject with an adequate blood level of Antabuse, there occurs within a few minutes a characteristic response, the alcohol-Antabuse reaction. This consists of flushing, injection of the conjunctivae, sweating, a sensation of warmth, and tachycardia; in 20 to 30 minutes, additional symptoms may appear—headache, dizziness, chest pain, palpitation, dyspnea, pallor, and nausea. With more severe reactions, vomiting, hypotension, vasomotor collapse, and sometimes convulsions may occur. Chronic alcoholics who sincerely wish to stop drinking are kept on a maintenance dose of Antabuse as an aid to control while other more specific therapeutic measures are utilized. Antabuse treatment is a form of deconditioning and as such it is to be considered adjunctive therapy; used alone, it is ineffectual in curing alcoholism.

anthropo- (an'thrō-pō-) Combining form meaning *man, human being.*

anthropocentrism (an-thrō-pō-sen'triz'm) The doctrine or belief that man is the center of the universe to which all else has reference.

anthropology (-pol'ō-ji) The science of man or mankind in the widest sense; the history of human society. This term designates the extensive branch of natural science which studies the developmental spects of man as a species, using archaeology as one of its main methods.

Although anthropological research covers the history of human society regardless of time and space, it is primarily related to early times and primitive people, as it deals not only with the question of the earliest appearance of man and his rise from lower forms, but also with all the problems concerning the differential development of human races, languages, and cultural forms. The individual person has little, if any, significance in these studies and is bound to disappear in the cultural or racial groups to which he belongs, since there exists no record of individual activity for prehistoric times.

Anthropology is usually subdivided into: (1) zoological anthropology, investigating the evolutionary conditions of humanity; (2) descriptive anthropology or ethnology, describing the division of mankind into races and studying the origin, distribution, and relations of these racial groups; (3) general anthropology, dealing with the evolution of mankind as a human society.

The last division is anthropology proper and, according to Franz Boas (*General Anthropology,* Heath, Boston, 1938), includes the following three main problems: (1) the reconstruction of human history; (2) the determination of types of historical phenomena and their sequences; and (3) the dynamics of change.

anthropology, psychological That branch of anthropology which deals with the psychology of different civilizations and cultures and which studies especially the folklore, the myths, and other expressions of the mentality of the people. Through comparisons the psychological investigations throw light on many observations made in children or in mentally sick persons in our culture. See *ethnology.* (Hinsie, L.E. *Understandable Psychiatry,* Macmillan, New York, 1948)

anthropometry (-pom'e-trē) The scientific method preeminently applied in the field of *anthropology* (q.v.), which uses the measurement of the human body for the description of the typical anatomical variability of a population. In anthropology, more attention must be given to the bony structure than to any other part of the body, since a comparison between present and past conditions can be based only on comparisons of skeletons.

The size of the body is measured by stature, by weight, and sometimes by volume. The length of the limbs is measured on the skeleton by the length of the long bones; on the living, by the determination with the greatest possible accuracy of the corresponding lengths. The head measures most commonly used on the living are length of head, measured from the glabella to the most distant point of the occiput; the greatest transversal diameter of the head; and the greatest width of the face measured between the zygomatic arches. 'These are preferred on the living, because they can be taken with the greatest accuracy, since the points from which the measurements have to be taken are well defined and the soft parts covering these regions are rather thin.' (Boas, F. *General Anthropology,* D.C. Heath, Boston, 1938)

anthropomorph (an'thrō-pō-mawrf) An expression used by some authors to designate a member of the group of psychologists and philosophers who in the past century studied the mental activity of animals and interpreted them in terms of human adult logic. (Sladen, F.J. *Psychi-*

atry and the War, Thomas, Springfield, Ill., 1943)

anthroponomy (-pon'o-mi) Hunter's term for his behavioristic psychology.

anthropophobia (an-thrō-po-fō'bē-à) Fear of man in general.

anthropos (an'thrō-pos) Primal man; one of Jung's archetypes. See *archetype; archetype, mother.*

anthroposcopy (an'thrō-pos'kō-pi) This obsolescent term is used in reference to various debatable procedures of character-reading from the features or other parts of the human body.

anthrotype (an'thrō-tīp) *Biotype* (q.v.); this term is used in some systems of constitutional medicine, to classify various constellations of all the morphological, physiological, immunological, and psychological characteristics making up the human individual. It is usually interpreted in terms as general as those of biotypology, that is, in the sense of including the entire phenotypical make-up of human organisms.

antibody-barrier system See *barrier, blood-brain.*

anti-cathexis *Counter-investment;* the energy that must be expended by the ego to maintain repression or otherwise block the entrance of id derivatives into consciousness.

anticipation The act of dealing with, doing, foreseeing, or experiencing beforehand. Anticipation of the future is characteristic of the ego and is necessary for judgment and planning of suitable later action. Anticipation is dependent upon reality testing, by trying in an active manner and in small dosage what might happen to one passively and in unknown dosage. With the development of speech, name symbols can be substituted for things, and thus anticipation can take place in the imagination in the model world of words. This affords the possibility of judging reality and is an important factor in development of the ability to tolerate tensions.

anticipatory maturation See *maturation, anticipatory, principle of.*

antidepressants See *psychotropics.*

antifetishism (an-tē-fe'tish-iz'm) Hirschfeld's term for aversions that many latent homosexuals develop as a protection against conscious recognition of their homosexuality.

'One man dislikes women with large feet, another is repelled by women with hair on their bodies. Such a woman causes him to have a distinct nausea. . . . His search is endless because he is truly, though secretly, attracted by the male. His sexual goal is man.' (Stekel, W. *Bi-Sexual Love*, tr. by van Teslaar, J.S., Badger, Boston, 1922)

anti-instinctual force See *anti-cathexis; counter-cathexis.*

antikinesis (-ki-nē'sis) *Obs.* Bethe's term for all forms of nervous response; those recurring regularly and in a definite manner in response to stimulation he termed *reflexes*, while all the volitional responses in which there is a variable factor due to the greater complexity and elaboration in the physiological mechanism he called *antiklises.*

antiklisis (an-ti-klī'sis) See *antikinesis.*

anti-nodal behavior See *behavior, nodal.*

antipsychotics See *psychotropics.*

antisocial activity, concealed See *activity, concealed antisocial.*

antisocial personality *Psychopathic personality* (q.v.) or constitutional psychopathic state; in DSM-II, 301.7.

antithesis, neurotic Opposition, contrast. Adler uses this term to indicate that the neurotic measures a thing, a force, or an event, by an opposite which is fitted to it.

'Among these I have regularly found the following: (1) Above-beneath, (2) masculine-feminine. One furthermore always finds an arrangement of memories, feelings and actions according to this type of *antithesis* in the sense the patient takes them (not always in the generally accepted sense), i.e., inferior — beneath, feminine;

powerful—above, masculine.' (Adler, A. *The Neurotic Constitution,* tr. by Glueck, B. and Lind, J.E., Moffat, Yard, New York, 1917)

antlophobia (ant-lō-fō'bē-à) Fear of floods.

anus Termination of the alimentary canal. See *anal-erotism; anality.*

anus feminarum amatarum lambere (à'nōōs fe-mē-nà'room àmà-ta'room làmba're) The impulse to apply the lips to the anal zone; anilingus.

anxietas (àngk-sē'e-tàs) A nervous condition of unrest; anxiety.

anxietas praesenilis (prī-se-nē'lis) Farrar describes three main forms of involutional melancholia. First, melancholia vera, characterized essentially by a clinical syndrome resembling manic-depressive psychosis; second, anxietas praesenilis, in which there is extreme anxiety with feelings of unreality; third, depressio apathetica, the central symptom of which is apathy.

anxietas tibiarum (tē-bē-ä'room) A nervous agitation, continually impelling the patient to change the position of his legs.

anxiety An affect that differs from other affects in its specific unpleasurable characteristics. Anxiety consists of a somatic, physiological side (disturbed breathing, increased heart activity, vasomotor changes, musculoskeletal disturbances such as trembling or paralysis, increased sweating, etc.) and of a psychological side. The latter includes '. . . a specific conscious inner attitude and a peculiar feeling state characterized (1) by a physically as well as mentally painful awareness of being powerless to do anything about a personal matter; (2) by presentiment of an impending and almost inevitable danger; (3) by a tense and physically exhausting alertness as if facing an emergency; (4) by an apprehensive self-absorption which interferes with an effective and advantageous solution of reality-problems; and (5) by an irresolvable doubt concerning the nature of the threatening evil, concerning the probability of the actual appearance of the threat, concern-

ing the best objective means of reducing or removing the evil, and concerning one's subjective capacity for making effective use of those means if and when the emergency arises.' (Piotrowski, Z. *Perceptanalysis,* Macmillan, New York, 1957) Anxiety is to be differentiated from fear, which lacks characteristics (4) and (5). Fear is a reaction to a real or threatened danger, while anxiety is more typically a reaction to an unreal or imagined danger.

Freud's earlier view was that anxiety arises by transformation of libido which cannot otherwise be discharged. He later abandoned this view and came to believe that anxiety arises automatically whenever the psyche is overwhelmed by an influx of stimuli too great to be mastered or discharged. Such *automatic anxiety* may arise in response to stimuli either of external or of internal origin, but most frequently it arises from the id, that is, from the drives *(id anxiety).* When anxiety develops automatically according to this pattern, the situation is called a traumatic one. Automatic anxiety is characteristic of infancy, when the ego is weak and immature, and of so-called 'actual' anxiety neurosis of adult life.

There is a second type of anxiety, characteristic of the psychoneuroses, which Freud called *signal anxiety.* In the course of development, the child learns to anticipate the advent of a traumatic situation and reacts to this possibility with anxiety before the situation becomes traumatic. The unpleasure arising from this threat of a danger situation automatically sets into operation the pleasure principle. The latter acts by enabling the ego to check or inhibit whatever id impulses might be giving rise to the danger situation. There is a series of typical danger situations which occur in sequence in the child's life; these persist to some degree throughout life in the unconscious, and it is one or another of these dangers which the psychoneurotic patient unconsciously fears. The first of these dangers, characteristic of ego development up to about 1½ years, is separation (known also as loss of the love object, and as primal anxiety); the second, seen at 1 to 2 years, is loss of love; the third, seen at 2½ to 3 years, is castration or other genital injury; and the fourth, which is seen after the age of 5 or 6 years, when the superego has been formed, is guilt (disapproval and punishment by the superego).

'We understand from our discussion of anxiety that when the ego opposes the emergence of an id impulse it does so because it judges that the emergence of that impulse will create a danger situation. The ego then produces anxiety as a signal of danger, wins the help of the pleasure principle in this way, and is able to offer successful opposition to the emergence of the dangerous impulses. In psychoanalytical terminology we speak of such opposition as the *defense* or as the defensive operation of the ego.' (Brenner, C. *An Elementary Textbook of Psychoanalysis,* International Universities Press, New York, 1955.)

'Anxiety is a biological reaction of the ego with the aim of self-preservation. In infancy, the ego and the id are scarcely differentiated, and it is almost impossible to determine whether a reaction belongs to the id or to the ego. It is thus irrelevant whether the anxiety of the infant (and actual anxiety) is psychic or not. According to Freud's formulation, psychic processes are somatic processes which are originally unconscious. It is only in the course of development that id reactions (which are unconscious) are taken over by the ego and thus gain access to the perceptive and motor end of the psychic apparatus. In other words, when the ego is differentiated from the id, the affect of anxiety reaches the system Cs. of the ego and is experienced there and expressed by the psychic complex "anxiety."' (Nunberg, H. *Principles of Psychoanalysis,* International Universities Press, New York, 1955.)

anxiety, anal castration Fear of castration displaced, through regressive distortion, onto the anal area. Thus many 'toilet phobias,' such as a fear of falling into the bowl or a fear that some monster will emerge from the toilet and crawl into one's anus, reveal themselves in analysis to refer to castration anxiety.

anxiety-attack, equivalent of The physical symptoms often associated with manifest anxiety may alone constitute the anxiety-attack. These *equivalents* (physical symptoms) take on a variety of forms; for example, attacks of sudden diarrhea or attacks of sweating, often nocturnal.

anxiety, automatic See *anxiety.*

anxiety, basic Horney's term for a feeling of loneliness and helplessness toward a potentially hostile world. This concept is more comprehensive than Freud's 'real' anxiety. (Horney, K. *The Neurotic Personality of Our Time,* Norton, New York, 1937)

anxiety, castration Fear of genital loss or injury; see *anxiety.*

The castration complex has its foundation laid down in the pregenital stage of development. Alexander, for example, refers to the many deprivations and losses suffered by the infant from the time of birth. He says that the child loses its mother's body and its fetal membrane at birth. A pleasure-giving organ is replaced by a painful condition. The next important loss is the pleasure-giving nipple (Staercke's oral primal castration); then the pleasure-giving stool is lost (Freud's anal primal castration); finally, there is fear of the loss of the penis.

These early losses, first expressed organically, are indelibly imprinted upon the psyche and appear later in the form of character traits, depending upon the way they were solved or resolved in the early years.

anxiety, conscious and unconscious A psychoanalytic term which stresses the power that unconscious anxiety maintains in causing symptomatic traits, attitudes, and actions. Unconscious anxiety, i.e. anxiety of which the individual is unaware, results in compulsive and impulsive behavior which is then secondarily rationalized to conform with conscious realistic motives. In this way unconscious anxiety functions in the unconscious as a well-spring for character-rooted symptomatic trends toward action. In other words, unconscious anxiety is not felt in consciousness as anxiety per se, but rather as a tense urge toward action, and its presence in the unconscious is inferred from this conscious urge. On the other hand, conscious anxiety is apprehended in consciousness as such by the individual, and motivates voluntary actions striving toward the relief of the unpleasant sensations of conscious anxiety.

anxiety, death A form of depression in

which fear of death, poverty, etc. is the most prominent complaint.

anxiety-depersonalization neurosis See *depersonalization.*

anxiety-depression Reactive depression. See *depression; depression, (psycho) neurotic; depression, reactive.*

anxiety, depressive The specific anxiety observed in a person afflicted with depression. '. . . the preservation of the good internalized objects with whom the ego is identified as a whole. In the latter case—which is the case of the depressive—the anxiety and feelings of suffering are of a much more complex nature. The anxiety lest the good objects and, with them, the ego should be destroyed, or that they are in a state of disintegration, is interwoven with continuous and desperate efforts to save the good objects both internalized and external.' (Klein, M. *Contributions to Psycho-analysis* 1921-1945, The Hogarth Press, London, 1948)

anxiety, discharge of The process by which unconscious anxiety (tension) is chronically, repetitively, and more or less constantly nullified through action and deed in the integral activity of everyday life. The reality activities of everyday life are utilized for the gratification of unconscious drives and urges. If this gratification did not occur more or less constantly and repetitively, these urges would succumb to repression and thus form the nidus for symptomatic anxiety and symptom formation. The trend toward the excessive utilization of this method of nullifying anxiety in contrast to such other common methods as the suppression of feeling or the guarding over thinking has been called 'the flight into reality.'

Sexual activity, with orgastic discharge, is a specific activity frequently employed as a method of discharging anxiety of unconscious origin.

anxiety, dramatization of The tendency of many patients to act out their unconscious conflicts in the presence of and for the benefit of the analyst with whom they are working.

anxiety, ego The threat of internal dangers to the ego in contrast to fear, which refers to the threat of external dangers to the ego. See *anxiety.*

anxiety, elemental See *panic, primordial.*

anxiety, erotized A paradoxical reaction to anxiety in which, instead of flight from the source of anxiety, the tendency is to head directly toward the source and enjoy it. 'We have called this reaction, where fear of danger is replaced by love of danger, eroticized anxiety.' (Laforgue, R. *The Relativity of Reality,* Nervous and Mental Disease Monographs No. 66, New York, 1940)

anxiety, examination It is the opinion of Freud that the anxiety attendant upon examinations is intensified by experiences of the past, usually unconscious, which had to do with 'the punishments we suffered as children for misdeeds we had committed—memories which were revived in us on the *dies irae, dies illa* of the grueling examination at the two critical junctures in our careers as students.' (Freud, S. *The Interpretation of Dreams,* 3rd ed., tr. by Brill, A.A., Macmillan, New York, 1933)

anxiety, free-floating Anxiety that is neither attached to ideational content nor otherwise channeled into substitutive symptoms; it is characteristic of *anxiety neurosis* (q.v.).

anxiety-hysteria Phobic neurosis (300.2); a primitive reaction type and the most frequent neurosis of childhood. The main symptom is a specific fear (see listings under *fear of*) which has usually arisen from the binding of primary diffuse anxiety to a specific content. The thing that is feared may be feared because it represents a temptation (especially a situation which would ordinarily call forth an aggressive or a sexual response), or it may be feared because it represents the punishment for the forbidden impulse either directly or indirectly through symbolism, or it may be feared because of a combination of these factors. Further, the phobia may be a fear that the anxiety will return; this is seen in some agoraphobics whose initial attacks occurred in the street. The phobia may not represent castration and punishment directly, but may be concerned mainly with a fear of loss of love.

The defense in anxiety-hysteria is (1) through anxiety itself, which gives warning to the ego so that the situation can be avoided; (2) repression of the impulse by development of substitutes for the real fear; (3) by projection of an internal instinctual danger onto an external perceptional danger (this is the most frequent type of displacement in anxiety hysteria); (4) by regression to childhood in order to ward off the wishes of the genital Oedipal complex.

The two most famous cases of phobia in psychoanalytic literature are those of little Hans (Freud 1902) and the wolf man (Freud 1918).

anxiety, ictal See *emotions, ictal.*

anxiety, id See *anxiety.*

anxiety, instinctual A term used by Freud interchangeably with the term 'neurotic anxiety.' In discussing the meaning and significance of anxiety, Freud distinguishes between true anxiety and neurotic anxiety: true anxiety is anxiety in regard to a known real danger threatening from some external object; neurotic anxiety is anxiety in regard to an unknown danger. Upon investigation, this latter danger is found to be an instinctual danger. Accordingly, the term instinctual anxiety is used to refer to neurotic anxiety. But there are some cases in which neurotic anxiety is intermingled with true anxiety. In these cases the danger is known and real, 'but the anxiety in regard to it is disproportionately great, greater than in our judgment it ought to be.' See *anxiety.*

anxiety-neurosis (300.0) In 1894, Freud detached the particular syndrome of anxiety-neurosis from neurasthenia and described the clinical characteristics of anxiety-neurosis as: general irritability, anxious expectation and pangs of conscience, the anxiety-attack, and phobias. In anxious expectation there is a quantum of anxiety in a free-floating condition which is ever ready to attach itself to any suitable ideational content. Thus common physiological dangers, such as snakes or vermin, are exaggeratedly feared; and the affect of anxiety is also commonly attached to locomotion, as in agoraphobia. But this is not a true hysterical channeling, for it does not originate in a repressed idea. The anxiety attack includes cardiac disturbances, respiratory disturbances, sweating, tremor and shuddering, ravenous hunger often with giddiness, diarrhea, vertigo, congestion and vasomotor neurasthenia, paresthesiae, awakening in fright (the pavor nocturnus of adults), urinary frequency, seminal emissions, blurring of vision, tinnitus, general fatiguability, etc.; in other words, the somatic symptoms may involve any or all of the bodily systems.

Anxiety-neurosis is very uncommon in pure form. Freud considered that the etiology of the anxiety-neurosis was a current or contemporary one, in which forced abstinence, frustrated sexual excitement, incomplete or interrupted coitus, sexual efforts which exceed the psychical capacity, etc. all unite in disturbing the equilibrium of psychical and somatic functions in sexual activity, and in hindering the psychical co-operation necessary to relieve the nervous economy from sexual tension. He found that it appeared in females in the following cases: as virginal anxiety or anxiety in adolescents, provoked by their first meeting with the sexual problem; as anxiety in women whose husbands suffer from ejaculatio praecox or from impaired potency; and as anxiety in women whose husbands practice coitus interruptus or reservatus; as anxiety in widows and voluntarily abstinent persons, when it is often combined with obsessional ideas; as anxiety in the climacteric during the last great increase in sexual need. Anxiety-neurosis appears in men in the following cases: the voluntarily abstinent, in prolonged sexual frustration as in a long courtship without intercourse, in men who practice coitus interruptus, and in aging men.

Freud considered the basis of anxiety-neurosis to be a deflection of somatic sexual excitation from the psychical field, and the symptoms to be substitutes for the specific activity which should follow upon sexual excitation, should such activity be allowed. Neurasthenia, on the other hand, he considered to result from a deflection of methods of sexual gratification from more to less satisfactory means. Anxiety-neurosis would thus be the somatic counterpart of hysteria; the excitation is from the soma and chemically mediated, and it cannot be mastered by the psyche and so is deflected into somatic channels. In hysteria, the excitation results from intrapsychic (rather than somatic) conflict which cannot be mastered and so is deflected into somatic channels.

anxiety, neurotic Freud distinguishes between objective anxiety and neurotic anxiety. He says that the latter is encountered in three forms. 'Firstly, we have free-floating, general apprehensiveness, ready to attach itself for the time being to any new possibility that may arise in the form of what we call expectant dread, as happens, for instance, in the typical anxiety-neurosis. Secondly, we find it firmly attached to certain ideas, in what are known as *phobias,* in which we can still recognize a connection with external danger, but cannot help regarding the anxiety felt toward it as enormously exaggerated. Thirdly and finally, we have anxiety as it occurs in hysteria and in other severe neuroses; this anxiety either accompanies symptoms or manifests itself independently, whether as an attack or as a condition which persists for some time, but always without having any visible justification in an external danger.' (Freud, S. *New Introductory Lectures on Psycho-Analysis,* tr. by Sprott, W.J.H., Norton, New York, 1933)

anxiety-object The displacement of anxiety to an object that is a symbolic representation of the individual who originally caused the anxiety. For example, a child fears a horse. The horse elicits marked anxiety in the child because the horse is a symbolic representation of the father who was the original focus for anxiety.

anxiety, objective See *anxiety-preparedness.*

anxiety, oral A psychoanalytic term denoting the infantile anxiety occurring at the primary or oral stage of libidinal (personality) development. (See *libido, displaceability of* and *phase, oral incorporative.*) It is assumed that such massive expressions of infantile rage and fear are associated with or stem from phantasy images within the infant, of an immense internal object in countless small pieces. This image, theoretically an analytic reconstruction, has its origin in the ideas of swallowing, incorporating, and chewing up a dangerous or loved object, i.e. the parent, a body organ, or part thereof.

E.F. Sharpe (*Collected Papers on Psycho-analysis,* The Hogarth Press and The Institute of Psychoanalysis, London, 1950) states: 'There must be some correlation between the excessive anxiety in oral stages, which is associated with the phantasy of a huge image of pieces inside; and the fact that at this time there is as little coordination of the bodily as of the psychical ego.'

anxiety, organic The anxiety that is associated with organic pain and that can be markedly attenuated in the dream state by the process of denial, transformation, and displacement; these mechanisms represent attempts at cure through wish-fulfillment.

anxiety, phobic Anxiety associated with a phobia.

anxiety-preparedness The increased sensory attention and motor tension which accompany anxiety and fear.

anxiety, primal See *anxiety.*

anxiety, psychogenic Anxiety states conditioned by mental causes, such as phobias, obsessions, doubts, indecisions, etc.

anxiety-reaction According to the 1952 revision of psychiatric nomenclature, this is the acceptable term for conditions formerly diagnosed anxiety state, or anxiety-neurosis. See *anxiety-neurosis.*

anxiety, real Anxiety produced by actual danger in the external world of reality. Freud calls it *Realangst* (real anxiety).

anxiety, resolution The therapeutic process through which the unconscious roots of anxiety are brought into consciousness and there mastered. The key to the resolution of anxiety is the recovery, in consciousness, by the patient, of repressed, albeit 'forgotten' infantile, instinctual, conflict-ridden experiences, which have been mastered or overcome, and which remain fixation and regression focal points in the pseudo-adult character. Full ego maturity, in the neurotic, cannot be achieved except through this arduous path. All the forces of defense and resistance combine and conspire to defeat this process.

anxiety, separation The reaction seen in a child who is isolated or separated from its mother, consisting usually of tearfulness, irritability, and other signs of distress. This is considered by most to be an indication that the child is attempting to adjust to the changes imposed upon him and, therefore, presumptive evidence of good emotional reactivity. Although these symptoms of protest may culminate in an acute physical upset and in temporary or even prolonged refusal to adjust, the separation symptoms are not in themselves thought to be evidence of personality defect or unbearable trauma. For a discussion of more pathologic reactions to separation, see *depression, anaclitic.*

anxiety, signal See *anxiety.*

anxiety, signal of The use of anxiety by the ego as a signal that an increase in unpleasure is impending.

anxiety, simple MacCurdy's term for a type of depression in which fears of sexual assault and bodily harm are prominent.

anxiety-state, pre-release The anxiety phenomena which some inmates of penal institutions develop through fear of being set free and having to face the world again. (Seliger, R.V., et al. *Contemporary Criminal Hygiene,* Oakridge Press, Baltimore, 1946)

anxiety, superego Anxiety caused by the unconscious functioning of the superego, which itself can become a source of continual danger.

anxiety, true See *anxiety, basic.*

anxiety, urethral Tension, anxiety, fear, and inhibition associated with urination.

anxiety, virginal Anxiety provoked by the first meeting with heterosexuality; see *anxiety neurosis.*

anxiolytic See *psychotropics.*

anypnia (ȧ-nip'nē-ȧ) *Obs.* Sleeplessness.

aochlesia (ā-ō-klē'sē-ȧ) *Obs.* Catalepsy.

A-P psychiatrist Analytic-psychological psychiatrist; Hollingshead and Redlich so designated that group of psychiatrists whose approach is essentially nondirective and utilizes a psychodynamic orientation with acceptance of such basic psychoanalytic concepts as unconscious mental activity, conflict, repression, and transference. See *D-O psychiatrist.*

APA Abbreviation of American Psychiatric Association; founded as the Association of Medical Superintendents of American Institutions for the Insane in 1844, its name was changed to American Medico-Psychological Association in 1891, and to American Psychiatric Association in 1921. In 1969, approximately 17,000 members were recognized by the Association.

apallic Akinetic; see *syndrome, apallic.*

apandria (ȧ-pan'drē-ȧ) Aversion to men.

apanthropia, apanthropy (ap-an-thrō'pē-ȧ, ȧ-pan'thrō-pi) *Obs.* Aversion to man, to human society.

apastia (ȧ-pas'tē-ȧ) Abstinence from food as a symptom of a psychiatric disorder.

apathetic (ap-ȧ-thet'ik) Without feeling; listless; hebetudinous.

apathy Want of feeling; absence of affect. The term refers to absence of feeling from the psychical, not from the somatic or physical point of view. It is observed in vivid form as a symptom in deep, stuporous states of depression and in certain schizophrenic syndromes.

apathy, disorganization Despair, one of the two great manifestations of chronic demoralization, the other manifestation being discouragement. Disorganization apathy constitutes a problem of morale.

apathy, emotional Hebetude.

apathy, euphoric This is an expression used by C.G. Jung, who says that 'we notice the same in the euphoric apathy of dementia praecox.' *(The Psychology of Dementia Praecox).* He refers to happy indifference, analogous to the 'belle indifference' of the hysterical subject.

apeirophobia (à-pī-rō-fō'bē-à) Fear of infinity.

apepsia hysterica (à-pep'sē-à hēs-ter'ē-kà) *Anorexia nervosa* (q.v.).

aphalgesia (af-al-jē'si-à) 'It consists in pain, which is caused, either in a particular region or in any part of the body, by contact with some special substance, such as copper, tin, silver or gold. To these may be added juice of lemons, peach-skins, and many other things which produce feelings of repugnance in some patients, even with their eyes closed (idiosyncrasies).' (Tanzi, E. *A Text-Book of Mental Diseases,* tr. by Robertson, W. and Mackenzie, T.C., Rebman, New York, 1909)

aphanisis (à-fan'i-sis) Extinction of sexuality. The concept "castration" should be reserved, as Freud pointed out, for the penis alone, and should not be confounded with that of "extinction of sexuality" for which the term "aphanisis" is proposed. Privation in respect to sexual wishes evokes with the child the fear of aphanisis, i.e., is equivalent to the dread of frustration.' (Jones, E. *Papers on Psycho-Analysis,* 4th ed., Wood, Baltimore, 1938)

aphasia (à-fā'zhē-à) A general term for all disturbances of language due to brain lesions but not a result of faulty innervation of the speech muscles, involvement of the organs of articulation, or general mental or intellectual deficiency. The word, 'language,' as used in this definition, refers not only to the expression or communication of thought by word, writing, and gesture, but also to the reception and interpretation of such acts when carried out by others and also to the retention, recall, and visualization of the symbols involved. Thus aphasia would technically include the agnosias and the apraxias.

Head has aptly termed the present state of opinion on the aphasias as 'chaos.' There are many systems of classification, some primarily anatomical (e.g. Bastian, Broadbent, Wernicke), others primarily functional or physiologic (e.g. Jackson, Marie, Goldstein, Head). Anatomical classifications have subdivided the aphasias into the motor type, with lesions in the lower precentral region, and the sensory type, with lesions in the superior temporal, the angular, or the supramarginal gyri. The sensory type is further divided into the cortical, subcortical, and transcortical groups.

Head classified the aphasias as follows:

A. Verbal aphasia—disability in the formulation of words.

B. Syntactical aphasia—inability to arrange words in proper sequence.

C. Nominal aphasia—defective use of words, inability to name objects.

D. Semantic aphasia—inability to recognize the full significance of words.

Following Weisenburg, the following classification has been suggested:

A. Expressive aphasia—apraxia; an inability to execute purposive movements or complex acts in the absence of paralysis of the motor apparatus for carrying out such acts; this group includes oral expressive aphasia or aphemia (comparable to Broca's motor aphasia and Head's verbal aphasia), and usually follows lesions in the lower motor area; also included are agraphia, acalculia, paragraphia or jargon writing, asymbolia, and amimia.

B. Receptive aphasia or agnosia; visual receptive aphasia or visual sensory aphasia or visual agnosia, including alexia (word blindness); auditory receptive aphasia, including word deafness, agrammatism, paraphasis, jargon aphasia.

C. Expressive-receptive aphasia, including total or global aphasia.

D. Amnesic aphasia—comparable to Head's nominal aphasia.

Brain suggests the following classification:

A. Pure word-deafness and word-blindness. In pure (subcortical) word-deafness, the patient distinguishes words from other sounds but does not understand them; the lesion is believed to be in the subcortical white matter beneath the left first temporal convolution. In pure or subcortical word-blindness (visual aphasia), the patient can visualize colors but cannot recognize words, letters, or colors; the lesion is in the lingual gyrus.

B. Visual asymbolia (cortical word-blindness). A combination of visual aphasia with agraphia due to a lesion of the left angular gyrus.

C. Central aphasia (syntactical aphasia). Difficulty in understanding spoken speech is associated with gross disorder of thought and expression, due to a lesion in the left temporo-parietal region; included are such forms as paragrammatism, paraphasia, jargon aphasia, and total aphasia.

D. Nominal aphasia (amnestic aphasia). The patient has difficulty in comprehending spoken and written language due to failure to recognize the meaning of words; the lesion here is usually between the angular gyrus and the first temporal gyrus on the left side.

E. Expressive aphasia (cortical motor aphasia, verbal aphasia). The patient may be completely speechless or he may be reduced to constant repetition of the same word or phrase; the lesion is usually in the third frontal convolution (Broca's area) and the lower part of the precentral convolution.

F. Pure word-dumbness (subcortical motor aphasia). Uttered speech is disturbed as in expressive aphasia, but inner speech is intact, comprehension is unimpaired and writing is normal. The lesion is thought to lie in the white matter in Broca's area.

G. Agraphia, acalculia, amusia. In idiokinetic agraphia, the patient may be able to copy but is unable to write spontaneously; the lesion is in the left angular gyrus. Agraphia may also be produced by a lesion in the second frontal convolution. In acalculia, there is a defect in the use of mathematical symbols; this usually occurs as a part of aphasia of the expressive type. (Cf. Brain, W.R. *Diseases of the Nervous System*, 4th ed., Oxford University Press, 1951.)

aphasia, amnestic Nominal aphasia; a difficulty in finding the right name for an object, even though the subject usually insists that he knows what the object is. In its mildest form, nominal or amnestic aphasia is a common disturbance and is seen following anxiety, fatigue, intoxication, or senility. When due to a focal cerebral lesion, amnestic aphasia usually indicates a lesion between the angular gyrus and the posterior part of the first temporal gyrus on the left side.

aphasia, auditory Word-deafness. 'In pure or subcortical word-deafness the patient distinguishes words from other sounds but does not understand them, so that his own language sounds to him like a foreign tongue. Sometimes he recognizes the meaning of an individual word, but not of a whole sentence. Owing to this defect

he cannot repeat words or write to dictation, but there is no other change in speaking, reading or spontaneous writing. . . . The lesion is thought to be in the subcortical white matter beneath the posterior part of the left first temporal convolution.' (Brain, W.R. *Diseases of the Nervous System*, 4th ed., Oxford University Press, 1951.)

aphasia, central Syntactical aphasia. 'In central aphasia, the difficulty in understanding spoken speech is associated with gross disorder of thought and expression. Spoken speech is fluent, in marked contrast to the speech of the patient with expressive aphasia, but is is disordered by verbal and grammatical confusions — paragrammatism — difficulty in evoking words as names for objects, actions, and qualities, and the utterance of non-existent or incorrect words — paraphasia (the syntactical aphasia of Head). The comprehension of spoken speech is impaired, but reading is less affected,and the patient can usually understand what he reads silently, though if he reads aloud he may be confused by the inaccuracies in his verbal expression of what he sees. Writing is usually less affected than articulate speech. Defective comprehension of spoken speech prevents the patient from noticing his own errors in speaking, and in severe cases he pours forth a stream of unintelligible jargon (jargon aphasia). The lesion responsible for central aphasia is situated in the left temporo-parietal region.' (Brain, W.R. *Diseases of the Nervous System*, 4th ed., Oxford University Press, 1951.)

aphasia, congenital A more or less general term used in the fields of neurology and neuropsychiatry. It refers to the inborn or constitutionally determined clinical symptomatic appearance of varied types of verbal or symbol-handling difficulty. The specific disability may appear in the fields of speaking, reading, writing, spelling, arithmetic, and even musical appreciation. The reading disability (dyslexia, i.e. congenital word-blindness) has received the most intensive study.

Specific reading, writing, and spelling difficulty is often found connected with a tendency to reverse letters and words in reading and writing. This condition has been named *strephosymbolia*.

'Congenital word-deafness, a rare form

of congenital aphasia, is characterized by the inability of otherwise intelligent children to comprehend the meaning of words heard. Deafness, in the ordinary sense, is not present.'

Certain forms of congenital aphasia, like stuttering, seem connected with the whole question of *handedness, eyedness, footedness, laterality,* or the predominance, physiologically, of one cerebral hemisphere over the other in motor function. (Hunt, J.McV. *Personality and the Behavior Disorders,* Vol. 2, Ronald, New York, 1944.)

aphasia, expressive See *aphasia, motor.*

aphasia, global Total aphasia, which results from massive destruction of the fronto-temporal region of the left hemisphere.

aphasia, jargon A type of central or syntactical aphasia in which the patient pours fourth a stream of unintelligible jargon. See *aphasia, central.*

aphasia, motor Expressive aphasia; verbal aphasia; word-dumbness. 'In this form of aphasia the expressive aspect of speech suffers severely. In severe cases the patient may be completely speechless or able to say only "yes" or "no," and even these words may be inappropriately used and cannot be repeated to order. He may be limited to the same phrase constantly repeated—a recurring utterance, Emotional speech suffers less than "propositional," and an otherwise almost speechless individual may be able to swear or utter other emotional ejaculations. . . . When the patient cannot think of the right word himself he will recognize it when it is offered to him.' (Brain, W.R. *Diseases of the Nervous System,* 4th ed., Oxford University Press, 1951.) The lesion responsible for motor aphasia is usually in the posterior part of the third frontal convolution (Broca's area) and the lower part of the precentral convolution.

Brain also differentiates a type of aphasia called pure word-dumbness or subcortical motor aphasia in which uttered speech is disturbed in the same way as above but in which there are no associated disturbances in inner speech, comprehension or writing. The lesion here is thought to be deep in the white matter in Broca's area.

aphasia, nominal See *aphasia, amnestic.*

aphasia, semantic The inability to grasp the meaning of words or speech. The patient may be able to utter words but does not understand their significance. He perceives the words, but does not apperceive them.

aphasia, sensory Receptive aphasia; inability to perceive speech by the senses, regardless of the retention of the power of using speech, which is usually meaningless and confined to parrot-like utterances. Sensory aphasia may combine visual aphasia and auditory aphasia.

aphasia, syntactical See *aphasia, central.*

aphasia, total Global aphasia; a combination of motor and sensory aphasia. See *aphasia, global.*

aphasia, verbal See *aphasia, motor.*

aphasia, visual Word-blindness. In pure (subcortical) form, the patient can visualize colors but cannot recognize words, letters, or colors, he can write spontaneously but cannot copy. The lesion is in the lingual gyrus.

Visual aphasia is more often combined with agraphia; this is known as visual asymbolia or cortical word-blindness and is produced by a lesion of the left angular gyrus. Inability to read is termed alexia.

aphelxia (af-elk'sē-à) See *ecphronia.*

aphemia (à-fē'mē-à) Speechlessness; loss of power of speech; *aphasia* (q.v.).

aphemia hysterica (hēs-te'rē-kà) Inability to speak, due to hysteria.

aphemia pathematica (pà-thā-mà'tē-kà) Loss of speech due to fright.

aphemia plastica (plàs'tē-kà) Voluntary *mutism* (q.v.).

aphemia, spasmodica (spàz-mô'dē-kà) Spasmodic speechlessness.

aphephobia (af-ē-fō'bē-à) Haptephobia; haphephobia; fear of being touched.

aphilanthropia (à-fi-lan-thrō-'pē-à) Asociability. An old term, coined by Wedelius.

aphonia, aphony (à-fō'nē-à, af'ō-ni) Voicelessness; dumbness. Aphony may be due to organic or psychic causes, though the term is generally used today with organic etiology in mind. Aphony conveys the idea that the patient is unable to use his voice owing to structural or organic changes.

aphoria (à-fō'rē-à) *Obs.* Asthenia and, particularly, the inability to increase energy or muscle tone through exercise; Janet thought it characteristic of neurotics.

aphoristic multiple sclerosis A type of multiple sclerosis characterized by pyramidal signs in both lower extremities, with subjective symptoms limited to one extremity. See *sclerosis, multiple.*

aphraenous (a-frē'nus) An older term for *insane.*

aphrasia (a-frā'zhē-à) Inability to utter or understand words connected in the form of phrases. A subdivision of *aphasia* (q.v.) which involves only the order of words in the phrase and goes a stage beyond individual words: the patient's power (1) *expressive* (motor), i.e. to utter, or (2) *perceptive* (sensory), i.e. to understand *single words* may be unimpaired, whereas *groups* of words forming phrases may baffle him completely as far as using or understanding them is concerned. See also *speech disorders.*

aphrasia paranoica (par-à-nō'i-kà) *Obs.* The clinical syndrome characterized by stupor followed by talkativeness.

aphrenia (a-frē'nē-à) *Obs.* Dementia. At one time aphrenia was used synonymously with apoplexy, but that usage is now obsolete.

aphrodisia (af-rō-diz'ē-à) The state of sexual excitation.

aphrodisia phrenitica (frā-nē'tē-kà) An older term for a psychiatric state due, as was thought, to sexual causes.

aphrodisiac Characterized by sexual excitation; also, any agent (e.g. odor) that stimulates sexual activity.

aphrodisiomania (af-rō-diz-iō-mā'nē-à)
The state of excessive sexual excitement; morbid desire for venery; erotomania.

aphronesia (af-rō-nē-zē-à) *Obs.* Dementia.

aphthongia (àf-thông'ē-à, àf-thông'jē-à) A form of motor aphasia characterized by spasm of the speech muscles.

apiphobia (à-pi-fō'bē-à) Morbid dread of bees.

aplasia (à-plā'zē-à) Complete or partial failure of tissue to grow or develop; arrested development; agenesis. It is to be distinguished from atrophy, which refers to the loss or diminution of structure which once had normal or average development. When tissue growth is partial, the term *hypoplasia* is used; when above average, *hyperplasia.*

aplastic (à-plas'tik) Without power to grow toward normal, healthy tissue.

aplestia (ap-les'tē-à) Greediness.

apocarteresis (ap-ō-kär-tē-rē'sis) Suicide by hunger or starvation.

apoclesis (ap-ō-klē'sis) Aversion to, or absence of desire for, food.

apomathema (ap-ō-math'ē-mà) *Obs.* Loss of memory.

apoplectic See *habitus apoplecticus.*

apoplexia cataleptica (ap-ō-plek'si-à kat-à-lep'ti-kà) *Obs.* Catalepsy.

apoplexy Stroke; see *accident, cerebrovascular.*

apopnixis (à-pop-nik'sis) Globus hystericus (Moschion).

apositia (à-pō-si'shē-a) *Obs.* Loathing of food.

apostle of the idiots The title generally applied to Edouard Séguin (1812-80), a French psychiatrist whose life-work was the care and welfare of the mentally deficient.

apparatus, autonomic All the vital organs, including the ductless secretory glands, unstriped muscles and the ganglionic nervous systems that have to do with the *assimilation, conservation, distribution* and *expenditure* of energy-giving metabolic products and the *elimination* of the waste products. This includes the entire digestive, circulatory, respiratory and urinary systems, sex organs, glands of internal secretion, glands of external secretion and the autonomic nervous system.' (Kempf, E.J. *Psychopathology*, Mosby, St. Louis, 1921)

apparatus, autonomic affective This is an expression used by Kempf, who says that 'the various systems of the body, if grouped according to their functions, form two great divisions, the *autonomic apparatus* and its *projicient apparatus*. The sensory streams flowing from the periphery of different segments of the autonomic apparatus constitute the affective cravings or feelings, and the sensory streams flowing from the projicient apparatus, as it is compelled to work by the affective stream, constitutes the kinesthetic stream.'

apparatus, lie detector See *detector, lie.*

apparatus, mental A more or less colloquial term for mental structure.

apparatus, projicient (prō-jish'ent) 'The striped muscle apparatus and the cerebrospinal nervous system proper constitute the *projicient apparatus* which has been developed by the autonomic apparatus in order to master the enviornment.' (Kempf, E.J. *Psychopathology*, Mosby, St. Louis, 1921)

apparition *Rare.* Visual hallucination or visual illusion, particularly when such phenomena occur as part of an organic delirium. Such visual illusions result from the visual distortion of an object and the interpretaion of the object in terms of the (usually unconscious and morbid) impulses of the patient. In alcoholic delirium, for instance, any object may be regarded as a person who is about to kill the patient.

apperception Conscious realization; awareness of the significance of a percept and particularly interpretation of what is apprehended by relating it to similar, already existing knowledge. See *distortion, apperceptive.*

apperception, scheme of By this term Adler indicates that the individual perceives what he wishes to perceive, and selects from his whole experience what is useful in view of his directive fiction, forgetting or rejecting the rest of reality.

apperceptions, Gestalt See *intelligence.*

appersonification, appersonation The act of embodiment or impersonation of another. From the psychiatric point of view it generally implies a form of unconscious identification with another in part or in whole. While the phenomenon occurs in many psychiatric conditions, it is very overtly expressed in patients with schizophrenia. A patient is thoroughly convinced that he is Christ; another says that he is the person who died in the next bed; a third affirms that she has the cancer her husband had.

appetite, depraved *Obs.* Pica.

appetitus caninus (à-p-pe-tē'toos kà-nē' noos) (L. 'doglike appetite') *Obs.* Bulimia.

apprehensio (à-p-pre-hen'sē-ō) P. Zacchias used this term for catalepsy.

apprehension Royce defines the term as '(1) The intellectual act or process by which a relatively simple object is understood, grasped, or brought before the mind. (2) A relatively simple or elementary intellectual act itself (without regard to its object), as opposed to a complex act, such as judgment, or a more finished sort of knowledge, such as comprehension.' (Baldwin, J.M. *Dictionary of Philosophy and Psychology*, vols. 1-2, Macmillan, New York, 1928, p. 62)

If the object is not understood correctly, the expression misapprehension is used. Apprehension is 'merely a simple cognition.' (ibid.). In his *Critique of Pure Reason*, Kant regards apprehension as a synthetic act, in which a perceived object is described in terms of time and space.

The history of the word apprehension shows that it has been used synonymously with a variety of words: intellectuality, cognition, perception, conception, retention, attention, memory, imagination, emotion, etc. In psychiatry such synonymous use has been abandoned.

There is a tendency today to disregard also another meaning of the term, viz. a mental concept from which one judges what may happen in the future. The inclusion of a prophetic implication is now less frequently associated with the word, when used by psychiatrists. When it is used in this sense, it is almost invariably connected with the feeling of fear, anxiety, or dread. States of so-called apprehension are common in psychiatric practice and are generally identified with fear of impending danger. There is a tendency, however, to use more circumscribed expressions, such as anxiety, in place of such a general term as apprehension.

apprehension, irresistible Kraepelin's term for what is now termed 'compulsive-obsessive psychoneurosis.'

apprehensiveness The faculty of apprehending, of seizing quickly with the mind. Psychiatrists seldom use the term today to refer to the act of ready and quick apprehension. But the tendency to use the adjective apprehensive to imply anticipation of evil or harm is common.

approach, environmental From the standpoint of the psychiatric social worker 'the *personal approach* is through the interview as it is employed to explore emotional reactions, interpret conflicts, suggest new points of view and stimulate interest in new lines of action. The *environmental approach* covers essentially manipulation of the material situations presented by physical illness, financial difficulty, employment, neighborhood conditions, etc.; this manipulation of the environment is exercised to relieve undue external pressure and call forth new and better attitudes in the client toward his responsibilities so that ultimately he may carry them unassisted.' (*Proceedings of the American Association of Hospital Social Workers,* 1926). See *treatment, psychiatric social.*

apraxia (à-prak′sē-à) A disorder of voluntary movement in which the patient is more or less completely incapacitated to carry out purposeful movements, in spite of the absence of paralysis or other motor or sensory impairment. Apraxia of gait, for example, is inability to use the lower limbs in walking even though no sensory impairment or motor weakness is demonstrable. Object apraxia (less correctly called objective apraxia) consists of im-

pairment in the handling of objects, as in the patient who slips his right foot into his left shoe.

There is no general agreement concerning the way in which apraxia is produced. It may occur in diffuse or more focalized cortical lesions, perhaps especially if the corpus callosum is involved, but it may also result from subcortical lesions.

apraxia, akinetic A condition in which the ability to carry out spontaneous movements is lost.

apraxia, amnestic Inability to carry out a movement on command, owing to inability to remember a command—though there is the ability to perform that movement.

apraxia, constructional or constructive A type of apraxia in which the patient, when asked to reproduce simple geometric patterns with matches, for example, is unable to connect the separate parts correctly; the end result is disorder and chaos. The defect is not related to intelligence and the patient with this kind of apraxia often recognizes his errors. See *Gerstmann syndrome.*

apraxia, dressing A type of apraxia in which the patient is unable to don his clothes properly, putting his jacket on upside down, for example. Dressing apraxia is seen most commonly in parietal lobe lesions, such as occur in Pick's disease.

apraxia, ideational Sensory apraxia; loss of the conceptional process. The patient does not know the use of objects; he may fumble with a toothbrush, pen or cigarette, but will not know what to do with them.

apraxia, motor Along with ability to understand and name objects, the inability to carry out the purposive movement with them.

apraxia, sensory See *apraxia, ideational.*

aprosexia (ap-rō-sek′sē-à) Inability to maintain attention. The condition is common in organic states that affect the brain and psychiatric conditions in which (1) there are present overwhelming emotions that constantly interfere with thought processes; (2) ideas are sparse, as in states of pronounced depression; (3) ideas are so abundant that the patient cannot fix attention upon external objects, as in productive mania; (4) fixed ideas of the patient compel his constant attention. The patient may show excellent attentive capacity when his special interests are involved, that is, aprosexia may be selective for certain matters.

apsithyria, apsithuria (ap-si-thī'rē-à, thū'-rē-à) *Obs.* Aphonia.

apsychia (ap-sik'ē-à, à-sī'kē-à) *Obs.* Loss of consciousness.

apsychognosia (à-sī-kog-nō'zē-à) Lack of awareness of one's own personality or mental state; used particularly to refer to the chronic alcoholic's typical lack of awareness of the outside world's reaction to his drinking.

apsychosis *Rare.* In Barnes's terminology, absence of mental functioning and particularly of thinking, as in stupor. Barnes also speaks of *hyperpsychosis* (exaggeration of mental functioning), *hypopsychosis* (diminution of function), and *parapsychosis* (perversion of function). Barnes, F.M. *An Introduction to the Study of Mental Disorders*, 2nd ed., Mosby, St. Louis, 1923)

aptitude In occupational therapy, the ability and natural skill of a patient in certain lines of endeavor. See also *test, aptitude.*

aquaphobia (ak-wà-fō'bē-à) A special morbid fear of water, i.e. of going (for bathing or swimming purposes) into a *body* of water where one may drown.

arachnephobia (à-rak-nē-fō'bē-à) fear of spiders.

arachnoid (a-räk'noid) See *meninges.*

arachnoiditis See *pseudotumor cerebri.*

arc de cercle (ärk dē ser'kl) (F. 'arc or segment of a circle') A pathological posture characterized by pronounced bending of the body, anteriorly or posteriorly. In describing a phase of so-called hystero-epilepsy, one author says: 'a period of disordered movements commences,

which generally begins with the phenomenon called a "segment of a circle" (l'arc de cercle), very analogous to that observed in some tetanic patients; the body rests on the feet and occiput only; the trunk is raised, and according to the expression of the patients forms a kind of "bridge" on the bed; most frequently this segment of the circle consists in opisthotonos, more rarely pleurosthotonos, sometimes also in emprosthotonos.' (Tuke, D.H. *A Dictionary of Psychological Medicine*, vols. 1-2, Blakiston, Philadelphia, 1892)

arc, psychic reflex Ferenczi's term for that primitive onto- and phylo-genetic stage of development in which adaptation is not achieved by a modification of the outer world, but instead by modifications of the organism itself, and particularly by simple motor discharge. Freud called this the *autoplastic* stage of development.

archaeology The science of antiquities. This term denotes the science which studies the history, use, and meaning of prehistoric objects in different countries, in order to throw light on the remote past of mankind (see *anthropology*). 'Under unusually favorable conditions *archaeological* data give us information on the gradual changes of material culture and allow also inferences regarding a few aspects of the inner life of the people.' (Boas, F. *General Anthropology*, Heath, Boston, 1938)

archaic Antiquated; stemming from a primitive or prehistoric age. The psyche appears to have its own ancestral past just as the soma possesses its historical background. It seems that, from the psychical point of view also, ontogeny repeats phylogeny. Thought and language in their development progress from feeling, concreteness and perception to reasoning, differentiation and abstraction. Psychiatrists recognize psychical material (primordial images) which is representative of the distant past of humanity or which is expressed in the framework of primitive mentality. Archaic modes of thinking and expression are seen most frequently in the schizophrenias. See *paleologic.*

archaism From the standpoint of analytical psychology (Jung), archaism means 'the *ancient* character of psychic contents and functions. By this I do not mean archaistic, i.e., imitated antiquity, as exhibited for instance in later Roman sculpture or the nineteenth century "Gothic," but qualities which have the character of *survival*. All those psychological traits can be so described which essentially correspond with the qualities of primitive mentality. It is clear that archaism primarily clings to the phantasies of the unconscious, i.e., to such products of unconscious phantasy-activity as reach consciousness. The quality of the image is archaic when it possess unmistakable mythological parallels.' (Jung, C.G. *Psychological Types*, tr. by Baynes, H.G., Harcourt, Brace, New York and London, 1923)

archeopsychism (ar-kē-ō-sī'kiz'm) See *archaism.*

archetype (är'kē-tīp) 'In the theory of C.G. Jung, an inherited idea or mode of thought, derived from the experience of the race, and present in the unconscious of the individual, controlling his ways of perceiving the world.' (*Webster's New International Dictionary*, 2nd ed., Merriam, Springfield, Mass., 1948.) An understanding of Jung's concept of these archetypes, especially with regard to his application of them in therapy, is basic for an understanding of Jung's system of psychology.

The unconscious part of the mind is separated by Jung into two subdivisions, termed by him the *personal* unconscious and the *collective* unconscious. (1) The *personal* unconscious lies directly beneath consciousness and contains psychic material that is not in consciousness, yet is subject to conscious recall. Because it has to do with the person's life-experience this material can be made conscious, at least theoretically, since we are dealing with the actual person whom it concerns. Thus the term personal unconscious is particularly apt. (2) Constituting by far the largest area of the mind, and situated beneath the personal unconscious, is the *collective* unconscious. The material contained in this area is *not* derived from the life-experience of the person, but from the life-experience of the person's progenitors, *all of them*, and, therefore, of the entire human race. The whole history of human psychic functioning, the collective experience of humanity, is the inheritance of each individual psyche. The record of this history and experience contains ideas, modes of thought, patterns of reaction that are fundamental and typical in all humanity: the archetypes are their representations in the collective unconscious.

Jung believed that the collective unconscious represented the wisdom of the ages and, in consequence, contained tendencies superior to the individual's. This conception 'had a significant influence on his therapeutic approach. A part of the process of self-development consisted in bringing a person into contact with his collective unconscious. This was done to a great extent through the interpretation of dreams. Jung saw the dream as having meanings on several levels. There was the personal meaning relating to the immediate life of the patient. If one pushed associations beyond that, one finally reached the collective unconscious meaning. Thus a dream about the father would finally come to a conception of all fatherhood, the father archetype. At this level supposedly the knowledge acquired by mankind through the centuries becomes available to the patient.' (Thompson, C. *Psychoanalysis: Evolution and Development*, Hermitage House, New York, 1950)

'In the language of the unconscious, which is a picture-language, the archetypes appear in personified or symbolized picture form. Their number is relatively limited, for it corresponds to the "possibilities of typical fundamental experiences," such as human beings have had since the beginning of time. Their significance for us lies precisely in that "primal experience" which they represent and mediate. The motives of the archetypal images are the same in all cultures. We find them repeated in all mythologies, fairy tales, religious traditions, and mysteries. What else is the myth of the night sea-voyage, of the wandering hero, or of the sea monster than our timeless knowledge, transformed into a picture of the sun's setting and rebirth? Prometheus, the stealer of fire, Hercules, the slayer of dragons, numerous myths of creation, the fall from Paradise, the sacrificial mysteries, the virgin birth, the treacherous betrayal of the hero, the dismembering of Osiris, and many other myths and tales portray psychic processes in symbolic-imaginary form.

Likewise the forms of the snake, the fish, the sphinx, the helpful animals, the World Tree, the Great Mother, and otherwise the enchanted prince, the *puer aeternus,* the Magi, the Wise Man, Paradise, etc., stand for certain figures and contents of the collective unconscious. The sum of the archetypes signifies thus for Jung the sum of all the latent potentialities of the human psyche — an enormous, inexhaustible store of ancient knowledge concerning the most profound relations between God, man, and the cosmos.' (Jacobi, J. *The Psychology of C.G. Jung,* Kegan Paul, Trench, Trubner, London, 1942)

archetype, mother 'The archetype "Mother" is pre-existent and superordinate to every form of manifestation of the "motherly." It is a constant core of meaning, which can take on all the aspects and symbols of the "motherly." The primordial image of the mother and the characteristics of the "Great Mother" with all paradoxical traits are the same in the soul of present-day man as in mythological times.' (Jacobi, J. *The Psychology of C. G. Jung,* Kegan Paul, Trench, Trubner, London, 1942) See *Magna Mater; individuation.*

archi-sleep See *dream.*

area, catchment See *psychiatry, community.*

area, delinquency A neighborhood or community with a disproportionately high rate of juvenile delinquents. It is typically an area adjacent to the central business district or a major industrial development and 'characterized by physical deterioration, decreasing population, high rates of dependency, high percentages of foreign-born and Negro population, high rates of adult offenders and marked deterioration of the traditional institutions and neighborhood organization.' (Shaw, C.R. and McKay, H.D. *Social Factors in Juvenile Delinquency,* National Commission on Law Observance and Enforcement, Government Printing Office, Washington, D.C., 1931)

area striata (â'rē-à strē-à'ta) See *lobe, occipital.*

arecoline A parasympatho-mimetic drug which has been noted on occasion to pro-

duce short-lived intervals of lucidity in schizophrenic subjects.

argininosuccinic acidurea (ar-jin-ēn-ō-suk-sin'ik as-id-ūr'ē-à) A metabolic defect characterized by a high quantity of argininosuccinic acid in the cerebrospinal fluid and urine; associated with this are epilepsy, EEG dysrhythmia, and mental retardation (31x.2). Known also as Allan-Dent disease.

Argyll Robertson pupil (Argyll Robertson, Scottish physician, 1837-1909) A pupil, usually myotic, which responds to accommodation but does not respond to light and reacts slowly to mydriatics. It is usually found in patients with neuro-syphilis, although it may appear in other conditions (traumatic brain injury, brain tumor, infectious diseases of the brain, multiple sclerosis, etc.).

Ariëns Kappers (ä'ri-ens käp'ērs) *Cornelius Ubbo,* (b. 1877) Dutch neuropathologist.

aristogenic (a-ris-tō-jen'ik) Best-endowed eugenically. A term describing the individuals whose parenthood is to be encouraged through *positive* eugenic measures. See *eugenics.*

arithomomania (à-rith-mō-mā'nē-à) A morbid impulse to count. The condition may be observed in a variety of psychiatric disorders, but most commonly in obsessive-compulsive neurosis.
'Case 6. Obsession of arithmomania. A woman became obliged to count the boards in the floor, the steps in the staircase, etc. — acts which she performed in a state of ridiculous distress.
Reinstatement. She had begun the counting in order to turn her mind from obsessive ideas of temptation. She had succeeded in so doing, but the impulse to count had replaced the original obsession.' (Freud, S. *Collected Papers,* vol. 1, tr. by Riviere, J., Leonard and Virginia Woolf and the Institute of Psychoanalysis, London, 1924-25)

Arnold-Chiari malformation (Friedrich Arnold, German anatomist, 1803-1890; Hans Chiari; German physician, 1851-1916) A congenital abnormality of the central nervous system characterized by protusion of the medulla and cerebellum into the spinal conal. Hydrocephalus is usually present and, commonly, there is an associated meningomyelocele and lumbosacral spina bifida.

arousal Cortical vigilance, or readiness, or tone, which is presumed to be in response to sensory stimulation (? via the reticular activating system). See *formation, reticular*

arrangement, neurotic The construction and marshaling of erroneous ideas on the part of a neurotic patient in order to justify his neurosis with apparently logical reasons, by rearranging the events of his life to suit his neurosis. These patients have an ingenious way of accounting for their failures; for instance, a man asserted that he had a 'historic mission' to accomplish in life, yet did nothing in that direction and justified his hidden inferiority by saying to himself: 'If you had sound nerves, if you did not suffer from night terrors, you would have gone far.' This type of neurotic arrangement does not confine itself to the simple construction of erroneous ideas but may also be present in the somatic sphere: the patient magnifies an existing organ inferiority or creates one if it does not exist. (Stekel, W. *The Interpretation of Dreams,* Liveright, New York, 1943)

arreptio (a-rep'shō) *Obs.* Insanity.

arrhostia (a-rōs'tē-à) *Obs.* Imbecillitas.

ars amandi (ärs' à-màn'dē) A poetical expression for sexual potency, coined in connection with a famous work of erotic poetry, *De Arte Amatoria* in three books, by the Roman poet Publius Ovidius Naso (43 B.C. - 17 A.D.).

arsphenamine hemorrhagic encephalitis (ärs-fen'à-mēn hem-o-raj'ik en-sef-à-lī'tis) A toxic and probably idiosyncratic reaction (hence more correctly termed an encephalopathy) to the intravenous administration of arsphenamine. This is a rare complication and usually occurs onc to two days after injection. Vomiting and headache are rapidly followed by restlessness and delirium, passing into coma with stertorous respiration and often generalized convulsions. In fatal cases, there is edema of the brain, capillary engorgement, and perivascular hemorrhage, and also non-hemorrhagic perivascular areas of necrosis and demyelination.

art The study of artistic productions has thrown much light upon questions of psychology and psychopathology. Like dreams and phantasies, art is regarded as representing factors or themes of the psyche. From the psychiatric standpoint art is analyzed in much the same way that dreams and phantasies are. Freud applies his methods of investigation also to the problem of artistic creativeness, its nature and sources. He says: 'the artist is originally a man who turns from reality because he cannot come to terms with the demand for the renunciation of instinctual satisfaction as it is first made, and who then in phantasy-life allows full play to his erotic and ambitious wishes.' (Freud, S. *Collected Papers,* vol. 4, tr. by Riviere, J., Leonard and Virgina Woolf and The Institute of Psychoanalysis, London, 1924 - 25).

Jung says: 'Art, like every other human activity, proceeds from psychic motives. . . .' Speaking of poetic art, he quotes Gerhart Hauptmann, to wit: 'Poetry means the distant echo of the primitive word behind our veil of words.' Jung expresses a similar idea when he asks 'to what primordial image of the collective unconscious can we trace the image we see developed in the work of art?' He adds that 'the shaping of the primordial image is, as it were, a translation into the language of the present which makes it possible for every man to find again the deepest springs of life which would otherwise be closed to him.' (Jung, C.G. *Contributions to Analytical Psychology,* tr. by Baynes, H.G. and C.F., Kegan Paul, Trench, Trubner, London, 1928)

arterenol (ar-te-rē'nol) Norepinephrine; see *epinephrine.*

arteriogram *Angiogram* (q.v.).

arteriosclerosis, cerebral (àr-te-rē-o-sklerō'sis, se-rē'bral) Hardening of the arteries of the brain, the most common causes of which are: primary degeneration of the intima of the cerebral vessels, degeneration secondary to hypertension, endarteritis (usually syphilitic), thromboangiitis, polyarteritis nodosa or periarteritis nodosa, and temporal arteritis. Pathological changes are of two types —hyperplastic or hypoplastic degeneration of the internal elastic membrane. Hyperplastic degeneration produces focal parenchymatous lesions and mainly neurological symptoms (convulsions, aphasia, agnosia, apraxia, paralysis of the upper motor neuron type, tremor, chorea, athetosis, Parkinsonism); mental changes appear late in the course of the disorder.

Hypoplastic degeneration, on the other hand, produces gross hemorrhagic softenings and mainly mental symptoms: signs of frontal lobe damage such as *Witzelsucht* (q.v.), callousness, and euphoria; basal ganglia signs such as impulsiveness and whining; temporal lobe signs such as depression and visual hallucinations; and with parietal lobe involvement often hypochondriacal trends. In addition, there are general intellectual dulling with memory defects, emotional. lability, hostility to all change, paranoid trends, loosely constructed delusions, confusion, and finally profound dementia.

arthralgia hysterica (är-thrȧl′gē-ȧ hēste′rē-kȧ) Hysterical joint-pain; arthropathia hysterica.

arthritism (är′thri-tiz′m) See *diathesis, arthritic.*

arthritism, infantile In constitutional medicine this refers to the arthritic diathesis or arthritism which manifests itself in young children. See *diathesis, arthritic.*

arthro-, arthr- (är′thrō-, är′thr-) Combining form meaning *joint, articulation.*

arthropathy (är-throp′-a-thē) Joint disease, especially neuroarthropathy or trophoneurosis of the joint. Tabetic arthropathy, or Charcot's joint, consists of edema and effusions within the joints, associated usually with painless swellings; proliferation and destruction of the cartilage, capsule, and bone surface may occur with formation of new bone, fragments of which may be free within the joint ('joint mice').

articulation, disorders of See *speech disorders.*

artificial neurosis See *neurosis, experimental.*

artificialism Piaget's term for the child's tendency to believe that natural phenomena are caused by some human agency.

'as if' This term, borrowed from the philosopher Vaihinger, is used by Adler to indicate the fictitious and imaginary goal of complete superiority which some persons set for themselves. '. . . This goal introduces into our life a hostile and fighting tendency . . . whoever takes this goal of godlikeness seriously or literally, will soon be compelled to flee from real life and compromise, by seeking a life within life; if fortunate,—in art, but more generally,—in pietism, neurosis or crime.' (Adler, A. *The Practice and Theory of Individual Psychology,* tr. by Radin, P., Kegan Paul, Trench, Trubner, London, 1924) 'As if' also is used to refer to a personality type seen typically in schizophrenics before or between acute episodes. See *personality, as if.*

as-if performances Sullivan's term for those dramatizations in which a person ordinarily assumes various roles in order to avoid punishment or get tenderness; also included are those preoccupations in which a child loses himself in order to combat anxiety.

'as-if,' pseudo See *'pseudo as-if.'*

asaphia (ȧ-saf′ē-a) *Obs.* Indistinctness of voice.

aspholalia (ȧ-sȧ-fō-lā′lē-ȧ) Indistinct or mumbling speech.

ascendance, ascendancy Dominance; used especially to refer to character traits and interpersonal or group relationships. See *submissiveness.*

asceticism See *character, ascetic.*

Aschaffenburg, Gustav (ȧ-shäf′en-boorK) (b. 1866) German psychiatrist.

Aschner ocular phenomenon (Bernhardt Aschner, Viennese physician, b. 1863) Pressure exerted over the eyeball produces a slowing of the pulse; also known as the oculocardiac reflex.

Aschner treatment of schizophrenia A method of 'constitutional' therapy employed by the Viennese physician Bernhardt Aschner (b. 1863) in the treatment of schizophrenia; the method includes the use of cold baths, sweats, drastic purgatives, emmenagogues, emetics, blisters, and periodic blood-letting.

asemasia (as-ē-mā'zhē-à) *Asemia* (q.v.)

asemia (à-sē'mē-à) Loss of the ability, previously possessed, to make or understand any sign or token of communication, whether of organic or emotional origin. See *speech disorders*.

As in all speech disorders the perceptive and the expressive (or sensory and motor) aspects may manifest themselves singly or both combined, when the disability may be called total. The subdivisions of asemia are: amimia, alexia, agraphia. It includes the trainman's or switchman's inability to grasp the meaning of signs by semaphore or colored lights, the bellboy's irresponsiveness to the various buzzes or bell-combinations, the telegrapher's inability to convey or 'read' messages on the ticker, the student's blindness to letters, figures, and mathematical signs and symbols, the pianist's blank stare at a page of formerly familiar music, though he may still be able to play the piece from memory, the soldier's 'disregard' of bugle calls, etc.

asexuality Magnus Hirschfeld defines asexuality as the absence of sexual desire or feeling, due, he believes, to the 'loss of sexual glands.' The loss of sexual interests may also be observed in many psychiatric conditions in which no pathology of the sexual apparatus may be demonstrated, as in depressed patients.

asitia (à-sish'ē-à) Anorexia.

asocial Not social; indifferent to social values; without social meaning or significance.

aspermia, psychogenic (a-sper'mē-a) See *impotence, psychic.*

assembly, cell *Engram* (q.v.); any group of neurons that has come to function as a unit by reason of repeated stimulation.

assimilation In analytical psychology (Jung), 'the absorption or joining up of a new conscious content to already prepared subjective material, whereby the similarity of the new content with the waiting subjective material is specially emphasized, even to the prejudice of the independent quality of the new content. Fundamentally, assimilation is a process of apperception . . . which, however, is distinguished from pure apperception by this element of adjustment to the subjective material.' (Jung, C.G. *Psychological Types,* tr. by Baynes, H.G., Harcourt, Brace, New York and London, 1923)

Jung maintains that *dissimilation* 'represents the adjustment of subject to object, and a consequent estrangement of the subject from himself in favour of the object, whether it be an external object or a "psychological" or inner object, as for instance an idea.' (ibid.)

In Fromm's theory of character, assimilation is one of two ways of relating to the world (the other is socialization). Assimilation types relate to material things rather than to people, and Fromm distinguishes five subtypes: (1) *receiving* —the person feels that the only way to get what he wants is to receive it passively from some outside source; (2) *exploiting* —the person feels that he can get what he wants only by stealing it or by using some artful, cunning scheme; (3) *hoarding* —the person doubts that he can ever get what he wants, so whatever he has must be saved and hoarded (similar to the anal character is other classifications); (4) *marketing*—the person values himself only in terms of salability to others and is dependent upon personal acceptance by them; such a person becomes alienated and estranged from his actions and his own life-forces, an automaton who is ruled by the institutions of industrial society; (5) *working*—the only productive type in this group, characterized by the ability to reason objectively, to love unselfishly, and to work productively.

assimilation, social The process or processes by which peoples of diverse social origins and different cultural heritages, occupying a common territory, achieve a cultural solidarity.' (Park, R.E. *Encyclopaedia of the Social Sciences,* vol. 2, Macmillan, New York, 1930, p. 281)

Assimilation is generally considered in terms of the fusion of immigrants or of members of a minority group into the national culture, but it applies equally to the nature and degree of participation of a newcomer in a group, institution, or neighborhood.

association Relationship. In psychiatry, association refers particularly to the relationship between the conscious and the unconscious ideas in the former being connected to the latter.

Associations may be free or induced. When a person without prompting is allowed to raise and to expand upon an idea or ideas, the process is known as 'free' association. This is one of the methods used by psychoanalysts in tracing the origin and development of ideas or groups of ideas.

Induced associations involve the giving of stimulus words; 'the experimenter calls out a word to the test-person, and the test-person immediately replies with the next association that comes into his mind.' (Jung, C.G.)

Originally the test was employed as a means by which complexes were revealed. It is still used by some for that purpose. As a rule, however, for practical, therapeutic purposes, the free association method is used, not alone for uncovering complexes, but principally for gaining information on the organization and development of the contents of the mind.

Freud 'maintains that, when a subject is asked to make free associations from a given theme to which he is attending, and wholly to suspend the active-selective criticism that under such circumstances is instinctively exercised towards the incoming thoughts, the associations must be directly or indirectly related, in a causative manner to the initial theme.' (Jones, E. *Papers on Psycho-Analysis*, 4th ed., Wood, Baltimore, 1938)

Jung uses the term association-method to mean the procedure; the tests are called association-experiments.

association, clang An association based on similarity of sound, without regard for differences in meaning;; most frequently observed in the manic phase of manic-depressive disorder and in the schizophrenias.

association-disturbances See *associations, disturbances of.*

association-experiment See *association.*

association, false Stekel's term for the dreamer's various identifications simultaneously with several persons who, nevertheless, represent the same love-object, these associations (given by the dreamer) being only partly valid, inasmuch as they correspond to incomplete situations and typically to two different situations reported by the patient as being only one.

This type of association may lead the analyst to details concerning one of the persons with whom the dreamer identifies his love-object, when in reality this association pertains to another person, also a partial substitute for the real love-object. (Stekel, W. *The Interpretation of Dreams*, Liveright, New York, 1943)

association fibers See *commissure.*

association, free The trends of thought or chains of ideas which spontaneously arise when restraint and censorship upon logical thinking are removed and the individual orally reports everything that passes through his mind. This fundamental technique of modern psychoanalysis assumes that when relieved of the necessity of logical thinking and reporting verbally everything going through his mind, the individual will bring forward basic psychic material and thus make it available to analytical interpretation. 'Mistakes of everyday life, and dreams in which the partial liberation from fetters of logic and repression is already achieved, constitute a particularly interesting material in this respect.' This method was originally introduced by Freud after he had been disillusioned with the results of hypnosis. In trying to overcome the posthypnotic amnesia, Freud found out that, when urged to make an effort, the hypnotized individual was able to recall almost everything that had been said to him, although he could not remember anything that had happened during the hypnotic trance.

Freud applied the same technique to patients he could not hypnotize. He urged them to tell him everything that came to their minds, to leave out nothing, regardless of whether they considered it relevant or not. He persuaded them to give up all conscious reflection, abandon themselves to calm concentration, follow their spontaneous mental occurrences, and impart everything to him. In this way he finally obtained those free associations which lead to the origin of the symptoms. As he developed this method, he found that it was not as simple as he had thought, that these so-called free associations were really not free, but were determined by unconscious material which had to be analyzed and interpreted. He, therefore, designated this new technique psycho-analysis.'

The combined work of repressive influences of the ego prevents the unconscious material from entering into the field of consciousness. Such material can be obtained only through the technique of free association. In other words, free association overcomes, or sidetracks, the repressive forces and makes it possible for the psychic unconscious material to come forward into consciousness. In this manner the psychiatrist is able to reach the inner layers of the mental life of the patient, interpret them, and finally bring them into the range of the patient's insight. The methodological principle of free association is a common basis for the classical Freudian analysis and the Jungian type of analysis. (Freud, S. *The Basic Writings of Sigmund Freud,* tr. by Brill, A.A., Random House, New York, 1938; Schilder, P. *Pschotherapy,* Norton, New York, 1938)

association, induced See *association.*

association-method See *association.*

association, psychosis of A form of psychosis in which certain of the mental symptoms of one patient (the principal) appear in similar or identical form in one or more other people (the associates) who are closely associated with the first. This association is typically intrafamilial, as in two siblings, or in parent and child, or in husband and wife; but it has also been reported among pairs of patients on a psychiatric ward and in pairs of friends who have been in intimate social contact over a period of time. When the number of people involved is two, the condition is sometimes called *folie à deux* (q.v.); there may be three *(folie à trois),* four *(folie à quatre)* or many *(folie à beaucoup)* involved. Other names by which the condition has been known are: infectious insanity (Ideler, 1838); psychic infection (Hoffbauer, 1846); familial mental infection (Séguin, 1879; reciprocal insanity (Parsons, 1883); collective insanity

(Ireland, 1886); double insanity (Tuke, 1887); influenced psychosis (Gordon, 1925); mystic paranoia (Pike, 1933).

Most writers agree that psychosis of association is limited to paranoid and depressive forms of psychosis, and in the case reports in the literature even purely depressive forms are a relative rarity. Four types of psychosis of association are recognized: (1) imposed (described by Laseque and Falret, 1877), in which the associate accepts the delusions of the principal with little elaboration, and separation of the patients typically results in disappearance of the delusions in the associate; (2) simultaneous (described by Regis, 1880), in which there is simultaneous appearance of identical symptoms in more than one subject, and these symptoms are typically depression and/or persecutory ideas; (3) communicated (described by Marandon de Montyel, 1881), in which the associate takes over the delusions of the principal and works them into his own system, often with elaboration, and these delusions are usually maintained even after separation of the two; and (4) induced (described by Lehmann, 1885), wherein a second receptive patient adds the principal's delusions to his own symptoms.

association-test See *association.*

associationism That school of psychology which holds that mental development consists mainly of combinations and recombinations of basic, irreducible, mental elements; see *reductionism.*

associations, contiguity of An internal connection which is still undisclosed will announce its presence by means of a temporal proximity of associations; just as in writing, if "a" and "b" are put side by side, it means that the syllable "ab" is to be formed out of them.' (Freud, S. *Collected Papers,* vol. 3, tr. by Strachey, A. and J., Leonard and Virginia Woolf and The Institute of Psychoanalysis, London, 1925)

As an example, Freud refers to the case of Dora (Analysis of a Case of Hysteria) in which Dora recognizes that Frau K. would always fall ill whenever Herr K. returned from one of his long journeys, to be able to escape the conjugal duties which she so much detested. At this point Dora referred to her own alternations between good and bad health during the first years of her girlhood. Freud then suspected that her states of health depended upon something else, in the same way as Frau K.'s.

associations, disturbances of One of Bleuler's fundamental symptoms of the schizophrenias. The associations are the innumerable related threads which guide thinking, and in the schizophrenias the associations are interrupted and lose their contiguity. As a result, thinking becomes haphazard, seemingly purposeless, illogical, confused, incorrect, abrupt, and bizarre. Among the many possible association-disturbances are clang associations, indirect associations, stereotypy in speech, dearth of ideas to the point of monoideism, 'thought-deprivation' (blocking), 'naming' (echopraxia) or 'touching,' pressure of thoughts, inappropriate application of cliches, Klebedenken, impoverishment of thought, replacement of thinking proper by a senseless compulsion to associate.

associations, indirect One of the disturbances of associations seen often in the schizophrenias. With indirect associations, A may be connected to B and B may be connected to C, but the connecting link B is unexpressed so that the listener finds the statement incomprehensible, illogical, or bizarre.

associative thinking See *thinking, associative.*

assortative See *mating, assortative.*

astasia (à-stā′zhē-à) The inability to stand, when there is no organic reason for the disability. See *astasia-abasia.*

astasia-abasia A form of hysterical ataxia with bizarre inco-ordination and inability to stand or walk, even though all leg movements can be performed normally while sitting or lying down.

astereognosis (às-ter-ē-og-nō′sis) Loss of power to perceive the shape and nature of an object and inability to identify it by superficial contact alone, in the absence of any demonstrable sensory defect; sometimes called tactile agnosia, although in astereognosis there is a defect in the higher correlation of proprio-

ceptive sensations as well. Some use astereognosis for minor defects in which the patient cannot recognize form, and tactile agnosia for more profound defects in which there is inability to identify objects. Astereognosis follows lesions of the parietal lobe, especially in the posterior portions.

asterixis A lapse of posture consisting of momentary loss of a fixed position of the hands or arms followed by a jerking recovery movement that restores the limb to its original position; also known as *flapping tremor,* it usually occurs in association with tremulousness in patients with some degree of central nervous system dysfunction secondary to metabolic disorders such as liver disease, uremia, etc.

asthenia (as-thē′nē-à) Want or loss of strength, debility, diminution of the vital forces. In the field of constitutional medicine it does not imply the specific meaning conveyed by the adjective *asthenic.* See *type, asthenic.*

asthenia, mental Diminution of the capacity for mental work, usually related to hypoboulia and/or difficulty in concentration.

asthenia, neurocirculatory A clinical syndrome, also called effort syndrome, characterized by palpitation, shortness of breath, labored breathings, subjective complaints of effort and discomfort, all following slight exertion; other symptoms may be dizziness, tremulousness, sweating, insomnia. Neurocirculatory asthenia is most typically seen as a form of *anxiety neurosis* (q.v.).

asthenic (as-then′ik) See *type, asthenic.*

asthenic personality A *personality disorder* (in DSM-II, 301.6), characterized by low energy level, easy fatigability, incapacity for enjoyment and lack of enthusiasm, and oversensitivity to physical and emotional stress. See also *neurasthenia.*

asthenology (as-thē-nol′ō-ji) The doctrine of diseases or anomalies, structural or functional, associated with weakness or debility. In psychiatry the term has special, though not exclusive, reference to matters pertaining to constitutional medicine, including such concepts as constitutional inadequacies, early structural or functional wearing out of organs or systems of organs, imbalance of organic systems, etc. For example, it is believed that among certain psychiatric patients, particularly the schizophrenic, the cardiovascular system retains puerile structure and function, as a consequence of which adult parts of the body have to get along with puerile parts. Such anomalies often lead to debility of a greater or lesser order. Asthenology includes studies of such disability or debility.

asthenophobia (as-thē-nō-fō′bē-à) Fear of weakness.

asthenopia (as-thē-nō′pē-à) Weakness of vision or sight.

asthma, bronchial (305.2) A respiratory disorder characterized by recurrent attacks of bronchiolar spasm, which traps air in the lungs and results in paralysis of the expiratory muscles, assumption of the inspiratory position, and use of all the accessory muscles of respiration. Asthma may be an anaphylactic reaction, or primarily hereditary, or a combination of extrinsic factors such as allergy with any number of intrinsic factors, including emotional and psychologic elements. In some asthmatics, the asthmatic attack may be an anxiety equivalent related to threat of separation from the protecting, encompassing mother and a cry for help. Maternal rejection is a recurrent motif in the history of such asthmatics, who are often of the obsessive-compulsive personality type with an anal-sadistic orientation.

asthma, sexual The asthmatic condition induced by the act of coitus.

astraphobia, astrapophobia (as-tra-fō′bē-à, -pō-fō′bē-à) Morbid fear of thunder and lightening.

astrocyte (as′trō-sīt) See *neuroglia*.

astrology Thy study of planets particularly in their influence on the destiny of the universe including human beings, their actions, personality, body, and health. The medicine of the Middle Ages was strikingly dominated by demonology, witchcraft, sorcery, and astrology, and

statements which assumed that there existed no infirmity or disease not due to the influence of some planet or planets were not uncommon. Saturn was assumed to govern the spleen; Jupiter ruled over the lungs, liver and semen; Mars controlled the kidneys; Venus, the uterus, breasts, and genitals of the female; Mercury stood for the mental processes; and the Sun ruled the brain and the nerves, the right half of the body, and the left eye of the woman. Paracelsus expanded this school of medical thought considerably: among other things he believed that with a magnet he was able to shift the diseases of the body into the earth. (Hinsie, L.E. *Understandable Psychiatry*, Macmillan, New York, 1948)

astyphia (à-stif′ē-à) Sexual impotence.

astysia (à-stis′ē-à) Sexual impotence.

asyllabia (à-si-lā′bē-à) A form of aphasia (agraphia or alexia); inability to combine individual letters (or sounds) into syllables. See also *speech disorders*.

asylum An old term defined as a 'place safe from violence or pillage. The ancients set apart certain places of refuge where the vilest criminals were protected, and the name later on got to be applied specially to an institution which afforded a place of refuge or safety for the infirm or unsound of mind.' (Tuke, D.H. *A Dictionary of Psychological Medicine*, vols. 1-2, Blakiston, Philadelphia, 1892)

asymbolia (as-im-bō′lē-à) Inability to make or understand symbols or signs. A term proposed by F.C. Finkelburg in 1870 for what is now denoted by the more generally accepted term *asemia* (q.v.) suggested by Steinthal. Kussmaul argued that asymbolia is less comprehensive, because back of *symbol* stands an *idea* and thus it is narrower than *sign* or *token*, which frequently has merely a *feeling* back of it. See also *speech disorders*.

asymbolia, pain A type of disordered recognition of the body, such as is seen in parietal lobe lesions, in which the patient, although able to perceive painful stimuli, 'shows a morbid poverty of emotional reaction to them. In every case described the lesion has been found in the left hemisphere but the whole of the body shows the abnormal response to pain.' (Mayer-Gross, W., et al. *Clinical Psychiatry*, 2nd ed., Williams and Wilkins, Baltimore, 1960)

asymbolia, visual See *aphasia, visual.*

asymmetry Absence of symmetry or congruence between two or more parts of a whole. Generally the term is used in medicine to designate anatomical disharmony of homologous parts.

Psychiatric patients may believe that their bodies are entirely asymmetrical, in spite of normal asymmetry. One patient asserted that the right side of his body was absent; he called the right side the masculine side; the delusion was equated with castration. Another patient—and this is not uncommon—believed that the anatomy and physiology of his right side were masculine while those of his left were feminine. In this instance the delusion of asymmetry was based on the delusion of bisexuality.

asymmetry, mental The disparity in form and the unbalanced relationship between two opposite mental processes. In this regard, one may assert that a very frequent symptom in compulsion neurosis is the patient's tendency to compare various parts of his body with one another: some patients spend hours in front of a mirror comparing the two sides of their faces and even may often assert that they are of different form (asymmetric). This is but an expression of their mental disparity and unbalance and their conclusions are drawn merely with reference to their own egos. The patient compares not only different parts of his own body but also 'compares himself with his father, with his brothers and sisters, and with other people.' He compares also various achievements in his life, especially homosexual and heterosexual trends. (Stekel, W. *Compulsion and Doubt,* Liveright, New York, 1949)

asymptotic See *wish-fulfillment, asymptotic.*

asyndesis (às-in-dē'sis) A language disorder seen most commonly in the schizophrenias and to a lesser extent in other organic brain syndromes in which there is juxtaposition of elements without adequate linkage between them. Images and meanings which are connected in the mind of the patient are superimposed on each other in a sentence without explanation as to what the connecting links are; to the listener, the language then seems disjointed and disconnected. 'One of our patients, for example, when asked what caused the wind to blow, said it was "due to velocity, due to loss of air, evaporation of water . . . the contact of trees, of air in the trees."' (Cameron, N., in Kasanin, J.S. (ed.). *Language and Thought in Schizophrenia,* Univerisity of California Press, Berkeley, 1944) See *thinking-aside.*

asynergia (às-i-nēr'jē-à) See *ataxia.*

asynergia of Babinski, major Inco-ordination in standing and walking as a result of involvement of the cerebellum.

asynergia of Babinski, minor As a consequence of involvement of the cerebellum, there results a decomposition of movements giving rise to a 'breaking up' of simple acts; when the patient attempts to carry out such acts as kneeling on a chair, elevating the leg while in a supine position, sitting up from a recumbent position, etc. the movements are disjointed and awkward.

asynesia (às-in-ē'zē-à) Profound mental dullness; stupidity.

asynesis (à-sin'ē-sis) *Obs.* Aphasia.

asynetous (à-sin'ē-tus) *Obs.* Stupid, foolish.

at In Rorschach scoring, anatomy response, i.e. any response containing the image of a part of a human or animal organism that is not visible without cutting the body open. The *at* responses indicate attempt to compensate for a feeling of intellectual inferiority.

ataraxy (a'tar-ak-sē) Absence of anxiety or confusion; untroubled calmness. The ataractic drugs are commonly called tranquilizers. See *psychotropics.*

atavism (at'à-viz'm) When mental or physical traits, dormant for one or more generations, reappear in the offspring, the condition is known as atavism. The term is commonly used in biology and less frequently in psychiatry. There are no clear-cut examples of atavism, strictly speaking, in psychology or psychiatry, although it is not unlikely that the many components of the sphere of the unconscious that constitute the 'collective' unconscious of Jung may be regarded as atavistic, particularly when they are expressed overtly in the daily life of the person (as in schizophrenia).

ataxia (a-tak'se-a) Absence or lack of order. In this general sense it may refer to the absence of order of any bodily function or system, physical or mental. It is most commonly used in the field of neurology to designate a loss of power of muscular co-ordination. The condition may be due to disorder in the brain or spinal cord. There is a form called autonomic or vasomotor ataxia, resulting from imbalance of the sympathetic and parasympathetic nervous systems.

The term ataxia is used also in conjunction with certain psychic functions. Stransky coined the expression intrapsychic ataxia, regarding it, as Urstein did, as a cardinal symptom of schizophrenia; it refers to lack of co-ordination between thoughts and feelings. A schizophrenic patient may laugh heartily, while he believes that his body is being cut into millions of pieces. Intrapsychic ataxia is most vividly expressed in schizophrenia; it is not uncommon in hysteria; it may appear in other psychiatric and non-psychiatric states.

ataxia, Friedreich's A familial, hereditary, and slowly progressive disorder consisting of degeneration of the posterior columns and the spinocerebellar tracts of the spinal cord, mainly in its lower portion, and of the pyramidal tracts. Onset is between 5 and 15 years of age, with ataxia, loss of deep reflexes, nystagmus, dysarthria, intention tremor, and, because of early degeneration of the pyramidal tracts, development of pes cavus. The Babinski and Romberg are usually positive and there is often a mild dementia. Death usually occurs within 20 years from first appearance of symptoms.

ataxia, hysterical See *astasia-abasia*.

ataxia, intrapsychic Stransky introduced this term in an effort to describe the condition of the emotions in schizophrenia. He stressed the thought that patients with

that disorder seemed not to show destruction of the feelings, but rather a separation of them from other mental phenomena; he spoke of *ataxic feelings*.

ataxia, locomotor See *tabes*.

ataxia, Marie's hereditary cerebellar (Pierre Marie, French physician, 1853-1940) A familial, hereditary disorder consisting of cerebellar and pyramidal tract degeneration and, in some cases, optic atrophy. Onset is during or after adolescence. Symptoms include ataxia, nystagmus, dysarthria, and intention tremor; in contrast to Friedreich's ataxia, reflexes are normal, pes cavus is not seen, and the Babinski and Romberg reflexes are negative. It would appear that this is a mixed group rather than a pure clinical or pathological entity.

ataxia, mental Intrapsychic ataxia. 'In dementia praecox there is marked ataxia between the emotions and the intellectual and volitional powers of the mind. The dementia praecox patient may be depressed and have apparent reason to be so, yet his conduct at the time of apparent depression is in absolute opposition to the content of his consciousness. He cries when he should laugh, and vice versa.' (Bowers, P.E. *Manual of Psychiatry*, Saunders, Philadelphia, 1924)

ataxia spirituum (a-tak'se-a spe-re'too-oom) *Obs.* Nervous diathesis.

ataxophemia (a-tak-so-fe'me-a) Impaired co-ordination of words; incoherence.

atelesis Absence of integration or successful completion. The term has been used to refer to the three major dysjunctions prominent in schizophrenic psychopathology: dysjunction of inner world and environment (autism), dysjunction of ego and the contents of consciousness ('splitting;' or 'ego anachoresis'), and dysjunction of experience contents and the elementary forms of mental perception ('destruction of categories').

atelia (a-te'le-a) The doctrine of incomplete development.

ateliosis (a-te-le-o'sis) A form of dwarfism. The term means incomplete development of the mind or body or both. While usually synonymous with infantilism, it is broad enough to include incomplete development or arrest at any stage of growth. In general it may be said that development may be arrested in one or both of the two major systems, the psyche or the soma (the physique). Usually defects in one system are associated with defects in the other. More specifically arrested development may appear preponderantly in the field of experience, emotions, intelligence, organic physiology, and anatomy.

From a strictly psychiatric point of view, psychogenic mental disorders may be a reflection of arrested development or fixation of feelings and interests at one of the earlier stages of growth. For instance, schizophrenia may be a form of psychic infantilism or puerilism or puberism. Feeble-mindedness may represent incomplete development of intellectual faculties, while microsomia (small physique) refers to generalized arrest of perhaps all the tissues of the body.

atephobia (ā-tē-fō'bē-à) Fear of ruin.

ater succus (ä'ter sook'koos) (L. 'black juice or sap.') *Obs.* Melancholia.

athetosis (ath-ē-tō'sis) Irregular, slow, objectively purposeless movement with some apparent pattern, occurring mainly in the toes and fingers, in the form of extension and flexion and spreading of the digits.

Athetosis results from a lesion in the extrapyramidal pathways, usually the corpus striatum, or from other lesions which interrupt the circuit of the suppressor reaction between cortical areas 4s and 4.

athletic See *type, athletic.*

athymia (à-thim'ē-à, thī'mē-à) Hippocratic term for melancholia.

atom, social 'The social atom consists of the psychological relations of one individual to those other individuals to whom he is attracted or repelled, and their relation to him. It is the smallest social structure in a community. Developing from the time of birth, it first contains mother and child. As time goes on, the child adds from the persons who come into his orbit such persons as are unpleasant or pleasant to him, and, vice versa, those to whom he is unpleasant or pleasant. Persons who do not leave any impression, positive or nega-

tive, remain outside of the social atom as mere acquaintances. The feeling which correlates two or more individuals is called tele. The social atom is, therefore, a compound of the tele relationships of an individual. As positively or negatively charged persons may leave the individual's social atom and others may enter it, the social atom has a more or less ever-changing constellation.' (Moreno, J.L. *Who Shall Survive?* Nervous & Mental Disease Publishing Company, Washington, D.C., 1934)

atomism (at'um-iz'm) See *psychology, atomistic.*

atonic (à-ton'ik) Relating to or characterized by atonia, i.e. by lack of tone or vital energy. It refers to the whole body, to a particular system of the body or to single organs, especially to contractile organs.

In the system of constitutional types described by Pende the term is used in a more specialized sense to indicate a sub-group of the *megalosplanchnic hypervegetative* (q.v.) constitution and also a sub-group of the *microsplanchnic hypovegetative* (q.v.) constitution. 'We can understand the importance of our division of the great megalosplanchnic group into two sub-groups, one of which we designate as the atonic and flaccid, and the other as the hypertonic and hypersthenic. The first includes individuals morphologically hypoevolute in almost all their organs, with a dominant parasympathicotonia and a torpid orientation of the animal nervous system and psyche; with slow metabolism; and with lymphatic plethora, a deficiency in the development of the arterial portion of the heart as compared with the venous, and of the blood as compared with the lymph.' (Pende, N. *Constitutional Inadequacies,* tr. by Naccarati, S., Lea & Febiger, Philadelphia, 1928)

Similarly there is a distinction between the atonic and hyposthenic sub-group and the hypersthenic and hypertonic sub-group of the microsplanchnic hypovegetative constitution. In the former sub-group we have the slender type with small skeleton and muscles and also with hypoevolutism of the cardiovascular system and the endocrine glands.

The concept of an *atonic constitution* is further used in the system of Rostan, in which it refers to a type characterized by atonia of all systems, corresponding to the *lymphatic* (q.v.) type of classical antiquity and also in the system of Stiler, in which it is identical with the *ptotic habitus* (q.v.).

atony, atonicity, atonia (at'ō-nē, à-tō-nis'i-tē, à-tō'nē-à) The tonus or state of tonicity of body tissues is normally described in terms of the tonicity of the neuro-muscular apparatus. All tissues of the body are normally under a given physiological tension.

It is presumed also that the psyche has its own tonus, conceived as mental pressure. When the mental pressure is below average, the term atony is used. Thus, depressed patients often claim that the mind is dead, that ideas and emotions have gone from them, that there is no psychic initiative or drive. The musculature as a whole usually participates in this expression of atonicity.

atrabiliary, atrabilious (at-rà-bil'i-er-ē; -bil'yus) An old term meaning depressed or melancholic.

atrophy, optic (at'rō-fē) A degenerative process involving the optic nerve fibers. The condition is primary or secondary. Primary optic atrophy may occur in tabes, multiple sclerosis, or may be due to poisons such as methyl alcohol, tryparsamide, lead, atoxyl, quinine, carbon bisulphide, and nitrobenzol. Occasionally, the condition may occur following severe hemorrhage and in malaria. Ophthalmoscopically, the disk is grayish white in color, with some 'cupping,' the margins being sharply outlined.

Secondary optic atrophy may occur as a result of optic neuritis and choked disk. Here the fundus, disk, and vessels usually manifest residual signs of the previous condition.

Tumors of the pituitary gland, of the optic chiasm, and in some cases of the frontal lobe frequently give rise to optic atrophy—usually unilateral for a time.

atrophy, peroneal muscular Charcot-Marie-Tooth's disease; neural progressive muscular atrophy. A hereditary disorder, transmitted as a Mendelian dominant, more often affecting males, beginning between the ages of 5 and 10 years, with wasting of the small muscles in the peripheral limbs secondary to degeneration of the peripheral nerves and spinal cord. The muscular wasting results in a steppage gait, 'fat bottle' calf when the lower part of the calf is wasted, and 'inverted champagne bottle' limb when the lower third of the thigh is wasted. The disease runs a slow course and may become arrested at any stage; it does not shorten life, and there are no associated intellectual changes.

atrophy, progressive muscular See *sclerosis, amyotrophic lateral.*

attachment, liquidation of P. Janet uses this term to mean freedom from painful situations. 'In this connexion, our first aim must be to put an end to the unceasing efforts occasioned by "attachments." We must "disattach" the patients, we must unravel, as far as may be, the complicated situations in which they find themselves, and in which they have become enmeshed.' (Janet, P. *Psychological Healing,* vols. 1-2, tr. by Paul, E. and C., Macmillan, New York, 1925)

attack, first An illness occurring for the first time, whether or not it results in hospitalization, is a first attack.

attack, obsessive Rado's term for the major symptoms (as distinguished from obsessive character traits) of the *obsessive-compulsive psychoneurosis* (q.v.): (1) spells of doubting and brooding, (2) bouts of ritual making, and (3) fits of horrific temptation. According to Rado, obsessive attacks are derived from the temper (rage) tantrums of childhood, but the discharge of rage is slow and incomplete since it is always opposed by guilty fear. He terms this an interference pattern of discharge, i.e. a mechanism for the alternating discharge of opposite tensions. In the motor sphere, alternating discharge is expressed as bouts of ritual making; in the thinking sphere, as brooding spells.

attack, psychomotor A term sometimes used interchangeably with the term *psychic equivalent* of epilepsy. See *equivalent, epileptic.*

attention Conscious and wilful focussing of mental energy on one object or one component of a complex experience and at the same time excluding other emotional or thought content; the act of heeding or taking notice or concentrating. Attention depends upon consciousness and is thus a part of what is meant by the more general term, *sensorium* (q.v.). *Attention span* (also known as *perceptual span*) is the number of briefly-presented objects that can be recalled immediately; it is used as a test of immediate memory. See *memory*.

In Burrow's phylobiology: partitive attention, (1) because it selects a part-element or item of an object which thereafter constitutes the sign or symbol of it, and (2) because the process of attention is then invariably involved in secondary, extraneous affect-elements which tend either to re-route man's basic feeling or to partition it off from the organism's primary empathic channels of activation. See also *affect; partitive; social image*. Contrasted with cotention. Synonyms: symbolic attention, projective attention. (Burrow, T. *The Structure of Insanity*, Kegan Paul, Trench, Trubner, London, 1932, pp. 27, 80)

attention, blocking of See *blocking*.

attention, deterioration of Bleuler lists this as one of the fundamental symptoms of the schizophrenias, where often there is seen an impairment in the ability to heed, observe, and concentrate on external reality. This fundamental symptom appears to be related to deterioration of affectivity (another fundamental symptom) and the patient's disinterest in many things about him. The impairment of attention is inconstant and shifting, for attention may appear normal when it is directed to something the patient wants to do. Inability to concentrate is seen also in other psychiatric disorders, but in this latter case it is almost always secondary, i.e. a result of emotional pressure, while in the schizophrenias it appears to be primary.

attention-getting Any means of gaining attention and recognition when the ego is starved for them, as observed most often in a child who feels unloved. At first the child will attempt to do whatever he feels the parents like and will gain their attention. If this is not successful,

the child will develop temper-tantrums or other behavior disorders, preferring a display of displeasure or even a harsh disciplinary measure to no attention at all.

attention, vigility of 'The *vigility* of the attention is a term used by some clinicians to indicate the fact that the direction of the stream of energy is dirigible' (i.e. controllable). (Paton, S. *Psychiatry*, Lippincott, Philadelphia and London, 1905)

attitude A readiness of the psyche to act or react in a certain direction. . . . To have a certain attitude means to be ready for something definite, even though this definite something is unconscious, since having an attitude is synonymous with an *a priori* direction toward a definite thing, whether this be present in consciousness or not.' (Jung, C.G. *Psychological Types*, tr. by Baynes, H.G., Harcourt, Brace, New York and London, 1923)

Attempts have been made to measure attitudes but they have been criticized as measuring opinions rather than attitudes.

attitude, abstract See *abstract attitude*.

attitude, captative In the early ego development 'things of the external world it conceives of only from its own veiwpoint and in their relation to itself. We agree with Pichon in qualifying as "captative" this attitude of the ego.' (Laforgue, R. *The Relativity of Reality*, Nervous and Mental Disease Monographs No. 66, New York, 1940)

attitude, catatonoid A type of behavior that resembles catatonia. According to Fenichel, it may be found in individuals who 'are on the verge of becoming psychotic.' Apparently, this phrase refers to a certain lack of the expected emotional response in personal or social situations: instead, there is found a stereotyped response, which never varies from situation to situation. For example, if the same vacant smile adorns an individual's countenance when he hears his friend's story of a recent personal tragedy or is told an uproarious anecdote, the individual demonstrates a catatonoid attitude. These stereotyped responses on the part of 'schizoid characters,' which occur when the individual becomes psychotic, would be easily recognized as catatonic symptoms. (Fenichel, O. *The Psychoanalytic Theory of Neurosis*, Norton, New York, 1945)

attitude, collective An *attitude* (q.v.) which is peculiar 'not to one individual, but to many, at the same time, i.e. either to a society, a people, or to mankind in general.' (Jung, C.G. *Psychological Types*, tr. by Baynes, H.G., Harcourt, Brace, New York and London, 1923)

attitude, concretizing The tendency of many schizophrenic patients to transform abstract parts of their life into concrete representations. Thus the patient who feels that his wife poisons his life may express his feelings concretely by developing the delusion that she poisons his food.

attitude, fear An expression used by Kanner to designate a fear reaction observed in some children 'who are literally *always afraid of everything*.' (Kanner, L. *Child Psychiatry*, Thomas, Springfield, Ill., 1935)

attitude, inner Soul, according to Jung's point of view.

attitude, listening The expectation that one is about to hear something; S. Arieti emphasizes that such an attitude typically precedes hallucinations in schizophrenic patients: 'If the patient learns to catch himself in the act of putting himself into the listening attitude, he, after some training, can prevent himself from doing so.' (*Archives of General Psychiatry 6*, 112-122, 1962)

attitude, masculine, in female neurotics. See *masculine attitude in female neurotics.*

attitude, mummy Henderson and Gillespie use this expression to denote the inactive, immobilized patient in the state of catatonic stupor.
'Then a state of dull stupor develops, with mutism, refusal of food, and with such a diminution of all activities that the patient may sit idly in one position, with the hands stretched out on the knees, and the head bowed between the shoulders,

the whole aspect being that of a mummy.' (Henderson, D.K. and Gillespie, R.D. *A Text-Book of Psychiatry*, 4th ed., Oxford University Press, London, 1936)

attitude, preadaptive The initial reaction to a stimulus or experience, before the subject has become accustomed to it. P. Steckler (*Archives of Neurology and Psychiatry 80*, 625-628, 1958) notes that the preadaptive attitude of schizophrenics to hallucinations or feelings of estrangement is of a fairly consistent pattern: anxiety, fear, search for reassurance, doubts as to sanity, search for a rational explanation and, finally, autonomic and muscular system reactions.

attitude, referential An attitude of expectancy seen in some schizophrenic patients who, feeling themselves to be victims of hostility from others, search for references that will justify the underlying mood. See *attitude, listening.*

attitude therapy See *therapy, attitude.*

attitude-tic See *tic, attitude.*

attitude-type See *function-type.*

attitudes passionelles (à-ti-tüd pa-syō-nel) See *hysteria.*

attonity (at-on'i-tē) Attonity is a clinical state of stupor with complete or almost complete immobility. Bleuler believes that the condition occurs most frequently in the catatonic form of schizophrenia, though it is also observed in states of depression; it is then known as melancholia attonita. Other authorities consider that the latter designation refers also to the catatonic type of schizophrenia.

atypical development See *development, atypical.*

audile (aw'dīl) Ear-minded; i.e. understanding better by hearing than by seeing.

audiogenic seizure (aw-di-ō-jen'ik) See *seizure, audiogenic.*

audition, thought A form of auditory hallucination in which everything the patient thinks or speaks is repeated by the voices; also known as *thought echoing* or *echo des pensées.*

auditory feedback See *feedback.*

auditory nerve See *nerve, acoustic.*

aulophobia (aw-lō-fō′bē-à) Fear of seeing, handling, or playing a flute or similar wind instrument, which can serve as a phallic symbol.

aura (aw′rà) A premonitory symptom that warns of some approaching physical or mental disorder. It is a symptom of a special nature in that it is not regarded as an essential part of the disease or disorder, because it disappears or loses its force after it has performed its function of warning.

The term is usually restricted to certain symptoms that appear in genuine epilepsy before the major symptoms set in. Bleuler says: 'the attack is often preceded by prodromata which last a few hours, more rarely days; most frequently they are represented by "moods," but also by any ill-feeling, more rarely hallucinations and twilight states. In most instances these prodromata disappear in a trice with the attack.' (Bleuler, E. *Textbook of Psychiatry*, tr. by Brill, A.A., Macmillan, New York, 1930)

In the grand mal type of epilepsy, an aura precedes loss of consciousness in about 60 per cent of cases (the others are known as the 'thunderclap' variety). The aura localizes the epileptogenic focus in the brain and thus appears in many forms, depending upon the specific location of the lesion: (1) psychic aurae—complex mental states such as feeling of unreality, or feeling of familiarity and déjà vu and déjà fait, disembodied feeling, intense but inexplicable fear; (2) sensory aurae—olfactory and gustatory hallucinations, visual hallucinations with complex scenes or simple flashes of light or balls of fire, auditory hallucinations of words, phrases, or merely crude sounds, and various paresthesiae; (3) visceral aurae—vertigo, epigastric discomfort; (4) motor aurae—as in cursive epilepsy.

aura cursoria (ou′rà koor-sô′rē-à) A condition, usually associated with epilepsy, occurring immediately before a seizure and characterized by aimless running.

aurae, auditory (aw′rē) A form of epilepsy described as sensory seizures in which buzzing noises may occur suddenly, last a short period of time, and then disappear without the patient's having a grand mal attack. This would indicate a focus in the temporal lobe. In grand mal attacks, the patient occasionally may have an auditory aura just prior to the grand mal seizures, as a warning that a convulsive seizure is about to occur.

aurae, visual A form of epilepsy described as sensory seizures in which flashes of light may occur suddenly, last a short period of time, and then disappear without the patient's having a grand mal attack. This would indicate a focus in the temporo-occipital area. In grand mal attacks, the patient occasionally may have a visual aura just before the grand mal seizure, as a warning that a convulsive attack is about to occur.

auroraphobia (aw-rō-rà-fō′bē-à) Fear of northern lights.

autarchy (aw′tär-ki) Supreme, autocratic power, absolute sovereignty; used in psychiatry in reference to the early infantile period, when no demands are made on the child and, insofar as possible, his instinctual demands are satisfied immediately. During this period the child is indeed absolute ruler—his slightest cry brings instinctual gratification, there is no need to deny himself pleasure, and there need be no deferral of pleasure.

autemesia (awt-ē-mē′zē-à) Idiopathic vomiting, usually psychogenic in origin.

authoritarianism (aw-thor-i-tâ′ri-an-iz′m) P. Janet writes that 'we are apt to think that the habit of domination, and a passion for command, are appropriate to persons of energetic temperament, to those whose will is active and powerful. We therefore feel surprised to find that authoritarianism is one of the symptoms of psychological depression. But the feeling that there is something paradoxical here can be dispelled by drawing a distinction between the genuine domination exercised by the strong, and the authoritarianism of the weak, which is but a parody of true domination.' (Janet, P. *Psychological Healing*, vols. 1-2, tr. by Paul, E. and C., Macmillan, New York, 1925)

authoritative imperative See *imperative*, authoritative.

authority, irrational Power or command over others that, contrary to reason and logic, is based on neurotic craving for power and has no justification in competence; authority imposed on others through sheer will power, without their consent. Fromm distinguishes this from rational authority, which is based on genuine ability and competence and is exemplified by the teacher imparting knowledge to a pupil. The person who resorts to irrational authority for security may find power by being a *magic helper* (q.v.) or from various forms of intimidation; he may also find that power through identification with the authoritarian force, be it a person, a group, or an idea. Hence, Fromm considers Freud's super-ego as a manifestation of authoritarian power.

The classical legend based on a vivid account by Pliny the Elder *(Historia Naturalis, XXXV,* 10, 36, § 85) which gave rise to a widespread saying is a striking illustration of the gulf between rational and irrational authority. The great Greek painter Apelles (fl. 330 B.C.), valuing the opinion of the common folk, was in the habit of showing a new canvas in his (porch) studio and, hiding behind a painting, would listen to their observations. A passing shoemaker found fault with one sandal-loop being smaller than the other. The artist redrew it later in the day. The next morning the same shoemaker, emboldened by the artist's compliance, began to jeer about the leg. Emerging from his hiding place, Apelles squelched the glib critic with the crushing: 'A cobbler should not judge above the sandal.' ('Shoe-maker, stick to your last.')

authypnobatesis (awth-hip-nō-bà-tē′sis) *Obs.* Spontaneous somnambulism.

autism (aw′tiz′m) A form of thinking, more or less genuinely of a subjective character; if objective material enters, it is given subjective meaning and emphasis. Autism generally implies that the material is derived from the subject himself, appearing in the nature of daydreams, phantasies, delusions, hallucinations, etc. The content of thought, in other words, is largely endogenous. In classical instances of autistic thinking, such as occurs in schizophrenia, the unconscious sphere makes the largest contribution to autism.

Autism is a form of narcissism, yet a narcissist is not restricted in the content of the conscious mind to subjective material; he is one who interprets material largely in terms of himself.

Autism, dereism and introversion are closely allied to one another. Some authorities speak of the autistic temperament, meaning by it 'the bashful, retiring type that shrinks from all contact with life. The subject is "shut-in," inaccessible and introverted, a day-dreamer.' (Bridges, J.W. *An Outline of Abnormal Psychology,* 2nd ed., Adams & Company, Columbus, 1921)

Autism, when it is a pervasive and generalized dereistic life-approach, is one of the fundamental symptoms of the schizophrenias (Bleuler).

In the autistic life-approach, the 'Me' predominates, often to the exclusion of the 'Not-Me,' external reality gradually loses more and more of its significance, and the patient is attuned to and guided only by the inner workings of his being. He is totally selfish, in the most literal (and yet non-pejorative) sense of the term, for he is unable to turn his energies onto objects outside himself. He exaggerates the importance of inner physical sensations as well as his own ideas and emotions. He becomes involved in pseudo-philosophical speculations and has no time for mixing with his peers. He feels different from others, complains that he has never realized his potentialities, and is concerned with establishing an identity for himself.

autism, early infantile A syndrome described by Kanner consisting of: (1) primary symptoms, including (a) withdrawal and (b) anxious, obsessive desire to maintain the status quo; and (2) secondary symptoms, including (a) exceptional object relationships, (b) intelligent, pensive facies despite low intelligence and, often, auditory impairment, (c) language disturbances, (d) monotonously repetitive motor behavior, and (e) fear of moving objects and loud noise.

Symptoms appear early in life or are present from the beginning: self-absorption, inaccessibility, aloneness, inability to relate, highly repetitive play and rage reactions if interrupted; predilection for rhythmical movements such as rolling, jumping, rocking and whirling; and many language disturbances such as pronominal reversals, inability to accept synonyms, echolalia, etc.

Kanner and others maintain that early infantile autism is different from childhood schizophrenia (295.8) while others include it within the latter group. In support of his view, Kanner cites the following differences: the autistic disorder is present from early infancy, while the schizophrenic appears 'normal' for the first two years of life; the autistic child appears physically healthy, while the schizophrenic shows many disturbances in maintaining homeostatsis and many vasovegetative symptoms; the electroencephalogram is usually normal in autistics, but abnormal in many schizophrenic children; the autistic child is unresponsive, stiff, detached, and more isolated than the schizophrenic, who often shows excessive motor compliance and molding to the body of the adult; autistics have if anything a lower incidence of mental disorders in their ancestors, while schizophrenics have a higher incidence; and the parents of autistic children fit a unique and highly consistent pattern in terms of high intelligence, status, and accomplishment, and they appear aloof, mechanized, emotionally frigid, and obsessive about rearing 'perfect' children.

autisme pauvre (aw-tēsm′ pōvr′) Literally, impoverished autism; Minkowski's term for the schizophrenic's withdrawal and detachment from reality that is not a deliberate retreat into phantasy life but is instead a product of will and affect disturbances which cut the patient off from meaningful contact with his environment.

autismus infantum Early infantile autism. See *autism, early infantile.*

autistic (aw-tis′tik) Relating to mentation that is more or less subjective.

autistic psychosis See *psychosis, symbiotic infantile.*

auto-analysis See *analysis, self.*

autocastration, anticipatory A symbolic self-castration appearing as either a symptom or a personality trait, to forestall castration which under the circumstances is unconsciously perceived by the patient as an unavoidable threat. This anticipatory autocastration may be the unconscious reason for 'feminine' behavior in boys: if the boy 'castrates himself' by acting like a girl, he can no longer be threatened with actual castration.

Fenichel explains this behavior as a manifestation of primitive thinking. If the threatened individual punishes himself, he will be protected by the threatening force, which is the father or super-ego in unconscious terms. This thinking is clearly seen in prayer or in sacrifices to the gods, where the individual ingratiates himself with the gods by a self-inflicted lesser or symbolic punishment and thus wards off a more severe punishment.

Actual autocastration, however, takes place in some cases and apparently a 'passive-submissive merging' with the omnipotent person is obtained thereby: by abandoning all activity, the individual shares the omnipotence. By these means religious fanatics endeavor to obtain a union with God. (Fenichel, O. *The Psychoanalytic Theory of Neurosis,* Norton, New York, 1945)

autocatharsis Self-expression, especially as a form of therapy wherein the patient is encouraged to write down his experiences, thoughts, and feelings in order to rid himself of disturbing emotions.

autocentric (aw-tō-sen′trik) Self-centered. 'In its most fundamental sense, conversion is a natural, normal, universal, and necessary process at the stage [i.e., adolescence] when life pivots over from an autocentric to an heterocentric basis.' (Hall, G.S. *Adolescence,* vol. 2, Appleton, New York, 1908, p. 301)

autochiria (aw-tō-kī′rē-à) *Obs.* Suicide.

autochthonous (aw-tok′thō-nus) Aboriginal to the site of appearance, brought about by the independent activity of the structure in which the activity appears. See *delusion, autochthonous.*

autochthony The state of originating in an organ itself, independent of any essential influences outside of the organ in question. Many organs of the body act in part in virtue of forces inherent in the organs and in part because of forces or factors coming from distant sources. The heart, for instance, continues to beat for a time after it has been removed from the body. It is then said to function autochthonously. The same principle of independent action may be applied to the psyche, in the sense that the psyche can and does originate many of the forces found in it. The expression *psychogenic* carries this implication, for it means 'born in the psyche.' It is believed, for example, that dreams are products of the psyche; they are autochthonous to the psyche; they are psychogenic.

autoctonia (aw-tok-tō'nē-à) *Obs.* Suicide.

auto-echolalia (aw-tō-ek-ō-lā'lē-à) Verbigeration; that type of stereotypy in which the patient repeats over and over again some word or phrase of his own. The condition is most commonly observed in the patient with the catatonic form of schizophrenia.

auto-echopraxia (-prak'sē-à) That form of stereotypy in which the patient, usually schizophrenic, constantly repeats an action which he had formerly experienced. The patient echoes, so to speak, his own motions. When he echoes that of another person, one speaks of echopraxia. Kraepelin says that 'the patients stand or kneel for hours, days, or still longer, on the same spot, lie in the most uncomfortable positions in bed, fold their hands spasmodically, even till pressure-sores appear, take up the position of fencing.' (Kraepelin, E. *Dementia Praecox and Paraphremia,* tr. by Barclay, R.M., Livingstone, Edinburgh, 1919)

autoerotism, autoeroticism Havelock Ellis invented the term 'auto-erotism' to mean 'the phenomena of spontaneous sexual emotion generated in the absence of an external stimulus proceeding, directly or indirectly, from another person.' (Ellis, H. *Studies in the Psychology of Sex,* vol. 1, 3rd ed., Davis, Philadelphia, 1919, p. 161)

Common usage has made autoerotism synonymous with masturbation. The latter, however, is a special subdivision of autoerotism. The term onanism has likewise been diverted to mean masturbation or autoerotism, though, as Ellis says, 'Onan's device was not auto-erotic, but

was an early example of withdrawal before emission, or *coitus interruptus*.' (ibid, p. 163)

Autoeroticism is also a phase in the development of object relationships (see *ontogeny, psychic*). The drives are present from the beginning of life and at first are amorphous energy potentials in the undifferentiated psyche. Since there are no object relationships at birth, these energies are, perforce, directed to the infant himself. This is the period of autoeroticism, when no distinction is made between the self and the non-self, when little if any heed is paid to the external environment.

In psychoanalytic psychology, autoerotism is considered to be the most primitive form of relationship to the environment; it is followed by the narcissistic stage out of which objects develop. Freud appears to have held concurrently three contradictory views on the nature of the earliest relationship to the environment; in one view autoerotism was considered primary, in another, narcissism, and in still another, the most primitive relationship was considered to be primary object-love. See *narcissism, primary*.

According to Abraham, the autoerotic stage first becomes manifest during the oral sucking period. It is the opinion of some (Rickman) that autoerotism is distinguished from narcissism in that the former is objectless, while in narcissim the 'I' is recognizable. When the infant takes his own body as the love object, the condition is known as narcissism.

autoerotism, secondary This is an expression suggested by Sadger to refer to that form of self-pleasure indirectly connected with the erogenous zones. For example, the pleasure associated, not with the act of urination, but with the urine itself, is called secondary autoerotism. A patient in the manic phase of manic-depressive psychosis drank her own urine.

autofellatio (-fel-lä'tē-ō) Putting one's own penis into his mouth.

'. . . a considerable portion of the population does record attempts at self-fellation, at least in early adolescence. Only two or three males in a thousand are able to achieve the objective, but there are three or four histories of males who had depended upon self-fellation as a masturbatory technique for some appreciable period of time—in the case of one thirty-year-old-male, for most of his life.' (Kinsey, A.C., et al. *Sexual Behavior in the Human Male*, Saunders, Philadelphia, 1948.)

autofetishism Hirschfeld's term for the state of loving a material object (e.g. article of clothing) of one's own possession. The object acts as a sexual excitant.

autoflagellation Hirschfeld's term for the act of whipping oneself as a sexual excitant.

autogeny, autogenic(aw-toj'en-i, -to-jēn'ik) See *endogenous; endogeny.*

autognosis (aw-tog-nō'sis) Knowledge of oneself.

auto-hypnosis (-hip-nō'sis) Self-hypnosis. In one of Freud's early communications (on the *Psychical Mechanism of Hysterical Phenomena*, 1893), he emphasized the need on the part of the patient not only to remember the painful experience, but to live out its affect at the same time. He called this abreaction. Some patients are able to abreact on occasion when under the influence of auto-hypnosis.

autoimmunity An immunologic aberration in which antibody or sensitized lymphocyte reacts with the organism's own tissue. Whether the autoantibody causes, results from, or is merely coincident to human disease is unknown, even though it is a common belief that autoantibody attacks tissue and thereby causes auto-immune disease *(A.I.D.)*—among which are warm- and cold-antibody acquired hemolytic anemia, lupus erythematosus, chronic membranous glomerulonephritis, Hashimoto's thyroiditis, rheumatoid arthritis, mysasthenia gravis, scleroderma, and perhaps ulcerative colitis and some types of rheumatic heart disease. An alternative hypothesis is equally tenable—that autoimmunity may be due to genetically determined immunologic deficiencies which render the organism unable to respond immunologically to antigens (e.g. bacterium, virus, myoplasm, or other microorganism) that a normal immune system would readily eliminate. According to such an hypothesis, autoantibodies may be a secondary mechanism designed to eliminate the tissue killed or damaged by the antigen and/or designed to protect the attacked organ from further damage.

auto-infection, mental With this term Kornfeld in 1897 denoted a psychotic state in which the person believes himself wronged and brings every misfortune and unpleasant event into relation with his delusion. (Kornfeld, H. 'On Mental Auto-Infection,' *Journal of Mental Science* 43, 96, 1897)

autointoxication An obsolescent term denoting toxicity allegedly due to the absorption of the waste products of metabolism or of the products of intestinal decomposition.

autokinesis Self-movement; frequently used in a specific way to designate the phenomenon of seeing and tracing the 'movement' of a stationary pinpoint of light in a dark room. Persons with high autokinetic perception are said to demonstrate greater ego autonomy and more independent, non-conforming attitudes.

auto-libido See *libido.*

automagnetization Baragnon's term for autosuggestion.

automasochism (aw-tō-maz'ok-iz'm) A term used by Hirschfeld synonymously with Freud's conception of *masochism* (q.v.).

automatic seizures A type of psychomotor epilepsy. See *epilepsy.*

automatism (aw-tom'à-tiz'm) A condition in which activity is carried out without conscious knowledge on the part of the subject. Automatic actions and speech are seen in clear form in the catatonic form of schizophrenia in which incessant repetition may prevail without the patient's awareness. Automatisms are common also in other clinical states, particularly in those associated with a fugue.

'Automatic actions are not directly noticed by the patient himself; he neither feels that he wishes to accomplish the action, nor that he executes it. If the action lasts for some time, he takes notice of it like a third person, by observing and listening.' (Bleuler, E. *Textbook of Psychiatry*, tr. by Brill, A.A. Macmillan, New York, 1930) See *obedience, automatic.*

automatism, ambulatory A rhythmic form of automatic activity.

automatism, ambulatory comitial (kō-mish'al) A term devised by D.H. Tuke to denote automatic acts often observed in epileptic patients.

automatism, command When a patient strictly obeys a command, without the exercise of any critical judgment, he is said to show command automatism. The condition may be induced through hypnosis. It is not uncommon during the stage of hypersuggestibility in the catatonic form of schizophrenia; the patient may 'automatically' follow orders that lead to dangerous results.

'As an outward contrast to negativism there is sometimes found in our patients an automatic obedience to given commands. . . .' (Bleuler, E. *Textbook of Psychiatry*, tr. by Brill, A.A., Macmillan, New York, 1930)

automatism, post-ictal See *epilepsy.*

automatism, primary ictal A type of psychomotor epilepsy. See *epilepsy.*

automatization (aw-tōm-à-ti-zā'shun) The process whereby an action becomes routine and automatic, without conscious effort or direction. While discussing the probable fundamental reason for the development of a neurosis, Waelder defines a neurosis as 'the automatization of anxiety reaction,' the individuals 'remaining perpetually infantile in an important part of their being.' A neurotic subject is therefore regarded as an automaton, acting at the mercy of his infantile impulses. The schizophrenic patient, whose life is built around concepts of infancy, succumbs completely to the deeply lying forces of his unconscious. The compulsive neurotic must give automatic obedience to his symptoms.

automonosexualism *Rare.* The term, coined by Rohleder, is synonymous with narcissism.

automysophobia (aw-tō-mī-sō-fō'bē-à) Morbid dread that the person himself is filthy or smells bad—not infrequently a symptom of psychoneurosis.

autonomasia (-nō-mā'zhē-à) A variety of amnesic aphasia, characterized by an inability to recall names or substantives.

autonomic nervous system Vegetative nervous system. 'The autonomic nervous system consists of a series of cerebrospinal nuclei and nerves with widely distributed ganglia and plexuses which subserve the vegetative functions of the body. In its peripheral ramifications the system is characterized by a series of synaptic junctions which are situated outside the central nervous system. From anatomic and physiologic points of view there are two primary divisions, (1) the parasympathetic, or craniosacral, and (2) the sympathetic, orthosympathetic or thoracicolumbar. This subdivision is based upon the point of outflow from the central nervous system, the distribution of peripheral ganglia, the general antagonism in physiologic effects on visceral tissues most of which receive innervation from both divisions, and the response to pharmacologic agents. Each peripheral division of the autonomic nervous system is characterized by a two-neuron chain and consists of two histologic elements, the preganglionic neuron which terminates in a peripheral ganglion, whence the postganglionic neuron of the second order, carries impulses to their destinations on the viscera. No impulse goes directly to an organ of termination. Anatomically the two divisions are designated the craniosacral and the thoracicolumbar portions, or outflows, but clinically favored terms are either parasympathetic and sympathetic systems or parasympathetic and sympathetic divisions.' (De-Jong, R.N. *The Neurologic Examination,* Hoeber, 1950)

The autonomic nervous system is under control of higher centers, the most important of which is the hypothalamus. The hypothalamus appears to be the chief subcortical center for the regulation of both sympathetic and parasympathetic activities and for the integration of these. The anterior and medial nuclei of the hypothalamus are chiefly concerned with parasympathetic functions, while the lateral and posterior hypothalamic nuclei are chiefly concerned with sympathetic regulation.

autonomic-affective law See *law, autonomic-affective.*

autonomy (aw-ton'ō-mē) The quality or state of being self-governing. The living organism does not represent merely an inactive element but is, to a large extent, a self-governing entity. The biological process, therefore, is not entirely a resultant of external forces, but is in part governed by specific biological forces which are endogenous. The organism possesses a certain degree of freedom in the sense of Spinoza: it acts according to its own inherent nature, which is based on intrinsic forces, and not under the compulsion of outside influences. (Angyal, A. *Foundations for a Science of Personality,* The Commonwealth Fund, Oxford University Press, New York, 1941)

autonomy-heteronomy (-het-ēr-on'ō-mē) The autonomy of the organism is not absolute: the self-determination is restricted by outside influences which are heteronomous with relation to the organism. Every organismic process is always a resultant of two components, autonomy and heteronomy (endogenous and exogenous factors). In living beings of different species we find marked variations in the importance of autonomous and heteronomous determinants in their lives. Autonomy essentially means self-government; heteronomy means government from the outside. The expression autonomy-heteronomy is also used on the symbolic level, for instance, in relation to self-awareness. There is no absolute separation between the biological subject and the envirgnment and, therefore, there is no sharp boundary between the experience of the self and the outside world. There are only degrees of ego proximity and ego distance. The degrees of ego proximity and ego distance are the symbolic expressions of the gradient of autonomy-heteronomy. (Angyal, A. *Foundations for a Science of Personality,* The Commonwealth Fund, Oxford University Press, New York, 1941)

autonyctobatesis (aw-tō-nik-tō-bà-tē'sis) *Obs.* Somnambulism.

autopathic (aw-tō-pa'thik) A term used by Burrow to signify feeling that has been distorted by self-consciousness and bias. Contrasted with *orthopathic*(q.v.).

autopathy (aw-top'à-thē) Disease or disorder without apparent cause.

autophagy (aw-tof'à-jē) Biting or eating one's own flesh.

autophilia (aw-tō-fil'ē-à) Self-love; narcissism.

autophobia (-fo'bē-à) Morbid fear of being alone; fear of self.

autophonia (-fō'nē-à) *Obs.* Suicide.

autophonomania (-fō-nō-mā'nē-à) *Obs.* Suicidal insanity.

autoplasty The process of adapting by changing one's self, rather than by altering the external environment. Autoplastic adaptation may be normal and healthy (the patient's change in the course of psychoanalytic treatment, for example, which results from an autoplastic identification with the analyst), or they may be neurotic (as in symptom formation). See *alloplasty.*

autopsyche (aw-tō-sī'kē) The mind of one's self.

autopsychosis, moral (-sī-kō'sis) *Obs.* Wernicke's term for 'moral insanity,' i.e. psychopathic behavior traits, based on schizophrenia.

auto-sadism (-sad'iz'm) *Masochism* (q.v.). 'The first stage of sadism is thus aggression linked with activity against an outside object. The second stage, which may appear as a form of defense, consists of a turning against the subject which is identical with a change of object (auto-sadism). If the object is entirely absorbed by the ego, then the sadism is transformed into secondary masochism, which then grafts itself upon the primary masochism preceding the sadism, and strengthens it.' (Nunberg. H. *Principles of Psychoanalysis,* International Universities Press, 1955)

autoscopy Seeing one's 'self' or 'double' usually 'as the face and bust which imitate the movement and facial expressions of the original. The double typically appears misty, hazy or semi-transparent, and associated auditory, kinesthetic, and emotional perceptions are frequent. The commonest emotional reactions are sadness and bewilderment. Two forms of autoscopy are recognized: (1) symptomatic autoscopy, on an organic basis (such as irritative lesions in the temporoparietal lobes); and (2) idiopathic autoscopy, presumably a wish-fulfilling mechanism.

autosome (awt'ō-sōm) Ordinary chromosome which has no relation to sex and is distinguishable from the heterosome or sex chromosome. See *sex determination; chromosome.*

auto-somnambulism Somnambulism occasioned by 'self-hypnosis.'

auto-suggestibility The state of influencing oneself; self-suggestibility.

auto-suggestion When suggestion comes from the subject himself it is called auto-suggestion, in contradistinction to heterosuggestion or that which emanates from another.

autosymbolism Silberer's term for hallucinations which represent, in symbolic form, what is thought or felt at a given instant. Autosymbolism is a phenomenon of the hypnagogic state, when neither full sleep nor full waking is predominant. It consists, essentially, of translation of thoughts into pictures and to this extent is identical with dream formation, differing from the latter only in that the other factors in dream-work are absent.

autosynnoia (aw-tō-sin-oi'à) *Obs.* Complete or almost complete self-centeredness.

autotelik (-tē'lik) Pertaining to behavior and traits that express the central aims of the person, such as self-preservation.

autotomia (-tō'mē-à) In zoology this term refers to the severance of a part of the body; according to Ferenczi, this phenomenon appears to have its analogue in human activity. Some patients mutilate or cut off parts of the body that offend them. 'A similar tendency for freeing oneself from a part of the body which causes pain is demonstrated in the normal "scratch-reflex," where the desire to scratch away the stimulated part is clearly indicated, in the tendencies to self-mutila-

tion in catatonia and in the like tendencies symbolically represented in the automatic actions of many tic patients. . . .' (Ferenczi, S. *Further Contribution to the Theory and Technique of Psychoanalysis,* London, 1926.)

autotopagnosia (aw-tō-top-ag-nō'sē-à) Inability to identify or orient the body or the relation of its individual parts, i.e. a defect in appreciation of the body scheme. This type of agnosia occurs in lesions of the thalamoparietal pathways of the cortex in the region of the angular gyrus. The patient with such a lesion behaves as if he had no arm or leg on that side, even though he may feel stimuli on that side if his attention is called to the limb.

avalanche, law of See *law of avalanche; conduction, avalanche.*

Avellis' syndrome (George Avellis, German laryngologist, 1864-1916) A bulbar syndrome due to involvement of the vagus nerve and the bulbar portion of the spinal accessory nerve. Symptoms are: homolateral paralysis of the soft palate, pharynx, and larynx, and contralateral dissociate hemianesthesia, with loss of pain and temperature but not of touch and pressure.

average, arithmetic The mean; the sum of all items in a group divided by the number of items in the group. Example: the average age of four children aged 7, 10, 12, and 15 years, is the sum of their ages (44) divided by the number of children (4), which is 11 years.

aversion, partial *Antifetishism, Magnus Hirschfeld* (q.v.).

aversion therapy See *therapy, aversion.*

avoidance A defense mechanism, akin to *denial* (q.v.), consisting of refusal to encounter situations, objects, or activities because they represent unconscious sexual or aggressive impulses and/or punishments for those impulses. Avoidance is a major defense in *phobia* and *anxiety-hysteria* (qq.v.).

avoidant Negatively oriented or moving away from; an avoidant drive or behavior or response is a situation which results in behavior drawing away from the stimu-

lus. Withdrawal behavior and defense reactions are types of avoidant behavior.
Also known as abient behavior.

awakening, delayed See *paralysis, sleep.*

Awl, William M. (1799 - 1876) American
psychiatrist; one of the 'original thirteen'
founders of The Association of Medical
Superintendents of America (the forerunner of The American Psychiatric Association).

axon, axone See *neuron.*

aypnia (a-ip′ni-à) Insomnia, sleeplessness.

B

babbling A form of speech preceding articulate speech, characterized by sound combinations devoid of meaning.

Babinski-Nageotte's syndrome (Joseph François Felix Babinski, Paris physician, 1857-1932, and Jean Nageotte, Paris histologist, b. 1866) A bulbar syndrome produced by scattered lesions of the glossopharyngeal, vagus, spinal accessory (bulbar portion), and trigeminal nerves. Symptoms are: homolateral paralysis of the tongue, pharynx, and larynx; homolateral loss of taste in posterior tongue; homolateral Horner's syndrome; homolateral loss of pain and temperature sense in the face; homolateral asynergia and ataxia with a tendency to fall to the side of the lesion; contralateral hemiplegia, and contralateral dissociate hemianesthesia with loss of pain and temperature sense but preservation of touch and pressure.

Babinski's reflex Described by Joseph Babinski (1857-1932), a French neuropathologist, in 1898 and 1903, as extension of the toes instead of flexion when stimulating the sole of the foot. It 'consists in the comparatively slow dorsal extension of the great toe when the plantar reflex is tested and at the same time there is a slight spreading apart of the toes.' (Jelliffe, S.E. and White, W.A. *Diseases of the Nervous System,* 6th ed., Lea & Febiger, Philadelphia, 1935). The same phenomenon (great toe extension) may be produced by other tests—under *reflex* see *Oppenheim, Gordon, Chaddock.*

baby talk A form of speech characterized by defective articulation of certain consonants; it is rapidly outgrown unless adults in the environment contribute to its maintenance by using it themselves in conversing with the child. In severe behavior disorders and schizophrenia, the patient may revert to this type of speech.

bacillophobia (bȧ-sil'ō-fō'bē-ȧ) Morbid fear of bacilli or of microörganisms in general.

background *Ground* (q.v.).

backlash A type of *feedback* (q.v.), referring to the effect of its own overt responses upon the organism.

backwardness Educational retardation due not to intrinsic, but to extrinsic causes (in DSM-II, 31x.8). When these causes can be removed the arrears are usually made up, although in some cases this may not entirely take place. They compose about one-third of all retarded children. The causes of extrinsic backwardness are numerous, but they may be grouped under the heading of (1) environmental or social; (2) physical.' (Tredgold, A.F. *A Text-book of Mental Deficiency,* 6th ed., Wood, Baltimore, 1937)

bad object See *object, bad.*

bad self See *self, bad.*

Baillarger, Jules (1809-90) (bȧ-yär-zhā') French psychiatrist; investigated manicdepressive insanity as *folie à double forme* (1853-54) and *cretinism* (1873).

balance, group The result of grouping patients in accordance with clinical and personal criteria, in order to prevent intensification of a specific problem or set of problems.

balbutiate (bal-bū'shē-āt) *Rare.* To stammer.

balbuties (bal-boo'tē-ēz) *Stammering* or *stuttering* (qq.v.). Some authorities differentiate between *balbuties praecox* (starting before the age of 3 years), *balbuties vulgaris* (onset between the ages of 3 and 7), and *balbuties tarda* (onset after the age of 7).

ballistophobia (ba-lis-tō-fō'bē-ȧ) Abnormal fear of missiles.

balneology (bal-nē-ol'ō-jē) Study of waters used in baths.

balneum arenae (bȧl-ne-oom ȧ-rā'nī) Sand bath.

balneum calidum (kȧ'lē-doom) Hot bath.

balneum frigidum (frē'gē-doom) Cold bath.

balneum tepidum (te'pē-doom) Warm bath.

Baló's disease Concentric demyelination. See *sclerosis, diffuse.*

baragnosis (bar-ag-nō'sis) Absence of ability to recognize weight of objects, generally tested by placing objects in the hand; indicative of parietal lobe lesion.

barbiturates (bar-bi'tūr-ātes, -tūr'ātes) A group of central nervous system depressants which are chemical derivatives of barbituric acid (malonyl-urea); among them are phenobarbital, amytal, pentobarbital, seconal, evipal, and pentothal.

Of particular interest in psychiatry is the increasingly important role the barbiturates have been playing as addicting drugs (304.2). The barbiturate addict develops a high tolerance to the drugs (a daily dose of 10 Gm. i.e. 100 capsules of 1½ grains strength is not unheard of) but the tolerance is incomplete. As a result the addict may suddenly react to his usual daily dose as though he had never taken a barbiturate before and develop symptoms of acute intoxication.

On empirical grounds, a person is considered to be an addict if his daily intake exceeds 0.8 Gm. The barbiturates are mentally deteriorating, in that they depress the cortex and cerebellum. Symptoms of addiction include impairment of all mental functions, defective emotional control, poor judgment, confusion, nystagmus, ataxia, and sometimes a toxic psychosis. Abrupt withdrawal of barbiturates from an addict is not without danger; within 30 to 48 hours after withdrawal, 75 per cent of cases manifest convulsions and 60 per cent develop deliria (which may be fatal). See *dependency, drug.*

baresthesia (bàr-es-thē'zē-à) Pressure sense.

barognosis (bar-og-nō'sis) The sense of weight-differences, usually by lifting objects in the hand.

barophobia (bar-ō-fō'bē-à) Fear of gravity.

barrier Boundary; limit; obstruction; separation. In psychiatry, the word is generally used in three contexts: (1) the neurophysiolgic, to refer to the functional obstruction to the free flow of constituents of the blood into the brain (see *barrier, blood-brain*); (2) the interpersonal, to refer to an absent or defective ability to form adequate relationships with people—the *schizophrenic barrier* is thus considered a type of autistic behavior based upon an ego defect, although the phrase is on occasion used to refer to a lack of relatedness between different parts of the schizophrenic's personality; and (3) in projective testing where *barrier response* is used to indicate a response that emphasizes the periphery of a percept and highlights the boundary (e.g. "turtle with shell," "man in armor"). Responses that emphasize weakness and permeability (e.g. "a gaping wound" "a torn rug") are called *penetration responses.* Schizophrenic patients tend to have fewer barrier responses and more penetration responses than neurotic or 'normal' subjects.

barrier, blood-brain An hypothesized resistance or obstruction to the free flow of various constituents of the blood into the brain; also known as *hemato-encephalic barrier.* The glial protoplasm (of astrocytes and/or dendroglia) has been proposed as the possible anatomical site of the fixed blood-brain barrier. It is probable that many other factors influence entry of metabolites into the brain, such as carbon dioxide content of blood (which affects permeability of brain capillaries) and circulating antibodies. 'The term barrier-antibody system is thus proposed to denote both fixed and circulating barrier components, whose functions are defense, and the maintenance of a selective internal environment for the brain.' (Bogoch, S. *Archives of Neurology and Psychiatry 80;* 221, 1958)

barrier, incest The ego's defenses against incestuous impulses, which are formed mainly in the latency period by deflection of infantile impulses from their sexual aims, with resultant desexualization of impulses.

baryglossia (bar-i-glos'ē-à) *Obs.* Thick, heavy speech, usually implying a disorder of the tongue.

barylalia (-lā'lē-à) An indistinct and thick speech, observed principally in patients with an organic lesion, often in the central nervous system (Broca's area). It is common in advanced states of general paresis.

baryphonia (-fō'nē-à) A heavy quality of voice; generally deep and hoarse.

barythymia (-thī'mē-à) *Rare.* Depression of emotions. It is generally accompanied by difficulty in thinking and acting.

basal ganglia Masses of gray matter lying deep within each cerebral hemisphere. The basal ganglia are composed of: (1) corpus striatum, including (a) pallidum (globus pallidus), (b) neostriatum (putamen and caudate nucleus) and (c) amygdala and claustrum; and (2) the internal capsule. The lenticular nucleus is used to refer to the outer putamen and the globus pallidus. The corpus striatum is an important unit of the *extrapyramidal system* (q.v.). The neostriatum receives fibers from the thalamus and the cortex (frontal cortex and pyramidal tract) and sends efferents mainly to the pallidum. The pallidum sends efferents to the thalamus, hypothalamus, subthalamus, substantia nigra, midbrain, pons, and medulla.

Lesions in the corpus striatum may cause various symptoms, including muscular rigidity, involuntary movements (e.g. tremor, chorea, athetosis), and hypotonia. Lesions of the globus pallidus or substantia nigra are most commonly associated with muscular rigidity and tremor, as in Parkinsonism.

It has been suggested, incidentally, that the source of instinctual energy might be the basal ganglia, and perhaps especially the globus pallidus (Ostow, M. *International Journal of Psycho-Analysis XLII*, 486, 1961)

The internal capsule is a band of white fiber tracts separating the lenticular nucleus from the caudate and thalamus. It contains all the fibers which ascend to and descend from the cortex: pyramidal tract, thalamocortical fibers, optic radiation from the lateral geniculate body, auditory radiation from the medical geniculate body, fronto- and temporo-pontine tracts, fibers of the corpus striatum, and the corticothalamic tracts. Lesions in the internal capsule, common in cerebrovas-

cular accidents, result in contralateral spastic hemiplegia.

Basedow's disease Hyperthyroidism or overactivity of the thyroid gland. Karl A von Basedow, German physician (1799-1854), described the disease exophthalmic goiter in 1840. It is characterized by enlargement of the thyroid gland, protrusion of the eyeballs, rapid heart action fine muscular tremors and so-called general nervousness. It is as commonly called Grave's disease and less frequently Begbie's, Marsh's, Parry's, Parsons', or Flajani's disease.

basic mistakes In Adlerian psychology incidents, concepts and attitudes of early childhood that have determined or contributed to a person's life style, which must be corrected if the patient is to be helped. They are revealed through exploration in psychotherapy of the patient's early recollections. See *constancy.*

basic trust See *relatedness.*

basiphobia (bā-si-fō'bē-à) Morbid fear of walking. It is common in the psychoneu roses, less so in the psychoses. Generally it is related to fear of collapse and death rather than to fear of objects while walking.

basistasiphobia (bā-si-stas-i-fō'bē-à) See *stasibasiphobia.*

basophobia (bā-sō-fō'bē-à) Basiphobia.

basostasophobia (bā-sō-stas-ō-fō'bē-à) *Stasibasiphobia* (q.v.).

Bastian's law (Henry Charlton Bastian English neurologist, 1837-1915) In severe crush or complete interruption of the spinal cord, there results a total and permanent loss of reflexes with flac cid paralysis; death ensues within a few days or weeks.

bath, Brand See *bath, cold.*

bath, cold 'Cold baths, usually referred to as the Brand baths, are occasionally employed in states of high temperature and deliria caused by it. The temperature is usually from 70° to 85°F. The patient is covered with a sheet and the body immersed in a cold tub. Friction of the body is immediately instituted and continued as long as the patient is in the tub. The patient should not be permitted to remain longer than fifteen minutes in the cold bath. He should then be removed and covered with dry, warm blankets.' (Sands, I.J. *Nervous and Mental Diseases for Nurses,* 3rd ed., Saunders, Philadelphia and London, 1937)

bath, continuous 'The *continuous bath* is a valuable therapeutic agent in the management of the very excited, delirious, and exhausted patients. The tub is arranged for a continuous inflow and outflow of water at a constant temperature of approximately 98 ° F. The patient is permitted to lie comfortably in a canvas suspended in the tub, and the body immersed in water. . . . He may be kept in the tub from four to twenty-four hours, or even longer.' (Sands, I.J. *Nervous and Mental Diseases for Nurses,* 3rd ed., Saunders, Philadelphia and London, 1937)

bath, drip A form of hydrotherapy. Standing in a tub filled with just enough water at a temperature of 105 °F. to cover the ankles, the patient is soaked with cool water applied to the torso; this is followed by vigorous friction.

bath, hot air As a rule, a hot air bath is given in a cabinet heated by electric light bulbs. It is said that when a tonic effect is desired the temperature of the air surrounding the body should range from 110 ° to 120 °F. For eliminative purposes the temperature is maintained around 160 °F.

bath, sitz The sitz bath is given locally to the pelvis, in a tub of special construction. Depending upon the action desired these may be hot, cold, neutral, or prolonged. A blanket is placed about the patient and pinned at the back of the neck. The patient is then seated in the tub, and the feet placed in a foot bath at a temperature of 105 °to 110 °F. The upper edge of the blanket is brought up around the shoulders and over the edge of the tub, and the lower edge covers the foot bath.' (Bailey, H. *Nursing Mental Diseases,* 3rd ed., Macmillan, New York, 1935)

bath, whirlpool 'This is a local bath given in a small tub for either arm or leg. There is a mixer to provide both hot and cold water and to make it possible to control the temperature. The temperature of the whirlpool bath ranges from 104 °to 120 °F. Air under pressure enters the tub under the surface of the water. Whirlpool baths are given for from 15 to 45 minutes.' (Steele, K.M. *Psychiatric Nursing,* Davis, Philadelphia, 1937)

bathophobia (bath-ō-fō′bē-à) Morbid dread of depths. The term commonly refers to fear of height, that is, fear of losing control of oneself while in a high place; it is a fear of falling from the height and of thus being killed. The fear is common among normal individuals, who, however, are able to control the impulse without much anxiety. It is morbid when the anxiety is intense and lasting and leads to measures to avoid high places. Common to many psychiatric conditions, it gains particular prominence among psychoneurotic subjects. It is symbolic of an unconscious impulse, the nature of which is unknown to the individual ruled by the fear.

bathyesthesia (ba-thi-es-thē′z[h]ē-à) Deep sensibility; sensibility of the parts of the body beneath the surface. 'Here deep pressure pain, muscle and joint sense and bony sensibility are to be tested. Deep pressure with the thumb and fingers, or a special instrument (baresthesiometer) is used. The pressure should be sufficient to cause pain.' (Jelliffe, S.E. and White, W.A. *Diseases of the Nervous System,* 6th ed., Lea & Febiger, Philadelphia, 1935)

batophobia (ba-tō-fō′bē-à) Fear of (being on or passing) high objects or buildings.

batrachophobia (bat-rà-kō-fō′bē-à) Fear of frogs.

battarismus (bat-ar-iz′mus) Stammering; stuttering; hesitating speech.

battered child See *syndrome, battered child.*

battle fatigue See *shell-shock.*

Battle's sign Postauricular and subconjunctival ecchymosis in cases of fracture of the base of the skull.

Bayle's disease Antoine Bayle, French

physician (1799-1858), first described it in 1822. *Obs.* Commonly known as general paralysis or paresis; dementia paralytica.

bdelygmia (dē-lig′mē-à) A Hippocratic term referring to a morbid loathing of food.

Beard, George Miller (1840-83) American psychiatrist; introduced the term *neurasthenia* in a paper, 'Neurasthenia or Nervous Exhaustion,' *Boston Medical and Surgical Journal LXXX*, 217-21, 1869.

beating Flagellation. Beating phantasies accompanying masturbation were discussed as a form of perversion by Freud. In the girl, beating phantasies typically go through three stages of development: first the father is beating a sibling, next he beats the girl herself, and finally he beats other children again, but these are boys and need not be siblings. In the boy, beating phantasies develop in two stages: in the first, the father is beating a boy, and in the second it is the mother who is beating him. In both sexes, the phantasies originate from an incestuous attachment to the father; the boy evades the threat of homosexuality by transforming the beating father into the beating mother, while the girl transforms herself in phantasy into a man and derives masochistic pleasure from what appears on the surface to be a sadistic phantasy.

Bechtereff-Mendel reflex V.M. Bechtereff, Russian neurologist (1857-1927); Kurt Mendel, German physician (b. 1874). Also known as the cuboidodigital or dorsocuboidal reflex; by striking the outer part of the dorsum of the foot, there results normally a dorsal flexion of the toes; in abnormal conditions such as pyramidal tract disease, there is plantar flexion.

Bedlam The name of the Priory of St. Mary of Bethlehem, founded in London in 1247, turned into a mental hospital in 1402 and incorporated in 1547 as the Hospital of St. Mary of Bethlehem. The proper name of this first English 'lunatic asylum' became a common appellation for 'lunatic asylum' in general and, still later, synonymous with states of frenzy, excitement, wild tumult, pandemonium.

bedlamism *Rare.* A word or act which is

characteristic of psychosis or of psychotic individuals; a trait of psychosis.

bedlamite *Obs.* Psychotic person.

Beers, Clifford W. (1876-1943) In 1909 founded National Committee for Mental Hygiene (now called National Association for Mental Health); wrote *A Mind That Found Itself.*

Beevor's sign (Charles Edward Beevor, British neurologist, 1854-1908) Upward excursion of the umbilicus, observed when the lower half of the abdominal muscles are paralyzed.

beggar, emotional A term describing that type of person who is always 'holding his mental palm out to people, yet always expecting it to be slapped down. . .' The emotional beggar has been unable to detach himself from his parents (usually the parent of the opposite sex). 'He cannot get away from the desire to possess and be possessed' by the parent and 'is always seeking more, no matter how close to the parent he has managed to attach himself emotionally. This impulse usually begins in infancy, the person never having been weaned physically or emotionally. 'His general reaction to people is a suckling one.' (Hinsie, L.E. *Understandable Psychiatry,* Macmillan, New York, 1948)

behavior The manner in which anything acts or operates. With regard to the human being the term usually refers to the action of the individual as a unit. He may be, and ordinarily is, acting in response to some given organ or impulse, but it is his general reaction that gives rise to the concept *behavior.* Each component of the body has its own special ways of reacting; when the action of individual parts is meant, terms such as physiology and pathology are used. A hungry man seeks food; the seeking constitutes behavior. Food gets into his stomach; the stomach acts and reacts, that is, it exhibits physiology or pathology.

Healy, Bronner, and Bowers define behavior as 'the sum total of responses to stimuli, internal and external.' (Healy, W., Bronner, A.F., Bowers, A.M. *The Structure and Meaning of Psychoanalysis,* Knopf, New York, 1930)

To the special school of psychology called behaviorism the expression means that all human action, normal or abnormal, can be understood in terms of the reflex arc, reflex action, and conditioned reflexes.

behavior, catastrophic A term introduced by Kurt Goldstein in 1939 to describe a certain type of behavior disorder that seemed more or less characteristic, or specific, for patients suffering from those disturbances of language and thought that had been grouped under the general diagnostic term *aphasia*. This symptomatic behavior takes the form of an inability to carry on a simple course of action once it is interrupted. The patients 'become agitated and fearful and more than usually inept. when presented with once simple tasks that they can no longer do.' Goldstein interprets such traits of behavior as characteristic of a trend toward fanatical orderliness and the reaction of disinterest and aversion as defensive methods of avoiding 'catastrophic' embarrassment. It would seem that the catastrophic reaction stems from the personality (or psychological) response to the organic brain injury that underlies so many aphasia cases. (Hunt, J.McV. *Personality and the Behavior Disorders*, vol. 2, Ronald, New York, 1944)

behavior, chaotic An extreme disorderliness in organizing one's humdrum affairs, with respect to the time to be made available for different needs, the necessary money for various expenditures, or the disposition of personal effects—all suggesting or betokening a straying from mental health. Fenichel states that chaotic behavior appears usually as a character trait of hysterical individuals. He explains that chaotic behavior 'represents a striving to get rid of traumatic impressions by actively repeating them.' (Fenichel, O. *The Psychoanalytic Theory of Neurosis*, Norton, New York, 1945)

behavior, collective The behavior which results when every individual in a group, an assemblage or a public 'is moved to think and act under the influence of a mood or state of mind, in which each shares and to which each contributes.' (Park, R.E. *Collective Behavior; Encyclopaedia of the Social Sciences*, vol. 3, Macmillan, New York, p. 631)

In the broadest sense all group behavior is collective behavior. In the narrow sense collective behavior is applied not so much to customary and conventional behavior as to the emergence of new forms of behavior under conditions of inter-stimulation wherein 'individuals reflect one another's states of feeling and in so doing intensify this feeling.' (Blumer, H.E., in Park, R.E. *Principles of Sociology*, Barnes & Noble, New York, 1939)

Elementary forms of collective behavior are to be observed in the street crowd, the acting crowd, the expressive crowd, the mob, the gang, the panic, the riot, the stampede, and the mutiny; intermediate forms in mass behavior, the public, public opinion, the party, and crusades; and more highly organized forms in propaganda, advertising, religious movements, nationalistic movements, fashion, reform, and revolution.

behavior, criminotic Terms such as criminotic, criminotic behavior, criminosis have been introduced into psychiatric literature by Arthur N. Foxe. The word criminosis is coined on the pattern of neurosis and psychosis in regard to form, but differs in meaning in that it does not specifically connote mental illness. The criminotic is not necessarily mentally or emotionally ill, but the term criminosis would imply or decribe his condition. And the term criminotic behavior would refer to the crime-committing activities of that person, as constituting the evidences of criminality or *criminosis* (q.v.).

behavior disorders This term refers to a group of psychiatric disorders in children and adolescents which are not secondary to somatic diseases or defects or to convulsive disorders and which are not part of a well-defined psychosis or psychoneurosis. The primary behavior disorders are considered to be reactions to an unfavorable environment; they appear as problems of personality development, as persisting undesirable traits or unfavorable habits (the so-called habit disorders, including nail-biting, thumb-sucking, enuresis, masturbation, temper tantrums, etc.), as delinquency or conduct disorders (truancy, fighting and quarreling, disobedience, untruthfulness, stealing, forgery, setting fires, destruction of property, use of alcohol, use of drugs, cruelty, sex offenses, vagrancy, etc.), as certain neurotic traits (such as tics and habit spasms, sleep-walking, overactivity and fears), and as problems of school and general educational or vocational difficulties. In the past, children with such disorders were referred to as 'problem children.'

In DSM-II, *Behavior Disorders of Childhood and Adolescence* are classified as follows:

308.0 Hyperkinetic reaction; see *impulse disorder, hyperkinetic.*
308.1 Withdrawing reaction.
308.2 Overanxious reaction.
308.3 Runaway reaction.
308.4 Unsocialized aggressive reaction.
308.5 Group delinquent reaction.
308.9 Other reactions of childhood or adolescence which are more stable, internalized, and resistant to treatment than transient situational disturbances, but less serious than psychoses, neuroses, and personality disorders.

behavior, expiatory See *expiation.*

behavior-language This term means that the actions of the child, before he learns to speak, constitute a real language or means of expression. The crying, fretting, anxiety, quiescence, satiety, smiling, and self-activity are the words of a language the infant uses before acquiring the capacity of producing articulate sounds. (Sladen, F.J. *Psychiatry and the War,* Thomas, Springfield, Ill., 1943) See *jargon, organ.*

behavior, multidetermined Human behavior, healthy or disordered, can be conceived of as being carried out at four fundamental levels: (a) the eugenical; (b) the physiological; (c) the psychological, and (d) the environmental. Multitudinous factors stemming from past experience, on the one hand, and the current, present environmental situation on the other constantly interact and interreact to determine the current behavior at the present cross-sectional level.

In the field of prevention, this important concept of the multidetermined origin of human behavior is the basis for the 'all out,' 'gun shot,' 'total push,' eclectic methods of approach toward psychiatric treatment and prevention.

behavior, nodal In group therapy, the peak of hyper-aggressivity and hilarity on the part of children. This high peak is always followed by a period of quietude, which is the *anti-nodal phase.* This alter-nation of the quiet and action occurs in cycles. The frequency of this manifestation decreases as therapy progresses.

behavior theory A theory of the genesis of neurotic behavior, based upon learning theory; among its leading exponents are Eysenck, Jones, and Wolpe. The theory postulates that neurotic symptoms are learned patterns of behavior which are unadaptive. If neurotic symptoms are learned, then they should be amenable to 'unlearning,' and behavior therapy is directed to the inhibition and/or extinction of the learned neurotic responses. One form of behavior therapy is J. Wolpe's *reciprocal inhibition psychotherapy:* 'If a response antagonistic to anxiety can be made to occur in the presence of anxiety-evoking stimuli so that it is accompanied by a complete or partial suppression of the anxiety responses, the bond between these stimuli and the anxiety responses will be weakened.' (*Psychotherapy by Reciprocal Inhibition,* Stanford University Press, 1958)

behavioral genetics See *genetics.*

behavioral reaction See *personality disorder.*

behavioral sciences 'A multidisciplinary pursuit of knowledge about behavior in its roots and manifestations, in man and animals, in individuals, groups, and cultures, and in all conditions, normal, exceptional, and pathological. Behavioral scientists remain specialists in their respective fields, while striving to unify their diverse theories and concepts.' (Bry I. et al. *Mental Health Book Review Index Vol. 5,* No. 1, January 1960) Among the many disciplines contributing to the behavioral sciences are all those ordinarily subsumed under the groupings: 'The Natural Sciences, which explore the inanimate and animate universe in which man finds himself; The Social Sciences, concerned with the political, social, legal, and economic structure he has given to the world around him; and the Humanities, the study of man's lasting intellectual and artistic creations.' (ibid.)

behaviorism A term coined by J.B. Watson in 1913 ('Psychology as the Behaviorist Views It,' *Psychological Review XX;* also *Behaviorism—An Introduction to Com-*

parative Psychology, Holt, New York, 1914) to indicate that all habits may be explained in terms of conditioned glandular and motor reaction.

'Behaviorism, on the contrary, holds that the subject matter of human psychology is the *behavior or activities of the human being.* Behaviorism claims that "consciousness" is neither a definable nor a usable concept; that it is merely another word for the "soul" of more ancient times.' (Watson, J.B. *Behaviorism,* The People's Institute, New York, 1924)

Bell, Luther V. (1806-62) American psychiatrist; one of the 'original thirteen' founders of the Association of Medical Superintendents of America (the forerunner of The American Psychiatric Association); *Bell's mania* (q.v.).

belle indifference See *hysteria.*

Bell's mania (Luther V. Bell, 1806-62, American physician) A term used by Luther Bell in 1849 for what is now designated as acute manic excitement.

Bell's palsy See *nerve, facial.*

belonephobia (bel-ō-nē-fō′bē-à) Fear of needles.

belongingness A feeling of being a part of and/or being accepted by another person or group. A lack of this feeling is often a complaint of schizophrenic patients. See *autism.*

Bender, Lauretta (1897-) American neuropsychiatrist; Visual Motor Gestalt test; child psychiatry, especially schizophrenia and brain damage.

bends, the See *disease, caisson.*

Benedikt's syndrome (Moritz Benedikt, Austrian physician, 1835-1920) The symptoms following a lesion of the red nucleus in the midbrain which involves the oculomotor fibers passing through the midbrain: homolateral oculomotor paralysis, contralateral hyperkinesis.

benign (bē-nīn′) In psychiatry, referring to a disorder with good prognosis. It does not refer to the intensity of the clinical syndrome. A benign psychosis may be extremely intense, as the benign stupor

state, from which the patient generally recovers or experiences appreciable amelioration.

Benommenheit (be-nom′en-hīt) Literally, a benumbing; Bleuler's term for one of the acute syndromes of the schizophrenias in which there is a slowing of all psychic processes but no dejection of mood or self-depreciatory ideas. Patients with Benommenheit are unable to deal with any relatively complicated or unusual situation; they make many mistakes and show marked apraxia and impaired comprehension. This syndrome may persist for long periods, even decades, but it is not otherwise indicative of a poor prognosis.

Benzedrine ® dependency (304.6) Symptoms include an inability to abstain from the drug, need for increasing dosage (high tolerance is developed, e.g. 1500 mg. may be the usual daily dose), insomnia, restlessness, irritability, gross errors in judgment, loss of impulse control (especially aggressive impulses), ideas of reference and delusions of persecution, and hallucinosis with auditory and visual hallucinations. The last named usually clears within four or five weeks; males are much more prone to develop such symptoms than females.

berdache (ber-dash′) Transvestite.

Berger rhythm, Berger wave See *electroencephalogram.*

Bernheim (bârn-hâN′), **Hippolyte-Marie** (1840-1919) French psychotherapist; hypnotism and suggestibility.

bestiality Any type of human behavior which resembles that of beasts; more specifically, sexual congress between humans and animals.

beta rhythm or wave See *electroencephalogram.*

beta-arc See *alpha-arc.*

Betz cell See *lobe, frontal.*

bewildered A term often used to describe the lost, dazed, perplexed, puzzled patient who appears to be confused but shows a sort of numb apathy about his confusion. Bewilderment is often associated with conscious ambivalence, with dereistic or autistic thinking, with preoccupation, and with vacuity or sterility of thinking.

Bianchi, Leonardo (1848 - 1927) (bē-äng′-kē) Italian psychiatrist and neurologist.

bias (bī′us) A tendency to err, usually because the sample from which conclusions are drawn is not representative of the group to which the conclusions are applied.

biased apperception Seeing things only as one wants to see them, considered by Adler a prerequisite for social participation since, without it, social movements would be stifled by indecisiveness. The person who cannot make a move unless he is certain to be right, for example, cannot usually move very much. The normal person, by contrast, takes a chance and chooses in accordance with his preferences and his subjective evaluation of the situation.

biblioclast (bib′lē-ō-klast) One who destroys or mutilates books.
   'Among biblioclasts some act in groups *cornering* copies of a rare book and making a *"pool" of any volumes which are not immaculate;* from among these they *complete or perfect* as many copies as possible, and destroy the remainder. . . .' (Jackson, H. *The Anatomy of Bibliomania,* Scribner's, New York, 1932)

biblioklept (-klept) One who steals books.

bibliokleptomania (-klep-tō-mā′nē-à) Morbid tendency to steal books.

bibliomania Book-madness; an intense desire to collect and possess books, especially rare and curious ones.

bibliophobia (-fō′bē-à) A morbid dread or hatred of books.

bibliotherapy (-ther′à-pē) Utilization of reading as an adjunct to psychotherapy. Books may be recommended to patients for the following reasons: (1) to help the patient understand better his own psychological and physiological reactions to frustration; (2) to remedy insufficient or erroneous knowledge; (3) to facilitate

communication between patient and therapist by helping the patient understand the terminology of therapy; (4) to stimulate the patient to discuss and verbalize certain problems by helping to remove the fear, shame, or guilt related to those problems; (5) to stimulate the patient to think constructively between interviews; (6) to reinforce accepted social and cultural patterns and thereby inhibit certain infantile patterns of behavior; (7) to stimulate the patient's imagination and give him vicarious satisfactions which reality cannot afford without danger; (8) to enlarge the patient's sphere of interest; (9) as an adjunct to a program of vocational rehabilitation. The reading matter recommended must, of course, be selected individually for the specific patient, depending on the goals of therapy, the intellectual capacities of the patient, and his stage of achievement in therapy.

Bichat, Law of (Marie François Xavier Bichat, French anatomist, 1771 - 1802) According to Bichat there are two great body systems, called by him the vegetative and the animal. The former provides for assimilation and augmentation of mass, while the latter provides for the transformation of energy, 'that is, for the relations with the environment.' The two systems 'are in inverse ratio of development in ontogenetic evolution — the greater the development of the vegetative system, the less developed is the system of relation.' (Pende, N. *Constitutional Inadequacies,* tr. by Naccarati, S., Lea & Febiger, Philadelphia, 1928)

Biedl-Moon-Laurence syndrome See *syndrome, Laurence-Moon-Biedl.*

Bielschowsky's disease (Max Bielschowsky, German neuropathologist, 1869 - 1940) See *amaurotic family idiocy.*

bind, double This term is approximately equivalent to dilemma and is used particularly to refer to a type of interaction said to be characteristic of families containing schizophrenic members. The parent of a schizophrenic, for example, is perceived by the patient as emitting '. . . signals of an incongruent nature. This incongruence is perhaps most clear when one half of the parent's behavior precedes an act of the patient and the other half follows. The parent will, for example, invite the patient to express a courageous opinion, and when that opinion is expressed, will disparage it as unloving, disloyal, disobedient, etc.' (Bateson, G. 'Cultural Problems Posed by a Study of Schizophrenic Process' in Auerback, A., ed., *Schizophrenia—An Integrated Approach*, Ronald, New York, 1959, Chap. 6) As a result of repeated entrapment in the double-bind, which he can neither ignore nor attack directly by commenting upon the incongruity, the schizophrenic learns to strip all his communications of material that might be maltreated in this way. This is believed by some to be the mode of development of certain of the schizophrenic's fundamental symptoms.

J.H. Weakland and D.D. Jackson (*Archives of Neurology and Psychiatry* 79, 554, 1958) define the double-bind as 'a hostile dependent involvement where one of the parties insists on a response to multiple orders of messages which are mutually contradictory, and the other (the schizophrenic patient to be) cannot comment on these contradictions or escape from the situation.'

A. Ferreira (*Archives of General Psychiatry* 3:359, 1960) terms the double-bind described above a 'unipolar message. He notes that the double-bind can hardly represent the full cause of schizophrenia, since the double bind is not confined to the schizophrenogenic relationship. But what is seemingly characteristic of schizophrenics is that the contradictory messages emanate from a single (unipolar) source, usually the mother. In delinquent behavior, on the other hand, the source of the messages is split (bipolar), with message A emanating from the father and message B (a comment about message A with the effect of opposing or destroying it) emanating from the mother, or vice versa. Ferreira calls this the 'split double bind.'

Binet-Simon tests See *tests, Binet-Simon*.

binge eating See *syndrome, night-eating*.

Bini, Lucio (1908-1964) Italian psychiatrist. Co-discoverer (with Ugo Cerletti) of electric convulsive therapy, first demonstrated in Rome on 28 March, 1938. The idea of inducing convulsions electrically rather than pharmacologically was Cerletti's, but the elaboration of the technique and bitemporal placement of the electrodes was Bini's.

Binswanger, Otto (1852-1929) (bĕn'-swäng-gĕr) German neurologist and psychiatrist.

Binswanger's disease See *encephalopathy, subcortical arteriosclerotic*.

bioanalysis (bī-ō-à-nal'i-sis) '. . . The question presents itself to me whether the term psychoanalysis is really broad enough and whether another more comprehensive and more all-inclusive term, such as *bioanalysis* or *psychobioanalysis* should not be substituted for it, especially if we would include the analysis of the somatic symptoms of the psychoneuroses, psychoses, and other psychic states as well as the multiform conduct of man at every stage of evolution and development.' (Solomon, M. 'Plea for Broader Standpoint in Psychoanalysis,' *Psychoanalytic Review 2*, 66, 1915)

biodynamics (bī-ō-dī-nam'iks) Masserman's system of psychoanalytic psychiatry; '. . . biodynamics derives some of its essential dynamic orientations from analysis, and serves no greater practical function than to generalize fundamental analytic concepts and to demonstrate their theoretical, experimental and clinical applicability to a wide range of phenomena in animal and human behavior.' (Masserman, J.H. *The Practice of Dynamic Psychiatry*, Saunders, Philadelphia, 1955.) The four principles of biodynamics—motivation, milieu, adaptation and conflict—are stated as follows: (1) all organisms are actuated by their physiologic needs; (2) every organism reacts to its own interpretations of its milieu in terms of its individual needs, special capacities, and unique experiences; (3) whenever an organism's goal-directed activities are frustrated by external obstacles, the organism either changes its techniques to reach that same goal or changes its goal; (4) when two or more urgent motivations conflict so that the adaptive patterns attendant to each are mutually exclusive, the organism experiences anxiety and its somatic and muscular behavior becomes either ambivalent, poorly adaptive, and ineffectively substitutive (neurotic), or progressively more disorganized, regressive, and bizarrely symbolic (psychotic).

biogenetic law of Haeckel See *law, biogenetic mental.*

biogenetics See *genetics.*

biogenic amines See *amine.*

biography in depth The use of established psychoanalytic knowledge to contribute to the understanding of the personality of the subject being studied. See *pathography, psychoanalytic.*

biology, mathematical That branch of biology concerned with the development of conceptual or mathematical models of various biological phenomena. From those models, various mathematical consequences are deduced which are then compared to actual experiments or other observed phenomena. Successful mathematical theories have been developed for a large number of biological phenomena, including nerve excitation, endocrine secretions, conditioning and learning.

biometry (bī-om′e-trē) The measurement of life; specifically, calculation of the probable duration of life and study of all the factors, endogenous and exogenous, that enter into the determination of the duration of life.

bionegativity (bī-ō-neg-à-tiv′i-tē) A personality constellation in which one or more part processes disturb the total function of the organism. In an entirely healthy organism the various part processes are integrated in such a way that they subserve and promote the total function of the organism, while in an abnormal condition the integration is impaired and one or more part functions impede or disturb instead of promote the total function. Instead of being viewed as an abnormality such an impairment is, therefore, conceived as an integrational state, a specific relation between part and whole, and is called bionegativity.

bionics The study of biological functions and mechanisms from the point of view

of applying them to electronic devices, such as computers.

bionomics (bī-ō-no′miks) *Ecology* (q.v.); bionomic factors are those external, environmental factors that limit the development of an organism.

biophilia (bī-ō-fil′ē-à) Instinct of self-preservation.

biosphere (bī′ō-sfēr) The realm or sphere of life in which the total biological process takes place. The biosphere includes both the individual and his environment not as interacting parts or constituents that have an independent existence, but as aspects of a single reality which can be mentally separated only by abstraction. The limits of life extend as far as the organism is able to exert an influence on the events outside of him. (Biosphere corresponds to the German term *Lebenskreis.*)

biostatistics (-stà-tis′tiks) Vital statistics; the numerical representation of conditions associated with life.

biothanatos (-than′à-tos) *Obs.* Suicide.

biotype All individuals who equal each other *genotypically,* whether or not their *phenotypical* appearance may show any obvious resemblance. The phenotypical features of two individuals belonging to the same biotype may be dissimilar to a considerable extent, since every hereditary predisposition has a certain amount of variability of manifestation.

biotypogram In Pende's system of constitutional medicine, a variety of constitutional formulae as they are to be recorded in the individual's *'book of health'* for the purpose of a 'diagrammatic representation' describing the various types in all their somatic and psychological aspects.

biotypology (bī-ō-tī-pol′ō-jē) The systematic study or doctrine of biotypes. In this sense it no longer corresponds to the original biological meaning of biotype. Although the genetic concept of biotype applies to individuals equaling each other *genotypically,* it has been taken in the field of constitutional studies, especially by the Italian school, to indicate the phenotypical constellation of all characteristics making up the 'somatic-psychic individuality' of a human being, including the morphological, physiological and psychological aspects of the given type.

bipolar double-bind See *bind, double*.

bipolarity (bī-pō-lar'i-tē) *Ambivalence* (q.v.).

Birnbaum, Karl (b. 1878) (bērn'boum) German psychiatrist; forensic psychiatry.

birth, anal In psychoanalytic theory this term refers to the sexual phantasies or dreams directly connected with anal erotism when these phantasies or dreams are expressed in the symbolic form of a wish to be reborn through the anus. In this respect, Freud gave the following dream as example: 'Spending the summer beside Lake _____ she flings herself into the dark waters at the place where the pale moon is mirrored.' Freud defined this dream as an expression of anal birth. The interpretation of the dream reveals that 'she flings herself into the water' means 'she comes out of the water, that is to say, 'that she is born.' The moon represents an anal symbol derived from the French language in which the 'derriere' (the 'behind') is vulgarly spoken of as 'la lune' (the moon).

birth control Prevention of conception for the purpose of limiting the number of offspring, particularly among those who are termed *cacogenic* (q.v.). 'Planned parenthood' is a better term than 'birth control' to characterize the eugenic objectives. In many instances what is sought is not a reduction in the size of families, but the proper 'spacing' of children, so that they will come when the mother, the home, and the family budget are best prepared for their advent into the world.

Various contraceptive measures have been medically devised for the practice of birth control. Within the special program of 'negative' eugenic measures proposed for application to those hopelessly insane and mentally defective individuals who are considered unfit to have *any* children, the most drastic form of birth control is sterilization.

birth injury Any damage to the fetus-neonate as a result of the birth process; often used in a more limited way to refer to brain damage due to the birth process (including that due to instrument delivery). See *brain damage*.

birth, multiple In biology and vital statistics the term applies to all instances in which women produce more than one child at the same birth. The tendency to multiple births seems to run in certain families, although it has not yet been proved that it is based on a specific hereditary factor.

Twins come about once in every 90 births in most of the American and European countries. The proportion of fraternal to identical twins is approximately 3:1 (see *twin*).

Triplets occur once in about 8,000 births. They also may be identical or 'unmatched' multiples, that is, developed either from one egg or from three separate eggs. The third possibility is that only two members of a set of triplets are identical, developed from one egg, and the third is a fraternal, developed from a different egg.

Quadruplets are reported by Scheinfeld to occur once in about 700,000 births, with only a few sets surviving. Here the following combinations are possible: (1) all four identicals; (2) three identicals and one fraternal; (3) two identicals and two fraternals, and (4) most rarely, all four fraternals.

The birth of five humans at one time is believed to have occurred spontaneously not more than sixty times in the last five hundred years. In most cases, however, these *quintuplets* perished soon after birth.

bisexuality The presence of the qualities of both sexes in the same person. The term is synonymous with hermaphroditism, though the latter term appears to have gained almost exclusive reference to the organic manifestations of the condition. The term intersex, introduced by Goldschmidt, is used 'to designate hermaphrodites as individuals who started out either male or female from a genetic standpoint but who after a certain period completed their sexual development in the opposite direction. In the intersex there is first a female phase and later a male phase, or vice versa, and in the second phase a typical mixture of both sexes exists.' (Young, H.H. *Genital Abnormalities, Hermaphroditism and Related Adrenal Diseases* Williams & Wilkins, Baltimore, 1937)

In the classical sense a bisexual or hermaproditic individual is one 'who has the gonads and external genitalia of both sexes and is capable of living as either a man or a woman.' (ibid)

Bisexuality manifests itself also in the psyche. 'It would seem palpably obvious that the repression and the formation of the neurosis must have originated out of the conflict between masculine and feminine tendencies, that is, out of bisexuality.' (Freud, S. *The Basic Writings of Sigmund Freud*, tr. by Brill, A.A., Random House, New York, 1938)

'But, since the nature of the human being unites masculine and feminine elements, a man can live the feminine in himself, and a woman the masculine in herself.' (Jung, C.G. *Contributions to Analytical Psychology*, tr. by Baynes, H.G. and C.F., Kegan Paul, Trench, Trubner, London, 1928)

'Psycho-analysis has proven that all homosexuals, without exception, show heterosexual tendencies in early life. There is no exception to this rule. *There are no monosexual persons!*' (Stekel, W. *Bi-Sexual Love*, tr. by van Teslaar, J.S., Badger, Boston, 1922)

bivalence (bī-vā′lens, biv′à-lens) Some authors use the terms bivalence and ambivalence interchangeably. See *ambivalence.*

bizarreness Striking incongruity or eccentricity; discordant, disharmonious, contradictory behavior such as is seen most commonly in schizophrenic patients.

black-out 1. Loss of consciousness, usually secondary to brain anemia. When the loss of consciousness is only partial, *gray-out* is the term applied; this is seen frequently in pilots when they rapidly change altitude, as in a dive.

2. The alcoholic's amnesia for his behavior during drinking episodes (sometimes termed *dim-out* to differentiate it from the acute syncopal episode described above). Such black-outs are indicative of beginning, but still reversible, brain damage *(intermediate brain syndrome due to alcohol)*. Typically, the black-out follows moderate drinking, and the drinker converses reasonably and carries out elaborate activities without signs of intoxication, but the next day he has no memory of what he said or did.

bladder, automatic The filling and spontaneous evacuation of the urinary bladder occurring in cases of transsection of the spinal cord.

blaesus (blē′sus) *Obs.* General paralysis.

-blast, blasto- (blas′tō-) A combining form meaning *sprout, shoot, germ, embryonic*, from Gr. *blastós*, sprout, shoot, twig.

blast concussion See *neurosis, postconcussion.*

blastomere (blas′tō-mēr) Cell(s) formed by the first cell divisions of a fertilized egg undergoing the process of *cleavage* (q.v.).

blastophthoria (blas-tof-thōr′ē-à) Degenerative effect on germ cells of poisons such as alcohol and lead; many temperance adherents claim that alcohol has a blastophthoric effect that is manifested in mental retardation in the alcoholic's children, but no such effect has ever been demonstrated in scientific studies.

blastopore (blas′tō-pōr) See *gastrulation.*

blastula (blas′chū-là) In this embryological stage of a human organism, there is continued cell division beyond the 32-cell stage and the appearance of an enlarging central cavity, the blastocele, in the fertilized egg undergoing the segmenting process of *cleavage* (q.v.).

At first the blastula is a hollow sphere whose wall is a single layer of morphologically and functionally identical cells, the primitive *ectoderm* (q.v.). Only in the later stages of this *monodermic* blastula condition one finds those larger cells at the pole opposite that of the location of the polar bodies, which foreshadow the future *entoderm* (q.v.).

blepharospasm (blef′à-rō-spaz'm) The spasmoid closing of the orbicular muscle of the eyelid. It is not infrequently observed in psychiatric patients, in whom a relatively large quantum of emotions is referred to the external ocular apparatus. In extreme instances, as in catatonic states, the lids may be held tightly approximated in the effort to shut off all light stimuli coming from the environment. In other cases, it appears as a winking tic. See *blinking.*

Bleuler, Eugen (1857-1939) (bloi'lēr) Swiss psychiatrist, dementia praecox. In 1911, Bleuler suggested the term 'schizophrenia' to replace dementia praecox. His monumental treatise, *Dementia Praecox or the Group of Schizophrenias,* differentiated between the fundamental and the accessory symptoms of schizophrenia, and it remains today the authoritative source book on the development and manifestations of schizophrenic symptoms.

blindism Undesirable mannerisms and habitual movements seen in blind patients, and particularly in children, such as repeated rubbing of the eyes, shaking and rolling the body, poking at the eyes or ears, shaking the hands when excited and, if there is some vision, fanning the fingers in front of the eyes. Usually the blindism is given up as the child grows older.

blindness, circumferential See *field defect.*

blindness, cortical psychic A condition usually due to bilateral occipital lobe lesions producing a loss of topographical orientation, of optic memory image and spatial orientation.

blindness, hysterical Blindness as a symptom of conversion hysteria. In principle it bears out the popular belief that we see what we want to see and are blind to the things we do not want to see. Hysterical blindness is of the same order. A young woman, inordinately fond of her father, tried frantically to drive him out of her mind. Realizing the unnaturalness of her love for him, she became blind, owing to her strong sense of guilt and because she could no longer look upon her father.

blindness, mind Psychic blindness; objects and space dimensions are seen by the eye, but the patient has an erroneous idea of the size of objects and the three dimensions of space. Sometimes he sees objects as flat, or as small (see *micropsia*). Uncertainty over object relationships may be a basic element in the development of such symptoms. Schilder described the case of a patient, who, during analytical treatment, had the impression of seeing the analyst seated in a chair very far away. In anxiety cases the distance between the individual and the beloved person is the only space that seems real to the patient. Accordingly, when the beloved person is away, or out of sight, the space seems to become immense. 'In some phobias connected with walking the patients occasionally dream that their feet do not touch the ground.' This, according to the psycho-analytical interpretation of Schilder, symbolizes the distance of their genitals from mother. (Schilder, P. *Mind, Perception and Thought,* Columbia University Press, New York, 1942)

blinking Quick, involuntary, apparently purposeless and repetitious movement of the eyelids (alone or associated with similar movements involving other groups of muscles and belonging to the category of tics or habit spasms) observed in nervous children. See *blepharospasm.*

block See *chromosome.*

block, affect Inability to discharge emotions adequately or appropriately, seen typically in obsessive-compulsives, who often appear cold, unfeeling and emotionally stiff and overcontrolled, and also in some schizophrenics. Freud termed this 'isolation of affect.' 'In such cases a fantasy connected with a wish or a crucial memory from the past may have ready access to consciousness, but the emotion, usually a painful one, which should be connected with it does not become conscious. Moreover, such patients usually manage to keep from feeling too much emotion of any sort. . . . However, in some unfortunate individuals it goes so far that in the end the individual has hardly any awareness of emotions of any kind and seems like a caricature of that equanimity which ancient philosophers put forward as an ideal." (Brenner, C. *An Elementary Textbook of Psychoanalysis.* International Universities Press, New York, 1955.)

block, partial genetic See *disease, genetotrophic.*

blockade, narcotic Inhibition, removal, or diminution of the euphoria produced by narcotic drugs such as heroin. Some have advocated the use of methadone in narcotic addicts to produce blockade, but others have pointed out that a search for euphoria or avoidance of withdrawal symptoms may not be the only determinant in addiction to narcotics.

blocking Sudden cessation in the train of thought or in the midst of a sentence. The patient is unable to explain the reason for the sudden stoppage, which may occur in the absence of intellectual defect or sensorial disorder. 'Often thinking stops in the middle of a thought; or in the attempt to pass to another idea, it may suddenly cease altogether, at least as far as it is a conscious process (blocking). Instead of continuing the thought, new ideas crop up which neither the patient nor the observer can bring into any connection with the previous stream of thought.' (Bleuler, E. *Dementia Praecox or the Group of Schizophrenias,* International Universities Press, New York, 1950.) Blocking is also known as 'thought-deprivation.' It is usually experienced by the patient as unpleasant. Bleuler considered a positive response by a patient to the question of whether or not he had ever experienced thought-deprivation pathognomonic of schizophrenic association-disorder. See *obstruction.*

In experimental psychology, blocking consists of temporary complete cessation of work during a period of continuous practice. Blockings of this sort are more frequent in schizophrenics than in normals.

blocking, counter-impulse in The opposite of the impulse that is blocked. Kraepelin particularly stressed that counter-drives may cause blocking. Bleuler points out that '. . . the denial of any impulse is so very often associated with a counter-impulse that, in stressing the counter-impulse, we only emphasize a different aspect of the same process, but we do not gain a new perspective.' (Bleuler, E. *Dementia Praecox or the Group of Schizophrenias,* International Universities Press, New York, 1950) One schizophrenic patient demonstrated blocking whenever he was asked about his father. Further investigation indicated that the patient had marked ambivalence toward his father, and questioning him touched upon his hatred for the father and at the same time upon his love for the father. Here the impulse appeared to be canceled out, as it were, by the counter-impulse, and blocking resulted.

boarding-out system See *system, boarding out.*

bodies, geniculate See *geniculate bodies.*

body build, index of A standard devised by Eysenck in his studies on the relationship between somato-type and psychosis. The I.B. consists of a measurement of stature and transverse chest diameter;

$$\text{I.B.} = \frac{\text{stature} \times 100}{\text{transverse chest diameter} \times 6}.$$

body cell See *cell, body.*

body-image See *image, body; ego, body.*

body-language The expression of feelings or thoughts by means of bodily movements. See *language, primitive psychosomatic.*

body-memory A memory retained by the body as opposed to a mind-memory which is retained by the mind. The theory of body-memories holds that the body remembers and repeats. This is noted particularly during psychoanalytical treatment. Although frequently the treatment cannot recover memories from the early years of life, the patient behaves like an infant: he exhibits tantrums, grimaces, or peevishness; cries for attention or yells and screams; flails his limbs when not getting what he wants, and he may assume the posture of an infant. In this way the patient speaks a body-language. His behavior 'looks like a throwback to infancy and the appearance is frequently supported by what the patient says.' These infantile activities are explained by the theory that the body remembers and repeats. Indeed 'some patients say that they do not think, their bodies do.' (Hinsie, L.E. *Understandable Psychiatry,* Macmillan, New York, 1948.) See also *engram.*

body-mindedness *Psychosomatic* (q.v.).

body of Luys (Jules Bernard Luys, French physician, 1828 - 1898) See *subthalamus.*

body, polar In sexual reproduction, the female germ cells or oögonia divide into two unequal daughter cells the smaller of which is called the first or second polar body, according to whether it is produced by the first or second meiotic division. Only the larger cells or oöcytes have a reproductive function, while the polar bodies gradually disintegrate and disappear. See *egg*.

body-protest See *protest, body*.

body-scheme See *ego, body*.

bogeyman A spirit or goblin who will punish the child for misdoings or for 'being naughty.' The childhood fear of the bogeyman has its precise psychoanalytic interpretation, as a result of what is called 'internalized parental prohibitions.' The growing child soon discovers that there are many things he might receive pleasure from which are prohibited by his parents. Through the double fear of punishment and losing his parents' affection he begins to follow out these prohibitions even when his parents are not on hand. As a result a part of the child's mind is continually on guard so that he may not behave in such a way that the parents' disapproval will be aroused. These 'internalized parental prohibitions' are forerunners of the super-ego. One way in which the child handles these terrible threats of punishment is to project them onto persons in the external world. Thus the bogeyman is in reality what Fenichel calls an 'externalized pre-super-ego.' And the fear of this terrifying being is in reality the terror of punishment arising from 'internalized parental prohibitions.' (Fenichel, O. *The Psychoanalytic Theory of Neurosis*, Norton, New York, 1945)

Bonhoeffer, Karl (1868-1939) (bôn'hĕf-ēr) German psychiatrist and neurologist; alcoholism; forensic psychiatry.

Bonnier's syndrome (Pierre Bonnier, French physician, 1861-1918) Symptoms resulting from a lesion involving the acoustic, glossopharyngeal, and vagus nerves: paroxysmal vertigo (Ménière's disease), contralateral hemiplegia, aphonia, dysphagia, and loss of gag reflex.

borderline psychosis An inexact term, often used to describe a patient who is potentially psychotic (usually schizophrenic, 295.5) but has not, as yet, broken with reality. See *schizophrenia, ambulatory; schizophrenia, pseudoneurotic*. 'Schizophrenic mechanisms are differ-

ent from neurotic mechanisms. It certainly is not true that psychoses represent a kind of higher degree of neurosis. It is possible that the same person may develop both types of mechanisms. There are neurotic persons who, without developing a complete psychosis, have certain psychotic trends, or have a readiness to employ schizophrenic mechanisms whenever frustrations occur. . . . To this group belong queer psychopaths, abortive paranoids, the many "apathic" individuals whom one may call hebephrenoid personalities, all the types who, as adults, retain or regain a large part of their primitive narcissism because they are able to answer narcissistic hurts with simple denials and with protective increase in their narcissism; they tend to react to frustrations with the loss of object relationships, although this loss frequently is only partial and temporary.' (Fenichel, O. *The Psychoanalytic Theory of Neurosis*, Norton, New York, 1945)

boredom A feeling of unpleasantness due to a need for more activity, or a lack of meaningful stimuli, or an inability to become stimulated. The last form is generally considered pathological and may be expressed as a need to maintain the status quo and as a stubborn clinging to stimuli which are without interest or meaning to the subject. Pathological boredom usually represents a defense against libidinal or aggressive strivings.

boundary, ego A concept introduced by Federn to refer to 'the peripheral sense organ of the ego.' The ego boundary discriminates what is real from what is unreal. Because the boundary is flexible and dynamic, it will vary in accordance with different ego states. There are two main ego boundaries, the inner and the outer. The inner ego boundary is the boundary toward the repressed unconscious. This is strengthened by countercathexes (anticathexes) and thus is able to prevent the entrance of repressed material. Its flexibility is demonstrable in hypnagogic states and in normal falling asleep, where the ego and its boundaries lose cathexis and unegotized material enters. The external or outer ego boundary is the boundary toward stimuli of the external world. The external ego boundary includes the sense organs but it is more than mere summation of these, for the sense of reality of an object comes not alone by stimulation of a sense organ but further requires that the non-ego material impinges upon a well-cathected external ego boundary. If the boundary loses cathexis these perceptions, no matter how vivid, will have a strange, unfamiliar, or even unreal quality.

bouquet de malades (boo-kä' dē málàd') The distinctive odor said to be characteristic of psychiatric patients.

Bourneville's disease (Dé'siré'-Magloire Bourneville, Paris neurologist, 1840-1909) Tuberous sclerosis (31x.3).

bouts of ritual making See *ritual-making.*

Bovarism (From the title character in the novel *Madame Bovary,* by Gustave Flaubert) Confusion of daydreaming with the facts of the perceptual world; failure to differentiate between phantasy and reality.

bovina fames (bô-vē'nà fà'mes) L. 'ox-like hunger') Bulimia.

boxer's traumatic encephalopathy (en-sef-à-lop'à-thi) See *dementia, boxer's.*

brachuna (brà-kū'nà) Acrai; nymphomania and/or satyriasis.

brachy- (brăk'i-) Combining form meaning (abnormally) short.

brachycephaly, brachycephalism (-sef'à-li, -liz'm) A skull with shortened antero-posterior diameter. See *index, cephalic.*

brachylineal (-lin'ē-al) Brachymorphic.

brachymorphic (-mawr'fik) Relating to or characterized by brachymorphy. In the systems of constitutional types of the Italian school, this is equivalent to the *megalosplanchnic* type of Viola, although in analogy to eumorphic and normosplanchnic, the difference in the etymology of brachymorphic and megalosplanchnic indicates a difference of the criteria used for assessing the type, namely, general structure in contrast to visceral size and its effect. It has been affirmed, however, that there is a complete correspondence between the incidence of these general and external morphological cri-

teria on the one hand, and those of the internal anatomy and its results on the other.

Generally speaking, the *brachymorphic type* is built along lines that are shorter and broader than the normal figure, and corresponds roughly to the *pyknic* type.

brachymorphy (-mawr'fē) Shortness of stature. See *brachymorphic.*

brachyskelic (-skel'ik) Characterized by an excessive shortness of the legs. See *type, pyknic.*

brachytypical (-tip'i-kal) Synonymous with *brevilineal* (q.v.) and *brachymorphic* (q.v.).

brady- (brăd'i-) Combining form meaning slow, from Gr. *bradys.*

bradyarthria (-àr'thrē-à) Slowness of speech, due to some disorder in the central or peripheral apparatus connected with speech. See *bradylogia,* the implication of which is psychical.

bradyglossia (-glos'ē-à) Slowness of speech or bradyglossia carries with it the idea that the slowness is the result of difficulties in the movements of the tongue. The original cause may be distant from the tongue.

bradykinesis, bradykinesia (-ki-nē'sis, -sē-à) Slow or retarded movement; it may be organically or psychically determined. It is common in depressive states and is often observed in schizophrenia.

bradylalia (-lā'lē-à) Abnormal slowness of speech, or bradyarthria. It may, like bradylexia, be occasioned by organic or psychological pathology or both. It is common in depressed states.

bradylexia (-lek'sē-à) Abnormal slowness in reading, which may be organically or psychologically (emotionally) determined or both. It is observed that, in the depressed patient, for instance, slowness in reading is but one of the many phenomena of mental retardation. Bradylexia may or may not be associated with intellectual incapacity as such.

bradylogia (-lo'jē-à) Slowness of speech whether of physical or psychical origin.

When it occurs, for example, in general paresis, it is usually, though not always, the consequence of organic lesions. When it is observed in depressive states (e.g. the depressive phase of manic-depressive psychosis), it is believed to be a reflection of psychic (emotional) inhibition.

bradyphasia (brad-i-fā'zhē-à) Slowness of speech.

bradysphrasia (-frā'zhē-à) Slowness of thought.

bradyphrenia (-frē'nē-à) Sluggish mentality. It is used by some as the equivalent of feeblemindedness, by others as the equivalent of psychomotor retardation.

Bradyphrenia may be symptomatic of any acquired disorder that interrupts the functioning of intelligence.

Bradyphrenia is focal when there is retardation in the presence only of disagreeable or painful ideas; it is diffuse when it is vague and unvarying irrespective of the topic in mind.

Slowness in thinking is often associated with states of intense emotion, as in severe anxieties and depressions; in the latter there may be a marked paucity or such a profusion of ideas as to lead to great difficulty in concentrated thinking. Bradyphrenia, like intellectual retardation, may be initial, that is, slowness in starting, or consistent, that is, slowness in continuing.

bradypragia (-prā'jē-à) Unusually slow action. The expression is more frequently employed in reference to physical than to psychical matters. When, for instance, the thyroid gland is underactive, the physiology of the body in general is diminished. Some authorities apply the word also to slow mentation, although bradyphrenia is the term relating directly to the mind.

bradytrophism (-trō-fiz'm) This term was introduced in constitutional medicine by Bouchard to designate a syndrome which is caused by a slowing down of the nutritive movement. The condition may be generalized or localized, and is characteristic of such diseases as gout, diabetes, asthma, various chronic or recurrent rheumatisms, and various forms of lithiasis and of pruritic and chronic or recurrent desquamative dermatosis.

General bradytrophism results in products of imperfect metabolism and chronic autotoxemia. *Local* bradytrophism is best understood as a nutritive torpor of the organs which leads to the accumulation of lymph and waste material in their interstitium and gradually produces fatty infiltration, sclerosis, and early aging of the organs.

braid-cutting A perversion, relatively rare nowadays, consisting of the cutting of the hair from the victim. This perversion is a form of sadism combined with a fetishistic preference for hair. It expresses the idea, 'I am the castrator, not the castrated one,' and often also the complementary idea, 'I am only a pseudo-castrator, not a real castrator.' The knowledge that the hair will grow back is an important part of the reassurance which the patient gains from the perverse act in that it proves to him that castration need not be final.

braidism (brād'iz'm) The theory of hypnosis named after James Braid, English surgeon (1795-1861), who published in 1843, *Neurypnology, or, the Rationale of Nervous Sleep, considered in relation with animal magnetism.*

brain The part of the nervous system confined in the skull; it includes the cerebrum, mid-brain, cerebellum, pons, and medulla.

brain damage Intracranial birth injury and/or its results; among the most important causes are excessive or otherwise abnormal compression due to abnormal presentations, contracted pelvis, or instrumentation; excessive longitudinal stress producing tears of the dura and rupture of venous sinuses; certain methods of resuscitation, which predispose to sinus rupture; prematurity, which predisposes to intracranial hemorrhage. See *syndome, organic.*

brain-damage behavior syndrome See *impulse-disorder, hyperkinetic; syndrome, organic.*

brain disorder A term used in DSM-I to refer to any psychiatric syndrome caused by impairment of brain tissue function; this group corresponds in general to that formerly called the 'organic psychoses' or the 'organic reaction types.' The brain disorders are termed acute or chronic depending upon their reversibility; those which are ordinarily temporary and reversible are called acute, while those from which full recovery is not anticipated are called chronic. In DSM-II, brain disorders are termed *organic brain syndromes (OBS)*; see *syndrome, organic*.

brain-stem This term refers to the *pons* (q.v.) and the *medulla oblongata* (q.v.).

brain syndrome associated with systemic infection Organic reaction (psychotic 292.x, non-psychotic 309.0) occurring as a complication of the acute or convalescent stages of such disorders as pneumonia, typhoid fever, rheumatic fever, scarlet fever, malaria, influenza, small pox, and typhus; also known as infective-exhaustive psychosis, acute toxic encephalopathy, acute toxic encephalitis, and acute serous encephalitis. The chief types of reaction, which occur mainly in children, are delirious, epileptiform, stuporous or comatose, hallucinatory, and confusional. The most common form is the toxic delirium.

brain trauma See *brain damage; compression cerebral; concussion; contusion, brain; syndrome, organic*.

brain tumor See *tumor, intracranial*.

brain, visceral See *rhinencephalon*.

brain-washing See *deprivation, sensory; menticide*.

breakdown, nervous A sudden onset of severe painful emotions such as anxiety, tension, or feeling of guilt, etc. which may also be accompanied by various physical symptoms such as headaches, dizziness, tremors, fainting spells, nausea, vomiting, diarrhea, etc., all without a real physical basis. With people who have gone along at a certain level of adaptation to their environment and handled their problems of ordinary living fairly well without suffering too much distress in the various situations in which they find themselves, this adjustment is utterly disrupted and a nervous breakdown occurs. These breakdowns may afflict already neurotic as well as normal people and among their manifold causes may be involved such things as physiological stress, certain particularly disturbing experiences, physical illness, fatigue, and many other factors. (Fenichel, O. *The Psychoanalytic Theory of Neurosis,* Norton, New York, 1945)

breakdown, social See *syndrome, social breakdown*.

break-off A phenomenon that occurs in aviators when flying alone, at high altitudes, and when relatively unconcerned about flying details; the phenomenon consists of a feeling of physical separation from the earth. It is more frequent in emotionally unstable flyers, and can itself precipitate an acute phobic reaction that may develop into a general fear of flying.

Breuer, Joseph (1841 - 1925) (broi'ēr) Viennese neurologist; published (1895) with Freud, *Studien über Hysterie*.

brevilineal (brev-i-lin'ē-al) In constitutional medicine, this term refers to one of the two constitutional types distinguished by Manouvrier on the basis of the configuration of the body as a whole. In contradistinction to the longilineal type, it designates the type built along lines that are shorter and broader than the average figure.

Persons of this type correspond roughly to the *pyknic* type of Kretschmer, the *brachymorphic* type of Pende and to their equivalents in other systems.

bribe In psychoanalysis, a compromise. The symptoms of a neurosis are regarded as symbolic representations of repressed impulses. At first the ego rejects the symptoms; later it becomes reconciled with them, since they afford a certain protection to the security of the ego. The symptoms are accepted by the ego in the nature of a bribe, but the acceptance carries certain favorable elements. For instance, there is the so-called secondary gain from suffering. The repressed impulse is released in the guise of symptoms; the patient does not recognize the released impulse in its new manner of expression. Moreover, in order to placate the *superego* or inner conscience, the ego bribes it by suffering. Thus, forbidden pleasure gratification, by being presented to the Ego as a punishment, is made acceptable.

At the same time, the Super-Ego itself, which recognizes the latent meaning of the symptom in spite of disguise, is "bribed with suffering."' (Healy, W., Bronner, A.F., and Bowers, A.M. *The Structure and Meaning of Psychoanalysis,* Knopf, New York, 1930)

Brickner, Richard (1896 - 1959) American neurologist; multiple sclerosis, physiology of the frontal lobes.

brief psychotherapy See *psychotherapy, brief.*

Briggs' law See *law, Briggs'.*

Brigham, Amariah (1798 - 1849) American psychiatrist; founded *American Journal of Insanity* (1844), now the *American Journal of Psychiatry;* 'moral treatment.'

Brill, A.A. (1874 - 1948) First American psychoanalyst; translated Freud's works into English.

Briquet, Paul (1796 - 1881) (brē-kā') French psychiatrist; author of a monumental treatise on hysteria (1859).

Brissaud's syndrome (brē-sō') (Edouard Brissaud, French physician, 1852 - 1909). Infantilism due to thyroid dysfunction; cretinism.

Broca's speech area (Broca, Paul, Parisian anthropologist and surgeon, 1824 - 1880) The motor speech area; areas 44 and 45 of Brodmann; the inferior end of the motor area in the third left frontal convolution. Lesions here in a right-handed subject result in motor aphasia; in pure motor aphasia, the patient is able to write or otherwise indicate his desires, but articulate speech either is impossible or is restricted to a few ill-pronounced expletives.

bromidism Bromide intoxication (psychotic, 294.3; non-psychotic 309.14) which may be manifested in several ways: (1) simple intoxication—with mental dulling, memory disturbances, enfeeblement, tremor (especially of the hands, face, and tongue), ataxia, incoordination, acneform dermatitis, fetid breath, and coated tongue; (2) delirium, with disorientation in all spheres; (3) hallucinosis with marked fear reactions; in contrast to delirium tremens, bromide hallucinosis lasts weeks rather than days; (4) schizophreniform psychosis; or (5) pseudoepilepsy.

bromidrosiphobia (brō-mi-drō-si-fō'bē-à) Morbid dread of the alleged offensive odors of the body.

bromidrosis (-drō'sis) Perspiration with foul odor.

brontophobia (bron-tō-fo'bē-à) Fear of thunder; astrophobia. It is related in part to the dread of allegedly demonical phenomena of nature, akin to personalization of such phenomena by primitive man; it may also be related to fear of real persons, and especially of the father or father-figure.

brooding Anxious or moody pondering, usually about very abstract matters. Brooding is seen frequently in obsessive-compulsive neurotics as a *thinking compulsion,* a need to worry very much about apparently insignificant things. This is a form of displacement onto a small detail and represents an attempt to avoid objectionable impulses or affects by escaping from the world of emotions into a world of intellectual concepts and words; also termed 'intellectualization.'

brooding-spells One of Rado's subdivisions of obsessive attacks is called *spells of doubting and brooding:* a swinging back and forth between the same pros and the same cons without reaching a decision. Since this may invade any mental activity, the patient soon finds he can trust no belief, no memory, not even his own observations, and as a result he must check and re-check his every move, to make sure that it has been right.

Brown-Séquard's syndrome (brown-sā-kàr') (Charles Brown-Séquard, French neurologist, 1817 - 1894). Hemisection of the spinal cord (as in cord tumor, syringomyelia, stab wound, etc.) producing homolateral lower motor neuron paralysis in the segment of the lesion, homolateral upper motor neuron paralysis below the lesion, homolateral anesthesia in the segment of the lesion, homolateral hyperesthesia below the lesion, homolateral loss of proprioception, vibratory and two-point discrimination below the lesion, contralateral hyperesthesia in the segment of the lesion, and contralateral loss of pain and temperature below the lesion.

Brudzinski sign See *sign, Brudzinski.*

Bruns's sign (Ludwig Bruns, German neurologist, 1858-1916) Headache, vertigo, and vomiting associated with sudden movements of the head, occurring in cases of tumor of the fourth ventricle.

bruxism (bruk′siz′m) Gnashing or grinding of the teeth, which occurs typically at night, during sleep. It is said to be especially common in alcoholics and to indicate repressed aggressivity or hostility.

bruxomania (bruk-sō-mā′nē-à) Grinding, pounding or setting of the teeth apart from the normal activity of mastication. There results a loosening of the teeth and a bleeding of the gums.

B.S.T. Brief stimulus therapy. See *therapy, brief stimulus.*

buffoonery-psychosis See *psychosis, buffoonery.*

bufotenin (bu-fō′te-nin) Dimethyl-serotonin. An analogue of serotonin which, unlike serotonin itself, is psychotomimetic in the cat, monkey, and man and produces effects similar to those seen following lysergic acid or mescaline administration. It has been suggested that conversion of serotonin into bufotenin rather than breakdown by monoamine oxidase into 5-hydroxyindole acetic acid may be of significance in the etiology of endogenous psychoses.

bug, cocaine One of the more common unpleasant tactual paresthesiae which occurs during withdrawal of cocaine in a cocaine addict. Also known as formication. The patient typically interprets the sensation as an itching, biting, crawling, or sticking due to an insect.

bugger Colloquial for a homosexual, especially one who practices anal intercourse.

bulbar Referring to the bulb (medulla oblongata).

bulbocapnine (bul-bō-kap′nin) One of the drugs used relatively early in the many experiments of H.H. DeJong in experimental production of catatonia.

bulbotegmental reticular formation (bulbō-teg-men′tal) See *formation, reticular.*

bulimia, bulimy (bū-lim′ē-à, bū′li-mē) Insatiable hunger.

Bumke, Oswald (b. 1877) (boom′kē) German psychiatrist and neurologist.

Burrow, Trigant (1875-1951) American psychoanalyst, later developed *phyloanalysis* (q.v.).

Buscaino, Vito Maria (b. 1887) (booskà-ē′nô) Italian neurologist.

Butler, John S. (1803-90) American psychiatrist; one of the 'original thirteen' founders of Association of Medical Superintendents of America (forerunner of American Psychiatric Association).

by-idea The secondary or manifest thought, concept, symbol, or idea onto which the primary or latent idea is displaced. While discussing speech disorders in dream, Kraepelin said: 'The common feature in all these observations (dream paraphasias) is the displacement of the basic thought by the entrance of a by-association, for an essential link of the chain of ideas. The derailment of speech or of thought to a by-association is due, in my opinion, to lack of distinctness in the ideas.' He also said: 'The by-idea causing the displacement of thought was distinctly a narrower and more comprehensive idea which suppressed the more general and more shadowy one.' He referred to this condition as *metaphoric paralogia.* (Kraepelin, E. *Dementia Praecox and Paraphrenia,* tr. by Barclay, R.M., Livingstone, Edinburgh, 1919)

C

C In Rorschach scoring, a color response, i.e. response of an object imagined to have the same chromatic colors as those which stimulated the response. The color responses measure the degree of emotional responsiveness to the environment, whether positive or negative. The greater the role of the form element in color responses (scored as FC), the more the subject considers others in his emotional attitudes. The greater the role of color in relation to form (the CF responses), the more blind, self-centered and inconsiderate is the subject in his emotional reactions. A lack of C responses indicates apathy and flatness of emotions.

c In Rorschach scoring, that type of shading response determined by the light shades of gray on the blots and uninfluenced by the form of the area. See *ShR.*

c′ In Rorschach scoring, that type of shading response determined by the dark or black . areas and uninfluenced by the form of the area. See *ShR.*

C*n* A Rorschach scoring symbol for color-naming.

CA Abbreviation for chronological age.

cacergasia (kas-ēr-gās′ē-à) *Obs.* Deficient mentality.

cachexia (kà-kek′sē-à) Malnourishment proceeding to wasting of body tissues, seen usually as part of a chronic disease process. See *cachexia, hypophysial; anorexia nervosa.*

cachexia, hypophysial (hǐ-pō-fiz′ē-al) A condition due to necrosis or other destruction of the anterior lobe of the pituitary gland, occurring most commonly in women. Characteristic symptoms are: marked asthenia, great loss of weight with extreme emaciation, chilliness, slow pulse, anemia, low basal metabolic rate, loss of hair, amenorrhea or impotence, somnolence, apathy, poor memory, and occasionally hallucinations and delirium. Also known as Simmonds's disease (Morris Simmonds, a Hamburg pathologist [1855 - 1925]). See *anorexia nervosa.*

cachinnation (kak-i-nā′shun) Inordinate laughter without apparent cause; it is common in the hebephrenic form of schizophrenia.

caco- (kak′ō-) combining form meaning bad, vitiated, distorted, from Gr. *kakós,* bad, evil.

cacodaemonomania (-dē-mon-ō-mā′nē-à) A condition in which the patient believes himself to be, or to be inhabited by, or possessed of, a devil or some evil spirit; it is not uncommonly a symptom of the hebephrenic form of schizophrenia.

cacogenic (-jen′ik) The term (the opposite of *aristogenic* or *eugenic,* q.v.) means 'giving rise to a deteriorated race' and refers to deteriorating agencies in heredity. A. Myerson cites a case of ·artificial insemination in a woman with a prominent family history of otosclerosis and paranoid mental disease. The woman herself was delusional and was not fully desirous of impregnation. The procedure in this case would be termed cacogenic insemination.

cacogeusia (-gū′sē-à) A bad taste; a frequent complaint in idiopathic epilepsy, in patients receiving tranquilizer therapy, and in somatic delusional states.

cacopathia (-path′ē-à) A Hippocratic designation for a severe mental disorder.

cacosomnia (-som′nē-à) *Obs.* Sleeplessness.

cacothymia (-thim′ē-à, -thī′mē-à) *Obs.* 'Any mental affection with depravation of the morals.' (Tuke, D.H. *A Dictionary of Psychological Medicine,* vols. 1 - 2, Blakiston, Philadelphia, 1892)

cadiva insania (kà-dē′và in-sà′nē-à) (L. 'falling or epileptic insanity') *Obs.* Epilepsy.

caduca passio (kà-doo′kà pàs′sē-ō) (L. 'falling disease') *Obs.* Epilepsy, 'the falling sickness.'

caducus morbus (kȧ-dōō'koos môr'boos) (L. 'falling sickness.') *Obs.* Epilepsy.

cainophobia (kī-nō-fō'bē-ȧ) See *kainotophobia; neophobia.*

cainotophobia (kī-nō'tō-fō-bē-ȧ) See *kainotophobia; neophobia.*

Cairns' stupor Akinetic or diencephalic stupor: stupor, rigidity, postural catatonia, absence of spontaneous movement and emotion. See *mutism, akinetic.*

caisson disease See *disease, caisson.*

calcarine area See *lobe, occipital.*

calf-love The fleeting mild infatuation of a susceptible teen-ager with a member of the opposite sex, abruptly ending only to be followed by a fresh adventure with another object of affection. The term probably originated in the seemingly inexplicable antics of a calf ceaselessly transferring its attentions and attachments to various members of a herd or group of cattle. See also *puppy-love.*

callipedia (kal-i-pē'dēȧ) The desire to give birth to a beautiful child. Some people believe that if a gravid woman concentrates her attention upon a beautiful child, or the picture or thought of one, she will give birth to its equal. The idea is associated with the magic of thought and with other primitive concepts concerning reproduction.

callomania (kal-ō-mā'nē-ȧ) *Obs.* Love of beauty and grace.

callosal gyrus *Cingulate gyrus* (q.v.).

calorie, psychic In psychiatric literature this term is used to describe a transference relationship. Without the psychic calories (i.e. sustenance) obtainable through the analyst's person, those patients who are too dependent on the analytic relationship cannot achieve a realization of their own self. (Baynes, H.G. *Mythology of the Soul,* Williams and Wilkins, Baltimore, 1940)

camisole A canvas shirt with very long sleeves, used to restrain a violently psychotic person; the shirt is put on and securely laced, and then the patient's arms are folded and the ends of the sleeves are fastened behind the back; sometimes simply a square of canvas fastened behind with a buckle, binding the arms to the sides of the body.

camouflage, neurotic A term for neurotic endeavor to disguise. 'It represents an attempt to reconcile two psychic processes which tend to go in opposite directions. The patient wishes to be obedient to the compulsion imposed by the neurosis, but at the same time he feels impelled to heed the psychic necessity of making his behavior conform to the requirements of his social milieu. . . I venture to assert that social camouflage constitutes a typical feature in the behavior of all psychoneurotics at a certain stage of development of their neurosis.' (Reik, T. 'Neurotic Camouflage and Thought-Rehearsal, *American Imago 2,* 86, 1941.) The neurotic camouflage is particularly evident in the obsessive-compulsive patient, whose need to conform often drives him to obsessional rehearsal. See *rehearsal, obsessional.*

campimeter (kam'pi-mē-têr) A chart upon which the visual field is plotted or projected. See *field defect.*

camptocormia (kamp-tō-kôr'mē-ȧ) Functional bent back; first described by Brodie in 1837, named camptocormia by Souques in 1915. It consists of persistent lumbar pain, anterior bending of the trunk of the body, and an anthropoid posture with head and trunk parallel with the ground and the arms swinging. Often there is a history of trauma, and almost always there is an accompanying psychic impotence. Most cases reported have been in soldiers, and the condition is extremely rare in the female (Kosbab reported the only known case in a woman, in 1961). In many of the cases the symptom has served as a conversion defense against an underlying schizophrenic process.

canalization (kȧ-nal-i-zā'shun) Restriction of behavior patterns, and particularly the choice of one way of satisfying a drive in reference to all other possible ways. Janet used the term to refer to substitutive discharge of tension.

cancer, fear of The fear of cancer occurs quite frequently, especially in older persons, but sometimes it is seen as a phobia in younger patients too. It often represents a fear of castration and/or a fear of being devoured by an introjected object.

canchasmus (kang-kaz′mus) *Obs.* Inordinate laughter sometimes observed in hysterical and schizophrenic patients.

canina appetentia (kà-nē′nà àp-pe-ten′-tī-à) (L. 'dog-appetite') *Obs.* Bulimia.

cannibalistic In psychoanalysis, referring to the hostile, sadistic aspects of (usually oral) introjection or incorporation. Schizophrenic patients may express cannibalistic impulses openly; but in psychoneurotic patients such impulses, if they are present at all, are usually thickly veiled or highly disguised.

Cannon hypothalamic theory of emotion Cannon and Bard offered a more modern version of Head's thalamic theory: afferent impulses from peripheral receptors may evoke patterned efferent 'emotional' responses directly through reflex pathways at the thalamic level, and/or indirectly through arousal of 'conditioned responses' at the cortical level, which in turn release diencephalically integrated patterns of emotional response from cortical inhibition. At the same time, upward discharges from the activated diencephalon reach the cortex, thus adding a patterned 'quale' to the sensory experience and transforming the 'object-simply-apprehended' to the 'object-emotionally-felt.'

Capgras See *syndrome, Capgras'.*

capsule, internal See *basal ganglia.*

captation (kap-tā′shun) An old term used by Descourtis to denote the first stage in hypnosis.

captivation Max Hirsch's term for the state of light hypnosis; Hirschlaff called the state one of pseudo-hypnosis.

caput obstipum (kà′put ob′sti-pum) See *torticollis.*

carbon dioxide inhalation See *therapy, carbon dioxide inhalation.*

card-sorting See *tests, sorting.*

cardiazol (kär′dē-à-zōl) Metrazol.

cardiopathia adolescentium (kär-dē-ô-pà′thē-à à-dô-les-ken′tē-oom) Individuals with an asthenic type of body build, the asthenic habitus first described by Stiller, often possess anomalies of the heart that represent immaturity. For example, the heart frequently assumes a vertical position; it is often below average in size, though it may be small only in comparison with the size of the body as a whole; the condition called drop heart may also be present. De Giovanni and Benecke have demonstrated that the right side of the heart may predominate over the left, a condition characteristic during childhood, but anomalous when continued into adulthood.

cardio-renal disease, psychosis with Organic brain syndrome associated with circulatory disturbance. This diagnosis is made on those patients with heart disease, especially in the stages of decompensation, who show psychotic symptoms. These symptoms usually take the form of deliria or temporary periods of confusion, often worse at night. Memory may be impaired and concentration may be defective; at times, fearful hallucinations may occur. (In DSM-II, coded 293.1 if psychotic, 309.3 if non-psychotic.)

carebaria (kar-ē-bà-rē′à) Unpleasant head sensations, such as pressure or heaviness in the head.

caregiver Any person involved in the identification or treatment or prevention of illness, and in the rehabilitation of patients. The *primary physician* (typically, the general practitioner in the community to whom the patient comes for help, no matter what the nature of his problem or illness) is often termed the front line caregiver. Another type of caregiver is the *indigenous worker*—the person from the population being serviced who has had special training in diagnostic or treatment techniques, and whose function is '. . . to find out from the residents of the neighborhood how they saw their needs, and to explore with them the ways in which we [i.e. the professionals of the Community Mental Health Center] could or could not be helpful.' (Peck, H.B., Roman, M., and Kaplan, S.R. *Psychiatric Research Report 21,* American Psychiatric Association, April 1967)

carnivorous Though in zoology it applies to animals (carnivora) adapted to flesh-eating, in constitutional medicine the term refers to a type described by Bryant and corresponds roughly to Kretschmer's *asthenic*. See *type, asthenic*.

carotodynia (kȧ-rot-ō-dī'nē-ȧ, -din'ē-ȧ) Pain in the malar (cheek) region, in the back of the neck, and about the eyes due to pressure on the common carotid artery.

carphology (kär-fol'ō-ji) Aimless picking or plucking (Galen's term). It is not uncommon among those with a senile psychiatric disorder, although it may be a symptom in any patient in a delirious state. The patient picks aimlessly, usually at his clothes or bed coverings.

carrier See *taint-carrier; trait-carrier.*

carus catalepsia (kȧ'roos kat-a-lep'sē-ȧ) Catalepsy.

carus lethargus (lā-thär'goos) Lethargy.

case, index (Genetics) The case in a family or group which is the subject of investigation.

case work, social 'Social case work is one of the major divisions of social work along with social group work and community organization or social welfare planning.' '. . . its concern is with social relationships and its disciplines directed toward the release of individual capacities and the relieving of environmental pressures. There have not been any notable changes in the accepted definitions since the well-known one by Mary Richmond in 1922. . . . "Social adjustments, consciously effected, individual by individual, between man and his social environment." Seven years later, the report of the Milford Conference . . . showed that more stress was being laid on the client's own purposes, and that the "distinguishing concern of social case work is the capacity of the individual to organize his own normal social activities in any given environment." (Hamilton, G. in *Social Work Year Book 1939*, edited by Kurtz, R.H., Russell Sage Foundation, New York)

caste A caste is composed of 'persons who can live with, eat with, and marry only individuals of the same group.' (Sighele,

S. *Psychologie des Sectes.*) Under the caste system, accordingly, a person cannot rise from a lower to a higher caste. 'It is in India that the caste has had its completest development.' (Kroeber, A.L. *Encyclopaedia of the Social Sciences*, vol. 3, Macmillan, New York, 1931, p. 255). Other illustrations of caste are the Eta of Japan and the Negro in the United States, particularly in the Southern states.

castrate Castrated person; eunuch. Although practically this term denotes a man deprived of manhood through loss of the testicles, and is thus in a sense identical with *eunuch*, the original meaning of the term naturally applies to individuals of either sex whose gonads were removed, that is, the ovaries in the female and the testes in the male. See *castration; eunuchism; eunuch.*

castration In its original and broadest biological sense, this term simply means the surgical operation of removing the sex organs (gonads) which are essential to reproduction as well as to the development of the secondary sex characters, that is, the ovaries in the female or the testes in the male. The operative removal of the ovaries is usually called *ovariotomy* or *oöphorectomy*, of the testes, *orchidectomy*.

Castrating operations are now performed in both sexes for medical reasons only. Castration as a eugenic policy, as previously executed in sex-offenders especially, is no longer practiced in civilized countries. For eugenic purposes, *sterilization* by *vastectomy* or *salpingectomy* is now preferred, as these sterilizing operations affect only the capacity for reproduction but not the secondary sex characteristics.

When performed or occurring *after* puberty, castration has in neither sex such drastic effects as are observed following surgical removal of the sex organs in early life, when the secondary sex characters of the organism have not yet developed. Castration *before* puberty results in *eunuchoidism* or *enunuchism*—the development of the secondary sexual characteristics of the opposite sex. *Eunuchoid women* are recognizable by male body proportions, deep voice, and hairiness of body and face, and *eunuchoid men* by large hips, narrow sloping shoulders, absence of beard and body hair, high-pitched voice, etc.

In psychological medicine castration implies the penis alone.

Psychoanalysts are in agreement that the castration complex is universal. It is intimately bound up with the Oedipus situation. The manner in which the castration complex is handled determines in a large measure the fate of the Oedipus complex.

During the late infancy period, an unusually large volume of libido converges upon the genital area, giving rise to what is called the phallic stage. See *ontogeny, psychic.*

Children of either sex first believe that everyone is born with a penis. When the male child finds out that there are some people (girls) who have no penis, he became intensely alarmed, because he is now faced with proof to support his phantasy that he might lose his own organ, just as in the past he had lost other valuable possessions. During the oral stage the nipple was taken from him; during the anal stage he lost the feces, to which he had attached so much importance. Owing to these previous experiences and their many representations, the thought of something disastrous befalling his penis gains in intensity. The boy believes that the girl once had such an organ as his, but it was taken away from her. At about this time he begins to feel that if he continues to show sexual interest in his mother, his penis will be removed. The Oedipus situation becomes acute with such a dread and is amplified with the many sexual and non-sexual threats that come from both parents.

In the normal person the castration complex and its many associations, principally the Oedipal, give way in a large measure to the reaction-formations, sublimations, substitutions, extra-parental identifications, etc. that characterize the so-called latency period. During the latency period the threat of castration, especially that from the father, causes the son to identify himself with his father, thus setting up within himself the latter's prohibitions. The castration complex is in this way internalized, 'covered up'; it is also free from external authority, until it is reanimated at puberty. See *superego.*

The castration complex in the girl is not as clearly defined as it is in the boy. 'Nevertheless,' Freud says, 'we know that the female child is extremely sensitive about the lack of sex organ equal to that of the male child. Accordingly, the girl comes to consider herself inferior to the boy, developing a condition of "penis envy" from which may be traced a whole chain of reactions characteristic of the female.' (Freud, S. *Collected Papers,* vol. 2, tr. by Riviere, J., Leonard and Virginia Woolf and The Institute of Psychoanalysis, London, 1924-25). The girl feels that she has been injured in her infancy and she generally blames her mother for it. Thus the castration phantasy plays an important role in the development and termination of the Electra complex or, as it is also known, of the female Oedipus complex.

castrophilia See *transvestism.*

castrophrenia (kas-tro-frē'nē-à) See *noöklopia.*

cat-cry syndrome See *syndrome, cat cry.*

catabolic (kat-à-bol'ik) Pertaining to, or characterized by, *catabolism* (q.v.). In constitutional medicine the term applies to the *anabolic-catabolic balance,* which, according to the theories of Pende, is the most fundamental criterion in describing or typing human beings (see *anabolic*).

On the basis of this concept, the *catabolic biotype* constitutes the fundamental underlying type to which the more superficial characterizations of the types called *microsplanchnic, dolichomorphic,* and *sympathicotonic* (q.v.), among others, apply.

catabolism (kà-tab'ō-liz'm) In physiology and general medicine, this means *destructive metabolism* (q.v.), or a downward series of changes by which complex bodies are broken down into simpler forms. In certain cases, of course, catabolism can be constructive, especially in botany.

catabythismomania (kat-à-bith-iz-mō-mā'-nē-à) *Obs.* Morbid impulse to commit suicide by drowning.

catabythismus Suicide by drowning.

cataclonia (kat-à-klō'nē-à) Cataclonus.

cataclonus (-klō'nus) Rhythmic convulsive movements, especially when psychically determined.

catagelophobia (kat-à-jel-ō-fō'bē-à) Fear of ridicule.

catalentia (-lent'ē-à) *Obs.* A. Paracelsian term for epilepsy.

catalepsia cerea (-lep'sē-à kā'rē-à) *Obs.* Catalepsy.

catalepsy [1] (kat'à-lep-sē) Inordinate maintenance of postures or physical attitudes. The term is usually synonymous with flexibilitas cerea. 'The muscular system may be in a condition of *waxy flexibility*, permitting of the molding of the limbs into any position where they remain indefinitely— *catalepsy.*' (Jelliffe, S.E. and White, W.A. *Diseases of the Nervous System*, 6th ed., Lea & Febiger, Philadelphia, 1935, p. 1031) Catalepsy is regarded as a high degree of suggestibility and is often associated with other forms of suggestibility, such as echopraxia, echolalia, command automatism, etc.

Wax-like postures may also appear with rigid rather than flexible musculature, so-called rigid catalepsy.

Cataleptic states may appear in a wide variety of clinical syndromes, but are most common in schizophrenia, epilepsy, and hysteria. It may be psychically induced through hypnotism. 'Cerebellar patients, also, and certain types of cases with fronto-cerebellar pathway disturbances show what is known as *cataleptic rigidity* in this (erect) position.' (Jelliffe, S.E. and White, W.A. *Diseases of the Nervous System*, 6th ed., Lea & Febiger, Philadelphia, 1935, p. 79)

catalepsy [2]
In the 17th century catalepsy was 'also called *catoche, catochus, congelatio*; and by Hippocrates, *aphonia*; by Antigenes, *anaudia*; by Coelius Aurelianus, *apprehensio, opressio*; and also by some *apoplexia cataleptica, detentio; encatalepsis; prehensio, comprehensio, deprehensio.*' (Motherby, G. *A New Medical Dictionary*, 5th ed., for J. Johnson, St. Paul's Church-Yard, etc., London, 1801)

catalepsy, artificial Catalepsy occurring during induced hynosis.

catalepsy, epidemic Cataleptic states appearing simultaneously in many persons, as a consequence of imitation or identification.

catalepsy, rigid See *catalepsy.*

catalexia (kat-à-lek'sē-à) A type of reading disability characterized by a tendency to reread words and phrases.

catalysator, catalyzator (kat'à-li-zā-tēr) An external stimulus that serves to loosen inhibitions; a catalyzer.

catamite (kat'à-mīt) *Rare.* A boy who submits to pederasty.

catamnesis (kat-am-nē'sis) The medical history of a patient following a given illness, the so-called 'follow-up' history; sometimes used to refer to the history of the patient and his illness following the initial examination.

cataphasia (kat-à-fā'zhē-à) The repetition of words or phrases, seen in pronounced form in the catatonic form of schizophrenia; see *sterotypy; verbigeration.*

cataphora (kà-taf'ō-rà) A form of coma which may be interrupted by transitory states of partial consciousness; coma somnolentium.

cataplectic attack (kat-à-plek'tik) See *cataplexy.*

cataplexy (kat'a-plek-si) Temporary 'paralysis' or immobilization. 'Cataplexy denotes paroxysmal attacks of loss of muscle tone (often without loss of consciousness), so that the patient sinks to the ground. It is usually associated with narcoleptic attacks (paroxysms of sleep).' (Henderson, D.K. and Gillespie, R.D. *A Text-Book of Psychiatry*, 4th ed., Oxford University Press, London, 1936)

cataplexy of awakening See *paralysis, sleep.*

cataptosis (kat-ap-tō'sis) Galen's term for an epileptic or apoplectic seizure.

catastrophe See *theory, catastrophe; behavior, catastrophic.*

catathymia (kat-à-thī'mē-à, -thim'e-à) The existence in the unconscious of a complex that is sufficiently charged with affects to produce effects in consciousness.

catatonia, depressive Synonymous with,

but rarely used today for, catatonic stupor. See *schizophrenia, catatonic.*

catatonia, katatonia (kat-à-tō'nē-à) A lowering of tension. From the clinical point of view many different syndromes have been called catatonia. Modern descriptions of the clinical condition were first given by Kahlbaum in 1874 (Die Katatonie) and the general concepts laid down by him have prevailed, save for minor changes. Kahlbaum regarded catatonia as a nosologic entity, but since the later works of Kraepelin it has been looked upon as a subdivision of schizophrenia. (See *schizophrenia, catatonic.*) It is true that catatonic or rather cataleptoid syndromes are not infrequently a part of other diagnostic groups (e.g. hysteria and manic-depressive psychosis), but the tendency is to restrict the term catatonia to the schizophrenic group. Cataleptoid states may also be observed in association with organic pathology, such as is found, for example, in lethargic encephalitis.

The clinical syndrome called *catatonia* is characterized as a rule by (1) stupor, associated with either marked rigidity or flexibility of the musculature or (2) overactivity in conjunction with various manifestations of stereotypy.

catatonia, manic *Rare.* Catatonic excitement. See *schizophrenia, catatonic.*

catatonia mitis (mē'tēs) A mild and relatively short course of catatonia, with stupor and immobility as the principal symptoms.

When the catatonic syndrome is more extensive, resembling that described under the heading *schizophrenia, catatonic,* the expression catatonia protracta is sometimes used.

catatonia protracta (pro-trak'tà) See *catatonia mitis.*

catatonia, Stauder's lethal See *paralysis, catatonic cerebral.*

catatonic cerebral paralysis See *paralysis, catatonic cerebral.*

catatonic schizophrenia (kat-à-ton'ik skiz-ō-frē'nē-à) See *schizophrenia, catatonic.*

catatony (kà-tat'ō-ni) A rarely used Anglicized form for catatonia.

catchment area See *psychiatry, community.*

catecholamine See *epinephrine.*

categorical attitude *Abstract attitude* (q.v.).

catharsis (kà-thär'sis) In psychiatry the term was first used by Freud to designate a type of psychotherapy. He tried through the methods of 'free-association' and hypnosis to bring so-called traumatic experiences and their affective associations into consciousness. Psychiatric symptoms or symbols are looked upon as disguised representations of forgotten and repressed ideas or experiences. When the latter are brought back into the sphere of consciousness and lived out fully (in a therapeutic sense), the method is called catharsis.

Abreaction and *catharsis* are often used synonymously.

catharsis, activity In psychotherapy, especially in activity group psychotherapy, a catharsis in which the patients convey their unconscious preoccupations and conscious intent through *action* rather than through language.

catharsis, community Abreaction in a group, as in *psychodrama* (q.v.).

catharsis, emotional *Catharsis; abreaction* (qq.v.).

catharsis, psychodramatic See *psychodrama.*

cathect, cathecticize (kà-thekt', kà-thek'-ti-sīz) To charge with, to infuse with psychic energy. See *cathexis.*

cathexis (kà-thek'sis) Concentration of psychic energy upon a given object. Investment of the psychic energy of a drive in a conscious or unconscious mental representation such as a concept, idea, image, phantasy, or symbol.

From the standpoint of general location of cathexis psychoanalysts refer to (1) ego-cathexis; when the psychic energy is attached to the conscious division of the ego. Hence, the expressions ego-libido or narcissism arise. Some use the term *self-libido* or *auto-libido* in contradistinction to *object-libido.* (2) Phantasy-cathexis; when psychic energy is attached to wish-formations or phantasies or to their original sources in the unconscious, the expression phantasy-cathexis is used. Both ego-cathexis and phantasy-cathexis are associated with primary narcissism. (3) Object-cathexis; the expression is employed to refer to psychic energy that is attached to some object outside of the subject himself or to its representation in the mind of the individual. Object-cathexis is less stable or fixed than the other forms, because it is associated with manifestations of secondary narcissism, which, in turn, are less durable than those of the primary kind.

When there is an overcharge of psychic energy in an object, the term *hypercathexis* is used; when an undercharge *hypocathexis.*

Other words are often prefixed to the term cathexis: (1) to signify the quality of the charge—adjectives, as in affective-cathexis, libidinal-cathexis, erotic-cathexis, instinctual cathexis; nouns, as in word-cathexis, thought-cathexis, thing-cathexis, or: (2) to express the degree of cathexis, as in hypercathexis, hypocathexis, acathexis.

catochus (kat′ō-kus) *Obs.* Catalepsy, especially that phase of ecstasy or trance in which the patient is conscious, but cannot move or speak.

caudate nucleus (kaw-′dāt) See *basal ganglia.*

causalgia (kaw-sal′jē-à) Sensation of burning pain in the distribution of a peripheral nerve, associated with glossy skin devoid of hair or wrinkles. Other associated changes include swelling, redness, sweating, and curling of the nails. Causalgia is usually due to irritation of a nerve by injury; the median or sciatic nerves are most commonly involved.

CAVD A measure of intelligence, devised by Thorndike, consisting of a battery of four tests: completion, arithmetic, vocabulary, and direction-following.

C.C.C. Citrated calcium carbamide; recommended in thy treatment of chronic alcoholism as superior to Antabuse (disulfiram) because it is said to have no undesirable side-effects and more rapid action.

Cd In Rorschach scoring, color denial, i.e. protestation that the color had nothing to do with the percept or that the color on the blot is wrong. Color denial indicates a neurotic avoidance of realistic attitudes and a wish for more intense emotional experiences.

cell In biology, the term denotes those minute structural units of protoplasmic nature which determine the different organic qualities of plant and animal bodies. Cells are ubiquitous and represent the fundamental elements of all organisms. They are so small—ranging ordinarily from 0.01 to 0.1 mm. in diameter—that there may be billions of them in a cubic inch of tissue.

Each cell consists of a denser protoplasmic body, the *nucleus,* which exerts a governing influence over all cellular activities, and the surrounding *cytoplasm.* All development from seed or egg involves cells, and each phase of hereditary transmission is guided and affected by cellular elements.

In embryonic development a great deal depends on how the cells are placed in relation to one another. All other cellular activities are governed by the rule that no cell works by itself in a multicellular animal, but every cell is influenced by others around it or even at a distance from it. (Shull, A.F. *Heredity,* 3rd ed., McGraw-Hill, New York and London, 1938). Dissolved substances pass through any of the ordinary envelopes around cells, although in certain tissues there are protoplasmic bridges from cell to cell. Only the vegetative cells of plants are usually surrounded by a rather rigid wall of cellulose, while most animal cells lack such a pronounced wall.

In the many-celled animals there are two genetically different classes of cells, the *somatic* or *body* cells, which are directly responsible for the actual manifestation of inherited characters but have nothing to do with their transmission, except in primitive types of reproduction; and the *germ* cells, which perform the transmission from generation to generation in the higher forms of reproduction. In animals, the somatic cells produce germ cells only very rarely, while the germ cells give rise in every generation to both somatic and germ cells, thus constituting a reserve out of which the genetic continuity of the germ cells and the repetition of the production of bodies in each generation are maintained (Shull, ibid.)

The process of cell division is initiated

and controlled largely by the nucleus and is commonly called *mitosis*.

cell, body That type of somatic cell which forms the somatoplasm of higher animals and does not produce germ cells. According to Weismann's germ plasm theory, the body cells have nothing to do with the hereditary transmission of inherited characters, but are responsible only for their phenotypical manifestations, at least in the higher forms of reproduction. See *plasm, germ; somatoplasm*.

cell, germ That type of cell which transmits inherited characteristics from generation to generation. See *cell*.

cell, padded A room used for isolation of acutely disturbed patients who are potentially destructive to themselves or others. The room usually has a large mattress on the floor and padding on the walls. Often restraints are applied to the patient within the room. Modern psychiatry utilizes sedation and individual attention to the patient's need rather than the padded cell.

cell, Purkinje (Johannes Evangelista Purkinje, Bohemian physiologist, 1787-1869) See *cerebellum*.

celom (sē'lom) In the tridermic stage of embryological development, the split-like cavity formed by the lateral plates of the middle germ layer or *mesoderm* (q.v.).

cene-, coene- From Gr. *koinós*, common or general.

cenesthesia (sē-nes-thē'zē-à) The general sense of bodily existence (and especially the general feeling of well-being or malaise), presumably dependent upon multiple stimuli coming from various parts of the body, including sensations of internal organ activity even though these are not necessarily on a conscious level.

cenesthesic (-es-thē'sik) Relating to mental constituents caused by stimuli from organs other than the one in which the constituent appears.

cenesthopathy (-es-thop'à-thē) The feeling or sense of general physical ill-being. The feeling ordinarily is not referable to any special part of the body, but is more in the nature of a general feeling of ill-

ness, and is commonly expressed in psychiatric patients.

cenophobia (-ō-fō'bē-à) See *kenophobia*.

cenotrope, coenotrope (-ō-trōp) Instinct; behavior characteristic of all members of a group having the same biological and experiential background.

censor, endopsychic (en-dō-sī'kik) See censorship.

censorship A non-specific term referring to the critical and evaluative scrutiny to which any instinctual quality or drive impulse is subjected before it is allowed to pass into a higher level of mental organization. Both ego and superego have censorship functions and most typically, at least in the adult, these require some modification of the original drive.

'But we shall do well not to regard this complication as a difficulty, but to assume that to every transition from one system to that immediately above it (that is, every advance to a higher stage of mental organization) there corresponds a new censorship.' (Freud, S. *Collected Papers*, vol. 4, tr. by Riviere, J., Leonard and Virginia Woolf, London, 1925)

'The characteristic function of consciousness is the exercise of this censoring influence. . . . It is probable that between preconscious and conscious processes a censorship action is also interposed, of the same kind as that between unconscious and preconscious processes.' (Jones, E. *Papers on Psycho-Analysis*, 4th ed., Wood, Baltimore, 1938)

censorship, dream Dreams are highly disguised representations of unconscious impulses. They are under the constant rule of censoring influences. 'The stricter the domination of the censorship, the more thorough becomes the disguise, and, often enough, the more ingenious the means employed to put the reader on the track of the actual meaning.' (Freud, S. *The Interpretation of Dreams*, 3rd ed., tr. by Brill, A.A., Macmillan, New York, 1933)

Center, Community Mental Health See *psychiatry, community*.

center, psychical (sī'ki-kal) This is an older concept, intended to convey the idea that the mind and intelligence were localized as centers in the brain.

center, psychomotor The part of the cerebral cortex around the central fissure, embracing the centers of voluntary muscular movement; psychocortical center.

centering Goldstein's term for perfect integration of the organism with its environment.

central constant See *constant, central.*

central excitatory state See *summation.*

central integrative field factor The sum total of previous experience that forms the basis for *apperception* (q.v.) and incorporation of new experiences.

central nervous system deviation See *impulse-disorder, hyperkinetic.*

centrencephalic system See *system, centrencephalic.*

centrifugal (sen-trif'ū-gal) Radiating or flying off from a center. See *centripetal.*

centripetal (cen-trip'e-tal) Directed toward the center. In psychiatry the term implies a moving toward the psyche. It is said, for example, that the psychoanalysis of Freud is essentially a centripetal psychology. 'For Freud the aims of empirical science, with its centripetal bias towards a minute and detailed analysis of observable facts, were absolute; whereas for Jung a purely objective psychology was not enough, in that it entirely omitted the undeniable reality and power of the idea.' (Baynes, H.G. Translator's Preface to Jung's *Psychological Types,* Harcourt, Brace, New York and London, 1923)

The opposite of centripetal forces (of the mind) are centrifugal ones. Jung is today the outstanding upholder of the centrifugal point of view, the principal representation of which is his *collective unconscious.* Baynes says: 'To Jung the psyche is a world which contains all the elements of the greater world, with the same destructive and constructive forces —a pluralistic universe in which the individual either fulfils or neglects his essential role of creator.' (ibid.)

centrolobar sclerosis (cen-trō-lō'bar skle-rō'sis) See *sclerosis, diffuse.*

centrosome (sen'trō-sōm) Central body. This biological term refers to a central cytoplasmic particle which is thought to be important in the mechanism of cell division. See *cytoplasm.*

cephalalgia (sef-al-al'jē-à) Headache.

cephalalgia, histaminic (his-ta-min'ik) See *histamine.*

cephalea, epileptic (sef-à-lē'à) A type of visceral epilepsy, more common in children than adults, in which paroxysmal headache is the most prominent symptom.

cephalogenesis (sef-al-ō-jen'e-sis) In embryological development, the stage which follows *notogenesis* (q.v.) and is associated with the origin of the primordia of the head.

This stage is initiated by the appearance of the *neural plate,* the primordium of the nervous system, and the formation of the head-fold which delimits the head end of the embryo from the extra-embryonic blastoderm. The neural plate forms the floor of the *neural groove,* which is bounded along both borders by a *neural fold* developing subsequently into the *neural tube,* lined with neural ectoderm, from an overlying epidermal ectoderm. The cephalic portion of a neural tube produces three dilatations which later become forebrain, midbrain, and hindbrain, the primordia of the future cerebrum, cerebellum, and pons and medulla oblongata. The later steps in cephalogenesis lead to the formation of the face and the head as well as of the eyes and the ears.

ceraunophobia (sē-raw-nō-fō'bē-à) See keraunophobia.

cerchnus (sērk'nus) *Obs.* Hoarseness.

cerea flexibilitas (ka're-à flek-sē-bē'lē-tàs) See *catalepsy.*

cerebellum (sēr-e-bel'loom) A large, oval structure with a laminated appearance which lies in the posterior fossa of the skull behind the pons and medulla oblongata. It is joined to the brain-stem by three peduncles, the superior, middle, and inferior, and appears grossly to be divided into two lateral lobes (the cerebellar hemispheres) and an unpaired median lobe (the vermis). Morphologically, however, 'the cerebellum has two primary divisions: (1) the flocculonodular lobe, the most primitive part, with connexions which are entirely vestibular, and (2) the corpus cerebelli, itself divided into (i) a palaeocerebellar division, receiving vestibular and spinocerebellar fibres, and composed anteriorly of lingula, centralis, and culmen, and posteriorly of pyramis, uvula, and paraflocculi, and (ii) a neocerebellar division, constituting the greater part of the corpus cerebelli, with connections mainly corticopontine.

'The cerebellum consists mainly of white matter which is covered with a thin layer of grey matter, the cerebellar cortex, and contains several grey masses, the nuclei. These are divided into lateral nuclei, the nuclei dentatus and emboliformis, and middle and roof nuclei, the nuclei globosus and fastigii.

'Microscopically the cortex consists of three principal layers of cells, the molecular layer, which lies most superficially, the granular layer, which is the deepest, and the layer of Purkinje cells, which lies between the two.' (Brain, W.R. *Diseases of the Nervous System*, Oxford University Press, London, 1951)

'. . . the neocerebellum is essentially a reinforcing and co-ordinating organ which plays an important part in graduating and harmonizing muscular contraction, both in voluntary movement and in the maintenance of posture.

'The anterior lobe and the roof nuclei are concerned with the regulation of stretch reflexes and the anti-gravity posture. The flocculonodular lobe is an important equilibratory centre and lesions of this region cause swaying, staggering, and titubation. The neocerebellum regulates voluntary movement.' (ibid) Thus the cerebellum maintains orientation in space and it brakes volitional movements, especially those requiring checking or halting, and the fine movement of the hands.

Lesions of the cerebellum may produce the following symptoms: dysmetria, intention tremor, inability to perform alternating movements (dysdiadochokinesia), ataxia, decomposition of movement, rebound, nystagmus, vertigo, dysarthria, plurosthotonus, hypotonia, skew deviation of the eyes, and cerebellar 'fits.' To a considerable extent, however, other parts of the nervous system are able to compensate for loss of cerebellar function.

cerebral embolism (ser'e-bral em'bō-liz'm) See *accident, cerebrovascular.*

cerebral hemorrhage (hem'or-raj) See *accident, cerebrovascular.*

cerebral palsy *Little's disease* (q.v.).

cerebral peduncle (ped'ung-k'l) See *midbrain.*

cerebral syphilis (sif'i-lis) See *syphilis, cerebral.*

cerebral thrombosis (throm-bō'sis) See *accident, cerebrovascular.*

cerebrasthenia (ser-ē-bras-thē'nē-à) *Obs.* Neurasthenia relating to the head.

cerebration (-brā'shun) Lewes used this term for 'cerebral actions consecutive on a perception'; today it generally means any kind of conscious thinking.

cerebration, unconscious *Obs.* Mental activity occurring without conscious direction. Hamilton referred to it as *latent thought.*

cerebria (ser-ē'brē-à) A term used by Pinel for mental derangement in general.

cerebria acuta (ke-re'brē-à a-kōō'tà) (L. 'acute mental derangement') Pinel's term for mania.

cerebria chronica (krô'nē-kà) (L. 'chronic mental derangement') *Obs.* Imbecility.

cerebria partialis (pär-tē-ä'lēs) (L. 'partial mental derangement') *Obs.* Monomania.

cerebria sympathetica (sēm-pà-thā'tē-kà) (L. 'sympathetic mental derangement') *Obs.* Hypochondriasis or hysteria.

cerebro-psychosis (ser-ē-brō-sī-kō'sis) This is an old term and concept referring to 'those forms of mental disturbance which result from disease of the psychic centres, such as mania and general paralysis. Also used in a generic sense for all mental affections.' (Tuke, D.H. *A Dictionary of Psychological Medicine*, vols. 1-2, Blakiston, Philadelphia, 1892)

cerebrotonia (-tō'nē-à) A personality type, described by Sheldon, which is associated with the ectomorphic body build and is characterized by restraint, inhibition, alertness, and a predominantly intellectual approach to reality.

cerebrovascular accident See *accident, cerebrovascular.*

cerebrum (se-rē'brum, ser'e-brum) The major portion of the brain; the *forebrain* (q.v.) or prosencephalon.

ceremonial, compulsive A term used to describe the ritualistic behavior that is characteristic of the compulsion-neurotic. As in all neurotic symptoms, the compulsive ceremonials defend against certain unconscious instinctual demands which are threatening to the ego. According to Freud, this ritualistic behavior demonstrates the use of two types of defense mechanisms in particular: 'undoing' and 'isolation.' Through motor means, that is, by a gesture or act which is symbolic and is repeated countless times, the patient tries to undo an undesirable or traumatic experience. For example, a patient with a washing compulsion is undoing a previous dirtying action (either real or imaginary). The dirtying action is usually masturbation, which by anal regression (characteristic of the compulsion-neurotic) is conceived of as dirty. Through order, routine, and system the compulsive neurotic tries to isolate his experiences and rid them of their emotional concomitants. In analysis he finds it extremely difficult to associate or to experience any emotional reactions no matter how exciting his ideas may be.

The mechanism of isolation is seen most vividly in compulsive ceremonials which center around the taboo of touching. Many compulsion-neurotics have routines concerning which objects should not be touched and which should, and, in the latter case, in which order the objects should be touched. These rituals frequently concern routines to be followed in washing or bathing, but they may involve any ordinary daily activity such as crossing thresholds, handling doorknobs, etc.

ceremonial, defensive A more or less elaborate pattern of actions unconsciously devised by a person as a defense against anxiety and compulsively executed by him whenever this anxiety threatens.

In traumatic neuroses, for example, 'A large group of patients have symptoms that are chiefly unconscious defense reactions against the original trauma.' For example, '. . . the symptom may be a more complete elaboration of a defensive reaction that was not carried out on the original traumatic occasion.' (Kardiner, A., and Spiegel, H. *War Stress and Neurotic Illness*, Hoeber, New York, 1947.) Whatever actions might be gone through in this

elaboration of the incompleted defensive reaction would constitute a defensive ceremonial.

A 'defense ceremonial has the nature of a compulsory act which the patient carries out without knowing exactly why, but which relieves him of anxiety.' It is '. . . usually carried out with no more control of the will than is shown in the ordinary compulsive ritual. . . The ceremonial which the patient unconsciously devises takes form some years after the original traumatic event.' (ibid.)

Cerletti, Ugo (1877-1963) Italian neuropsychiatrist; in 1938, with L. Bini, introduced electrical form of convulsive therapy.

certification See *commitment.*

certify Formally to declare a person insane.

ceruloplasmin (ser-ū-lō-plas'min) An alpha globulin which contains almost all the copper in blood serum. Among other substrates, ceruloplasmin acts on serotonin and norepinephrine (which have been suggested by some to be the central neurohumors for the parasympathetic and sympathetic nervous systems, respectively). Ceruloplasmin tends to be elevated in many chronic diseases; it tends not to be elevated in chronic schizophrenia, although it is often elevated in acute schizophrenia. The reasons for such elevation are unknown, but it has been suggested that in schizophrenia an abnormal ceruloplasmin (? taraxein) is formed through a metabolic error and that the abnormal ceruloplasmin fails to neutralize certain naturally occurring, noxious metabolites such as adrenoxine and adrenolutin. Others have hypothesized that ceruloplasmin is elevated in acute schizophrenia to compensate for taraxein, a substance closely related to ceruloplasmin and reported to have been found in schizophrenic serum. Taraxein may produce schizophrenic symptoms by lowering the resistance of the blood-brain barrier to various potentially toxic substances which are then able to attack certain portions of the brain (especially the septal region or the limbic lobe). According to this hypothesis, the taraxein and/or the toxic substances may arise as a result of genetically determined metabolic error.

Related to the increase of ceruloplasmin

in schizophrenia are: (1) the more rapid oxidation of adrenalin by schizophrenic serum, and (2) the more rapid oxidation of N-N-dimethyl-paraphenyline diamine by schizophrenic serum.

Vitamin C antagonizes ceruloplasmin, and some workers disavow both of the above hypotheses, claiming that the more rapid oxidations and the relative increase in ceruloplasmin that have been observed reflect only a vitamin C deficiency induced by dietary inadequacies in long-term hospitals.

c.e.s. Central excitatory state. See *summation.*

CF Rorschach scoring symbol for a response determined by color and form, with color dominant.

chaero-, chairo-, chero- (kī-ro-) From Gr. *chairein,* to rejoice.

chalasis (kal'ȧ-sis) Inhibition of resting posture. Hines, in her studies on the maturation of excitability in the precentral gyrus, describes chalastic foci which cause inhibition of resting posture.

chalastic fits, postdormital See *paralysis, sleep.*

chance-action An action that is executed by mere chance and has no conscious aim or purpose, but nevertheless subserves the execution of an unconscious intention. Under this heading Freud distinguishes three separate categories: (a) habitual actions such as fingering one's hair; (b) actions which are usual under certain circumstances, such as doodling, coin-jingling, etc.; and (c) isolated chance actions. One example of the last variety might be the loss of a wedding ring on the honeymoon, indicating an unconscious wish to dissolve the marriage. Another might be the leaving of personal articles such as gloves, a cigarette lighter, etc. in the psychotherapist's office, indicating the patient's difficulty in tearing himself away.

Freud separates these 'symptomatic' or 'chance' actions from those carried out erroneously. In the latter we have to do with an action that has a conscious intention but is carried out erroneously, this erroneous execution reflecting the person's unconscious intention. Manifestly, the line

of demarcation between these two categories is not definite.

change agent See *psychiatry, community.*

change, social Changes in culture or the social heritage, which characteristically take place through invention, that is, through any new element in culture. (Ogburn, W.F. *Encyclopaedia of the Social Sciences,* vol. 3, Macmillan, New York, 1931, p. 331) Major social changes have resulted from technological inventions as the bow and arrow, writing, printing, the steam engine, etc. Social changes taking place in modern society give rise to many problems of personal and social adjustments.

changing, compulsive A symptom found in some compulsion-neurotics, expressing itself in a tendency to change continuously. This changing apparently has no limitations and may involve anything anywhere: personal habits, dress, work, social relations, opinions, etc. The changing is an effort 'to bring the world into accord with . . . [the patient's] . . . system.' Apparently through compulsive changing the patient can avoid the reality that the world does not obey his compulsive system. (Fenichel, O. *The Psychoanalytic Theory of Neurosis,* Norton, New York, 1945)

character In current usage, approximately equivalent to *personality;* it consists of the totality of objectively observable behavior and subjectively reportable inner experience. It includes the characteristic (and to some extent predictable) behavior-response patterns that each person evolves, both consciously and unconsciously, as his style of life or way of being in adapting to his environment and in maintaining a stable, reciprocal relationship with the human and non-human environment. The character or personality reflects the nature of the person's psychologic defense system, his autoplastic and alloplastic maneuvers, and the ego defenses that he automatically and customarily employs to maintain intrapsychic stability. The character is the agency through which inner personal and outer environmental forces are brought together, critically evaluated, and acted upon; it is, in other words, a compromise between inner drives, the claims of the superego, and reality demands. Because the character or personality is ego-syntonic, it must be recognized that any diagnosis of *character disorder* or *personality disturbance* is fundamentally a social diagnosis, and made by people other than the subject himself, whose behavior is perceived by others as destructive, frightening, nonconforming, or otherwise deviant. See *defense, character.*

character, anal Obsessive-compulsive personality disorder (in DSM-II, 301.4).

The anal character is made up of three cardinal traits. The first is orderliness (reliability, conscientiousness, punctuality, etc.), the second is parsimony, which may be expressed as avarice, while the third is obstinacy and its closely allied traits (defiance, vindictiveness, irascibility, etc.). See *anal-erotism; defense, character.*

character, ascetic A mode of life characterized by rigor, self-denial, and mortification of the flesh. Asceticism is seen typically as a phase in puberty, where it indicates a fear of sexuality and a simultaneous defense against sexuality. Asceticism is also seen as an extreme type of masochistic character disorder, where almost all activity is forbidden because it represents intolerable instinctual demands. In such cases, the very act of mortifying may become a distorted expression of the blocked sexuality and produce masochistic pleasure. An example of this is the eccentric who devotes his life to the combating of some particular evil which unconsciously represents his own instinctual demands.

character, daemonic Masochism represents the existence of an impulse that has self-destruction as its aim; it is older than sadism and is of a repetitive-compulsive character. 'There are people who, all their lives, repeat, to their own detriment, the same reactions, without any correction, or who seem to be dogged by a relentless ill-fortune, though a closer investigation shows that they are unwittingly bringing this ill-fortune upon themselves. Thus we explain what is called a "daemonic" character as being due to the repetition-compulsion.' (Frued, S. *New Introductory Lectures on Psychoanalysis*, tr. by Sprott, W.J.H., Norton, New York, 1933)

character, epileptic Some epileptologists have described a special array of character traits which they consider constitute the epileptic character. The basic traits are built around extremely developed ambivalence. The patients vividly exhibit antithetic qualities; they love and hate intensely; they are piously religious at one time and utterly sacrilegious at another; they are remarkably meticulous, and presently they are careless; they alternate between high morality and the performance of all kinds of sexual perversions, between generosity and penuriousness, between insolence and obsequiousness, etc. See *personality, epileptic; personality, explosive.*

character, exploitative Fromm's term for a new presentation of the character pattern described by Abraham as *oral aggressive* (see *defense, character*), in agreement with the so-called cultural school of psychoanalysis, which has made its own classification of character types. Instead of viewing character structure as the result of libido sublimation or reaction formation, this school sees the character types as basic attitudes in the process of socialization and coping with each particular life situation. Accordingly, Fromm believes that such a person develops in a frustrating atmosphere and hence comes to feel that one can have only what one takes and that the only source of security lies in exploiting others. When threatened with danger, the exploitative character tries to manipulate the situation by flattery, cajoling, aggression, or any other means.

character, genital The genital character is the resultant of those character traits (handed down from the pregenital levels) which serve the interest of genitality and of the traits that issue from the Oedipus complex. During the pregenital stages the management of instinctual energies was largely of an autoerotic and narcissistic character; now, since the object of the genital impulses is outside of the person himself, the instincts strive toward alloerotic (homosexual and heterosexual) expression.

In the normal person the final formation of the genital character is relatively unnarcissistic and unambivalent. 'Generally speaking, we may say that when the child has been able to subdue his Oedipus complex with all its constituents, he has made the most important step toward overcoming his original narcism, and his hostile tendencies; and at the same time he has broken the power of the pleasure principle to dominate the conduct of his life.' (Abraham, K. *Selected Papers,* tr. by Bryan, D. and Strachey, A., Leonard and Virginia Woolf, London, 1927)

character, hysterical See *defense, character.*

character, neurotic See *neurosis, character.*

character, oral The personality traits based on oral erotism. According to Abraham there are two principal ways of expressing oral activity: (1) sucking and (2) biting, from each of which arise definite types of personality.

If the infant suffered no difficulties or privations during the sucking period, if the sucking phase was largely pleasurable, it is believed that the pleasure is carried over as a character trait, leading to the optimistic type of person who believes that he will succeed in any undertaking. Moreover, such a person may exhibit carefree indifference and perhaps inactivity. The mother's breast will 'flow for them eternally.' Because the infant was treated so generously, identification with the mother gives rise to generosity as an important trait in the child.

If, on the other hand, the infant failed to achieve gratification during the sucking period, it develops a pessimistic attitude. In later life the child is apprehensive and demanding; it is never satisfied and comes to believe it never will be.

The second or biting stage is said also to lead to the development of character traits: to a tendency to hate and to destroy. 'This fundamental difference extends to the smallest details of a person's behavior,' (Abraham, K., *Selected Papers,* tr. by Bryan, D. and Strachey, A., Leonard and Virginia Woolf, London, 1927)

character, paranoiac In this personality type, projection mechanisms are foremost, in that the subject constantly blames the environment for his difficulties. Moreover, he generally has greatest trouble in getting along with members of his own sex. The paranoiac usually superimposes his false claims upon some real circumstances in the environment, thus giving some degree of plausibility to his delusional formations.

The *paranoid personality* (301.0) possesses the same fundamental traits, but to a more marked degree. Furthermore, it is usually easy to detect the delusional basis for his trouble. See *personality disorders.*

character, receptive A type described by Fromm; such a person is passive, dependent, clinging, and compliant. This type is similar to the passive-oral or passive-dependent types of other writers. (in DSM-II, 301.81).

character, reformation of A psychoanalytic term referring to a form of defense that occurs in everyday life and also frequently as a way-station in the course of the psychoanalytic procedure. In this form of defense the patient leans over backward in the proverbial 'reformed rake' fashion. By his meticulosity and carefully guarded behavior, he denies the presence of the 'old' recently uncovered 'bad' traits and 'bad' instinctual desires. He is constantly preoccupied with 'selling' the picture of himself, as a reformed character, to himself, the analyst, and the world. The process of reaction-formation, i.e. leaning over backward against certain instinctual trends and developing the overlay of 'just the opposite' superficial traits, is nuclear in the 'character reformation' process as used in this sense.

E.F. Sharpe (*Collected Papers on Psycho-analysis,* The Hogarth Press and The Institute of Psychoanalysis, London, 1950) states: 'We have to demonstrate that the same impulses are discernible in the reformation as before it, that obedience has in it the same factors as disobedience—that black is white and white black . . . that anxiety is being allayed by this system of goodness and obedience.'

character structure See *structure, character; defense, character.*

character, unit See *unit-character.*

character, urethral A character type, mentioned briefly by Freud and Ferenczi and belonging to the classificatory group which stresses the libido origin of character structure (see *defense, character*). The urethral character commonly gives a history of bed-wetting beyond the usual age. The behavioral characteristics of this type depend on reaction formation in relation to the specific fear of urethral eroticism, which is shame. Burning ambition, a need to boast of achievement, and great impatience are typical traits.

Charcot, Jean-Martin (1825-93) (shàr-kō') French neurologist and psychiatrist; localization of function in cerebral disease; hysteria; hypnosis; the first modern physician to make a serious attempt to treat emotional disorders on an individual psychotherapeutic basis.

Charcot triad See *sclerosis, multiple.*

Charcot-Marie-Tooth's disease (Jean-Marie Charcot; Pierre Marie, French physician, 1853-1940; and Howard Henry Tooth, English physician, 1856-1926) See *atrophy, peroneal muscular.*

Charcot's syndrome Multiple sclerosis.

charge, mental *Cathexis* (q.v.).

charm Light hypnosis; hypotaxis.

chart, life See *sketch, biographic.*

chasmus hystericus (kàz'moos hēs-te'rē-koos) Persistent yawning, usually on a hysterical basis.

chastity, conjugal The state of husband and wife living in celibacy.

cheimaphobia (kī-mà-fō'bē-à) Fear of cold.

cheiro- See *chiro.*

chemopallidectomy (kē-mō-pal-i-dek'tō-mē) Injection of small amounts of alcohol into the globus pallidus, used in the therapy of basal ganglia hyperkinetic disorders.

chemo-psychiatry A psychiatric term intended to designate the application and effect of chemical substances in psychiatry. See *psychotropics.*

cher- See *chaer-.*

cheromania (kē-rō-mā'nē-à) *Obs* Morbid impulse to gaiety. The elated syndrome of manic-depressive psychosis.

cherophobia Morbid aversion to gaiety.

Cheyne-Stokes psychosis See *psychosis, Cheyne-Stokes.*

child, battered See *syndrome, battered child.*

child, bright A generic term originating in the desire to establish categories in the large group of children with superior intellectual abilities. Clinical observation and intelligence testing are the two main avenues of approach for establishing these categories. In its specific meaning, the term 'the bright child' has become a tool in the technical equipment of those dealing, in the main, with the problems and concepts of child guidance. In general, children of superior ability have been divided into four groups: (a) the bright child; (b) the superior child; (c) the gifted child; (d) the prodigy.

(a) The special ability of the *bright child* can best be ascertained by intelligence tests. A bright child, as contrasted with the dull or subnormal child, is one who possesses average qualifications, when judged by the mental level of our civilization. The brightness of the child consists specifically in his ability to perceive, grasp, and absorb communicated knowledge more quickly than is usual with his own age group. Bright children assimilate more easily and may offer more original products in creative work.

(b) *Superior children* are more than bright. They have extraordinary capabilities, usually being endowed with some particular superiority in their special field.

(c) *Gifted children* are those with a specific talent against a background of bright, average, or dull abilities. Gifted children are usually one-sided, or have a tendency to overdevelop in the direction of their ability only.

(d) The *prodigy* (among superior children) is rare, and is a child who from the earliest stage of his life shows an unusual and practically untrained capability in one or more fields. Most frequently such children are seen on the concert stage, but some attract attention in the fine arts, literature, and science. (Harms, E. *Handbook of Child Guidance,* Child Care Publications, New York, 1947)

child-centered In educational psychology, a school whose primary concern is fulfilling the child's present needs rather than preparing him for adult life.

child, gifted See *child, bright.*

child guidance Used especially in the psychiatric, sociological, and psychological study and treatment of the developing child, this psychiatric term intends to emphasize preventive or prophylactic measures directed toward the goal of minimizing the chances of mental and emotional disorders developing in adult life. These measures are focused mainly upon the familial, educational, and social environmental milieu of the developing child.

Child guidance strives to influence the child's developmental familial and social milieu mainly through education, support, insight, and understanding, directed at both the child's immediate family and such influential parent surrogate figures as the doctor, the minister, the nurse, and the teacher. A major portion of this preventive program is directed toward alleviating the neurotic anxiety of parents and parent surrogates as it is acted out in their close relationship with the child, and easing the anxiety of the child, who is inevitably, albeit unconsciously, affected in the process.

child, intelligent See *child, bright.*

child-penis-feces See *concept, feces-child-penis.*

child, problem A child whose behavior presents deviations from the norm, such as would warrant investigation and treatment by methods of clinical guidance, child psychiatry, etc. The deviations are manifested primarily in the adaptation to the social group, but may be related to habit training or neurotic traits which make social adaptation difficult.

child prodigy See *child, bright.*

child, superior See *child, bright.*

childbirth, envy of According to some authorities the boy has an envy of the girl's ability to bear children, which in its intensity matches the girl's envy of the boy's penis. Fenichel does not believe this to be the case. He points out that both boys and girls may have a 'passionate wish to give birth to babies, a wish that is doomed to frustration.' On the other hand, however, little boys 'can actually get pleasure from their penis.' This is clearly not the case in the girl's side of the situation, i.e. since little girls can in no possible way bear children any better than can little boys. (Fenichel, O. *The Psychoanalytic Theory of Neurosis,* Norton, New York, 1945)

childhood The period of life from birth to puberty. See *developmental levels.*

childhood, land of Jung used this expression to describe 'that time in which the rational consciousness of the present was not yet separated from the "historical soul," the collective unconscious, and thus not only into that land where the complexes of childhood have their origin but into a prehistorical one that was the cradle of us all. The individual's separation from the "land of childhood" is unavoidable, although it leads to such a removal from that twilit psyche of primordial time that a loss of the natural instincts thereby occurs.' (Jacobi, J. *The Psychology of C.G. Jung,* Kegan Paul, Trench, Trubner, London, 1942.) 'The consequence of this is want of instinct and therefore disorientation in general human situations. The separation has, however, also the result that the "land of childhood" remains definitely infantile and so becomes a constant source of childish inclinations and impulses. Naturally these intruders are highly unwelcome to consciousness, which therefore represses them. This repression merely increases the separation from the source and intensifies the want of instinct to the point of sterile rationalism. Consciousness therefore either is overwhelmed with infantility or must constantly defend itself against it in vain. The one-sidedly rational attitude of consciousness must, in spite of its undeniable successes, be regarded as unadapted and contrary to the demands of life. Life is dried up and longs to return to its source. The source, however, can only be found in the "land of childhood," where one, as formerly, can receive directions from the unconscious. Not only he is childish, though, who remains a child too long but also he who parts himself from his childhood and supposes it has therewith ceased to exist. For he does not know that everything pertaining to the psyche has a double face. The one looks forward, the other back. It is ambiguous and therefore symbolic, like all living reality . . . In consciousness we stand upon a peak and childishly imagine that the road leads on to greater heights beyond the peak. That is the chimerical rainbow-bridge. In order to gain the next peak one goes nevertheless—one must go, if one will reach it—down into the land where the roads first begin to branch.' (Jung, C.G. *The Integration of* *the Personality,* Farrar and Rinehart, New York, 1939)

children, ego deviant A term suggested by Beres as a diagnostic label for those children whom others would classify as childhood schizophrenia or early infantile autism.

chionophobia (kī-ō-nō-fō'bē-à) Fear of snow.

chiro- From Gr. *cheir,* hand.

chiromania (kī-rō-mā'nē-à) *Obs.* Masturbatic psychosis; morbid impulse to masturbate. See *psychosis, masturbatic.*

choc fortuit (shawk' fawr-twē') (F. 'accidental shock') In 1887 Binet coined this expression to denote an accidental shock to the psyche. The shock or psychic trauma is usually of a sexual character and is influential in modifying to a greater or lesser degree the subsequent adjustment of the person.

choice, object An object (usually a person) upon which psychic energy is centered.

choice, of neurosis See *compliance, somatic.*

choleric See *type, choleric.*

cholinergic (kōl-in-er'jik) A term used for all nerves which release acetylcholine at their terminals, viz. all postganglionic parasympathetic nerves, all autonomic preganglionic fibers whether parasympathetic or sympathetic, and postganglionic sympathetic nerves to sweat glands and certain blood vessels, and the somatic nerves to skeletal muscles.

cholinesterase (kōl-in-es'ter-ās) See *process, elementary; acetylcholine.*

chorea (kō-rē'à) A disorder characterized by irregular spasmodic, involuntary movements of the limbs of facial muscles. Without a modifying word it usually means Sydenham's chorea or St. Vitus' dance.

chorea (Sydeham's), acute (Thomas Sydenham, English physician, 1624-1689). This condition includes acute and chronic mental disturbances associated with Sydenham's chorea. The latter is an infectious disease related to tonsillitis, rheumatism, and endocarditis and characterized by spontaneous, irregular, spasmodic, involuntary, and objectively purposeless movements of the various muscle groups. Restlessness, irritability, and insomnia occur. Memory disturbances, hallucinations, delirium, depression, or mania may be observed. The condition represents a toxic-infectious psychosis.

chorea demonomania (dē-mun-ō-mā'nē-à) Choreomania.

chorea, epidemic The convulsive dances of the Middle Ages which spread among the population like an epidemic. See *choreomania.*

chorea, Huntington's (G. Huntington, American neurologist, 1850-1916) Chronic degenerative hereditary chorea. A rare, hereditary and familial affection of the nervous system, occurring in adults from 30 to 50 years of age, and characterized by a chronic, progressive chorea, associated with mental deterioration which finally terminates in dementia. (In DSM-II, 290.1 if psychotic, 309.6 if non-psychotic.)

The symptoms include choreic movements which gradually become widespread and violent; facial grimacing, bizarre, dancing, jerking gait; speech impairment; smacking of the tongue and lips, etc.

Mental symptoms include, in the early stages, impairment of memory; poor attention; irritability; at times, apathy and suicidal tendencies. The mental deterioration progresses gradually until total dementia occurs. There are usually no delusions or hallucinations.

chorea, hysterical When choreiform movements constitute the outstanding symptoms of hysteria, the condition is known as hysterical or mimetic chorea.

chorea insaniens (kō-rā'à ēn-sä'nē-ens) (L. 'raving chorea') Chorea with delirium. See *chorea, maniacal.*

chorea magna (màg'nà) (L. 'great chorea') *Obs.* 'Severe associated contractions of a choreic character, but which do not seem to be a special disease, but rather a form of hysteria or some epidemic psychosis, or it may be malingering.' (Tuke, D.H. *A Dictionary of Psychological Medicine*, vols. 1-2, Blakiston, Philadelphia, 1892)

chorea major *Obs. Chorea magna* (q.v.).

chorea, maniacal 'A name given to those cases of chorea in which the mental disturbance is very great. It occurs chiefly in females, at or soon after puberty, or during pregnancy. The mental disturbance may precede or accompany the chorea, which may remain slight, while the mental symptoms assume an intense form. There are delusions with wild, violent, and aimless excitement, accompanied by garrulity, rarely partaking, however, of the incoherent type of acute mania; food has to be administered by force. . . . The excitement subsides after a short period, and leaves dullness and apathy, taciturnity, and sometimes persistent hallucinations. The mental condition may slowly improve, but occasionally persists for weeks or months after the cessation of the chorea.' (Tuke, D.H. *A Dictionary of Psychological Medicine*, vols. 1-2, Blakiston, Philadelphia, 1892) See *chorea, Sydenham's.*

chorea, mental *Obs.* Mania with incoordination of ideas; probably a form of catatonic excitement.

chorea, methodical A form of chorea in which the movements take place at definite intervals.

chorea, mimetic See *chorea, hysterical.*

chorea, nutans (noō'tàns) A hysterical symptom characterized by rhythmical nodding; also called *chorea oscillatoria*, though the latter term refers to rhythmical hysterical movements seen in any part of the body.

chorea oscillatoria (os-kil-à-tor'ē-a) See *chorea nutans.*

chorea, psychogenic The frequent involuntary repetition of the same movement met with in children, and often mistaken for Sydenham's chorea. It is really a habit tic or spasm, in the nature of a compulsion.

chorea, rhythmic Methodical chorea.

chorea rotatoria (kō-rā'à rō-tà-tō'rē-à) A form of chorea characterized by rotation or oscillation of the head, trunk, or limbs, many times a minute.

chorea saltatoria (sàl-tà-tō'rē-à) A form of chorea in which the patient involuntarily jumps rhythmically or irregularly.

chorea, Sydenham's (sī'den-hams) (Thomas Sydenham, English physician, 1624-1689) St. Vitus' dance; an acute toxic disorder of the central nervous system secondary to rheumatic infection (although it has also been reported in association with other infections, e.g. scarlet fever, diphtheria, and chicken-pox). It occurs chiefly in children and young adolescents, in females more than in males, and in the white race more than in the colored. Chief symptoms are involuntary movements which resemble fragments of purposive movements haphazardly performed, hypotonia and hyperextensibility, and often emotional instability of an agitated, overactive kind. On occasion, persistent excitement and insomnia are seen—*maniacal chorea.* Recovery is the rule, although the patient may have several recurrences. Sedatives and cortisone are of value in treatment. See *chorea, maniacal.*

chorea, tetanoid (kō-rē-a, tet'à-noid) See *degeneration, hepatolenticular.*

choreatiform syndrome See *impulse-disorder, hyperkinetic.*

choreiform (kō-rē'i-fawrm) Resembling chorea, choreoid.

choreo-athetosis (kō-rē-ō-a-the-tō'sis) A combination of the clinical features of *chorea* (q.v.) and *athetosis* (q.v.). Both chorea and athetosis physiologically present features which are the opposite of the symptoms of Parkinsonism, and it has therefore been suggested that while Parkinsonism represents a loss of function of the corpus striatum, chorea and athetosis are due to a disorganization of its activity and are due to lesions involving especially the caudate nucleus and the putamen. 'We do not at present know what determines the difference between chorea, athetosis, and torsion-spasm. That these disorders are closely allied is indicated by their possession of common physiological features, and by the occurrence of intermediate forms. Their differences may depend upon whether the striatal lesion is diffuse or focal, and whether or not other structures are also involved.' (Brain, W.R. *Diseases of the Nervous System*, 4th ed., Oxford University Press, 1951.)

choreomania (kō-rē-ō-mā'nē-à) Dancing mania; epidemic chorea. At different times in different countries epidemics of frenzied dancing have taken place. During the fourteenth and fifteenth centuries such epidemics were prominent in western Germany, where they were known as *Tanzwut;* later they were called *chorea Germanorum* to distinguish the condition from *chorea Anglorum* or the form of chorea first described by Sydenham.

choriomeningitis, acute lymphocytic (kō-rē-ō-men-in-jī'tis, lim-fō-si'tik) A virus infection, spread by mice, involving the leptomeninges, the ependyma of the ventricles and the choroid plexuses, and ganglion cells of the brain. Children are most commonly affected, and complete recovery is the rule (psychotic 292.3; nonpsychotic, 309.0).

chrematophobia (krē-mà-tō-fō'bē-à) Fear of money.

Christotherapy Marcus Gregory, in his *Psychotherapy, Scientific and Religious* (1939) thus calls the psychotherapeutic methods used by Christ.

chromatic In genetics the term relates to the protoplasmic cell substance called *chromatin* which stains the nuclear network and constitutes the morphological basis of heredity.

chromatid (krō'mà-tid) In genetics the term is used with reference to the chromosomes which originate in the nucleus of a cell during the meiotic process of cell division (see *chromosome*).

According to Sinnott and Dunn: 'In the prophase of the first division the two members of each elongated pair approach each other side by side and become so closely associated that they sometimes seem to have fused into a single *bivalent* chromosome. During synapsis, or previously, each member of the bivalent pair splits longitudinally into two exactly equal daughter chromosomes or chromatids, so that for a time a *tetrad* is formed

consisting of four chromatids.' (Sinnott, E.W. and Dunn, L.D. *Principles of Genetics*, 3rd ed., McGraw-Hill, New York and London, 1939)

chromatin (krō'mà-tin) Stainable tissue. *Biol.* This collective biological term refers to a reticulum of protein substances in the nucleus of a cell, which are readily stainable and render the nucleus conspicuous in dyed tissues. See *chromosome*.

chromatophobia (krō-mà-tō-fō'bē-à) Morbid dread of certain color or colors.

chromatopsia (-top'sē-à) A condition, most often due to ingestion of certain drugs, in which all objects appear to be of the same color or hue.

chromesthesia (krō-mes-thē'zhē-à) A form of synesthesia in which colors are seen in association with other forms of sensation, and especially in association with sounds (colored hearing).

chromidial neuroplasm See *neuron*.

chromidrosis (krō-mi-drō'sis) Colored perspiration.

chromomere (krō'mō-mēr) Minute nodules in the chromosomes of a cell nucleus which form a chain of chromatic bodies, particularly in the early stages of mitosis, and are strung like beads on a fine thread. They show persistent differences in size and distribution and presumably have also different chemical compositions. There are sound reasons for believing that many chromomeric nodules are too small to be visible. See *chromosome*.

chromophobia (krō-mō-fō'bē-à) Fear of color(s).

chromosomal, chromosomic, chromosomatic (krō-mō-sō'mal, -som'ik, -sō-mat'ik) The adjectives not only refer to the minute chromosome particles themselves into which the scattered chromatin of a cell nucleus separates at the beginning of cell division, but are also used to characterize that part of the mechanism of heredity which is based on the activities of the chromosomes.

chromosome Any of the minute, deeply-staining, thread-like structures which appear in the nucleus of the cell during mitosis. See *division, cell.*

During the process of growth, each cell may divide many hundreds of times. To maintain a constant number of chromosomes per nucleus, at each cell division the chromosomes must also divide; two new cells are formed from one old cell, and two new chromosomes for each old chromosome. Thus the double, or *diploid,* number of chromosomes that is characteristic for each species of animal or plant is maintained. The identical members of a pair of chromosomes are known as homologs (or homologues).

In 1956, Tjio and Levan showed that the number of chromosomes in man is 46, and not 48 as was previously believed. The 46 chromosomes are composed of 22 pairs of *autosomes* and one pair of sex chromosomes (*heterosomes*). The latter are XX in the female, and XY in the male.

In the usual type of cell division as described, one cell thus divides to form two new cells; in sexual reproduction, on the other hand, two cells (the germ cells or *gametes,* one from the paternal side and one from the maternal side) join together to form a single new cell. In order to maintain the correct number of chromosomes in the new cell, the gametes must each contain exactly half the full number of chromosomes. The process by which this reduction division to the *haploid* number occurs is termed *miosis* (q.v.) At miosis (or *meiosis*) the paired chromosomes (homologues) are halved; the resultant gamete with the haploid number is ready to unite with the gamete from the other parent to form the *zygote* (q.v.) with the full, diploid number of chromosomes.

Genes, the basic units of inheritance, are submicroscopic entities located at various points along the chromosomes. The zygote receives either one of a pair of homologous chromosomes, along with the genes it carries, but not both chromosomes. See *gene.*

An hereditary trait or disorder is not inherited as such, but is, rather, the end result of a long line of interactions, some of which were initiated by gene action and some of which were initiated by environmental action. The gene exerts its action through its chemical properties — it instructs the cells or metabolic processes under its influence by means of a chemical code. In the many chains of chemical events that constitute metabolism, each

gene directs one specific action. The original proposition of Beadle and Tatum that one gene controls one enzyme has more recently been refined into the proposition that one gene controls one polypeptide chain. Genetic disorders arise when the gene's chemical code is misinterpreted at any step in its conversion into the specific order of amino acids that will form protein.

Recent biochemical advances have identified *deoxyribonucleic acid (DNA)* as the chemical carrier of the hereditary code. Genetic material is composed of nucleic acids, which are of two types: DNA, found only in the chromosomes, and *ribonucleic acid (RNA),* located mainly in the cytoplasm. DNA contains the coded instructions which are transferred and translated into protein synthesis by RNA. The chemical structure of DNA, according to the generally accepted *Watson-Crick model* (after American biologist James Watson, who shared the 1962 Nobel prize for this work with the English scientists Francis Crick and Maurice Wilkins), consists of a double helix of about 200,000 attached nucleotides that spiral around a central axis like a spiral staircase. The sides of the staircase, which carry very little genetic information, are composed of monotonously repeating sugar molecules joined one after another by phosphate bonds. The actual alphabet of the hereditary language is found in the steps of the staircase which consists of pairs of weakly bonded nitrogenous bases (nucleotides). The nucleotides are only four in number: guanine (G), cytosine (C), adenine (A), and thymine (T); and they are always paired with the same partner to form the step: guanine with cytosine (G : C), and adenine with thymine (A : T). Even though these four chemical 'letters' make up the whole alphabet, the long chain formed by 200,000 pairs of them in the DNA molecule constitutes a tape of coded instructions with almost infinite variations. In a molecule with only 40 nucleotides, for example, there are five billion trillion possible arrangements of the four base letters.

Translating such genetic coding into action requires that the sequence of base pairs in DNA somehow be converted into the sequence of amino acids in a protein. The necessary conversion is achieved through the medium of concerted action of different species of RNA, which translate the code into a message that can be re-coded into a message comprehensible to the next 'translator' along the way.

RNA is structurally similar to DNA, except that it is a single strand rather than a double one, its sugar contains an extra hydroxyl group, and among its four bases uracil substitutes for thymine. It occurs in three different forms: ribosomal RNA, messenger RNA, and transfer RNA. Protein synthesis occurs largely in association with ribosomes, spherical particles of ribonucleoprotein located in the cytoplasm that contain about 60% ribosomal RNA and 40% protein.

The genetic code of DNA is transmitted within the nucleus to the more mobile messenger RNA, whose single strand anneals to or couples with the single strand of DNA that has resulted from a splitting of the double helix down the center of the staircase (that is, each step of the staircase splits at the point where the two bases are weakly joined to each other). Such a division has left one side of the staircase structure of DNA carrying projecting spokes; each spoke consists of one base or nucleotide from the pair that had previously made the unbroken step. Thus, if three consecutive steps of the original chain ladder were G : C,

$$A : T$$
$$A : T$$

splitting would produce two chains: G:

A:

A:

and :C. The single strand of messenger

:T

:T

RNA then joins itself to the corresponding exposed nucleotide chain of the split DNA. Thus, if the G: chain is joined, the

A:

A:

messenger RNA would align itself alongside the DNA chain in such a way as to match the nucleotides appropriately — that is, C to join with G, and U (uracil, which as noted above, substitutes for T in RNA) to join with A. The sequence of nucleotides in the messenger RNA chain is determined, in other words, by one of the two chains of a double DNA helix acting as a template, against which RNA nucleotides are ordered in proper sequence. (And new DNA chains, incidentally, are constructed alongside old ones in exactly the same fashion).

In the next step, messenger RNA migrates into the cytoplasm and becomes associated with a number of ribosomes. Meantime, the various amino acids are being activated and bonded enzymatically to RNA molecules of another kind, transfer RNA. The latter is relatively small and of low molecular weight; hence it is also known as *soluble RNA*. It has the unique property of binding enzymatically to amino acids (hence it is also known as *activating RNA*), and there is at least one specific transfer RNA for each amino acid. Each molecule of transfer RNA is constructed of 80 to 90 ribonucleotides and is folded back on itself in the shape of a hairpin. The end where the amino acid attaches has the base triplet A-C-C, and the base -G- is at the other end. The specificity of each molecule of transfer RNA is determined by the triplet of nucleotide bases located on the turn of the hairpin. That triplet aligns itself to corresponding triplets along the messenger RNA molecule, like sprockets on a wheel finding their correct perforation; and just as with the alignment of DNA with messenger RNA, C must bind itself to G, and A must bind itself to U. By determining the exact sequence of bases, the corresponding alignment also fixes the particular sequence of amino acids that are carried to the alignment by transfer RNA. Peptide bonds are then formed between the aligned amino acids and a new protein is constructed; the transfer RNA which has carried the amino acids is then free to combine with other amino acid units and repeat the sequence.

Mutations, whether naturally occurring or induced by mutagens, arise if the alphabet code is misread at any step along the way, that is, if the sprocket inserts itself into the wrong perforation (or does not insert itself at all). As a result, wrong nucleotides may be added, others may be deleted, or substitutions or rearrangements of nucleotides may occur. Any of these possibilities will alter or erase a polypeptide or enzyme that is essential for one step in a metabolic pathway; consequently, a biochemical *block* develops at the expected site of action. The absence of the usual end product of the metabolic pathway may produce disease, and/or the accumulation of intermediate products (that would ordinarily have been broken down and removed) may produce disease. An example of the former kind of heritable deficiency disorder is succinylcholine sensitivity, due to absence of the enzyme pseudocholinesterase. Phenylketonuria and galactosemia, on the other hand, are examples of the second kind of mutation, where accumulation of an intermediate metabolic substance (or a derivative) is responsible for development of the symptoms characteristic of the disorder.

Since the entire process of transmitting the instructions carried within DNA to amino acids in protein is a mechanical one, once a mutation has occurred it will be copied faithfully forever after. It is as though a secretary were to make each copy of a letter not from a corrected master copy, but from the last version she had herself done, complete with all the mistakes. (And one might note that the probability is high she would add more mistakes each time.)

Thus new mutations can arise, and do, within each generation; because they are copied faithfully, they are then passed on to succeeding generations and may ultimately emerge as heritable disorders. See *heredity; law, Mendelian; Mendelism; mutation.*

It has been estimated that each year, between three and four million persons are born with a significant genetic defect (i.e. 4% to 5% of births); probably another million abortions, stillbirths, and neonatal deaths are caused by genetic defects. Of the first group, approximately one-third have defects that are well understood; 70% of these are dominant autosomal traits, 25% are recessive autosomal traits, and 5% are sex-linked. A second third of the group demonstrates gross chromosomal abnormalities, and the remaining third has developmental abnormalities the nature of which is only poorly understood.

Among recognized genetic disorders are: albinism, alkaptonuria, cystinuria, pentosuria, phenlketonuria, galactosemia, aniridia, one form of muscular dystrophy, microphthalmus, arachnodactyly, chondrodystrophy, sickle cell disorder, hemophilia, color blindness, epiloia, amaurotic idiocy, Wilson's disease, Huntington's chorea, retinoblastoma, neurofibromatosis, and — at least according to some — certain forms of epilepsy, manic-depressive psychosis, schizophrenia, Pick's disease, Alzheimer's disease, senile psychosis, and adult male homosexuality. Hormonal abnormalities that are recognized as genetically determined are diabetes insipidus, diabetes mellitus, and one form of goitrous cretinism. Diseases known to be due to gross chromosome abnormalities are mongolian idiocy (Down's syndrome or 21-trisomy), Turner's syndrome (with XO sex chromosomes instead of XX or XY), Klinefelter's syndrome (XXY), superfemale (XXX), and chronic granulocytic leukemia.

It must be recognized that genes are not static units that inevitably produce fixed results; rather, they are initiators of specific biochemical events, each of which occurs in the context of many other biochemical events proceeding from the actions of other genes. Thus, given different conditions, there can be marked variability in the effects produced by any gene. Under certain conditions, the gene, gene-pair, or gene-complement for the trait (or disease) in question may produce no discernible effect in the phenotype, or its effect may be considerably reduced or modified. (And the terms *penetrance* and *expressivity* refer to such variability: *penetrance* is the percentage of cases which carry the gene that in fact show some or any of its effects; while *expressivity* is the degree to which the penetrant gene manifests itself phenotypically.)

Furthermore, hereditary information can determine only the qualitative patterns of the amino acids, while quantitative control comes from the physicochemical environment of the gene and cell. The genes are not constantly and continuously active at equal rate; if they were, all genetic abnormalities would appear in the embryo and never after birth, and there would be no such things as tissue differentiation, tissue repair, growth, and maturation. Instead, the genes are part of a self-regulating system that contains a pool of enzymes producing different metabolites, the sum of which in turn determines what enzymes will be made from the pool. In short, even genetically determined disease can occur only through an interplay of hereditary and environmental actions.

chromosome, sex See *sex-chromosome.*

chronaxia, chronaxy (kron-ak′sē-à, krō′-nak-sē) The shortest duration which a current of a certain defined strength takes to flow through a nerve in order to produce a muscular contraction.

chronic brain syndrome See *brain disorder; syndrome, organic.*

chronograph, interaction A mechanical device, developed by E. D. Chapple, which enables the observer of a standardized psychiatric interview to record certain temporal aspects of verbal and gestural interactions between interviewer and subject. Chapple's interaction theory of personality assumes that personality can be assessed without recourse to intrapsychic or other psychodynamic formulations, and that its assessment involves merely the process of observing the time relations in the interaction patterns of the subject.

chronophobia (krōn-ō-fō'bē-à) A neurotic fear of time. This is the most common psychiatric disorder in prison inmates, and sooner or later almost all prisoners suffer chronophobia to some degree: it occurs in every potential neurotic who goes to prison. The duration and immensity of time are terrifying to the patient, and the passage of time throws him into a panic. The frequency of chronophobia in prisoners has led to the condition's being called prison neurosis.

Chronophobia appears suddenly, without warning, at the time the inmate comes to grips with his sentence. The introductory phase of imprisonment is ordinarily marked by hopes and plans for a new trial or the like, by uncertainty, and by a studied indifference or carefree attitude. After the novelty of prison has worn off, and the real length of the sentence is felt, chronophobia sets in. The prisoner goes into a panic, usually while in his cell, and fears his enclosure and restraint, but this apparent claustrophobia arises from fear of time, as represented by the prison. After the first attack, more or less constant anxiety, restlessness, insomnia, dissatisfaction with life, numerous hypochondriacal complaints, and progressive inability to adjust himself to his surroundings appear. The intensity of the crisis usually passes within a few weeks or months, though mild relapses may occur. But the prisoner becomes essentially a phlegmatic, indifferent automaton who serves the rest of his sentence by the clock and lives wholly in the present, one day at a time.

chronotaraxis (kron-ō-târ-ak'sis) Confu-sion for time, as for date, season of year, time of day, and overestimation or underestimation of duration of time; this symptom has been reported as occurring as a result of bilateral lesions of the dorsomedial and anterior thalamic nuclei.

chthonic (thon'ik) Relating to the depths of the earth. Jung likens the psyche to the earth. Speaking of psychic archetypes, he says that 'they are essentially the chthonic portion of the mind—if we may use this expression—that portion through which the mind is linked to nature, or in which, at least, its relatedness to the earth and the universe seems most comprehensible.' (Jung, C.G. *Contributions to Analytical Psychology,* tr. by Baynes, H.G. and C.F., Kegan Paul, Trench, Trubner, London, 1928)

cibophobia (sib-ō-fō'bē-à) Fear of food. Sitophobia.

ciliospinal reflex (sil-ē-ō-spī'nal) A superficial reflex; scratching or pinching of the skin on the side of the neck produces dilatation of the pupil; strong light and accommodation must be avoided in this test.

cingulate gyrus (sin'gū-lāt jī'rus) The arched, crescent-shaped convolution on the medial surface of the cerebral hemisphere that lies immediately above the corpus callosum. Also known as gyrus cinguli callosal gyrus. Part of 'Papez's circle'; see *emotion, Papex's theory of.*

cipher method A method in secret writing. While writing on the question of dream interpretation Freud refers to the 'cipher method,' which 'treats the dream as a kind of secret code in which every sign is translated into another sign of known meaning, according to an established key.' (Freud, S. *The Interpretation of Dreams,* 3rd ed., tr. by Brill, A.A., Macmillan, New York, 1933). The method is said by psychiatrists to possess no scientific value.

circle, closed See *theory, immanence.*

circle, Papez's See *emotion, Papez's theory of.*

circuit, reverberating Lorente de No's hypothesis to explain enduring reflex responses to a single stimulus; the hypothesis assumes that several internuncial neurons are intercalated between the sensory fibres and the anterior horn cells and that these several neurons discharge in sequence rather than simultaneously and thus produce an enduring cerebral excitatory state and enduring reflex discharge.

circular In psychiatry the term is used in characterizing manic-depressive psychosis, because the psychosis is often characterized by cycles of mania and depression.

circumscription, monosymptomatic (mon-ō-simp-tō-mat'ik) When a patient has but a single symptom psychiatrists speak of monosymptomatic circumscription. See *monoideism; monomania.*

circumstantiality A disorder of associations seen in schizophrenic patients in which too many associated ideas come to consciousness because of too little selective suppression. Many things which are implicit in ordinary conversation are explicitly communicated and, typically, to an absurd and bizarre degree. One of Bleuler's patients, for example, wrote the following in a letter to his mother: 'I am writing on paper. The pen I use for it is from a factory called Perry & Co., the factory is in England. I am assuming that. After the name Perry Co. the city of London is scratched in; but not the country. The city of London is in England. That I know from school.' Some patients who are aware of their circumstantiality will describe an accompanying subjective experience that the central idea has not been communicated until all of its facets have been considered in detail. This same sort of uncertainty and doubt about adequacy of communication may be seen in obsessional disorders where it usually appears as overmeticulousness, precision, or ostentatious honesty.

Circumstantiality also occurs in epileptic dementia.

cistern puncture See *puncture, cistern.*

cisvestite (sis-ves'tīt) One who keeps to wearing clothes within the conventions of one's sex.

cisvestitism (sis-ves'ti-tiz'm) Dressing in the clothes of one's own sex, but in clothes inappropriate to one's station in life. When an adult dresses as a child, or a child as an adult, or a citizen as an army officer—such acts are called cisvestitism. See *transvestitism.*

cittosis (si-tō'sis) *Pica.* (q.v.).

claim, neurotic Horney's term for the belief held by certain patients (whom Freud called 'the exceptions') that they are in some way superior and that others should fulfill their wishes and needs.

clasp-knife phenomenon See *rigidity, decerebrate.*

class 'Any portion of a community which is marked off from the rest, not by limitations arising out of language, locality, function or specialization, but primarily by a sense of social distance [which involves also as a rule objective differences, income levels, occupational distinctions and so forth, within a society.' (McIver, R.M. *Society, Its Structure and Changes,* Smith, New York, 1931)

classical technique See *parameter.*

classification, mechanistic The reference herein is to the classification suggested by Kempf, who speaks of 'mechanistic classification of neuroses and psychoses produced by distortion of the autonomic-affective functions.' He states that 'it seems, therefore, much more practical to use a system of classifying psychopaths according to the nature of their autonomic-affective difficulties and their attitudes towards them, because this keeps the dynamic factors directly in psychiatric attention and permits of revision as the cases change.' (Kempf, E.J. *Psychopathology,* Mosby, St. Louis, 1921)

Kempf designates all psychiatric conditions as neuroses, which may be benign or pernicious. There is a further subdivision into: (1) suppression, (2) repression, (3) compensation, (4) regression, and (5) dissociation neuroses.

classification of disordered behavior (Rado) See *disordered behavior, classification of.*

classification of post-traumatic and post-encephalitic syndromes See *post-traumatic* *and post-encephalitic syndromes, classification of.*

classification of psychiatric disorders See *nomenclature, DSM-II.*

claudication, cerebral intermittent (klaw-di-kā'shun) A vasomotor phenomenon in which transient spasm and closure of the lumen of an artery occurs, temporarily depriving a part of the brain of its blood supply, producing transitory hemiplegia. This condition is usually observed in the course of cerebral arteriosclerosis.

claudication, mental Transitory spasm of the blood vessels of the brain. Some authors hold that mental claudication may be responsible for sudden fleeting episodes of mental confusion.

claustrophilia (klaws-trō-fil'ē-à) A pathological desire to be confined and enclosed within a small space—the exact opposite of *claustrophobia.* Claustrophilia is a manifestation of a strong tendency to withdraw in a somatic way and is seen in many catatonic episodes. It has been suggested that certain criminals have adopted a psychopathic reaction pattern, thus inviting incarceration, which represents a protected withdrawal from unbearable environmental tension. In these cases claustrophilia is interpreted psychoanalytically as an escape from the world and a tendency to return to the womb. A disposition to claustrophilia is often seen in asthmatics, who symptomatically withdraw into their own respiratory cavities. Such patients show a predilection for introversion and isolation, often with a strong need for solitude and silence.

claustrophobia (-fō'bē-à) (300.2) Fear of being locked or shut in; fear of enclosed places, such as tunnels, elevators, theaters, classrooms, boats, narrow streets, etc. Like all phobias, this fear may represent a feared temptation (e.g. a fear of sexual excitement which in some patients is manifested in feelings of constriction and painful vegetative sensations, or a fear of phantasies of being in the mother's womb, or a fear that one might not escape his own excitement once it has reached a certain intensity), or it may represent punishment for yielding to temptation,

or (as is most common) it may represent a combination of both the foregoing. *See anxiety-hysteria.*

claustrophoboid Lewin's term for a person afflicted with claustrophobia; *claustrophobiac* is the more correct form.

claustrum (klaws'trum) See *basal ganglia.*

clavus (klā'vus) Severe head pain, sharply defined, and typically described as feeling like a nail is being driven into the head; usually regarded as a conversion symptom.

clavus hystericus (klā'voos hē-ster'ē-koos) See *clavus.*

cleavage In the developmental process of any organism originating by sexual reproduction, this term denotes the stage in the embryological development of a fertilized egg, which follows fertilization and, in fact, is initiated by it. Reproduction occurring without prior fertilization is known as *parthenogenesis* (q.v.).

The mode of cleavage is conditioned by the character of the egg; it is of the miolecithal type (with little yolk) in the case of the human egg.

The character of the egg with respect to yolk-content imposes a particular type of cleavage, influencing the whole series of subsequent stages in the earlier development. Miolecithal eggs segment totally and produce *blastomeres* as the result of segmentation, which are equal in size. This type of cleavage is known as *holoblastic equal* segmentation or, as is true in the case of human cleavage with blastomeres of almost, but not quite, equal size, as *adequal holoblastic* segmentation.

Up to and including the 32-cell stage, the product of the cleavage of the miolecithal egg is a solid sphere of cells, called a *morula.* Subsequently a central cavity appears and the segmenting egg becomes a *blastula.* See *reproduction.*

Clérambault-Kandinsky complex See *complex, Clérambault-Kandinsky.*

client Psychiatric social workers' term for a patient.

client-centered therapy See *therapy, client-centered.*

climacophobia (klī-mak-ō-fō′bē-à) Fear of stairs.

climacteric (klī-mak-ter′ik) Of or pertaining to the so-called involutional period of life, characterized in the woman by the cessation of the menses and less definitely characterized in men.

climacterium (-ter′ē-um) A critical period of life; most commonly, in present-day usage, that period generally designated as the involutional period when the endocrine and reproductive glands undergo a decrease in functional activity. In the male, the climacterium is generally considered to fall between the ages of 50 and 65 years; in the female, between 40 and 55 years. See *psychosis, involutional; developmental levels.*

climacterium, male An ill-defined syndrome in males, in middle life, and thought of as analogous to the menopause in females. The major symptoms are usually nocturnal frequency, fatigue, indecision, flushes, decreased sexual desire, and decreased erective and intromissive potency. Various other symptoms may be present also. It is a moot question whether this syndrome constitutes a separate and distinct clinical entity, or whether it is not a symptomatic manifestation of a psychoneurotic breakdown in middle life, revolving, in the main, around psychogenic impotence and anxiety. In a very small percentage of cases, a true organic, or gonadal, endocrine etiology, secondary to testicular atrophy and degeneration, has been diagnostically validated by means of the therapeutic test with androgens and gonadotrophic assays of the urine. Heller and Meyer state: 'Whereas, in the female, the menopause is an invariable and physiologic accompaniment of the aging process, in the male, the climacteric is an infrequent and pathologic accompaniment of that same process.' (Weiss, E., and English, O.S. *Psychosomatic Medicine,* 2nd ed., Saunders Company, Philadelphia and London, 1949) See *psychosis, involutional.*

climacterium virile (klē-màk-tā′rē-oom vē-rē′le) A term introduced by Kurt Mendel in 1910 to designate the period of life when procreative power ceases in the male sex. As a rule the climacterium

in males is reached between the age of 50 to 60. There is a psychiatric state, known as involutional melancholia, taking its name from the period (climacterium, involutional) at which it occurs. See *psychosis, involutional.*

climax Peak; acme; often used synonymously with *orgasm* (q.v.).

clinical psychologist See *psychologist, clinical.*

clithrophobia (klith-rō-fō′bē-à) *Obs.* Claustrophobia.

clitoris (klī′tō-ris) A female organ, the analogue of the penis. It is about an inch and a half in length and is composed of two corpora cavernosa capped by a glans. It is part of the external genitalia.

According to psychoanalysis, the first genital belief of the child is that everyone possesses a penis. The little girl regards her clitoris as an undeveloped penis. Deutsch stresses that in the beginning of the phallic stage the clitoris possesses for the girl the same pleasure-giving capacities as the penis has for the boy. There is clitoral primacy just as there is phallic primacy.

clitoromania (klī-tor-ō-mā′nē-à) Nymphomania.

cloaca (klō-ā′kà) The cloaca is an embryological organization of the rectum and urogenital sinus. In the embryo the rectum and the urethra have a common opening. Later when the anal membrane ruptures, the rectum acquires its own orifice.

In psychoanalysis emphasis is placed upon the child's cloaca phantasy, the so-called 'cloaca theory,' that babies are expelled by way of the anal aperture. At the time that children develop this concept their interests are largely coprophilic; hence, there is nothing illogical to them in the belief that babies follow the same anatomical course as feces. Nor do children at this early age know that only females bear children; they believe both sexes can perform that function.

It is believed that to the child's imagination the abdomen is merely a receptacle where food goes and feces come out. The knowledge that the baby grows in the body of the parent is associated with the idea of eating and of expulsion. Hence *baby* and *feces* are equated.

clone, clon (klōn, klon) A group of organisms which have originated from a single individual by asexual reproduction. Since all these organisms must be endowed with the same hereditary equipment, it may generally be assumed that differences in their phenotypical appearance are due to modifying conditions of their environment. See *modification.*

clonus (klō′nus) A rhythmical series of contractions in response to the maintenance of tension in a muscle, often appearing in pyramidal lesions as a manifestation of exaggerated tendon reflexes.

clonus, ankle *n.* A clonic rhythmical tremor of the foot elicited by placing the leg in semiflexion, holding the leg with one hand, grasping the foot with the other and briskly dorsiflexing the foot one or more times. See *clonus.*

clonus, patellar (pà-tel′ēr) Patellar clonus is elicited by extending the leg, grasping the patella (knee cap) between index finger and thumb, and briskly pushing the cap down one or several times. See *clonus.*

closing-in A symptom of constructive apraxia in which the patient tends to close-in on the model when performing constructive tasks. For example, when attempting to copy from a model, the patient moves toward the model; or, in setting-up exercises, he will bring his hands ever closer to those of the demonstrator. The symptom, which becomes worse with an increase in the difficulty of the task, may be the result of a fear of empty space, but more likely it represents an attempt to perform better when there is a disturbance in the ability to make an abstract copy from a concrete model. (*Journal of Nervous and Mental Disease* 88, 1, 1938)

closure, law of and life-course A person's course of life is described by a general law of Gestalt dynamics, the *law of closure.* This means that every uncompleted whole tends to a kind of continuation which is in accordance with the inherent system of that given whole. In

the early phase of life only a few initial lines of the life patterns are apparent, and the continuation patterns may take many different directions. The more the pattern nears completion, the less variation in the pattern continuation is possible. (Angyal, A. *Foundations for a Science of Personality,* The Commonwealth Fund, Oxford University Press, New York, 1941)

clouded states, epileptic See *epileptic clouded states.*

cloudiness See *sensorium.*

clouding (of consciousness) A condition, seen most commonly in the acute and chronic brain disorders (the organic reaction types), in which there is impairment of orientation, perception, and attention.

Clouston, Sir Thomas Smith (1840 - 1915) British psychiatrist and neurologist.

clownism A popular term denoting clownish, grotesque attitudes assumed by certain psychiatric patients; seen especially in the so-called Faxenpsychosis and buffoonery psychosis and, to a lesser extent, in Ganser state.

clumsiness, arranged An unconsciously prepared inaptitude through which the neurotic prevents himself from properly performing certain acts which he secretly fears. In a general sense, arranged clumsiness is an escape mechanism by means of which the performance of certain acts is avoided through the pretence of lack of skill. In a more specific way, this expression is used in relation to the unconsciously prearranged inability to find the vaginal entrance in an attempt to perform coitus, and to other inadequacies in the performance of sexual acts.

cluster headaches See *headaches, cluster.*

cluttering Rapid, confused and jumbled speech, commonly associated with motor awkwardness and personality and behavior changes (e.g. behavior is erratic, disorganized, impulsive, untidy). Other language disorders such as delay in beginning to speak, reading disability, and spelling disability are common. Family history frequently reveals clutterers in the same family and the condition is often mistaken for tammering. Like stammering, it is more common in boys, but cluttering tends to persist throughout life and the cluttered speech is characteristic. It is hurried, even precipitate (tachylalia), and confused. 'The child starts a sentence in several different ways before he can proceed. Finally, having gotten started, he continues to mix his words and thoughts so that he ends up with a different idea from the one with which he started. Words, phrases, and even short sentences are repeated while the speaker gropes for the proper ones. . . . The position of words is confused, some being inserted too early, others too late. . . . The clutterer has great difficulty in finding the right words, and he may, consequently, get panicky while talking. Hoarseness and stammering episodes are frequent.' (Bakwin, H., and Bakwin, R.M. *Clinical Management of Behavior Disorders in Children*, Saunders, Philadelphia, 1953.)

'Probably the most famous clutterer was the Reverend W.A. Spooner, Warden of New College, Oxford, whose word confusions have come to be known as spoonerisms. Typical examples include The two great English poets, Kelly and Sheets' (for 'Shelley and Keats') and The Lord is a shoving leopard' (for 'loving shepherd').' (ibid.)

Cluttering is also sometimes called agitolalia.

CMHC Acronym for Community Mental Health Center; see *psychiatry, community.*

CMMS Columbia Mental Maturity Scale, designed primarily for use with patients with cerebral palsy.

Cn In Rorschach scoring, color naming, i.e. the naming of a chromatic color that is proffered by the patient as a complete response requiring no further elaboration. The Cn indicate superficial, labile affectivity and are produced most commonly by organic brain cases.

C.O. Abbreviation for community organization, community organizer. See *social policy planning.*

cocainism (kō-kān'ism, -kā'in-ism) Cocaine poisoning or cocaine dependency (304.4); symptoms are referable to sympathomimetic discharge (e.g. rise in blood pressure, sweating) and to central nervous system excitation (subject is more active mentally, overestimates his physical and mental capacities, may have pleasurable illusions and hallucinations which may be of the Lilliputian variety). After these effects wear off, there may be motor incoordination, moroseness and suspiciousness, and sometimes convulsions. See *dependency, drug.*

cocainomania (-ō-mā'nē-à) Morbid craving for cocaine.

coccygodynia (kok-sig-ō-din'ē-à) Pain at the tip of the coccyx.

cochlear nerve (kok'lē-ēr) See *nerve, acoustic.*

cocktail, lytic A mixture of neuroleptic drugs (usually chlorpromazine, promethazine, hydergin, atropine, etc.) used in the treatment of acute or impending delirium.

co-conscious, co-consciousness 'conscious states that we are not aware of, simply because [they are] not in the focus of attention but in the fringe of the content of consciousness. The term would also include pathologically split-off and independently acting co-conscious ideas or systems of ideas such as occur in hysteria, reaching their apogee in conscious personalities and in automatic writings.' (Prince, M. *The Unconscious,* Macmillan, New York, 1916)

In psychoanalysis the term preconscious is in general equivalent to co-conscious.

Co-conscious, preceded by *the,* is often used as a noun.

codification (kō-di-fi-kā'shun) The act of systematizing or classifying; in communications theory, the phrasing of signals in such terms as to be understandable to others.

coefficient, correlation See *correlation.*

coefficient of reality See *reality, coefficient of.*

coefficient, regression See *correlation.*

coelom (sē'lom) Celom.

coene See *cene-.*

cognition, paranormal Obtaining knowledge by means outside of the normal process of perceiving the thinking, as in extra-sensory perception. See *perception, extra-sensory.*

cognitive See *conation.*

cognitive dissonance In information theory, *incongruity* (q.v.).

cohabitation See *coitus.*

coitophobia (kō-i-tō-fō'bē-à) Fear of the sexual act.

coitus, coition (kō'i-tus, kō-ish'un) Sexual intercourse per vaginam between male and female.

In medicine *coitus, copulation, cohabitation* and *sexual intercourse* are used synonymously, though the words have a widely different meaning in their original setting.

coitus a tergo (à ter-gō) See *pederasty; coitus more ferarum.*

coitus, external Perineal coitus.

coitus, incomplete *Coitus interruptus* (q.v.).

coitus inter femora (kô'ē-toos ēn'ter fem'ô-rà) Sexual relations by the insertion of the penis between the thighs of the partner.

coitus interruptus (ēn-ter-roop'toos) Cessation of sexual intercourse before emission; synonymous with *onanism.* (Popular usage, however, has equated onanism with masturbation.)

coitus more ferarum (mō're fe-rä'room) (L. 'sexual intercourse in the manner of [wild] beasts') The carrying out of the act of heterosexual intercourse in the 'natural' position of lower animals, that is, from the rear, and usually with the female on hands and knees. The penis is inserted into the vagina; when it is inserted into the rectum, the act is called anal intercourse. This latter practice is called *pederasty* (q.v.) when the partner is a boy, and *sodomy* (q.v.) when the sexual relation is with an animal through the vagina.

Coitus more ferarum is not sodomy, but is thought of as primitive. The axis of th vagina, in this position, is in direct co respondence with the axis of the penis i erection. This might indicate the prim tive biological congruity of this positior Certain elements of tenderness, which ar dominant in the so-called 'normal,' o face-to-face, position, are, however, ex cluded in this approach. R. Sterba (*Ir troduction to the Psycho-analytic Theor of the Libido,* Nervous and Mental Dis ease Monographs No. 68, New York 1942) states: 'Pleasure satisfaction in th anal sadistic zone, or the buttocks, is indi cated by the preference of many peopl for coitus more ferarum, or "a tergo (from the rear.)'

coitus oralis (ō-rä'lēs) *Fellatio.* (q.v.).

coitus per anum (per ä'noom) *Pederast* (q.v.).

coitus, perineal (kō'i-tus, per-i-nē'al) Ex ternal coitus; Lacassagne coined the ex pression for the act of rubbing the peni against the perineal region.

coitus, psychic Ellis writes: 'Brooding o sexual images, which the theologian called *delectatio morosa,* may lead t spontaneous orgasm in either sex, even i perfectly normal persons. Hammond de scribed as a not uncommon form of "psy chic coitus," a condition in which the simple act of imagination alone, in the presence of the desired object, suffice to produce orgasm.' (Ellis, H. *Studies i the Psychology of Sex,* 3rd ed., vol. 1 Davis, Philadelphia, 1919)

coitus reservatus (kô'ē-toos re-zer-wä'toos Sexual intercourse in which the male partner delays or withholds his orgasm until the female partner has hers, or in definitely as a means of birth control.

colic, hysterical Hysterical pain felt ir the abdominal region.

collaboration As used by Sullivan, a type of interpersonal relationship in which there is not only co-operation but also sensitivity to the needs of the other person.

collateral Any person related by blood to a series of siblings, but not descended from the same line of immediate ancesors. A first cousin is the most closely related instance of a collateral.

The term also means 'indirect' when applied to this line of descent of an individual or to the form of inheritance of Mendelian factor as characteristic of recessiveness (q.v.), that is, the transmission of a trait to the descendants of the siblings of a trait-carrier.

olleague-centered consultation See *onsultant.*

ollecting, collection See *soteria; mania, ollecting.*

ollection The impulse to collect is given much prominence in psychoanalysis. 'To objects we have grown to like through use, or because of their esthetic value, we obviously have a personal relationship which is quite analogous to sexual attraction. There are many different degrees of this kind of object-love. Many persons have almost no needs in this respect, while others are completely under the domination of their passion for certain objects. . . . A passion for collection is frequently a direct surrogate for a sexual desire; and in that case a delicate symbolism is often concealed behind the choice of objects collected.' (Abraham, K. *Selected Papers,* tr. by Bryan, D. and Strachey, A., Leonard and Virginia Woolf and The Institute for Psychoanalysis, London, 1927)

It is the belief of psychoanalysts that the desire to possess and control is a reflection also of early oral and anal conditions. In the oral stage the motive is to gain, in the anal it is to hold. 'The possessiveness of anal love shows itself clearly in the collector; the objects collected are associated symbolically with excrement.' Healy, W., Bronner, A.F., and Bowers, A.M. *The Structure and Meaning of Psychoanalysis,* Knopf, New York, 1930)

'That the collecting mania is a reaction to an unconscious need, to an inner feeling of voidness concerning some particular craving, is best seen in the collections made by the insane.' (Brill, A.A., *Fundamental Conceptions of Psychoanalysis,* Allen & Unwin, London, 1921)

'All collectors are anal-erotics, and the objects collected are nearly always typical copro-symbols; thus, money, coins (apart from current ones), stamps, eggs, butterflies—these two being associated with the idea of babies—books, and even worthless things like pens, old newspapers, etc.' (Jones, E. *Papers on Psycho-Analysis,* 4th ed., Wood, Baltimore, 1938)

collective 'All those psychic contents I term collective which are peculiar not to one individual, but to many, at the same time, i.e., either to a society, a people, or to mankind in general. Such contents are the "mystical collective ideas" ("representation collectives") of the primitive described by Levy-Bruhl; they include also the *general concepts* of right, the State, religion, science, etc., current among civilized men. . . . The antithesis of *collective* is *individual.*' (Jung, C.G. *Contributions to Analytical Psychology,* tr. by Baynes, H.G. and C.F., Kegan Paul, Trench, Trubner, London, 1928)

Jung refers to two divisions of the unconscious, the *personal* and the *collective.* The former 'embraces all the acquisitions of the personal existence—hence the forgotten, the repressed, the subliminally perceived, thought and felt. But, in addition to these personal unconscious contents, there exist other contents which do not originate in personal acquisitions but in the inherited possibility of psychic functioning in general, viz. in the inherited brain-structure. These are the mythological associations—those motives and images which can spring anew in every age and clime, without historical tradition or migration. I term these contents the *collective unconscious.*' (ibid.)

collective life handicap See *handicap, collective life.*

colloidal gold reaction See *Lange's colloidal gold reaction.*

colloidoclastic diathesis (kol-oi-dō-klas′tik di-a-the-sis) See *diathesis, colloidoclastic.*

coloboma (ko-lō-bō′mà) A cleft or defect, especially of the eye; of significance in neuropsychiatry in that choroido-retinal coloboma is one of the elements of a familial syndrome which also includes dysplastic body build and mental retardation. The coloboma appears as a white patch of exposed sclera below the optic disc and causes a scotoma in that region.

colony, Gheel See *Gheel.*

Columbia Mental Maturity Scale See *CMMS*.

coma The profoundest degree of stupor in which all consciousness is lost and there is no voluntary activity of any kind. Among the various conditions which may produce coma the most common are: encephalitis, cerebral hemorrhage, cerebral thrombosis, cerebral embolism, subarachnoid hemorrhage, intracranial tumor, head injury, post-epileptic coma, diabetic coma, hypoglycemic coma, hypertensive encephalopathy, uremic coma, acute alcoholism, intoxication with opiates or other sedatives, hypothalamic lesions, congestive attacks of general paralysis, hysterical trance, and catatonic stupor.

coma somnolentium (kō′ma sôm-nô-len′tē-oom) (L. 'coma of the somnolent') *Cataphora* (q.v.).

coma-vigil Coma in which the eyes remain open. Coma-vigil occurs in certain acute brain syndromes associated with systemic infection (the infective-exhaustive psychoses, also known as acute toxic encephalopathy, acute toxic encephalitis or acute serous encephalitis). See *mutism, akinetic.*

combat exhaustion Same as *combat fatigue.* See *shellshock.*

combination In genetics, this term refers to the hereditary variations which represent the effect of *hybridization* and which occur in crossbred products originating from the union between two individuals with unlike hereditary equipment. The formation of new hereditary combinations which account for the majority of genetic differences among animals and plants and also explain why hybrids do not breed true, takes place in accordance with the *Mendelian law,* which governs the reassortment of the different genetic factors involved in a given cross (see *variation*).

Pearson has used this term to refer to what he considers the earliest mechanism of learning: the unification of sensory impressions from the outside with perceptions arising from instinctual (internal) stimuli.

combined degeneration of the spinal cord See *sclerosis, posterolateral.*

cometophobia (kom-e-tō-fō′bē-à) Fear o comets.

comfort-dream See *dream, convenience*

comic Freud says: 'The comic is conten with only two persons, one who finds th comical, and one in whom it is found The third person to whom the comica may be imparted reinforces the comi process, but adds nothing new to it.' H adds that, because of the many difficultie in understanding the comic, 'we ma therefore expect that we shall lear nothing about the nature of the comi other than that which we have alread become aware of in wit.' (Freud, S. *Th Basic Writings of Sigmund Freud,* tr. b Brill, A.A., Random House, New York 1938)

command, posthypnotic See *suggestion posthypnotic.*

commission, lunacy See *lunacy commis sion.*

commissure (kom′i-shêr) Transverse o commissural fibers; those portions of th white substance of the cerebral hemis pheres made up of medullated nerv fibers connecting the two hemispheres The commissural fibers are to be dis tinguished from the two other types o myelinated nerve fibers found in th white matter: *projection fibers,* whicl connect the cerebral cortex with lowe portions of the brain and spinal cord and *association fibers,* which connec different portions of the same hemisphere

commitment Depriving a person of hi liberty by putting him under the guard ianship of another (whether menta hospital, prison, or other institution, o in the custody of a probation officer). I psychiatry, commitment is a proces whereby one or more doctors explain t a court why a patient's mental problem necessitate forfeiture of his freedom Such explanation is usually in the form o a certificate signed by the examinin physician(s), and it is the process of com pleting this certificate that is properl labelled *certification.* In practice, how ever, the terms commitment and certifi cation are interchangeable.

communication Transmission of emotions

ttitudes, ideas, and acts from one person
) another. Through communication
habits of doing, thinking, and feeling
are transmitted) from the older to the
younger. . . . Society . . . may fairly be
said to exist *in* transmission, *in* communi-
ation.' (Dewey, J. *Democracy and Edu-
ation*, Macmillan, New York, 1916)

The distinction is made between the
rimary techniques of communication
ommon to all men, as language, gesture,
he imitation of overt behavior and social
uggestion, and the *secondary* techniques
vhich facilitate communication, as writ-
ig, symbolic systems including stop-and-
o lights, bugle-calls and other signals,
nd physical conditions allowing for com-
nunication, including the railroad, the
teamship, the telegraph, the telephone,
he motion picture, the radio, and the
irplane. (Sapir, E. 'Communication,'
Incyclopaedia of the Social Sciences, vol.
:, Macmillan, New York, 1931, pp. 78 -
0.)

ommunication, physiognomonic Non-
verbal communication, such as by ges-
ure, mime, facial expression, and/or any
umber of minimal cues by which mean-
ng is transmitted from one organism to
another.

ommunication, privileged Information
vhich a patient discloses to his physician
vhile the latter is attending him in a
professional capacity; such information is
ermed privileged because in some states
and according to ethical precepts of the
nedical profession the physician is not
allowed to divulge such information without the patient's consent. This is, in other
words, the patient's privilege of silence
n regard to confidential matters on the
part of his physician.

communication unit The essential components of transmission of information
from one person to another; these components are the source (the person sending
the message), the transmitter (the motor
apparatus through which the message
will be expressed), and the destination
(the person to whom the message is sent,
who picks up the message through his
receiver, or sensory apparatus).

communion, magical According to psychoanalytic theory, in unconscious thinking, 'by incorporating objects one becomes

united with them.' That is, to eat something or be eaten by someone is an unconscious way of achieving union with
that object. In countless experiences of
everyday living one shares ideas, emotions, activities with others. Some of these
experiences of sharing with others present
as their unconscious significance, psychoanalytically, the type of mystical or magical union described above. This magical
communion of 'becoming the same substance' takes place when the same food
is jointly eaten or the respective bloods
of the individuals involved are mixed.
The latter type of communion is seen in
many tribal rites of friendship, and, symbolically, in our custom of handshaking.
The magical union mediated through
food is seen not only in the old idea that
friendship and hospitality are associated
with breaking bread together, but also
and particularly in the well-known religious rites of the Eucharist, the bread
and wine (distributed to the parishioners)
symbolizing, as in the Last Supper,
Christ's body and blood. (Fenichel, O.
The Psychoanalytic Theory of Neurosis,
Norton, New York, 1945)

community 'A group (of persons) occupying a territorial area (and) sharing a
whole set of interests wide enough and
complete enough to include their lives.'
(McIver, R.M. *Society, Its Structure and
Changes*, Smith, New York, 1931) Comprised under the term community are not
only hamlets, villages, towns, cities, and
local areas within the city, but also metro-
politan regions, states, nations, and the
world. In the literature two different aspects of the community are stressed 1)
as structure in terms of an 'aggregation of
individuals residing in a specified area or
locality, characterized by greater or lesser
mutual interdependence and maintaining
primary institutions, such as the church
and the school, and 2) in terms of consensus, socialization and solidarity.' (Lin-
derman, E.C. 'Community as Process,'
Encyclopaedia of the Social Sciences, vol.
1, Macmillan, New York, 1931, pp. 102 -
5.)

community-feeling The sense of relationship between the individual and the community. Adler states that out of commu-
nity-feelings 'are developed tenderness,
love of neighbour, friendship and love,
the desire for power unfolding itself in a

veiled manner and seeking secretly to push its way along the path of group consciousness.' (Adler, A. *The Practice and Theory of Individual Psychology*, tr. by Radin, P., Kegan Paul, Trench, Trubner, London, 1924)

Community Mental Health Center See *psychiatry, community.*

community organization See *social policy planning.*

community, therapeutic A psychiatric or mental hospital which emphasizes the importance of socioenvironmental and interpersonal influences in the therapy, management, resocialization and rehabilitation of the long-term patient. Self-control, dignity, and trust are employed rather than excessive imposed controls, restrictions, regimentation, and meaningless rituals. 'It seeks continually to solve its problems in terms of interpersonal relations, by helping the patient to identify himself with a social group and through identification modify his social attitudes and behavior because of his growing awareness of his role in relationship to other people.' (Wilmer, H.A. 'Toward a Definition of the Community,' *American Journal of Psychiatry 114:* 824-33, 1958.)

companion, imaginary It has often been observed that a child will create an imaginary companion for himself and will endow this product of phantasy with the qualities of reality. The imaginary companion will have a name, a definite appearance and personality—even an imaginary family created for it, and so on.
   Imaginary companions are created mostly by only children, or by children whose siblings are much older, or who for any reason are without real playmates. The imaginary companion thus fulfills the child's need for intimate companionship and friendship and serves an important function in his emotional life. For the imaginary companion is freely taken into confidences from which these are distinctly barred and becomes 'someone to tell its troubles to' and 'to share its secret pleasures with.' In general, the imaginary companion is so created by the child that it has everything the child desires but lacks. The play *Harvey* presents an amusing and not dissimilar instance of this imagery, a huge white rabbit created

as an imaginary companion. Though i is an animal and the imaginary crea tion of an adult, its origin and func tion are much the same as those of th imaginary companions of children.

compartmentalization Isolation; keepin separate parts of one's personality whicl should be kept together; psychic fragmen tation.

compensation From the standpoint o analytical psychology Jung defines *com pensation* 'as a general functional adjust ment, an inherent self-regulation of th psychic apparatus. In this sense, I regare the activity of the unconscious as a com pensation to the onesidedness of the gen eral attitude produced by the functior of consciousness.' He adds that 'in th normal condition the compensation i unconscious, i.e., it performs an uncon scious regulation of conscious activity. Ir the neurotic state the unconscious appear in such strong contrast to the consciou: that compensation is disturbed. The ain of analytical therapy, therefore, is t make the unconscious contents consciou: in order that compensation may be rees tablished.' (Jung, C.G. *Psychologica Types*, tr. by Baynes, H.G., Harcourt Brace, New York and London, 1923)

compensation, autonomic From the stand point of Kempf's psychopathology '*com pensation* is one of the most fundamenta attributes of living tissue and occurs par ticularly where there exists some sort o painful irritation or the tendency of the au tonomic-affective apparatus to be force into the *fear state*. The cause of the fea state may be due to pain from the diseas or injury of some organ (as the heart lung, kidney, skeleton, skin) or the poten tial danger of injury, failure, persecution prosecution, loss of social esteem or prop erty, etc. . . . If the cause of *fear* is a segmental compulsion within ourselves ar attempt to *eliminate* it, or, if regarded a: a social inferiority, an attempt to *compen sate* by some estimable work is reflexly initiated.' (Kempf, E.J. *Psychopathology* Mosby, St. Louis, 1921)

compensation-ideal This term is used by Adler to indicate a substitution in drean or phantasy of some superior image fo an inferior one.
   Adler says: 'Napoleon, Jesus, Jeanne

'Arc, the Virgin, as well as the Kaiser, father, uncle, mother, brother, etc. are frequent *compensation-ideals* of the intensified lust for superiority and represent at the same time, the directive and emotionally-steeped preparations of the psychic life of the neurotic.' (Adler, A. *The Neurotic Constitution*, tr. by Glueck, B. and Lind, J.E. Moffat, Yard, New York, 1917)

compensation-neurosis See *neurosis, compensation.*

competence, mental See *incompetence.*

competition The struggle for existence and for a livelihood. Competition may be either unconscious or conscious; as it becomes self-conscious it tends to pass over into social conflict. 'Competition is a term . . . which associates the fact of a struggle with the function of order. . . . It is by competition . . . that the fittest survive: individuals, instruments and institutions of different capacities are given places in a going society and an industrial system . . . is adapted to new conditions. Competition is at once a process of selection, an economic organization and an agency of social development.' (Hamilton, Walton, 'Competition,' *Encyclopaedia of the Social Sciences*, vol. 4, Macmillan, New York, 1931, pp. 141-2)

complacency, principle of W.B. Cannon formulated the thesis that 'instincts' and 'drives' are in a sense attempts on the part of the organism to maintain its optimal body economy (homeostasis). R.B. Raup called it the principle of complacency, thereby indicating that every organism is a physiological system which tends to preserve its stationary condition or to restore the stationary condition as soon as it is disturbed by any variation occurring within or outside the organism. In a sense all needs and desires are behavior patterns, such as withdrawal, or attack, or flight, in direct or indirect consequence of this general tendency to keep a physiological condition constant.

complaint habit *Hypochondriasis* (q.v.).

complementarity A state of harmony or balance between the emotional needs of the interacting members of a group, or the degree to which such a balance

has been achieved. N.W. Ackerman *(The Psychodynamics of Family Life,* New York, Basic Books, 1958) describes a *minus form* of complementarity in family role relations that is limited to neutralization of the disintegrating effects of conflict and anxiety. The *plus form,* in addition to such neutralization, promotes further growth and creative development in the family unit and in the individual members of the unit.

complementarity, reciprocal In sociology, the hypothesis of reciprocal complementarity postulates that moral and social codes, rather than being arbitrary conventionalities which are antagonistic to man's emotional drives, are an intrinsic factor in human functioning and that homeostasis exists in relation to the social environment fully as much as it exists in relation to the internal milieu.

complementary Mutually supplying each other's lack; used most often to refer to a type of relationship within a family, or between husband and wife. 'In a *complementary* relationship, behavior of one sort by one partner—such as dominance—is met by behavior of another sort, in this case submission, by the spouse. In a *symmetrical* relationship, both partners exchange the same kind of behavior—both are giving, or both are domineering, for example. In contemporary America, a husband often has to deal with a wife who demands a symmetrical relationship on the one hand, and insists that she be treated as an equal, but at the same time demands that her husband dominate her in a complementary relationship. Such an incompatibility of messages constitutes paradoxical communication, or what has been termed by Bateson, Jackson, and their co-workers, a "double bind."' (Campbell, R. J. 'Sexual Adjustment in Marriage' in *Marriage: A Psychological and Moral Approach,* edited by W. Bier, Fordham University Press, New York, 1964).

complex A group of repressed ideas interlinked into a complex whole, which besets the individual, impelling him to think, feel, and perhaps act after a habitual pattern. Jung, who introduced the term *complex* to psychiatry, describes it as the grouping 'of psychic elements about emotionally-toned contents.' He adds that it 'consists of a nuclear element and a great number of secondarily constellated associations.' Apparently the contents of a complex may be in consciousness or in the unconscious. It is believed that the nuclear component is always in the unconscious. Jones defines a complex as 'a group of emotionally invested ideas partially or entirely repressed.' (Jones, E. *Papers on Psycho-Analysis*, 4th ed., Wood, Baltimore, 1938)

In general it may be said that fundamental psychic conflicts, usually those derived during the stages of infantile sexuality, may give rise to a complex. Thus, one speaks of the Oedipus, Electra and castration complexes.

complex, active castration The ideas centered around the fear of losing the penis and the emotions linked with these ideas. The passive castration complex is the idea that the penis has already been lost and/or the wish to lose the penis.

complex, anti-Oedipus Any attitude adopted in an attempt to overcome the Oedipal conflict.

complex, apprentice The time in a boy's life when he aims to be like his father and will act as a pupil or apprentice: in psychoanalytic terms, will have a penis like his father. To achieve this, he is submissive, passive, with the idea or phantasy that by this method, in the future, he will be prepared to be masculine and active, like his father.

Sometimes this attitude toward the father and father figures in the individual's environment is exaggerated and persists as the individual matures. According to Fenichel, such is the case in 'pregenitally oriented compulsive characters' and in some homosexuals. In these individuals there are 'mobilized (the aforementioned) pregenital passive aims toward the father . . . connected with the penis.' (Fenichel, O. *The Psychoanalytic Theory of Neurosis*, Norton, New York, 1945)

complex, Atreus See *complex, Medea.*

complex, authority A group of emotionally invested ideas centering around the concept of authority. These emotions are entirely or partly repressed together with the original ideas concerning authority to which they are attached. If a person's earliest experiences with authority have been sufficiently painful, it is likely that both the experiences and the associated affects have undergone repression. The material thus repressed constitutes a complex and is termed an authority complex. The person will always react to authority just as he did originally, although he will not be aware of this fact. Unconsciously overdetermined reactions to authority either in the direction of rebellion against it or in submission to it are common in neurotic patients.

complex, autonomous 'All those psychic formations which at first are developed quite unconsciously, and only from the moment when they attain threshold-value are able to break through into consciousness. The association which they then make with consciousness has not the importance of an assimilation, but rather of a perception; which means to say, that the autonomous complex, although certainly perceived, cannot be subjected to conscious control, whether in the form of inhibition or of voluntary reproduction. The autonomy of the complex reveals itself in the fact that it appears or vanishes when and in such guise as accords with its own intrinsic tendency; it is independent of the option of consciousness.' (Jung, C.G. *Contributions to Analytical Psychology*, tr. by Baynes, H.G. and C.F., Kegan Paul, Trench, Trubner, London, 1928)

complex, breast Substitution of the possessed penis for the mother's breast which has been denied or withheld from the boy. The breast complex may be expressed in the phantasy of vagina dentata (a vagina with teeth), where the vagina represents the mouth which originally wanted to tear off the mother's breast. The complex may also be expressed in breast envy, which in turn may be expressed in that type of overt homosexuality in which the penis of the subject and/or his partner unconsciously represents the breast.

complex, brother See *complex, Cain.*

complex, Cain An expression synonymous with *brother complex;* rivalry, competition, aggression, or destructive impulses directed against a brother.

complex, castration See *castration.*

omplex, chronological See *complex, ubject.*

omplex, Clérambault-Kandinsky (klä'-äN-bô kän-dēn'ski) (Gatian G. de Clérambault, 1872-1934, French psychiatrist.) A psychotic syndrome which may e associated with any clinical picture in which the patient feels that his mind is ontrolled by another person or by an utside power.

omplex, Clytemnestra This refers to the wife who kills her husband so that she may possess one of his male relatives.

omplex, dart and dome The spike and wave type of electroencephalographic racing seen in petit mal epilepsy. See *pilepsy.*

omplex, Demosthenes The neurotic need o achieve mastery over inferiority feelngs through words and language in the process of speaking.

omplex, Diana The wish of a female to be a male.

omplex, Electra (Electra, the daughter of Agamemnon, King of Mycenae, induced her brother Orestes, just returned after long years of self-exile, to wreak on their mother Clytemnestra and her former paramour, and new husband, the effeminate Aegisthus, vengeance for having together butchered Agamemnon in his bathtub. The dark broodings over the dismal fate of her beloved hero-father possessed the wedlock-scorning Electra ill death, a tragic image immortalized for posterity by the great Greek dramatists Aeschylus, Sophocles, and Euripides.) *Obs.* The female Oedipus complex.

complex, emotional See *memory, automatic,* for viewpoint of Morton Prince.

complex, Eshmun Castration complex. Here apparently Eshmun, the beautiful youth, castrates himself to escape the incestuous situation, and thereafter his activities become associated with a more neutral or perhaps feminine type function. . . .' (Lewis, N.D.C., 'The Psychology of the Castration Reaction,' *Psychoanalytic Review 15:* 174, 1928)

complex, femininity Psychoanalysts believe that, in the infantile life of the boy, there is a phase equivalent to the 'penis' phase in the little girl. Girls believe that they once possessed a phallus just like the one that boys have, but through some misdeed on their part it was taken from them. The male child develops the same fear of frustration (castration phantasy), which Klein calls a *femininity complex.* In essence it is the inferiority complex of Adler. The boy thinks that the mother is the castrator. In order to save his phallus from the fate suffered by girls he identifies himself with his mother and wishes for a vagina and breasts. There is thus 'vaginal envy' in boys as there is 'penis envy' in girls. At the same time there is a dread on his part against the feminine role which castration would bring about. The dread may appear as its opposite, aggression. 'A tendency to excess in the direction of aggression which very frequently occurs has its source in the femininity-complex.' (Klein, M. *The Psycho-Analysis of Children,* tr. by Strachey, A., Norton, New York, 1932)

complex, flatus The infant's interest in the production of intestinal gas.

complex, function This term, used principally by Jung, denotes the purpose or function of a psychic structure. 'Thus, the persona is a function-complex which has come into existence for reasons of adaptation or necessary convenience, but by no means is it identical with individuality. The function-complex of the persona is exclusively concerned with the relation to the object.' (Jung, C.G. *Psychological Types,* tr. by Baynes, H.G., Harcourt, Brace, New York and London, 1923)

complex, grandfather The desire to become the parent of one's own parents. Some children 'may even entertain the belief that just in proportion as they grow bigger, so will their parents grow smaller, till in time the present position of affairs will be completely reversed. This curious construction of the imagination, which is probably one of the sources of the belief in re-incarnation, is evidently closely connected with incestuous wishes, since it is an exaggerated form of the commoner desire to be one's own father.' (Jones, E. *Papers on Psycho-Analysis,* 4th ed., Wood, Baltimore, 1938)

complex, Griselda (Griselda, or Griselidis, was a paragon of womanly purity, virtue, and endless patience, widely celebrated in medieval romances.) The name given by Putnam to the father's complex in regard to his daughter. In the father-daughter complex, or the Griselda complex as Putnam called it, the father unconsciously grudges giving up his daughter to another man, not wishing to part with her himself. According to Jones, parental complexes are ultimately derived from infantile ones of the Oedipus type, the father's complex in regard to his daughter being a later development and manifestation of his own original Oedipus complex for his mother. Contemplation of the marriage of his daughter—the future mother—reactivates the older Oedipal yearning for his own mother. The father's reluctance to give up his daughter to another man is often thinly disguised under the pretext of altruistic solicitude for the daughter's welfare. (Jones, E. *Hamlet and Oedipus,* Norton, New York, 1949)

complex, heir of the Oedipus See *heir of the Oedipus complex.*

complex, Heracles The hatred of a father for his children.

complex, incest See *incest.*

complex, inferiority See *inferiority; inferiority, feeling of.*

complex, Jocasta The term proposed by Raymond de Saussure (*Internationale Zeitschrift fur Psychoanalyse VI,* No. 2, 118 - 22, 1920) for the morbid attachment of a mother for her own son—from the marriage of Jocasta to her son Oedipus (see *Oedipus complex*). The Jocasta complex represents a type of perverted mother love and has 'various degrees of intensity—from the maternal instinct slightly deformed to a frank sexual attachment in which both physical and psychic satisfaction is found.'

complex, masculinity Rebellion against castration in the girl, leading to masculine attitudes and behavior. This term is used by Freudian psychoanalysts in much the same way that Adler uses *masculine attitude in female neurotics* (q.v.).

complex, Medea The hatred and/or hom-icidal wishes of the mother toward he child. The death-wishes against the of spring are usually motivated uncor sciously by a desire for revenge again: the father. Fritz Wittels has used the ter in a more limited way to indicate mother's death-wish against her daughte: Strictly speaking, this is not correct, fc the Medea of Euripides had only son. The term Atreus complex has been sug gested for a father's death-wishes again: his offspring. The Medea complex i probably the clue to an explanation c the baseless accusation of ritual murde practiced by the Jews on Christian chi dren. The accusation likely represents projection of the accuser's death-wishe against his own children. The Mede complex may lead to dyspareunia, pre vention and interruption of pregnancy failure of breast feeding, and other source of marital discord. (Stern, E.S. 'Th Medea Complex,' *Journal of Mental Sc ence,* 321, 1948)

complex, not-knowing The phrase *no knowing* is sometimes referred to as complex. A child's inferiority may b considerably re-enforced when he is le to believe that there are many thing about which he should not know. Wher for instance, adults carry on conversation with an air of secrecy and mystery, th child's curiosity impulse is aroused, bu because it cannot know what the adult are talking about it develops a 'not-know ing' complex, the influences of which ma modify the child's later personality growt] to a great extent.

complex, nuclear In psychoanalysis, syn onymous with Oedipus complex.

complex, obscenity-purity T. Schroede says: 'I have found that the zeal of th Puritan or religious denunciation of an) particular manifestation of sex, is an exac measure of the intensity of its lure fo such a person.' *(Encyclopaedia Sexualis.*

complex, Oedipus According to Greel mythology, Oedipus was a son of Laius King of Thebes, and Jocasta, his wife The King learned from an oracle tha he was fated to be killed by his son When a boy was born, the King gave him (with a spike driven through hi: feet) to a shepherd to leave him on Mt Kithaeron to die. However, the compas onate shepherd gave the infant to the hildless King of Corinth, Polybus. When edipus reached the age of puberty and n oracle told him that he would kill his ather and form an incestuous union with is mother, he decided not to return to orinth to his alleged father. In his jourey he met Laius, whom he slew in a uarrel. When Oedipus arrived at Thebes he Sphinx presented a riddle for soluon. Oedipus solved the riddle and the hebans in gratitude gave him Jocasta s wife. When finally he discovered the elationship between him and his wife he linded himself, while Jocasta hanged erself. Oedipus wandered away, accomanied by his daughter, Antigone, being inally destroyed by the avenging deities, he Eumenides. The principles of the edipus situation are regarded by psychonalysts as characteristic of all persons. uring the phase of late infancy, the child hifts a quantum of energy into sexual nterests in the parents. Normally the oy becomes chiefly attached to his nother, the girl to her father. The soluion of the struggle determines the charcter of the child's later reactions. During he latency period the Oedipus complex s normally relinquished in favor of extraparental activities and interests. With he advent of puberty the original, infanile Oedipus situation is again aroused, nd is normally dissolved by the centering f interests in others.

However, the average psychiatric paient never successfully manages his Oedius complex. Schizophrenia serves as an xcellent example. A schizophrenic paient believed implicitly that he was not he child of his parents, that his mother vas his wife and that his brothers and isters were his children; he maintained hat his father did not exist. The same atient also insisted that he was blind; n other occasions he spoke of having een castrated. The schizophrenic patient elives the Sophoclean tragedy often with ninute precision, even to the point of laiming royal birth.

The same theme is common to psychoneurotic patients, but it is often highly ymbolized as a fear, a compulsion, or a conversion phenomenon.

Freud is responsible for the introducion of the Oedipus concept into psychiary. 'One says rightly that the Oedipus complex is the nuclear concept of the neuroses, that it represents the essential

part in the content of the neuroses. It is the culminating point of infantile sexuality, which through its after-effects decisively influences the sexuality of the adult.' (Freud, S. *Three Contributions to the Theory of Sex,* 4th ed., tr. by Brill, A.A., Nervous and Mental Disease Publishing Company, New York and Washington, 1930)

complex, Oedipus, passing of The passing of the complex is considered by many psychoanalysts as finally accomplished during the first half of the adolescent period with the energy formerly given to the complex now distributed upon objects apparently unrelated to the parents. In psychiatric conditions, however, there is never a complete dissolution; indeed, it is usually very incomplete.

According to Freud the immediate determinant (in the boy) for the dissolution of the Oedipus complex is the castration complex which 'literally smashes to pieces the Oedipus complex.' *(The Passing of the Oedipus Complex)* It is also called *dissolution of Oedipus complex.*

complex, Orestes (Orestes, the son of the Mycenaean King Agamemnon, who killed his own mother Clytemnestra and her paramour Aegisthus for murdering her husband Agamemnon.) The psychiatric term proposed for a son's killing, or desire to kill, his own mother. Frederick Wertham believes this is a universal complex, like the Oedipus complex. The majority of psychoanalysts disagree with this view and feel, instead, that when it occurs the Orestes complex is an outgrowth of the Oedipus complex and is a reaction by the male child to rejection or frustration by the Oedipal love-object, the mother. *(Psychoanalytic Quarterly 12, 582-3, 1943)*

complex, parental See *complex, Oedipus.*

complex, passive castration See *complex, active castration.*

complex, perceptual It is one of the characteristics of the mentality of primitive peoples and of schizophrenic patients that they think in terms of percepts or images. 'The distortions and condensations of schizophrenics can be explained in an analogous manner. Their root is in the mode of thinking in perceptual complexes, which, in schizophrenics, has to a greater or lesser extent supplanted logical and rational thinking.' (Storch, A. *The Primitive Archaic Forms in Schizophrenia*, tr. by Willard, C., Nervous & Mental Disease Publishing Company, New York and Washington, 1924)

complex, Phaedra This refers to the mother who is in love with her son.

complex, Polycrates *Polycratism* (q.v.).

complex, power 'The total complex of all those ideas and strivings whose tendency it is to range the ego above other influences, thus subordinating all such influences to the ego, quite irrespective of whether they have their source in men and objective conditions, or spring from one's own subjective impulses, feelings, and thoughts.' (Jung, C.G. *Psychological Types*, tr. by Baynes, H.G., Harcourt, Brace, New York and London, 1923)

complex, Pygmalion *Pygmalionism* (q.v.).

complex, quality 'In schizophrenia, instead of a content of consciousness composed of separate parts organized in a definite structure, we find in the mind of the patient absolutely undifferentiated, diffuse, total expressions, resembling emotions rather than ideas, often only vague fragments of ideas, echoes, or mere reverberations of some content or another not in itself present in consciousness at all.' (Storch, A. *The Primitive Archaic Forms in Schizophrenia*, tr. by Willard, C., Nervous & Mental Disease Publishing Company, New York and Washington, 1924) Such undifferentiated, primitive groupings of psychic material Storch calls 'quality complexes.'

complex, Quasimodo Emotional conflict, personality disorder, or social maladaptation developing as a result of disfigurement or deformity.

complex, self-reference While discussing the processes involved in the forgetting of names, Freud says that the memory loss protects the individual against some unpleasant' narcissitic trauma; if the name were recalled it would bring to consciousness the unpleasant affect associated with it. Freud calls the condition a self-reference complex.

complex, small penis While speaking o the dread of castration, Jones says: 'Th whole group of ideas is strongest in me with a "small penis" complex, often ac companied by impotence, and it is wit them that one gets the clearest insight int the genesis. What such a man is reall ashamed of is not that his penis is "small, but the reason *why* it is "small."' (Jone: E. *Papers on Psycho-Analysis*, 4th ed Woold, Baltimore, 1938)

complex, spike and wave The dart an dome type of electroencephalographi tracing seen in petit mal epilepsy. Se *epilepsy.*

complex, subject A systematized comple made up of 'subjects or departments c human experience.'
A systematized complex that embrace 'the experiences of certain epochs of ou lives rather than the subject material in cluded in them' is called a *chronologica. complex* or *chronological system.*
A systematized complex constitutin 'certain dispositions toward views of lif which represent natural inclinations, d sires, and modes of activity, which for on reason or another, we tend to suppress c are unable to give full play to, is called *disposition* or *mood* system.' (Prince, M *The Unconscious*, Macmillan, New York 1916)

complex, symptom *Syndrome.* 'Syndrome are complexes of symptoms that belon together genetically.' (Bleuler, E. *Test book of Psychiatry*, tr. by Brill A.A., Mac millan, New York, 1930)

complex, systematized Morton Princ says: 'In contrast with the limited grou of fixed ideas, organized with one or mor emotions (i.e., instincts) I have been de scribing, are the large *systems* of com plexes or associated experiences whicl become organized and fairly distinctly dif ferentiated in the course of the develop ment of everyone's personality. In many at least, of these systems there will b found a predominant emotion and certai instinctive tendencies, and a predomina feeling tone—of pleasure or pain, of exal tation or depression, etc. It is quite possi ble that careful investigation would dis close that it is this conflicting affectiv force which is responsible for the differen tiation of one system from another wit opposing affects and tendencies. . . . among such systems may here be mentioned those which are related to certain subjects or departments of human experience, or are related to *time*, or to certain dispositions of *moods* of the individual. The first may be called *subject* systems, the second *chronological* systems, and the last *mood* systems.' (Prince, M. *The Unconscious*, Macmillan, New York, 1916)

ompliance Self-effacing submission or obedience to the overt and implied demands of others; when used in clinical psychiatry the term implies a neurotic degree of over-submissiveness. It is seen most commonly as a part of the obsessive-compulsive character's defensive system.

ompliance, motor A type of response noted in many schizophrenic children, in whom light palm contact is enough to make them turn or change position. Such children show marked dependence on contact with others—they melt into the lap of the examiner and show many disturbances in motility. See *schizophrenia, childhood.*

ompliance, somatic The degree to which the individual's organic structure coincides with his psychological mechanism in the symptomatic expression of his pathological defenses. In conversion symptoms, for instance, the entire cathexis of the objectionable impulses is condensed into a definite physical function. The ability of the affected function to adsorb this cathexis is its somatic compliance. The function may be chosen because the organ in question presents a locus minoris resistentiae (see *inferiority, organ*), or because the erogeneity of the afflicted part corresponds to the unconscious phantasies seeking expression (as in the case of a person with oral fixations who, when symptoms are developed, will show primarily oral symptoms), or because of the situation in which the decisive repression occurred (the organ or function under highest tension at the decisive moment is likely to become the seat of disturbance), or because of the organ's ability to symbolize the unconscious drive in question (thus convex organs such as the hand, nose, and breasts may symbolize the penis and represent masculine wishes).

component-instinct *Part-instinct* (q.v.);

component impulse. See *impulse, component.*

compos mentis (kom'pos men'tis) L. 'sound of mind.'

composition See *dream, agreement in.*

comprehension Understanding, especially as opposed to mere apprehending or cognition. In examining the sensorium, mental grasp, and capacity of a patient, the examiner often presents the subject with a *comprehension test,* which commonly consists of having the patient read or listen to a narrative paragraph and then asking him questions to determine how much he grasped of the significance of the story.

compression In *The Interpretation of Dreams,* Freud uses this term interchangeably with *condensation* (q.v.).

compression, cerebral This term is used to refer to any degree of head injury (concussion, brain contusion, or cerebral laceration) which is followed by intracranial hemorrhage. The latter may be subdural (which is twice as common) or extradural. Acute subdural hemorrhage is usually the result of severe cerebral laceration; extradural hemorrhage is usually due to laceration of the middle meningeal artery by fractured bone, and in this case the posterior branches of the artery are more frequently involved than the anterior.

compromise-distortion In contradistinction to *compromise-formation* as occurring in normal and neurotic development, Freud used the term *compromise-distortion* to describe an analogous process in a psychosis. Owing to a compromise between the resistance of the ego and the strength of the idea under repression the return of the repressed becomes distorted into a delusion or a hallucination. 'A circumstance quite peculiar to paranoia . . . is that the repressed reproaches return as thoughts spoken aloud. They must thereby suffer a two-fold distortion, first, through a censorship, which leads to their substitution by other associated ideas or to a disguise by indefinite kinds of expressions, and secondly, through their relation to current experiences which are merely analogous to the original.' (Freud, S. *Collected Papers,* vol. 1, tr. by Riviere, J., Leonard and Virginia Woolf and The Institute of Psychoanalysis, London, 1924-25)

compromise-formation In psychoanalysis, a substitutive idea or act representing a repressed conflict. Freud held that as a consequence of the ego's contacts with reality, four typical danger situations arise, each derived from some stage of infantile sexuality. They are (1) danger of separation, i.e. loss of the love object; (2) danger of the loss of love; (3) danger of castration; and (4) danger of the loss of superego approval, i.e. guilt. See *anxiety.*

All psychogenic symptoms are compromises, for they arise on the basis of repressed material and thus serve to give release to the pressure or tension resident in the repressed complex.

compulsion A repetitive, stereotyped, and often trivial motor action, the need for whose performance insistently forces itself into consciousness even though the subject does not wish to perform the act. Failure to perform the act generates increasing anxiety, while completion of the act gives at least temporary surcease of tension. Compulsions are obsessions in action and, like the latter, are ego-alien and therefore always resisted. See *obsession.*

compulsion, external Outside cultural rules to which the child reacts with manifestations of defiance. (Stekel, W. *Compulsion and Doubt,* Liveright, New York, 1949)

compulsion, internal (**organ**) The child's primitive urge to obtain pleasure through the satisfaction of his organic functions.

compulsion, masked A mental mechanism by which the neurotic individual hides his real obsessive idea behind a compulsion. This compulsion acts only as a disguise (= mask) for the obsessive idea. Such is the case of the patient who has the compulsion of constantly complaining of pain when, in reality, what he is trying to do is to avoid the knowledge of the real cause of his trouble, which is produced by the existence of obsessive ideas. The patient complains of pain instead of obsessions because in this way he can continue with these same obsessions. 'It is

diagnostically important that the usual sedatives are always ineffective in these cases or, if forced upon the patient, may lead to narcoto-mania.' (Stekel, W. *Compulsion and Doubt,* Liveright, New York, 1949)

compulsion, repetition See *repetition-compulsion.*

compulsion, thinking See *brooding.*

compulsive-obsessive psychoneurosis See *obsessive-compulsive psychoneurosis.*

compulsive personality See *personality trait disturbance; defense, character.*

conarium (kō-nā′ri-um) The point of contact of mind and body in Cartesian philosophy. The basic tenet of this philosophy was that the human mind is a thinking substance in intimate association with the body. The Cartesian conarium was renamed the *id* by Freud, who regarded it as the place in which the instincts in both their organic and their psychic manifestations are localized and from which they spread to diverse sections of the body and the mind. The Cartesian philosophy is to a large extent dualistic, but holds that mind and body are in intimate contact with each other. Freud's *id,* however, is not perceived from a dualistic point of view. (Hinsie, L.E. *Understandable Psychiatry,* Macmillan, New York 1948)

conation (kō-nā′shun) Striving, inclination, tendency to do actively or purposively. Many psychologists distinguish between three categories of mental functioning: the cognitive (perceptual or intellectual), the emotional, and the conative. Conation includes instincts, drives, wishes, cravings, etc.

concentration See *attention.*

concentric demyelination (dē-mī-ē-li-nā′ shun) Balo's disease. See *sclerosis, diffuse.*

concept, body See *image, body.*

concept, feces-child-penis According to psychoanalysis, many factors connected with the anal stage have significant bear g upon the Oedipus and castration com-exes. As Freud says: 'The handing over feces for the sake of (out of love for) meone else becomes a prototype of cas-ation; it is the first occasion upon which a individual gives up a piece of his own dy (it is such that feces are invariably eated by children) in order to gain the vor of some person whom he loves. So at a person's love for his own penis, hich is in other respects narcissistic, is t without an element of anal-erotism.' he same reasoning applies to the concept child and the breast, and the symbolic uation breast-feces-penis-child is at e root of many pregnancy phantasies. reud, S. *Collected Papers*, vol. 3, tr. by rachey, A. and J., Leonard and Virginia oolf and The Institute for Psychoanaly-s, London, 1925)

onception In biology, the process by hich a female's egg or eggs are fertilized d thus enabled to form an embryo.

onception-hallucination. See *hallucina-on of perception.*

onceptive *Biol.* Capable of conceiving, at is, of being fertilized and forming an mbryo.

oncordance Agreement; in statistics, used imarily in twin studies to refer to the roportion of a representative sample f affected twins whose co-twins are or ill be similarly affected. To be con-asted with *frequency*, which refers only incidence of illness among twins, with-ut regard to incidence in their co-twins.

oncrete attitude See *abstract attitude.*

oncretism In analytical psychology con-retism is defined as 'a definite peculiar-y of *thought* and *feeling* which repre-ents the antithesis of abstraction. The ctual meaning of concrete is "grown to-ether." A concretely-thought concept is ne that has grown together or coalesced ith other concepts. Such a concept is not bstract, not isolated, and independently hought, but always impure and related. t is not a differentiated concept, but is till embedded in the sense-conveyed aterial of perception. Concretistic think-ng moves among exclusively concrete oncepts and views; it is constantly re-lated to sensation.' (Jung, C.G. *Psycho-logical Types,* tr. by Baynes, H.G., Har-court, Brace, New York and London, 1923)

concretization The act of making or being concrete and specific, as opposed to gen-eral and abstract. In psychiatry, the term generally connotes an overemphasis on specific detail and on the events of im-mediate experience especially in the sub-ject's verbal productions, in which case the concretization is considered to be an association defect. See *associations, dis-turbances of*

Example: A graduate university stu-dent with an I.Q. of 134 gave the follow-ing concretistic responses to a word as-sociation test—

1. When someone looks at me, "I have someone in front of me."
2. My father always "has a head and shoulders."
3. If I were queen I would "be seated and have a scepter."

concussion Widespread paralysis of brain function, due to a blow on the head, with a strong tendency to spontaneous recov-ery, and not necessarily associated with gross organic brain damage. Experimen-tal evidence suggests that this functional disturbance is due to a direct physical injury to the neurone which is reversible, the rate of recovery being proportional to the severity of the injury. See *com-pression, cerebral.*

concussion, blast *See neurosis, postcon-cussion.*

condemnation With Freud the term means 'rejection based on judgment.' In his com-munication *Repression,* he discusses the fate of libido. He says that one cannot flee from internal stimuli; 'with an in-stinct, flight is of no avail, for the ego can-not escape from itself. Later on, rejection based on judgment *(condemnation)* will be found to be a good weapon against the impulse.' (Freud, S. *Collected Papers,* vol. 4, tr. by Riviere, J., Leonard and Virginia Woolf and The Institute of Psy-choanalysis, London, 1924-25)

condensation The process whereby an idea is made to contain all the emotion associated with a group of ideas. A single word or phrase may be over-cathected or over-charged with emotion when it stands for something else of a much larger order.

This process of emotional condensation is characteristic of almost all dreams. As Jones expresses it, a person in a dream 'may be constituted by the fusion of the memories of several different actual persons.' (Jones, E. *Papers on Psycho-Analysis,* 4th ed., Wood, Baltimore, 1938)

A second meaning of condensation is a corollary of the first. Many ideas or allied experiences may be compressed into a single thought or word. Thus, a phobia is never an entity; it is representative of a chain of circumstances; it is a symbol that expresses a number of experiences.

'The incompleteness of ideas facilitates the formation of *condensations* which are consequently unusually frequent in schizophrenia. Various lovers, various places of residence are no longer kept apart, sometimes one lover and one place are the representatives of the entire total conception. . . .' (Bleuler, E. *Textbook of Psychiatry,* tr. by Brill, A.A., Macmillan, New York, 1930)

condensation, dream 'The first thing that becomes clear to the investigator when he compares the dream-content with the dream-thoughts is that a tremendous *work of condensation* has been accomplished. The dream is meagre, paltry and laconic in comparison with the range and copiousness of the dream-thoughts. The dream, when written down, fills half a page; the analysis, which contains the dream-thoughts, requires six, eight, twelve times as much space.' (Freud, S. *The Interpretation of Dreams,* 3rd ed., tr. by Brill, A.A., Macmillan, New York, 1933). See *condensation.*

condition, hysteriform See *hysteriform.*

condition, paranoid See *paranoid.*

conditionalism In Jung's usage, approximately equivalent to determinism. Conditionalism thus endeavors 'to conceive strict causality by means of interplay of conditions, to enlarge the simple significance of the relation between cause and effect by means of the manifold significance of the relations between effects. Causality in the general sense is not thereby destroyed, but only accommodated to the many-sided living material.' (Jung, C.G. *Seminar on Children's Dreams*)

conditioning The experimental procedure in which an adequate stimulus (e.g. presentation of food, causing salivation in the experimental animal) is paired with an inadequate stimulus (e.g. ringing of a bell which of itself has no effect on salivation) until the previously inadequate stimulus is by itself able to evoke the response. The original, adequate stimulus (food in the above example) is termed the unconditional stimulus (US), and the response to the unconditional stimulus is termed the unconditional response (UR). The other stimulus (ringing of a bell in the above example) is termed the conditioned or conditional stimulus (CS) and the response to it once conditioning is established is termed the conditioned or conditional response (CR). Because conditioning as thus defined was first described by I.P. Pavlov, it is often known as Pavlovian conditioning or classical conditioning.

conditioning, operant Consequence-governed behavior; B.F. Skinner's term for the process of reinforcing a subject's spontaneous activities. The experimenter waits for the subject to perform an action and once the deed is done the subject is rewarded. It has been suggested that many forms of psychotherapy are applications of operant conditioning, in that the patient's speech is rewarded by (reinforced by) remarks or other behavior on the part of the therapist. The patient learns what the therapist expects or wants to hear, and he modifies his own speech and behavior accordingly.

conduct 1. As a rule the word *conduct* refers to the action or behavior of the total individual rather than to parts of him (such as movement of an extremity and an isolated act). *Conduct* implies psychic as well as somatic activity.
2. Self-conscious behavior as determined by the standards set for the person by his social environment.

conduct-disorder See *behavior disorders.*

conduction, avalanche Spread of nerve impulse to many more neurons so that an effect disproportionate to the initial stimulus is produced. See *law of avalanche.*

confabulation In psychiatry, the act of replacing memory loss by phantasy or by reality that is not true for the occasion. The gaps in memory are filled by all sorts of *confabulations* or *fabrications* which are narrated in great detail and with perfect appearance of lucidity (thus sometimes termed *opportune confabulation*).

The term implies also lack of insight, in the sense that the subject fully believes his answers to be correct. Confabulation is found in organic brain diseases in which intellectual impairment is a prominent feature. For example, the patient with a Korsakov syndrome often fills in the memory gaps with incorrect details. A patient, bed-ridden in the hospital for months, said that he had just returned from a European journey and gave many details of the trip, believing thoroughly in his account.

Confabulation is to be differentiated from *pseudologia fantastica* (q.v.), which occurs mainly in the 'psychopathic' group and in other conditions in which acting-out is prominent. In pseudologia fantastica, the phantasy is believed only momentarily and will quickly be dropped if the patient is confronted with contradictory evidence. The confabulator, in contrast, will stick steadfastly to his story.

In describing the perceptual, thought, and language disturbances of schizophrenic children, W. Goldfarb terms *confabulations* those misconceptions that the child is seeing different people when he is really seeing the same person in different settings.

confabulation, suggestion 'In many cases [of Korsakov's psychosis] the fabrications can be suggested by leading questions and the patient may be led to make almost any statement, no matter how contradictory—*suggestion confabulation.*' (White, W.A. *Outlines of Psychiatry,* 12th ed., Nervous & Mental Disease Publishing Company, Washington, D.C., 1929)

confabulosis A type of symptomatic psychosis characterized by systematized confabulations in a setting of relatively clear consciousness; other than confabulations, memory disturbances are mild, and orientation is relatively intact. Confabulosis typically occurs at the stage of recovery from an acute brain syndrome.

confession-dream See *dream, confession.*

confidence, level of A quantitative expression of the degree of reliability of an inference; a 5 per cent level of confidence, for example, is a statement that the particular inference would be wrong 5 per cent of the time. Thus the per cent specified is seen to be negatively related to the degree of confidence involved, and a small per cent denotes a high degree of confidence or a low degree of uncertainty.

configuration Gestalt. See *psychology, Gestalt.*

conflict In psychiatry, a mental struggle occasioned by the simultaneous operation of opposing or mutually exclusive drives, impulses, wishes, or external or internal demands. When an instinct leaves its original source, the id, and goes in the direction of the environment, it encounters the critical scrutiny of several different forces, each of which demands that the instinct conform to certain requirements before it can take the next step forward. The drive (instinct) opposes the successive forces it encounters, namely, the superego, ego, ego-ideal and reality. Consequently there is a *conflict* leading to one of many results, such as repression, symbolization, etc. See *defense.*

'From the very beginning our view was that men fall ill owing to the conflict between the demands of their instincts and the internal resistance which is set up against them.' (Freud, S. *New Introductory Lectures on Psycho-Analysis,* tr. by Sprott, W.J.H., Norton, New York, 1933)

conflict, actual 'A conflict precipitating the crisis. It occurs when the struggle begins between the conscious and unconscious forces. This must be differentiated from *root conflict* which represents the early source of the struggle, which has been dormant in the unconscious since childhood and repressed.' (London, L.S. *Libido and Delusion,* Mental Therapy Publications, 2nd ed., enlgd., Washington, D.C., 1946)

conflict, basic Horney's term for the intrapsychic struggle between opposing neurotic trends, such as self-effacing vs. expansive solutions, or proud self vs. despised self. See *conflict, central.*

conflict, central Horney's term for the intrapsychic struggle between the healthy, constructive forces of the real self and the neurotic, obstructive forces of the idealized self. In general, the central conflict involves the whole self (and not just part of the self as is the case with basic conflict), is more severe than basic conflict, and is encountered during the course of psychoanalytic treatment.

conflict, experimental An artificial situation created through hypnotic suggestion in order to demonstrate to the patient his inner attitude toward the real conflict. Accordingly one may refer to it as 'an experimental neurosis' deliberately induced by the hypnotist so as to direct his patient toward awareness of the true motivations of his real neuroses. (Wolberg, L.R. *Hypnoanalysis,* Grune and Stratton, New York 1945) See *neurosis, experimental.*

conflict, inner 'A distinct conflict within the personality between two or more opposing impulses or desires which tend to irresolution, tension, or neurotic behavior.' (Hamilton, G. *A Medical Social Terminology,* Presbyterian Hospital, New York, 1930)

conflict, root In psychiatry, a term that refers to the earliest source of the patient's struggle, lying at the root of the conflict. 'There was no doubt that the roots of masturbation and other sexual traumas occurred earlier in his life, but they were too deeply submerged and could not be brought to the conscious level. . . His actual conflict began when he was rejected as a suitor. His root conflict was only disclosed by hearsay, the story of his reactions when his mother gave her affections to his younger sister of whom he was jealous.' (London, L.S. *Libido and Delusion,* Mental Therapy Publications, 2nd ed. enlgd., Washington, D.C., 1946)

confluence Used in individual psychology (Adler) to refer to the flowing together of several instincts into a single object. In genetics, the combined influence of heredity and environment.

conformity, automaton The course of blindly adopting the pattern of culture of one's environment and bowing submissively to its dictates: the person accepts the way to live, to feel, and to think as implicitly or explicitly recommended by the group. The effects of culture on personality have been greatly emphasized by Fromm. Man has today become aware of himself as a separate entity. The growing realization of his separateness gives him a sense of isolation and a longing to return to the earlier feeling of solidarity with others. So he uses certain irrational methods of relating back to the group. These are termed mechanisms of escape and include sadomasochism, destructiveness, and automation conformity.

confusion A state of disordered orientation; a disturbance of consciousness in the sense that awareness of time, place, or person is unclear. Confusion may be occasioned by organic or psychic causes.

confusional state, acute An acute stress reaction, occurring typically in adolescents when they are placed in an unfamiliar environment, such as college, and are expected to manifest a degree of psychological maturity that they have not as yet achieved. (307.2) The reaction is precipitated by some minor frustration and is characterized by rage, followed by the confusional state itself (inability to concentrate, estrangement, depersonalization, feelings of loneliness, sometimes impulsive suicidal attempts). Unless the subject is otherwise predisposed to the development of psychosis, the acute confusional state is self-limiting and the subject slowly reintegrates his ego-defenses.

congelatio (kôn-ge-lä′tē-ō) *Obs.* Rigid state of the body in catalepsy; same as *gelatio.* See *catalepsy².*

congenital Existing or possessed since birth. In biology applied to an attribute, or anomaly, possessed and manifested by an individual since *birth.* Opposed to *hereditary* (q.v.).

congruent Consistent, dependable; in harmony with or concordant to what would generally be considered proper, reasonable, or appropriate. Rogers emphasizes the need for the therapist to be congruent; that is, to be dependably real and to act in accordance with the feelings or attitudes he is in fact experiencing, rather than to adopt a stereotyped demeanor (e.g. of loving acceptance) that is rigidly maintained no matter what happens between him and his client.

conjunctive In Sullivan's terminology, tending to promote harmony among different and even contradictory factors and situations.

connotation The significance of a word as it applies to a whole class rather than to a specific or concrete embodiment of the word. Thus, the connotative meaning of the word *chair* would include all the qualities essential to any chair and would be most closely indicated by the phrase *chair in general as a physical entity*. This is to be distinguished from denotation, or denotative meaning, which (in this case) would refer to certain chairs or to a specific chair.

It has been noted that schizophrenics typically demonstrate a reduction in their connotation ability and are able to define words only as they apply to specific objects and not in their general sense as representative of a group or class. As a result, there is relative overemphasis on denotation and thinking comes to be pathologically concretized. (See *concretization*.) This would also appear to be an important factor in the schizophrenic's overliteralness and inability to use metaphor.

Conn's syndrome *Aldosteronism* (q.v.).

Conolly, John (born between 1794 and 1796; died 1866) British psychiatrist; psychotherapy.

conquassationes animi (kôn-kwȧs-sȧ-tē-ō′nes ȧ′nē-mē) (L. 'severe shakings of the soul') *Obs.* Mental derangement.

consanguinity In contradistinction to *affinity* or the relation by marriage, *consanguinity* means relation by blood or descent from a common ancestor within the same family stock. See *kinship*.

conscience Those psychical organizations that stand in opposition to the expression of instinctual actions. Conscience relates to the moral and esthetic and ethical attitudes of the individual. When the parental

attitudes, prohibitions, and commands take up their position in the unconscious to form the superego, it is the superego that is conscience. Later in development, when the child begins to emulate others outside the family circle and develops an ego-ideal, he acquires another conscience. There is, however, a continuity between the two. See *superego*.

The function of conscience is to warn the ego to avoid the pains of intense guilt feelings. 'Conscience becomes pathological when it (a) functions in too rigid or too automatic a manner, so that realistic judgment about the actual outcome of intended actions is disturbed ("archaic superego") or (b) when the breakdown toward "panic" occurs and a greater or lesser sense of complete annihilation is experienced instead of a warning signal, which is the case in severe depressions.' (Fenichel, O. *The Psychoanalytic Theory of Neurosis*, Norton, New York, 1945.)

conscience, double Dissociation and splitting of consciousness leading to the production of abnormal states of consciousness; a fundamental manifestation of hysteria.

conscience, inner A term used by L.E. Hinsie to designate the superego. (*Understandable Psychiatry*, Macmillan, New York, 1948)

conscience-instinct See *instinct, conscience.*

conscience, outer A term used by L.E. Hinsie to designate the ego-ideal. The ego-ideal is a mental organization formed by the child's teachers, playmates, and other associates. This organization constitutes a conscious standard guiding the individual. Through the formation of the ego-ideal or outer conscience some of the individual's mental energy is diverted from the parents to others. (*Understandable Psychiatry*, Macmillan, New York, 1948)

conscience, primitive A type of superego derived from man's archaic past.

conscious In psychiatry *conscious* is used: (1) (less frequently) as an adjective descriptive of a function of consciousness or of the conscious realm as a perceptive faculty. As such, it is synonymous with:

aware; having knowledge of; present in the field (or realm) of consciousness. (2) (usually) as a noun, to denote a particular division of the psyche. In such use it is practically synonymous with *consciousness*, and is invariably preceded by the definite article: *the conscious*, as is generally the case with *the preconscious, the unconscious, the collective unconscious*.

'The conscious is that part of mental life, proportionately infinitesimal, of which the individual is aware at any given time. Though consciousness is a continuum during normal waking life, its content is extremely transitory, constantly changing.' (Healy, W., Bronner, A.F., and Bowers, A.M. *The Structure and Meaning of Psychoanalysis*, Knopf, New York, 1930)

Kempf's definition of consciousness is as follows: 'The phenomena of consciousness of self or of the environment is the result of all the [autonomic] segments reacting together more or less vigorously, as a *unity*, to the sensational activity of any one or several of its parts.' (Kempf, E.J. *Psychopathology*, Mosby, St. Louis, 1921)

consciousness See *conscious*.

consciousness, clouding of See *sensorium*.

consciousness, disintegration of 'The vast majority of mental diseases, in so far as they are not of a definitely organic nature, are due to a disintegration of consciousness caused by an irresistible inundation of unconscious contents.' (Jung, C.G. *Contributions to Analytical Psychology*, tr. by Baynes, H.G. and C.F., Kegan Paul, Trench, Trubner, London, 1928.) This means that material from the unconscious more or less gradually causes the disruption and disintegration of the contents of consciousness.

consciousness, double; dual See *personality, alternating*.

consciousness, dream See *ego, dream*.

consciousness, splitting of When a set of experiences, a mental constellation exist, as for instance, in hysteria, essentially alone in consciousness, without associations with other components of consciousness, it is said that there is a splitting of consciousness. See *hysteria, defense*.

consciousness, subliminal See *tendency, subliminal*.

consensual light reflex When light enters the pupil of one eye only, the iris of the other eye contracts; the phenomenon is known as the consensual light reflex.

consensual validation See *distortion, parataxic*.

consensus Agreement reached by the resolution of conflict. (Kallen, H. 'Consensus.' *Encyclopaedia of the Social Sciences*, vol. 4, Macmillan, New York, 1931, pp. 225-6) Four types of group agreement have been differentiated: by authority, by compromise, by majority determination, and by integration. (McIver, R.M. *Society, Its Structure and Changes*, Smith, New York, 1931)

conservation In Morton Prince's terminology, memory retention or preservation.

consolidation See *memory*.

constancy Steadfastness or stability; Adler assumed a constancy of personality, i.e. that a person remains fundamentally the same once his personality has been well established in early childhood. Such constancy of personality constitutes the *life style* of the person, the characteristic way in which he pursues his long range goals. 'There are two areas for investigation of the life style. First, we determine the family constellation, the interaction between all the members of the family, and thereby perceive the movement of the patient in contrast to the movement of his parents, siblings, and others in the family group. The second . . . pertains to the significance of *early recollections*. They permit a rather clear and reliable perception of the person's outlook on life, because he remembers, of the millions of early childhood experiences, only those which fit into it.' (Dreikurs, R. *The Adlerian Approach to Psychodynamics* in *Contemporary Psychotherapies*, edited by Stein, M.I., Free Press, New York, 1961)

constant, central Burrow's term for the primary principle governing the organism's total action pattern. Essentially homeostatic, this principle, on the basis of phyloorganismic behavior, relates the organism of man-as-a-species to its environment. Contrasted with extrinsic constant. Synonym: intrinsic constant. (Burrow, T. *The Biology of Human Conflict*, Macmillan, New York, 1937, pp. 341-3).

constant, extrinsic Burrow's term for the secondary, symbolic principle in organism-environment relationship. It refers to the partial reaction-patterns mediated through the cortex and conforms symbolically to the consistency of phenomena throughout the external world. The organism's extrinsic constant regulates the secondary, partial system of word-conditioned reflexes, and is subordinate to the organism's primary principle or central constant. Contrasted with intrinsic constant. (Burrow, T. *The Biology of Human Conflict*, Macmillan, New York, 1937, pp. 341-3.)

constant, intrinsic See *constant, central.*

constellation A group of allied thoughts, centering around a nuclear idea. 'The nuclear element has a constellating power corresponding to its energic value. From this power there follows a specific constellation of the psychic contents; and thus is developed the complex, which is a constellation of psychic contents dynamically conditioned by the energic value.' (Jung, C.G. *Contributions to Analytical Psychology*, tr. by Baynes, H. G. and C.F., Kegan Paul, Trench, Trubner, London, 1928)

constellation, emotional All the persons to whom one is strongly attached and by whom he is chiefly influenced. In the Freudian doctrine, the center of this constellation is, in a general sense, the mother or the father. Stekel speaks of 'infantile constellation' in reference to the hatred of the child toward the father. This, in fact, constitutes one of the manifestations of the Oedipus complex. (Stekel, W. *The Interpretation of Dreams*, Liveright, New York, 1943)

constellation, family The particular setting of the family in which a person develops; Adler emphasized the interaction between all members of the family, children as well as parents, as being a determinant of the life style of a person. See *constancy.*

constellation, infantile See *constellation, emotional.*

consternatio (kon-ster-nä′tē-ō) (L. confusion, consternation) *Obs.* Night terrors in children.

constitution 'Constitution is the relatively constant physiological composition and biological make-up of the human organism by which its resistances are governed.'

More complex definitions are found in different schools of constitutional medicine. Draper defines constitution as 'that aggregate of herediterial characters, influenced more or less by environment, which determine the individual's reaction, successful or unsuccessful, to the stress of environment.' (Draper, G. *Disease and the Man*, Macmillan, New York, 1930)

Pende conceives of the constitution as 'the morphological, physiological and psychological resultant (variable in each individual) of the properties of all the cellular and humoral elements of the body, and of the combination of these in a special cellular state having a balance and functional output of its own, a given capacity for adaption and a mode of reaction to its environmental stimuli.' This resultant is believed to be 'determined primarily by the laws of heredity and secondarily by the disturbing influences exercised by the environment upon the individual's hereditary plan of organization.' (Pende, N. *Constitutional Inadequacies*, tr. by Naccarati, S., Lea & Febiger, Philadelphia, 1928)

The concept of Kretschmer who defined constitution as 'the totality of all individual peculiarities which are referable to heredity, i.e., which have a genetic basis' seems oversimplified to a similar extent as that of Johannsen, who described it as 'the totality of all the morphological, functional and evolutionary elements of an organism which are inherited or inheritable.'

In interpreting the physical and mental resistance of an individual in the dynamic terms of the capacity of producing *compensatory reactions* to pathogenic influences, Lewis conceives of the constitution as 'the expression of the integration of formative elements comprising the inherited organic units, cosmic elements, subhuman living environment, psychological influences, including those more or less rigid patterns determined by tradition, social ideas, moulding childhood experiences, and the influence of contact-persons in the human environment.' (Lewis,

N.D.C. *Constitutional Factors in Dementia Praecox,* Monograph No. 35 of the Nervous & Mental Disease Publishing Company, New York, 1923). As this synthetic conception seeks to unite the morphological, physiological, and psychological aspects of the individual, it certainly constitutes a promising working hypothesis for approaching the field of constitutional medicine from all possible angles.

Few expressions in contemporary medical literature are applied with so little unanimity and exactness as is the term *constitution.* Its identification with the phenotype, body build, or genotype of an individual is almost as common as its usage—with or without the epithet 'hereditary'—for denoting the general biological make-up or the particular genetic structure of an organism. Many authors still use the term 'constitutional' in connection with diseases which are caused 'internally' or affect, as do gout or diabetes, the whole organism. Another school describes the constitution in terms of the different types of physique and seeks in them the primary etiologic basis of variations in clinical pathology.

This inaccuracy in terminology and conception is understandable when one considers that the knowledge of constitution is almost as old as medicine itself, and that all definitions of constitution incorporate the special ideas of both the time and the branch of medicine in which they have been formulated. From Hippocrates to the present there have been systems of constitutional types and diseases, which changed in content and could be more finely subdivided when further knowledge was added. Up to the nineteenth century, all diseases not localized in the pathology of a single organ were constitutional. When the knowledge of pathogenesis advanced, the number of these so-called 'constitutional' diseases was correspondingly reduced.

Following the discovery of the physiological and chemical cell processes in the bacteriological era, constitutional research was almost forgotten and had to retreat to the classification of different physical types. Although these studies were to some extent successful, especially in psychiatry and under the influence of Kretschmer's systematic work, there were many disappointments in other fields of medicine so long as the study of constitution was confined to purely anthropological investigation of the individual and the concept of constitution was not founded on accurate genetic principles. The classification of constitutional disease groups as clinical entities was bound to remain useless, because there is no disease which is purely constitutional, and there is no constitutional system which is alone the basis for a specific pathology.

According to the principles of modern physiological genetics the furthest one can go is to distinguish between predominantly hereditary and predominantly peristatic diseases (see *peristasis*). Consequently, the concepts of heredity and constitution have become practically inseparable, although it is clear that the constitution is not to be identified with either the genotypical structure or the phenotypical make-up of a person. While the phenotype is the *changeable* picture of the manifest appearance of an organism and is always modified by its external life-situation, constitution represents a *relatively constant* state of the person and classifies this person according to his biological values. It is therefore best understood as an auxiliary concept of medical classification and general pathology.

constitutional Pertaining to those elements in the biological make-up of an individual organism which are inherent in its given constitution, that is, in the relatively constant physiological composition and biological make-up of the human organism by which its resistances are governed. See *hereditary.*

If the concept of *constitution* is thus to have its own precise meaning which neither coincides with the genotype or the phenotype of an individual nor disagrees with the other definitions of the biological structure and development of a human being, as they appear in the light of modern physiological genetics, it is based on the distinction of three different factors determining the final nature of an individual; namely, the inherited elements which make up the *genotype* and are again transmissible, the *peristatic* conditions of the environment, and the *dispositional response* of the individual organism. A change in any of these factors is bound to modify the phenotypical appearance of the organism, although the genotypical structure is of primary importance to the prospective biological development in that it expresses the actual equipment of the individual as a classified member of a particular species or group, and demarcates the limits and qualities of all future reactions of the given organism to its individual life situation.

constitutional mania See *disposition, constitutional manic.*

constitutional type See *type, constitutional.*

constitution, carcinomatous (kär-si-nom′-à-tus, nō′mà-tus) Introduced by Beneke, this term denotes a constitutional type believed to be predisposed to carcinoma by a particular physique, practically identical with the *neoplastic diathesis.*

constitution, epileptic psychopathic E. Bleuler (*Texbook of Psychiatry,* Macmillan, New York, 1930) says: 'Specific psychic peculiarities are connected with epilepsy, which as a rule increase with the duration of the disease. According to the degree, one speaks of an epileptic character, epileptic psychopathic constitution, and, in severe cases, of epileptic dementia.' See *epilepsy; personality, epileptic.*

constitution, hydropic (hī-drop′ik) This constitutional anomaly is a form of *exudative diathesis* in children, which is characterized by thermic lability, instability of body weight, a tendency to edema and the accumulation of water and salt in the tissues, and a marked instability of the combining property of water in the tissues themselves. These features are often supplemented by the development of certain nervous disorders, especially in the sphere of the vegetative nervous system.

constitution, hyperadrenal (hī-per-ad-rē′nal) A type associated with oversecretion of the adrenal gland (medulary portion?). The type's physical characteristics are an apoplectic habitus with muscular overdevelopment and hypertonia, marked muscular strength, hypertonic peripheral arteries with a blood pressure above the average, hypertrichosis, hyperglycemia, and hypercholesteremia. The psychological features are said to be characterized by euphoria and great moral and intellectual energy. 'In the female there is general tonic

adiposity with wealth of hair of masculine type and premature sexual development with a tendency to dissociation of sexual characteristics and to a masculine character, which when present to a marked degree constitutes the condition of *precocious matronism.*' (Pende, N. *Constitutional Inadequacies,* tr. by Naccarati, S., Lea & Febiger, Philadelphia, 1928)

constitution, hyperpituitary (-pi-tū′i-ter-ē) A type characterized by oversecretion of the pituitary gland occurring after or toward the end of the period of normal growth, as compared with such oversecretion occurring earlier in life and producing *gigantism.*

The general constitutional aspects of this *hyperpituitary* type correspond to Kretschmer's *athletic* type with *dysplastic* features and mainly consist of strong long bones, massive face, hands, and feet, thick oily skin, scanty scalp with seborrhea, large external genitalia, a tendency to tachycardia, hypertension, and arteriosclerosis, increased basal metabolism, and a restless mental attitude with reason prevailing over passion.

constitution, hyperthymic (-thī′mik) In the system of constitutional types described by Pende and Berman, this term denotes a type associated with overdevelopment of the thymus gland and its persistence into adulthood.

In infancy, this constitutional type is represented by the angelic type, with pretty and well-proportioned features, transparent skin, silky hair, delicate body proportions, exceptional grace of motion and an alert mind. These children seem to be models of beauty, but they are unfit for the struggle with life and fall easy victims to tuberculosis, meningitis, and other infections.

After puberty, all hyperthymic constitutions are distinguished by a strong tendency to inversion of physical and mental sex characteristics, hypoplastic hearts and arteries, insufficient muscular strength, and a tendency to sudden circulatory imbalance which often leads to sudden death or a rupture of the hypoplastic arteries. While the *male* hyperthymic is characterized by elegant feminine body outlines, long thorax, rounded pelvis, soft skin and milky color, the *female* type shows delicate skin and nails, little hair, deficient mammary development, delayed menstruation and, in some cases, a certain persistent adiposity and juvenility.

On the psychic side, there is a certain moral irresponsibility, with definite tendencies to homosexuality or masochism, impulsiveness, incapability for adaptation to the difficulties of social life, and a tendency to crime and suicide.

constitution, hyperthyroid (-thī'roid) This constitutional type is associated with excessive secretion of the thyroid gland and is said to be characterized by youthfulness, well-developed sexual characteristics, well-formed nails and teeth, large brilliant and sometimes rather prominent eyes, hyperpigmentation of the skin, slightly enlarged thyroid, swiftness of all functional reactions, marked irritability of the sympathetic nervous system, and general hyperemotivity and instability. The physical and psychological aspects of this type correspond to those of the *asthenic*.

constitution, hypoadrenal (hī-pō-ad-rē'-nal) The constitutional type associated with a deficient secretion of the adrenal gland (medullary portion?) and described by Pende as characterized by a hypoplastic trunk, slender bones, habitual leanness, marked developmental deficiency of both skeletal and smooth muscles, an accentuated universal lymphatism with or without hyperplasia of the thymus, marked arterial hypotention, lymphocytosis, and a hypotrophic skin with increased pigmentation, especially on the exposed parts of the body, and often an abundance of pigmented moles. 'Psychologically there is a tendency to melancholia, while the intelligence is normal or supernormal.' (Pende, N. *Constitutional Inadequacies*, tr. by Naccarati, S., Lea & Febiger, Philadelphia, 1928)

constitution, hypopancreatic (-pan-krē-a' tik) See *constitution, hypoparathyroid.*

constitution, hypoparathyroid (-par-à-thī'roid) This constitutional type is distinquished by deficient secretion of the parathyroid glands and is said by Pende to be characterized by hyperkinesis and hyperreflexia of the striated as well as the smooth muscles, sensory hyperexcitability, fragility of the incisors, a tendency to rickets in infancy, and anomalies of the calcium metabolism. There is also a

frequent association of this type with the *hypopancreatic* constitution, which results from a diminished tolerance for carbohydrates and constitutes a transition to true diabetes.

constitution, hypopituitary (-pi-tū'i-ter-ē) In the system of constitutional types described by Pende this term refers to a type associated with deficient secretion of the pituitary gland. The general constitutional aspects of this type correspond to the *hypoplastic* group in Kretschmer's system, although age and sex considerably modify them.

The *infant* type is characterized: (a) in *both sexes,* by defective stature and growth, increased adiposity, small head, short bones, irregular dentition, thin lips, poorly spaced eyes with scanty eyebrows, small hands, and circular mouth; (b) in the *male,* by small external genitals and, sometimes, by cryptorchism; and (c) in the *female,* by a feminine appearance even in early childhood.

The *adult* (adolescent) type is characterized: (a) in the *male,* by delicate facial features, smooth bony contours, silky hair, large pelvis, feminine distribution of fat and pubic hair, hairless trunk and extremities, small hands, and defective sex activity; (b) in the *female,* by small breasts, frigidity, and the tendency to sterility and masculinism; and (c) in *both sexes,* by muscular asthenia, vagotonia, low blood pressure, slow pulse, increased carbohydrate tolerance, polyuria, and general mental torpor.

constitution, hypothyroid (-thī'roid) In constitutional medicine, this term refers to a type with a deficient secretion of the thyroid gland. While the body build of this type generally corresponds to that of a *pyknic* or *megalosplanchnic* individual, its further characteristics mainly consist of generalized adiposity with special fatty deposits on face and neck, large head, thick neck, short and stubby hands, small and expressionless eyes, short and thick nose, round face with poorly marked features, poor pigmentation of the skin, premature baldness, dystrophic teeth and nails, torpid vasomotor reactions, normal sex development, acrocyanosis, habitual hypoglycemia with great carbohydrate tolerance, diminished basal metabolism, and a torpid and apathetic mental attitude.

constitution, paranoid (par'a-noid) See *character, paranoiac.*

constitution, personality The personality as it exists prior to the development of a psychiatric condition. Several forms of personality constitution have been described, among which may be mentioned the schizoid (schizothymic), cycloid (cyclothymic), epileptoid, and hysteroid.

From the standpoint of Jung there are two general reaction types, the introverted and the extraverted, each of which is subdivided into four functional types, namely, thinking, feeling, sensation, and intuition.

Psychoanalysts describe types of personality in terms of their relationship with the major influences of infantile components. Among the personality or character forms, according to psychoanalysis, are the anal, oral, and genital characters. See *defense, character.*

constitution, post-traumatic The clinical syndromes, subsumed under this heading, vary from person to person; the symptoms are often a mixture of both neurotic and psychotic phenomena. Friedmann's complex is one of the most common syndromes; it is said to be due to cerebral vasomotor disturbance and is characterized by headache, dizziness, insomnia, easy fatigue, irritability, and other character changes.

In 1904 Adolf Meyer described five types:

'a: Types with mere facilitation of reaction to alcohol, grippe, etc.

b: Types with vaso-motor neurosis.

c: Types with explosive diathesis.

d: Types with hysteroid or epileptoid episodes with or without convulsions (such as most reflex-psychoses).

e: Types of paranoiac development.' (Meyer, M. *American Journal of Insanity* LX, 439, 1904)

See post-traumatic and post-encephalitic syndromes, classification of.

constitution, psychic The original structure and function laid down in the individual as distinguished from acquired modifications; i.e. the phylogenetic inheritance of the psyche such as, in Jung's terms, the collective unconscious.

constitution, psychopathic See *psychopathic personality.*

constitution, sexual In psychoanalysis, this refers to the hereditary tendencies that account for the various erogenous zones being charged with different amounts of chathexis or different degrees of ability for discharge. Little is known about such constitutional factors.

constitution, traumatic A mental and nervous disorder following head injuries, which is characterized by such symptoms as headache, fatigability, irritability, emotional instability, and sometimes severe and serious dispositional changes. This condition is included, by most authors, among the *traumatic psychoses.* See *post-traumatic and post-encephalitic syndromes, classification of; psychosis, traumatic.*

constraint of movement See *constraint of thought.*

constraint of thought The idea, expressed especially by patients with dementia praecox, that the patients' thoughts are under the influence of other people.

'They never tire of describing this constraint of theirs in ever varying ways. The patient's *thoughts are influenced,* inspired, pressed on him; he must receive them like a telephone; they are forced on him by hypnotism and suggestion, act on him "by suggestion."' (Kraepelin, E. *Dementia Praecox and Paraphrenia,* tr. by Barclay, R.M., Livingstone, Edinburgh, 1919)

When the same idea of constraint prevails as regards the patient's movements, one speaks of *constraint of movement.*

It is to be noted that psychiatric usage differentiates between constraint and *constriction* (q.v.).

constriction When applied to thinking or movement, this term implies a reduction in range or variability. Constriction is associated with diminished spontaneity. It is to be noted that psychiatric usage differentiates between constriction and *constraint* (q.v.).

constructive 'This concept is used by me in an equivalent sense to *synthetic,* almost in fact as an illustration of the latter concept. Constructive means "building up." I employ "constructive" and "synthetic" in describing a method that is opposed to the reductive. The constructive method is concerned with the elaboration of unconscious products (dreams, phantasies, etc.). It takes the unconscious product as a basis or starting point, as a *symbolical* expression, which, stretching on ahead, as it were, represents a coming phase of psychological development.' (Jung, C.G. *Psychological Types,* tr. by Baynes, H.G., Harcourt, Brace, New York and London, 1923)

consultant In traditional medicine and psychiatry, an advisor to the treating physician on matters of diagnosis, treatment, rehabilitation, etc. Ordinarily, the consultant is a specialist whose expert advice is sought by the attending physician or, sometimes, by the patient. The consultant may or may not meet directly with the patient, but ordinarily he does not take actual charge of a case; instead, he advises or counsels the attending physician, although his advice is *patient-oriented.*

Another type of consultation is *colleague-centered;* here the consultant-specialist meets with one or more colleagues to advise, counsel, or educate them in the area of his specialized knowledge. Questions about the management of specific patients may legitimately be raised during the course of colleague-centered consultation, but the primary focus of the consultant is not a single patient, but the other physician(s). In psychiatric colleague-centered consultation, for example, the implicit goal is that the non-psychiatrist physician will understand and be sensitive to the emotional needs of the patient, to his family and the other biosocial systems with which he relates; that the physician will develop skills to meet those needs and thereby foster emotional growth and mental health in his patient; and that the physician will utilize collateral resources appropriate to those ends.

Still another type of consultation is *agency-centered;* here it is the entire organization or agency with whom the consultant meets and tries to help.

Consultation psychiatry may refer to any of the above types of consultation performed by a psychiatrist. Often, however, it is limited to the activity of the psychiatrist (diagnostic, therapeutic, teaching, research, etc.) in the non-psychiatric parts of a general hospital; when used in this sense, it is synonymous with *liaison psychiatry.*

contamination In a psychiatric sense the term *contamination* refers to an error of speech characterized by amalgamating a part of one word with that of another (Freud). Bleuler gives as an example the neologism 'gruesor,' derived from gruesome and sorrowful. Apparently the result of contamination is a neologism. Freud states that contamination is the first step in the process of condensation.

In Rorschach interpretation, contamination is a pathological response, pathognomonic of schizophrenia, characterized by the following: 'First the patient is unaware of what he is doing; second, the resulting response is perceptually unintelligible; third, at least two different percepts overlap so that the same area is covered by different percepts simultaneously; and fourth, the patient is unable to disjoin the condensed percepts at will and with clarity.' (Piotrowski, Z.A., *Perceptanalysis,* Macmillan, New York, 1957.)

contemplatio (kôn-tem-plä′tē-ō) *Obs.* Ecstasy.

content, dream See *dream-content; content, latent.*

content, latent This concept, particularly emphasized and developed by Freud, refers to the consideration that the bulk of psychiatric phenomena is made up of symbolic expressions. Phobias, compulsive-obsessive symptoms, delusions, hallucinations, conversion symptoms, dreams, etc., in themselves, do not reveal the nature of the disorder. They constitute what is called the *manifest content.* The real meaning of the symptoms or symbols is concealed, that is, latent. Thus, a patient must always perform an act a certain number of times; if he does not obey the compulsion something dreadful will happen to someone. That is the manifest content. Analysis reveals that the repetition compulsion is associated with his mother and that she is the one who will suffer death, if he does not repeat the compulsion. The underlying components constitute the latent content.

content, manifest See *content, latent.*

contentious Quarrelsome. Some patients, particularly those with a manic syndrome and those in the early stages of a paranoid reaction, feel that they and others are being treated unfairly; they see slights when none is present or intended, as a result of which they incessantly quarrel about discriminations.

'The fighting maniacs stand between those who feel in the right and forever appeal to the law, on the one hand, and the paranoid litigants, on the other.' (Bleuler, E. *Textbook of Psychiatry,* tr. by Brill, A.A., Macmillan, New York, 1930)

continuity of care See *psychiatry, community.*

continuity, social 'This concept is used to indicate that existing culture forms are outgrowths or modifications of antecedent forms.' (Willey, M. 'Continuity, Social,' *Encyclopaedia of the Social Sciences,* vol. 4, Macmillan, New York, 1931, p. 315) The chief agencies of social continuity are the family, the play group, the church, the school, and all other instrumentalities of communication.

contraception The act of interfering with the female's natural capacity, or process, of conception.

contraceptive Aiming at or producing contraception; preventing conception or impregnation.

contraction, habit See *tic.*

contraindication A reason for not doing something; more specifically, a feature or complication of a condition that countermands the use of a therapeutic agent that might otherwise be applied. Active pulmonary tuberculosis and aortic valvular insufficiency, for example, are ordinarily considered to be contraindications to the use of electro-convulsive therapy in depression.

contrary sexual An *invert* (q.v.).

contrasexual Jacobi's term for the 'repressed side' in Jung's theory of analytical psychology. Jung maintains that there is a male and a female side to everyone, the side which is not dominant being repressed; i.e. in the male the female side is repressed and vice versa. 'The second

stage of the individuation process [self-realization through Jungian analysis] is characterized by the meeting with the figure of the *"soul-image,"* named by Jung the *anima* in the man, the *animus* in the woman. The archetypal figure of the soul-image stands for the respective contrasexual portion of the psyche, showing partly how our personal relation thereto is constituted, partly the precipitate of all human experience pertaining to the opposite sex. In other words, it is the image of the other sex that we carry in us, both as individuals and as representatives of a species. "Jeder Mann trägt seine Eva in sich" (Every man carries his Eve in himself), affirms a popular saying. According to psychic law ... everything latent, unexperienced, undifferentiated in the psyche, everything that lies in the unconscious and therefore the man's "Eve" and the woman's "Adam" as well, is always projected. In consequence one experiences the elements of the opposite sex that are present in one's own psyche no otherwise than, for example, one experiences his shadow—*in the other person.* One chooses another, one binds one's self to another, who represents the qualities of one's own soul.

'The soul-image is a "more or less firmly constituted functional complex, and the inability to distinguish one's self from it leads to such phenomena as those of the moody man, dominated by feminine drives, ruled by his emotions, or of the rationalizing, animus-obsessed woman who always knows better and reacts in a masculine way, not instinctively." (Wolff, T. *Einführung in die Grundlagen der Komplexen Psychologie,* p. 112.) 'One has then the impression that another, a strange person, has "taken possession" of the individual, "a different spirit has got into him," etc., as proverbial speech so profoundly expresses it. Or we see the man who blindly falls victim to a certain type of woman—how often one sees precisely highly cultivated intellectuals abandon themselves helplessly to hussies because their feminine, emotional side is wholly undifferentiated!—or the woman who, apparently incomprehensibly, falls for an adventurer or swindler and cannot get loose from him. The character of our soul-image, the anima or animus of our dreams, is the natural measure of our internal psychological situation. It deserves very special consideration in the way of self-knowledge.' (Jacobi, J. *The Psychology of C.G. Jung*, Kegan Paul, Trench, Trubner, London, 1942)

contrectation Tumescence or the swelling of the penis; erection. Moll uses the term also in a more general sense, namely, as the 'instinct to approach, touch, and kiss another person, usually of the opposite sex,' i.e. the acts of pleasure, such as handling, that lead to genital excitation.

control In clinical psychiatry, control usually refers to conscious limitation of impulses, wishes, tendencies, etc., that is, to suppression of instincts and affects.

In experimental psychiatry, control refers to regulation of all known variables in the experimental situation except the variable which is under investigation. This is an attempt to insure that whatever effects are produced will be a function of the experimental variable and not due to extraneous factors. In assessing the value of a particular drug in the treatment of depression, for instance, a 'control group' may be formed by patients matched in age, clinical condition, and treatment conditions to the 'experimental group,' the only difference being that the control group does not receive the drug while the experimental group does. In such an experiment, a *placebo* (q.v.) may be used in place of the drug under investigation to mimic more closely all the extraneous factors which may influence the response of the experimental group to the experimental drug.

Control '. . . may be defined as any procedure or technique that allows the unequivocal establishment of the existence of a phenomenon, its equally unequivocal relation to a specific cause, and the elucidation of its ostensible, probable and actual natures.' (Bigelow, N. and Sainz, A. *American Journal of Psychiatry 118*; 889, 1962)

control analysis See *analysis, control.*

control, birth See *birth-control.*

control, co-twin A method used in biogenetics in which one member of an identical twinship is trained, treated, etc. while the other is not.

control, social The influence upon the

behavior of a person exerted by other persons, particularly as members of a social group or of a society.

The formal control of society over its members exemplified by law and by institutions derives its effectiveness in large part from their conformity to the folkways, the mores, and public opinion.

contusion, brain A diffuse disturbance of the brain, secondary to head trauma, with edema and multiple intracerebral hemorrhages, most commonly at the poles of the hemispheres. Typically, cerebrospinal fluid pressure is raised and this plays an important part in the production of symptoms (coma, stupor, drowsiness, or confusion). A late result of the edema of the brain may be localized, severe demyelination. Although a patient may recover rapidly and completely from cerebral contusion, persistent disabling symptoms are extremely common. The three cardinal late symptoms are headache, dizziness, and mental disturbances (typically, a mild dementia, with inability to concentrate, memory impairment, and anxiety). In DSM-II, such mental disturbances are coded 293.5 if psychotic, 309.2 if nonpsychotic.

conventions, social Standards of conduct or behavior prescribing what is to be done or not to be done by the members of a given group or community.

convergence See *accommodation.*

conversion Symbolic representation of psychical conflict in terms of motor or sensory manifestations. The symbolization is the means by which repressed instinctual tendencies gain external expression; usually, as for instance in hysteria, the symbolization also contains the defense set up against the instinctual impulses.

There is probably no psychiatric disorder in which conversion symptoms may not appear. See *hysteria.*

conversion hysteria See *conversion; hysteria.*

conversion-reaction See *conversion; hysteria.*

convulsion An involuntary, violent muscular contraction; a 'fit.' See *epilepsy.*

convulsion, clonic Convulsion characterized by alternate contraction and relaxation of muscular tissue.

convulsion, static Special forms of motor aurae of epilepsy, such as procursive epilepsy. See *epilepsy, procursive.*

convulsion, tonic Sustained contraction of a muscle.

co-operation 'A form of interaction of two or more persons directed toward some goal, the result of whose common action, mutual helpfulness, will benefit them.' (Young, K. *An Introductory Sociology,* American Book Company, New York, 1934)

Two chief forms of co-operation should be distinguished: *economic* co-operation, in which individuals act together to obtain the advantages of combined effort, and *societal* co-operation, which results from mutual identification and social solidarity. In addition there is 'competitive co-operation in which the incidental results of activity unintentionally react to the benefit of others.' (Reuter, E.B. and Hart, C.W. *Introduction to Sociology,* McGraw-Hill, New York, 1933)

co-operation, antagonistic Alexander uses this term to describe the organizational nature of our present-day society. He says that in our free and competitive society we are at one and the same time both friends and rivals: we live in an 'antagonistic co-operation' with our fellowmen. This life pattern can lead to fears and hostility, frustrations and thwarted hopes, exaggerated ambitions and discouragement, all of which can cause disturbed human relations and can lead to mental and nervous symptoms. (Alexander, F., and French, T.M. *Studies in Psychosomatic Medicine,* Ronald Press, New York, 1948)

coping Adjusting; adapting; successfully meeting a challenge. Coping mechanisms are all the ways, both conscious and unconscious, which a person uses in adjusting to environmental demands without altering his goals or purposes.

copro- (kop'rō) Combining form meaning feces, filth, from Gr. *kopros,* dung, ordure, filth.

coprolagnia (-lag-nē-à) Sexual pleasure from handling feces. See *anal erotism; sadism, anal.*

coprolalia (-lāl'ē-à) Literally, fecal speech; hence, the involuntary utterance of vulgar or obscene words, seen in some schizophrenics who play with words as though they were feces. See *coprophrasia.*

coprophagy (kop-rof'à-jē) The ingestion of feces.

coprophemia (kop-rō-fē'mē-à) Obscene speech. E. Jones speaks of the curious perversion of coprophemia in which 'the sexual act consists solely of uttering indecent words to women.' (*International Journal of Psychoanalysis I,* 258, 1920)

coprophilia (-fil'ē-à) Love of feces or filth. According to psychoanalysis, *anal-erotism* (q.v.) possesses two chief aspects, the first concerned with the retention and expulsion of fecal material, and the second with pleasure in the product itself. During the stage of sphincter-training the aim is twofold—to perform regularly and not to soil. The discipline associated with so-called anal training is later carried over in the form of character traits, while a certain quantum of libido remains fixed in its original form. A third possibility exists, namely, that the interest in the product is later transferred to other objects which resemble or symbolize feces, even though there may be no conscious awareness of the resemblance. Thus Ferenczi traces the development from feces through its various forms of symbolizations, namely, mud pies, sand, pebbles, marbles, buttons, jewels, coins, currency, securities, etc. Hence, ownership of valuables is traced chiefly, but not exclusively, to early anal interests; that is, it is a coprophilic interest.

Coprophilic interest may also be sublimated in such forms as painting, sculpturing, cooking and the like. Some patients exhibit coprophilia more literally. Thus, one patient hoarded his feces as earlier he had hoarded his money. Another patient 'decorated' himself, as he put it, with feces. A third said she loved her feces 'as if it were her child.' A fourth could experience sexual potency only when thinking of feces.

coprophobia Fear of rectal excreta, sometimes seen in obsessive-compulsive psychoneurosis. More typically, the fear is expressed symbolically, as fear of dirt or of contamination (e.g. fear of an infectious disease, or fearing to touch anything lest the patient acquire some ailment). Coprophobia is generally a reaction-formation against unconscious coprophilic impulses, that are derivatives of the anal stage. See *anal-erotism*.

coprophrasia (-frā'zhē-à) Coprolalia. 'If the interjection is an obscene or offensive word, as when the patient in talking with the friend who has come to visit him hisses in his face the word *"merde"* (feces) or *"cochon"* (pig) (cases of Charcot and others), or another word very frequent in the low speech of certain Southern countries, the automatism is stronger, and it goes under the name of *coprolalia*, or, better, *coprophrasia.*' Bianchi, L. *A Text-Book of Psychiatry*, tr. by MacDonald, J.H. Baillière, Tindall & Cox, London, 1906)

copulatia analis (kô-poo-lä'tē-ō ā-nä'lis) (L. 'anal coitus') *Pederasty* (q.v.).

copulation See *coitus.*

Cornell, William Mason (1802-95) American psychiatrist; mental hygiene.

corpora quadrigemina (kor'por-a kwa-dri-gēm-in-à) Four raised eminences, arranged in pairs, on the dorsal surface (tectum) of the midbrain. The two superior colliculi and the two inferior colliculi make up the four corpora. The superior colliculi are optic reflex centers and receive fibers from the lateral geniculate body via the superior quadrigeminal brachium. The more prominent inferior colliculi are associated with the auditory system and are the termination of the lateral lemniscus. The inferior colliculi project to the medial geniculate body via the inferior quadrigeminal brachium.

corpus callosum (kor'poos ka-lō'soom) A broad, white fiber-tract which connects the cerebral hemispheres and forms the roof of the lateral and 3rd ventricles. Most of its fibers arise in various parts of one hemisphere and terminate in the symmetrical area of the opposite hemisphere.

corpus striatum (kor'poos strē-à-toom) See *basal ganglia.*

corrective emotional experience See *experience, corrective emotional.*

correlation Mutual relation. (A) Tendency to concomitant change in two variables. (1) If the change, whether positive or negative, in one is accompanied by a like (i.e. in the same direction) change in the other variable, the correlation is positive with a maximal coefficient of $+1$. (2) If an increase in one corresponds to a decrease in the other (or, vice versa, a decrease in one corresponds to an increase in the other) the correlation is negative, with a maximal coefficient of -1. (3) If there is no change in the second variable, the correlation is 0.

(B) The principle of correlation is frequently useful as evidence of heredity when other signs fail. It indicates 'a connection between two properties of the individuals of a population such that, as one of the properties varies, the other tends to vary.' (Shull, A.F. *Heredity*, 3rd ed., McGraw-Hill, New York and London, 1938.) If as one property increases the other tends to increase, the correlation is *positive*. If as the one property increases the other tends to decrease, the correlation is *negative*. Positive correlation means that the two qualities have part of their physiological bases in common, and the physiological bases are frequently genetic.

The most commonly used measure of correlation is Pearson's coefficient of correlation, while the best method describing an individual in terms of the degree to which he possesses the factors that vary *independently* of one another is constituted by the analysis of a person according to 'independent variables' as devised by Spearman, Cohen, and others (see *type, constitutional*).

With factors which are related, the change which takes place in one factor for a unit change in the other can be computed; this statistic is known as the 'regression coefficient.' Computation of this latter allows the value of one factor to be estimated when the value of the other factor is known. Even when the correlation is very high, however, the error of this estimate may be large.

To be noted in any consideration of correlation is the fact that evidence of association is not necessarily evidence of causation, and the possible influence of other factors common to the ones for which correlation is discovered must always be remembered in interpreting correlation coefficients. 'It is one of the first lessons a student of statistics learns, that *correlation does not imply direct causation* and must not under any circumstances be so interpreted without *additional experimental proof.* It is curious that psychologists, almost without exception, have thrown this principle overboard and have interpreted the usually quite low correlations actually found as proof of environmental hypotheses without even considering hereditary or reactive hypotheses.' (Eysenck, H.J. *Handbook of Abnormal Psychology*, Basic Books, New York, 1960, p. 8)

In illustrating the pitfalls attendant upon disregard of this 'first lesson,' Eysenck cites a study of the relationship between early weaning and the later appearance of oral aggressive character traits (see *defense, character*). The finding that mothers who practiced early weaning had children who developed oral aggressive traits was interpreted as evidence that early weaning causes aggression. But 'This argument clearly has no logical validity at all; there are many other alternative hypotheses which account equally well for the observed facts. One alternative . . . may be called the hereditary theory. Using the same facts as before we may argue that aggressive parents wean their children early, and that the children inherit the parents' aggressiveness. . . . The second alternative theory can be called the reaction theory. According to this hypothesis, aggressive children behave aggressively to their mothers, reject the breast, etc. They therefore cause their mothers to wean them early. . . . Many other possibilities could be envisaged, but these two will suffice to show that the known facts cannot be used to support the environmental theory in any unequivocal manner. Essentially, the facts offered are *correlational.*' (*ibid.*)

correlative Pertaining to the values of a reciprocal relation between biological phenemena as indicated by the method of correlation.

cortex, cerebral (kor'teks, ser'e-bral) The most anterior portion of the telencephalon; the cerebral cortex is made up of the two cerebral hemispheres, each of which is subdivided into the frontal lobe, parietal lobe, occipital lobe, temporal lobe, and insula. Strictly speaking, the rhinen-

cephalon is not considered part of the cerebral cortex, although by implication the rhinencephalon is included where the term cerebral cortex (or cerebrum) is used.

For a more detailed description of function, see under the various divisions of the cortex—e.g. *lobe, frontal.* See also *isocortex.*

cortex, motor See *motor cortex.*

cortex, olfactory (ol-fak'to-rē) See *rhinencephalon.*

cortex, visual See *lobe, occipital.*

corticalization *Encephalization* (q.v.).

corvus (kawr'voos) Fellator. See *fellatio.*

cosmic Relating to the universe.

cosmic identification See *identification, cosmic.*

cosmos The world or universe; see *identification, cosmic.*

Cotard's syndrome [Jules Cotard. French neurologist, 1840-87] A psychotic state characterized by anxious depression, suicidal tendencies, and ideas of negation. The patient feels he no longer has a body.

cotention Burrow's term for the type of attention concomitant to a specific distribution of internally perceptible tensional patterns. It marks the organism's total tensional reaction to environmental situations. In the cotentive reaction the organism's generalized tensional patterns are sensed as contrasted with the more definitely localized tensions characteristic of the symbolic segment. The reaction of cotention appears to be coterminous with the arrest or reduction of the eye-movements concomitant to habitual mental or symbolic attention. To this extent cotention precludes the usual play of wishful phantasies with their affects and strivings as well as the partitive reaction of competitiveness and concern unconsciously adhering to man's traditional social imagery. Contrasted with *at*tention, in which a partfunction of the organism focuses upon selective objects of the environment and is adapted to them through symbolic or projective processes. (Burrow, T. *The Structure of Insanity*, Kegan Paul, Trench,

Trubner, London, 1932, p. 24; *The Biology of Human Conflict*, Macmillan, New York, 1937, p. 215)

co-therapy See *psychotherapy, multiple.*

co-twin control See *control, co-twin.*

cough, convulsive, of puberty A condition characterized by paroxysms of coughing, lasting about a minute, and based, presumably, on hysterical mechanisms. Sometimes called *cynobex hebetis.*

counseling *Guidance* (q.v.); a type of psychotherapy of the supportive or re-educative variety; often the term is applied to behavioral problems not strictly classifiable as mental illness, such as vocational or school or marriage problems. See *psychotherapy.*

counseling, genetic Also known as *genetic guidance,* or *family counseling;* the provision of advice in regard to genetically rooted family problems. Such counseling involves more than merely presenting the client with some idea of the 'genetic odds' that his offspring might develop a particular pathologic condition; equally important in family guidance is the presentation of scientifically valid information in such a way that it can be assimilated and used constructively by the client in planning future actions or arriving at a decision, and not in such a way as to traumatize the client by compounding his anxiety with perplexity and despair.

counseling, marriage '. . . the process through which a trained counselor assists two persons to develop abilities in resolving, to some workable degree, the problems that trouble them in their interpersonal relationships. A basic assumption is that all individuals grow to greater adequacy and maturity in their relationships if not blocked by such obstacles as loneliness, fear, hostility, guilt and their displacements, or transferences which prevent a person from experiencing the present as it really is and hence behaving effectively. New experience in communication is offered, and a search for more realistic solutions of present difficulties is made in an atmosphere of acceptance and understanding. The process is not encumbered with detailed consideration of conflicts in the past, their devious and

disguised transferences, or with intense and difficult ventilations of feeling.' (Appel, K.E. et al. *American Journal of Psychiatry 117,* 709, 1961)

counseling, pastoral The application of the principles of mental health by the clergyman to the management of the problems presented to him by those who seek his help. Pastoral counseling is a type of supportive or guidance therapy in which the clergyman, in his role of interpreter of personal and societal values, attempts to relate the contributions of the behavioral sciences and the resources of religion to the needs of his parishioners.

cortico-striato-spinal degeneration See *degeneration, cortico-striato-spinal.*

counter-affect See *affect, inversion of.*

counter-cathexis (-kȧ-thek′sis) *Anti-cathexis* (q.v.).

counter-compulsion A compulsion secondarily developed to fight the original compulsion, when the patient finds himself deprived of the means to continue the performance of such original compulsion. The patient supplants the original compulsion with the new one in order to continue his compulsive behavior. In the opinion of Stekel, 'every compulsion causes a counter-compulsion in the same way that every pressure causes a counter-pressure.' The compulsion to keep silent is in opposition to the compulsion to talk. (Stekel, W. *Compulsion and Doubt,* Liveright, New York, 1949)

counter-ego Stekel's term for the unconscious part of the self which acts antagonistically toward the ego proper or consciousness.

counter-formula A new formula often resorted to by a compulsive patient under certain (insurmountable) circumstances and constituting the *exact opposite* of his hitherto established *tenet.* A tenet characteristic of the compulsive patient might be: 'If I do not perform this action my father will die.' Very often, however, it is impossible to carry out the particular action. When such an impossibility is encountered, the patient goes through a series of compulsions and obsessions until he eventually finds a solution, by amending his formula in the following manner: 'My father will die if I *do* perform this action.' The final version is called the counter-formula. (Stekel, W. *Compulsion and Doubt,* Liveright, New York, 1949)

counter-identification A form of *counter-transference* (q.v.) in which the analyst identifies with the patient.

counter-impulse See *blocking, counter-impulse in.*

counter-investment *Anticathexis* (q.v.).

counterphobia Preference for or seeking of the very situation which the phobic person is, or was, afraid of. Probably the basic component of the pleasure derived from the counterphobia is the gratification which the person takes in the fact that indulging in the particular pleasure is now possible without anxiety. The counterphobic attitude is similar to the mechanism (seen normally in childhood and frequently in cases of traumatic neurosis) of striving to master excess anxiety through repeated coping with danger. Such repetition makes possible the transformation of passivity into activity; and it may also indicate libidinization of the anxiety or a flight into reality.

countershock Non-convulsive electrical stimulation usually applied for a one-minute period immediately after an electroconvulsive shock. Some claim that countershock relieves postconvulsive amnesia or confusion; others find that countershock may even increase amnesia.

counter-transference Annie Reich (*International Journal of Psychoanalysis 32:* 1-7, 1951) defines counter-transference as the effects on his understanding or technique of the analyst's unconscious needs and conflicts. The patient's personality, or the material he produces, or the analytic situation as such represents an object from the analyst's past, onto which past feelings and wishes are projected. A broader definition would include not only situations in which the patient serves as a real object onto whom something is transferred, but also those where the patient serves merely as a tool to gratify some need of the analyst, such as alleviation of anxiety or mastery of guilt feelings. Counter-transference is a necessary part of psycho-analytic therapy, for it is within the framework of counter-transference that the analyst's unconscious perception and understanding of his patient's productions come about, typically by means of partial and short-lived identifications with the patient at which points the analyst gains insight and comprehension of the patient's previously incomprehensible and confusing productions. But the analyst must be able to give up this identification and swing back into his objective role, thus preserving the neutrality of his reactions to the patient's emotions which makes the patient's transference possible.

Ideally, the analyst's unconscious mechanisms will be sublimated successfully into the qualities necessary for the practice of psychoanalytic technique. If this has not occurred, however, there may appear various undesirable counter-transference manifestations. These may be acute, temporary, and short-lived, and such manifestations are often based on identification with the patient or on reactions to the specific content of the patient's productions. As an example of the former, Reich cites the case of the analyst who was in pain and taking analgesics. His patient began to make aggressive demands for attention which irked the analyst because he was himself in a situation which would justify similar demands, but he was forced to control himself. As an instance of reaction to specific content, Reich describes the analyst who became sleepy and found it hard to concentrate or remember when his patient produced material which he perceived as relating to the primal scene; in the therapeutic situation, he reacted with the same defenses which he had himself used as a child when exposed to the primal scene.

More serious, however, are long-lasting, frequently recurring, or even permanent manifestations of counter-transference; these are usually based on deeply ingrained personality disturbances. Thus passive masochistic wishes in the analyst may make it impossible for him to analyze resistances in the patient; instead, he accepts them at face value and lets the patient accuse and mistreat him. Or unconscious agression may make the analyst overconciliatory, hesitant, and unable to be firm. Unconscious guilt feelings may lead to boredom or therapeutic overeagerness.

A not uncommon type of counter-transference is based on a paranoid attitude in the analyst so that he unearths in the patient what he wants not to see in himself, even if such content exists in only a small degree in the patient. A need to show that he is unafraid of the unconscious and its manifestations may produce a compulsion in the analyst to understand the unconscious intellectually, but such isolation renders him unable to understand defense mechanisms. If the analyst doubts the veracity of unconscious expressions, he may be afraid to make any interpretations, or he may overcompensate by making too early and too deep interpretations whenever any small bit of unconscious material is recognized. When analysis represents mainly a source of narcissistic gratification for the analyst, he will see himself as a magic healer who restores potency and heals castrations; this will lead to therapeutic overambitiousness, overestimation of patients, and hostility toward patients who do not improve. A pedagogic attitude in the analyst results in reassurance therapy rather than analytic therapy, for in essence he is saying to the patient: 'You see the world is not as bad as you think, and I do not mistreat you as you were mistreated in childhood.'

counter-volition Counter-will, as is evidenced frequently in dreams in the form of being physically unable to perform some action (such as running away) or being unable to attain some goal of reason of the particular dream situation (e.g. the dreamer wishes to visit his sweetheart but is unable to find her house, even though he has been there many times before).

counterwill, hysterial An impulse or a wish, unconsciously determined, which expresses the opposite of a conscious wish. 'A child who is very ill at last falls asleep, and its mother tries her utmost to keep quiet and not to wake it; but just in consequence of this resolution (hysterical counterwill) she makes a clucking noise with her tongue.' (Freud, S. *Collected Papers*, vol. 1, tr. by Riviere, J., Leonard and Virginia Woolf and The Institute of Psychoanalysis, London, 1924-25)

counting, compulsive See *arithmomania*.

coupling The capacity of hereditary characters to remain associated in several generations, without regard to the Mendelian principle of independent assortment.

The tendency of genetic factors to stay together in inheritance was discovered in 1906 by Bateson and Punnett. Like the mechanism of *repulsion,* it results in the formation of an excess of the parental combinations of genes and a deficiency of the new type of combinations, and is now regarded as an instance of the important phenomenon called *linkage* (q.v.).

cousin marriage See *intermarriage*.

couvade (kōō-vȧd′) A custom, found in some primitive tribes, consisting of the father taking to his bed after the birth of his child, as though he himself had given birth to the child.

cover-memory See *memory, screen; screen*.

Cp In Rorschach scoring, color projection, i.e. a response of color to an area of the blot that contains only gray. Color projection seems to replace a conscious determination to appear happy despite inner sadness; it occurs most frequently in organic brain disorders and in mild or early schizophrenias.

C.R. Abbreviation of conditional response; see *conditioning*.

CR Critical ratio; a measure of the significance or stability of a statistic, obtained by comparing the statistic to its standard error.

cramp, memory 'In conditions of fatigue or exhaustion patients frequently complain of the constant and annoying recurrence of certain tunes, melodies, phrases, verses of poetry, etc., which they have heard. The more aggravated forms, on account of their sudden startling appearance in consciousness, are in many ways analogous to muscular cramps. Certain authorities have spoken of them as "reproduction" or "memory cramps." Ribot has referred to them as characterized by a semi-tetanized attention. . . .' (Paton, S. *Psychiatry*, Lippincott, Philadelphia and London, 1905)

cramp, musician's An occupation neurosis, affecting instrumentalists and usually named according to the instrument played. See *neurosis, occupational.*

cramp, reproduction See *cramp, memory.*

cramp, seamstress's An occupation neurosis, similar to writer's cramp, occurring in needlewomen. See *neurosis, occupational.*

cramp, writer's See *neurosis, occupational.*

craniosynostosis (krā-nē-ō-sin-os-tō'sis) A congenital anomaly in which there is premature closure of the cranial sutures, resulting in oxycephaly (the most frequent form, due to closure of the coronal and lambdoid sutures), scaphocephaly (due to closure of the sagittal suture) or acrocephaly (due to closure of the coronal suture).

cratomania (krat-ō-mā'nē-à) *Obs.* 'The monomania of power, preeminence, and superiority.' (Tuke, D.H. *A Dictionary of Psychological Medicine,* vols. 1-2. Blakiston, Philadelphia, 1892)

craving, acquisitive-assimilative 'The autonomic-affective craving for food, which is a typical *acquisitive-assimilative* craving and the autonomic-affective craving to urinate, which is a typical *emissive-avertive* craving, indicate that probably all the *acquisitive* or *avertive* emotions or affective cravings and the most delicate sentiments, such as hunger, love, fear, anger, grief, sympathy, pity, joy, can probably be best understood as having a peripheral origin in characteristic variations of postural tension of autonomic or visceral segments. In its essential respects this is the James-Lange theory of the emotions.' (Kempf, E.J. *Psychopathology,* Mosby, St. Louis, 1921).

craving, autonomic-affective An expression peculiar to the psychopathology of Kempf. 'The postural tensions of the hollow viscera, although they vary in degree, are also continuously active, and this gives rise to a continuous, complex, converging affective stream from all parts of the autonomic musculature, *to which the organism as a unity is constantly, reciprocally adjusting itself.* Most of the time this afferent affective stream from a

visceral or autonomic segment is subliminally active and does not cause the organism to adjust overtly *as a unity,* that is, to become conscious of the segment's activities. When, however, the tension of some viscus is increased, the sensory stream is felt in the form of *craving,* that is, a more or less intermittent, persistent *itching* (which in the stomach causes a craving or wish for food, or in the bladder causes a craving or wish to urinate).' (Kempf, E.J. *Psychopathology,* Mosby, St. Louis, 1921)

craving, conditioned By this expression Kempf refers to the conditioning of the autonomic segments 'through an endless variety of experiences.'

craving, emissive-avertive See *craving, acquisitive-assimilative.*

craving, segmental From the point of view of Kempf's psychopathology, affective cravings arise through increased tensions of different segments of the autonomic apparatus. 'The term "segmental craving"' means that the craving 'originates in some autonomic segment, i.e., some viscus or organ such as the stomach, bladder, throat, heart or genitalia. As *physiological segments* they include their nerve and circulation division. As excised *anatomical segments* or dead organs we do not usually consider the circulatory and innervating systems, but in psychopathology we must deal with organs as they function in life.' (Kempf, E.J. *Psychopathology,* Mosby, St. Louis, 1921)

creation, replacement Any symptom formed by means of displacement of drive energy. 'The symptoms are replacement-creations (*Ersatzbildungen*), which takes the place in consciousness of the painful and repressed complexes.' (Jones, E. *Papers on Psycho-Analysis,* 4th ed., Wood, Baltimore, 1938)

creativity The ability to create something new, presumed to be a derivative of sublimation.

cremnophobia (krem-nō-fō'bē-à) Fear of precipices.

cretinism Cretinism is classified by Tredgold as one of the forms of deprivative amentia. Cretinism, which may be sporadic or endemic, is associated with the absence or insufficiency of secretion of the thyroid gland. The signs and symptoms are mental and physical, usually appearing at about the sixth month of life; among the symptoms may be mentioned apathy, lethargy, protrusion of tongue, skin changes, thickening of features, prominence of abdomen, breathing difficulties (the 'leathery' cry), defective speech, difficulty in posture and gait, generalized underdevelopment, and intellectual impairment.

cretomania (krē-tō-mā'nē-à) *Obs.* The form of insanity sometimes associated with the cretinoid state. Mania with lust and satyriasis.' (Tuke, D.H. *A Dictionary of Psychological Medicine*, vols. 1-2, Blakiston, Philadelphia, 1892)

Crichton, A. (1763-1856) British psychiatrist.

crime 'Defined legally as a violation of law.' (Sutherland, E.H. *Principles of Criminology*, Lippincott, Chicago, 1939)
'Crime within the group is essentially and primarily antisocial in that the criminal who is expected to contribute positively to the welfare of his group acts instead against it and breaks the principles of social solidarity not merely by not doing what these principles prescribe, but by doing something exactly opposite.' (Thomas, W.I. and Znaniecki, F. *The Polish Peasant in Europe and America*, Knopf, New York, 1927)

crime à deux (krēm à dü) *Folie à deux* (q.v.) in which one or more crimes are committed as part of the psychotic behavioral pattern. The term was introduced by Moreau de Tours in 1893.

crime and mental disorder There is no invariable relationship between crime and mental disorder, although criminals as a group have a greater incidence of psychiatric abnormalities than non-criminals. Many studies have shown that some degree of mental retardation is found in unexpectedly high frequency in prison inmates (20 to 25%, as opposed to the expected 1 to 3%); while such findings may indicate that the retardate is defective in his ability to control agressive or other antisocial impulses, it may equally indicate that the retardate is less adept in escaping detection, more likely because of his suggestibility to be influenced by others to act against society, and/or is poorly equipped to defend himself once he is brought to trial.

Other disorders with a higher than expected incidence of crime are schizophrenia, epilepsy and other organic brain disorders, alcoholism (especially states of acute and pathological intoxication), drug use and abuse, amnesic episodes, and fugue states. The greatest proportion of habitual offenders however, rather than belonging to any of these categories, fall instead into the group labeled antisocial or psychopathic personality. Many of these latter have had an arrested emotional development, have learned a style of delinquent life in unfavorable psychosocial settings, have had no proper models for constructive identification and have had to resort to models from disapproved subcultures (in Erikson's terminology, *malignant identity diffusion*), and/or have been reared in a society which aroused expectations in them but then denied them opportunity to fulfill those expectations

One of the major interests of the psychiatrist in crime and mental disorder, and in the *criminally insane*, revolves about the question of responsibility of the accused for the criminal action he is alleged to have committed. See *responsibility, criminal.*

crime, preventives of Any program set up to attack crime and delinquent behavior at their sources. A program of this nature needs the constant and comprehensive collaboration of psychiatrists, social workers, educators, lawmakers, and public officials, since crime is a social problem and it should be treated as such.
'Some crime preventives which should be mentioned are as follows: (1) The insurance that every child will be decently born and that his home life be socially and economically adequate; without socially mature parents the child is handicapped at the start; thus parental education, integrated with the public school system, should be developed now. (2) A more meaningful educational program which would emphasize ideals of citizenship, moral integrity, and respect for the

law and the police. (3) A periodic check made for potential delinquents throughout the public schools and treatment provided if possible; and if not, proper segregation in institutions. (4) Careful attention paid to press, movies, and radio so that crime may no longer appear to be glamorous. This can be done by women's clubs, civic bodies, and other educational groups exerting pressure on the movie syndicates and broadcasting companies to free their productions of the tawdry and lurid characteristics of crime and criminals.' (Seliger, R.V., *et al. Contemporary Criminal Hygiene,* Oakridge Press, Baltimore, 1946)

criminal, from sense of guilt A person with an unconscious need for punishment stemming from repressed oedipal wishes; this unconscious need propels him into commission of a crime for which punishment is certain.

criminal intent See *intent, criminal.*

criminalism, compulsive-neurotic Frequent repetition of criminal acts in a compulsive manner. Like most symptoms of the compulsive-neurotic, such antisocial acts are closely related to feelings of hostility and aggression, often against the father. Because these acts are symptomatic, they afford only temporary relief and are therefore repeated. One patient with compulsive-neurotic criminalism was apprehended after breaking into a hardware store and stealing money. He later confessed to many similar incidents over the preceding two years. At the same time it was apparent that he stole only for the sake of stealing. He did not need the money he thus obtained and had no special plans for using it.

criminally insane See *crime and mental disorder.*

criminology, biological In criminology, an approach that is concerned with the criminal in relation to his body-build as a factor in the crime committed. (Abrahamsen, D. *Crime and the Human Mind,* Columbia University Press, New York, 1944)

criminology, psychiatric The branch of criminology dealing with the components

of the criminal's personality that precipitate the perpetration of the crime: the criminal's experiences, inherited traits, and the causes of the crime as they pertain to his mind. (Abrahamsen, D. *Crime and the Human Mind,* Columbia University Press, New York, 1944)

criminology, sociological That branch of criminology, or the science of crime, which investigates all aspects of environment as causes of crime. (Abrahamsen, D. *Crime and the Human Mind,* Columbia University Press, New York, 1944)

criminosis (krim-i-nō'sis) 'The writer [A.N. Foxe] and others have for some years used the word criminotic to describe the individual who commits crimes, and the word *criminosis* to [describe?] the condition of such an individual.' (Branham, V.C., and Kutash, S.B. *Encyclopedia of Criminology,* Philosophical Library, New York, 1949.) The word *criminosis* is patterned after neurosis and psychosis in form, but differs in that it does not specifically connote mental illness. The criminotic individual is not necessarily emotionally or mentally ill, but the term criminosis would imply such a condition.

In his work as a prison psychiatrist Foxe encountered the problem of how to classify the prisoners who show none of the customary symptoms of mental disease. As a solution he suggested classifying criminals according to criminal behavior. 'Just as the psychiatrist studies mental symptoms as evidences of mental disease, so he must study criminal manifestations as evidence of criminality or *criminosis.'* (Foxe, A.N. *Studies in Criminology,* Nervous and Mental Disease Monographs No. 76, New York, 1948)

criminotic See *criminosis.*

crises, urban See *social policy planning.*

crisis, adolescent The emotional changes that take place during adolescence: the psychological events during this period constitute a kind of crisis, the last battle fought by the individual before reaching maturity. The ego must achieve independence, the old emotional ties must be cast off and new attachments made. Biological development brings in its train great qualitative and quantitative changes, in both the physiologic and the psychologic fields, and as a result the adolescent ego is confronted with new difficulties. Because they are closely connected with instinctual life, the emotions are affected more than is any other part of the personality by the problems of growth and therefore represent a challenging problem for the adolescent. (Stekel, W. *Compulsion and Doubt,* Liveright, New York, 1949)

crisis, catathymic (ka-ta-thī'mik) Usually, an isolated, non-repetitive act of violence which, though occurring suddenly, develops from a background of intolerable tension.

crisis, hemoclastic (hē-mō-klas'tik) Reversal of the normal white blood cell and blood pressure response to the ingestion of protein. In the normal, ingestion of protein results in leukocytosis and rise of blood pressure. In contrast, 'hemoclastic' patients show a fall in blood pressure, leukopenia, altered differential white blood count, and a reduction in the refractive index of the blood. Hemoclastic crisis is said to be particularly frequent in schizophrenia, depression, and anxiety states, and to be correlated with a poorer prognosis than in patients with a normal response.

crisis-intervention See *psychiatry, community.*

crisis, oculogyric See *spasm, oculogyric.*

crisis, physiologic Bender's term for any sudden change, endogenously produced, which occurs in the course of apparently normal maturation and development. Physiologic crisis is always seen in the history of childhood schizophrenics and is often a precipitating factor in onset of psychosis. The physiologic crisis appears to depend upon embryonal plasticity and a maturational lag.

crisis, psycholeptic (sī-kō-lep'tik) Eruption of irrational unconscious elements into consciousness. Baynes analogizes breaking in of unconscious material with the psycholeptic outbreak, which is essentially the feeling of a catastrophe, namely, the end of the world. Epileptic patients often have ideas of impending destruction. There, too, the breaking of unconscious material into the conscious-

ness is assumed to be responsible for this ideation. (Baynes, H.G. *Mythology of the Soul,* Williams and Wilkins, Baltimore, 1940.)

crispation (kris-pā'shun) Slight spasmodic or convulsive muscle-contraction, — the creeps. A synonym for *dysphoria* (q.v.).

critical flicker (fusion) frequency See *flicker.*

criticizing faculty See *faculty, criticizing.*

cross-association, telepathic The phenomenon that occurs when a thought or phantasy in one mind suddenly intersects a thought or phantasy articulated by another. It is assumed that such factors as coincidence, intuition, suggestion, or sympathetic identification of the one individual with the other are not at play. Jule Eisenbud ('Telepathy and Problems of Psychoanalysis,' *Psychoanalysis Quarterly 15,* 61, 1946) gives the following example of telepathic cross-association occurring in the course of his analysis of a patient: 'I had just come from a conference on hypertension and coronary thrombosis. During an analytic hour I began to ponder the question of differential organic neurotic adaptations. Why hypertension or coronary spasm in some cases and convulsive seizures or migraine in others? All have the factor of repressed aggression. So has the obsessive and depressed middle-aged patient on the couch before me; yet he has no physical symptoms and no clinically demonstrable organic difficulty. How is it that with his lifelong neurotic conflicts he has still managed to escape organic injury? Perhaps he is the "silent" type who will one day get a sudden coronary attack. At this point my patient, who had been weeping and complaining about his unhappy lot, said, "Why don't I die? Why don't I simply get a heart attack and die? Others do."' This phantasy was completely new to the patient and intersected the analyst's thoughts in two respects; the patient mentioned a heart attack, and also the fact that others under similar circumstances do get coronary disease.

cross dressing *Transvestism* (q.v.).

crossing over The genetic mechanism by which a chromosomal linkage group is broken up, so that some of the linked genes are able to separate and to enter different gametes and new *recombinations*. Since this interchange of genes between members of a pair of homologous chromosomes tends to involve large parts of chromosomes, that is, blocks of genes rather than single genes, mixed chromosomes, composed of both paternal and maternal gene units, originate either by *single* or *double* crossing over.

That crossing over occurs only between chromatids is due to the fact that it does not take place until after the chromosomes have each split into a pair of chromatids, early in prophase.

The new linkage groups are again as permanent as those that preceded them. It is clear, however, that a second crossing over not only undoes the genetic effect of a single crossing over, but also prevents single crossings over from occurring in more than 50 per cent. If exactly 50 per cent of crossing over took place, the numerical result would be the same as if free assortment were operating.

If there is only little crossing over between two genes, the linkage is said to be *strong* or *close*. If there is much crossing over taking place, it is said that the linkage is *weak* or *loose* (see *linkage*).

crossover See *recombination*.

croup, hysterical A hysterical cough accompanied by a croupy sound and paroxysms of dyspnoea.

crowd A group of persons in a state of sympathetic responsiveness to each other and with their attention focused upon a particular object or objective which leads to their consequent collective action.

Four types of crowd have been differentiated: the *casual* or street crowd; the *conventionalized* as spectators at college football games; the *acting* as the lynching mob; and the *expressive,* or dancing crowd observed in the origin of religious sects. (Blumer, E.H., and Park, R.E. *Principles of Sociology,* Barnes & Noble, New York, 1939)

crowding, thought By this expression Bleuler denotes what may be called enforced thinking. 'In superficial contradistinction to obstruction, schizophrenics often feel a "crowding of thoughts"; they are forced to think.' Bleuler adds that it is to be distinguished from obsessive thinking in that 'in the former the obsession lies in the subject-matter, while in the latter it is in the process.' (Bleuler, E. *Textbook of Psychiatry,* tr. by Brill, A.A., Macmillan, New York, 1930)

cruciata, hemiplegia See *hemiplegia cruciata.*

crush A popular term, denoting an amorous interest of an adolescent girl for an older girl or woman, but particularly for a teacher (woman or man).

cry, epileptic (ep-i-lep′tik) A peculiar discordant cry or yell occasionally uttered at the beginning of an epileptic fit, just before respiration is arrested. It is believed to be due to the expulsion of air through the glottis, which is narrowed at the time of the tonic spasm. The epileptic cry is sometimes referred to as the *initial cry.*

cry, initial See *cry, epileptic.*

crying cat syndrome See *syndrome, cat cry.*

cryogenic Relating to refrigeration, and especially to methods of producing very low temperatures. In neuropsychiatry, used particularly to describe methods of producing brain lesions; the technique is generally reported to produce less severe blood loss and lower mortality than other types of surgery.

cryptesthesia (krip-tes-thē′sē-à) A general term for clairvoyance, clairaudience, and other types of paranormal cognition in which the sensory stimulus is unknown.

cryptomnesia (krip-tom-nē′zhē-à) When a forgotten experience is recalled, but it appears to the subject that the experience is completely new to him, the condition is known as cryptomnesia.

crystallophobia (kris-tal-ō-fō′bē-à) Fear of glass.

C.S. Abbreviation of conditional stimulus; see *conditioning.*

Cs. Abbreviated form of *conscious.*

cue, minimal The smallest quantum or most elemental aspect of a stimulus presentation that will elicit a response or a major portion of the total response. The responder is typically unaware of the significance or even the presence of the stimulus, and his response in many respects is similar to the conditional response in clinical or operant *conditioning* (q.v.). The mechanisms involved, at least at times, are also analogous to those operative in the production of temporal *summation* (q.v.) through subliminal excitation.

Cullen, William (1710-90) A Scottish physician who emphasized the endogenous nature of mental disorders and their relationship to irritability of the nervous system; Dr. Benjamin Rush was among his students.

culmen (kul'men) See *cerebellum*.

cultural psychiatry See *psychiatry, comparative*.

culture 'The totality of the social heritages viewed as an organized body of achievement.' (Reuter, E.B. and Hart, C.W. *Introduction to Sociology*, McGraw-Hill, New York, 1933)
   'Culture comprises inherited artifacts, goods, technical processes, ideas, habits and values. Social organization cannot be understood except as a part of culture.' (Malinowski, B. 'Culture,' *Encyclopaedia of the Social Sciences*, vol. 4, Macmillan, New York, 1931, p. 621)
   ". . . the man-made part of the environment, man's symbols, ideas, values, traditions, institutions, pots and pans, and technology. As the late Sir John Myres put it, culture is what remains of man's past working on his present to shape his future." (Montagu, A. *American Journal of Psychiatry 118:*15, 1961)
   The distinction is made between *material* culture, including tools, shelter, goods, technology; and *non-material* culture, as values, customs, institutions, and social organization.

cunnilinction (kun-i-lingk'shun) Apposition of the mouth to the female genitals.

cunnilingus (-ling'gus) One who practices the apposition of the mouth to the vulva or to any part of the external female genitals, usually clitoris. From the woman's standpoint the act is completed when she achieves an orgasm.

cunnus (kun'us) Pudenda; vulva; female external genitalia.

curdling *Rare.* A term, coined by Masselon, for emotional dementia; it refers to the fixation of affects upon infantile or early childhood experiences.

cure, transference See *flight into health*.

curiosity, infantile Curiosity concerning matters of a directly sexual nature, indulged in by most children at one time or another, is referred to by psychoanalysts as infantile curiosity. The children exhibit a kind of foolish, witless behavior, and inept kind of funniness and silliness, motivation for which, says Jones, is 'to simulate innocence and often extreme childishness, even "foolishness," in order to delude their elders into regarding them as being "too young to understand" or even into altogether disregarding their presence. The purpose of the artifice is that by these means children can view and overhear various private things which they are not supposed to. It need hardly be said that curiosity thus indulged in is in most cases concerned with matters of a directly sexual nature; even marital embraces are in this way investigated by quite young children far oftener than is generally suspected or thought possible.' (Jones, E. *Hamlet and Oedipus*, Norton, New York, 1949.) See *pseudoimbecility*.

Currens formula See *responsibility, criminal*.

current, action See *action current*.

curve, Lange's colloidal gold See *Lange's colloidal gold reaction*.

Cushing's syndrome (Harvey William Cushing, American surgeon and neurologist, 1869-1939.) Hyperadrenocorticism; see *adenoma, basophile*.

custom 'The totality of behavior patterns which are carried by tradition and lodged in the group, as contrasted with the more random personal activities of the individual.' (Sapir, E. 'Custom,' *Encyclopaedia of the Social Sciences*, vol. 4, Macmillan, New York, 1931, p. 658)
   The customs of society become the habits of its individual members. W.G. Sumner classified customs into the *folkways* (q.v.) and the *mores* (q.v.).

Cutter, Nehemiah (1787-1859) American psychiatrist; one of the 'original thirteen' founders of Association of Medical Superintendents of America (forerunner of American Psychiatric Association).

cutting, braid See *braid-cutting.*

CWF Cornell Word Form. See *test, Cornell Word Form.*

CVA Cerebrovascular accident; see *accident, cerebrovascular.*

cybernetics (sī-bēr-ne'tiks) The study of messages and communication in humans, social groups, mechines, etc., especially in reference to regulation and control mechanisms such as feedback. The field of cybernetics is particularly associated with the name of Norbert Wiener, who hypothesizes a similarity between the human nervous system and electronic machines.

Cyclazocine See *methadone.*

cycle, life See *life-cycle, evolutionary.*

cycle, manic-depressive See *psychosis, manic-depressive.*

cycloid The type of personality (in DSM-II, 301.1) characterized by alternating states of increased psychic and motor activity, usually with feelings of well-being, and of diminution of the same factors. The personality is said to alternate from the one to the other. *Cycloid* commonly describes the normal or usual personality of many who subsequently develop manic-depressive psychosis, although the development of the psychosis is not a necessary result of such a personality.

Cycloid and cyclothymia are regarded by many as synonymous, although the latter term generally refers to personality problems that are more than cycloid and less than manic-depressive reactions.

cyclophrenia (sī-klō-frē'nē-à) Rare. Manic-depressive psychosis; thymergasia. See *psychosis, manic-depressive.*

cycloplegic See *mydriasis.*

cyclothemia (sī-klō-thē'mē-à) An older form for *cyclothymia.*

cyclothymia (-thī'mē-à, -thim'ē-à) Mild fluctuations of the manic-depressive type that almost have the stamp of normal mood shifts come under the heading of cyclothymia. There need not be fluctuations from psychomotor overactivity to underactivity. Some cases give a history only of periodic excitements, while others have one of periodic depressions.

The depressive phase may be clouded by the predominance of physical complaints, to which the term neurasthenia may be applied. 'Here is a group of cases who during their attacks regularly seek the specialist and are subjected to all sorts of gastro-intestinal treatment, gastric lavage, special dietaries, gynecological manipulations of one sort and another, metabolism experiments, endocrine therapy, eye-strain and almost everything in the category of medical specialism. . . .' (Jelliffe, S.E. and White, W.A. *Diseases of the Nervous System,* 6th ed., Lea & Febiger, Philadelphia, 1935)

Jelliffe and White include certain paranoid reactions under the heading of cyclothymia. 'Another group of these cases are the paranoid type. These patients present typical paranoid symptoms with emotional accompaniments that seem to be hardly in excess of what is demanded as normal reactions to the delusional state.' (ibid.)

cyclothymic personality See *personality disorders.*

cyclothymosis (-thī-mō'sis) A term suggested by Southard for manic-depressive reactions.

cynanthropy (sī-nan'thro-pē) A symptom in which the patient believes himself to be a dog; it is sometimes seen in the hebephrenic form of schizophrenia.

cynobex hebetis (cē-nō-beks hē-bē-tis) See *cough, convulsive, of puberty.*

cynophobia (sī-nō-fō'bē-à) Fear of a dog, or of rabies, Cynophobia, sometimes called pseudo-hydrophobia, is a morbid mental state, usually hysterical in character, sometimes precipitated by the bite of a dog.

cynorexia (-rek'sē-à) Dog's appetite. Bulimia.

cypridophobia (sip-ri-dō-fō'bē-à) Fear of contracting venereal disease.

cystathianineuria (sist-à-thī-à-nēn-ūr'ē-à) A metabolic defect associated with mental deficiency (31x.2).

cytheromania (si-ther-ō-mā'nē-à) *Nymphomania.* (q.v.).

cytoarchitecture Cell structure; used primarily in neurohistology. See *isocortex.*

cytogenetics (sī-tō-jen-e'tiks) That branch of biology dealing with heredity and variation at the cellular level; specifically, the study of the chemical structure of genes, the specific arrangement of gene units on chromosomes, and effects of quantitative chromosomal irregularities. See *gene; chromosome.*

cytomegalic disease Congenital, cytomegalic, inclusion body disease is a viral disorder which may infect the fetus and produce mental retardation (31x.0); inclusion bodies are demonstrable in the cells of cerebrospinal fluid, tissues, and urine.

cytoplasm (sī'tō-plas'm) The outer protoplasmic substance of a cell, exclusive of the nucleus. According to Sinnott and Dunn, its groundwork is a clear, viscous, colorless liquid which contains, in addition to various differentiated protoplasmic structures, numerous bodies of nonprotoplasmic and chiefly nutritive nature, such as oil globules and starch grains.

A system of cytoplasmic rays, the *aster,* usually surrounds in animal cells the *centrosome* or *central body* which takes a leading part in cell division. Almost all cells also embrace smaller granular bodies of mainly lipoid composition, the *mitochondria* or *chondriosomes,* which are suspected by some biologists of having a

certain function in heredity, too. The *Golgi apparatus* or *Golgi material* occurs only in animal cells as a special series of platelike bodies (fibrils), while the *plastids,* oblong bodies with specialized functions, are found exclusively in certain cells of plants. (Sinnott, E.W. and Dunn, L.D. *Principles of Genetics,* 3rd ed., McGraw-Hill, New York and London, 1939)

cytoplasmic, cytoplasmatic (sī-tō-plaz'-mik, -mat'ik) Pertaining to cytoplasm. *Cytoplasmic* originally referred to all biological qualities of the cytoplasm, but is now predominantly used in connection with that particular mode of non-Mendelian inheritance which is supposed to be based on a system of *plasmons* or genelike entities in the cytoplasm.

Although evidence for the existence of a plasmon has been derived from various sources, it seems safe to say that the problem of *cytoplasmic inheritance* is still far from a satisfactory solution. It is generally recognized now that the cytoplasm is very closely associated with the nucleus and constitutes the most immediate and intimate part of the environment in which the genes operate, thus playing an important role both in the origin of differentiation and the development of hereditary characters. According to Sinnott and Dunn, however, the part played in hereditary transmission by the cytoplasm alone is 'a relatively minor one and clearly subsidiary to the dominant genic mechanism in the nucleus,' while the opeartion of independent cytoplasmic determiners for characters other than those which have — like the plastids — their physical basis in the cytoplasm itself, must still be regarded as an open question. (Sinnott, E.W. and Dunn, L.D. *Principles of Genetics,* 3rd ed., McGraw-Hill, New York and London, 1939)

D

D In Rorschach scoring, a response to details of the ink blot which are selected frequently by healthy subjects. Piotrowski considers the D to be a measure of practical intelligence.

d In Rorschach scoring, a rare-detail response, i.e. a response to a part of the ink blot which is neither a *W*, a *D*, nor a *Dr* (qq.v.). Numerous *d* in a record indicate the subject's tendency to alleviate anxiety by occupying himself with small, precise, exacting tasks; such records are most commonly seen in schizophrenics, organic brain disorders, and obsessive neurotics.

Da Costa's syndrome Effort syndrome; neurocirculatory asthenia; soldier's heart. See *asthenia, neurocirculatory.*

dacrygelosis (dak-rē-je-lō'sis) *Obs.* Condition characterized by spells of alternate weeping and laughing; seen most frequently in hebephrenic schizophrenia.

daemonophobia (dē-mon-ō-fō'bē-à) A morbid fear of ghosts, spirits, devils, etc.

DAF Abbreviation for delayed auditory feedback. See *feedback, delayed auditory.*

D.A.H. An abbreviation for disordered action of the heart; the syndrome is known as neurocirculatory asthenia or effort syndrome. See *asthenia, neurocirculatory.*

Daltonism Red-green color blindness.

dance, St. Vitus' See *chorea, Sydenham's.*

danger-situation See *anxiety.*

DAP Draw-a-person. See *test, draw-a-person.*

dart and dome The spike and wave type of electroencephalographic tracing seen in petit mal epilepsy. See *epilepsy.*

Darwin, Charles Robert (1809-82) The scientific work of this famous British naturalist has received so much acclaim for having placed the principle of the *evolution* of living forms on a firm biological basis, that his name and the *evolutionary* theory have practically become inseparable.

Darwin was born at Shrewsbury on February 12, 1809, and there he received his early education. After he had completed his studies at the Universities of Edinburgh and Cambridge, he spent five years in a surveying expedition on the ship *Beagle*, which took him to all corners of the earth. His later life was equally active and extremely productive. His contributions to comparative zoology alone would have been sufficient to make him rank as one of the first biologists of all time. Moreover, in his *The Expression of the Emotions* he made an outstanding contribution to psychology. He died on April 19, 1882, and was buried in Westminster Abbey.

Darwin's works with their assumption of Man's descent from lowlier animal forms —particularly his *Origin of Species*, published in 1859—were interpreted by literalist theologians and religionists, including Wilberforce and Gladstone, as contradicting the biblical doctrine of the special creation of Man. He thus became the subject of hostile attacks in which his doctrines were misrepresented and caricatured, although he had an able defender in T.H. Huxley.

Even if he could not support all of his postulates, Darwin certainly was the first to succeed in establishing the truth of organic descent and to place great importance not only on the hereditary transmission of well-established characters from parents to progeny, but also on the development of certain new characters which the old-style naturalist had ignored. He proved the value of breeding experiments as a means of settling problems of ancestry, and in doing so he anticipated *genetics*, the study by which the ways of descent are discovered (see *evolution*).

Darwinism, Darwinianism Both terms relate to the branch of biology that deals with, or is in favor of, the doctrine of Charles Darwin postulating the evolution of all forms of living organisms from a few forms of primitive life (see *evolution*).

[177]

Dasein (dä-sīn') 'A being who is here'; a term used in *existentialism* (q.v.) to refer to the distinctive character of human existence, the capacity to become aware of one's own being at any particular point in time and in space and thereby to accept responsibility for what one is to become in the immediate future.

Dauerschlaf (dow'er-shlaf) Prolonged sleep treatment with drugs (usually barbiturates), used mainly in status epilepticus, acute psychotic episodes, and drug addiction.

day-dream Phantasy; idle indulgence of the fancy during the waking hours; wishful thinking. Often, as in schizophrenia, day-dreams assume pre-eminence in the mind of the patient, in whom they take the place of action in the real environment. In schizophrenia day-dreams acquire the value of reality for the patient; that is, they become symptoms of the psychosis. When the latter takes place one no longer speaks of the phantasies as day-dreams, because reality has been abandoned for the unconscious strivings and their presentation in the form of symptoms.

Freud says that day-dreams hover in a curious medley of the past, present, and future. Some thought of the present creates a desire; the desire courses back to some earlier pleasant experience, which is lived out again in the mind with the idea of future fulfilment.

The driving force behind day-dreaming is a conscious or unconscious wish or striving. Day-dreams serve an appeasing function (Maeder), in that they give partial release to strong, unconscious affects. The process involved is in the nature of abreaction (Varendonck). Federn says that abnormal day-dreaming is analogous to sexual fore-pleasure in that neither represents the fulfillment of the final aim. See *phantasy-life*.

day hospital A type of treatment for mentally ill patients consisting of a psychiatric hospital program (including individual and group psychotherapy, somatic treatment, nursing care, social case work, psychological evaluation, occupational and recreational therapy, etc.) in which the patient participates during the day; but, at night, he returns to his home, family, and community. The first day hospital was set up by Dr. Ewen Cameron at the Allan Memorial Institute, Montreal (Canada), in 1946. In 1954, the first *night hospital* (with patients partaking of hospital care at night but returning to their homes and occupations during the day) was established at the Montreal General Hospital.

Both the day hospital and the night hospital are types of *partial hospitalization*, another form of which is the weekend hospital. See *psychiatry, community*.

daymare Anxiety-attack; a condition 'of great temporary mental terror or distress, arising without apparent cause, or from very slight causes in a person in a state of wakefulness.' (Tuke, D.H. *A Dictionary of Psychological Medicine*, vols. 1-2, Blakiston, Philadelphia, 1892)

day-residue See *regression, topographical*.

Dd Rorschach scoring symbol for an unusual detail response.

dD In Rorschach scoring, a confabulated detail response; it is the use of a single, small detail as the basis for interpretation of a larger area of the ink blot. Such responses are always poorly conceived and thus of poor form quality.

dd Rorschach scoring symbol for a very small detail response.

Dds Rorschach scoring symbol for a detail response to a small white space on the card.

DdW Rorschach scoring symbol for an unusual detail response which is elaborated in such a way that the whole is perceived in the form of the detail.

de Rorschach scoring symbol for edge detail.

deadly nightshade poisoning See *poisoning, deadly nightshade*.

deafness, word Auditory aphasia. See *aphasia, auditory*.

de-analize Instincts are said to be *de-analized* when they are shifted from the anal region to another object or form of expression. For example, interests in feces may later be expressed as interests in mud, still later in money, securities, etc. Part of he interests may be expressed as a character trait (e.g. cleanliness).

death Cessation of life, physical and mental; total and permanent cessation of the functions or vital actions of an organism. Among certain psychiatric patients the term 'death' does not imply cessation of life, save in the sense that the patient ceases to continue in the environment in which he lives. Death is regarded simply as a preliminary step to re-birth, without any essential alteration of the body or psyche. This concept is common in schizophrenia.

In others (e.g. hysterical women), death may represent punishment for carrying out a forbidden impulse, such as incest. Or it may represent reunion with the Oedipal love object.

Another symbolic meaning of death occurs in depressive states, in which suicide unconsciously represents the means by which the death of another is accomplished.

death-instinct See *instinct, death.*

death-rate See *rate, death.*

death-trance n. A state of apparent death; so-called suspended animation as may be seen in hysteria and catatonic schizophrenia.

death-trend. See *suicide.*

debilitas animi (dā-bē'lē-tås å'nē-mē) (L. 'infirmity of the spirit') An older term for imbecility.

debilitas erethisica (er-e-thē'zē-kå) *Obs.* Morbid irritability.

debilitas memoriae (me-mô'rē-ī) (L. 'weakness of memory') *Obs.* Defect or weakness of memory.

debilitas nervosa (ner-vō'zå) (L. 'nervous debility') *Obs.* Neurasthenia.

debility Asthenia.

decadence The retrogression of a person, group, or society which results from social rather than from physical or biological change (see *degeneration*).

decades, involutional Roughly, the period

from 40 to 60 years of age; in women, the involutional period is usually considered to include the years between 40 and 55, in men the years between 50 and 65.

decapitation, fear of Castration anxiety dread (that his penis will be cut off) which in the psychoanalytic context assumes the form of a fear that he will be decapitated. Castration anxiety appears in boys at the age when a high concentration of pleasurable sensations from the penis begins to arise. This anxiety may take many forms depending on the history of the particular person, and one of these forms is a fear of decapitation.

deception Simulation; malingering.

deception, reduplicative memory An expression used by Pick for a form of false memory sometimes observed in patients with organic brain disease. The patient claims, for instance, that he has already been examined by the same doctor, in the same examining room, with the same nurse in attendance, although the entire situation is in fact new to him. See *déjà fait.*

decerebrate rigidity See *rigidity, decerebrate.*

decidentia (dā-kē-den'tē-å) *Obs.* Epilepsy.

decompensation Breakdown or failure in the functioning of the defense system such as occurs in relapses in schizophrenic patients.

decompose In a psychiatric sense: *to divide* oneself or another into separate and distinct personalities.

decomposition Division of a person into separate components, or, more correctly, personalities. It is often observed among patients with the paranoid form of schizophrenia that they decompose or split the persecutor into separate entities.

'If we take a survey of the delusions as a whole we see that the persecutor is divided into Flechsig and God; in just the same way Flechsig himself subsequently splits up into two personalities, the "upper" and the "middle" Flechsig and God into the "lower" and "upper" God. In the later stages of the illness the decomposition of Flechsig goes further still.'

(Freud, S. *Collected Papers*, vol. 3, tr. by Strachey, A. and J., Leonard and Virginia Woolf and The Institute for Psychoanalysis, London, 1925)

decomposition, in dreams The gradual dissolution of the whole structure (i.e. its manifest content) of the dream into its component parts (i.e. its latent content) by the process of free association.

decomposition of ego See *ego, decomposition of.*

decomposition of movement This condition, described by Babinski, is characterized by irregularity in the successive flexion or extension at the various joints, instead of steady, well-timed movements.

dedifferentiation Loss of higher levels of organization and function; regression; usually applied to the simultaneous acceleration and retardation of development found in schizophrenic children and approximately equivalent to what Bergmann and Escalona termed *fragmentation of the ego,* to Erikson's *interference with psycho-embryological schedule of ego functions,* to what Eckstein and Wallerstein termed *fluctuating ego states,* and to Rank's *atypical development.*

deep interpretation See *interpretation, deep.*

de-erotize To remove libidinal cathexis from the psychic representation of an object.

defecation Act of discharging excreta. See *anal-erotism.*

defect, field See *field defect.*

defectio animi (dā-fek′tē-ō à′nē-mē) (L. 'deficiency of mind') *Obs.* Mental deficiency.

defective, mental One who is subnormal intellectually; feebleminded. In New York State a mentally defective individual is defined as 'any person afflicted with mental defectiveness from birth or from early age to such an extent that he is incapable of managing himself and his affairs, who for his own welfare or the welfare of others or of the community requires supervision, control or care and who is not insane or of unsound mind to such an extent as to require his commitment to an institution as provided by this chapter (*Handbook of the Department of Mental Hygiene, New York State,* State Hospitals Press, Utica, N.Y., 1939) See *retardation, mental.*

defemination See *eviration.*

defense, defence A mental attribute or mechanism or dynamism, which serves to protect the person against danger arising from his impulses or affects. See *anxiety.*

The ego arises in response to the frustrations and demands of reality on the organism; it learns to follow the reality principle. But the id follows the pleasure principle only, so that often there are conflicts between the two. This is the essential neurotic conflict. The superego may take either side, and if the world and external reality appear to the ego to be sources of temptation, the conflict may appear to be between the world and the ego.

The mechanisms of defense are developed as a means of controlling or holding in check the impulses or affects which might occasion such conflicts. The various motives for the development of defense-mechanisms are: (a) anxiety, arising when the ego believes the instinct is dangerous; (b) guilt, with anxiety of the ego toward the superego and fear of annihilation or decrease of narcissistic supplies (c) disgust, when the ego must reject the impulse or it will have to be vomited out, and (d) shame, a fear of being looked at and despised if the impulse is not rejected.

Various defense-mechanisms have been described. Anna Freud (*The Ego and the Mechanisms of Defence,* Hogarth Press, London, 1948) lists the following: regression, repression, reaction-formation, isolation, undoing, projection, introjection, turning against the self, reversal, and sublimation or displacement of instinctual aims. O. Fenichel (*The Psychoanalytic Theory of Neurosis,* Norton, New York, 1945) includes: regression, repression, reaction-formation, isolation, undoing, projection, introjection, sublimation, displacement, denial, postponement of affects, affect equivalents, and change in the quality of affects.

Evidently both Anna Freud and Fenichel use introjection and identification interchangeably, although technically introjection is the mechanism by which *identification* (q.v.) is accomplished. L. E. Hinsie (*Visual Outline of Psychiatry,* Oxford University Press, New York, 1940) lists 16 mental mechanisms; repression, reaction-formation, isolation, undoing, projection, introjection, identification, sublimation, displacement, condensation, rationalization, transference, symbolization and transposition, conversion, phantasy, and day-dreaming.

defense, character In the early 1920's, many psychoanalysts had become pessimistic about the value of therapy. Wilhelm Reich (*Character Analysis,* 3rd ed., Orgone Institute Press, New York, 1949) undertook an evaluation of therapeutic failures and pointed out that many chaotic analyses are the result of failure to recognize a latent negative transference. This negative transference is commonly hidden behind the character traits of the person, which serve as a protective armor against stimuli from the outer world and against his own libidinous strivings. In the course of the conflict between instinctual demands and the frustrating outer world, the character armor develops in the ego and becomes a chronic and habitual pattern of reaction to threatened or actual frustration from the outer world. Also, in psychoanalytic treatment the character armor serves as a compact defense mechanism, and this character resistance or character defense must be overcome if the analysis is to proceed properly. The ego employs other mechanisms of defense, such as repression, regression, reaction-formation, isolation, undoing, introjection, turning against the self, reversal, and sublimation. Although any or all of these mechanisms may be involved in the development of the character defense, they correspond essentially to a single experience, whereas the character represents a specific way of being and is an expression of the total past.

There are four main types of character defense: (1) hysterical; (2) compulsive; (3) phallic-narcissistic; and (4) masochistic.

(1) In the hysterical (which includes the passive-feminine) character (in DSM-II, *hysterical personality,* 301.5), obvious sexual behavior is combined with a specific kind of bodily agility which has a definitely sexual nuance. Such behavior traits are combined with outspoken apprehensiveness, which is increased when the sexual behavior comes close to attaining its goal. The hysterical character represents an apprehensive defense against incest wishes inhibited by the anxiety related to any genital expression.

(2) The compulsive character (in DSM-II, *obsessive-compulsive* or *anankastic personality,* 301.4) has a pedantic concern for orderliness, a tendency to collect things, and thriftiness or avarice. Thinking is circumstantial and ruminative in type. This character armor is a defense against sadistic and aggressive impulses.

(3) The phallic-narcissistic character appears self-confident and arrogant; behavior is either cold and reserved or derisively aggressive. Most forms of active homosexuality and of schizophrenia fall into this group. Phallic-narcissistic attitudes are a defense against passive-feminine tendencies and represent an unconscious tendency of revenge against the opposite sex. The character resistance is seen in aggressive depreciation of the analysis and a tendency to take over the interpretation work.

(4) The masochistic character shows chronic tendencies to self-damage and self-depreciation and subjectively has a chronic sensation of suffering. The masochistic self-punishment is a defense against punishment and anxiety in that it represents a milder substitute punishment. The masochistic character avoids anxiety by wanting to be loved, but the excessive demand for love is disguised in grandiose provocation of the love-object. The purpose of this is to make the provoked person react with behavior which will justify the reproach: 'See how badly you treat me.'

The classification above is in terms of the clinical picture. There is another classification which stresses the libido origin of character. In this system, the character attitudes are assumed to be reaction-formations or sublimations of the libido of the stage in question. Thus: (1) The oral receptive character is considered a sublimation of the earliest sucking stage of life. Such people are characterized by friendliness, optimism, and generosity and expect the whole world to mother them. When frustrated they become pessimistic and act as if the bottom had fallen out of the world.

(2) The oral aggressive character represents a sublimation of the oral biting stage. Aggressiveness, envy, ambition, and

a tendency to exploit others are typical features.

(3) The anal character corresponds to the compulsive character described as (2) in the other classification above.

(4) The phallic character has also been described.

(5) The urethral character has burning ambition and a need to boast of achievement, and is impatient; there is often a history of bed-wetting beyond the usual age.

(6) The mature or genital character is no longer dominated by the pleasure principle, shows features characteristic of the preceding stages, but in a combination conducive to the greatest effectiveness. The mature character is able to care for and contribute to the welfare of another.

defense-mechanism The means by which the organism protects itself against impulses and affects. See *defense.*

defense-neuro-psychosis See *psychosis, defense.*

defense-neurosis See *psychosis, defense.*

defense, pathogenic A defense against instinctual demands, pathogenic in its nature, because the opposed unconscious impulse cannot find discharge.

For many reasons, as the person develops, he learns to 'ward off' his own impulses, his instinctual drives. First, as an infant he required external help to satisfy these demands and since this help was not always immediately at hand, the infant found himself in traumatic situations as a result of his instinctual excitations. Secondly, both education and nature's own prohibitions (such as being burned upon grasping a flame) engender fear of instinctual acts. Education is effective not only because of the adult's physical power, but also because of the child's need of affection from the adult. Thirdly, the child thinks animistically and, accordingly, believes that his own instinctual demands are identical with those of his environment. Also, since the child feels that any of his acts might provoke the same response from the environment, he will fear fantastic dangers from the environment in connection with his own instinctual impulses. For example, on meeting a rebuff in his phantasies of devouring the environment, the child may phantasy that he might be eaten by the parents. These are some of the reasons for the development of forces opposing the discharge of instinctual impulses. These forces are known as ego-defenses. When successful, the ego-defenses are called sublimations. The instinctual drives find an adequate discharge in these sublimations. When unsuccessful, however, these defenses are called pathogenic. The opposed pregenital impulses do not find discharge but remain in the unconscious and in fact keep on gaining strength, because of the continued functioning of their physiological sources. These warded-off instincts continue to seek discharge. 'A state of tension results and a breakthrough may occur.' This breakthrough is the basis of neurotic symptoms which express simultaneously both a repressed drive and the defense against it. An unsuccessful defense is therefore pathogenic, in the sense that it is the basis for the subsequent neurotic symptoms, in which the drive, formerly opposed by the defense, has broken through and is expressed in the neurotic symptom.

The pathogenic defenses are mechanisms which consist of 'a partial cessation of certain functions of the ego.' Some examples of these pathogenic defenses are denial, projection, introjection, repression, reaction-formation, undoing, isolation, and regression. In many of these defenses the ego's function of reality-testing has been conspicuously suspended and, in some of them, old archaic modes of thinking, perceiving, and relating to reality have been utilized again. (Fenichel, O. *The Psychoanalytic Theory of Neurosis,* Norton, New York, 1945)

defense-psychoneurosis. See *psychoneurosis, defense.*

defense-psychosis. See *psychosis, defense.*

defenses, Ur See *Ur-defenses.*

defensive-reaction See *reaction, defensive.*

deficiency, mental Mental retardation; intellectual inadequacy, feeble-mindedness, hypophrenia, oligophrenia, oligergasia. In the 1952 nomenclature (DSM-I), the term denoted intellectual defect existing since birth, without demonstrated organic brain disease or known prenatal cause. As thus used, the term was equivalent to the older term, familial or idiopathic mental deficiency. Mental retardation is the term preferred currently; see *retardation, mental.*

deficiency, moral An early term for moral insanity. Most psychiatrists today prefer to use the term *psychopathic personality* (q.v.) for such cases. See *anethopathy.*

defloration The act of perforating the hymen during the first coitus of a virgin. From the psychiatric point of view, such an event is, of course, extraordinarily important, inasmuch as it constitutes an experience which, in general, is a vital consequence in the development of a woman's personality. A careful study of all the details concerning this act supplies to psychoanalytic theory and practice valuable material in which the analyst may unearth the clue for elucidating many emotional conflicts seemingly unrelated to defloration, but in fact linked with and stemming from this experience.

In the interpretation of dreams, defloration and its symbolic representations often play a role of paramount importance.

deformation While in general medicine this term is identical with *disfigurement* or *want of harmony,* in the field of constitutional medicine it refers to De Giovanni's particular hypothesis, the *'law of deformation,'* which is basic to his concepts of constitutional types: that individuals having a small trunk tend to assume a *longilinear* body which corresponds to the *phthisic habitus* (q.v.). Analogously, individuals having a large trunk are thought to be inclined to assume a *short* body which corresponds to the *habitus apoplecticus* (q.v.), and individuals having a normal trunk are said to be inclined to maintain *normal* proportions of the body.

defusion In psychoanalysis, the separation or detachment of the instincts, so that they operate independently.

Normally, the energy of the aggressive or death instinct is fused with the sexual. With regression, however, this unification and organization of part-instincts crumbles; the destructive instincts are freed and often work directly against the sexual instincts. This is the process of defusion, which in severe form will lead to such prepotency of the destructive instincts that negation of life is the result.

degeneration *Deterioration* (q.v.); reduction to a lower type of personal and social conduct as defined by existing moral and organic laws to which the person is expected to conform. Often the term is used in a pejorative sense to imply a sexual offense.

degeneration, cerebromacular *Amaurotic family idiocy* (q.v.).

degeneration, cortico-striato-spinal Spastic pseudosclerosis; Jakob-Creutzfeldt's disease; usually classified as one of the presenile dementias (290.1). The condition begins slowly, with apathy, some memory impairment, unpredictability of behavior, and speech disturbances. Neurological symptoms (ataxia, dysarthria, spasticity of the limbs, choreo-athetoid movements and other extrapyramidal symptoms) become increasingly severe and are accompanied by rapidly progressing dementia until finally speech becomes an incoherent jumble, gross spasticity and paralysis appear, and sphincter control is lost. Death usually occurs within 6 to 24 months after appearance of symptoms.

Etiology is unknown. Pathological changes, most prominent in the cerebral cortex, basal ganglia, cerebellar cortex, optic thalamus, substantia nigra, and anterior horn cells, include ganglion cell atrophy, degeneration of the corticospinal tracts, and widely distributed senile plaques and neurofibrillary changes.

degeneration, hepatolenticular (he-pa-tō-len-tik-ū-lêr) Tetanoid chorea of Gowers; Westphal's pseudosclerosis; progressive lenticular degeneration; in DSM-II, coded 31x.2. A hereditary disorder of copper metabolism characterized by degeneration of the corpus striatum (especially the putamen) and cirrhosis of the liver, with decreased serum ceruloplasm and increased urinary excretion of copper and amino acids. The disease begins early in life (10 to 25 years of age) and is progressive. The initial symptom is usually tremor, which is increased by voluntary movement. This is followed by rigidity, similar to that seen in Parkinsonism, and including a vacant, expressionless appearance or a vacuous smile. Involuntary laughing and crying may occur and also some degree of mental deterioration.

In a certain number of cases, a zone of golden-brown granular pigmentation (the Kayser-Fleischer ring) can be seen in the cornea; some would distinguish these patients from those with Wilson's disease and term the syndrome Westphal-Strümpell's pseudosclerosis. Untreated cases are invariably fatal, half of them within six years from onset of symptoms; more recently, treatment with BAL (British anti-lewisite) to remove copper from the body has afforded some hope of at least temporary amelioration.

degeneration, neuro-axonal Also known as *Seitelberger's disease;* the syndrome consists of spastic paraplegia, equilibrium disturbances, ocular tremor, and mental retardation (31x.3). Pathology includes eosinophilic spheroid masses throughout the cerebral grey matter, spongiosis of the globus pallidus, and demyelination of the pyramidal tracts.

degeneration-psychosis See *psychosis, degeneration.*

degeneration, subacute combined See *sclerosis, posterolateral.*

degeneration, Wallerian (Augustus Volney Waller, English physician, 1816 - 70) Myelin sheath degeneration of the axon distal to the point of severance from the cell body.

dégénérés superieurs (dā-zhā-hā-rā′ sü-pā-ryēr′) (F. 'high-class degenerates') Magnan's term for those sexual deviates whose perversions serve as an inspiration for great achievements in some special field of endeavor—social, artistic, ethical, etc. An example is the sadistic pedophile who built and maintained a home for disadvantaged children.

degenitalization (dē-jen-i-tal-ī-za′shun) *Desexualization* (q.v.).

degradation, senile *Obs.* for *senile deterioration.*

dehypnotize (dē-hip′nō-tiz) To bring one out of the hypnotic state.

déjà entendu (de-zhà′äN-täN-dü′) (F. 'already heard, perceived') The feeling, not demonstrable in fact, because it never was associated with reality, that one had at some prior time heard or perceived what one is hearing in the present.

déjà eprouvé (ā-proo-vā′) (F. 'already experienced, tested, tried out') Many patients, on the basis of the wish, have the distinct feeling that an act or experience, in which they had actually never engaged, had already been carried out by them. It is not an uncommon delusional phenomenon among psychotic patients.

déjà fait (de-zhà′fe′) (F. 'already done') Pierre Marie's term for a type of paramnesia in which the patient believes that what is happening to him now has happened to him before. Thus one hebephrenic believed he had experienced exactly one year before, everything that was happening to him at the time. 'The very same visitor in exactly the same clothes was here one year ago today and said the same things.' This sort of paramnesia is common in schizophrenia.

déjà pensé (päN-sā′) (F. 'already thought (of)') A patient's feeling, verging on certainty, that he has already thought of the matter. 'The *déjà vu* and *déjà pensé* phenomena that are a part of many psychomotor attacks . . . suggest that many of them are associated with disorders localized to the temporal lobes.' (DeJong, R.N. 'Phenurone in the Treatment of Psychomotor Attacks,' *American Journal of Psychiatry CVII,* No. 11, May 1951)

déjà raconté (rà-kawN-tā′) (F. 'already told, recounted') Sometimes, when a forgotten experience, particularly one from the distant past, is recalled, the individual may feel as if he had known all the time that the experience had been told to him. The phenomenon is known as *déjà raconté.* The term is also applied to the conviction of the patient in psychoanalysis that he has already related an episode to the analyst, when in fact he has not.

déjà voulu (voo-lü′) (F. 'already desired') Pierre Marie's term for a type of paramnesia in which the patient believes that his present desires are exactly the same as the desires he had some time before. See *déjà fait; déjà vu.*

déjà vu (vü′) (F. 'already seen') Feeling of familiarity. When a person, upon perceiving something that he has never seen before, has the distinct feeling that he had had the experience some time in the past, the expression *déjà vu* is used. It is not uncommon among psychiatric patients, particularly those with hysteria and epilepsy. A patient, for example, while visiting a town for the first time in his life may feel certain that he has been there on some previous occasion.

Freud suggested that déjà vu feelings correspond to the memory of an unconscious phantasy; the experience probably represents a combination of ego defenses in a situation that both symbolizes and stimulates the revival of an anxiety-provoking memory or phantasy. The ego defenses include wish-fulfillment (in the form of 'Don't worry; you have been in the same situation before and came out all right') and regressive reanimation of omnipotent feelings (in the form of predicting the future). (Arlow, J.A. *Journal of the American Psychoanalytic Association* 7, 611-631, 1959)

dejectio animi (dā-yek′tē-ō ä′nē-mē) (L. 'depression of spirit') Melancholia.

dejection Melancholy. The word dejection refers to the mood-tone change which is part of a clinical depression and is approximately equivalent to the word depression as used by the layman. In psychiatry, depression has a more specific meaning and should not be used when only a lowered mood tone is meant.

Déjérine (dā-zhē-rēn′) **Jules-Joseph** (1849-1917) French neurologist and psychiatrist.

de Jong, H. Holland (1895-1956) Dutch psychiatrist, in later years in U.S.; production of symptoms of mental illness in animals (especially catatonia).

delayed auditory feedback See *feedback*.

delibidinization (dē-li-bi-di-ni-zā′shun) Technically, the act of removing libido from an object. In practice, this term is used to refer to an interpersonal relationship which is predicated on spiritual, objective, or non-emotional grounds. In certain Jewish forms of culture, for example, the father's authority rests primarily on his status as an exponent of the

religious and scholarly tradition, rather than on the status of comforter, nurse, or donor of material or emotional comforts. 'Insofar as is possible to a living creature, a father's personality is delibidinized.' (Landes, R. and Zborowski, M. 'Hypotheses concerning the Eastern European Jewish Family,' *Psychiatry 13*, 447, 1950)

delinquency The term delinquency, which includes faults, misdeeds, and certain types of misbehavior, is applied (*technically* speaking) only to the offenses of young people under the age of sixteen or eighteen, and refers to all offenses committed by them. Heredity, family influences, environmental competition, idleness and monotony in the life of the child, emotional maladjustment, and psychosexual development are among the more important factors to be studied as causes of delinquency. Nevertheless, one may assert that, in gross personality disturbances, the delinquent does not differ markedly from the general run of the population, and although the delinquent suffers less from the neuroses and is not sharply inferior (in mental deficiency rates) in comparison with the corresponding classes of the population, he is, on the other hand, more often the victim of psychoses and psychopathic states.

Immaturity, egocentricity, and inability to establish emotional relationship with others are characteristics of the delinquent personality.

Immaturity: This involves the inability to deny oneself a present pleasure, even though its indulgence may carry with it an immediate penalty or may interfere with the attainment of future aims.

Egocentricity: The delinquent selfishly seeks personal pleasure, has little or no consideration for others, has no sense of guilt, and often believes that he is right and the rest of society is wrong.

Inability to establish emotional relationship with others: The delinquent is pressed by family, school (or class), and communal competition and, as he fails to reach standards that are quite beyond him, his inadequate behavior becomes delinquent to compensate for his inadequacy. He develops an antisocial attitude through his inability to make the necessary healthy identifications, or through actual and direct hostility to adverse surroundings.

Heredity: 'Figures most prominently in

the causes of crime through the production of feeblemindedness and the lessening of emotional inhibition.'

Family influences: 'The unharmonious atmosphere of the home whose members are constantly fighting and where the children are made a buffer between quarreling parents who have "fallen out of love" is much more likely to result in delinquency than are parental separations and family breakups. The emotional relationships in the family are most important, particularly those based on the child's feeling of rejection or on the manifestation of overprotection by a parent. The child's need for affection and sense of security and of personal adequacy, which is ordinarily satisfied in the normal family, is not so met in the psychologically broken home, whose bickering and disharmony is anything but reassuring to the sensitive child mind. The situation is particularly serious, if the youngster is made to feel that he is not wanted.'

Environment: The life of children in a 'bad' neighborhood atmosphere is likely to be hostile to the normal development of the individual. 'There is not sufficient opportunity for social activities and wholesome outdoor play. Delinquent schools, of which there are some, as a rule are closely associated with delinquent communities. The rigid, theoretical curriculum of the public school makes it difficult for non-bookish, non-academic youngsters to get along well. The final blunder of society is its failure to provide school activities that will interest and intrigue these peculiar types of youths, who are likely to turn delinquent when frustrated, disappointed, and discouraged.'

Idleness and monotony: Long periods of idleness in the life of children, especially in the slum districts of large cities, may be considered a factor of importance as a crime breeder. Monotony is unbearable to adventurous youth . . . Many times juvenile crime is nothing more or less than an unconscious attempt to escape boredom.'

Psychosexual development: While more complete sex instruction 'has done much to lessen sex worries and anxiety, it has done but little, if anything, to improve sexual morals. There is just about as much of the sex element in juvenile delinquency today as a generation ago. It represents one of the major divisions of juvenile crime; in fact, among girls, it is the outstanding delinquency . . . Many times sex offenses are committed by young people for the same reason that they resort to the use of alcohol—to convince themselves and others that they have "grown up."

These abnormal sex drives are also exhibited by "rippers" and "slashers," those boys who cut pieces of clothing from girls' dresses or snip off locks of their hair. Many times these sexual delinquents are intelligent youths, good students, and otherwise very well-behaved socially . . . undoubtedly many sexual delinquents are on the borderline of insanity. This will explain certain types of sex perversion, criminal sexual assaults, and chronic exhibitionism. This group of psychotic sex offenders will not be helped very much by ordinary methods of treatment.' (Sadler, W.S. *Modern Psychiatry,* Mosby, St. Louis, 1945; Seliger, R.V. *et al. Contemporary Criminal Hygiene,* Oakridge Press, Baltimore, 1946)

delinquency area See *area, delinquency.*

delinquent, defective In some states it is recognized that 'there are individuals who are not of sufficiently low mentality to be called legally irresponsible for their anti-social acts, or incapable of standing trial, but who are, nevertheless, of more or less subnormal mentality, and who require special institutional treatment.' (Weihofen, H. *Insanity as a Defense in Criminal Law,* Commonwealth Fund, Oxford University Press, New York, 1933.) Such individuals are known as defective delinquents and the condition is known as defective delinquency.

'The Massachusetts law provides that in any case involving an offense not punishable by death or life imprisonment, if the court shall find that the defendant is mentally defective and has shown himself to be an habitual delinquent or shows tendencies towards becoming such, and that such delinquency is or may become a menace to the public and that he is not a proper subject for commitment as an insane or feebleminded person, the court may commit him as a defective delinquent.' (ibid.)

deliquium animi (dā-lē′kwē-oom a′nē-mē) *Obs.* Mental deficiency.

deliramentum (dā-lē-rá-men'toom) (L. 'nonsense, absurdity') *Obs.* Delirium.

deliratio senum (-rä'tē-ō se'noom) (L. 'dotage of the old') *Obs.* Senile psychosis.

deliration (del-i-rā'shun) *Obs.* Delirium.

délire (ā-lēr') (F. 'delirium') An uncertain term, which sometimes refers to *delirium* (q.v.), at other times to *delusion* (q.v.) or to *compulsion* (q.v.). In general, the term could best be described as referring to a complex or system of ideas which forms a prominent part of the patient's mental condition.

délire aigu (ā-gü') (F. 'acute delirium') Acute mania.

délire alcoolique (ál-kô-lik') (F. 'alcoholic delirium') Delirium tremens.

délire ambitieux (äN-bē-syē') (F. 'highfalutin delirium') Maniacal excitement with grandiosity.

délire à quatre (á-katr') (F. 'quadruple insanity, foursome insanity') A psychiatric constellation, usually consisting of systematized delusions of persecution, involving four people. The delusions are found first in one person, and then are taken over, as in a contagious disease, by a second, third, and fourth person. See *association, psychosis of.*

délire chronique à évolution systématique (krô-nēk' á ā-vô-lü-syawN' sē-stemá-tēk') (F. 'chronic delirium with organized development') See *paranoia completa.*

délire crapuleux (krá-pü-lē') (F. 'dissolute delirium') Delirium tremens.

délire d'emblée (däN-blā') (F. 'delirium at one blow') Bleuler says: 'Some delusions, especially in schizophrenia, suddenly appear in consciousness as finished products (délire d'emblée, primordial delusion).' (Bleuler, E. *Textbook of Psychiatry,* tr. by Brill, AA., Macmillan, New York, 1930)

délire de négation (dē ne-gá-syawN') (F. 'delirium of negation') See *negation.*

délire de négation généralise (zhā-ne-rá-lē-zā') (F. 'generalized delirium of negation') Church and Peterson write: 'Another interesting form of depressed delusion is that of negation (délire de négation généralise), which has its origin usually from an idea of having sinned. The patient thinks he must be the devil himself, his sin is so great; consequently he can never die, he must suffer forever; then with the growing idea of the enormity of his sin, he comes to believe that God and mankind and the world exist no more.' (Church, A. and Peterson, F. *Nervous and Mental Diseases,* 8th ed., Saunders, Philadelphia and London, 1916)

délire d'énormité (dā-nawr-mē-tā') (F. 'mania of vastness') Bleuler says that in *délire d'énormité* the patients may not use a chamber because they would flood the entire institution or the whole world; they are swollen up so big that they fill up the entire house and city, and choke everybody. . . . In a certain sense the opposite of this is *micromania* which also occurs only in organic depressions.' (Bleuler, E. *Textbook of Psychiatry,* tr. by Brill, A.A., Macmillan, New York, 1930)

délire depressif (dā-pres-ēf') (F. 'depressive delirium') Melancholia.

délire des grandeurs (dā-gräN-dēr') (F. 'mania of grandeurs') Delusional grandiosity.

délire des persécutions (dā per-sā-kü-syawN') (F.) Persecutory delusional state.

délire du toucher (dütoo-shā') (F. 'mania for touching') Compulsion to touch objects; see *touching.*

délire ecmnesique (ek-mnā-zēk') (F. 'ecmnesic delirium') See *ecmnesia.* By this expression Pitres denotes preoccupation with events which transpired years before. He describes the condition in conjunction with hysteria, pointing out that the patient in this state lives almost entirely in the past.

délire en partie double (äN pár-tē'doo'-bl') (F. 'double-entry delirium') Induced 'insanity'; *folie à deux.* See *association, psychosis of.*

délire onirique (aw-nē-rēk') (F. 'oneiric delirium') See *deliria oneirica*. Dreamlike delirium.

délire terminal See *hysteria*.

délire tremblant (träN-bläN') (F. 'trembling delirium') Delirium tremens.

délire vésanique (ve-za-nēk') (F. 'insane delirium') *Vesania* (q.v.).

deliria (dā-lē'rē-à) An older term, meaning 'insanity' in general.

deliria oneirica (ô-nā'rē-kà) Bianchi says: 'These deliria are constituted of scenes from dreams, changing, varied, and uninterrupted, the subject being as if he were in a somnambulic dream. These occur generally at night, but sometimes they continue after waking. On recovery the patient has no recollection of his delirium.' (Bianchi, L. *A Text-Book of Psychiatry*, tr. by MacDonald, J.H., Baillière, Tindall & Cox, London, 1906)

delirious reaction See *syndrome, organic*.

delirium (dē-lir'ē-um) An acute organic reaction consisting of alteration of consciousness and attention (the patient alternates at various times between preoccupation and coma); impaired orientation and (especially recent) memory, which give rise to illusional falsifications and hallucinations of dreamlike scenes; delusions which are fleeting, unsystematized, and illogical because they are often secondary to the hallucinatory experiences; emotional lability and incontinence; and marked restlessness and agitation. The most common causes are intoxicants, drugs, infections, avitaminoses, metabolic disturbances (such as diabetes, uremia, and hyperthyroidism), and trauma; but a delirious reaction can occur in the course of any organic brain disorder.

Delirium at one time was used in a general way to indicate insanity, psychopathy, and almost any psychopathologic manifestation; now obsolete, such usage explains such appellations as depressive delirium (melancholia), persecutory delirium (paranoia), touching delirium (compulsive touching), etc.

delirium, abstinence When a state of delirium, usually delirium tremens, follows the immediate withdrawal of alcohol from a chronically alcoholic individual, the condition is known as *abstinence delirium*. The syndrome may be observed in any form of drug addiction.

delirium alcoholicum (dā-lē'rē-oom àl-kō-hô'lē-koom) Delirium tremens.

delirium ambitiosum (dā-lē'rē-oom àm-bē-tē-ō'zoom) (L. 'conceited delirium') *Obs.* Megalomania.

delirium, asthenic (as-then'ik) *Obs.* Delirium occasioned by fatigue.

delirium, chronic (kron'ik) *Obs.* Insanity.

delirium, chronic alcoholic This is a nosologic term synonymous with *psychosis, alcoholic Korsakov* (q.v.).

delirium, collapse Thus Kraepelin designates a condition, usually associated with high fever, characterized by marked disorientation, illusions, unsystematized delusions and emotional variability; the condition is marked by physical collapse.
This term is also sometimes used to refer to delirious mania (Bell's mania).

delirium ebriosorum (dā-lē'rē-oom ā-bri-ō-zō'room) (L. 'delirium of drunkards') Delirium tremens.

delirium, emotional This is a term used by Morel for the mental state in which the patient unqualifiedly accepts a false idea.

delirium e potu (dā-lē'rē-oom ā pō'tōō) (L. 'delirium from drinking') Delirium tremens; used by some to refer to pathological intoxication. See *intoxication, alcoholic*.

delirium ferox (dā-lē'rē-oom fe'rôks) (L. 'wild, savage, fierce') A psychiatric state characterized by violence.

delirium, fever See *delirium, initial*.

delirium furibundum (dā-lē'rē-oom foo-rē-boon'doom) (L. 'raging delirium') *Obs.* 'The delirium of insanity.' (Tuke, D.H. *A Dictionary of Psychological Medicine*, vols. 1-2, Blakiston, Philadelphia, 1892)

delirium furiosum (dā-lē′rē-oom foo-rē-ō′zoom) (L. 'furious delirium') *Obs.* Mania.

delirium grandiosum (dā-lē′rē-oom grăn-dē-ō′zoom) Megalomania.

delirium grave (dā-lē′rē-oom gră′ve) Collapse delirium. Also used by some to refer to delirious mania (Bell's mania).

delirium, idiopathic *Obs.* Name for psychiatric states occasioned by brain injury or toxic cerebral conditions.

delirium, initial *Obs.* A delirious reaction to toxic-infectious origin in which delirium appears before the fever is at its height. The term *fever-delirium* is similarly used to indicate a delirious reaction occuring at the height of the fever, while *collapse delirium* is sometimes used for delirium following high fever.

delirium, intellectual *Obs.* Hysterical mania.

delirium maniacum (dā-lē′rē-oom mà-nē′à-koom) Mania.

delirium melancholicum (dā-lē′rē-oom me-làn-kô′lē-koom) Melancholia.

delirium, metamorphosis *Obs.* The state in which the patient believes that his body is transformed into that of a beast.

delirium, micromaniacal (mī-krō-mà-nī′-à-kal) 'The form of insanity in which the patient believes himself to be a little child or a dwarf with shrunken limbs.' (Tuke, D.H. *A Dictionary of Psychological Medicine*, vols. 1 - 2, Blakiston, Philadelphia, 1892)

delirium mite (dā-lē′rē-oom mē′te) (L. 'mild, calm, gentle') A mental state characterized by low, delirious muttering. See *delirium, muttering.*

delirium mussitans (dā-lē′rē-oom moos′-sē-tàns) Delirium mite. See *delirium, muttering.*

delirium, muttering A severe form of delirium in which movements are reduced to tossing or trembling and speech is disorganized by iteration, perseveration, slurring, and dysarthria.

delirium nervosum (dā-lē′rē-oom ner-vō′zoom) (L. 'nervous') This older term had many meanings, chief of which was delirium associated with organic brain disease.

delirium, occupational See *hyperactivity, purposeless.*

delirium, oneiric Dream delirium; see *deliria oneirica.*

delirium palingnosticum (dā-lē′rē-oom pà-lēng-gnaws′tē-koom) 'A term applied to that form of insanity which is merely a translation into belief or actuality of a sensation sometimes experienced by any one on first going into a new place, that he has been there before; the insane conversion of this sensation makes the patient assert that he has been for years in a spot to which he has only recently come, and that he has seen places which he has really never visited.' (Tuke, D.H. *A Dictionary of Psychological Medicine*, Vols. 1 - 2, Blakiston, Philadelphia, 1892) See *déjà fait; déjà vu.*

delirium persecutionis (per-se-kōo-tē-ō′nēs) (L. 'mania of persecution') Paranoid condition.

delirium placidum (dā-lē′rē-oom pla′kē-doom) (L. 'gentle, quiet, placid') Quiet delirium.

delirium, post-traumatic Adolf Meyer (*American Journal of Insanity LX*, 1904) described four subdivisions:
'a. Pre-eminently febrile reactions.
b. The delirium nervosum of Dupuytren, not differing from deliria after operations, injuries, etc.
c. The delirium of slow solution of coma with or without alcoholic basis.
d. Forms of protracted deliria usually with numerous fabulations, etc. (with or without alcoholic or senile basis).'

delirium potatorum (dā-lē′rē-oom pô-tä-tō′room) Delirium tremens.

delirium, psychasthenic See *delusion, psychasthenic.*

delirium, rhyming A symptom of the manic phase of manic-depressive reaction characterized by utterances in rhyme.

delirium, senile One form of *senile psychosis* (q.v.) (290.0). Onset is usually acute and often follows head injury, infection, or surgical anesthesia. Its principal characteristics are clouded consciousness, hallucinations, marked insomnia, restlessness, resistance, and wandering. The delirium may be intermittent, or it may be prolonged with only occasional return to clear consciousness. The chief danger to the patient is exhaustion.

delirium, sensorial A mental state characterized by hallucinations and illusions.

delirium sine materia (dā-lē′rē-oom sē′ne mà-tē′rē-ä) (L. 'without matter, pus') *Obs.* 'Delirium without appreciable cerebral lesion; a term applied to various forms of insanity.' (Tuke, D.H. *A Dictionary of Psychological Medicine*, vols. 1-2, Blakiston, Philadelphia, 1892)

delirium, subacute Subacute delirious state; 'a syndrome in which incoherence of thought, speech and movement appear together with perplexity, in a setting of clouding of consciousness, fluctuating in degree. The state may follow a typical delirium or appear independently. It may persist over a considerable period, weeks or months, outlasting the signs of the underlying physical illness, but always ending in recovery.' (Mayer-Gross, W. et al. *Clinical Psychiatry*, Williams and Wilkins, Baltimore, 1960).

delirium, toxic See *brain syndrome associated with systemic infection.*

delirium, traumatic A mental disturbance characterized by an acute delirium occuring immediately after head or brain injury as a result of force directly or indirectly applied to the head. Other patients, following such injury, may show a protracted or chronic delirium with marked disorientation, confabulation, and memory defect, but with apparent superficial alertness. This latter condition may resemble the Korsakov syndrome.

delirium tremefaciens (dā-lē′rē-oom treme-fà′kē-ens) (L. 'shaking delirium') Delirium tremens.

delirium tremens (dē-lir′i-um tre′mens) An acute brain syndrome (in DSM-II, 291.0) due to alcohol intoxication, characterized by an acute hallucinatory delirium and a coarse, generalized tremor which involves particularly the fingers, face, and tongue. Delirium may appear at any time in the chronic alcoholic, but it is usually precipitated by intercurrent infection, injury, or a prolonged debauch or it may appear as an *abstinence delirium* in the malignant, addictive alcoholic.

The syndrome begins suddenly with fever, rapid pulse, leukocytosis, profuse perspiration, headache, anorexia, nausea, weakness, and dehydration. Along with the tremor there are seen ataxia and hyperreflexia, and all these appear to be due to an encephalosis involving mainly the fronto-ponto-cerebellar pathways. Increased cerebrospinal fluid pressure and increased globulin in the cerebrospinal fluid are usual, and in about 50 per cent of cases a mild transitory albuminuria is seen. Epileptiform convulsions may also occur; these *rum fits,* as they are sometimes called, are probably due to pyridoxine vitamine B_6 deficiency.

The delirium itself begins within a few days after onset of the disorder. Persecutory delusions are common and are usually in reference to a gang of the same sex or some obvious castration fear. These delusions may lead to suicide or homocide. Illusions are frequent and are easily suggested. Visual hallucinations are the most common of the hallucinatory elements, and these are typically of animals, such as snakes or rats, which symbolize mainly sexual fears (pink elephants, incidentally, are most uncommon). Haptic hallucinations, of animals crawling over the skin, are also seen, but many of these are probably illusions based on paresthesiae. Auditory hallucinations, when they occur, are usually of a derogatory and/or homosexual nature. In the midst of the delirium, disorientation is marked; there is loss of attention and memory impairment, most marked for recent memory. There is an incontinence of emotions— panic, anxiety, and terror most commonly, although some few show euphoria or indifference to their hallucinations and illusions. Misidentification is common, and patients are highly suggestible and can easily be made to confabulate.

The delirium usually lasts three to six days; the patient usually has an amnesia for the delirium and frequently returns to his pattern of heavy drinking and thus there is often an early repetition of the syndrome. Auditory hallucinations usually indicate that the course will be prolonged. In uncomplicated cases, death is rare (3-4 per cent). If there is not full recovery, there is usually progression into a Korsakov syndrome (in about 15 per cent of cases).

The pathological picture consists of nuclear destruction of the nerve cells, with all degrees of granular degeneration and disintegration of the nuclei. In most patients, the cortex is mainly affected, but in those tending clinically to progress into a Korsakov psychosis, the brain stem is affected to a greater degree.

delirium verborum (dā-lē'rē-oom ver-bō'room) (L. 'delirium of words') Psychiatric state characterized by great loquacity.

delirium vesanicum (dā-lē'rē-oom vā-sä'-nē-koom) *Obs.* 'The delirium or incoherence, delusions, hallucinations, illusions, restlessness, watchfulness, etc., of insanity.' (Tuke, D.H. *A Dictionary of Psychological Medicine*, vols. 1-2, Blakiston, Philadelphia, 1892)

delta rhythm or wave See *electroencephalogram.*

delusion A false belief, born of morbidity. A belief engendered without appropriate external stimulation and maintained by one in spite of what to normal beings constitutes incontrovertible and 'plain-as-day' proof or evidence to the contrary. Further, the belief held is not one which is ordinarily accepted by other members of the patient's culture or subculture (i.e. it is not a commonly believed superstition).

Like hallucinations, delusions are condensations of perceptions, thoughts, and memories and can be interpreted much the same as hallucinations and dreams. Delusions are misjudgments of reality based on projection. The sequence of events in the formation of delusions is often seen to be as follows: the patient's relationship to objects is an archaic, ambivalent one; he attempts to incorporate the object, which then becomes a part of his own ego; the object is then reprojected into the external world and becomes the persecutor. Persecutory delusions thus represent projections of the patient's bad conscience; since the superego (conscience) is usually an introjected object of the same sex, the struggle against the superego represents also a struggle against the patient's homosexuality. The imagined persecutors, however, not only threaten and punish the patient; often also they are perceived as tempters who lead the patient into sin or weaken his potency. 'This can be explained by the fact that . . . the hallucinations and delusions of reference represent not only the superego but also, at the same time, the (ambivalent) loved object; the sexual wish for this object is perceived as a destructive sexual influence that emanates from him.' (Fenichel, O. *The Psychoanalytic Theory of Neurosis,* Norton, New York, 1945). See *paranoia.*

delusion, abortive Fenichel says: 'As to "abortive delusions," we may refer to erythrophobia, in which there is a feeling of being watched by persons to see whether one will blush—a state of mind reminiscent of delusions of reference.' (Fenichel, O. *Outline of Clinical Psychoanalysis,* tr. by Lewin, B.D. and Zilboorg, G., The Psychoanalytic Quarterly Press and Norton, New York, 1934)

delusion, allopsychic (al-ō-sī'kik) See *delusion, autopsychic.*

delusion, asthenic (às-then'ic) Psychasthenic delusion (Janet).

delusion, autochthonous Primary delusion, i.e. one that arises as an immediate experience, out of the blue, with no external or objective cause or explanation, but nonetheless with a strong feeling of conviction. Autochthonous delusions are characteristic of the schizophrenias; unlike delusions seen in other psychiatric disorders, they are not a disturbance of perception in which the subject tries to rationalize changes that he perceives in himself or in the outside world. Neither are they disturbances of apperception or intellect, for the subject can understand what specific objects in external reality are. Rather, autochthonous delusions are disturbances of symbolic meaning: because the legs of a chair are twisted, the world is twisted.

delusion, autopsychic (aw-tō-sī'kik) When a delusional concept refers to the person's own personality, it is called an autopsychic delusion; when it relates to the outside world, it is known as an allopsychic delusion; when it has to do with one's own body, it is called a somatopsychic delusion. This classification was suggested by Wernicke.

delusion, expansive See *megalomania.*

delusion, explanatory Bleuler , uses this expression to refer to delusions that give reasons for the false belief. A patient who believes that men are persecuting him, explains the delusion by 'showing' that they open his mail, that they publish photographs of him, that they assemble to discuss methods of injuring him.

delusion, healthy In his review of *The Maggid of Caro,* C.B. Farrar feels that 'whether a hallucination is agreeable with health or symptomatic of illness seems to depend upon circumstances. A deranged person may express ideas regarding sin and future penalties that we unhesitatingly set down as pathologic delusions; but identical ideas are found in the Holy Writ and presumably accepted by persons whose mental health is not under suspicion. Are these then *healthy* delusions?' (*American Journal of Psychiatry CVII*, No. 9, March 1951, p. 720)

delusion, infidelity See *paranoia, amorous.*

delusion, interpretation An interpretation or a meaning of a delusion as given by the patient himself.
'Paranoia . . . turns to another source in forming symptoms; the delusions which, by means of a compromise, succeed in becoming conscious (symptoms of the return of the repressed) absorb the thought-processes of the ego until they finally become accepted without contradiction. Since the delusions themselves are not to be influenced, the ego must accommodate itself to them; and thus the combinatory delusion-formations, such as *interpretation-delusions* ending in a *change within the ego*, correspond to the secondary defense in the obsessional neurosis.' (Freud, S. *Collected Papers*, vol. 1, tr. by Riviere, J., Leonard and Virginia Woolf and The Institute of Psychoanalysis, London, 1924-25)

delusion, Mignon (mē-ñon′) The belief

that one is the offspring of some distinquished family (e.g. royalty) rather than one's own parents. This delusion is seen most frequently in the schizophrenias, although it may appear as a more or less disguised wish in almost any psychiatric entity. See *romance, family.*

delusion of observation Delusion of reference; delusion of being watched.

delusion, primordial See *delire d'emblée.*

delusion, psychasthenic (sīk-as-then′ik) Janet's term for delusions occasioned by fatigue.

delusion, residual This is an expression used by Neisser to refer to delusions, formed in an acute state, which are carried over into a chronic state.

delusion, secondary With Bleuler this denotes a delusion that is based upon a primary one. 'When the patient is convinced that the physician wants to murder him and after taking medicine he feels indisposed, then it is a conclusion, based on logical probability, that the physician has prescribed poison (secondary delusion).' (Bleuler, E. *Textbook of Psychiatry*, tr. by Brill, A.A., Macmillan, New York, 1930)

delusion, somatic (sō-mat′ik) The subjective reports and complaints made by patients that their body is perceived, or felt, by them as disturbed or disordered in all, or individual, organs or parts. In 1935, Angyal reported that a depersonalized schizophrenic patient reported to him that he felt the floor waving. Angyal analyzed the phenomenon as an 'exteriorization' of the pulse in the plantar region of the foot. The complaints stemming from such somatic delusions in unrecognized ambulatory schizophrenics are frequently the source of much useless medical and surgical treatment, and thus of 'iatrogenic' illnesses. (Hunt, J.McV. *Personality and the Behavior Disorders,* vol. 2, Ronald Press, New York, 1944)

delusion, somatopsychic (sō-mat-ō-sī′kik) See *delusion, autopsychic.*

demand See *feeding, demand.*

dement (dē-ment′) A person with an absence or reduction of intellectual faculties in consequence of known organic brain disease. Earlier writers used the term for deteriorated schizophrenics. Thus the paranoid dements of Kraepelin are those with unstable and unorganized delusions, apparent marked reduction in intellectual capacities, and a break in psychic unity.

dementia (dē-men'shē-à) Absence or reduction of intellectual faculties in consequence of known organic brain disease.

In years gone by, the term dementia has had various meanings. It was once synonymous with madness, insanity, and lunacy; in the early part of the 17th century it was synonymous with delirium. Nowadays, however, in recognition of the fact that many psychotic persons possess very keen intelligence, the term is not used sweepingly for all psychiatric states. It is often limited to those who show primary memory loss due to disorders in brain tissue, and as used today the term stresses the irreversibility of the intellectual defects, whatever their origin. The term 'deterioration' also refers to progressive loss of intellectual faculties, but without intimating a specific cause and without stressing the permanency of the change. The term 'regression,' on the other hand, stresses the reversibility of the change, and with Freud this term came to refer primarily to emotional disturbances rather than to loss of intellectual ability. See *dementia, schizophrenic; syndrome, organic.*

dementia, abiotrophic atrophic See *dementia, atrophic.*

dementia, acute Anergic stupor, such as is seen in catatonic stupor and hysterical trance states. The term is little used today; in the past, however, it was considered a distinct nosological entity.

dementia adventitia (dā-men'tē-à àd-ven-tē'tē-à) (L. 'adventitious dementia') *Rare.* A generic term denoting psychiatric conditions arising in individuals who had previously been mentally well adjusted.

dementia, affective (dē-men'shi-à) See *hebetude; affectivity, disturbances of.*

dementia agitata (dā-men'tē-à à-gē-tä'tà) This expression, introduced by Krafft-Ebing, refers to agitated states in patients with dementia praecox (schizophrenia).

dementia, alcoholic (dē-men'shi-à) This is the term used to refer to lack of recovery and progression of *Korsakov's psychosis* (q.v.). Alcoholic dementia consists of impairment of memory and intellectual capacity, emotional instability, moral deterioration, carelessness in dress and personal cleanliness, and, frequently, delusions of marital infidelity.

dementia apathetica (dā-men'tē-à à-pà-thā'tē-ka) (L. 'apathetic dementia') *Obs.* Dementia with listlessness.

dementia apoplectica (à-pô-plek'tē-kà) (L. 'apoplectic dementia') Apoplectic attacks, associated with cerebral arteriosclerosis, may be due to hemorrhage or to softening of brain tissue. Usually there are prodromes of variable duration; they may appear as headache, dizziness, fainting attacks, together with ideational and emotional changes. Depending upon the nature and severity of the arteriosclerotic process, the apoplectic ('stroke') condition may be followed by diffuse cerebral atrophy, giving rise to the organic type of dementia. Clinically the last condition is known as apoplectic dementia.

dementia, apperceptive (dē-men'shē-à) Used by Weygandt to denote a type of dementia induced primarily by disorder in the volitional and intellectual spheres. Weygandt applied the term to dementia praecox (schizophrenia), conceiving the so-called deterioration in the light of 'disintegration' of the will, which in turn interrupted the normal train of thought, the final effect appearing as dementia.

dementia, arteriosclerotic See *psychosis, arteriosclerotic.*

dementia, ascending paretic General paresis with grandiose delusions. See *paresis, general.*

dementia, atrophic Atrophic dementia, known also as *abiotrophic atrophic dementia,* refers to the presenile organic reactions or brain syndromes, e.g. Pick's disease and Alzheimer's disease (290.1).

dementia, boxer's One type of chronic cerebral disorder seen in boxers, expecially those who have sustained many head blows; also known as dementia pugilistica. Boxer's dementia is a chronic, slowly progressive disorder with pathologic changes similar to those seen in post-encephalitic Parkinsonism.

The other common cerebral disorders in boxers include (1) boxer's traumatic encephalopathy, where predominantly neurological defects are directly related to head blows, and (2) paranoid and catatonic psychoses, the nature of whose relationship to oft-repeated brain traumata is incompletely understood.

dementia, chronic *Obs.* Dementia praecox (schizophrenia).

dementia, circular Thus Kraepelin denotes a form of dementia praecox (schizophrenia) characterized by alternating phases of excitement and depression. Currently, this would be classified as the schizo-affective form of schizophrenia.

dementia, depressive Kraepelin's designation for a special subdivision of dementia praecox (schizophrenia). The syndrome resembles that of *simple depressive dementia,* save that all symptoms are more intense and the course of the illness is protracted. *Rare* in the United States.

dementia, driveling *Rare.* This is an expression used by Kraepelin to denote 'the general *decay of mental efficiency'* observed in the terminal states of certain syndromes of dementia praecox (schizophrenia).

'Here also are still found, as a rule, hallucinations and delusions, the senselessness of which distinctly proves the mental weakness.' (Kraepelin, E. *Dementia Praecox and Paraphrenia,* tr. by Barclay, R.M., Livingstone, Edinburgh, 1919.)

dementia, epileptic (ep-i-lep'tik) Two forms of psychoses are seen in epilepsy: typical 'organic psychoses' and a chronic form which progresses to a Korsakov psychosis or an epileptic dementia. See *personality, epileptic.*

Epileptic dementia refers to the progressive mental and intellectual deterioration seen in a small number of epileptics (not more than 5 per cent, and there are many famous epileptics who showed no such dementia: Helmholtz, Flaubert, Dostoyevsky). The resultant mental deficiency is more likely when the attacks have begun early in life. It is probable that both this and the convulsions are expressions

of some unknown physiological abnormality, although some believe that the dementia is due to nerve cell degeneration secondary to vascular disturbances during the convulsive episodes.

In a small group of epileptics, more complicated clinical psychiatric syndromes are seen, with mainly depressive or mainly schizophrenic symptoms. It will thus be noted that epilepsy and schizophrenia are not antagonistic, even though a belief to the contrary afforded a rationale for the electro-convulsive treatment of schizophrenic psychoses.

dementia, foolish Kraepelin's term for hebephrenic schizophrenia.

dementia, hallucinatory (ha-lū'sin-à-tor-ē) See *dementia paranoides gravis.*

dementia, higher Van Guden's term (Hoch calls it *parlor dementia*) for a condition in persons 'who absorb school material quite well, under given conditions even excellently, and can even use it in certain combinations, but in spite of great activity they are failures in life. Their behavior is the reverse of the oligophrenics; they have much knowledge and can do nothing.' (Bleuler, E. *Textbook of Psychiatry,* tr. by Brill, A.A., Macmillan, New York, 1930)

Bleuler refers also to *relative dementia,* not sharply distinguished from the foregoing. About it he says: 'There are people whose understanding suffices for a usual attitude of life, and often even for one a little above the average, who, however, are too active, and constantly adjudge to themselves more than they can grasp, and therefore commit many stupidities and suffer shipwreck in life.' (ibid.)

dementia infantilis (dā-men'tē-à ēn-fàn-tē'lēs) (L. 'infantile (or childhood) dementia) A term suggested by Heller to designate a variety of infantile schizophrenia. It has been also referred to as *Heller's disease.* In discussing it Kanner (*Child Psychiatry,* 2nd ed., Thomas, Springfield, Ill., 1948) writes: 'It was customary to list Heller's disease among the varieties of infantile schizophrenia. Corberi's findings make it more plausible that this condition represents a cerebral degenerative process akin to Tay-Sachs disease and to "amaurotic idiocy without amaurosis" (Kufs-Walter).' Schilder stated categorically: 'I assume as a matter of course that *dementia infantilis* (Heller) has nothing to do with schizophrenia, but is an organic process.' (Schilder, P. 'Reaction Types Resembling Functional Psychoses in Childhood on the Basis of an Organic Inferiority of the Brain,' *Mental Hygiene 19*, 439-48, 1935)

Infantile dementia occurs in children at three to four years of age. The patient becomes resistive, whining, and anxious, shows a general loss of acquired functions with mutism, dementia, and posturing, but an intelligent facial expression is usually retained.

Up to the present time, no cases of infantile dementia have been reported in the American literature.

dementia naturalis (nä-tōo-rä'lēs) (L. 'natural, inborn dementia') *Obs*. Idiocy.

dementia paralytica (pà-rà-lē'tē-kà) (L. 'paralytic dementia') See *paresis, general.*

dementia paranoides (pà-rà-nô'ē-dās) Paranoid schizophrenia.

dementia paranoides gravis (grà'vēs) 'Those paranoid morbid states, which, it is true, begin with simple delusions, but which as time goes on terminate in severe so-called deterioration, 'a *peculiar disintegration of the psychic life.*' (Kraepelin, E. *Dementia Praecox and Paraphrenia*, tr. by Barclay, R.M., Livingstone, Edinburgh, 1919)

The *milder* type of paranoid schizophrenia, hallucinatory feeblemindedness, Kraepelin called *dementia paranoides mitis*, when the patient has hallucinations and 'the substance of the personality seems to be less seriously damaged.' Today Kraepelin's term is used only occasionally and even then not in the diagnostic sense assigned to it by Kraepelin.

dementia paranoides mitis (mē'tes) See *dementia paranoides gravis.*

dementia paratonita progressiva (pà-rà-tō'nē-tà prô-gres-sē-và) Alexander Bernstein's term for catatonic schizophrenia, which he also sometimes called *paratonia progressiva.*

dementia, parlor (dē-men'shi-à) See *dementia, higher.*

dementia, partial *Rare*. A form of dementia praecox (schizophrenia) in which the patient retains some healthy mental components.

dementia, periodic See *dementia praecox, circular.*

dementia, post-traumatic (pōst-trawmat'ik) An absence or diminution of intellectual faculties secondary to brain injury. Post-traumatic dementia comprises 0.6 per cent of annual admissions to mental hospitals. Less severe disturbances with memory impairment and minor personality changes are more frequent. Psychologic changes following head injury become prominent approximately two months after the injury and generally subside within the next three months (in DSM-II, coded 293.5 if psychotic, 309.2 if non-psychotic). In 50 per cent of cases, symptoms persist for at least six months, and in 15 per cent, for a year or more. There is no correlation between severity of the injury and severity of the post-traumatic psychiatric sequelae. Persons with pre-traumatic psychoneurotic personalities, and those with many complicating factors, such as pending litigation, anxiety about compensation, occupational stresses, or associated bodily injuries, are more likely to develop post-traumatic psychiatric sequelae. Traumatic epilepsy develops within two years in about 10 per cent of cases who manifest psychiatric sequelae.

dementia praecocissima (dà-men'tē-à prī-kô-kēs'sē-mà) (L. 'premature dementia') In a paper on neuropsychiatric disorders in young children DeSanctis calls attention to a disorder named by him *dementia praecocissima*. (*Neuropsichiatria infantile*, Rome, Stock, 1925, pp. 623-61.) According to DeSanctis this condition, occurring in young children, sometimes as early as the fourth year, is characterized by a more or less abrupt appearance of symptoms indicative of catatonia. Sterotypy, fixed postures, negativism, angry outbursts, echolalia, emotional blunting are particularly noticeable. Marked intellectual deterioration is present. DeSanctis ascribed the cause of the disorder to a hereditary predisposition due to paternal alcoholism. Its development was hastened by acute or chronic toxic disease such as pertussis, rickets, pleurisy, and intestinal infections.

Kanner feels that the case material presented by DeSanctis as dementia praecocissima includes a variety of pathologic conditions. He writes: 'Some of the cases are indistinguishable from childhood schizophrenia (Bromberg), others represent rapidly progressing brain diseases (Lutz; Schilder). An autopsy performed by Ciampi showed chromatolysis of the pyramidal cortical cells.

'Rapid disorganization after a fairly normal start is encountered in small children on rare occasions and offers baffling problems of diagnosis. Some cases prove to belong to the group of Heller's disease (*dementia infantilis*), some few are cases of Tay-Sachs's disease with or without the characteristic eye ground findings, others are instances of even more unusual cerebral disease processes. The custom of including them under the heading of schizophrenia should be discouraged.' (Kanner, L. *Child Psychiatry*, Thomas, Springfield, Ill., 1948)

dementia praecox (dē-men'shē-a prē'koks) A term coined by Morel in 1857 to describe those psychoses ('vesania') with a poor prognosis, i.e. those ending in deterioration (dementia) and incurability. Praecox was meant to refer to the fact that the onset of the disorders was early in life—typically, in adolescence. In the years following the introduction of this term, various symptom complexes were described which later were included in the group, dementia praecox. Thus, Kahlbaum described catatonia, Hecker described hebephrenia, Pick and Sommer described simple deterioration, and Zieber described paranoia. In 1896, Kraepelin made the important differentiation between manic-depressive psychosis and dementia praecox, and he included the aforementioned entities as subgroups of dementia praecox. He, too, emphasized the poor prognosis in dementia praecox and believed that those cases which could be cured permanently or arrested for very long periods were really instances of manic-depressive psychosis.

In 1911, Bleuler introduced the term *schizophrenia*, which in present-day psychiatry has largely replaced the term 'dementia praecox.' Bleuler rejected the latter term because, in his experience,

dementia is not a constant end-product of the disorder (or group of disorders), and because at least 40 per cent of cases did not manifest gross disturbances until after their twenty-fifth year.

Some contemporary authorities, and particularly European psychiatrists, continue to use the term dementia praecox in a fairly restricted sense to refer to 'nuclear' or 'process' schizophrenia, i.e. unquestionable cases with a high tendency to deterioration and little tendency to remission or recovery. See *schizophrenia*.

dementia praecox, agitated Certain schizophrenic patients show marked agitation. Kraepelin classified them as having the agitated form of dementia praecox. As a rule psychiatrists have not accepted the classification. In America, patients with agitation are grouped in accordance with other phenomena. They may be classed as hebephrenic, catatonic, or paranoid.

dementia praecox, catatonic (ka-ta-ton'ik) This term is equivalent to 'catatonic schizophrenia.' See *schizophrenia*.

dementia praecox, circular Kraepelin's term for what today would be called the schizo-affective type of schizophrenia.

dementia praecox, hebephrenic (hē-be-frē'nik) This term is equivalent to 'hebephrenic schizophrenia.' See *schizophrenia*.

dementia praecox, paranoid (par'à-noid) This term is equivalent to 'paranoid schizophrenia.' See *schizophrenia*.

dementia praecox, simple A subdivision of the group formerly called *dementia praecox* (q.v.) and now generally called *schizophrenia* (q.v.). Sometimes the word 'simplex' is substituted for 'simple.' It is also known as dementia simplex, schizophrenia simplex, and primary dementia.

dementia praesenilis (dā-men'tē-à prī-se-nē'lēs) See *senium praecox*.

dementia, precocious (dē-men'shi-à) Dementia praecox (schizophrenia).

dementia, premature *Obs.* Dementia praecox (schizophrenia).

dementia, primary Synonymous with *dementia praecox, simple* (q.v.)

dementia pugilistica (dā-men′tē-à pōō-gē-lē′stē-kà) See *dementia, boxer's.*

dementia, relative (dē-men′shi-à) See *dementia, higher.*

dementia, schizophrenic (skiz-ō-frē′nik) One of the fundamental symptoms of the schizophrenias (Bleuler). Schizophrenic patients, despite generally adequate preservation of their intellectual potentialities, are often not able to make use of this potential in a constructive, appropriate, purposeful, goal-directed way. Knowledge, although present, is not always available to them at the moment it is called for. Schizophrenic dementia seems to be the result of disturbances of primary elemental functions, such as associations, affectivity, attention and concentration, and will.

Schizophrenic dementia reveals itself in various forms; e.g. stupid, foolish mistakes; senseless generalizations; gullibility; faddism; pseudomotivations; vacuity and banality of thought; an insipid, unintegrated, disconnected quality in thought and speech; difficulty in forming new concepts; ellipsis in thought and speech; treating the concrete as though it were abstract, etc. On psychological testing, probably the most frequent expression of schizophrenic dementia is 'scattering.'

dementia, secondary *Obs.* The schizophrenic syndrome that follows what was known as the initial 'acute' attack or dementia simplex. In the psychiatry of today no such differentiation is made, the entire course of the illness, whether periodic or continuous, being known merely as schizophrenia.

dementia sejunctiva (dā-men′tē-à sā-yoongk-tē′và) *Obs.* Dementia praecox; schizophrenia.

dementia, semantic (dē-men′shē-à) The inability to experience or evaluate the meaning of things. In psychiatry this term has been used by Cleckley ('Semantic Dementia and Semi-suicide, *Psychiatric Quarterly 16*, 521, 1942) to refer to the inability of the psychopathic personality to evaluate or experience life as a totally integrated organism. Although the psychopath can react verbally, as though he understood love, pride, grief, shame, or the other emotions, he has no real experience of these human values or connotations. Cleckley believes that failure to function at this level provokes regression, which is expressed in a drive toward failure and folly, a destruction of the self at the personality or cultural level.

dementia, senile Simple senile deterioration (290.0). See *senile psychoses; deterioration, simple senile.*

dementia, sequential (sē-kwen′shal) *Obs.* Synonymous with *secondary dementia.*

dementia, simple depressive *Stuporous dementia,* one of Kraepelin's subdivisions of dementia praecox (schizophrenia).

The syndrome is characterized by depression, resembling that seen in the depressive phase of manic-depressive disorder; the projection mechanism appears to a greater or lesser degree. The condition often tends toward periodicity, but not with the same sharpness that marks clear-cut depressive states.

dementia, simple senile See *deterioration, simple senile.*

dementia simplex (dā-men-tē-à sim′pleks) See *dementia praecox, simple.*

dementia, traumatic (dā-men′shē-à, trawmat′ik) When dementia, intellectual or affective, or both, is directly or indirectly caused by an injury, usually to the head, the condition is known as traumatic dementia. See *dementia, post-traumatic.*

'Common to most of them are rapid exhaustion, irritability, tendency to spontaneous and reactive moods, up to the most intensive anger, which is in part labile and in part of a more torpid persitent affect.... Not rarely epileptic attacks appear in which the typical *epileptic dementia* may occur (traumatic epilepsy). Pictures similar to catatonia can last for a long time.' (Bleuler, E. *Textbook of Psychiatry,* tr. by Brill, A.A., Macmillan, New York, 1930)

demenza primitiva (dā-men′tsà prē-mē-tē′và) (It. 'primitive edementia') Dementia praecox (schizophrenia).

demissio animi (dā-mēs′sē-ō à′nē-mē) (L. 'lowering of the spirit') Melancholy.

demi-vierge (dē-mē'vyerzh') (F. 'semi-virgin') The French novelist Marcel Prevost describes women who, he says, are spiritually, not bodily, deflorated, that is, deprived of their virginity. The concept is common, for example, among schizophrenic patients, who express the delusion that men steal into their beds nightly and have sexual intercourse with them.

demography (dē-mog'ra-fē) The statistical study of populations, including births, marriages, mortality, health, geographic distribution, population shifts, etc.

demonia (dē-mo'nē-à) Demonomania.

demoniac *Obs.* One affected with madness.

demonolatry (dē-mun-ol'à-trē) A form of mental deviation in which a patient worships a demon or devil.

demonomania (dē-mun-ō-mā'nē-à) Morbid dread of demons. Freud believes that the original pleasurable affect associated with an act, such as masturbation, is first repressed, then transformed into anxiety, which contains features of punishment in it and brings dread of an evil spirit as the next stage.

demono-melancholia   (-mel-an-kō'lē-à) Demonomania.

demonopathy (dē-mun-op'à-thē) Demonomania.

demophobia (dē-mō-fō'bē-à) Morbid fear of crowds; ochlophobia.

demoralization, personal The repudiation by the person in a crisis situation of 'old habits and restraints without reorganizing his life.' (Park, R.E. and Miller, H.A., *Old World Traits Transplanted*, Harper, New York, 1921)
'Demoralization is the decay of the personal life-organization of an individual member of a social group. . . . Prevalent social disorganization, in those periods when the old system which controlled more or less adequately the behavior of the group members is decaying so rapidly that the development of a new social situation cannot keep pace with this process of decadence, is particularly favorable for the growth of individual demoralization.'

(Thomas, W.I. and Znaniecki, F. *The Polish Peasant in Europe and America*, Knopf, New York, 1927)

demorphinization (dē-mor-fin-i-zā'shun) The process of gradual or rapid withdrawal of morphine in the treatment of addicts.

demyelination (dē-mī-e-lin-ā'shun) The process of destruction of the myelin sheaths of the nerve fibers. There is a large group of neurologic diseases, the 'demyelinating diseases of the nervous system,' characterized by foci of demyelination. These foci are usually in the white matter and vary in size, shape, distribution, and in the acuteness of the pathological process. Classification of these disorders is unsatisfactory; their etiology is unknown, their differential pathology is indistinct, and clinical forms are often transitional, presenting features common to more than one of the specific diseases recognized. The four major forms, divided on the basis of clinico-pathologic manifestations, are: acute disseminated encephalomyelitis (following acute infections); disseminated myelitis with optic neuritis (Devic's disease); multiple sclerosis (disseminated sclerosis); and diffuse sclerosis (Schilder's disease, Balô's disease, etc.).

demyelination, concentric Balô's disease. See *sclerosis, diffuse.*

denarcissism (dē-när'si-sis'm) The state of being unselfish, altruistic. In early infancy instinctual energy is incorporated almost completely within the infant himself. In the very early stages it is bound to the soma. Later, with the development of the psyche, much of the energy is transferred to it. When psychic energy is devoted to one's own psyche, the condition is known as *narcissism* (q.v.). Still later, for healthy mental growth, a part of the psychic energy must be objectivated, externalized, detached from its very personal value to the individual. When psychic energy exists in what may be called an impersonal state, that is, it exists in something not strictly related to the individual himself, it is said to be in a state of denarcissism.

dendrite, dendritic zone See *neuron.*

dendrophilia, dendrophily (den-drō-fil'ē-à, drof'i-lē) Love of trees, which may often be phallic symbols. Magnus Hirschfeld defines it as 'a sexual obsession for trees.' He reports: 'A few years ago a man confided in me who was having an "affair" with an oak tree in Machnow near Berlin. He had, as he said, an idolatrous veneration for it, and often in the darkness, when he felt quite safe from observation, he would press his naked member against the "venerable trunk," until an ejaculation resulted.' (Hirschfeld, M. *Sexual Pathology*, tr. by Gibbs, J., Emerson Books, New York, 1939)

dendropsychosis (den-drō-sī-kō′sis) *Obs.* Intense interest in trees.

denial Refusal to admit the reality of, disavowal of the truth of, refusal to acknowledge the presence or existence of. Known also as *negation*, denial is a primitive *defense* (q.v.), consisting of an attempt to disavow the existence of unpleasant reality. Because denial must ignore data presenting themselves to the perceptory system and garnered by the memory apparatus, such a defense can operate only in the undeveloped, infantile psyche, or in persons whose ego is weak or disturbed (as in the psychoses), and even so, denial succeeds best against single internal perceptions of a painful nature. Denial and negation are also used, more loosely, to refer to any form of *resistance* (q.v.).

denotation See *connotation.*

de-orality The state in which instinctual activity, formerly connected with the oral region, is expressed through some other agency. It is said by psychoanalysts that the pleasure of suckling at the breast may in later life assume the form of a pleasure in being morally dependent upon a maternal person.

deoxyribonucleic acid See *chromosome.*

depatterning D.E. Cameron uses this term almost synonymously with 'regressive' ECT. He uses intensive ECT and prolonged sleep with chlorpromazine and barbiturates to treat chronic paranoids.

dependence, oral The unconscious wish for maternal protection, to be encompassed by the mother, to regain the peace, protection, and security of her sheltering arms. This stems from the original intense and forgotten gratifications of the infantile nursing period, when the infant's prehensile mouth anchored it to the mother's nipple and breast. To the child, to be fed means to be loved, i.e. to be protected, ergo, to be secure. The nostalgic urge toward the reinstatement of such security has been found nuclear in asthmatics. (Alexander, F. *Psychosomatic Medicine*, Norton, New York, 1950)

dependency State of being dependent. With social workers this means 'a form of behavior which suggests inability to make decisions; marked inclination to lean on others for advice, guidance, support, etc.' (Hamilton, G. *A Medical Social Terminology*, Presbyterian Hospital, New York, 1930)
Dependency reflects needs for mothering, love, affection, shelter, protection, security, food, warmth, etc.
In Horney's terminology, *morbid dependency* is a form of self-effacement manifested in a compulsive need to surrender to and unite with a stronger person.

dependency, drug Psychic craving for, habituation to, or addiction to a chemical substance; the term is gradually replacing 'drug addiction' which emphasizes physiologic dependence upon a drug rather than the psychologic craving that is the essential element in those whose life, in whole or in part, revolves about their need for a specific effect of one or more chemical agents on mood or state of consciousness. Drug dependency thus includes what has heretofore been classified under drug addiction; but in addition, it includes drug abusers whose pathologic craving for certain drug effects seems unrelated to physical dependency upon those chemical agents. See *addiction.*
The following types of drug dependency have been differentiated:
(1) 304.0, dependency on opium, opium alkaloids, and their derivatives—such as morphine, heroin, codeine, dilaudid, laudanum, paregoric; see *opium;*
(2) 304.1, dependency on synthetic analgestics with morphine-like effects—such as Demerol and Methadone;
(3) 304.2, dependency on barbiturates (other classifications have included alcoholism and alcohol addiction within

this general category); see *barbiturates;*
(4) 304.3, dependency upon other
hypnotics, sedatives or 'tranquilizers';
(5) 304.4, dependency on cocaine; see
cocainism;
(6) 304.5, dependency on Cannabis
sativa (hashish, marijuana, etc.); see
marijuana;
(7) 304.6, dependency on other psychostimulants—such as the amphetamines; see *benzedrine dependency;*
(8) 304.7, dependency on hallucinogens
—such as lysergic acid;
(9) 304.8, a miscellaneous group, not
of great importance in the United States,
although elsewhere in the world other
drugs (e.g. khat) are separately specified
because of the prevalence of their use.

depersonalization A non-specific syndrome in which the patient feels that he
has lost his personal identity, that he is
different or strange or unreal. Derealization, the feeling that the environment is
also strange or unreal, is usually part of
the syndrome. Other frequent symptoms
are mood changes (e.g. dejection, apathy,
bewilderment, or a feeling of emotional
emptiness); difficulty in organizing,
collecting, and arranging thoughts; and
cephalic paresthesiae (e.g. numbness of
head or a feeling that the brain has been
deadened). Depersonalization has been
reported in depression, hysterical and
dissociative states, schizoid personality,
schizophrenia, toxic psychoses, temporal
lobe epilepsy, and in states of fatigue. It
most commonly occurs in the third and
fourth decades and is more common in
women. It may last for one or two years
before disappearing spontaneously; it
rarely responds to treatment of any sort.
M. Roth (*Proceedings, Royal Society of
Medicine 52, 587, 1959*) has described
a more specific syndrome, the phobic
anxiety-depersonalization neurosis (sometimes also called pseudo-schizophrenic
neurosis) (300.6). In this neurosis, phobic
anxiety is combined with depersonalization; the patient often complains of giddiness, swaying feelings, and fears of
collapse or loss of self control in public.
Roth suggests that the neurosis may be
at least in part related to some disorder
of the temporal lobes, the limbic system,
or the cerebral mechanisms regulating
awareness.

depravity, insanity and An old medico-

legal and psychiatric term dating back
to the early nineteenth century and embodying mainly moralistic attitudes toward behavior disorders involving clashes
with society and the law. The phrase is
particularly used and applied to the borderline cases between personality deviation, habitual criminality, and perversion
on the one hand, and those minimal ambulatory psychotics with predominantly acting-out trends on the other. The early
concepts of 'moral insanity,' 'constitutional (inborn) psychopathic inferiority,'
'psychopathic personality,' 'psychopathic
inferiority,' 'moral imbecility,' 'moral insanity,' 'moral lunacy' all refer to this
borderline group, the fundamental understanding of which, even today, is an open
question.

deprehensio (dā-pre-hen′sē-ō) *Obs.* Catalepsy.

depressio apathetica (dā-pres′sē-ō ä-pà-
thā′tē-kà) See *anxietas praesenilis.*

depression In psychiatry, depression refers
to a clinical syndrome consisting of lowering of mood-tone (feelings of painful dejection), difficulty in thinking, and psychomotor retardation. The general retardation, however, may be masked by
anxiety, obsessive thinking, and agitation
in certain depressions, especially those of
the involutional period ('involutional
melancholia').

Depression is '. . . a pathological state
of conscious psychic suffering and guilt,
accompanied by a marked reduction in
the sense of personal values, and a diminution of mental, psycho-motor, and even
organic activity, unrelated to actual
deficiency.' (Nacht, S., and Racamier,
P.C. *International Journal of Psycho-
Analysis XLI,* 481, 1960)

As used by the layman, the word depression ordinarily refers only to the mood
element, which in psychiatry would more
appropriately be labeled dejection, sadness, gloominess, despair, despondency,
etc.

Depression, even as defined above, may
occur in the course of any psychiatric disorder although it is most commonly seen
in the psychotic group, particularly in
the manic-depressive reactions, the involutional psychoses and the chronic brain
disorders associated with senile, circulatory, or metabolic disease. See *psycho-*

sis, manic-depressive; psychosis, involu-tional.

depression, acute See *melancholia.*

depression, adolescent 'Such depressions are so frequently seen in youth of both sexes that the term "adolescent depression" would not be out of place. But they occur whenever the adult sex problem becomes acute, for instance, following engagement or marriage. They are never pure depressions, because the repression is never complete. Symbolic outlets, representing unconscious solutions of the problem, carry off much of the libido and only what is left, which tends to appear in the form of crude infantilism, is repressed. There are, therefore, many anxieties and worries and much hypochondria, with only a general background of depression.' (MacCurdy, J.T. *The Psychology of Emotion*, Harcourt, Brace, New York, 1925)

depression, agitated Any *depression* (q.v.) in which restlessness and increased psychomotor activity are a prominent part of the clinical picture. Sometimes the term is used interchangeably with involutional melancholia, where agitation rather than psychomotor retardation is the rule.

depression, ambivalent (am-biv′à-lent) Minkowski's term for cases of depression in which ambivalence is a prominent symptom.

depression, anaclitic (an-à-klit′ik) A term used by Spitz to refer to the syndrome shown by infants who are separated from their mothers for long periods of time. Initially, the infant gives indications of distress, but after three months of separation '. . . the weepiness subsided, and stronger provocation became necessary to provoke it. These children would sit with wide open, expressionless eyes, frozen immobile face, and a faraway expression, as if in a daze, apparently not perceiving what went on in their environment. . . . Contact with children who arrived at this stage became increasingly difficult and finally impossible. At best, screaming was elicited.' (Spitz, R. *The Psychoanalytic Study of the Child*, vol. 2, International Universities Press, New York, 1946.)

In Spitz's series, the reaction occurred in children who were six to eight months old at the time of separation, which continued for a practically unbroken period of three months. This reaction was seen in full form only in children who had left a 'good' mother-child relationship; those with a 'bad' relationship did not develop the syndrome.

Bakwin noted a similar syndrome, with listlessness, emaciation and pallor, relative immobility, quietness, unresponsiveness, indifferent appetite, failure to gain weight despite adequate diet, frequent stools, poor sleep, an appearance of unhappiness, proneness to febrile episodes, and absence of sucking habits. Bakwin and others refer to this syndrome as 'hospitalism.'

The anaclitic depression is reversible if the mother is restored to the child within three months.

depression, anancastic (an-an-kas′tik) Lion uses this term to refer to dejection or depression accompanied by tension, perplexity, anxiety, and obsessive and paranoid ideas which occurs in individuals whose premorbid personality was of the rigid, obsessive anancastic type. See *anancasm.*

depression, anxious See *depression, classification of.*

depression, autonomous (aw-ton′ō-mus) See *depression, classification of.*

depression, classification of In the 1968 revision of psychiatric nomenclature (DSM-II), depression is considered in the following groups: (1) involutional melancholia, 296.0, (2) manic-depressive illness (manic type, 296.1; depressed type, 296.2; circular type, 296.3), (3) psychotic depressive reaction, 298.0, (4) schizophrenia, schizo-affective type, 295.7, and (5) depressive neurosis, 300.4.

An older scheme after Kraepelin classified manias and depressions (or melancholias) under the general heading Affective Psychosis, as follows:
(A) Manic-Depressive Psychosis
       (1) Manic phase
             (a) hypomania
             (b) acute mania
             (c) delirious mania
                   (Bell's mania)
             (d) chronic mania

(2) Depressive phase
    (a) simple depression
    (b) acute depression
    (c) depressive stupor
(3) Periodical psychoses
    (a) recurrent mania
    (b) recurrent melancholia
    (c) alternating insanity
    (d) circular insanity
(4) Mixed states
    (a) maniacal stupor
    (b) agitated depression
    (c) unproductive mania
    (d) depressive mania
    (e) depression with flight of ideas
    (f) akinetic mania
    (g) perplexity state
(B) Involutional Melancholia
    (1) depressed type (agitated depression)
    (2) paranoid type

Various authors have suggested other classificatory schemes, but these seem to compound rather than alleviate the difficulties inherent in categorizing disturbances whose etiology is only poorly understood. Thus Gillespie speaks of reactive, autonomous, and involutional depressions. Reactive depression, in this scheme, is characterized by lack of activity and thought; autonomous depression has more activity, restlessness, and self-accusatory tendencies; involutional depression is chiefly distinguished by a hypochondriacal trend.

Mira y Lopez differentiates the following types: (1) physiogenetic or symptomatic depression; (2) simple affective depression, (3) melancholic depression, with self-destructive tendencies; (4) anxious depression; (5) psychogenic depression; (6) depression associated with aboulia or other disturbances of the will; (7) schizophrenic depression.

depression, constitutional See *disposition, constitutional depressive.*

depression, cyclical (sī'kli-kal, sik'li) Recurrent episodes of depression which may or may not alternate with periods of exaltation. Cases of cyclical depression can be divided into two groups, those in which 'outer exciting causes do not seem to play any decisive part' and can, therefore, be described as spontaneous; and those that can 'easily be traced back to mental traumata.' In their clinical

manifestations the two types are markedly similar and both may end in mania.

In the second type the trauma, in the end, results in the real or emotional loss of a loved object (such as a failure of some sort, a monetary loss, the death of a loved person, a disappointment in love). From the psychoanalytical point of view the next step is the introjection of the lost object by the ego: the patient's ego becomes identified with the object. Finally, the ego-ideal, or superego, violently attacks both the ego and the object now identified with the ego. These rebukes and attacks upon the object are experienced by the patient as delusions of inferiority, as self-depreciation, and self-reproaches. At bottom, these symptoms represent the ego's revenge upon the lost object.

According to Freud, the just described rebellion of the ego against the ego-ideal is also at work in the spontaneous cyclical depression. In these patients, there is a sharp conflict between the ego and superego, 'a conflict in which the ideal, in an excess of sensitiveness, relentlessly exhibits its condemnation of the ego in delusions of inferiority and in self-depreciation.' This occurs as the ego periodically rebels against the ego-ideal. (Freud, S. *Group Psychology and the Analysis of the Ego,* International Psycho-analytical Press, London, 1922)

depression, ictal (ik'tal) See *emotions, ictal.*

depression, involutional (in-vō-lū'shun-al) See *psychosis, involutional.*

depression, melancholic (mel-an-kol'ik) See *depression, classification of.*

depression, physiogenetic (fiz-i-ō-ge-net'ik) See *depression, classification of.*

depression, post-infectious See *neurasthenia, post-infectious.*

depression, psychasthenic (sī-kas-then'ik) Depression occurring in psychasthenic person.

depression, psychogenic (sī-ko-gen'ik) See *depression, classification of.*

depression, (psycho)neurotic (sī-ko-nū-rot'ik) In the 1952 A.P.A. revision of psychiatric nomenclature, the diagnosis, psychoneurotic depressive reaction is synonymous with reactive depression (see *depression, reactive*). 'The anxiety in this reaction is allayed, and hence partially relieved, by depression and self-depreciation. The reaction is precipitated by a current situation, frequently by some loss sustained by the patient, and is often associated with a feeling of guilt for past failures or deeds.' (*Mental Disorders: Diagnostic and Statistical Manual*, American Psychiatric Association, Washington, D.C., 1952). To be considered in differentiating this group from the corresponding psychotic reaction are the following points: '. . . (1) life history of patient, with special reference to mood swings (suggestive of psychotic reaction), to the personality structure (neurotic or cyclothymic) and to precipitating environmental factors and (2) absence of malignant symptoms (hypochondriacal preoccupation, agitation, delusions, particularly somatic, hallucinations, severe guilt feelings, intractable insomnia, suicidal ruminations, severe psychomotor retardation, profound retardation of thought, stupor),' (ibid.)

In the 1968 revision of psychiatric nomenclature (DSM-II) this entity is termed *depressive neurosis*, 300.4.

It is recognized that attempts to differentiate between psychotic and neurotic depressions, either on phenomenological or on psychodynamic grounds, are inadequate. While it is obvious that severe dejection can be superimposed upon any nosologic entity (and is particularly common in phobics and obsessional neuroses), that this should justify a special diagnosis of depression is questionable.

depression, psychotic (298.0) In the 1968 revision of psychiatric nomenclature (DSM-II) 'psychotic depressive reaction' refers to those severely depressed patients with gross misinterpretation of reality (including delusions and hallucinations) who do not have a history of previous depressions or of marked mood swings, but whose symptoms are reactive (i.e. attributable to some identifiable experience) and of psychotic degree.

depression, reactive When a depressive state is directly occasioned by some external situation and is relieved when the external situation is removed, the condition is known as a reactive depression. A

mother, intensely joyous at the expectation of rejoining her children after a long absence abroad, was held by federal authorities until the legality of her admission to the country was established. She remained acutely depressed until a decision favorable to her was rendered.

'Reactive *depressions*, which become aggravated to a mental disease, are quite rare in the light of present views.' (Bleuler, E. *Textbook of Psychiatry*, tr. by Brill, A.A., Macmillan, New York, 1930)

Some use this term synonymously with psychoneurotic depressive reaction or depressive neurosis (300.4).

depression, retarded See *melancholia*.

depression, simple affective See *depression, classification of*.

depression, stuporous (stū′por-us) See *melancholia*.

depression, symptomatic (sim-tō-ma′tik) See *depression, classification of*.

depression, unreality 'Patients suffering from this psychosis do not labour with the diffuse inhibition assailing the retarded cases. In fact, they may seem to be perfectly normal, from an objective standpoint, and even intimates may fail to observe their trouble. Yet they tell a sad story. All kinds of activity to which they force themselves fail to reward them with any emotional satisfaction. They can make themselves laugh in company with others, but the joke does not feel funny, they only know it is. They can recognize intellectually the beauty in any work of art, but there is no glow of pleasure in the sight. Above all in their human relationship they feel themselves lacking. Affection for others who ought to be dearest to them simply will not come. Consequently they sum up their subjective woes in the expression *unreality*.' (MacCurdy, J.T. *The Psychology of Emotion*, Harcourt, Brace, New York, 1925)

depressive neurosis (300.4) See *depression, (psycho)neurotic*.

depressive position See *position, depressive*.

deprivation, emotional (de-pri-vā′shun) Isolation of an infant from its mother to the degree that identification with the maternal figure is not made, with the result that personality development is impaired. The validity of the general proposition regarding the adverse effects of emotional deprivation has been established by two sets of observations—studies of children who were reared in institutional settings and whose adjustment difficulties reflected early distortions in personality development; and studies of infants' reactions to separation from their mothers. See *depression, anaclitic* for a description of the latter.

deprivation, maternal The absence of a positive and continuous relationship between infant and mother or mother-surrogate. Many workers in developmental psychology and related fields have maintained that maternal deprivation has important deleterious short-range as well as long-range effects upon personality development; data accumulated within the 1950's and 1960's, however, have cast considerable doubt upon the validity of such a hypothesis. See *mother, schizophrenogenic.*

deprivation, perceptual (per-sep′choo-al) See *deprivation, sensory.*

deprivation, sensory Perceptual deprivation; perceptual or sensory isolation; informational underload. These terms are ordinarily used to refer to experimental techniques which either reduce the absolute intensity of stimuli reaching the subject, or reduce the patterning of stimuli or impose a structuring of stimuli upon the subject. One of the methods employed to reduce intensity of stimuli, for example, is to suspend the subject, wearing only a blacked-out head mask for breathing, in a tank of water maintained at a constant temperature of 34.5° C. Such experimental sensory deprivation is considered to be similar to 'brain-washing' and the isolation experienced by many explorers and shipwrecked persons, who under conditions of severe environmental stress are known to develop mental abnormalities. The following features are common to the various situations, whether 'naturally' or experimentally produced: intense desire for extrinsic sensory stimuli and bodily motion, increased suggestibility, impairment of organized thinking, oppression, depression and, in extreme cases, hallucinations, delusions, and confusion.

It is believed that such abnormalities may be explained as follows: the correspondence between external reality and sensory neuronal activity is not a one-to-one relationship; perception is learned through motor interactions with objects in the environment, and when sleep or other states minimize or eliminate such interactions, percepts based upon previous experience will emerge from the brain itself in the form of hallucinations and delusions (e.g. in dreams). This may be because the sensory input from the viscera augments spontaneous neuronal activity, especially in the thalamus, to such an extent that impulses over relay tracts are initiated, giving rise to visceral hallucinations and similar phenomena.

deprivation, thought *Blocking* (q.v.).

depth-psychology (depth′-sī-kol′ō-ji) The psychology relating to the realm of the unconscious, in contradistinction to the psychology of the conscious part of the mind. In psychoanalysis (Freud), depth-psychology may be represented by the id and superego; in analytical psychology (Jung), by the collective unconscious. It is simply a term indicative of a psychic level.

derailment Abnormal deviation or disorganization of psychic processes. Thus, Kraepelin spoke of derailment of volition, speech, thought, etc. Derailment is a basic symptom of schizophrenia.

derailment of volition In writing on *parabulia,* Kraepelin says that 'gradual transitions from the simple changes of every-day purposeful actions lead to those disorders of volition which we may gather together under the name of parabulia. The side impulses which at first bring about only flourishes in action may gradually become cross-impulses which lead to complete derailment of volition.' (Kraepelin, E. *Dementia Praecox and Paraphrenia,* tr. by Barclay, R.M., Livingstone, Edinburgh, 1919.) The phrase thus comes to mean disorganization and disintegration of volition.

derailment, speech See *derailment. 'Derailments in linguistic expression* form an important domain in the speech disorders of dementia praecox. Vocal speech itself can be changed in the most varied way by side and cross impulses. The patients in speaking, bellow, screech, murmur or whisper, scarcely move their lips, keep their teeth closed, or often pass suddenly from low whispering to loud screaming.' (Kraepelin, E. *Dementia Praecox and Paraphrenia*, tr. by Barclay, R.M., Livingstone, Edinburgh, 1919)

derailment, thought 'A great many quite incomprehensible and disconnected utterances, in which it can scarcely be only a question of disorders of linguistic expression. . . .' (Kraepelin, E. *Dementia Praecox and Paraphrenia*, tr. by Barclay, R.M., Livingstone, Edinburgh, 1919)

deranged Mentally unsound.

Dercum, Francis Xavier (1856-1931) American neurologist.

derealization (dē-rē-al-i-zā′shun) The feeling of changed reality; the feeling that one's surroundings have changed. The symptom is usually (though not always) indicative of schizophrenia and is based on the sense of passivity toward the environment which is secondary to projection feelings. 'Everybody is doing things to me; something has happened to the whole world; the world has changed.' If severe enough, this feeling of changed reality may be expressed as a feeling of imminent or actual catastrophe. See *dereism; depersonalization.*

dereism (dē′rē-iz′m) Mental activity that deviates from the laws of logic and experience and fails to take the facts of reality into consideration. Among psychiatric patients dereism reaches its fullest development in schizophrenic states, in which psychic activity is largely expressed without respect to the realities of life. When a patient firmly believes that, as the Redeemer, he cures all illnesses by a simple gesture, his thinking is said to be out of harmony with facts, that is, dereistic.
'The separation of associations from experience naturally facilitates dereistic thinking in its highest degree, which is actually based on the very fact that natural connections are ignored.' (Bleuler, E. *Textbook of Psychiatry*, tr. by Brill, A.A., Macmillan Company, New York, 1930, p. 79) See *autism; depersonalization.*

derivation, psychological (sī-lō-loj′i-kal) 'When analysing agitation, I was led to consider the phenomenon of *psychological derivation.* I wrote: "Derivation occurs whenever the production of a superior phenomenon, one characterized by high tension, has begun, but when the production of the phenomenon has been checked by a lowering of mental tension which has rendered the appearance of phenomena of high tension impossible." When this happens, instead of the complete activation which culminates in decision, effort, and triumph, there occur convulsive paroxysms, tics questionings, interminable debates, multifarious visceral agitations. . . . When one psychological phenomenon is superior to another, the force requisite for its production may be adequate to produce a lower-grade phenomenon a hundred times over.' (Janet, P. *Psychological Healing*, vols. 1-2, tr. by Paul, E. and C., Macmillan, New York, 1925)

derivative See *substitute-formation.*

dermatography, dermatographia (dĕr-mȧ-tog′rȧ-fē, -tō-graf′ē-ȧ) Dermatography is commonly called skin-writing. It appears in exaggerated form, namely, as an urticaria, when the skin is stroked by a pointed instrument.
Dermatography 'may be divided into two types; one the dilator type, which is characterized by reddening, swelling and even exudation, following stimulation of the skin; the other, the constrictor type, characterized by pallor of the skin where it has been irritated by a firm stroke of the finger.' (Eppinger, H. and Hess, L. *Vagotonia*, 2nd ed., tr. by Kraus, W.M. and Jelliffe, S.E., Nervous & Mental Disease Publishing Company, New York, 1917)

dermatome (der′ma-tōm) The skin area supplied by the dorsal root of a single nerve segment.

dermatophobia (dĕr-mat-ō-fō′bē-ȧ) Fear of skin(-lesion).

dermatosiophobia (dĕr-mȧ-tō-si-ō-fō′bē-ȧ) Fear of (acquiring a) skin disease.

dermatozoic (dĕr′ma-tō-zō-ik) Of or pertaining to the sensation of animals in the skin. Dermatozoic delusions, also called *formication* (q.v.) are seen in toxic psychosis and in some (usually female) patients with depression.

dermographia, dermographism, dermography (der-mō-graf'ē-à, -graf'iz'm, der-mog'ra-fē) See *dermatography.*

desaggressivization (des-ag-gres-iv-i-zā'-shun) Neutralization of the aggressive drive (just as desexualization is neutralization of the sexual drive), so that the energy which would ordinarily be discharged is made available to the ego for carrying out its various tasks and wishes according to the secondary process.

desanimania (des-an-i-mā'nē-à) *Obs.* Psychosis with mental deficiency.

descriptive In psychiatry, concerned with the observable and the objective, rather than with the internal forces that may affect or determine overt behavior. Thus, *descriptive psychiatry* typically refers to any system of psychiatry that is based primarily on the study of symptoms and phenomena; often contrasted with *dynamic psychiatry,* which is primarily concerned with internal, unconscious drives or energies that are presumed to determine behavior.

desensitization (dē-sen-si-ti-zā'shun) The act of alleviating or removing a mental complex. 'Hand in hand with this analysis [i.e. distributive analysis] go corrective habit training, necessary specific treatment for somatic disorders, and the bringing to recognition and the enucleation of "sore-spots" or complex-determined topics, memories, associations and reactions which require desensitization and replacement by more wholesome resources and performances.' (Howard, F.E. and Patry, F.L. *Mental Health,* Harper, New York, 1935)

deséquilibrés (dā-zā-kē-lē-brā') (F. 'unbalanced persons') A term coined by Magnan for those affected by what was then known as inherited neurasthenia.

desexualization (de-sek-shoo-al-i-za'shun) Neutralization of the sexual drive so that the energy which would ordinarily be expended in immediate id discharge (the primary process) is held up and made available to the ego for its various tasks and wishes according to the secondary process.

design, factorial A method of research in which two or more variables are manipulated deliberately to allow study of the interaction between them as well as the main effect of each variable.

desire Until the introduction of modern concepts in psychopathology, the term desire was defined essentially from the standpoint of the conscious part of the mind. It meant, and continues to mean, a wish, a longing for, a craving, an inclination. With the development of fuller knowledge of the unconscious, the term desire was applied to many impulses or tendencies of that part of the psyche. There are forces in the unconscious that strive for expression in reality. To indicate this striving, the terms desire, wish, etc. have been retained, amid great opposition, because it is not conceded in general that there is, for example, a wish to die, a wish for incest, for exhibitionism, etc. That is true, from the standpoint of consciousness; yet, in the unconscious are impulses, the antitheses of conscious desires or wishes, that press for overt expression. They may be regarded as biological urges or 'wishes' or 'desires,' in contradistinction to the personal ones. To wish or desire generally carries the idea that it is done wittingly and consciously; we are not in the habit of thinking that we wish also unconsciously. It suits our morality to have unconscious impulses and conscious wishes.

'In other words, the latter (unconscious) consists of thoughts, desires, and wishes of a kind that are highly unacceptable to the conscious personality. . . .' (Jones, E. *Papers on Psycho-Analysis,* 4th ed., Wood, Baltimore, 1938)

desire, psychical (sī-ki-kal) This is a term for a conscious sexual feeling.

'In whole groups of cases anxiety-neurosis is accompanied by a very noticeable abatement of sexual libido, i.e. of *psychical desire.'* (Freud, S. *Collected Papers,* vol. 1, tr, by Riviere, J., Leonard and Virginia Woolf and The Institute of Psychoanalysis, London, 1924 - 25)

desocialization (dē-so-shal-ī-zā'shun) The

process of withdrawing or turning away from interpersonal contacts and relationships, such as is seen commonly in schizophrenics. These patients tend to replace social behavior and language habits with personal, highly individual behavior.

despeciation (dē-spē-shi-ā'shun) The presence in a person of a number of extreme variants of physical characteristics, such as a scaphoid shoulder-blade, a supernumerary breast, a deformed ear lobe, an anomalous distribution of hair, etc. The variants, when alone, have little pathogenic value or meaning, but the accumulation of them in a single individual is regarded as a sign of biological inferiority or despeciation (Apert). J. Bauer uses the term *degeneration* to refer to such marked deviations from the type of the species.

despondency Melancholy.

destiny, neurosis of (nū-rō'sis) Moral masochism; fate neurosis. This type of neurotic ailment afflicts the person who unconsciously arranges all of his life's experiences so that he is in the position of suffering continual reverses, while he consciously holds that destiny or fate brings them. His friends will always remark on his bad luck and continual ill fortune. Moreover, the patient invariably tends to blame his fate for his continual reverses, being unaware that he is responsible for them himself. See *masochism*.

As the 'all-consuming task of his life' this neurotic has in the first place the 'mastery of guilt-feelings,' which he hopes to accomplish through his own suffering, and thus ingratiate himself with an implacable superego. Secondly, the patient turns all of his life's activities into situations where he can experience this suffering. In Fenichel's words, he uses his environment solely as 'an arena in which to stage his internal conflicts.' All real-life actions 'are repetitions of childhood situations or attempts to end infantile conflicts rather than rational undertakings.' (Fenichel, O. *The Psychoanalytic Theory of Neurosis*, Norton, New York, 1945)

destructive instinct See *instinct, death.*

destrudo (des-trōō'dō) Edoardo Weiss coined this term to denote the energy associated with the death or destructive instinct (*Imago, XXI*, 393, 1935). It is the opposite of *libido*, the energy of the instinct Eros. See *thanatos*.

detachment Separation; in psychiatry, separation or divorce from emotional involvement. See *affect, detached.*

detachment, somnolent Withdrawal into sleep; as used by Sullivan, the infant's reaction of drowsiness and apathy to anxiety in the mother. As the infant withdraws from the situation and sleeps, the mother's anxiety will often subside and thus the cause of the infant's own anxiety is removed. But if such detachments persist, the infant may progress into a *marasmic state* in which he may die unless appropriate nursing care is brought to him.

detector, lie A machine designed to record the various physiological changes which accompany changes in emotional tone, such as changes in respiratory rate, pulse rate, blood pressure, skin moisture, etc.; sometimes called the *Keeler polygraph.* 'The lie detector is based upon the fact that the impact of emotionally charged ideas or the conscious suppression of a true recollection and the substitution of a false statement cause detectable physiologic changes through stimulation of the autonomic nervous system, over which one has no voluntary control.' (Guttmacher, M.S. *Psychiatry and the Law*, Norton, New York, 1952.) Although results are not always accurate, the technique of interpretation is constantly being improved; it appears that accurate diagnosis on the basis of the test is possible in 75 - 80 per cent of cases, that in 15 - 20 per cent results may be too indefinite for confident diagnosis, and that the remaining 5 per cent constitute the margin of probable error. Such errors as do occur are usually those on the side of failing to detect a guilty person rather than on the side of mislabeling an innocent person guilty.

detentio (dā-ten'tē-ō) *Obs.* The fixed attitude in catelepsy.

deterioration Worsening of the clinical condition; progressively increasing impairment in functioning. Compare with regression, *dementia* (q.v.).

Intellectual deterioration generally refers to diminution or impairment of the ability to remember, together with disorders attendant upon memory losses. Intellectual deterioration is usually observed in patients with destructive processes in the cerebral cortex.

deterioration, chronic alcoholic A complication of chronic alcoholism characterized by emotional blunting, organic memory defect, and deterioration in the moral and ethical spheres; in DSM-II, coded 291.5.

deterioration, emotional Emotional deterioration occurs mainly in patients suffering from schizophrenia: the patient becomes careless and indifferent about the surroundings and people around him, and shows no adequate emotional reaction to environmental stimuli.

deterioration, epileptic (ep-i-lep'tik) See *dementia, epileptic.*

deterioration, habit The abandonment of integrated and socialized behavior in favor of disintegrated and personal behavior. Habit deterioration is a reflection of regression.

'In all dementing psychoses, in dementia praecox and paranoides and in organic and senile dementias there occurs a failure of the habits appropriate to the patient's social standing. Habits of cleanliness; of decency in micturition, defaecation and eating, and of neatness in dress, together with the conventional social manners, all suffer degradation and are replaced either by the habits of a lower social level or by purely indifferent animal behaviour.' (Craig, M. and Beaton, T. *Psychological Medicine,* 4th ed., Churchill, London, 1926)

deterioration index or quotient An index of the degree of intellectual impairment, based on comparison of scores on those tests of the Wechsler-Bellevue that show little or no decline, with scores on those tests that generally show a steep age decline. The tests that do not decline are often termed 'Hold' tests: information, vocabulary, picture completion, and object assembly; those that do decline are often termed 'Don't Hold' tests: digit span, arithmetic, block design, digit symbol. The deterioration index, or D.I., is computed as follows:

$$D.I. = \frac{Hold - Don't\ Hold}{Hold}$$

deterioration, post-traumatic mental (post-traw-ma'tik) A nosologic entity included under the psychoses due to trauma as indicated in the Standard Classified Nomenclature of Disease, 1935. In DSM-I it was called chronic brain syndrome associated with trauma, with mental deficiency. Following a severe or an apparently slight injury to the head, with or without an acute or chronic delirium, some persons may develop a progressively increasing dementia or mental enfeeblement. Many of the symptoms included under post-traumatic personality disorders may also be present. In DSM-II, coded 293.5 if psychotic, 309.9 if nonpsychotic.

deterioration, simple senile One form of the *senile psychoses* (q.v.) (290.0) Symptoms include narrowing of interests, sluggishness of thought, misoneism, recent memory gaps which are filled in with fabrications, defective orientation, hoarding, inattentiveness except to immediate personal wants, apathy or irritability, and sometimes suspiciousness, ideas of persecution, and restless wandering from the home.

determinant See *determinant, dream.*

determinant, dominant See *determinant, dream.*

determinant, dream The real or principal motive or reason responsible for the production of the dream, since it is true that even if 'dreams are always abundantly overdetermined, one determinant is invariable in the dreams of neurotics.' This invariable determinant is called the 'dominant determinant' and is in direct connection with the dreamer's most important conflict. To discover the dominant determinant is no easy task: most of the time it is not revealed through association and may be discovered only by the use of the interpreter's intuition. (Stekel, W. *The Interpretation of Dreams,* Liveright, New York, 1943)

determination, sex See *sex-determination.*

determinative idea See *idea, determinative.*

determiner A cause or determinant; in genetics, a *gene* (q.v.).

determining quality See *quality, determining.*

determinism (dē-tēr'min-iz'm) 'It is the concept which states, first, that our actions can change nothing in the events of life which were firmly established through causal connection, and, second, that man is not free to dispose of his own will and to choose between good and evil in his actions.' (Bleuler, E. *Textbook of Psychiatry,* tr. by Brill, A.A., Macmillan, New York, 1930)

Spinoza said: 'In the mind there is no absolute or free will, but the mind is determined by another cause, and this last by another cause, and so on to infinity." (Spinoza, B. de, *Ethic,* tr. by White, W.H.)

determinism, biological In the field of mental deficiency this term means that only those whose retardation is constitutionally determined should be classed as 'feebleminded.' The clinical differentiation of constitutionally determined mental defectives from those defectives not so determined is frequently difficult, if not impossible. For example, the intellectually subnormal not constitutionally determined may become social failures because of unfavorable environmental factors, and the constitutionally defective may be socially successful in a favorable environment. This opinion contrasts with that of *biosocial determinism* (q.v.).

determinism, biosocial In the field of mental deficiency, the theory of biosocial determinism maintains that when social failure or inadequacy occurs it is a result of the combined action of biological and environmental factors in a total situation. Just as persons of average intelligence may be socially effective or inadequate because of environmental factors, so the higher grade mentally defective may behave according to accepted social standards or be forced into behavior viewed as being feebleminded in nature. The intellectually subnormal and the feebleminded do not differ as groups, except in terms of social success or failure.

dethronement See *parents, dethronement of.*

detumescence (dē-tū-mes'ens) Subsidence of erection and genital engorgement as a result of emptying of the genital blood vessels. See *contrectation; tumescence.*

deuteropathy (dū-tēr-op'à-thē) A secondary disease, disorder, or symptom.

deutero-phallic (dū-tēr-ō-fal'ik) See *protophallic.*

development, atypical A term used by some (notably Beata Rank, Putnam, and Kaplan) as a diagnostic label for those children whom others would classify as childhood schizophrenia or early infantile autism.

development, genital-psychical (jen'i-tal-sī'ki-kal) A psychoanalytic term which stresses the importance of psychosexual, developmental, emotional maturation as a true basis for genito-sexual potency—in contrast to mechanical, anatomical, physiological, and orgastic criteria which give rise to pseudo-potency and the masking of impotence. Genito-sexual potency is characterized by the ability to love in the adult sense and by a free, full, and satisfactory orgasm as well. Genito-sexual pseudo-potency is manifested in a masturbatory preoccupation with personal, orgastic, and tactile sensation. Even though orgasm in the pseudo-potent may be deceptively satisfactory, it is frequently entirely dependent upon thinly disguised perversion stimuli, and perversion auspices. Genito-sexual psuedo-potency is associated with self-love and self-satisfaction; in contrast the genito-sexual potency of the psychosexually mature is strongly marked by love of and consideration for the partner.

development, inhibition of See *pathogenesis.*

developmental levels Divisions of the life span in terms of chronological age; the following levels are generally recognized: (1) neonatal period, from birth to one month; (2) *infancy* (q.v.) from birth to one year; (3) early (pre-school) childhood, from one to six years; (4) mid-childhood, six to ten years; (5) late childhood or pre-adolescence, 10 to 12 years; (6) *adolescence* (q.v.) 12 to 21 years; (7) adulthood or maturity, beginning at 21 years and ending with old age according to some, but with others ending at (8) the involutional period or climacterium, 40 to 55 years for women, 50 to 65 years for men; (9) old age or the senium, beginning at 65 or 70 years.

developmentalism (dē-vel-op-men'taliz'm) The genetic, longitudinal view of human behavior. The term is used to describe Gesell's method at his center at Yale University, where the emphasis is on maturation as a biological process in a cultural setting. Each level of development of children's behavior is determined and standardized on the basis of long-term studies; there is little concern with interpretation of the inner life of the child.

deviant, deviate Any person differing markedly from what is accepted as the norm, the average, or the usual. Probably the most common use of the term is in relation to the sexual form. See *deviation, sexual.*

deviation, average See *deviation, mean.*

deviation, conjugate (kon'jū-gāt) See *nerve, oculomotor.*

deviation, ego See *children, ego deviant.*

deviation, mean (M.D.) A description of the variability of a frequency distribution; also called *average deviation* (or A.D.). The mean deviation from the mean is computed by tabulating the amount by which each individual score in distribution differs from the mean score, considering all these deviations as positive, and then computing their mean.

The *standard deviation* (S.D.) is similar to the mean deviation, except that each deviation from the mean is squared, the squared deviations are totaled and averaged, and the square root of the average is then extracted. This gives a more reliable measure of variability than the mean deviation and is in wider use because other statistical measures are calculated on the basis of the S.D. In any distribution which approximates the normal curve in form, about 65 per cent of the measures will lie within one S.D. of the mean, and about 95 per cent will lie within two S.D.'s of the mean. When used as a measure of variability the S.D. is known as the *standard error.*

deviation, median A description of the variability of a frequency distribution; also called Probable Deviation or Probable Error (P.E.) The median deviation from the mean is computed by tabulating the amount by which each individual score in a distribution differs from the mean score, considering all these deviations as positive, and then computing their median. The median deviation is the absolute amount of deviations from the mean that is exceeded by half the measures in a distribution.

deviation, probable See *deviation, median.*

deviation, sexual In the 1968 revision of psychiatric nomenclature, sexual deviation is a major category of personality disorders and includes:

302.0 *homosexuality* (q.v.)
302.1 fetishism (see *fetish*)
302.2 *pedophilia* (q.v.)
302.3 *transvestitism* (q.v.)
302.4 *exhibitionism* (q.v.)
302.5 *voyeurism* (q.v.)
302.6 *sadism* (q.v.)
302.7 *masochism* (q.v.)
302.8 other sexual deviation

deviation, skew Skew-deviation (Hertwig-Magendie phenomenon) is a rare cerebellar or collicular sign, characterized by downward and inward rotation of the eyeball on the same side of the lesion and upward and outward rotation of the eyeball on the opposite side.

deviation, standard (S.D.) The standard deviation is a summary of the variation of the items in a frequency distribution. It is the square root of the mean square of the deviation of each variable in the series from the mean of the series. See *deviation, mean.*

device, safety Karen Horney's term for any means of protecting the self from threat, especially the hostility of the environment; although a more general term, safety device is approximately equivalent to defense mechanism.

Devic's disease Neuromyelitis optica; ophthalmoneuromyelitis; disseminated myelitis with optic neuritis. An acute demyelinating disease which is sometimes self-limited but which in 50 per cent of cases is relapsing, progressive, and fatal. It consists of massive foci of demyelination in the optic nerves and chiasma and spinal cord, which may undergo softening and cavitation. Etiology is unknown and there is no definitive treatment.

devolution (dev-ō-lū'shun) Hughlings Jackson's term, approximately equivalent to *regression* (q.v.). 'He called the tendency "devolution" as it was an undoing, a reversal, of evolution. The cornerstone of psychoanalytic theory is just this principle applied to mental functions, here called "regression."' (MacCurdy, J.T. *The Psychology of Emotion,* Harcourt, Brace, New York, 1925)

dextrality-sinistrality (deks-tral'i-ti-sin-is-tral'i-ti) These yoked terms refer to the clinically observed phenomenon that the 'uninfluenced' child will spontaneously favor and develop skill in the use of one hand, eye, and foot in a kind of primacy and choice over the other. The predominance of the right hand, eye, and foot is called *dextrality* (right-handedness), while that of the left hand, eye, and foot is called *sinistrality.* It is theoretically assumed that this motor predominance is correlated with a corresponding cerebral physiological pattern. Thus, the neurophysiological theory concludes that the left cerebral hemisphere is predominant over the right in children with dextrality, while the right cerebral hemisphere is physiologically predominant over the left in those with sinistrality.

It is contended that 'handedness,' right or left, can be converted through educational means, but that 'eyedness' seems resistant to such conversion. Some observers ascribe learning difficulties, speech difficulties, and other intellectual difficulties to this conversion process, which is usually the change of a 'natural' sinistrality into a converted dextrality. The validity of these correlations, as well as the neurophysiological and psychological interrelationships theoretically implicit in these clinical states, are still moot questions. It is generally agreed, however, that mixed and confused laterality is a frequent finding in minimal brain dysfunction. See *impulse-disorder, hyperkinetic.*

dextrophobia (deks-trō-fō'bē-à) Fear of objects to the right.

DFP See psychotomimetic.

D.I. Acronym for ˙*deterioration index* (q.v.).

di Rorschach scoring symbol for inside detail.

diabetic exophthalmic dysostosis (dī-à-bet'ik ek-sof-thal-am'ik dis-os-tō'sis) *Xanthomatosis* (q.v.).

diaboleptics (dī-à-bō-lep'tiks) Maudsley coined this term for those who claim to have supernatural communications.

diagnosis, negative Diagnosis by means of exclusion; 'wastebasket' diagnosis.

diagnosis, social Psychiatric social workers thus denote the conditions prevailing in the environment of the patient.

diamine (dī-am'in) Any substance that contains two amine groups. Such substances have recently received much attention in psychiatry because of certain indications that they may be of etiologic significance in the production of endogenously occurring psychoses. Thus, in the schizophrenias, 'The indications are that faulty enzyme production results in inadequate binding of amines, some of which are cerebrotropic, or exert their influence by reason of specific amino-sensitive cerebral areas. Both Baruk (France) and Buscaino (Italy) emphasize toxic and infectious (intestinal) causes, giving great importance to excessive or abnormal amine body production (especially diamines) due to liver or reticuloendothelial dysfunction or to gastro-intestinal diseases.' (Campbell, R. J., *Psychiatric Quarterly 32:* 318 - 334, 1958) See *amine; epinephrine; ergotropic; serotonin.*

diaphragma sellae (dē-à-fràg'mà sel'lē) See *meninges.*

diaschisis (dī-as'ki-sis) A term introduced by Monakow to indicate that when one 'center' of the brain is affected another distant 'center' which has a definite relation to the affected one, becomes functionally disordered.

diastematomyelia (dī-as-tem-à-tō-mī-ē'lē-à) Partial duplication of the spinal cord, usually in the thoracolumbar segments, with a column of connective tissue which sometimes contains bone or cartilage in the cleft between the two halves of the cord. Myelography shows a filling defect and dilatation of the vertebral canal, and also congenital deformity of two or more vertebrae.

diathesis (dī-ath'ē-sis) Constitutional disposition, or predisposition, to some anomalous or morbid condition 'which no longer belongs within the confines of the normal variability, but already begins to represent a potential disease condition.' These various *diathetic* conditions are distinguished by the fact that diathetic individuals respond with abnormal or truly pathological reactions to physiological stimuli, such as foods, or other ordinary conditions of life, such as sunlight, that are borne by the majority of individuals without injury. (Pende, N. *Constitutional Inadequacies,* tr. by Naccarati, S., Lea & Febiger, Philadelphia, 1928)

diathesis, arthritic (är-thrit'ik) Constitutional morbid condition which, according to the Italian school, includes the closely related exudative and hypersecretory diathesis as well as arthritism and is said to occur especially in the *megalosplanchnic hypervegetative* (q.v.) constitution.

Pende and Naccarati consider the hypersecretory diathesis as bearing out MacAuliffe's concept of a 'heavy type' and the chemical theories used to explain this type, although their own theory is based on neuro-chemism rather than on purely chemical principles.

Arthritic subjects are prone to syndromes grouped by the French school under the heading of diseases of *bradytrophism* (q.v.). Their organs have a tendency to sclerosis (fibroplastic diathesis) on account of the special primary hyperplasia and irritability of the visceral connective tissue.

Czerny's exudative diathesis readily becomes engrafted upon the overnourished megalosplanchnic constitution, inclined as it is to anomalies of metabolism, including those little-known anomalies which lie at the bottom of the exudative diathesis. This condition occurs in growing children and is so similar to the arthritic diathesis of adults that it has been called infantile arthritism.

There is general agreement that the arthritic manifestations differ somewhat in infancy because of the constitution peculiar to this age, namely, marked development of the connective and lymphatic tissue and a predominance of hormones stimulating the sympathetic nervous system, although the parasympathetic was originally predominant. The endocrine sympathetic condition accounts for the development and hardening of skin and mucosae, which are very delicate, fragile, and soft in the child, and for the ready appearance of phenomena due to the (originally predominant) parasympathetic nerves. It also explains the special localization of these neurovegetative disorders in the field of the skin and the mucosae as well as the special irritability and tendency to infection of the connective-lymphatic tissue, which functions actively in these first stages of life.

diathesis, colloidoclastic (ko-loid-ō-klas'-tik) A morbid condition in children which results from an imperfect albuminoid metabolism and leads to an unstable colloidoplasmatic equilibrium (colloidoclasia). The condition is believed to belong to the syndrome of *infantile arthritism* which is an *arthritic (exudative) diathesis* (q.v.) in children.

diathesis, eosinophilic (ē-ō-sin-ō-fil'ik) A subtype of the *arthritic diathesis* (q.v.). The condition is characterized by various degrees of eosinophila, which may range from 8 to 30 per cent and seems to depend on protein intoxication and anaphylactic crises.

diathesis, explosive A clinical subdivision of the traumatic psychoses characterized by intense irritability, particularly after the ingestion of alcohol; the irritability sometimes leads to acts of violence which appear unmotivated, that is, automatic.

diathesis, exudative (eks-ū'dȧ-tiv) This term, introduced by Czerny, designates a form of arthritic diathesis occurring in growing children and characterized by a constitutional condition called colloidoclastic diathesis by Widal.

The syndrome of arthritism in children is produced by irritating toxic products, which result from the protein metabolism and accumulate in the blood and interstitial lymph of the tissues, and especially in the skin and mucosae which possess the power of neutralizing toxins. The products of imperfect albuminoid metabolism stimulate these tissues and render them abnormally sensitive. They affect particularly the parasympathetic nerves, which are already in a state of hypertonia in the normal child. An unstable colloidoplasmatic equilibrium follows which is upset by ingestion of ordinary articles of diet, inducing the phenomena of protein shock, colloidoclasia, anaphylaxis and blood alkalosis. It is precisely to these phenomena that the syndrome of exudative diathesis applies.

diathesis, fibroplastic (fī-brō-plas'tik) A constitutional anomaly characterized by a sclerotic degeneration of various organs, due to a primary hyperplasia and irritability of the visceral connective tissue, and occurring in the course of a general arthritic diathesis.

diathesis, glial (glē̄al) A constitutional condition characterized by a hyperplastic or neoplastic tendency of primitive or more differentiated glial cells. The condition is believed to underlie a series of 'heredo-familial nervous diseases that usually develop on the soil of the lymphatic or hypoplastic constitution, and which include cerebral tuberous sclerosis and gliomatous cerebral hypertrophy, spinal gliosis and syringomyelia, glioma, neurofibromatosis, progressive lenticular degeneration, and other degenerative scleroses of the corpora striata.' (Pende, N. *Constitutional Inadequacies,* tr. by Naccarati, S., Lea & Febiger, Philadelphia, 1928)

diathesis, hypersecretory (hī-pēr-sē-krē'-tō-rē) See *diathesis, arthritic.*

diathesis, lithic (lith'ic) A constitutional morbid condition characterized by the metabolic anomaly of uricemia and a tendency to form urinary calculi. It is one of the most important manifestations of *arthritism* and is primarily a hereditary anomaly of metabolism rather than one of renal function, as it occurs especially in families in which various signs of a constitutional weakness of the urinary apparatus are found. See *diathesis, arthritic.*

A uric acid diathesis is often found in the same family or individual to be combined or alternating with gout and an oxalic acid diathesis leading to oxaluria and oxalic lithiasis. It is the autonomic system, together with the endocrine system, which plays a significant part in the pathogenesis of oxaluria and the related phosphaturia and calcinuria.

diathesis, neoplastic (nē-ō-plas'tik) Tendency of certain constitutional types to develop neoplastic conditions, especially carcinoma. Some typologists assign the equivalent of the pyknic or megaloplanchnic constitutions to persons with this tendency, while others postulate an association of the arthritic and the neoplastic diathesis, or an association between the cancerous and the *exudative* diathesis (q.v.).

In the literature, the assumption of an antagonism between cancer and active tuberculosis is widespread. It is said that both conditions are rarely found in the same person and that they favor different physiques, namely, the pyknic and asthenic types, respectively. The recent anatomical studies by Lewis have confirmed this assumption by revealing a high incidence of carcinoma in his hypercompensatory types and its absence in his regressive types. It must be mentioned, however, that the findings concerning a possibly genetic predisposition to cancer are still inadequate and contradictory, while there is already considerable evidence of the heredito-constitutional basis of the phthisic habitus.

diathesis, neuro-arthritic (nū-rō-är-thrit'-ik) Practically identical with *arthritic diathesis,* but the role of the autonomic system in this diathesis is stressed.

diathesis, neuropathic (nū-rō-path'ik) *Obs.* Neurasthenia.

diathesis, oxalic acid (oks-al'ik) See *diathesis, lithic.*

diathesis, traumatophilic (traw-mȧ-tō-fil'-ik) A predisposition to accidents, sometimes referred to as *accident proneness.* Fenichel considers this to be a manifestation of Freud's repetition compulsion. 'The repetition is desired to relieve a painful tension; but because the repetition is also painful, the person is afraid of it and tends to avoid it. Usually, therefore, a compromise is sought: a repetition on a smaller scale or under more encouraging circumstances. The ambivalence toward this repetition shows itself in the phenomena of traumatophilia and traumatophobia, in the fact that whatever these persons [of traumatophilic diathesis] undertake turns into a trauma; they fear this, and nevertheless they strive for it.' (Fenichel, O. *The Psychoanalytic Theory of Neurosis,* Norton, New York, 1945)

diathesis, uric acid (ū'rik) See *diathesis, lithic.*

didactic (dī-dak'tic) Fitted or intended to teach; used often to refer to formal teaching sessions, such as lectures, in contrast to discussion groups or seminars. Didactic psychoanalysis is also known as training or tuitional analysis. See *analysis, tuitional; analysis, orthodox.*

diecious, dioecious (dī-ē'shus) Sexually distinct, that is, being of one or the other sex and not hermaphroditic.

diencephalon (dī-en-sef'à-lon) See *forebrain.*

diencephalosis (dī-en-sef-à-lō'sis) A term used to refer to any of the many possible disturbances or functional alterations of the diencephalon and/or its interconnections. The following symptom groups are included: (1) lack of restraint and inhibition, (2) paradoxical co-existence of opposed functional disturbances, (3) alterations of biological rhythm, (4) various endocrine dysfunctions, (5) abnormalities of growth and development, (6) certain forms of psychopathy, (7) vascular lability, (8) dysthermia, (9) electroencephalograph abnormalities, and (10) cranioradiographic abnormalities. (Pende, N. 'Introduction to the Clinical Pathology of the Diencephalon.' *Medicina* 6: 197- 206, 1957)

differential fertility See *fertility, differential.*

differentiation, sex See *sex-differentiation.*

diffuse sclerosis See *sclerosis, diffuse.*

dihybrid (dī-hī'brid) A hybrid individual differing in two hereditary characters, or

hereditary traits based on two pairs of genes (see *hybrid*).

diisopropyl fluorophosphate (dī-ī-sō-prō-pil floo-ōr-ō-fos'fāt) See *psychotomimetic.*

dikephobia (dī-kē-fō'bē-à) Fear of justice.

dilapidation Deterioration; dementia.
'The minor degrees of incoherence are known as "scattering" and "dilapidation."' (Henderson, D. K. and Gillespie, R. D. *A Text-Book of Psychiatry,* 4th ed., Oxford University Press, London, 1936)

dilution, transference The diminution of the intensive transference toward the therapist owing to the presence of sibling and identification transferences to other members of a group. See *therapy, dilution.*

dim-out *Black-out* (q.v.).

dinomania (dī-nō-mā'nē-à) Dancing mania.

dionism (dī-on'iz'm) Heterosexuality. See *uranism.*

diplegia (dī-plē'jē-à) Bilateral paralysis of corresponding parts of the body.

diplegia, congenital spastic (kon-jen'i-tal spas'tik) *Little's disease* (q.v.).

diploid (dip'loid) The original stage in the maturation of a reproductive cell, in which the number of chromosomes is full, that is, not yet halved by the reduction division following the first or equation division. See *chromosome; maturation.*

diploidy (dip'loid-i) In the meiotic process of cell division the genetic term diploidy signifies the original quota of chromosomes, that is, the *full* number resulting from the duplicating equation division, prior to their reduction to the halved or haploid number through the reduction division (see *haploidy*).

diplopia (di-plō'-pē-à) Double vision; due to paralysis of the ocular muscles, which causes the image of an object to fall upon non-corresponding portions of the two retinae. See *nerve, oculomotor.*

diplopia, monocular (mō-nok'ū-lēr) A condition in which two images are seen with one eye. The existence of true monocular diplopia is questioned and when present is regarded as a sign of hysteria.

dippoldism (di'-pol-diz'm) Flogging of (school) children. The German schoolteacher, Dippold, was tried and convicted of manslaughter. Thereafter the act of flagellation came to be known as dippoldism. See *flagellation.*

dipsomania (dip-sō-mā'nē-à) A periodic mental disorder occasioned by alcoholic excesses. It is characterized mentally by a variety of responses peculiar to the individual. Some become shy and retiring; others quite boisterous and pugnacious; still others exhibit paranoid reactions. The alcoholic bout and its results last as a rule for several days, rarely for several weeks. 'In the intervals, that may last several weeks but also many months, most of these patients are temperate, and some are abstinent.' (Bleuler, E. *Textbook of Psychiatry,* tr. by Brill, A. A., Macmillan, New York, 1930). Dipsomania is usually regarded as a symptom or a syndrome of some more fundamental disorder, such as psychopathic personality, epilepsy, schizophrenia, etc. Bleuler includes dipsomania among the acute syndromes in the schizophrenias.

dipsosis avens (dēp-sō'zēs à v'ens) Excessive craving for alcohol.

directive In psychiatry, and particularly in the areas of psychotherapy and counseling, directive refers to an active and often authoritarian approach in which the therapist gives advice, suggests or demands that the patient follow certain courses of action, etc. See *D-O psychiatrist.*

disability A handicap, defect, or lack, especially when such defect interferes with adequate or normal functioning.

disadvantaged Lacking assets; in social psychiatry, the term usually refers to persons or groups who are economically poor and/or members of minority groups. Disadvantages typically include deprivations in housing, education, work opportunity, and medical (and particularly pre-natal) care and are associated with family disruption, faulty identity formation or malignant identity diffusion, and excessively high rates of juvenile offenses and of admissions to state mental hospitals.

disaggregation, mental (dis-ag-rē-gā'shun) According to Janet, '. . . a special form of weakness owing to which an elementary idea is left in isolation, and is not combined with others to form a higher unity.' 'It is a condition of natural and perpetual distraction, which prevents these persons from appreciating any other idea than the one which actually occupies their mind.' (Janet, P. *Psychological Healing,* vols. 1-2, tr. by Paul, E. and C., Macmillan, New York, 1925).

disaster, reactions to See *neurosis, traumatic.*

disattach See *attachment, liquidation of.*

discharge An unloading, release, dismissal. In neurophysiology, synonymous with *firing,* the delivery of excitation from one neurone to the next. In mental hospital statistics, the dropping of a patient from the rolls because of termination of services (patients transferred to other facilities and patients who die are not usually counted as discharges).

discharge, affective Release of emotion, usually an energetic reaction including the whole range of voluntary and involuntary reflexes, by which, according to experience, the emotions—from weeping up to a clear act of revenge—are habitually worked off.

'If this reaction occurs with sufficient intensity a great part of the affect disappears; common speech bears witness to these facts of everyday observation in the expressions "to cry out," "to storm oneself out."' (Freud, S. *Collected Papers* vol. 1, tr. by Riviere, J., Leonard anu Virginia Woolf and The Institute of Psychoanalysis, London, 1924-25)

discomfiture In social work, 'a failure in self-preservation in the sense of giving up the struggle; being overwhelmed by circumstances; defeatism.' (Hamilton, G. *A Medical Social Terminology,* Presbyterian Hospital, New York, 1930)

discriminanda (dis-krim-in-an'dà) See *intelligence*.

disease, Allan-Dent *Argininosuccinic aciduria* (q.v.).

disease, American An expression, introduced in Europe, for neurasthenia.

disease, association 1. Co-existing myoclonia and epilepsy; see *epilepsy, myoclonus*.
2. Schizophrenia; see *associations, disturbances of*.

disease, barbed wire Vischer's term for any reactive mental disturbance of prisoners, who are often held in barbed wire camps.

disease, Beard's (George M. Beard, American physician, 1839-1883) An old term for neurasthenia; named after the physician who introduced the name neurasthenia in 1869.

disease, Bell's Collapse delirium, delirious mania; the most severe of the manic type of manic-depressive psychosis. See *psychosis, manic-drepressive*.

disease, caisson Caisson disease *(diver's paralysis, the bends, tunnel disease)* is a circulatory disturbance occurring in the nervous system, observed when a person, subjected to high air pressure (e.g. in diving or working under compressed air in a caisson) returns too suddenly to normal atmosphere. There is a question as to whether the sudden release of pressure causes air emboli in the brain and spinal cord or whether the blood vessels dilate, giving rise to congestion and stasis. Pathologically, the spinal cord shows softening and necrosis.
The symptoms are acute in onset with headache, pains in the epigastrium, limbs and back, sufficient to double the patient up (the bends), dizziness, dyspnea, nausea, vomiting, coughing and partial or complete paralysis, usually of both lower extremities. Cerebral symptoms may occur, such as aphasia, double vision, confusion, coma, and convulsions.

disease, demyelinating (dē-mī'e-lin-ā-ting) See *demyelination*.

disease, Fahr's Idiopathic non-arteriosclerotic symmetrical calcification of cerebral vessels; a slowly progressive disorder, with onset between the ages of 30 to 50 years, manifested by organic dementia (293.1) and extrapyramidal motor dysfunction; first described by T. Fahr, a German neurologist, in 1930.

disease, flight into 'By means of *flight into the disease* one achieves definite aims through the disease; by an attack of rage one achieves a yielding; by a fainting spell, a new hat; and by the more protracted disease one gets a pleasant sojourn in a sanatorium. By means of all these one can at the same time compel consideration, secure care and tenderness, obtain power over others who have to adjust themselves to the disease, extort an allowance, evade tasks from the simple household duties up to the terrors of the trenches.' (Bleuler, E. *Textbook of Psychiatry*, tr. by Brill, A.A., Macmillan, New York, 1930) See *gain, epinosic; gain, morbid*.

disease, Friedmann's (Max Friedmann, German physician, 1858-1925) *Narcolepsy* (q.v.).

disease, Gaucher's (gō-shā') (Philippe Gaucher, French physician, 1854-1918) A familial disorder of lipoid metabolism (lipid histiocytosis) characterized by the deposition of kerasin in the reticuloendothelial cells of the liver and spleen and in the ganglion cells of the cerebral cortex, basal ganglia, and cerebellum. Onset of the disorder is usually between the ages of six and twelve months, typically in females. Symptoms include listlessness apathy, head retraction, hypertonicity bulbar signs, and sometimes mental retardation (31x.2).

disease, genetotrophic (ge-nē-tō-trō'fik) A disease 'in which the genetic pattern of the afflicted individual calls for an augmented supply of a particular nutrient (or nutrients) for which there develops, as a result, a nutritional deficiency.' (Williams R.J., et al. in Podolsky, E., *Management of Addictions*, Philosophical Library, New York, 1955.) 'On the basis of our studies with rats it seems likely that the basic etiologic factor in human alcoholism is genetotrophic, and that the sociological and psychological factors so generally considered as fundamental factors are only precipitating factors for the development of the clinical syndrome.' (ibid.) The factor described is believed to depend on one or more partial genetic blocks. 'Briefly described, such a block involves a heritable trait that is characterized not by a complete inability to carry out a specific enzymatic transformation, but by a diminished potentiality for producing the biochemical change. This in turn leads to an augmented requirement for some specific nutritional factor or factors.' (ibid.)

disease, Heller's See *dementia infantilis.*

disease, Jakob-Creutzfeldt's See *degeneration, cortico-striato-spinal.*

disease, Janet's (zhà-nāz') *Psychasthenia* (q.v.).

disease, Leber's (Theodor Leber, German ophthalmologist, 1840-1917) Hereditary familial primary optic atrophy, occurring between the ages of eighteen and thirty, more common in the male progeny, but transmitted from the female. It is a bilateral, slowly progressive condition, often remaining stationary or even regressing. There is a central scotoma and a normal peripheral field.

disease, Lindau's (Arvid Lindau, contemporary Swedish pathologist) An angioma of the brain occurring in connection with angiomatosis of the retina, occasionally familial and hereditary.

disease, Little's (William John Little, English surgeon, 1810-94) Includes the spastic diplegias, presumably due to bilateral congenital brain defects, involving especially the pyramidal motor system, or to lesions acquired at birth. Walking is retarded, the gait is spastic and the child walks on its toes (pes equinovarus). The thighs are adducted, the knees rub together, and the legs cross in progression (scissors gait). This spastic paralysis may involve both upper extremities as well. Frequently present are various grades of mental disturbance, ranging from hyperexcitability and irritability to imbecility or idiocy. Typical epileptic convulsions may occur. Strabismus, dysarthria, drooling,

and abnormal involuntary and associated movements may be observed.

disease-narcissism (-när'sis-is'm) See *narcissism, disease.*

disease, Niemann-Pick A familial disturbance in phospholipid metabolism (a lipid histiocytosis) characterized by mental deterioration (31x.2), progressive blindness, hepatosplenomegaly, and brownish discoloration of the skin. The disease is rapidly progressive and leads to death within two years of onset.

disease, Pick's See *Pick's disease.*

disease, pink *Acrodynia* (q.v.).

disease, sacred In Latin, *morbus sacer* (q.v.). Same as epilepsy.

disease, Saint Dymphna's (St. Dymphna, patron saint of the insane, a British noble-woman, murdered by her insane father, in Gheel, Belgium.) Any mental disease; insanity.

disease, Saint Mathurin's (St. Mathurin, patron saint of idiots and fools.) Epileptic psychosis.

disease, Saint Valentine's Epilepsy.

disease, sanatorium 'The habit of living in sanatoria can itself become a kind of disease that might be called *sanatorium-disease*; many people are by it completely estranged from their homes and occupations.' (Ferenczi, S. *Further Contributions to the Theory and Technique of Psycho-Analysis,* tr. by Suttie, J.I., Leonard and Virginia Woolf and The Institute of Psychoanalysis, London, 1926) Also called *hospitalitis.*

disease, Schilder's (Paul Schilder, American neurologist, 1886-1940.) Schilder's disease, or encephalitis periaxialis diffusa, is a slowly progressive degenerative disease of the brain occurring mainly in children and young people; it is characterized essentially by slowly advancing cerebral blindness and progressive mental deterioration terminating usually in complete amentia. In DSM-II, coded 31x.3. See *sclerosis, diffuse.*

disease, Simmonds's (Morris Simmonds, Hamburg physician, 1855 - 1925) See *cachexia, hypophysial.*

disease, Tay-Sach's Amaurotic family idiocy; it was first described by Warran Tay in 1881, who referred principally to the ocular changes; in 1887 Bernard Sachs described the brain changes in a paper entitled *Arrested Cerebral Development.* In DSM-II, coded 31x.2.

disease, tunnel *Disease, caisson* (q.v.).

disequilibrium, mental Mental imbalance.

disharmony, affective In writing on dementia praecox, White states: 'The lack of conformity of the emotional reaction and the ideational content—affective disharmony—is shown not only with reference to a given time, but in relations of succession. Moods and affects change in all possible ways without visible inner or outer causes.' (White, W.A. *Outlines of Psychiatry,* 12th ed., Nervous & Mental Disease Publishing Company, Washington, D.C., 1929)

disinfection, mental *Liquidation, mental* (q.v.).

disinhibition (dis-in-hi-bish'un) Removal of an inhibition. The inhibitory function of the cerebral cortex can be reduced by various agents—for instance, alcohol. If such a cortical function is impaired or reduced in its activity, the inhibitory influences of the cortex are diminished or removed and then a disinhibition takes place, indicating that without the high cortical control, lower vegetative or emotional functions are manifested. (Masserman, J.H. *Behavior and Neuroses,* University of Chicago Press, Chicago, 1943)

disintegration (dis-in-tē-grā'shun) Disorganization of psychic processes. 'We may therefore expect that a weakening or annihilation of the influence which general conceptions, higher emotions, and the permanent general trend of volition exercise on our thinking, feeling, and acting, must draw after it that inner *disintegration,* those "schizophrenic" disorders, which we meet with in dementia praecox.' (Kraepelin, E. *Dementia Praecox and Paraphrenia,* tr. by Barclay, R.M., Living-

stone, Edinburgh, 1919). See *integration; disruption.*

disk, choked See *papilledema.*

disk, herniated lumbar intervertebral (hẽr'ni-ā-ted lum'bẽr in-tẽr-vẽr'te-bral) Protrusion of the central portion of the intervertebral disk (the nucleus pulposus) through the surrounding annulus fibrosus, which holds the bodies of the vertebrae together. Such herniation is usually due to trauma, induced typically by lifting a heavy object in a bent-forward position or by a fall in a similar posture. Almost half of the cases begin in the fourth decade, and approximately three-quarters of the cases are male. Most herniations are between the fourth and fifth lumbar bodies, or between the fifth lumbar and first sacral bodies. Herniation of the disk results in compression of the spinal nerve running to the foramen one segment below; the clinical result is *sciatica,* i.e. pain beginning in the lumbar region and spreading down the back of one lower limb to the ankle, usually intensified by coughing or sneezing.

Four symptom-phases are recognized: (1) back pain, muscle spasm, and trunk tilt; (2) compression of the spinal nerve resulting in sciatica, with paresthesiae in the lateral calf and foot, muscle spasm, focal tenderness, and diminution of the ankle jerk; (3) paresis of the lower extremity and muscle atrophy; (4) paralysis of the affected extremity, marked sensory loss, and bladder and bowel disturbances.

In most cases, conservative treatment with analgesics and mobilization is adequate; in about 10 per cent of cases, interlaminar operation is indicated.

dismemberment, fear of A patient's fear that he is losing part of his body is called the dismemberment complex, or fear of dismemberment. It is most often seen in the involutional psychoses and in the schizophrenias. In some cases described by Schilder, the patient develops a strong feeling of persecution. This is explained in the following manner: Through the process of fear of dismemberment the individual projects to the outside world parts of his body, and then the endangered parts of the body retain their relation to the individual by coming back in

he form of persecutors. Such a mechanism is clearly illustrated in the example
of the depressive menopausic woman who
feared she was going to cut off all her
fingers every time she held a knife in her
hand. She later developed a persecution
complex in which five different enemies
were following her. (Schilder, P. *Psychotherapy*, Norton, New York, 1938)

disorder, affective determined An expression used by Adolf Meyer as equivalent
with manic-depressive psychosis.

disorder, behavior See *behavior disorders.*

disorder, personality See *personality-dis-
order.*

disordered behavior, classication of Rado
(*American Journal of Psychiatry, 110:*
406-416, 1953) offered the following
provisional classification of disordered behavior, based mainly on the psychodynamic phase of etiology:
  I. Over-reactive disorders. (1) Emer-
     gency dyscontrol; (2) Descending
     dyscontrol; (3) Sexual disorders; (4)
     Social overdependence; (5) Common
     maladaptation or combination of
     sexual disorder with social overde-
     pendence; (6) Expressive pattern;
     (7) Obsessive pattern; (8) Paranoid
     pattern.
 II. Mood cyclic disorders.
III. Schizotypal disorders. (1) Compen-
     sated schizo-adaptation; (2) Decom-
     pensated   schizo-adaptation;   (3)
     Schizotypal disintegration marked
     by adaptive incompetence.
 IV. Extractive disorders.
  V. Lesional disorders.
 VI. Narcotic disorders.
VII. Disorders of war adaptation.

disorders, episodic Any precipitous interruption in the life style of the subject, with
the appearance of behavior that is out
of character for the person himself and
usually out of context or inappropriate
to the situation at hand. Such bursts of
impulsivity or *acting-out* (q.v.) may be
the first sign of personality change in an
organic psychosyndrome, or they may
represent dyscontrol on a more purely
psychologic-motivational basis.

disorders, extractive See *psychodynamics,
adaptational.*

disorders, impulse See *impulse disorders.*

disorders, moodcyclic See *psychodynamics, adaptational.*

disorders, over-reactive See *psychodynamics, adaptational.*

disorientation (dis-ō-ri-en-tā'shun) Impairment in the understanding of temporal, spatial, or personal relationships.
See *syndrome, organic.*

disorientation, autopsychic (aw-tō-sī'kik)
Synonymous with impairment of insight;
see *orientation, autopsychic.*

disparagment, mania for A term used by
Janet, who says that 'one who feels himself to be a weakling and has a terrible
dread of effort, has a different idea of
competition. His aim is to triumph, not
by raising himself, but by lowering his
rival. Thus it is that the psychasthenic
secures a partial and thrifty success by preventing others from acting. . . . In many
instances, an additional factor is his
dread of others' success.' (Janet, P. *Psychological Healing*, vols. 1-2, tr. by Paul,
E. and C., Macmillan, New York, 1925)

dispersion, semantic See *dissociation,
semantic.*

displaced child syndrome See *syndrome,
displaced child.*

displacement 1. Transference of the emotions (affective cathexis) from the original ideas to which they are attached
—to other ideas. It is assumed in psychoanalysis that psychic energy may exist as
an entity, such as 'free-floating' libido,
that is, that it possesses a certain autonomy. It is sufficiently mobile to leave one
set of ideas and go to another. By such an
arrangement the affects may be able to
gain the realm of consciousness, attaching
themselves to ideas to which the patient is
ordinarily indifferent. By such an arrangement the patient is spared the pain of
knowing the original source of the affects.
A patient had a morbid fear that illuminating gas was issuing from the jet in his
room. The fear was not allayed in any way
by logic. The patient recognized how
ridiculous it was to let such an idea control his life. Upon analysis it was found

that the fear was associated with the repressed wish for his father's death.

Schizophrenic patients exhibit displacement of affects to a remarkable degree. What are seemingly the most inconsequential thoughts may be heavily emotionalized. A schizophrenic patient used to get into a state of uncontrollable rage over his shoestrings. Another patient was ecstatic over the word 'there.'

The displacement of affects presupposes also the displacement of ideas.

2. Shifting of id impulses from one pathway to another. When, for instance, aggression cannot express itself through direct motor discharge, as in fisticuffs, it may take the pathway of verbalization. Displacement manifests itself also with regard to organic zones. The instincts shift, for example, from the oral to the anal, to the genital zones, or to any other erotogenic zone. In conversion hysteria a psychic complex may be displaced upon any potentially acceptable organic structure. Or, all the issues connected with genitality may be displaced to the oral zone. Displacement 'from below upward' is a common phenomenon.

Dreams afford notable examples of displacement. See *dream.*

displacement from below to above See *displacement; above and below.*

displacement in dreams See *dream-displacement.*

displacement of affect See *affect, transposition of.*

displacement, retroactive Unconscious displacement that reaches back into the patient's early life. When we begin to investigate how far memory can go back into life, we find that quite often memories are concealed. 'If the content of the concealed memory belongs to the first years of childhood, but the ideas it represents belong to a later period of the individual's life, we speak with Freud about a retroactive displacement.' (Brill, A.A. *Basic Principles of Psychoanalysis,* Doubleday, New York, 1949)

displacement-substitute See *substitute, displacement.*

displacement-wit See *wit, displacement.*

disposing mind and memory 'A sound mind, capable of making a will; remembering the property to be disposed of and the persons who are the natural objects of bounty, and comprehending the manner in which the property is to be distributed.' (Singer, H.D. and Krohn, W.C. *Insanity and Law,* Blakiston, Philadelphia, 1924)

disposition, brain See *neurogram.*

disposition, constitutional depressive That type of person who is more or less consistently depressed throughout life. Such persons are retarded in thinking and acting, show a protracted pessimism as regards all life experiences, have difficulty in making and completing decisions, and lack self-confidence. Bleuler says they display the *melancholic mood.*

The term 'constitutional depression' is used by some to indicate endogenous depression, i.e. one in which precipitating factors are not clear or definite.

disposition, constitutional manic This denotes the type of personality that is more or less of a 'manic' disposition throughout life.

'The manic temperament of such people disposes to over-hasty acts and to a thoughtless manner of living in general, when it is not restrained by a particularly sound understanding and a particularly good morality. For that reason we find here on the one hand snobbish, inconsiderate, quarrelsome and cranky ne'er-do-wells, who have no staying powers in their transactions, but on the other hand "sunny dispositions," and people endowed with great ability, amounting sometimes to genius, and not rarely gifted with artistic ability who possess a tireless energy.' (Bleuler, E. *Textbook of Psychiatry,* tr. by Brill, A.A., Macmillan, New York, 1930) Bleuler says these people have the *manic mood.*

The term 'constitutional mania' is used by some as an equivalent of 'endogenous mania,' or mania without clear-cut precipitating factors.

disposition, personal See *Allport, Gordon Willard.*

disposition, polymorphous-perverse (pol-i-mor'fus-per-vers') See *perverse, polymorphous.*

disposition-system See *complex, subject.*

disruption Sudden loss of organization; although disruption is often used synonymously with *disintegration* (q.v.), the latter term more properly is reserved for slow or gradual loss of organization.

disseminated sclerosis (dis-em'in-ā-ted skle-rō-sis) See *sclerosis, multiple.*

dissimilation See *assimilation.*

dissimulation The act of pretending or feigning; *denial* (q.v.).

dissimulator One who dissimulates, dissembles, or pretends that he is not. One who puts up a bold front while faint with terror—dissimulates or dissembles his fear; at the same time he simulates or feigns intrepidity or a stout heart.

dissociate To split off some part or component of mental activity, which component then acts as an independent unit of mental life. See *dissociation.*

dissociation Segregation of any group of mental processes from the rest of the psychic apparatus; dissociation generally means a loss of the usual interrelationships between various groups of mental processes with resultant almost independent functioning of the one group that has been separated from the rest. As so defined, dissociation and 'splitting' are approximately equivalent; (for a discussion of differences between splitting in hysterical dissociative states and splitting in the schizophrenias, see *personality, multiple*); and the mental mechanism of *isolation* (q.v.) can also be considered a type of dissociation.

"Double" and "multiple" personality are the terms applied when the same individual at different times appears to be in possession of entirely different mental content, disposition and character, and when one of the different phases shows complete ignorance of the other, an ignorance which may be reciprocal. Each "sub-personality" (for the personality in these conditions at least is compounded of a series of sub- or partial personalities or "monads," as McDougall calls them) is said to be "dissociated" from the total personality, and from the other sub-personalities, on each occasion when its activities are fully conscious and control the motor apparatus of the individual.' (Henderson, D.K. and Gillespie, R.D. *A Text-Book of Psychiatry*, 4th ed., Oxford University Press, London, 1936)

Another form of dissociation is included in the definition framed by Strecker and Ebaugh: 'In effect, *dissociation is the separation of the mind or consciousness by a splitting off of one (sometimes more) component or system of ideas, the personality or remainder of the mind being unable to exert any control over the split-off portion.* This phenomenon of dissociation may be witnessed in the automatic writing of hysteria, in somnambulism, in double personality and in the many delusions of patients.' (Strecker, E.A. and Ebaugh, F.G. *Practical Clinical Psychiatry*, 4th ed., Blakiston, Philadelphia, 1935)

Another expression of dissociation has to do with the separation of ideas from their consonant affects. For example, a schizophrenic patient laughed heartily while discussing his delusion that he was cut into millions of pieces.

dissociation. semantic The distortion between symbol and meaning that is characteristic of the thought disorder of many schizophrenics. The term includes: (1) *enlargement of the semantic halo*—language becomes ambiguous, vague, indeterminate (schizophrenic systematic abstractionism), but is comprehensible and coherent; (2) *semantic distortion*—transfer of meaning to a new symbol (neologism) or to another word (paralogism); (3) *semantic dispersion*—meaning is lost or reduced; language becomes incoherent, agrammatical, asyntactic; and (4) *semantic dissolution*—complete loss of meaning and of communication ability; language is used as a game, or automatically. See *associations, disturbances of.*

dissociative reaction A type of conversion hysteria. See *conversion; hysteria.*

dissolution, insanity of See *insanity, dissolute.*

dissolution, semantic See *dissociation, semantic.*

dissonance, cognitive In information theory, *incongruity* (q.v.).

distemperature *Obst.* Mental derangement.

distortion The process of disguising, hiding, or otherwise modifying unconscious mental elements so that they are allowed to enter consciousness, whose censoring mechanisms would not allow them access to consciousness in undisguised form.

There are many ways in which distortion may be effected, e.g. dropping out (repression) of associative links between conscious content and unconscious impulse, displacement of activity onto a substitute object, replacement of objectionable impulse, displacement of activity onto a substitute object, replacement of objectionable impulse with another one which is associatively connected. 'It is the task of the analyst's interpretative work to undo and make retroactive the distortion caused by resistances.' (Fenichel, O. *The Psychoanalytic Theory of Neurosis,* Norton, New York, 1945)

distortion, apperceptive (ap-er-sep'tiv) A subjective interpretation of a perception which is dynamically meaningful in that perception of the contemporary stimulus is influenced by memories of previous percepts. The various projective tests (Rorschach, TAT, etc.) deal with apperceptive distortions of different degrees.

distortion by transference This term, employed by Freud, indicates that 'When there is anything in the complex-material (the content of the complex) which can at all suitably be transferred on to the person of the physician such a transference will be effected, and from it will arise the next association.' (Freud, S. *Collected Papers,* vol. 2, tr. by Riviere, J., Leonard and Virginia Woolf and The Institute of Psychoanalysis, London, 1924-25)

distortion, compromise See *compromise-distortion.*

distortion, ego An inexact term (at least at present), used mostly as a general term that is approximately equivalent to 'ego impoverishment,' 'ego deviation,' or 'ego immaturity.' Some writers, however, use 'ego distortion' in a more specific sense to refer to an inability to use the usual ego functions of defence in adapting to painful reality. Thus, S. Nacht (*International Journal of Psycho-Analysis 39,* 271-3, 1958) differentiates between (1) the classical disturbances of ego function, that stem primarily from memory falsi-fications of past experiences which are distorted by unconscious phantasies of the patient, and (2) ego distortion, where the ego is injured by objectively harmful events that occurred in reality rather than in phantasy.

distortion, memory See *displacement.*

distortion, parataxic (par-à-tak'sik) Any attitude toward any other person which is based on a phantasied or distorted evaluation of that person or on an identification of that person with other figures from past life.

Freud defined *transference* (q.v.) as a repetition of the attitude toward the parents at the time of the Oedipus complex. Almost invariably in the course of analysis, the patient begins to concern himself with the analyst in terms of these transferred attitudes. There are some classical analysts today who would confine the term transference to this original meaning. Others, however, accept character attitudes also as a part of transference, for these, too, are reaction patterns from the past which are applied indiscriminately to the analytic situation, where they are not suitable. In an attempt to avoid confusion, Sullivan has used the term parataxic distortion to include this whole picture. 'Sullivan uses neither the libido concept nor the repetition compulsion as formulated by Freud. Parataxic distortions, according to Sullivan, develop from early but essentially nonsexual integrations with significant people. One develops ways of coping with these people and then tends to apply these ways in later interpersonal integrations. However, the need to repeat is by no means as rigid a compulsion as Freud formulated in the repetition compulsion. Later experiences can modify the pattern consciously and unconsciously. In fact, the process of cure is an example of such a modification. The analyst, by his objectivity and insight, fails to conform to the patient's expectations and this, when the patient realizes it, constitutes a new interpersonal situation which helps to make clear the irrational nature of his own behavior.' (Thompson, C. *Psychoanalysis: Evolution and Development,* Hermitage House, New York, 1950.) One way to learn what is true and what is parataxic in thinking or feelings about another is to compare one's evaluations with those of others. Sullivan calls this comparison 'consensual validation.'

distortion, semantic See *dissociation, semantic.*

distractibility See *mania.*

distraction, suggestions by 'Many authorities have noticed that in certain patients suggestions made by insinuation, made gently without attracting attention, succeed better than imperative suggestions. I have myself written at considerable length about suggestions of this kind, terming them "suggestions by distraction." A great many subjects who are not ordinarily cataleptic will keep the arm raised if we raise it gently without their noticing it.' (Janet, P. *Psychological Healing*, vols. 1-3, tr. by Paul, E. and C., Macmillan, New York, 1925)

distributive analysis and synthesis See *psychobiology.*

disulfiram See *Antabuse.*

ditention Burrow's term, used to indicate the intrusion of affect or bias into the process of attention. In his view, ditention now characterizes man's interrelational behavior throughout. Contrasted with cotention. See *attention.*

diurnal Occurring each day, or in the daytime, as opposed to occurring at night (nocturnal).

divagation (dī-và-gā'shun) Rambling thought and speech.

division, cell In biology, cell division represents that genetically most important process by which new cells originate from old ones, following a definite order. The division of ordinary body cells takes place by *mitosis* and is initiated by the nucleus.

In the nucleus of a resting cell the chromatin is scattered and appears like a fine network. At the first indication of imminent division, however, it is formed in a long thread which breaks up into separate pieces, the *chromosomes.* The mitotic *prophase* is finished when each of the chromosomes splits longitudinally into two and the centrosome has also divided into two halves, which migrate to opposite poles of the nucleus.

In the *metaphase* of mitosis, the nuclear membrane breaks down, and a spindle-shaped mass of fiber-like structures accumulates beside the nucleus, converging toward two opposite poles. The split chromosomes arrange themselves in a plane across the equator of the cell, in such a manner that a spindle fiber is attached to each half chromosome, apparently connecting it with the adjacent pole.

The next stage, known as the *anaphase*, is characterized by a polar migration of the separated two halves of each chromosome. 'The result of this activity is the aggregation at each pole of a group of chromosomes, similar in number and all other visible respects to the single set of mother cell chromosomes from which they arose.' (Sinnot, E.W., and Dunn, L.D. *Principles of Genetics*, 3rd ed., McGraw-Hill, New York and London, 1939)

The last stage of division, the *telophase*, completes the replacement of one old cell by two new ones. The chromosomes of each polar group become surrounded by new nuclear membranes and reorganize daughter nuclei exactly like those of the mother cells. Finally, the cytoplasmic cell body is divided between the new nuclei, in animals by a cleavage furrow going inward from the periphery, and in most plants by a row of pellets forming a wall across the middle of the cell.

divorce See *marriage, psychiatric aspects of.*

divorce, emotional See *psychotherapy, family.*

Dix, Dorothea Lynde (1802-87) American reformer in the care of psychiatric patients.

dizygotic (dī-zī-got'ik) Pertaining to a twin pair produced by two eggs; preferable to the synonymous *fraternal, nonidentical.*

DNA Abbreviation of deoxyribonucleic acid. See *chromosome.*

Do In Rorschach scoring, an 'oligophrenic' response; according to Piotrowski, the Do indicates excessive intellectual caution and anxiety, rather than feeblemindedness.

D-O psychiatrist Directive-organic psychiatrist; Hollingshead and Redlich so designated that group of psychiatrists whose orientation is biological and whose psychotherapeutic approach is directive and authoritarian. In contrast to the *A-P psychiatrist* (q.v.), the D-O psychiatrist is often outspokenly antagonistic to psychoanalytic theory.

dodge, insanity Fictitious defense of insanity designed to evade punishment for a criminal act.

'It has been pretty widely assumed that insanity was used very frequently as a plea to save the criminal when all other means failed, and the "insanity dodge" has come into existence by popular consent as a symbol of sharp practice by unscrupulous attorneys and none-too-honest medical men.' (White, W.A. *Insanity and the Criminal Law,* Macmillan, New York, 1923).

'In the same connection, let it also be stated that the mere assertion of the accused that he has feigned insanity is by no means sufficient of itself to justify a court in declaring him sane and criminally responsible. It is not uncommon for an insane person, on finding that his acquittal on account of mental disorder will entail a longer period of confinement than would a conviction for the crime of which he stands accused, to declare he has feigned the symptoms of insanity.' (Jacoby, G.W. *The Unsound Mind and the Law,* Funk & Wagnalls, New York and London, 1918)

Dole-Nyswander program See *methadone.*

dolichocephaly (dol-i-kō-sef'a-lē) See *index, cephalic.*

dolichomorph (dol'i-kō-morf) A person with long thin stature.

dolichomorphic (dol-i-kō-mor'fik) Relating to long, thin stature.

Dolichomorphic is equivalent to *microsplanchnic* of Viola and corresponds closely to Kretschmer's *asthenic.* See *type, asthenic.*

dolichomorphy (dol'i-kō-mor-fē) The long, thin type of body build. There are at least two extremes in growth, representing excessive development in width or in length. Dolichomorphy refers to the lat-

ter and, in the psychiatric field, is frequently found in schizophrenics.

doll, amputation A doll which can readily be taken apart; used in play therapy with children; introduced by David Levy, who uses the doll in a specific situation, where it represents the mother. 'It is suggested that breasts be made of clay and attached to the mother doll. A baby doll may then be put to the breast. A brother or sister doll representing the child under investigation or treatment is added to the play setup. The child is encouraged to destroy the baby at the breast, the breasts, and also the mother. The patient may also punish the brother or sister doll.' (Bender, L. *Child Psychiatric Techniques,* Thomas, Springfield, Ill., 1952)

domatophobia (dō-mȧ-tō-fō'bē-ȧ) Fear of being in a house.

dominance Within the various phenomena of Mendelian inheritance, this term denotes the genetic mechanism by which one member of an allelic pair of hereditary factors is endowed with the capacity of expressing itself so strongly that it prevails over the contrasting factor and determines the visible appearance of a hybridized individual either completely or, at least, predominantly. The phenotype of any hybrid inheriting a *completely dominant* character from one of the parents exhibits no manifestations of the suppressed, or *recessive,* factor and is thus enabled to appear as a pure-bred organism in spite of its heterozygosity (see *recessiveness*).

In this dominant or *direct* mode of inheritance we observe as a rule that the phenotypically healthy children are also germinally healthy. Once a descending stock is free of a dominant anomaly, it is free forever. A diseased carrier of a dominant trait must always have one diseased parent and, on the average, 50 per cent diseased siblings and children.

Some genetic disorders (e.g. phenylketonuria) are recessive with respect to the occurrence of overt disease but dominant with respect to the chemical abnormality. It will accordingly be seen that the terms dominance and recessiveness are relative rather than precise and exact terms, and different authorities use the terms in different ways. Some, for example, define a dominant gene as one that causes expression of the disease when present in one parent, and a recessive gene as one that causes expression only when present in both. Genes that always cause the disease are termed 'fully penetrant,' while those that cause it only irregularly are termed 'partially penetrant.'

Since the heterozygotic hybrids of a dominant character appear phenotypically like the homozygotes, homozygosity of a trait-carrier can be assumed only if *both* parents are affected by the same trait. Such cases, of course, are very rare.

If a spontaneous interruption of the direct transmission of a dominant trait is found in some affected families, it must be concluded that the clinical pathology of the trait was either not diagnosed, or was inhibited by certain antagonistic factors, or could not be manifested because of the early death of the ordinary taint-carriers.

dominance, cerebral The tendency for certain functions of the brain to be concentrated on a single side of the brain. In right-handed persons, such functions tend to be concentrated in the left cerebral hemisphere; this is spoken of as 'left cerebral dominance.' Cerebral dominance is certainly associated with handedness, and attempts to alter a natural dominance may cause intellectual disturbances and speech disorders. But that dominance is the primary factor in all speech disorders, as has been maintained by some, is questionable.

dominance test See *test, Wada dominance.*

dominant In a strictly genetic sense, this term describes the particular faculty of a hereditary factor, transmitted to a hybrid by one of the parents, to constitute the only expressible member of a given pair of contrasting characters and, thus, to appear in the hybrid to the exclusion of the contrasted character transmitted by the other parent. See *dominance.*

dominant determinant See *determinant, dream.*

Don Juan (don jōō'an *or* dōn hwän) (Sp. 'Sir John') The Chronicle of Seville relates that Don Juan Tenorio (a member

of one of the city's 24 leading families) killed Comendador Ulloa at night and carried off his daughter. The father was buried in the St. Francis monastery in the family chapel and his statue erected there. The statue and chapel were destroyed by fire. To end the profligate's debauchery the Franciscan monks lured and killed him and spread the rumor that Don Juan had insulted the Comendador on his tomb and that the new statue had dragged the Don to hell. Tirso de Molina (1571-1648) dramatized the legend in 1630 and Mozart immortalized the story in his opera *Don Giovanni* (1787).

In psychiatry the term Don Juan refers to a type of male hypersexuality. Sexual activities are aimed toward contradicting inferiority feelings by proof of erotic successes. The Don Juan type is little interested in his woman partner of the moment; for having proved that he can excite her sexually, he must then allay his doubts about his ability to excite other women and so moves on to another conquest. The condition depends on intense narcissistic needs and fears of loss of love, with a pregenital and sadistic coloring of the total sexuality. The Don Juan type of erotomaniac is frequently a defense against unconscious homosexual impulses.

'Don Juans of achievement' are also recognized; these are people who must pile one success upon another in an attempt to undo previous failures and allay guilt.

donatism (don'à-tiz'm) Donato (professional name of the Belgian 'magnetizer' Alfred d'Hont, 1845-1900) demonstrated the role of imitation in hypnosis; the term donatism was given to that form of hypnosis in which imitation forms an important part.

door, revolving See *readmission.*

Doppelganger (dop'el-geNg-ger) A "double," such as is seen in the phantasy of an imaginary companion. Frequently the Doppelganger serves as an insurance against death by providing a second representation of oneself.

Dora The patient on whom Freud reported in his 1905 paper, 'Fragment of an Analysis of a Case of Hysteria.' Dora was an 18-year-old unmarried female whose neurotic symptoms began at the age of eight—chronic dyspnea, hemicranial headaches, and attacks of nervous coughing. Her later symptoms included suicidal threats, amnesic episodes, and periods of aphonia. Analysis of the patient was incomplete since she withdrew from treatment after three months. She died many years later in New York City but had all her life suffered a multitude of neurotic symptoms.

doraphobia (dō-rà-fō'bē-à) Fear of skin of animals.

Dorian love See *love, Dorian.*

dotage *Senile psychosis* (q.v.).

double bind See *bind, double.*

double-blind Referring to a research method, used primarily in drug investigations, in which neither subject-patient nor rater-evaluator knows whether the drug being studied or a placebo is being administered.

double personality See *personality, multiple.*

double simultaneous tactile sensation See *tactile sensation, double simultaneous.*

doubles, illusions of See *syndrome, Capgras'.*

doubt, obsessive An uncertainty that perpersistently forces itself on the mind of the patient and cannot be banished or reasoned away. Obsessive brooding and doubt may represent sexualization of thought, and their unconscious content is the same as in other symptoms of the obsessive-compulsive; viz., bisexuality, ambivalence (love versus hate), and id impulses versus superego demands.

doubting spells See *brooding-spells.*

douche, fan Fan-shaped water spray produced by holding the finger at the nozzle of a hose from which water is emitting.

douche, jet A form of hydrotherapy, consisting of a single stream of water directed at parts of the body.

douche, rain Shower bath.

douche, Scotch Alternating warm and cold jet douche.

Down's disease *Mongolism* (q.v.); (from W. Langdon-Down, contemporary English geneticist).

Dr In Rorschach scoring, a rare version of a normal or large detail such as one that includes more of the blot than is used in the usual detail response, or one that combines two or more detail responses.

dr Rorschach scoring symbol for an unusual (rare) detail.

dramatogenic (dram-à-tō-jen'ik) Moreno's term to denote people 'especially sensitive for collective experiences and able to dramatize them easily . . . Just as there are some people who are photogenic, there are some individuals who are dramatogenic . . .' (Moreno, J.L. 'The Concept of Sociodrama,' *Sociometry VI,* 4, Nov. 1947, p. 448)

drapetomania (drà-pē-tō-mā'nē-à) Uncontrollable impulse to wander; dromomania.

drawing, automatic The execution of drawings without a person's conscious volition, but often after being directed to do so in a hypnotic trance. Automatic drawing constitutes an important aid and method in hypnoanalytical technique: 'Drawing is both a form of motor expressiveness and a means by which the individual can reveal inner problems, wishes, and fears. It is an excellent method of gaining access to deep material where the patient is unable or unwilling to associate freely. Drawings have many of the characteristics of dreams. They provide symbolic ways of representing unconscious impulses. The patient condenses into his creations material that is to him of great emotional significance. He also injects into his graphic productions meanings that reflect his unconscious fantasies; this is similar to what occurs in the Rorschach test.' Automatic drawing can be done in a hypnotic trance (hypnotic drawing), or after awakening if the patient has previously, during the state of hypnosis, been instructed to do so. (Wolberg, L.R. *Hypnoanalysis,* Grune and Stratton, New York, 1945)

drawing, Goodenough See *test, Goodenough.*

dread A term that denotes anxiety related to a specific danger-situation. In his analysis of the nature of anxiety, Freud points out that it originates as the reaction to helplessness in a traumatic situation. Later on, as the ego develops, it anticipates that a situation of helplessness will occur or it is reminded of a previous traumatic experience by the present situation. The situation that is the cause of this anticipation or reminder is called the danger-situation. And the ego will now react with anxiety in this danger-situation. Thus anxiety has become an expectation of trauma in a danger-situation.

However, the affect of anxiety 'is endowed with a certain character of indefiniteness and objectlessness.' This objectlessness and indefiniteness pertain 'to the traumatic situation of helplessness which is anticipated in the danger-situation.' Freud states that in proper usage the term anxiety should be reserved for the original reaction of helplessness in a traumatic situation where no specific danger-situation is expected. The term dread should be used for the anxiety that relates to a specific danger, i.e. 'when it has found an object.' Therefore, 'dread in an individual is provoked either by the greatness of a danger or by the cessation of emotional ties (libidinal cathexes); the latter is the case of neurotic dread.' (Freud, S. *The Problem of Anxiety,* Norton, New York, 1936; *Group Psychology and the Analysis of the Ego,* The International Psychoanalytical Press, London, 1922)

dread, talion A fear of 'retaliation in kind' as punishment for forbidden acts or impulses. Psychoanalysts are familiar with the talion (retaliation) principle of psychology and the exactness with which the punishment is made to fit the crime.

A most vivid example of the use of the term in psychiatric context is seen in the Oedipus situation, wherein the boy fears loss of his penis, i.e. castration by his father, as punishment for his misuse of it (in incestual relationship with his mother): 'the boy's *talion dread* born of his incestual wishes toward his mother.' Another example is to be seen in the neurotic's fear of death and in the hysterical attacks during which he feels he is dying. The talion relationship of these phenomena with unconscious wishes for the death of another will readily be seen.

dream A psychic phenomenon occurring during sleep in which thoughts, images, emotions, etc. present themselves to the dreamer, usually with a definite sense of reality. Dreams are not random psychic productions, for they fulfill a vital purpose in the mental economy. They safeguard sleep; they foster a solution in phantasy of needs and conflicts too dangerous for solution in reality; they provide an outlet for the discharge of instinctual tension; they allow a working through of destructive and traumatic experiences which defy the coping capacities of the waking state. Dreaming is a universal psychic function, typical of the human mind. It is one of the vehicles by which impulses from the unconscious reach the level of consciousness.

Studies by Dement, Kleitman, Jouvet, and others have demonstrated that dreaming is an essential psychobiologic function, suppression of which may produce serious psychic disturbances.

Because sleep includes a shutting out of sensory receptors and progressive cortical inhibition, the dream itself works in the manner of the primitive mental apparatus. Visual images tend to replace words, thinking becomes archaic and prelogical and distorted, and there is a tendency toward a universal language.

Sleep itself seems to occur in two phases, involving two different neurophysiologic systems. The first phase, called *telencephalic sleep* or *neo-sleep,* depends upon inhibitory action of the cortex on the reticular activating system. The second phase, called *rhombencephalic sleep,* depends upon inhibitory action of the caudal pontile nucleus on the pontobulbar reticular system and on the limbic system. It is during rhombencephalic sleep that dreaming occurs. In the past, dreaming was considered to be a fleeting, instantaneous phenomenon superimposed on the physiologic state of sleep. It is now recognized, however, that dreaming occurs at specified periods during the night and is the subjective concomitant of a pervasive and distinctive physiologic state, the *D-state.* During the D-state rapid conjugate eye movements appear (hence it is also known as *Rapid Eye Movement* sleep or *REM* sleep) and the EEG becomes active (so another term for the state is *activated sleep*). This activity consists of a continuous hippocampal theta rhythm, pontine spindling, and a high rate of unit discharge in the mesencephalic reticular formation and in the visual and somatosensory cortex. Thus the D-state appears to be as intense as the most aroused wakefulness except that there is massive inhibition of motor expression, which is largely limited to the oculomotor apparatus in the form of REMs. During the D-state, autonomic activity is heightened, pulse and respiratory rates increase, and penile erections appear in the human male. The subjective duration of the dream experience is proportional to the length of the REM period or D-state, and there is a correspondence between specific directional patterns of REMs and the spatial orientation of events in the dream.

The recollected dream emerges as the 'manifest dream content,' which tends to be constructed out of events in the recent past. The 'latent dream content' is uncovered by analysis of the manifest content, usually by means of free association. Freud considered the dream a detour by means of which repression could be avoided. The day's residues (events of the waking day) establish contact with repressed, unconscious impulse(s), which attempt to find fulfillment in the material of the latent thoughts. Thus the latent content will include some or all of the following: early memories and experiences, attitudes and phantasies toward parents and siblings, defenses against early experiences and phantasies, present-day wishes (both acceptable and non-acceptable), and conflicts and defenses against these, habitual character strivings and character defenses, attitudes to therapy and attitudes toward the therapist. The unrecognizability, strangeness, and absurdity of the manifest dream are partly the result of translation of thought into archaic modes of expression and partly the result of the restrictive and disapproving dream-censorship of events in the dream.

Dream research has cast doubt on some of the teleological explanations that have traditionally been used in psychological theories. Dreaming does not appear to be a unique response to a specific psychological experiential factor; instead, it serves to maintain or re-establish homeostasis on a neuro-physiologic-biologic

level as well as on a psychologic one. It is not an unconscious wish that determines dreaming; rather, neurophysiologic changes in the sleep-wakefulness apparatus provide opportunities for representation of unconscious wishes, which 'ride along on' the waves of neurophysiologic disequilibrium, as it were, but which can hardly be credited with primary responsibility for dream production itself. Furthermore, it seems unlikely that repression is a major factor in producing amnesia for dreams, the majority of which are followed by a period of deep sleep that inhibits or prevents memory consolidation.

The processes which transform the latent into the manifest content are called the 'dream work': condensation, displacement, symbolization, dramatization, and secondary elaboration.

The *condensation* of latent thoughts, memories, and phantasies in a dream operates like a magnet gathering together out of the whole reservoir of past and present-day experiences all those pertinent to the magnet. *Displacement* is achieved by giving high interest in the manifest content to an element which will have little significance when the latent thoughts are evoked, or by representing an important latent thought as an insignificant detail in the manifest content. Similarly, the affective accompaniment may be very strong with the least important dream thought, but feeble with the most important thought. Displacement may also be achieved by reversal; e.g. representing the inside as the outside, or the bottom as the top, etc.

Symbolism is the chief method of distorting the latent content. Psychoanalytic experience has shown that the ideas symbolized concern the fundamental factors of existence—our bodies, life, death, procreation—in relation to ourselves and our families. Dream symbolism has many mechanisms in common with formation of figures of speech. The simplest figure of speech is 'simile,' i.e. the equation of two dissimilar things by means of a common attribute, the similarity being indicated by 'as' or 'like.' When these words are omitted, the compressed simile is known as 'metaphor.' These devices also occur in dreams. Personal metaphor involves the transference of human activities to the non-human, such as 'sighing oak.' A flowing stream in a dream will suggest a stream of urine or a flow of talk; or a particular type of tree may have special significance, such as 'pine' tree meaning someone longed for, etc. Through 'metonymy,' a name that has a usual or accidental connection with a thing is used for the thing itself, such as the 'bar' for the profession of law. 'Synecdoche' employs a part to represent the whole, such as a factory accommodating so many 'hands.' When the sounds of the words echo the sense, the term is 'onomatopoeia.' 'Antithesis' appears in dreams in the form of opposition in position, as in sitting. Parallels are used to convey similarity of position, such as sitting alongside a person. The repetition of a dream element is similar to the repetition of phrases in diction to secure emphasis. Through the 'implied metaphor,' abstract ideas are expressed in terms of the concrete; e.g. 'food for thought,' 'hot temper.' Although words acquire a second meaning and convey abstract ideas, they do not lose their original concrete significance in the unconscious; language itself, therefore, may yield significant information. Thus, 'She is her mother's spoiled darling' may mean she is pampered; but to the unconscious, spoiled also means dirty or ruined.

Dramatization is the representation in the manifest dream of an action or situation evolved from the latent thoughts by the dream mechanisms. It is the subjective attempt within the psyche to project anxiety and control stimuli. The mechanisms may attempt to draw a unity from the conflicting forces of many years, balancing and neutralizing affects. Different persons may represent conflicting parts of the psyche. If a balance is not achieved, the dream may leave a disagreeable affect or anxiety. *Secondary elaboration* molds the latent thoughts and wishes, disguised by the processes of condensation, displacement, and symbolization, into the semblance of a logical story. Ernest Jones considers it as being closely allied to rationalization. (Sharpe, E.F. *Dream Analysis*, Norton, New York, 1938)

Every dream is capable of many meanings, on many different psychic levels, and not all of them will necessarily be interpreted by the analyst. There are several choices possible in the technique of dream interpretation: to proceed chronologically and in order, to start with one particular element, to ask the dreamer what events of the previous day are asso-

ciated with the dream, or to let the dreamer begin where he will to free-associate. L. Wolberg (*The Technique of Psychotherapy*, Grune & Stratton, New York, 1954) lists the following techniques of interpretation: (a) summarizing for the patient the basic trends in the dream; (b) asking the patient for spontaneous associations; (c) tentative, unverbalized formulation of the dynamics based on therapist's knowledge of the patient (which formulation will take account of the setting of the dream, the characters in the dream, underlying wish or need, personality traits disclosed in the dream, mechanisms of defense, conflicts expressed in the dream, the movement and outcome of the dream, and the resistance and transference manifestations expressed); and (d) encouraging further associations by focusing the patient's attention on particular problems or conflicts as they seem to be expressed in the dream.

According to Adler, the dream has an anticipatory, prescient function. It foreshadows the preparations developed in connection with actual difficulties encountered by the dreamer's life-plan and the safeguarding purpose is never lost sight of. In other words, the dream attempts to influence the future complexion of things. It is an attempt to solve a problem and has no sexual connotation. It is an indication of power, a sign and a proof that both body and mind are making an attempt at anticipatory thinking and at anticipatory groping in order to justify the personality of the dreamer in connection with some approaching difficulty. It provides a glimpse of the dreamer's unconscious life-plan by means of which he strives to dominate the pressure of life and his own feeling of uncertainty. In dreams all the transitional phases of anticipatory thinking occur as if directed by some previously determined goal and by the utilization of personal experiences.

He sums up: The main function of dreams consists of simplified early trials and of warnings and encouragements favorable to the life-plan; and to have as their object the solution of some future problem.' (Adler, A. *The Practice and Theory of Individual Psychology*, tr. by Radin, P., Kegan Paul, Trench, Trubner, London, 1924)

dream, alternative in Freud says that

'dreams are quite incapable of expressing the alternative "either-or"; it is their custom to take both members of this alternative into the same content, as though they had an equal right to be there.' (Freud, S. *The Interpretation of Dreams*, 3rd ed., tr. by Brill, A.A., Macmillan, New York, 1933).

dream, antithesis in (an-tith′ē-sis) Freud's earlier view was that 'the attitude of dreams to the category of *antithesis* and *contradiction* is very striking. This category is simply ignored; the word "no" does not seem to exist for a dream. Dreams are particularly fond of reducing antitheses to uniformity, or representing them as one and the same thing.' (Freud, S. *The Interpretation of Dreams*, 3rd ed., tr. by Brill, A.A., Macmillan, New York, 1933)

dream, artificial Any dream which is apparently induced by sensory stimulation. Freud cites from Maury, who, when his neck was lightly pinched during sleep, dreamed that a blister was being applied. Freud holds that sensory stimuli may instigate a dream, but they cannot be held responsible for the content of the dream.

dream, biographical A type of dream in which the manifest content is mainly composed of fairly reasonable events connected with the life of the dreamer.

dream-censorship See *censorship, dream.*

dream, color in The specific report of having dreamed in color suggests that the color has analysable and significant meaning, including any or all of the following: to camouflage or to identify specific portions or excretions of the body; representation of a specific affect-system; synaesthetic representation of other sensory systems; to serve as a screen for traumatic experiences. Dreaming in color may also reflect some kind of neurophysiologic disturbance, for such dreams have been reported frequently in patients with epilepsy, migraine, and drug intoxication.

dream, comfort Synonymous with *dream, convenience* (q.v.).

dream, compensatory nature of Jung says: 'It is an assured finding of scientific experience that dreams, for example, almost invariably have a content which can act as an essential corrective to the conscious attitude. Hence our justification for speaking of a compensatory function of the unconscious.' (Jung, C.G. *Contributions to Analytical Psychology*, tr. by Baynes, H.G. and C.F., Kegan Paul, Trench, Trubner, London, 1928)

dream, conceptual content of As a rule, ideas in dreams are expressed in the form of visual images.
'The second quality peculiar to the dream alone, as distinguished from the day-dream, is that the conceptual content is not thought, but is transformed into visual images, to which we give credence, and which we believe that we experience. Let us add, however, that not all dreams show this transformation of ideas into visual images.' (Freud, S. *The Interpretation of Dreams*, 3rd ed., tr. by Brill, A.A., Macmillan, New York, 1933)

dream, consolation When dreams contain an encouraging note, they are known as consolation dreams.
'There are consolation-dreams, directed against another anxiety perceived in dreams—the fear of death. "To depart" is one of the most frequent and one of the most readily established of the death-symbols. The dream therefore says consolingly: "Reassure yourself, you are not going to die (to depart)," just as the examination-dream calms us by saying: "Don't be afraid; this time, too, nothing will happen to you." The difficulty in understanding both kinds of dreams is due to the fact that the anxiety is attached precisely to the expression of consolation.' (Freud, S. *The Interpretation of Dreams*, 3rd ed., tr. by Brill, A.A., Macmillan, 1933)

dream-content The material of which the dream is composed. Dreams have a latent dream-content, made up of dream-thoughts and manifest dream-content, usually presented in highly symbolic form. 'The dream-content is, as it were, presented in hieroglyphics, whose symbols must be translated, one by one, into the language of dream-thoughts.' (Freud, S. *The Interpretation of Dreams*, 3rd ed., tr. by Brill, A.A., Macmillan, New York, 1933)

dream, contradiction in See *dream, antithesis in.*

dream, convalescent Dreams can and do occur in *any* convalescence, but in no other period than the convalescence of traumatic neurosis is it true that *convalescent dreams* are of a specific type and *only* of that type. The nature and content of the dreams of a traumatic neurotic are characteristic of this particular disorder, so much so in fact that they may be taken as pathognomonic of the illness.

'In traumatic neurosis—especially in the early stages, within the first year of the trauma—the dream life is pathognomonic.' (Kardiner, A., and Spiegel, H. *War Stress and Neurotic Illness,* Hoeber, New York, 1947)

Moreover, in differential diagnosis this unique quality of the dream life in traumatic neurosis is a factor that may be used in differentiating this disorder from others which may resemble it (psychoneuroses, character neuroses, schizophrenia, malingering, etc.). The traumatic neurotic exhibits a stereotypy in his dream life. The most common content of the dream is the threat of annihilation, usually a representation of the original trauma. 'These . . . dreams say essentially the same thing in different ways; they all reproduce a helpless situation with its tremendous release of disorganized aggression. They all say: "I am as at birth, I perceive the world but can do nothing with it, hence it threatens me."' (ibid.)

dream, convenience While saying about convenience dreams that 'in truth all dreams may claim this designation,' Freud stresses certain types as such.

'Such convenience-dreams came very frequently to me in my youth. Accustomed as I had always to work until late at night, early waking was always a matter of difficulty. I used then to dream that I was out of bed and standing at the washstand.' (Freud, S. *The Interpretation of Dreams,* 3rd ed., tr. by Brill, A.A., Macmillan, New York, 1933) He calls this a lethargy-dream.

dream, corroborating A dream corroborating the material of a previous dream. 'In conclusion, I will mention a particular type of dream which, in the nature of the case, occurs only in the course of psychoanalytic treatment, and may bewilder or deceive beginners in practice. These are the corroborating dreams, which follow, as one may say, like "hangers-on"; they

are easily translated, and contain merely what has been arrived at by analysis of the previous few days' material.' (Freud, S. *Collected Papers,* vol. 2, tr. by Riviere, J., Leonard and Virginia Woolf and The Institute of Psychoanalysis, London, 1924-25)

dream, counter-wish According to Freud certain dreams seem not to be associated with a wish; in fact they seem to be of an opposite character, that is, to convey a counter-wish. The wish may be concealed behind its opposite. An impotent patient dreamed he had syphilis. He said that if he had syphilis it would signalize potency to him. A second motive for a counter-wish dream is seen in dream-distortion. A patient, who had often punished his brother, dreamed that the brother had foreclosed his (the patient's) mortgage on a house highly prized by the dreamer. Under analysis it was evident that the dreamer, out of a sense of guilt, was expressing a hidden wish for punishment.

dream-day The day before the night of the dream. It is significant because it often contributes something that stimulates the occurrence of a dream.

dream-displacement In principle dream-displacement does not differ from the displacement observed in other psychic structures. 'That which is obviously the essential content of the dream-thoughts need not be represented at all in the dream. The dream is, as it were, *centered elsewhere;* its content is arranged about elements which do not constitute the central point of the dream thoughts.' (Freud, S. *The Interpretation of Dreams,* 3rd ed., tr. by Brill, A.A., Macmillan, New York, 1933). See *displacement.*

dream-distortion 'We feel justified in connecting the unpleasant character of all these dreams with the fact of dream-distortion, and in concluding that these dreams are distorted, and that their wish-fulfilment is disguised beyond recognition, precisely because there is a strong revulsion against—a will to repress—the subject-matter of the dream, or the wish created by it. Dream-distortion, then proves in reality to be an act of the censorship.' (Freud, S. *The Interpretation of Dreams,* 3rd ed., tr. by Brill, A.A., Macmillan, New York, 1933). See *distortion.*

dream, egoism of Freud says: 'It has been my experience—and to this I have found no exception—that every dream treats of oneself. Dreams are absolutely egoistic. In cases where not my ego, but only a strange person occurs in the dream-content, I may safely assume that by means of identification my ego is concealed behind that person.' (Freud, S. *The Interpretation of Dreams*, 3rd ed., tr. by Brill, A.A., Macmillan, New York, 1933)

dream, embarrassment Dreams of embarrassment usually take the form of shame associated with nakedness. 'But the dream of nakedness demands our attention only when shame and embarrassment are felt in it, when one wishes to escape or hide, and when one feels the strange inhibition of being unable to stir from the spot, and of being utterly powerless to alter the painful situation.' (Freud, S. *The Interpretation of Dreams*, 3rd ed., tr. by Brill, A.A., Macmillan, New York, 1933.) The embarrassment dream is said to stem from similar experiences of childhood.

dream, examination Examination-dreams (Freud), or matriculation-dreams (Stekel), are dreams connected with examinations. See *anxiety, examination*.

dream, exhibition A dream of nakedness.

dream-forgetting During the waking stage there is 'an unmistakable intention to forget' dreams. During sleep there is a slackening of the censorship forces, the forces of resistance that keep unconscious material out of consciousness. The forces, however, gain their full powers when sleep is ended and they drive the memory of the dream into the unconscious sphere.

dream-formation The manner in which dreams are formed. See *dream*.

dream, fractional interpretation of Freud states that 'the interpretation of a dream cannot always be accomplished in one session; after following up a chain of associations you will often feel that your working capacity is exhausted; the dream will not tell you anything more that day; it is then best to break off, and to resume the work the following day. Another portion of the dream-content then solicits your attention, and you thus gain access to a fresh stratum of the dream-thoughts. One might call this the "fractional" interpretation of dreams.' (Freud, S. *The Interpretation of Dreams*, 3rd ed., tr. by Brill, A.A., Macmillan, New York, 1933)

dream-function Freud says: 'The dream is the (disguised) fulfilment of a (suppressed, repressed) wish.' (Freud, S. *The Interpretation of Dreams*, 3rd ed., tr. Brill, A.A., Macmillan, New York, 1933)

Jung holds that the general function of dreams is to reflect 'certain fundamental tendencies of the personality, either those whose meaning extends over the whole life, or those that are momentarily of most importance. The dream gives an objective statement of these tendencies, a statement which does not trouble itself about conscious wishes and convictions.' (Jung, C.G. *Contributions to Analytical Psychology*, tr. by Baynes, H.G. and C.F., Kegan Paul, Trench, Trubner, London, 1928)

While referring to Freud's dream theory Adler says: 'In reality these infantile wishes already stand under the compulsion of the imaginary goal and themselves usually bear the character of a guiding thought suitably arrayed, and adapt themselves to symbolic expression purely for reasons of thought economy.' (Adler, A. *The Neurotic Constitution*, tr. by Glueck, B. and Lind, J.E., Moffat, Yard, New York, 1917)

dream, functional According to Silberer, dreams that originate in physical disturbances of mental origin. Stekel uses the term in a looser sense to denote dreams that symbolize the function of the psyche, whether normal or morbid.

dream, hyper-determination of Most dreams have multiple determinants. 'In dream-formation the essential elements, those that are emphasized by intensive interests, may be treated as though they were subordinate, while they are replaced in the dream by other elements, which were certainly subordinate in the dream-thoughts.' (Freud, S. *The Interpretation of Dreams*, 3rd ed., tr. by Brill, A.A., Macmillan, New York, 1933). See *dream-displacement*.

dream-illusion A dream may be precipitated by an objective sensory stimulus.

A ringing alarm clock may set a dream in motion that has nothing to do with ringing or an alarm clock. The ringing stimulated a patient to dream of a locomotive swiftly passing by him. He was panic-stricken lest he be drawn into the path of the locomotive. The ringing of the clock had aroused a painful complex in him, that of castration. Of course, the locomotive was the illusory symbol.

Dream-illusions may be engendered also by subjective sensory stimuli. 'They are those very vivid and changeable pictures which with many people occur constantly during the period of falling asleep, and which may linger for a while even after the eyes have been opened. . . . According to Maury, if one wakes up shortly after such an experience (of hypnagogic hallucinations), it is often possible to trace in the dream the images which one has perceived before falling asleep as hypnagogic hallucinations.' (Freud, S. *The Interpretation of Dreams*, 3rd ed., tr. by Brill, A.A., Macmillan, New York, 1933)

Dream-illusions may come about as a consequence of organic, visceral stimulation. Thus, an organ, activated by disease or by any physiological urge, may stimulate memory-images that superficially have nothing in common with the source of the stimulus.

dream-inciter See *dream-stimulus.*

dream-instigator See *dream-stimulus.*

dream-interpretation The meaning given to a dream is dream-interpretation. The only kind of dream-interpretation used in current psychiatric practice is derived from the formulations of Freud, who includes many of the findings of others within his discipline. The Freudian form of dream-interpretation assumes that the dream has two contents: the manifest content is the dream as it actually appears to the dreamer; the latent content is made up of the hidden, disguised meaning of the manifest content. Dream-interpretation involves the application of the free-association method to the material comprising the manifest content for purposes of revealing the basic impulses resident in the latent content.

Usually dreams are analyzed by the 'fractional' method, that is, each item of the dream is considered separately for free-association. When this process is completed, the separate parts are used, in order to piece together a whole.

dream, lethargy See *dream, convenience.*

dream-life The activity of the mind, recorded in sensory images during sleep.

dream, lying According to Freud 'a dream is not the "unconscious" itself; it is the form into which a thought from the preconscious, or even from waking conscious life, can, thanks to the favouring conditions of sleep, be recast. . . . With our dreamer, the intention to mislead me, just as she did her father, certainly emanated from the preconscious, or perhaps even from consciousness; it could come to expression by entering into connection with the unconscious wish-impulse to please the father (or father-substitute), and in this way it created a lying dream.' (Freud, S. *Collected Papers*, vol. 2, tr. by Riviere, J., Leonard and Virginia Woolf and The Institute of Psychoanalysis, London, 1924 - 25)

dream, made-to-order A dream that the patient seems to produce at the analyst's direct suggestion, as if the patient dreams in response to the urgent demands of the psychiatrist. Of course, determined as they are by the relationship between the patient and the analyst, such dreams are often extremely distorted, and usually express a derisive attitude toward the physician.

dream, manifest The name given by Freud to the dream itself, as reported by the dreamer. The dream-text or manifest dream in itself is not intelligible as far as gaining new information about the patient is concerned. In the process of analysis of the manifest dream, however, information concerning the patient, which would otherwise be inaccessible, is obtained. This information which lies behind the dream is termed the latent dream-thoughts. The technique by which the latent dream-thoughts are derived from the manifest dream is called dream interpretation. This technique utilizes the associations of the patient to the various parts of the manifest dream and the meaning of certain symbols with which the patient often is unable to associate. The process by which the latent dream-thoughts become the manifest dream in the dreamer's mental life is called the dream-work. The two major techniques by which the dream-work is accomplished are condensation and displacement. (Freud, S. *New Introductory Lectures on Psycho-analysis,* Norton, New York, 1933)

dream, matriculation See *dream, examination.*

dream, nonsensical A dream seemingly senseless or void of logic. The illogicality of a dream does not necessarily mean that the patient himself is illogical in his waking life. 'On the contrary, the dreams that appear logical enough may be the fruit of a sick brain.' In the opinion of Stekel, a person of frank disposition, one who has nothing to hide (insofar as that is possible), will have dreams that are not essentially distorted, in opposition to persons who are perpetually fleeing from self-awareness and need distorted, so-called nonsensical dreams which are almost insoluble enigmas.

Of course, the analyst's failure to understand a dream does not inevitably imply that the dream is nonsensical. 'The dream has its own secret logic, so that we are justified in speaking of the inner logic of the dream,' because sometimes the apparently nonsensical parts of a dream are, as a matter of fact, the very spots that contain a clue to its meaning. (Stekel, W. *The Interpretation of Dreams,* Liveright, New York, 1943)

dream-pain Hypnalgia; pain occurring during the dream state.

dream, perennial A dream 'which, being first dreamt in childhood, recurs again and again in adult years.' (Freud, S. *The Interpretation of Dreams,* 3rd ed., tr. by Brill, A.A., Macmillan, New York, 1933)

dream-phantasy The manifest content of the dream.

dream, prophetic Stekel considers it justifiable to use the term 'prophetic' for describing those dreams that seem to forecast a wish of the dreamer and later on come true. To illustrate a dream of this type Stekel gives the example of the patient who was attached to his mother and his family with unduly strong ties and expressed symbolically, in a dream, his

wish to break these bonds. After the meaning of the dream was explained to him, he was able to fulfill his wish and become engaged to a girl with whom he had been in love for a long time. (Stekel, W. *The Interpretation of Dreams,* Liveright, New York, 1943)

dream-psychosis The mental state of the dreamer. Freud calls that state a psychosis, emphasizing that it is transitory, harmless, and disappears when relations with the external world are resumed.

dream, reconstruction In Levin's terminology, a dream in which a succession of events culminate, seemingly by chance, in a stimulus coinciding with an external stimulus of like nature which wakes the dreamer. Thus a dream that ends with a bell ringing when the ringing of an alarm clock wakes the sleeper is a reconstruction dream. It is probable that such dreams are mainly instances of the dynamic and 'economizing' purpose of dreams to protect the sleeper from disturbances. There seems to be no reason to doubt that reconstruction dreams are further utilized, as is any other dream, in the symbolic expression of unconscious conflicts: that is, reconstruction dreams are subject to psychoanalytic interpretation. (*Psychoanalytic Quarterly 10,* 685, 1941)

dream, secondary elaboration of The account of a dream given by the dreamer upon awakening, insofar as it differs from the original content, is referred to as secondary elaboration of the dream.

dream, Sisyphus Frustration dream. See *neurosis, traumatic.*

dream-source See *dream-stimulus.*

dream, speech in Freud says: 'The dream-work cannot compose a new speech. No matter how many speeches and answers, which may in themselves be sensible or absurd, may occur in dreams, analysis always shows us that the dream has merely taken from the dream-thoughts fragments of speeches which have really been delivered or heard, and has dealt with them in the most arbitrary fashion.' (Freud, S. *The Interpretation of Dreams,* 3rd ed., tr. by Brill, A.A., Macmillan, New York, 1933). The dream-work actually produces neologistic sentences.

What appears in the dream as speech often represents a command or prohibition stemming from the superego.

dream-stimulus The exciting cause of a dream. It may be (1) an external sensory stimulus, (2) an internal (subjective) sensory stimulus, (3) an internal (organic) physical stimulus, or (4) a stimulus from the psyche itself.

dream-synthesis A term used by Havelock Ellis to designate a study of dreams from the standpoint of statistics.

dream, telepathic By this expression Stekel describes a certain type of dream which seems to be engendered in the mind of the dreamer by transmission from other dreamers near him. The existence of such a type of dream is unquestionable according to Stekel, who asserts that he has collected 'numerous instances to show that persons who sleep in the same room influence one another's dreams.' (Stekel, W. *The Interpretation of Dreams,* Liveright, New York, 1943)

dream-text The manifest part of the dream, in contradistinction to its latent significance.

dream-thought The idea or ideas behind the dream and the special ways by which the material is expressed.

dream-waking *Obs.* Illusion or hallucination.

dream within a dream Sometimes part of a dream is regarded during the dream state as having been dreamed; the dreamer therefore does not consider that the dream within a dream belongs to the dream. He continues to dream, looking upon the continuation only as the real dream.
'The inclusion of a certain content in "a dream within a dream" is therefore equivalent to the wish that what has been characterized as a dream had never occurred.' (Freud, S. *The Interpretation of Dreams,* 3rd ed., tr. by Brill, A.A., Macmillan, New York, 1933). The attitude that the dreamer assumes toward it constitutes a repudiation of it.

dream-work See *dream.*

dreams, paired Alexander calls attention to what he describes as 'paired' dreams. They are based upon the concepts of punishment and gratification, in the sense that one is allowed to indulge in a forbidden act, if he has already paid the penalty for it. During the same night the subject may first dream that he is being punished; later he dreams that he is engaging in a forbidden act.

dreams, semantics in Dreams represent the language of the unconscious—the language of ancient mankind. Dreams are largely pictorial and perceptual, and over the ages newer and different meanings have been given to the pictorial language. Semantics in dreams refers to such language evolution. According to Freud, the language of dreams would be understood better and translated more easily if more were known about the development of language, for the thought-expression in dreams has the same regressive archaic character as is shown by primitive thought and its expression in language.
Freud gives the example of inversion in dreams—the process by which an element of the manifest dream may represent its opposite in the latent dream-thoughts. In many old and primitive languages, a fair number of the words have opposite meanings. This is true of the oldest roots of language, for, as the language develops, double meanings often disappear. For example, the Latin *altus* means both 'high' and 'deep,' and other examples may be drawn from other languages. Thus the prototype of the mechanism of inversion in dreams can be seen in the antithetical sense of many primitive words. (Freud, S. *The Antithetical Sense of Primal Words* in *Collected Papers,* vol. 4, Hogarth Press, London, 1925)

dreamy-state See *state, dreamy.*

drift, genetic A change in succeeding generation of the frequency of certain genes, due to chance rather than to selection.

drinker, problem See *alcoholism, chronic.*

drive 'A drive, then, is a genetically determined, psychic constituent which, when operative, produces a state of psychic excitation or, as we often say, of tension. This excitation or tension impels the individual to activity, which is also genetically determined in a general way, but which can be considerably altered by individual experience. . . . Thus we see that there is a sequence which is characteristic of the operation of the drive. This sequence we may call either tension, motor activity, and cessation of tension, or need, motor activity, and gratification, as we prefer. The former terminology deliberately neglects the elements of subjective experience, while the latter explicitly refers to it.' (Brenner, C. *An Elementary Textbook of Psychoanalysis,* International Universities Press, New York, 1955).

In present day psychoanalytic psychology, two drives are distinguished—the sexual or erotic (the energy of which is the libido), and the aggressive or destructive (the energy of which is the aggressive energy or, less commonly, destrudo).

drive, internal See *instinct.*

drive reduction theory See *reductionism.*

driveness, organic Kahn and Cohen's term for the overactivity of the brain-damaged individual, which is attributed to defective brain-stem organization.

driving, photic See *electroencephalogram.*

driving, psychic Continuously repeated playback of psychodynamically significant material which has been recorded on a device such as a tape recorder. Described by D.E. Cameron (*American Journal of Psychiatry 112:502-9,* 1956): 'Since this compels a continued response within a field largely limited by the cue material selected, it has been termed "psychic driving." The term "cue" is used to indicate that the material was selected because it triggers into expression a whole community of related topics.'

If the psychic driving is in response to the patient's own verbal cues, it is termed 'autopsychic'; if it is in response to cues verbalized by others but based on his known psychodynamics, it is termed 'heteropsychic.' The values of psychic driving are said to include penetration of defenses, elicitation of hitherto inaccessible material, and the setting up of a dynamic implant. (See *implant, dynamic*).

dromolepsy (drom'ō-lep-sē) A short spurt of running occurring just prior to and generally ending in an epileptic attack. By many it is believed to be the beginning of the attack. It is known also as *procursive epilepsy.*

dromomania (drō-mō-mā'nē-à) An abnormal impulse to travel is called dromomania; the term is frequently used by Hirschfeld to denote the desire to escape from a disagreeable sexual situation. It is also known as *vagabond neurosis.*

dromophobia (drom-ō-fō'bē-à, drō-mō-) Fear of (running across) a street.

dropout A student who leaves school before completing a grade or before graduation; a patient who withdraws from and terminates treatment. In the latter case, the term generally implies that the therapist has not concurred in the patient's decision to terminate.

drudge, household In social work, 'a person so tied down by housework or family cares as to have little time for rest, recreation, or self-development. There is usually lack of sympathy or understanding on the part of others of the household.' (Hamilton, G. *A Medical Social Terminology,* Presbyterian Hospital, New York, 1930)

drug, abreactive Any of the preparations, usually barbiturates, used in narcocatharsis. See *narcotherapy.*

drug abuse, drug dependency See *dependency, drug.*

drug, addicting See *addiction.*

drugs, psychosis due to (sī-kō'sis) Certain drugs such as bromides, cocaine, acetanilide, chloral, phenacetin, trional, sulphonal, etc. may by brief, excessive, or long continued use give rise to mental symptoms (in DSM-II, coded 294.3). Apathy and dullness may be apparent initially, sometimes followed by toxic delirium with confusion, auditory and visual hallucinations, confabulation, flight of ideas, misidentification, or paraphasia. When the drug is withheld, the symptoms usually disappear.

drunkards, acute hallucinosis of Wernicke's name for alcoholic hallucinosis. See *hallucinosis, alcoholic.*

drunkenness, maudlin Intoxicated state characterized by mawkish, silly, and blissful behavior. Bleuler regarded it as 'an abnormal reaction,' but he did not consider it as a psychosis.

drunkenness, pathological See *intoxication, alcoholic.*

Ds Rorschach scoring symbol for an associative response to a white space on the card.

DSD Abbreviation for *depression sine depression,* a recognition of the fact that a clinicial depression may be masked by or co-exist with symptoms that suggest other disorders, such as pyschosomatic disturbances or conversion hysteria.

DSM-II Diagnostic and Statistical Manual, 2nd edition; the 1968 revision of the nomenclature of mental disorders, prepared by the Committee on Nomenclature and Statistics of the American Psychiatric Association. See *nomenclature, 1968 revision.*

D-state See *dream.*

dual leadership See *psychotherapy, multiple.*

dual personality See *personality, multiple.*

dualism, psychic Co-existence of double consciousness or of two fairly distinctly formed superego streams (double conscience) as in multiple personality, where one personality may alternate with a second with complete amnesia of the active personality for the behavior of the inactive one, or where the two personalities live side by side, one or the other being predominant periodically but still influenced by the inactive one. But such co-conscious mentation may also be a normal phenomenon, as when one writes a letter and at the same time listens to the radio. Usually, however, when the co-conscious thinking is pathological, each of the co-conscious organizations strives to drive the ego in a different direction. Psychic dualism is perhaps responsible for critical self-observation, the ability of one conscious stream to observe the remainder of the personality. See also: *personality, alternating; personality, split.*

Dubois, Paul-Charles (1848-1918) (dübwả') French psychiatrist; psychotherapy.

dullard See *moron.*

dullness, mental 'The group comprised by the term "dull or backward" consists of those children who, at about the middle of their school career, are behind the normal average of their age to the extent of two years or two classes. This corresponds to a retardation of between 15 and 20 per cent of their age, or to about twice the "standard deviation," and roughly an I.Q. of between 80 and 85.' (Tredgold, A.F. *A Textbook of Mental Deficiency,* 6th ed., Wood, Baltimore, 1937)

dumbness, word See *aphasia, motor.*

dummy *Placebo* (q.v.).

dumpish A popular term meaning dull, stupid, morose; dumpy.

dunce (John *Duns* Scotus, a pedantic schoolman and theologian, [died 1308] .) Popular term for a stupid person.

duplicative reaction See *reaction, duplicative.*

dura mater (dōō'rả mả'ter) See *meninges.*

Durham decision, Durham test See *responsibility, criminal.*

DW In Rorschach scoring, a confabulated whole response in which a portion of the ink blot is used as the basis for interpretation of the whole picture. Such untenable extensions of percepts indicate an insistence that reality conform to the subject's wishes; they are seen most in the records of psychotics and psychopaths.

dwarfism Extreme deficiency in stature (under 105 cm. in white racial groups). It is identical with *microsomia* and is usually divided into the following three special forms:

(a) dwarfs with regular physical proportions and normal psychic development, going under such names as *nanosomia primordialis, heredo-familial essential microsomia,* and *pygmeism;*

(b) dwarfs with a serious hypogenesis of the skeleton except for a very large skull, falling under the heading of Paltauf's *nanism;*

(c) dwarfs with a combination of infantilism and premature senility, known as Gilford's *progeria* or the *senile nanism* of Variot and Pirronneau.

In addition to these specific forms, there is a heterogeneous group of *'infantilistic'* dwarfisms, or nanisms, of endocrine origin, which are said to 'assume different clinical forms according to the gland principally attacked by dysfunction.

'In these infantilistic dwarfisms we are naturally dealing with infantilisms in which a serious defect in stature and in the total bodily mass is the outstanding feature. Owing to this predominance of mass hypoevolutism they form a group by themselves, distinct from other glandular infantilisms in which bodily mass and proportions seem more evenly retarded in development. We do not fully understand the reason why in some cases the syndrome of infantilistic dwarfism and in others that of true infantilism develops.' (Pende, N. *Constitutional Inadequacies*, tr. by Naccarati, S., Lea & Febiger, Philadelphia, 1928)

dyad (dī'ad) In social psychiatry, a two-person relationship.

dynamic In psychiatry *dynamic* relates to the operation of mental forces or energy.

dynamic psychiatry See *descriptive*.

dynamics The word is used interchangeably with dynamism(s). See *psychodynamics*.

dynamism In psychiatry, the action of psychic structures and to the forces behind the action. A dynamism 'is a specific force operating in a specific manner or direction.' (Healy, W., Bronner, A.F., and Bowers, A.M. *The Structure and Meaning of Psychoanalysis*, Knopf, New York, 1930.) While the authors just cited prefer *dynamism* to *mechanism*, the latter is more commonly used. See *mechanism; defense*.

dynamogeny (dī-nȧ-moj'ē-nē) This term, used by P. Dubois, means 'the evolution of physical force.

dynamophany (-mof'ȧ-nē) The expression of psychic force (P. Dubois).

dynamopsychism (dī-nȧ-mō-sī'kiz'm) Geley's theory of libido or energy. The unconscious is the seat of both lower and higher functions, but the latter are purposely kept in abeyance during normal life in order to maintain the sense of limitation and deficiency necessary for ambition and progress. Thus a person forgets, because too much knowledge would remove the spurring to further efforts. But with impending death, the sense of limitation and deficiency is no longer necessary, so that the higher faculties are allowed to appear. The mind then becomes clearer and sharper, and certain manifestations such as clairvoyance and telepathy may occur. (Geley, G. *From the Unconscious to the Conscious*, tr. by S.De Brath, Harper, New York, 1921, p. 353)

dysapocatastasis (dis-ap-ō-kȧ-tas'tȧ-sis) *Obs.* Restless discontent.

dysarthria (-är'thrē-ȧ) Difficulty in articulation; partial impairment of articulatory speech.

dysautonomia (dis-aw-tō-nō'mē-ȧ) Dysfunction of the autonomic or vegetative nervous system, as a result of brain abnormality. Dysautonomia is often familial and bears many resemblances to childhood schizophrenia; the affected child is tense, irritable, subject to recurrent physical crises, defective in organizing complex behavior and adapting to change, and as a result typically develops any number of emotional disturbances.

dysbasia (dis-bā'zhē-ȧ) Any form of difficult or distorted walking, whether organically or psychically determined.

dysbulia, dysboulia (dis-bōō'lē-ȧ) Disturbance in the will or in the volitional aspects of the personality. See *will, disturbances of the*.

dyscalculia See *acalculia*.

dyschezia Inadequate evacuation of the stool from the rectum, commonly found in children who suffer from constipation on what is presumed to be an emotional basis.

dyscontrol, descending See *disordered behavior, classification of; psychodynamics, adaptational*.

dyscontrol, emergency See *disordered behavior, classification of; psychodynamics, adaptational*.

dyseneia (dis-e-nē′à) Defective articulation secondary to deafness.

dysergasia (dis-ēr-gas′ē-à) A term used by Adolf Meyer to designate those psychiatric syndromes which are presumably associated with disordered physiology of the brain. The dysergasias are generally known as toxic psychoses, one of the chief symptoms of which is delirium.

dysesthesia (-es-thē′zhē-à) Distortion of the sense of touch. It may be organically or psychically determined.

dysesthesia interna (dēs-thā′zē-à ēn-ter′nà) *Obs.* Amnesia.

dysgenesia (dis-jē-nē′zē-à) A morbid condition of the generative organs or functions.

dysgenesis (-jen′e-sis) (1) Faulty development and infertility in general or, (2) more specifically, a condition in which hybrids are sterile among themselves, but fertile with members of either parent stock.

dysgenic (-jen′ik) This term, specifically genetic, applies to various biological conditions which have a detrimental effect on the hereditary qualities of a stock or tend to counteract racial improvement through influences bearing on reproduction. In a more general sense, the term denotes any factor which is in contrast with *eugenic* principles by tending to impair the racial qualities of future generations (see *eugenics*).

dysgenics *Obs.* Term used by some eugenicists in reference to the study of 'racial degeneration.'

dysgeusia (dis-gū′sē-à) Impairment or perversion of the sense of taste; any aberration of the appetite.

dysglucosis Any disturbance in the blood sugar level, and particularly those disturbances in which the central nervous system (cortex, diencephalon, hypothalamus, or hypophysis) plays some role.

dysgnosia (disg-nō′sē-à) *Obs.* Intellectual impairment or anomaly.

dysgraphia (-graf′ē-à) Defective ability to write. As seen clinically, the dysgraphia is often dissociated in that the patient is unable to write spontaneously but is able to copy from printed material to script or vice versa. Dissociated dysgraphia is an almost constant finding in patients with primary reading retardation and in the Gerstmann syndrome.

dysidentity A term suggested by Rabinovitch to refer to what he considers the characteristic and basic problem of childhood schizophrenia: the child's inability to experience a clear-cut self-percept and to appreciate identities, their boundaries and limits. See *image, body.*

dyskinesia (ki-nē′sē-à) Distortion of voluntary movements; involuntary muscular activity such as a tic, spasm, or myoclonus.

dyskinesia, tardive Slow, rhythmical, automatic stereotyped movements in a single muscle group or more universally, occurring as an undesirable side effect in some patients treated with psychopharmacologic agents (especially the phenothiazines). Tardive dyskinesia typically appears late in treatment, often after several years; it is more common in patients over the age of 50 than in younger patients, in patients who have had previous ECT than in those who have not, and more in females than in males.

Acute dystonia is another type of neurologic side effect of tranquilizer therapy and consists of spasmodic movements of the limbs, torticollis, opisthotonus, oculogyric crises, swelling and protrusion of the tongue, and stridorous respiration. This complication typically begins after only a few doses of the drug have been administered, and it occurs more frequently in males than in females.

dyskinesis, professional (ki-nē′sis) Professional neurasthenia.

dyslalia (-lā′lē-à) Impairment of, partial disorder in, or specific inability for uttering (speaking).

dyslexia (lek′sē-à) Impaired ability to read or understand what is read; seen most commonly with parietal lobe lesions, and in many cases of minimal brain dysfunction. See *reading, disabilities of; impulse disorder, hyperkinetic.*

dyslogia (-lō′jē-à) Incoherence of speech.

dyslysimelia (dis-lī-si-mē'lē-á) A condition consisting of localized muscle contractions, which may be painful, occurring in both lower limbs during relaxation or sleep. The term is commonly shortened to 'dyslysis.'

dyslysis (dis-lī'sis) *Dyslysimelia* (q.v.).

dysmentia Pseudoretardation; impaired performance on psychological tests secondary to psychological factors rather than to primary or constitutional mental retardation. In DSM-II, dysmentia would ordinarily be classified as mental retardation with psycho-social (environmental) deprivation, 31x.8.

dysmetria (-mē'trē-á) Inability to gauge distance for bodily movements; elicited by asking patient to raise both arms and bring them quickly to a stop at the horizontal level; when one arm sinks below the horizontal level, correction is required for the dysmetria.

dysmimia (-mim'ē-á) Inappropriate mimicry.

dysmnesia (-nē'sē-á) Impaired memory. See *syndrome, organic.*
The term is sometimes used, either by itself or in the form of 'the dysmnesic syndrome' to refer to reversible Korsakov-like syndromes that may be seen after a delirium, especially in the middle-aged and older. The patient has amnesia for the acute delirious episode but in addition has difficulty in retaining recent events and a faulty orientation. Generally the syndrome clears rapidly within a few days, but occasionally it may abate only slowly, over a period of weeks or months.

dysmorphomania *Dysmorphophobia* (q.v.).

dysneuria (-nū'rē-á) *Obs.* Mental weakness.

dysnusia (-nū'sē-á) *Obs.* Mental enfeeblement.

dysorexia (-ō-rek'sē-á) Impaired or perverted appetite.

dysorthography *Dysgraphia* (q.v.).

dysostosis, diabetic exophthalmic (-ostō'sis, dī-a-bet'ik eks-of-thal'mik) *Xanthomatosis* (q.v.).

dysostosis multiplex See *syndrome, Hurler's.*

dyspareunia (-pa-rōō'nē-á) Dyspareunia is painful sexual intercourse. It is generally used to refer to pain in women.
'Pain at the beginning of intercourse generally indicates a lack of lubrication of the vaginal canal, and this, since it is functional, is generally due to an absence of sexual desire on the part of the female, or a fear of the results of a coitus even though the desire be present.' (Behan, R.J. *Pain,* Appleton, New York, 1920)
Jones defines dyspareunia as 'pain during intercourse; an hysterical symptom.' (Jones, E. *Papers on Psycho-Analysis,* 4th ed., Wood, Baltimore, 1938)

dysphagia (-fā'jē-á) Difficulty in eating; it may be organically or psychically determined, but the term generally implies an organic etiology.

dysphagia globosa (glô-bō'zá) *Globus hystericus* (q.v.).

dysphagia hysterica (hēs-te'rē-ká) Globus hystericus.

dysphagia spastica (spás'tē-ká) Impairment in swallowing, sometimes observed in hysterical subjects; it may also be due to organic causes.

dysphemia (-fē'mē-á) Stuttering; stammering.

dysphoria (-fō'rē-á) Dejection; disaffection; 'misery in various degrees'; 'perhaps the most frequent and widespread of all disorders of the mind, and that with the most numerous associations with other disorders. . . . The most frequent mental accompaniment of dysphoria is abasement, or underestimation of self on any or every level—physical, mental, possesive, or moral.' (Mercier, C.A. *A Text-Book of Insanity,* George Allen & Unwin, London, 1914)

dysphoria nervosa (ner-vō'zá) Fidgets.

dysphrasia (dis-frā'zhē-á) Impaired speaking due to intellectual defects.

dysphrasia, imitative Echolalia; echophrasia.

dysphrasia imitatoria (dēs-frá'zē-á ē-mē-tä-tō'rē-á) Echolalia; echophrasia.

dysphrenia (dis-frē'nē-à) An old and general term for mental disorder. Wolff used the term synonymously with dementia praecox (schizophrenia).

dysplasia (-plā'zhē-à) Abnormal tissue development. The term came into prominence in psychiatry particularly through the studies of Kretschmer on body configuration. According to him, there are three basic types of physique among psychiatric patients: the asthenic, athletic, and pyknic. The fourth, called the dysplastic, is a heterogeneous group, 'varing much among themselves, of which any one group contains only a few members.' Among the types described under this heading may be mentioned elongated eunuchoids, those with polyglandular syndromes, infantilism, and hypoplasia.

dysplastic (-plas'tik) See *type, dysplastic; dysplasia.*

dyspnea, neurotic (disp'-nē-à nū-rot'ik) The symptom of shortness of breath or other related breathing difficulties associated with the implication that the symptom is an expression of unconscious emotional conflict or neurosis. The neurotic or psychogenic etiology of this symptom demands careful diagnosis through the exclusion of all possible organic causes by the usual physical diagnostic methods, as well as a careful personality study and evaluation. Neurotic dyspnea is frequently associated with symptoms of weakness and exhaustion, and seems closely related to lone-standing repressed, denied, and undischarged hostility and resentment. When patients have adequately faced and 'aired' (abreacted) their resentment, the symptoms are frequently alleviated.

A 25-year-old young woman always complained of 'a smothering feeling and an inability to get the proper amount of air' and deeply resented the diagnosis that there was no organic cause for her symptoms. It became obvious that she harbored a great deal of resentment toward her brother and his wife. After the relationship between her exhaustion and the great amount of energy it had cost her to remain unaware (unconscious) of her denied and repressed hostility to her brother had been consciously established in her mind, it became possible for her to 'air' her hostility—and she began to breathe better She then began to 'relax and let more air in,' and then seemed to gain energy.

(Weiss, E., and English, O.S. *Psychosomatic Medicine,* 2nd ed., Saunders, Philadelphia and London, 1949)

dyspraxia (dis-prak'sē-à) Partial impairment of the ability to perform skilled movement, with no associated defect in the motor apparatus.

dysprosody Disordered rhythm, accent, or melody; clinically, used especially to refer to a cortical dysarthria, basically dyspraxic in nature and due to a frontal lesion, that makes the patient's speech sound foreign.

dysrhaphic (-raf'ik) Dysontogenetic; referring to disturbances of development and particularly to developmental disorders of the central nervous system such as the Arnold-Chiari malformation.

dysrhythmia, dart and dome (-rith'mē-à) See *pyknolepsy.*

dysrhythmia, major See *hypsarrhythmia.*

dysrhythmia, paroxysmal cerebral (parok'sis-mal ser'e-bral) *Epilepsy* (q.v.).

dyssocial See *sociopathic personality disturbance.*

dys-symbole (dis-sim'bō-lē) A state of mind characterized by the inability to formulate conceptual thoughts upon personal topics or to discriminate the gradations of personal emotions in language intelligible to others. Dys-symbole is certainly apparent in some schizophrenics, but many physicians believe that it is present in all schizophrenics. Whether dys-symbole represents a defect in the patient's semantic power or is indicative of a more basic emotional deficiency is not known.

dyssynergia (-si-nēr'jē-à) A failure to work in unison or harmony, such as is seen in the motor and gait disturbances that follow cerebellar lesions.

dyssynergia cerebellaris myoclonica See *syndrome, Hunt's.*

dysthymia (thī'mē-à) 1. *Obs.* Depression of less intense degree than seen in manic-depressive psychosis and characterized by associated neurasthenic-hypochondriacal symptoms. 2. Eysenck's term for the group of symptoms found in patients with a high degree of neuroticism and a high degree of introversion.

dysthymic (-thim'ik, -thī'mik) Pertaining to certain cyclothymic reactions that have the appearance of neurasthenia.

dystonia (dis-tō'nē-à) A state of abnormal tension or tonicity. It may be general, as in catatonic, or local, as in gastric, muscular, psychic, cerebral dystonia. See *dyskinesia, tardive.*

dystonia musculorum deformans (mus-kū-lor'oom dē-for'mans) See *dystonia, torsion.*

dystonia, torsion Oppenheim's dystonia musculorum deformans. Torsion dystonia is usually familial and is particularly common among Russian Jews. The characteristic lesion is *status marmoratus* (a disorder of glial formation leading to hypermyelination and giving a marble slab appearance), particularly in the caudate nucleus and putamen. The disease has its onset in childhood or adolescence and consists of involuntary movements which produce a torsion spasm of the limbs and spine. There is no muscular wasting, sensory loss, or reflex changes, and no mental deterioration. It appears that torsion dystonia is a symptom-complex rather than a specific disease, for it may occur in a number of disorders.

dystonic (-ton'ik) Relating to abnormal (muscular) tension. The psyche or personality is said to be dystonic when it is not in harmony either with itself or with its environment.

dystrophia myotonica (-tro'fē-à mī-ō-ton'i-kà) Myotonia atrophica; a hereditary disorder characterized by atrophy of the sternocleidomastoid muscles and the muscles of the face (leading to a 'hatchet-face' appearance), shoulder, forearm, and hand and of the quadriceps muscles. There is also myotonia and, usually, other dystrophic disturbances such as cataract and gonadal atrophy. Males are more commonly affected, between the ages of 20 and 30 years. Affected patients usually succumb to intercurrent illness in late middle life. The disease was first described by Déléage in 1890.

dystropy (dis'trō-pē) A term used by Adolf Meyer, meaning abnormality of behavior.

dystrophy, pseudohypertrophic muscular (dis'tro-fē, sū-dō-hī-pēr-trō'fik mus'kū-lēr) The commonest form of muscular dystrophy, first described by Duchenne in 1868. It is inherited as a sex-linked recessive and affects males six times as often as females. Onset is gradual, beginning at about five years of age. The child is noted to be clumsy and falls frequently. There is pseudohypertrophy, but weakness, of the muscles of the calves, the glutei, quadriceps and deltoids; the face and hands always escape. The patient adopts a waddling gait and an attitude of lordosis when standing; characteristically, he rises from the ground by climbing up on his own legs. Further progression of the disease leads to contractures in the muscles and fatal termination within 10 to 15 years.

DZ Abbreviation for *dizygotic* (q.v.).

E

Earle, Pliny (1809-1892) American psychiatrist; hospital administration; in 1877 published statistical study entitled *The Curability of Insanity.*

early infantile autism See *autism, early infantile.*

ear-pulling See *pulling, ear.*

eaten, fear of being Whether conscious or unconscious, the fear of being eaten originates early in the development of the infant's ego during what is termed the oral stage. During this stage the infant develops the normal aim of pleasure or satisfaction through eating and, in a more general sense, through the incorporation of objects. Frustrations of this erotic aim of eating or incorporating and fears of such frustration are of frequent occurrence. These anxieties take the form of a fear of being eaten, because of infantile animistic thinking which assumes that what the infant feels and does will also take place in the world around it. Clinically, it has been found that the archaic fear of being eaten may have another function—may be used as a cover for castration anxiety, disguised by being distorted through regression into the older fear of being eaten. Moreover, the patient's anxiety may contain both a fear of being eaten and a fear of being castrated. (Fenichel, O. *The Psychoanalytic Theory of Neurosis,* Norton, New York, 1945)

eaten, phantasy of being The phantasy of being eaten or incorporated frequently occurs as part of a certain type of relationship to a love-object. In this relationship the patient's only aim is 'to become part of a more powerful personality' whom he overestimates to an enormous degree, though having at the same time no interest in or idea about the partner's real personality. Patients who have this sort of aim, attitude, and phantasy are characterized by an overwhelming feeling of inadequacy and inordinate need for self-esteem. As a result they can never give love but have an extreme need to feel loved, and this they achieve in the way described above. In Fenichel's words, they 'never become complete individuals in their own right and, therefore, need participation in a greater union in order to be able to feel their own existence.' (Fenichel, O. *The Psychoanalytic Theory of Neurosis,* Norton, New York, 1945)

eating without saturation See *syndrome, night-eating.*

ebriecation (ē-bri-ē-kā'shun) A term coined by Paracelsus to denote mental disorder associated with alcoholism.

ébriécation celeste (ā-brē-ā-kȧ-syawN' sā-lest') (F. 'heavenly intoxication') A Paracelsian term, meaning religious excitement and enthusiasm in psychiatric patients.

ecdemomania (ek-dē-mō-mā'nē-ȧ) Morbid impulse to travel or wander about.

ecdemonomania (-nō-mā'-nē-ȧ) *Obs.* Uncontrollable impulse to wander; dromomania.

ecdysiasm (ek-di'si-az'm) A morbid tendency to disrobe in order to provoke useless erotic stimulation in the opposite sex.

echo des pensées (ā-kō' dā päNsā') (F. 'echo of thoughts') The imagined sound-reproduction of the patient's thoughts. 'A special form of auditory hallucinations is that in which the acoustic verbal images of the thought itself are projected outside in such a way that whatever the subject thinks, he hears repeated in speech. This *echo des pensées* not only repeats the patients' thoughts, but announces their future actions.' (Jacoby, G.W. *The Unsound Mind and the Law,* Funk & Wagnalls, New York & London, 1918)

echo-encephalography A technique of neurodiagnosis in which ultrasound is transmitted to the brain and its echo is recorded on an oscilloscope. A shift in echo may indicate the presence of a space-occupying mass.

echoing, thought Same as *echo des pensées* (q.v.).

echokinesis (ek-ō-ki-ne'sis) *Echopraxia.* (q.v.).

echolalia (-lā'lē-à) The pathological repetition by imitation of the speech of another, seen in some patients with the catatonic form of schizophrenia.

echomastism (ek-om'à-tiz'm) *Echopraxia* (q.v.).

echomimia (ek-ō-mim'ē-à) *Echopraxia* (q.v.).

echopalilalia (-pal-i-lā'lē-à) The morbid repetition (re-echoing) of words spoken by another person.

echopathy (ē-kop'à-thē) Pathological repetition through imitation of the actions or speech of another. It is encountered in vivid form in the catatonic phase of schizophrenia, when the patient assumes the postures, gestures, and speech of another in 'mirror' form, so to speak. See *echopraxia, echolalia.*

echo-phenomena By this expression Kraepelin refers to echolalia and echopraxia.

echophrasia (ek-ō-frā'zhē-à) *Echolalia* (q.v.).

echopraxia (-prak'sē-à) Echopraxia, a common symptom in the catatonic form of schizophrenia, is the repetition by imitation of the movements of another. Thus, a patient acted as the 'mirror image' of his physician in that he assumed the physician's postures and gestures as he saw them.

'Contrasting with negativism is the so-called *automatic obedience,* showing itself in echopraxia (repetition of actions seen), echolalia (repetition of words heard), and flexibilitas cerea (the maintenance of imposed postures).' (Henderson, D.K. and Gillespie, R.D. *A Text-Book of Psychiatry,* 4th ed., Oxford University Press, London, 1936)

'The echopractic patients imitate whatever strikes them in the actions or words of their surroundings. As far as we know, it is partly a question of hysteria-like mechanisms, as seen in the echopraxia of primitive people, and certainly in most cases of schizophrenia, and partly a matter of an incapacity to get away from a conceived idea, so that instead of giving an answer the question is repeated or instead of a new action the preceding act is imitated.' (Bleuler, E. *Textbook of Psychiatry,* tr. by Brill, A.A., Macmillan, New York, 1930)

echo-sign See *sign, echo.*

echo-speech Synonymous with *echolalia.*

eclactisma (ek-lak-tiz'mà) A synonym for epilepsy, in part descriptive of the movements of the lower limbs during the grand mal seizure.

eclecticism In psychiatry, the selection of compatible features from diverse (and, often, superficially incompatible) systems of metapsychology in an attempt to combine whatever is valid in any theory or doctrine into an integrated, harmonious whole.

eclimia (ek-lim'ē-à) Bulimia.

eclipse, mental An expression used by Janet to denote the 'stealing' of ideas from patients, particularly from patients with schizophrenia, who claim that whenever they have an idea, someone takes it away.

ecmnesia (ek-mnē'zhē-à) *Rare.* Synonym for anterograde amnesia.

ecnoea (ek-nō-ē'à) *Obs.* Mental disorder or disease.

ecnoia (ek-noi'à) A type of fear reaction seen in children consisting of a prolongation of what began as a normally motivated sudden fright; for days or weeks the child is startled by everything and sheds tears at the slightest provocation. During this period, sleep, appetite, and excretory functions may be affected. (307.1)

ecological systems model See *psychiatry, community.*

ecology (ē-kol'ō-jē) Study of the mutual relationships between living things and their environment. One of its basic principles is that no form of life can continue to multiply indefinitely without eventually coming to terms with the limitations imposed by its environment. Ecology includes such studies as the differential incidence of mental disorder in various populations and the distribution of crime and delinquency within a specified geographical area. The ecologist (or *social*

psychiatrist) is particularly interested in why one person falls ill while his neighbor (or sibling, or parent, etc.) maintains good health. 'The responses to stress vary from case to case between the widest extremes. The reasons for the variation lie in *genetical and constitutional differences* between individuals as well as in *developmental and psychological ones*. Genetical data are among the few solid facts we have, and hypotheses about the role of social factors in mental disease which take account of them are bound to be more fruitful than those which ignore them.' (Mayer-Gross, W. *Clinical Psychiatry.* Williams and Wilkins, Baltimore, 1960)
Ecology is also known as *bionomics;* psychiatric ecology is often called *social psychiatry.* See *psychiatry, community; psychiatry, comparative.*

ecomania (ē-kō-mā'nē-à) *Obs.* Morbid attitude toward the members of one's family. It used to be considered somewhat in the nature of a nosologic entity, but today, it is generally regarded as only one component of a syndrome. Also *oik(i)omania.*

Economo's disease (Konstantin von Economo, Austrian neuropathologist, 1876-1931) Encephalitis lethargica.

economic, economy 'By an *economic* point of view Freud means one in which the attempt is made to ascertain the laws covering the production, distribution, and consumption of definite quantities of physical excitation or energy, according to the economic principle of the greatest advantage with the least effort.' (Jones, E. *Papers on Psycho-Analysis,* 4th ed., Wood, Baltimore, 1938)

ecophobia (ē-kō-fō'bē-à) See *oikophobia.*

écouteur (à-kōō-tēr') One who obtains inordinate gratification through listening to sexual accounts. See *voyeur.*

ecphoria (ek-fō'rē-à) It is maintained 'that everything that has been psychically experienced leaves behind a lasting trace, or *engram.*' Memory involves 'the recurrence of a function resembling a previous experience, like an idea of something perceived, or of a function almost like it, like the repetition of a practiced motion. We designate this as an *ecphoria* of the en-

grams.' (Bleuler, E. *Textbook of Psychiatry,* tr. by Brill, A.A., Macmillan, New York, 1930)

ecphorize (ek'fō-rīz) To revive memories or engrams.

ecphronia (ek-frō'nē-à) *Obs.* 'Mason Good made the order *Phrenetica,* in the class *Neurotica,* and subdivided it into *ecphronia* (mania and melancholia), *empathema* (ungovernable passion), *alusia* (illusion), *aphelxia* (reverie), *paroniria* (sleep disturbance), and *moria* (fatuity).' (Mann, E.C. *A Manual of Psychological Medicine and Allied Nervous Diseases,* Blakiston, Philadelphia, 1883, p. 44)

ecplexis (ek-plek'sis) *Obs.* Galen's term for stupor.

ecstasy Formerly, a clinical syndrome 'in which a person presents opposite phases of mental action, some faculties being exalted and others depressed, sensation and locomotion being suspended. It is so allied to catalepsy that the term "cataleptic ecstacy" is often employed'; it was also known as *ecstatic trance* (Tuke, D.H. *A Dictionary of Psychological Medicine,* vols. 1-2, Blakiston, Philadelphia, 1892) and *contemplatio.*
In present-day psychiatry, the term ecstasy is confined for the most part to trance-states in which religious ideation or similar ideas of dedication and complete surrender occupy almost the entire field of consciousness.

E.C.T. Abbreviation of *electric convulsion therapy.* See *therapy, electric convulsion.*

E.C.T., regressive See *therapy, regressive electro-shock.*

ectoderm (ek'tō-dērm) The first, or outer, germ layer which in the embryo's monodermic *blastula* (q.v.) stage consists of an epithelial layer of more or less columnar cells, or to the primary tissues which are subsequently derived from this layer and, thus, are characteristically distinguished from the organs and tissues developed from the other germ layers, the *entoderm* and the *mesoderm* (qq.v.).
The *ectoderm* is early differentiated

into a thickened axial *neural plate,* and thinner lateral portions. When the neural canal has become closed, the surface ectoderm forms a continuous layer which gives rise to the *epidermis;* while the entire nervous system originates in the thickened walls of the dorsally situated axial groove which is subsequently converted into a canal (see *cephalogenesis*).

In addition to the epidermis, with hair and nails, and all neurons and neuroglia of the nervous system, the ectodermal tissue derivatives include the epithelium of mouth, anus, nostrils, conjunctiva, and lacrimal glands; the lens of the eye and the epithelium of the membranous ear labyrinth; the epithelium lining the central canal of the spinal cord and the ventricles of the brain; certain ductless glands such as the pineal, the nervous portion of hypophysis, and the adrenal medulla.

ectomorphic (-mor'fĭk) In Sheldon's system of constitutional types this means characterized by a predominance of its third component (linearity), that is, the physical structures developed from the *ectodermal* layer of the embryo. Persons of this type are contrasted with the *endomorphic* and *mesomorphic* types and correspond roughly to Kretschmer's *asthenic* type.

ectopia pupillae (ek-tō'pē-à pū-pil'ē) Displacement of pupil.

ectype (ek'tīp) Outstanding or unusual type. Types of physical or mental constitution that vary considerably from the average are called ectypes. From the physical point of view two ectypes are recognized, first the megalosplanchnic (brevilineal, brachymorphic) and, second the microsplanchnic (longilineal, dolichomorphic). There are likewise two personality ectypes, the introverted and the extraverted.

eczema, nervous (ek'zē-mà) A mixed dermatological and psychiatric diagnostic term for a skin disorder in which psychogenic factors are paramount in the etiology, understanding, and treatment of the condition. This concept does not exclude organic, chemical, irritant, or contact factors in the etiology. It does, however, emphasize the interaction of the psychogenic or emotional factors with the chemical or organic. In DSM-II, coded 305.0.

edema, angioneurotic (e-dē'mà an-ji-ō-nū-rot'ĭk) Angioneurotic edema (Quincke disease) is a condition which is said to represent an allergic or anaphylactic reaction to infectious, toxic, or autotoxic processes, occurring frequently in neurotic subjects with a hereditary predisposition. The disease is characterized by circumscribed edematous swelling of the skin and subcutaneous tissue and, less frequently, of the mucous membranes. In DSM-II, coded 305.0.

Edinger-Westphal nucleus See *accommodation.*

edipism (ed'i-piz'm) (From Oedipus, King of Thebes, who beat out his own eyes.) *Rare.* Self-inflicted injury to the eyes.

EDR Electrodermal response. See *reflex, psychogalvanic.*

education, progressive A movement within the field of education, founded by John Dewey, which emphasizes the needs of the individual and the individual's capacity for self-expression and self-direction.

educational-socialization   model See *psychiatry, community.*

eduction Sullivan's term for central processes, i.e. whatever lies between receptor functions and effector functions.

EEG *Electroencephalogram* (q.v.).

effect, placebo See *placebo.*

effeminated man See *man, effeminated.*

efferent (ef'-er-ent) See *afferent; reflex.*

effort, sustained In occupational therapy, continued exertion or attempt on the part of a patient to apply himself to some activity or achievement.

effort syndrome A type of anxiety-neurosis or anxiety reaction, approximately equivalent to soldier's heart, neurocirculatory asthenia, etc.

egersis (ē-gē 'sis) Intense wakefulness.

egg *Ovum.* Those germ cells in the process of sexual reproduction which are produced by the female. An egg is passive and relatively large as compared with the very small and actively motile germ cells of the male.

The most important biological characteristic of eggs is the phenomenon known as *miosis (meiosis)* or *maturation*. In typical miosis such a cell experiences two successive divisions, during which the number of chromosomes is reduced to one-half. The finally resulting egg only has one chromosome from each chromosome pair.

Prior to the commencement of miosis, the female reproductive cells or *oögonia* multiply by repeated cell divisions of the ordinary duplicating type. After these cells cease to divide by ordinary division and become *primary oöcytes,* in which the pairing of the chromosomes takes place, they grow considerably in size.

The first miotic division produces two very unequal cells. Only the large daughter cell, or *secondary oöcyte,* is functional. The other cell, which is very small and is usually called the *polar body,* gradually disintegrates and disappears (see *miosis*).

The next division is again very unequal, the large cell being the *mature egg,* the small cell another, or the *second, polar body*. In most sexually reproducing animals a mature egg must be fertilized before it can develop into a new individual (see *fertilization*).

ego (ē'gō) In psychoanalytic psychology, the ego is that part of the psychic apparatus which is the mediator between the person and reality. Its prime function is the perception of reality and adaptation to it. The ego is the executive organ of the reality principle and is ruled by the secondary process. The various tasks of the ego include: perception, including self-perception and self-awareness; motor control (action); adaptation to reality; use of the reality principle and the mechanism of anxiety to ensure safety and self-preservation; replacement of the primary process of the id by the secondary process; memory; affects; thinking; and a general synthetic function manifested in assimilation of external and internal elements, in reconciling conflicting ideas, in uniting contrasts, and in activating mental creativity. Unlike the id, the ego has an organization (i.e. it is not chaotic), it can generate co-ordinated action, and it is ruled by the secondary rather than the primary process. Its functions develop gradually, dependent upon physical maturation (and particularly, the genetically determined growth of the central nervous system) and upon experiential factors.

Ego strength, essentially, is the degree to which the ego's functions are maintained, even in the face of wide variations in the supply of instinctual energy to the ego.

Beginning at birth, stimuli from the external world act upon the organism; over the ensuing months and years, with the accumulation of more and more experiences, certain mental events have a peculiar intimacy and a new psychic structure, the ego, is formed. The ego mediates between the person and reality; it is a clearing-house for stimuli from both the unconscious and from conscious reality. It develops on the basis of unsatisfied demands (thus, if there were always to be satisfaction, there would be no development of reality). Birth floods the infant with excitation, and this becomes the model for all later anxiety. But the infant is still in the primary undifferentiated phase of consciousness; he is ignorant of any sources of pleasure other than himself and there is, at this stage of objectivation, no differentiation of the mother, or other objects, from himself. The breast is thought of as a part of his own body, and his slightest gestures are followed by satisfaction of his instinctive nutritional needs. This gives rise to the autarchic fiction of false omnipotence, and this is the stage of primary narcissism. The infantile ego only unwillingly orients itself to objects, which at this stage are seen only as ego-substance which satisfies instinctual demands. Thus, there is only ego and non-ego. Soon, however, reality makes increasing demands. Perceptions and memory system are differentiated, and the ego defends itself against stimulation by shutting off the perceptive system, by mastery through 'fascination' (empathy), or by mastery through swallowing and introjection. The infant develops the attitude that objects exist only for the ego's satisfaction, and the purified pleasure ego perceives anything which is unpleasant as non-ego. The ego believes itself to be omnipotent, but this is disproved by experience and frustration. The ego then comes to believe that the parents are omnipotent and partakes of their omnipotence by introjection. This is the primary identification: the putting into the mouth results in perception, and the ego imitates what is perceived in order to master the object. The imitation of the external world by oral incorporation is the basis for that primitive mode of thinking called magic. Even though reality destroys the feeling of omnipotence, the longing for this primary narcissism remains — the narcissistic needs — and self-esteem is the awareness of how close the ego is to the original omnipotence. The desire to partake of the parental omnipotence, even though it arose originally from the basic desire for the satisfaction of hunger, soon becomes differentiated from the hunger itself, and the ego craves affection in a passive way (passive object love), being willing to renounce other satisfactions if rewards of affection are promised.

By substituting actions for mere discharge reactions, the ego achieves the stage of active mastery. This is achieved through the interposing of time, the development of a tension tolerance, and the development of judgment (the ability to anticipate the future in the imagination by testing reality). Primary anxiety is the passive experiencing of excitation which cannot be mastered but which must be endured; with judgment, the ego declares that a certain situation might give rise to this primary anxiety, and instead of the original panic itself being experienced, a moderated, tamed fear is experienced which is anxiety in anticipation of what might happen.

The first fear is of a recurrence of the primal anxiety, and from this develops the fear that the child's own instinctual demands, which gave rise to the overwhelming excitation beyond his capacity to master, are dangerous in themselves. This fear is complicated by animistic thinking (the belief that the external environment has the same instincts as the self), for if the desire to recapture the primary narcissism is to be achieved by eating the parents, the child feels that the deed will be undone by his being devoured himself (talion principle). This is how anxieties of physical destruction originate; the most important representative of this group is castration anxiety.

The development of speech initiates a further decisive step in the development of reality testing, for tying up words and ideas makes thinking proper possible. Thinking is an anticipatory acting out done with reduced energy. The faculty of speech changes archaic, prelogical think-

ing ('primary process') into logical and orderly ('secondary process') thinking. With the arrival of speech and logical thinking, a final differentiation of conscious and unconscious is made. Now prelogical thinking will be used as a substitute for logical thinking only when the latter cannot master unpleasant reality.

The maturing ego must not only postpone action, but on occasion it must inhibit action completely. Thus the ego develops reactions of defense against instinctual impulses and turns against its own instinctual demands (countercathexis). There are various reasons for the development of these defenses: (1) instinctual demands that cannot be satisfied become traumatic in themselves; (2) prohibitions from the outside world, through education, experience, etc.; (3) the danger is phantasied because of a projective misunderstanding of the world; (4) the ego becomes dependent upon the superego (which has meanwhile developed), and anxiety is transformed into guilt. See *stress, ego.*

The above paragraphs outline the gradual development of the ego as theorized by the psychoanalytic school of psychology. Others conceive of the ego in somewhat different ways.

Jung says that the ego 'consists of record-images from the sense functions that transmit stimuli both from within and from without, and, furthermore, of an immense accumulation of images of past processes.' The record-images are innumerable. 'Therefore, I speak not merely of the ego, but of an ego-complex, on the established presupposition that the ego, having a fluctuating composition, is changeable, and therefore cannot be just simply *the* ego.' (Jung, C.G. *Contributions to Analytical Psychology,* tr. by Baynes, H.G. and C.F., Kegan Paul, Trench, Trubner, London, 1928)

From the standpoint of analytical psychology (Jung) the ego is 'a complex of representations which constitutes the centrum of my field of consciousness and appears to possess a very high degree of continuity and identity.' The ego 'is not identical with the totality of my psyche, being merely a complex among other complexes. Hence, I discriminate between the ego and the Self, since the ego is only the subject of my consciousness, while the Self is the subject of my totality: hence it also includes the unconscious psyche. In this sense the Self would be an (ideal) factor which embraces and includes the ego. In unconscious phantasy the Self often appears as a super-ordinated or ideal personality. . . .' (Jung, C.G. *Psychological Types,* tr. by Baynes, H.G., Harcourt, Brace, New York & London, 1923)

'I take it, then, that "the censor" on the one hand, and "the Ego" (together with "the Ego-Ideal") on the other, are two alternative designations for that part of the developed personality which I have called the sentiment of self-regard.' (McDougall, W. *Outline of Abnormal Psychology,* Scribner, New York, 1926)

According to the formulations of Kempf the ego 'is constituted of the inherent segmental functions that have become *conditioned* to seek stimuli in a manner that not only obtains gratification but also wins social justification and esteem. Hence, this egoistic unity must keep the asocial segments under control.' In another section of his book Kempf says: 'This general, incessant, autonomic compensation becomes essentially integrated into a unity to prevent any division from jeopardizing the unity. *This unity, having the capacity of reacting so as to be conscious or aware of any segment's activities constitutes the ego, and learns to speak of itself, as "I," "me," "myself," "I am," "I wish," etc.'* (Kempf, E.J. *Psychopathology,* Mosby, St. Louis, 1921)

In Parsons' *social role theory,* the ego is the subject in any process of interaction. The object with whom the ego interacts is the *alter.*

ego-alien *Ego-dystonic* (q.v.).

ego-alteration, reactive A type of anticathexis—that is, expenditure of energy in maintaining the repression of libidinal or aggressive impulses—in which the ego is altered by a reaction-formation against the particular libidinal impulses. Freud gives the example of the compulsion-neurosis in which an exaggeration of the normal character traits of pity, conscientiousness, and cleanliness is found. These character traits are the antithesis of the anal-sadistic impulses repressed by the compulsion-neurosis. Thus the ego is altered through an exaggeration of the abovementioned character traits which are a reaction against the repressed impulses; that is, some of the energy spent

in repressing these anal impulses is spent in reactive ego-alteration.

Another type of reactive ego-alteration occurs in hysteria. Freud gives as an example the way in which 'the ambivalency conflict in hysteria is resolved: hate for a loved person is kept submerged by an excess of tenderness towards him and anxious concern about him.' Unlike the compulsion-neurosis in which the reaction-formation takes the guise of a character trait, the reaction-formation in hysteria is confined to a specific situation, as illustrated by the hysterical woman who treats with an excess of tenderness the children she really hates, but who is therefore more tender neither in general nor toward other children. Freud contrasts the two types of reactive ego-alteration as follows: 'the reaction-formation of hysteria adheres tenaciously to a specific object and is not elevated to the status of a general disposition of the ego. Of compulsion-neurosis it is precisely this universalization, the looseness of object relationships, the displaceability marking object choice, which are characteristic.' (Freud, S. *The Problem of Anxiety,* Norton, New York, 1936)

ego-analysis See *analysis, ego.*

ego, auxiliary 'The auxiliary ego is an individual who identifies himself consciously with all the subject's expressions and purposes as far as organic limitations permit, thus strengthening the ego of the subject. The auxiliary ego, acting in the subject's behalf, is a genuine prolongation or extension of the subject's ego.

'An auxiliary ego operating upon the instinctive level is a function known as an "alter-ego." Illustrations of an alter-ego are the mother to her child, the lover, or the friend. This function received a new distinction when it became a conscious tool in therapeutic situations. In the case of an interpersonal difficulty, the consulting psychiatrist becomes an auxiliary ego of two or more persons involved. His function is to accept uncritically the subjective attitude of the patients and to stimulate their subjectivity and thus become ready to act in their behalf.

'In the psychodrama the function of the auxiliary ego is to enact such roles which the patient may require for presenting his situation adequately. Such roles may be upon the private level or the auxiliary ego may have to assist in embodying concrete persons in the patient's milieu, such as a specific father, wife or child. Or, the role may be upon a symbolic level, such as God, Judge, or Satan. Finally, the auxiliary ego may embody delusionary roles or peculiar symbolic combinations characteristic for the patient's world.' (Moreno, J.L. *Sociometry, 1,* 17, 1937)

ego, body That part of the perceiving portion of the ego around which all concepts of one's own ego are grouped. The body ego consists of the psychic representations of one's body and self—the memories and ideas connected with the body along with their cathexes. At first the various parts of the body, and eventually the body as a whole, occupy a particularly important place in the psyche throughout life.

The ego perceives not only external stimuli '. . . but also inner, mental processes (ideas, wishes, thoughts, strivings, sensations, and fantasies). External stimuli are intercepted by the sense organs and led to the central nervous system. Here they leave traces in the form of memories and ideas whose nature depends upon the particular sense organ which has received the stimulus (sight, hearing, touch). These precipitates in the psyche of external experiences, together with the internal processes, such as thinking, imagination, feelings, emotions, and visceral sensations, form what we call the psychic body scheme or image. The nucleus around which all concepts of one's own ego are grouped is the *body ego,* whose main function is perception.' (Nunberg, H. *Principles of Psychoanalysis,* International Universities Press, New York, 1955)

Federn used the term 'bodily ego-feeling' to refer to the body ego.

ego boundary See *boundary, ego.*

ego-cathexis (-kà-thek′sis) See *cathexis.*

ego-center Schilder's term for the nucleus, or inner part of the ego, surrounded by a peripheral part of the ego in the same manner that the nucleus of a cell is enclosed by the protoplasm.

The word 'ego' is used here not in the psychoanalytical sense but rather as a general psychological concept. According to Schilder, the various experiences of our life are at different distances from the center of the ego, some being closer than others. 'Our problems, emotions, feelings

and attitudes, in this respect, belong closer to the nucleus of the ego than experiences relating to the outward world, and to our body.' Some sensations are particularly close to this hypothetical nucleus of the ego, and specifically pain, sexual excitement, and anxiety seem to be in the very center of the personality. The fact that certain parts of the body are nearer than others to this center should be kept in mind during the study of post-operative neurosis and psychosis. It is worth while to point out that the importance of surgical operations varies in accordance with the part of the body operated upon: operations on genitals, breasts, or eye threaten the body parts that are nearer than others to the center of the ego. In schizophrenia and neurosis, the complexes are in the center of the personality, yet the experiences of organic brain lesions concern material which is rather impersonal. Those with organic diseases are generally much more objective toward their infirmity than are psychogenic cases. (Schilder, P. *Psychotherapy,* Norton, New York, 1938)

ego, collective The ego is 'not only a product of the individual but, at the same time in the measure that it reflects the group and its concepts and expresses its mentality, it is also the product of the group. Thus, as a whole, it is a composite of a collective ego and an individual ego.' (Laforgue, R. *The Relativity of Reality,* Nervous and Mental Disease Monographs, No. 66, New York, 1940)

ego, decomposition of The ego appears in the dream split up in its various tendencies, and represented by different persons, actions, things, or localities.

ego deviation See *children, ego deviant.*

ego distortion See *distortion, ego.*

ego, dream With this expression Jung (analytical psychology) designates 'a mere fragment of the conscious ego' that is active during the dream stage. 'In a dream, consciousness is neither fully awake nor fully extinguished; there is still a small remnant of consciousness. There is, for instance, nearly always some consciousness of the ego, but rarely of the ego as it appears to the consciousness of waking life. It is rather a limited ego, sometimes peculiarly transformed or distorted. . . . The psychic contents of the dream appear to the ego very like those external phenomena which appear to it in the waking state. Hence it happens that we find ourselves in situations like those in real life, but rarely exercise thought or reason about them.' (Jung, C.G. *Contributions to Analytical Psychology,* tr. by Baynes, H.G. and C.F., Kegan Paul, Trench, Trubner, London, 1928)

ego-drive Impulse toward self-preservation, ego-maximation, and group conformance, the development of which is deeply rooted in biological constitution and markedly influenced by the social nature of man's existence. Also called *ego-instinct* (q.v.).

ego, duplication of See *personality, multiplication of.*

ego-dystonic (-dis-ton'ik) Anything that is unacceptable to the ego. If an instinctual urge finds the ego unprepared to receive it, the impulse is said to be ego-dystonic. Stimuli from any source that are rejected by the ego or that are prevented from reaching the ego for its consideration are called ego-dystonic. Its opposite is *ego-syntonic* (q.v.).

ego, effective In his theory of traumatic neurosis, Kardiner introduced this term to denote the ego that has learned how to adapt itself to the environment and deal with it *effectively,* as differentiated from the infantile ego—helpless at birth and, therefore, *ineffective* in this respect. This learning process consists in the acquisition of adaptive techniques and manipulations and the integration of them into effective tools. To Kardiner, adaptation is 'a series of maneuvers in response to changes in the external environment, or to changes within the organism, which compel some activity in the outer world in order to continue existence, to remain intact or free from harm, and to maintain controlled contact with it. At birth only the automatic functions—anabolic and catabolic—are effective, with the aid of a few reflexes, the chief of which is sucking. The infant's adaptation is passive as far as the outer world is concerned; it has no controlled contact with the outer world except insofar as this is mediated through the mother. It cannot choose, avoid, or

seek out objects in the outer world necessary for its survival.' (Kardiner, A., and Spiegel, H. *War Stress and Neurotic Illness,* Hoeber, New York, 1947)

ego-erotism (-e'rō-tiz'm) Narcissism. See *ego-libido.*

ego, escape from the A phenomenon of psychic displacement by which the compulsive-neurotic shifts the goals of his own ego to another person by way of identification or differentiation. This is, for instance, the case of the rich man, suffering from a compulsion, who 'identifies himself with the man who sweeps the streets every day. The patient shares his life with the street-cleaner, he experiences his feelings, he participates in his humiliations, his deprivations, his small pleasures. This may go so far that the compulsive does not permit himself to enjoy a good meal at a restaurant, because the street-cleaner can afford only a modest one. On the other hand, the street-cleaner is under no obligation to maintain a high cultural standard. For this identification, the compulsive is rewarded with the pleasure that he does not have to restrain himself in certain other aspects: he may swear, curse, or tell vulgar stories in public, since it is the street-cleaner talking, not he, the man of his social position. In this way he can escape the culture-ego, even if he does so by denying himself luxury and many conveniences. However, he enjoys making these sacrifices, although he claims that he is troubled by this annoying compulsion, and threatens suicide, as all these patients do.' For another, and far more prevalent, mechanism of escape from the ego, see *ego, negation of the.* (Stekel, W. *Compulsion and Doubt,* Liveright, New York, 1949)

ego, extinction of A psychoanalytic term referring to the relationship between a punitive superego and a guilt-ridden ego. The guilt of the ego stems from the strength of denied and repressed unconscious hostility (or sexuality) of an infantile and primitive nature. The obsessional neurotic, for example, must constantly neutralize his infantile omnipotent destructive powers through equally omnipotent magical means, so that he can protect his loved objects from his repressed hostility. In this way he attains the right, or justification, for his own ego to continue to exist. When these ritualistic and magical processes fail, extreme guilt with deep inhibition, feelings of painful dejection, apathy, and nihilistic unworthiness overwhelm the ego (individual). It is this state that is tantamount to extinction of the ego through the wrath of the super-ego. E.F. Sharpe (*Collected Papers on Psycho-analysis*, Hogarth Press, and The Institute of Psychoanalysis, London, 1950) states: 'The ritual [of the obsessional neurotic] must never cease, or his unconscious destructive power will bring about the extinction of his ego . . .'

ego, fragmentation of See *dedifferentiation.*

ego-function See *ego.*

ego, ideal The ideal ego is the ego which feels as one with the id, as is the case with the unorganized ego of the child. This ideal condition begins to disappear with the first opposition to the gratification of his needs, and while all people presumably strive to recapture this state it is for the most part only in certain psychoses (e.g. manic and catatonic episodes) that the patient grants himself everything pleasurable and rejects everything unpleasurable. The phantasy of a return to the womb is an expression of the desire to return to the state of the ideal ego.

ego-ideal In psychoanalysis the term ego refers to a psychic structure that undergoes gradual evolution from the time that it makes its embryonic appearance as a modification of a part of the id until it acquires more or less final form late in life. As the ego expands, as it develops new structures and functions, its limits extend from the id to reality. The person is constantly identifying himself with others. The first important identifications are connected with the parents; hence, a part of the developing ego is set aside, so to speak, to contain the mental images of the parents. Later the composite image, constituting the superego, occupies a position in the unconscious, where it continues to act as the 'inner conscience' and controlling agency of the id. 'During the course of its growth, the super-ego also takes over the influence of those persons who have taken the place of the parents, that is to say of persons who have been concerned in the child's upbringing and whom it has regarded as ideal models.

Normally the super-ego is constantly becoming more and more remote from the original parents, becoming as it were more impersonal.' (Freud, S. *New Introductory Lectures on Psycho-Analysis,* tr. by Sprott, W.J.H., Norton, New York, 1933) That part of the ego devoted to the development of parental substitutes (parental imagos) and in which the parental imagos are laid down is called the ego-ideal. 'Identifications take place with these later editions of the parents as well, and regularly provide important contributions to the formation of character; but these only affect the ego, they have no influence on the super-ego, which has been determined by the earliest parental imagos.' (ibid.) The ego-ideal is a precipitation of the superego.

The ego-ideal may change from time to time as newer identifications are made. When the person's own narcissism is threatened, it is usually withdrawn from the ego-ideal of later development and regresses to what is called the narcissistic ego-ideal, namely, the mental image of perfection that the child constructs of himself.

See *ego; superego.*

ego-ideal, narcissistic See *ego-ideal.*

ego-instinct Jones defines the ego-instincts as 'all the non-sexual instincts.'

Freud states: 'The hypothesis of separate ego instincts and sexual instincts rests scarcely at all upon a psychological basis, but is essentially supported upon the facts of biology.' (Freud, S. *Collected Papers,* vol. 2, tr. by Riviere, J., Leonard and Virginia Woolf and The Institute of Psychoanalysis, London, 1924-25) For Freud's latest revision of the dual-instinct theory, see *instinct, death.*

ego-libido (-li-bēd′ō) When libido is attached to the ego it is called ego-libido. It is generally used in contradistinction to the expression *object-libido*. It is synonymous with ego-cathexis, when the latter refers to libidinal qualities. The ego may be cathected with libido (constructive instinctual quality) or with destrudo (destructive instinctual quality). The latter term (destrudo) has not found favor in psychoanalysis, though its meaning (sado-masochism) is extensively described.

Ego-libido and narcissism refer to the same conditions, namely, in the words of Karl Abraham, 'that stage in the development of the libido in which the child is himself the center of his own narrow world and in which he receives proofs of love from other persons without himself giving any return.' (Abraham, K. *Selected Papers,* tr. by Bryan, D. and Strachey, A., Leonard and Virginia Woolf and The Institute of Psychoanalysis, London, 1927)

ego, loss of boundaries of Often, as in schizophrenia, the usual sharp delineation of the ego is lost, the patient's ego merging with that of another or with the entire world (cosmic identity). A patient, quoted by Storch, said: 'Sometimes I cannot tell myself from other people. I just cannot understand it—sometimes she was my sister and sometimes I was the doctor.' 'We often found ourselves confronted by experiences in which the discrimination between the consciousness of self and the consciousness of the object were entirely suspended, the ego being no longer separated from the nonego; the subject no longer distinct from the object; the self and the world were fused in an inseparable total complex.' This is a common phenomenon in schizophrenia and in primitive mentality. (Storch, A. *The Primitive Archaic Forms in Schizophrenia,* tr. by Willard, C., Nervous and Mental Disease Publishing Company, New York and Washington, 1924)

ego-maximation Ego drives to maintain feelings of personal adequacy in competitive situations. See *self-maximation.*

ego, mental *See ego, body.*

ego, motor control of the The control exerted by the ego over one's motor activities. The mastery of the motor apparatus is a task gradually learned by the human infant. It learns to substitute 'actions for mere discharge reactions,' by acquiring a tolerance for the tension which arises from stimuli and which results in immediate reaction impulses. In addition, the infant must develop the function of judgment as a 'prerequisite for an action . . . This means the ability to anticipate the future in the imagination.' According to Fenichel, learning to walk, to control the sphincter, and to speak 'are the main steps in the development of the mastery of physical motor functions.' See *ego.* Disturbances in the ego's motor control can be seen in certain types of symp-

toms. One example of this type of symptom is 'psychogenic dystonia.' The patient suffers from either localized or general muscular spasms or hypotonic muscular attitudes. In some cases hypertonic and hypotonic states alternate. Whichever is the case, there is 'a partial weakening of the voluntary mastery of motility.' (These symptoms are a defense aimed at 'barring warded-off impulses from motility.')

Another example is the tic. Here, 'instead of acting as a means for voluntary and directed action, the musculature has become again . . . an instrument for immediate discharge.' This is another instance in which 'the ability for ego control of motor disturbances seems lacking or insufficient.' (Fenichel. O. *The Psychoanalytic Theory of Neurosis,* Norton, New York, 1945)

ego-narcissism *Narcissism* (q.v.).

ego, negation of the A mental mechanism through which the compulsive-neurotic avoids the responsibilities of his own ego by putting himself in the place of another person (identification) and then trying with all his might to differentiate himself from the chosen person (differentiation). The object in this case may be called a 'negative ruler of the soul.' The patient achieves the negation of his own ego through a negative and antagonistic attitude toward the person chosen as object. He will tell himself: 'I have no free will. I must do the opposite of what my object does. My actions are determined by his, but in such a manner that I become his opposite.'

This may be illustrated by the following example given by Stekel: 'A compulsive girl utilizes her neighbor for differentiation. This neighbor goes to her office at eight o'clock every morning. The patient anxiously watches for her behind the curtain. What kind of dress will the neighbor wear? What mood will she be in? Has she taken an umbrella along? The object appears, the patient inspects her closely—thus, the order of the day is given. The neighbor wore a dark dress. The patient will wear a light one. It is raining. The object carries an umbrella. The mechanism of the negation of the ego constitutes a type of flight from the ego. See *ego, escape from the.* (Stekel, W. *Compulsion and Doubt.* Liveright, New York, 1949)

ego-neurosis See *neurosis, ego.*

ego-nuclei (-nū′klē-ī) The smaller component elements of the ego. 'According to Edward Glover, the ego, at first but loosely organized, consists of a considerable number of ego-nuclei. In his view, in the first place an oral ego-nucleus and later an anal ego-nucleus predominates over the others.' (Klein, M *Contributions to Psycho-analysis* 1921-1945, Hogarth Press, London, 1948)

ego, perception Schilder's term for the censoring forces emanating from the ego and preventing certain psychic material from becoming conscious: 'the repressive forces originating from the ego are the representatives of the social functions of perception, action, and reality testing.' (Schilder, P. *Psychotherapy*, Norton, New York, 1938)

ego, pleasure The part of the ego made up of components agreeable with instinctual impulses. See *ego, reality.*

ego, preschizophrenic This term denotes the prepsychotic personality of the schizophrenic. The personality is characterized by impairment of ego synthesis; that is, the patient does not give the impression of a personal oneness which the normal person gives. The preschizophrenic child daydreams excessively, and the phantasies here have the aim of withdrawal from reality; in the normal child, phantasies have the goal of experimentation and preparation for mastery of reality. Often, during sleep, the preschizophrenic child has dreams of its own death; there is a predominance of regressive (even prenatal) phantasies; exaggerated conscience, bizarre somatic sensations, frequent severe temper tantrums, and a pervasive aggressiveness are typical. The boundaries of the prepsychotic ego are progressively constricted by aimless aggressiveness, whatever may be the serious obstacles preventing the healthy transformation of primitive aggresive drives into activity suitable for mastering reality, and adapting the "normal" individual to social existence. The inability adequately to test reality is closely connected with the limitation of the boundaries of the ego, a basic disturbance in schizophrenia . . . Thus, intrapsychic object representations and instinctual derivatives are detached from the ego, and come to be regarded as "real," as belonging to the outside world.' (Bychowski, G. 'The Preschizophrenic Ego,' *Psychoanalytic Quarterly 16*, 225, 1947)

ego, purified pleasure That stage in the development of the ego in which anything unpleasant is considered non-ego, anything pleasant is considered·ego. The purified pleasure ego strives to reverse the separation of ego from non-ego, thus expressing a longing for the original objectless state of affairs. By swallowing anything pleasant, the infant adjoins pleasurable stimuli to the ego and attempts to make parts of the external world flow into the ego. By 'spitting out' anything painful, the infant adjoins unpleasant stimuli to the non-ego and puts unpleasant sensations into the external world. See *ego.*

These mechanisms of the state of the purified pleasure ego may be used by the ego for defensive purposes. For example, projection is a derivative of the first negation of unpleasurable stimuli described above. Psychotics show the use of this mechanism most clearly, for, by narcissistic regression, the reality testing of their egos has been severely damaged. The boundaries between ego and non-ego are no longer clear. The psychotic perceives emotions or excitements which are unpleasant to him as being outside the ego. The offensive impulse is perceived in another person instead of in one's own ego.

ego, reality That part of the ego formed by the introjection of external objects. When the objects of reality are pleasurable they are absorbed by (introjected into) the ego. Hence, an object of reality, incorporated into the ego, helps to constitute that part of the ego known as reality-ego.

The ego absorbs both painful and pleasurable objects, but it separates them, retaining the pleasurable to form the *pleasure-ego* and projecting the painful back into the outer world as a hostile object. 'Thus the original *reality-ego*, which distinguished outer and inner by means of a sound objective criterion, changes into a purified *pleasure-ego*, which prizes above all else the quality of pleasure.' (Freud, S. *Collected Papers*, vol. 4, tr. by Riviere, J., Leonard and Virginia Woolf and The Institute of Psychoanalysis, London, 1924-25)

ego, reality life of A psychoanalytic concept referring to the practical everyday life of the patient with all its reality problems, in contrast to the goals and aims of the psychoanalytic procedure, as confined to the analyst's office. In the analyst's office, the patient's relationship to the analyst per se (i.e. the transference situation) is of paramount concern. The main task of the analyst is directed not at helping the patient with his reality problems but at assisting the patient in acquiring the courage to face the truth about himself. This is achieved mainly through the analysis of what are called defensive resistances. In this way, insuperable conflicts between powerful and primitive instinctive forces on the one hand, and horror-filled guilt-feelings on the other, stemming from childhood conscience pressures, can eventually be resolved. When this resolution has been brought about, symptomatic improvement in the reality life of the ego will usually ensue. (Sharpe, E.F. *Collected Papers on Psycho-analysis*, Hogarth Press and The Institute of Psychoanalysis, London, 1950)

ego, reasonable 'Lack of a reasonable ego' is discussed by Fenichel as a major factor to be considered in deciding whether or not psychoanalysis should be tried with a given patient. 'The method of psychoanalysis is based on the cooperation of a reasonable ego.' A part of the ego must be split off into a reasonable, judging portion. And 'this cleavage is accomplished by utilizing positive transference and transitory identifications with the analyst.'

In certain cases it may be difficult or even impossible to establish this co-operative reasonable ego. Some patients actually refuse to co-operate. In these cases the analyst must try to convince the patient that it is not that he simply does not wish to co-operate but that he is incapable of doing it. An interest in this inability to co-operate then becomes the patient's first motive for co-operation and other motives may follow. An extreme example of this type of patient is the generally frigid character who avoids emotions altogether. He does not understand the psychology of emotions and emotional connections and accepts only logical connections. Another example of this sort of

patient is the pseudo-emotional type of character whose intense and uncontrollable emotions have flooded everything. Such patients find 'reality full of representatives of the feared instincts' and 'lack the necessary detachment to form judgements' about their own emotions. Other patients in whom a reasonable ego may also be lacking are the schizophrenics. In these cases the problem is to establish a transference. A pre-analytic procedure may accomplish this and the transference thus formed will then be the basis of a later analysis. (Fenichel, O. *The Psychoanalytic Theory of Neurosis*, Norton, New York, 1945)

ego-resistance See *resistance, ego.*

ego-retrenchment The act of diminishing or removing the need for a given function of the ego is called ego-retrenchment. Thus inhibitions may make it unnecessary for the ego to form symptoms in order to appease an unconscious impulse.

ego, safety of A psychoanalytic term that refers to the function of conscious and unconscious ego defense-mechanisms in allaying or fending off anxiety. The ego is more or less constantly threatened from three different directions: (1) the objective reality of the outer world; (2) the severity of archaic and infantile conscience (superego); and (3) the urgent impulsive and compulsive power of instinctual drives.

ego, split in the By this term Freud designates the phenomenon in which the ego may develop several divergent yet co-existing attitudes toward the same thing. This situation exists (1) in the normal personality; (2) in neuroses, and (3) in psychoses.

(1) In the normal person 'The ego can take itself as object, it can treat itself like any other object, observe itself, criticize itself, and do Heavens know what besides with itself. In such a case one part of the ego stands over against the other. The ego can, then, be split; it splits when it performs many of its functions, at least for the time being. The parts can afterwards join up again' In particular, Freud describes that faculty of the ego which observes and criticizes the ego and he names it 'super-ego.' This is one example of a split in the ego, and the self-observation

and self-criticism demonstrate the existence of two attitudes toward whatever is being done by the person at the time.

(2) In neuroses, two contrary and independent attitudes are always present as regards some particular behavior, for the ego's defensive efforts to ward off danger are never completely successful and the weaker attitude which is repressed nevertheless leads to 'psychological complications,' such as the neurotic symptoms. This split in the ego is most vividly demonstrated when an effort is made to deny certain perceptions of the external world which represent painful demands of the external world on the person. The detachment from reality is always incomplete and the rejection is coupled with an acceptance. For example, the fetishist is trying to reject his perception of the fact that women have no penis, because then he must admit the fact that he, too, could be castrated. The fetish, a symbolic penis, is usually something that was seen at the same moment the women's genitals were seen or it is something suitable as a symbol for a penis. But many fetishists have a dread of castration. Thus these patients must also recognize the fact that women have no penis. The co-existence of fetishism and a dread of castration may be classified as a split in the ego.

(3) In psychotic episodes, the patients frequently verbalize the fact of a split in the ego when they relate that even during acute hallucinatory and delusional states one part of their mind was watching in an objective way the remainder of the patient and his feelings, behavior, and thoughts. This is particularly clear in those catatonic patients who, after the attack has ended, can report coherently on all their behavior and upon all that was going on about them during a catatonic episode in which they appeared to be completely out of contact. Here one attitude, the stronger one, arising from instincts, has detached the patient from reality, represented by a now weaker attitude. When the psychosis has been cured, the normal attitude which takes account of reality has become stronger and the attitude represented by the psychosis has become weaker and is now unconscious. (Freud, S. (1) *An Outline of Psychoanalysis,* Norton, New York, 1949; (2) *New Introductory Lectures on Psychoanalysis,* Norton, New York, 1933)

ego, stability of Health, strength, maturity, or normality of the ego. The usual differentiating criteria of the more normal ego, in contrast to the neurotic one, are the following: (1) less severe primitive or infantile hostility (id); (2) less severe self-punitive archaic conscience drive (superego); (3) fewer magical defensive systems; (4) less infantile omnipotent (wishful) thinking; (5) enhanced object reality functioning. In addition (6), E.F. Sharpe *(Collected Papers on Psycho-analysis,* Hogarth Press and The Institute of Psychoanalysis, London, 1950) states: 'The one essential difference I find between neurotic and normal . . . is a *reality system* of some kind in which the conflict is played out, or annulled, in connection with *real* people and *real* things.'

ego-strength The effectiveness with which the ego discharges its various functions. A strong ego will not only mediate between id, superego, and reality and integrate these various functions, but further it will do so with enough flexibility so that energy will remain for creativity and other needs. This is in contrast to the rigid personality in which ego functions are maintained, but only at the cost of impoverishment of the personality.

ego-subject When the ego is the object of its own instincts (ego-instincts), the ego is called the ego-subject. 'Originally, at the very beginning of mental life, the ego's instincts are directed to itself and it is to some extent capable of deriving satisfaction from them on itself. This condition is known as narcissism and this potentiality for satisfaction is termed autoerotic. The outside world is at this time, generally speaking, not cathected with any interest and is indifferent for purposes of satisfaction. At this period, therefore, the ego-subject coincides with what is pleasureable and the outside world with what is indifferent (or even painful as being a source of stimulation).' (Freud, S. *Collected Papers,* vol. 4, tr. by Riviere, J., Leonard and Virginia Woolf and The Institute of Psychoanalysis, London, 1924-25)

ego-suffering Guilt feelings and/or any of their substitute expressions such as attempts at atonement, punishment, or remorse. See *guilt.* While present in many psychiatric syndromes, including the character disorders, ego-suffering is most clearly evident in depressive states.

ego, supportive This term was first introduced by S.R. Slavson to denote one who is dynamic in activity group psychotherapy. In therapy groups it refers to the relation in which one member—because of his greater strength or maturity—helps a fellow-member to gain status in a group or to work out his intrapsychic problems. It has been observed that supportive-ego relations are temporary and progressive in nature. A weak child may attach himself to another weak child in order to forward his own adaptation to a group, but, growing stronger and less fearful, he makes friends with the stronger members of the group. Finally, the child functions on his own, without support from any one of his fellow-members.

ego-syntonic (-sin-ton′ik) Referring to the acceptability of ideas or impulses to the ego, which receives the impulses as consonant and compatible with its principles. Its opposite is *ego-dystonic* (q.v.).

egocentrism Healy, Bronner, and Bowers ask whether the term *egocentrism* might not be clearer and less confusing than *egoism*. The latter means self-centeredness, yet it is often used synonymously with narcissism. Freud makes a distinction when he says: 'I believe narcism is the libidinous complement of Egoism.' He states that one may be egoistic and still retain strong interest in libido-objects or 'one can be egoistic and at the same time preponderantly narcistic, that is, have a very slight need for an object.' (Freud, S. *Collected Papers*, vol. 4, tr. by Riviere, J., Leonard and Virginia Woolf and The Institute of Psychoanalysis, London, 1924-25) See *egoism*.

egoism Selfishness. *Egoism* refers to the condition of evaluating things in terms of oneself and of one's personal interests. 'Egoism is the feeling that demands for self an increase of enjoyment and a diminution of discomfort. Altruism is that which demands these results for others.' (Ward, L.F.) When the self-centeredness is heavily intermixed with the sense of self-importance, it is called *egotism*.

egoity (ē-gō′i-tē) Egohood; personality; individuality.

egoize (ē′gō-īz) To give excessive consideration to one's self.

egohood Personality; individuality.

egology (ē-gol′ō-jē) A term devised by S. Rado to mean study of the ego, the 'I'.

egomania (ē-gō-mā′nē-à) Exaggerated self-centeredness.

egomorphism (ē-gō-mor′fiz′m) The attributing of one's own needs, desires, motives, etc., to someone else; the tendency to build a system of thought and interpret the reactions of others in terms of one's own ego needs—*projection* (q.v.). It has been suggested that the interpretations a psychiatrist makes to his patient are based on the ego-morphism of the physician. This is one factor which has led psychoanalytic training institutes to require their students to undergo psychoanalysis.

egopathy (ē-gop′à-thē) Hostile behavior due to a psychopathically exaggerated sense of self-importance. Egopathic patients are characterized by a strong egocentric trend which compels them to deprecate others in their constant aggressive and unconceding attitude. The egopathic reaction, in a way, 'is not only characteristic of the psychopathic criminal, but also of the normal one.' Egopathic reactions are of different types and differ in their clinical significance. As an example of one of the types of egopathic reaction, Ralph Brancale gives 'the gunman who, with his compelling need to assert himself at the expense of others and to reassure himself of his strength and masculinity, works off his problems through aggression. He presents a different type of egocentricity than that of the relatively unaggressive, narcissistic swindler who tries to enact his vainglorious role through verbalism and deception.' (Seliger, R.V., *et al. Contemporary Criminal Hygiene*, Oakridge Press, Baltimore, 1946)

egotheism (ē′gō-thē-iz′m) Self-deification.

egotism See *egoism*.

egotropy (ē-got′rō-pē) Adolf Meyer's term for egocentricity or narcissism.

egregorsis (ē-grē-gor′sis) Egersis; intense wakefulness.

egrimony (eg′ri-mō-nē) *Obs.* Sadness, sorrow.

egritude (ē′gri-, eg′ri-tūd) *Obs.* Mental sickness.

eidetic (ī-det′ik) Pertaining to or characterized by clear visualization (even by a voluntary act) of objects previously seen. Eidetic images (also known as primary memory images) are clearer and richer in detail than the usual memory images and are also more intense and of better quality. Except that the subject recognizes the eidetic image as a memory experience, the phenomenon is analogous to a hallucination. Visual eidetic imagery is more common than auditory. Such imagery is rare in adults. See *imagery, eidetic.*

eidetic personification In Sullivan's terminology, any hold-over or representation of previous experiences that influences current behavior.

eisoptrophobia (ī-sop-trō-fō′bē-à) Fear of mirrors.

ejaculatio deficiens (ā-yà-koo-lä′tē-ō dā-fē′kē-ens) Absence of ejaculation.

ejaculatio praecox (ā-yà-koo-lä′tē-ō prī-kōks) The ejaculation of semen and seminal fluid during the act of preparation for sexual intercourse, i.e. before there is penetration; in DSM-II, coded 305.6.

Ejaculatio praecox (premature ejaculation) is usually based on a feminine orientation and/or a sadistic desire to soil the woman and/or intense urethral eroticism. Typically, such patients have marked masturbatory guilt. The sexual partner is identified with the mother, and the patient aims to have his genitals touched by the woman and then to ejaculate as though he were passing urine. This is in part determined by infantile narcissism, in that the penis and urinary activities are thought to exercise an irresistible charm over the woman. The praecox patient can only receive love, and his exhibitionism is a hostile attitude of contempt

for the woman. In ejaculatio praecox there is a defiant relapse into the infantile uncontrolled emptying of the bladder; in this way, the person takes revenge on every woman for the disappointments in love he suffered as a child at the hands of his mother.

ejaculatio retardata (rā-tár-dä′tà) When ejaculation during sexual intercourse is unduly delayed, the condition is known as *ejaculatio retardata.* It is often a manifestation of narcissistic and sado-masochistic object relations.

ejaculation (ē-jak-ū-lā′shun) From the sexual point of view ejaculation is the expulsion of semen and seminal fluid from the urethra; to be differentiated from *orgasm* (q.v.).

Ekbom's syndrome Restless legs syndrome, consisting of irregular, intermittent paresthesiae of the legs and a need to move the legs for relief. Etiology is unknown.

elaboration, secondary One of the four mechanisms of dream-making. These are: (1) condensation, (2) displacement, (3) dramatization, (4) secondary elaboration. The psychic material from which the dream is derived is transformed by these four mechanisms into the picture of the dream as it appears to the dreamer. In the process of transformation the psychic material undergoes great distortion. Jones writes: 'This [secondary elaboration] is the product of consciousness, and is brought about by the alteration undergone by the dream processes during their apprehension in consciousness. To it is due whatever degree of order and consistency there may be found in a dream. It particularly affects those parts of the dream that have been insufficiently distorted during the dream-making; its action continues after waking, so that a memory of a dream becomes more altered the greater is the period that has elapsed since it was experienced.' (Jones, E.J. *Papers on Psycho-Analysis,* Williams and Wilkins, Baltimore, 1949)

elan vital (à-laN′ vē-tàl′) Bergson's term for the creative life-force or life-impulse, the basis of evolutionary progress.

elation An affect consisting of feelings of

euphoria, triumph, intense self-satisfaction, optimism, etc.; an elated, though unstable, mood is characteristic of *mania* (q.v.).

electric convulsion therapy See *therapy, electric convulsion.*

electrodermal response See *reflex, psychogalvanic.*

electroencephalogram (ē-lek-trō-en-sef′ȧ-lō-gram) The graphic record of the electrical activity of the brain, usually obtained by means of electrodes attached to the scalp. The regular, spontaneous oscillations of the electrical potential of the brain are amplified and recorded on an oscillograph. Characteristic changes in type, frequency, and potential of the brain waves occur in various intracranial lesions.

The alpha wave or rhythm (also known as the Berger wave) is the most common wave form of the adult cortex. It is found mainly in the parieto-occipital area when the subject is at rest and consists of smooth, regular oscillations at a frequency of 8 to 12 per second. It is usually diminished ('blocked') by sensory stimulation and mental activity.

The beta rhythm has a frequency of 18 to 30 c./s. and is associated with alertness. The delta rhythm is an abnormal rhythm with a frequency slower than 4 c./s.; it is often found when the subject is in light sleep. The theta rhythm is a 4 to 7 c./s. rhythm, seen not uncommonly in the temporal region.

Various techniques are used to accentuate abnormal waves or to bring out latent abnormalities, among them overventilation, natural or drug-induced sleep, photic driving (rhythmic optic stimulation with a stroboscope), chemical stimulation (especially with metrazol, and often combined with photic driving) and hydration induced by pitressin, alcohol, hypoglycemia, or oxygen lack. Such activated EEGs, however, often give false positives and are, therefore, even more difficult to interpret than the standard record.

electroencephalograph The apparatus used in making a graphic record of the electrical activity of the brain.

electroencephalography (-en-sef-ȧ-log′rȧ-fē) The process or method of making (by a special electrical apparatus) a graphic record of the electrical activity of the brain (encephalon); a specific technique of investigation, neurophysiological in the main, consisting basically of the elaboration, recording, observation, and interpretation of the minute electrical action currents of the functioning cerebrum, or brain. These action currents, the result or concomitant of cerebral neurophysiological activity, are tapped off from the underlying brain tissue through fine electrodes inserted into the scalp, thus obviating the necessity of trephining or opening the skull.

Through an elaborate system of electrical amplification, the low-voltage electrical impulses are made discernible and readable through transformation into kymographic drum recordings. These kymographic drum records make visible the transformation of electrical impulses into the movements of a light-weight stylus over a revolving drum, covered with smoke soot, and are called electroencephalograms. Organic pathological and pathophysiological variations of the action currents of the brain have been standardized and can be compared with the standardized norms of the 'average,' the 'healthy,' or the 'normal.' The electroencephalogram (abbreviated *EEG*) is now an accepted and integral tool in the organic and physiological examination of the central nervous system, especially the brain. (Harms, E. *Handbook of Child Guidance,* Child Care Publications, New York, 1947)

electronarcosis (-när-kō′sis) A form of shock therapy requiring an electrical machine with electrodes which are applied to the patient's temples. 'Once the switch is thrown, the patient becomes unconscious immediately and tightens up (without breathing) for half a minute. The current is then turned off; the patient immediately relaxes, moves, and begins breathing. Then the current is carefully regulated to increase gradually till the patient reacts by sleeping, generally quiet and breathing easily. This procedure continues for five to seven minutes, after which the current is cut off and treatment is terminated.' (Polatin, P., and Philtine, E. *How Psychiatry Helps,* Harper, New York, 1949.) This treatment is used mainly in schizophrenia, but its effect is inferior to the effects of insulin in such diseases.

The electrical machine used for electronarcosis is more complicated technically than the electronconvulsive apparatus, but it has similar electrodes to apply the current.

electrophobia (ē-lek-trō-fō'bē-à) Fear of electricity.

electroplexy (ē-lek'trō-plek-sē) Electroconvulsive treatment; ECT.

electrostimulation Electric shock, usually of painful intensity, used as a technique of negative conditioning in aversion therapy. See *therapy, aversion.*

elementary process See *process, elementary.*

eleutheromania (ē-lū-thēr-ō-mā'nē-à) *Rare.* Excessive zeal for freedom.

Elgin check list A list of behavioral activities that occur frequently in a psychotic population but rarely in a normal one.

ellipsis (e-lip'sis) In psychiatry, essentially as in grammar: 'The omission of one or more words, leaving the whole to be understood or completed by the reader or hearer.' (The Century Dictionary)

In psychoanalysis Freud has stressed the omission of ideas, which are supplied by analysis. He quoted the following sentence from a patient: *'If you indulge in a coitus, something will happen to Ella.'* Freud writes: 'Here is another instance in which a solution can be reached by filling out an ellipsis. . . . When the omissions have been made good, we have: "Every time you copulate, even with a stranger, you will not be able to avoid the reflection that in your married life sexual intercourse can never bring you a child (on account of the lady's sterility). This will grieve you so much that you will become envious of your sister [Ella's mother] on account of little Ella, and you will grudge her the child. These envious impulses will inevitably lead to the child's death."' (Freud, S. *Collected Papers,* vol. 3, tr. by Strachey, A. and J., Leonard and Virginia Woolf and The Institute of Psychoanalysis, London, 1925)

Ellis, Henry Havelock (1859 - 1939) British sexologist.

elopement In psychiatry, escape; absenting oneself from a mental hospital without permission.

emancipation In psychiatry the term means detachment of instinctual qualities with particular reference to the Oedipus complex as it reappears at puberty. According to psychoanalysis the Oedipus situation loses many of its original manifestations at the close of the period of infantile sexuality and remains dormant during the latency period. At puberty it is reanimated and to it 'there is added a powerful current of unmistakable sensuality, which always at first attaches itself in the unconscious to the early incestuous objects of affection.' (Jones, E. *Papers on Psycho-Analysis* 4th ed., Wood, Baltimore, 1938) The child is obliged to relive the earlier complex, following which in normal instinctual growth he frees himself from the libidinal attachment to the parents and from dependence upon parental authority. The emancipation leads to heterosexual object-choice.

emasculation Castration; physical eviration; eunuchism.

embolalia (em-bō-lā'lē-à) *Embololalia* (q.v.).

embolism, cerebral (em'bō-lis'm ser'e-bral) Brain obstruction. Emboli (i.e. plugs or stoppers, usually detached clots) arising from the pulmonary circulation, from thrombosis of the arteries of the neck and head, or from vegetations on the heart valves, may interfere with cerebral circulation, causing cerebral softening and neurological or psychotic symptoms. Stupor or coma may be present with focal signs of hemiplegia or paralysis. Irritability and anger, dulling of general intelligence, and memory defects may occasionally be observed. See *accident, cerebrovascular.*

embololalia (em-bō-lō-lā'lē-à) A type of speech disorder, frequently associated with stuttering, in which the patient interpolates short sounds or words which are out of place in the structure of the sentence.

emboloplasia (-fā'zhē-à) Embolophrasia.

embolophrasia (-frā'zhē-à) 'A melancholic subject in my clinique became quite oppressive, because he interlarded his speech with "really, now." "Really, now, you cannot understand, really now, how much I suffer, really now. . . ." This dysphrasic disorder goes under the name of *embolophrasia.*' (Bianchi, L. *A Textbook of Psychiatry,* tr. by MacDonald, J.H., Baillière, Tindal & Cox, London, 1906)

emergence Epigenesis; the theory that mind or consciousness arises from living matter which has reached a certain state of complexity; the term emergence is used to indicate that such an end result is not predictable from a consideration or knowledge of its constituent parts.

emetomania (em-ē-tō-mā′nē-à) Morbid desire to vomit, usually a hysterical symptom.

emetophobia Morbid dread of vomiting, not an uncommon symptom in hysteria.

emission, nocturnal See *ejaculation; wetdream.*

emotion Feeling; mood; *affect* (q.v.). In current usage, emotion and affect are used interchangeably, although some use *emotion* to refer primarily to the consciously perceived feelings and their objective manifestations, and *affect* to include also the drive energies that are presumed to generate both conscious and unconscious feelings.

For Adler, emotions do not determine goals and hence are never the cause of undesirable or antisocial behavior; rather, goals are set in accord with cognitive processes (even though the subject may not be consciously aware of these). Emotions are generated secondarily to suit those goals, and to permit and support what the subject intends to do. 'People are not emotionally disturbed; they are deficient in their social movement, in their goals, in their form of social integration, because they have wrong concepts about themselves.' (Dreikurs, R. in Stein, M. *Contemporary Psychotherapies,* Glencoe, New York, 1961 p. 76)

'The usual way of thinking about emotional experiences and their facial or other bodily manifestations is that the emotional experience is excited by the perception of some object, and that the emotional feeling then expresses itself in the bodily manifestations in question.' (*Encyclopaedia Britannica,* 14th ed., vol. 12, p. 885) See *Cannon hypothalamic the-*

ory of emotion; emotion, Papez's theory of; ergotropic.

The James-Lange Theory of Emotions states that the so-called expressions or bodily changes are the direct results of the perception of the exciting object, and that the emotion is just the feeling of these bodily changes as they occur.

emotion, conversion of The psychosomatic process through which an unconscious emotional conflict concerning the function of one organ is displaced upon and expressed, vicariously, through the energizing of the functional disturbance of another organ. In this process symbolic representation of organ function plays a major role.

Blushing is a good example of the displacement of the erotic functions of congestion, tumescence, and erection from their primary phallic (clitoral or penile) glans, or head, onto the head (caput) of the body as a whole. In this process the body, as a whole, functions symbolically and unconsciously as a phallus, and is utilized to express and carry out conflicts that relate primarily to the genital area, and not primarily to the organ involved. (Weiss, E., and English, O.S. *Psychosomatic Medicine,* 2nd ed., Saunders, Philadelphia and London, 1949)

emotion, Papez's theory of A modification of Cannon's hypothalamic theory: the hippocampus, fornix, mammillary bodies of the hypothalamus, anterior thalamic nuclei, and gyrus cinguli form a circle ('Papez's circle') which elaborates the functions of central emotion and participates in emotional experience. The midbrain reticular formation is connected indirectly to Papez's circle by means of the olfactory tubercle and the amygdaloid and septal nuclei.

emotion, sources of A psychoanalytic term that is particularly used and useful in emphasizing the root origins, in the unconscious, of the personal shibboleths and prejudices of so-called 'normal' people. This is especially important for those with pretensions toward objective scientific observations and judgments. By working through the defensive resistances rooted in the character, a degree of self-knowledge is achieved, which is, in a way, the ideal goal of the personal analysis. Through this process the emotional sources of rationalizations, self-delusions, self-deceptions, and confused obstructions to lucidity and clear understanding are uncovered. It is only through the intimate knowledge of one's own unconscious life that the emotional sources of bias and prejudice can be recognized and overcome.

E.F. Sharpe (*Collected Papers on Psycho-analysis*, Hogarth Press and The Institute of Psychoanalysis, London, 1950) upbraids an imagined self-satisfied analyst: '"I am a normal person, and I do not need psychoanalysis." To think that, especially if the thinker is a practitioner, it is to be a conjurer or worker of magic. It is to be blind to the fact that we are all enmeshed in the magical thinking and doing that lies under the veneer of our civilization.'

emotionalism, respiratory See *pseudoasthma.*

emotionality, pathologic (ē-mō-shun-al'-i-tē, path-ō-loj'ik) A variety of emotional responses characterizing one type of psychopathic personality, which are usually held under control in the presence of superior strength or police force. The commonest pathologic emotion is pugnacity. A person afflicted with this type of malady is uncivil and bullying, and scorns the rights of others. Pathologic emotionality is also shown by inordinate bragging, by the individual's acting 'the part of beggars in order to gain money or favors,' or by his enacting 'sadness for purposes of attention.' In all these instances there is a certain slyness or cunning. (Hinsie, L.E. *Understandable Psychiatry*, Macmillan, New York, 1948)

emotionally unstable personality See *personality trait disturbance.*

emotions, Cannon-Bard theory of See *Cannon hypothalamic theory of emotion.*

emotions, emergency See *psychodynamics, adaptational.*

emotions, ictal (ik'tal) Any suddenly occurring and quickly disappearing emotional reactions, but especially depression and anxiety. While affective disturbances may accompany almost any organic cerebral disorder, they are most frequently associated with disorders of the temporal lobe. A.A. Weil (*American Journal of Psychiatry, 113,* 149-157, 1956) suggests that such disturbances may be due to subclinical 'hippocampal-amygdaloid-temporal lobe epilepsy' and/or after-discharge from these areas following manifest seizure activation.

emotions, welfare See *psychodynamics, adaptional.*

empathema (em-pà-thē'mà) *Obs.* Ungovernable passion.

empathema atonicum (à-tô'nē-koom) Mason Good's term for melancholy.

empathema entonicum (en-tô'nē-koom) Mason Good's expression for what is now known as the manic phase of manic-depressive psychosis.

empathema inane (ē-nä'ne) Mason Good's term for psychomotor 'violence.'

empathetic (em-pà-thet'ik) Relating to intellectual, in contrast to emotional, identification.

empathic (em-path'ik) In Burrow's phylobiology the organism's primary feeling-motivation and response. Contrasted with affects or projective feeling. (Burrow, T. *The Biology of Human Conflict*, Macmillan, New York, 1937, p. 385)

empathize (em'pà-thīz) To diagnose, that is to recognize and identify the feelings, emotions, passions, sufferings, torments through observing their symptoms is to *realize intellectually, to understand* them, in a remote way to identify oneself with the patient, without ever having personally experienced those feelings,—to *empathize,* as it is known in psychiatry.

On the other hand, to place oneself in the position of the patient, to get into his skin, so to speak, to be able to duplicate, live through, *experience* those feelings in a vicarious way, is closely to identify oneself with another, to *share his feelings with him,* to *sympathize,* from the Greek *syn,* together with, and *páthos,* suffering, passion.

empathy Putting oneself into the psychological frame of reference of another, so that the other person's thinking, feeling, and acting are understood and, to some extent, predictable. Carl Rogers defines empathy as the ability to accompany another to wherever the other person's feelings lead him, no matter how strong, deep, destructive, or abnormal they may seem.

emphrensy (em-fren'zē) Same as *enfrenzy.*

empirical self See *self.*

empiricism (em-pir'i-siz'm) A school of philosophic thought which holds that the only source of knowledge is observable fact or objective experience. Watson's behaviorism is a form of empirical psychology.

empresiomania (em-prē-sē-ō-mā'nē-à) Pyromania.

emprosthotonos (em-pros-thot'ō-nos) A forward bending of the body. It is the opposite of opisthotonos. See *arc de cercle; camptocormia.*

emulation Conscious, willful copying or imitating of another. Emulation is to be differentiated from *identification* (q.v.), which is an unconscious process.

enantiodromia (ē-nan-tē-ō-drō'mē-à) 'Enantiodromia means "a running counter to." In the philosophy of Heraclitus this concept is used to designate the play of opposites in the course of events, namely, the view which maintains that everything that exists goes over into its opposite.' Jung quotes from Zeller *(History of Greek Philosophy)* to wit: 'From the living comes death, and from the dead, life; from the young, old age; and from the old, youth; from waking, sleep; and from sleep, waking; the stream of creation and decay never stand still.' (Jung, C.G. *Contributions to Analytical Psychology,* tr. by Baynes, H.G. and C.F., Kegan Paul, Trench, Trubner, London, 1928)

enantiopathic (-path'ik) Tending to induce an opposite passion.

encapsulation Enclosure in a capsule or sheath; the process of walling off from surrounding areas, as in encapsulation of a brain abscess. Used in clinical psychiatry to refer particularly to the ability of some schizophrenic patients to keep their delusional life almost completely separated from their routine life in the

real, external world. See *orientation, double.*

encatalepsis (en-kà-tà-lep'sis) Hippocratic term for catalepsy.

encephalasthenia (en-sef-al-as-thē'nē-à) Mental exhaustion; *obs.* for *psychasthenia.*

encephalitis (en-sef-à-lī'tis) Any inflammatory process involving the brain.

encephalitis, acute serous (en-sef-à-lī'tis) See *organic brain syndrome associated with systemic infection.*

encephalitis, acute toxic See *organic brain syndrome associated with systemic infection.*

encephalitis, arsphenamine hemorrhagic See *arsphenamine hemorrhagic encephalitis.*

encephalitis, epidemic Encephalitis lethargica; von Economo's encephalitis; popularly known as sleeping sickness. First described by von Economo in Vienna in 1917; by 1918 the epidemic had reached Germany and Great Britain, and by 1920 the whole world. There was another peak incidence in 1924, but if the virus that is presumed to have been the etiologic agent now exists at all, it is not known to have produced an epidemic since 1927. The major reason for continued interest in this type of encephalitis is the discovery that it tended to persist in diverse chronic forms for many years after initial infection. Among the chronic stage syndromes are:

(1) parkinsonism—with rigidity of posture and movement, and subsequent appearance of tremor (in idiopathic Parkinson's disease, the sequence of symptoms is the reverse);

(2) sleep disturbances, including lethargy, insomnia, narcolepsy, or inversion of the sleep pattern;

(3) disturbances of vision, including misty vision, slight inequality of pupils, some impairment to accommodation, weakness of conjugate conversion, or oculogyral spasm;

(4) involuntary movements, such as torsion spasms, tremors, and tics, many of which were commonly misinterpreted as being primarily of psychologic origin;

(5) disturbances of respiratory rate and rhythm;

(6) rarely, metabolic and endocrine disorders, probably due to hypothalamic involvement; among these are obesity, polyuria and polydipsia, and hyperthyroidism;

(7) mental disturbances, particularly depression and, in children, behavior disorders of a restless and aggressive kind; in DSM-II, such mental changes are coded 292.2 if of psychotic proportions, 309.0 if non-psychotic. See *impulse disorder, hyperkinetic.*

encephalitis, Japanese B (292.3, or 309.0) A virus infection of the brain that occurs most often in summer epidemics. The brain stem, basal ganglia, and white matter of the cerebral hemispheres are mainly involved. Mortality is high (50 - 60%) but recovery, when it does occur, is rapid (10 - 14 days) and ordinarily complete. Mosquitoes are the vector for the virus.

encephalitis, myoclonic See *hypsarrhythmia.*

encephalitis periaxialis diffusa (en-sef-à-lē'tēs pār-ē-ak-sē-à'lēs dē-foo'sà) Schilder's disease. See *sclerosis, diffuse.*

encephalitis, purulent (en-sef-à-lī'tis) Brain abscess.

encephalitis, St. Louis (292.3, or 309.0) A virus infection of the brain that occurs most often in summer epidemics, spread through mosquito vectors. The brain stem, basal ganglia, and white matter of the cerebral hemispheres are mainly involved. Mortality probably does not exceed 20%; in the remainder, recovery is rapid (10 - 14 days) and ordinarily complete.

encephalitis, traumatic (traw-ma'tik) A term suggested by Osnato and Giliberti to replace *postconcussion neurosis,* because of actual cerebral injury in cases of concussion. (Osnato, M. and Giliberti, V. Archives of Neurology & Psychiatry *18,* 181 - 214, 1927) In current usage, the term 'traumatic encephalopathy' has superseded both older terms. See *encephalopathy, traumatic.*

encephalization (en-sef-al-i-zā'shun) In higher mammals the cerebral cortex has taken over more and more the task of controlling and exerting a regulative function on bodily processes and on emotions.

In the human being this process of encephalization has reached its highest degree. In humans, the cerebral cortex governs not the somatic system alone, but all systems involved in emotional expression, psychological tensions, fears, and phobias. It is possible that the complexity of such a regulation is due to the functioning of the cerebral cortex. The lower animals are regulated by the hypothalamus and other centers. In the human, the lower centers co-operate in directing the behavior, but are themselves increasingly dominated by the cortex. (Masserman, J.H. *Behavior and Neurosis,* University of Chicago Press, Chicago, 1943)

encephalocele (en-sef'à-lō-sēl) Hernia of the brain. A developmental anomaly of cerebral substance protruding through a cleft in the skull.

encephalogram An X-ray of the skull following replacement of cerebrospinal fluid by air by means of lumbar puncture.

encephalography, radio-isotopic A measurement of brain function that depends upon the uptake of radio-isotopes by different structures in the brain. The isotope is injected at a specific time before the examination, which consists of a *scanning* of the brain by an isotope-sensitive probe whose intensity of reaction is recorded in graphic form and compared with normal patterns. Positive brain scans (increased focal uptake) are found with some neoplasms, subdural hemotoma, brain abscess, and cerebral infarct.

encephaloleukopathia scleroticans (en-sef-à-lō-loo-kō-path'i-à sklēr-o'tē-kàns) See *sclerosis, diffuse.*

encephalomalacia (-mà-lā'shē-à) Softening of the brain.

encephalomyelitis, acute disseminated (mī-e-lī'tis, -lē'tis) Acute perivascular myelinoclasis; an acute demyelinating disease occurring in the course of infection with the causal virus of one of the exanthemata (e.g. measles, mumps, smallpox, chickenpox, vaccination, antirabic inoculation).

encephalomyelitis, equine (ek'wīn) A virus infection of the central nervous system transmitted by mosquitoes from bird and wood-tic reservoirs. Two types are recognized and are immunologically distinct: (1) Western, with lower mortality (ca. 10% and more complete recovery, usually within one or two weeks); and (2) Eastern with higher mortality (ca. 65%) and severe sequelae in those who do recover (e.g. mental defect, epilepsy, spastic palsies).

encephalomyelomalacia chronica diffusa (-mī-e-lō-mà-lā'shē-à kro'ni-kà di-foo'zà) See *sclerosis, diffuse.*

encephalopathia literatorum (en-ke-fà-lô-pà'thē-à lē-te-rä-tō'room) *Obs.* Mental disorder due to overstudy.

encephalopathia puerperalis (poo-er-pe-rä'lēs) Puerperal psychosis.

encephalopathy (en-sef-à-lop'à-thē) Disease of the brain.

encephalopathy, acute toxic See *brain syndrome associated with systemic infection.*

encephalopathy, boxer's See *dementia, boxer's.*

encephalopathy, hypertensive A diffuse, usually transient, cerebral disturbance that may complicate the course of arterial hypertension (as in glomerulonephritis, malignant or essential hypertension, and eclampsia). Increased intracranial pressure is evidenced by papilledema, raised cerebrospinal pressure, headaches, vomiting, convulsions, coma, etc. Onset is usually subacute, with focal signs (e.g. visual disturbances, aphasia, or hemiplegia), but in some cases onset is chronic and characterized by personality changes, poor judgment, and anxiety (psychotic, 293.1; non-psychotic, 309.3).

encephalopathy, lead A diffuse brain disease due to chronic *lead poisoning* (q.v.). It is usually occupational in origin, occurring in painters, plumbers, plasterers, and typesetters. Children may develop the disease from licking painted toys. Such substances as hair dyes, cosmetics, lead plasters, and salves, used over a long period of time, may cause lead poisoning.

Clinically, the disease may be characterized by headache, memory defects, con-

vulsions, delirium, hallucinations, hemiplegia, and blindness. Lead encephalopathy in children is characterized by increased intracranial pressure, convulsions, hypertension, and cerebral edema. In DSM-II, the mental disturbances are coded 294.3 if psychotic, 309.14 if non-psychotic.

encephalopathy, progressive degenerative subcortical See *sclerosis, diffuse.*

encephalopathy, subcortical arteriosclerotic (290.1 or 309.6) Also known as *Binswanger's disease;* one of the presenile dementias, not as clearly defined as *Alzheimer's disease* or *Pick's disease* (qq.v.).

encephalopathy, traumatic (traw-ma'tik) A diffuse organic brain disease due to injury to the brain. Clinical symptoms are: persistent headache, dizziness, spots before the eyes, poverty of memory, general mental and physical fatigability, poor concentration, loss of energy, irritability, outbursts of anger, and either drowsiness or insomnia; personality changes are commonly a part of the syndrome. In DSM-II, these are coded 293.5 if psychotic, 309.2 if non-psychotic.

encephalopsychosis (en-sef-à-lō-sī-kō'sis) A term suggested by Southard to refer to psychosis associated with cerebral lesions.

encephalopyosis (-pī-ō'sis) Brain abscess.

encephalosis (-lō'sis) A degenerative brain process produced by infectious disease. Clinically, it is characterized by headache, irritability, apathy, stupor, and convulsions. Pathologically, there occur petechial hemorrhages, anemic infarcts, endarteritis of small vessels, degeneration of ganglion cells, and brain hydration. Winkelmann introduced the term.

encoding In communications, the process of translating data (i.e. a message) into signals (a code) that can be carried by a communication channel.

encopresis (en-kop-rē'sis) Involuntary defecation not due to organic defect or illness. Encopresis in a child over two years old is a result of faulty training, mental retardation, or regression on a psychogenic basis.

end plate, motor That part of a nerve fiber making functional contact with the muscle spindle of an effector organ.

end-pleasure In psychoanalysis, the culmination of the sexual act in the mature, genital stage of psychosexual development. The term emphasizes the subservience of pre-genital satisfactions to adult genitality. At puberty 'the excitations . . . that gave satisfaction to the child's desires now come to contain a disagreeable component (*Unlust*) due to the feeling of tension experienced. Thus they constitute merely a "fore-pleasure" (*Vorlust*), which impels to further activities destined to produce the "end-pleasure" (*Endlust*) that relief of tension brings about.' (Jones, E. *Papers on Psycho-Analysis*, 4th ed., Wood, Baltimore, 1938)

ending, act Termination of an act, such as eating, that was begun in order to relieve tension, once tension release or drive satiation has been reached; also termed 'completion of the act.' Childhood schizophrenics often show impairment of such act ending and will continue to eat, for example, without evidence of satiation.

endocrinopathy (en-dō-kri-nop'à-thē) In general, a pathological state or abnormal functioning of an endocrine gland, with the clinical symptoms occurring in other parts of the body, although they are referable to the disturbance of the internal secretion of the gland in question.

Endocrinopathic conditions are usually named in accordance with the quantitative or qualitative alteration in the internal secretion of the gland involved, unless they are named after their discoverer (Basedow's disease, Graves' disease) or are given special names (myxoedema, acromegaly). In the case of the thyroid, for instance, we have hyperthyroidism where there is oversecretion; hypothyroidism where there is undersecretion; and dysthyroidism where qualitative alteration (underiodized thyroxin) is alleged.

Constitutional medicine views these various endocrinopathic syndromes from the standpoint of constitutional type rather than of disease. In fact, some authors go so far as to regard the glandular change as secondary to other constitu-tional traits, denying them a causal role in the symptoms commonly attributed to them.

The glandular constitutions of chief practical importance in constitutional medicine are the *hyper-* and *hypothyroid*, the *hyper-* and *hypopituitary*, the *hyper-* and *hypoadrenal* and the *hyperthymic* constitutions. Most of these types show features which have been included by Kretschmer in the description of his *dysplastic type* (see *type, dypsplastic*).

endocrinotherapy Treatment with hormone preparations, and especially replacement therapy for conditions caused by a deficiency or absence of circulating hormone.

endoderm (en'dō-dērm) Entoderm.

endogamy (en-dog'à-mē) Restriction of marriage to members of one's own social, religious, or cultural group.

endogenous, endogenic, endogenetic (en-doj'ē-nus, -dō-jen'ik, -jē-net'ik) In the modern era of psychiatry and physiological genetics, the term *endogenous* is preferably used for the general clinical classification of mental disorders, which are based primarily on special heredito-constitutional factors, thus originating predominantly *within* the organism itself and affecting the nervous system *directly*.

Schizophrenic and manic-depressive psychoses are the most characteristic types of endogenous disorders, while the so-called *'symptomatic'* psychoses which arise — as a secondary symptom of organic diseases in part of the body other than the nervous system — from causes *outside* of the nervous system, even though *within* the body, are quite reasonably classified today as exogenous (see *exogeny*).

endogeny, endogenism, endogenesis (en-doj'ē-nē, -niz'm, -jen'ē-sis) The term *endogeny*, relating in biology to any process of 'growing from within,' is used in medicine to denote physical and mental conditions which are known or suspected to arise predominantly from causes *within* the body, and more specifically, from causes inherent in that system of the body which is the seat of the morbid character in question.

The latter narrower definition seems to

be preferred in the province of psychiatry, particularly. In the case of mental disorders it has become customary to classify them as exogenous rather than as endogenous, if their primary causes act from within the nervous system, even though they may have originated within, or may have been brought into, another part of the organism. From this point of view, a traumatic psychosis would be no more an exogenous disorder than a case of alcoholic hallucinosis or a symptomatic psychosis due to pernicious anemia or cancer of the liver.

If this definition is accepted, the psychiatric meaning of endogeny becomes almost concordant with a heredito-constitutional etiology, even if the significance of this classification was not clear in its essential aspects when the theoretical distinction between endogenous and exogenous psychoses was introduced. The same view explains why the term *autogeny* has been used as synonymous with endogeny.

In any case, since psychiatric knowledge of the genetic and constitutional factors operating in the origin of 'autogenic' psychoses has meanwhile been considerably improved, it seems now more adequate to limit the application of the term endogeny to such disorders as are predisposed to by specific hereditary factors and cannot be produced, without their pre-existence, by purely external causes, for instance, the disease groups of schizophrenia or manic-depressive psychosis (see *exogeny*).

endomorphic (-mor'fik) In Sheldon's system this term describes the type characterized by a predominance of its first component (circularity), that is, the physical structures developed from the *endodermal* layer of the embryo. Persons of this type are contrasted with the *mesomorphic* and *ectomorphic* (qq.v.) types and correspond roughly to Kretschmer's *pyknic* type. See *type, pyknic*.

endomusia Silent recall of a melody; endomusia often appears as a type of obsessive thought.

endopsychic (-sī'kik) This term, characterizing something as being within the mind or psyche, is applied to those mental mechanisms that occur completely within the mind; thus *psychic suicide* is deter-

mined by the same processes that determine physical suicide, but in the case of the former the processes work endopsychically. Endopsychic structure refers to the structure of the psyche itself: the conscious, the preconscious, and the unconscious, the ego, the superego, and the id are all parts of the endopsychic structure.

endoreactive Endogenous; not related to external events. An unfortunate term in that the internal events to which he is supposedly reacting are usually unknown to the patient, in which case use of 'reactive' would seem to be inappropriate.

enelicomorphism (en-el-i-kō-mor'fizm) *Adultomorphism* (q.v.).

energizer See *psychotropics*.

energy, psychic The propelling force behind mental activity; in psychoanalytic psychology, the source of psychic energy is the id.

'Accompanying every mental process is a varying amount of psychical energy, which roughly corresponds with what we term the "affect."' (Jones, E. *Papers on Psycho-Analysis*, 4th ed., Wood, Baltimore, 1938)

'Instinctive mental processes have, for their emotional goal, bodily action. These processes are, then, a vehicle for expression of the energy of the whole organism, which they direct in somewhat the same way as an elaborate switch-board directs electrical energy.' (MacCurdy, J.T. *The Psychology of Emotion*, Harcourt, Brace, New York, 1925)

'The energic viewpoint on the other hand is in essence final; the event is traced from effect to cause on the assumption that energy forms the essential basis of changes in phenomena, that it maintains itself as a constant throughout these changes, and finally leads to an entropy, a condition of general equilibrium. The flow of energy has a definite direction (goal), in that it follows the fall of potential in a way that cannot be reversed.' (Jung, C.G. *Contributions to Analytical Psychology*, tr. by Baynes, H.G. and C.F., Kegan Paul, Trench, Trubner, London, 1928)

enfrenzy *Rare.* To madden, to make frenzied.

engineering, social See *social policy planning.*

engram In neurology, a neuronal pattern of an acquired skilled act. The term has been used somewhat loosely in psychiatry to refer to the persisting psychical traces (usually in the form of an unconscious or latent memory) of any experience.

engram, function See *function-engram.*

enomania (ē-nō-mā'nē-à) *Oinomania* (q.v.).

enosimania (en-ō-si-mā'nē-à) Obsessional belief of the patient that he has committed an unpardonable sin.

enosiophobia (en-ō-sē-ō-fō'bē-à) A morbid dread of having committed 'an unpardonable sin.'

entatic (en-tat'ik) Invigorating, aphrodisiac.

enterocolitis (en-tēr-ō-kō-lī'tis) Inflammation of the mucous membrane of the intestines. Déjérine and Gauckler say: 'the patients afflicted with this disease are, for the majority, neuropaths, characterized as such even by those specialists who are determined to refer the symptoms to an organic origin. There are no physicians who do not recognize that mucomembranous enterocolitis is almost certain to develop on a neuropathic soil.' (Déjérine, J. and Gauckler, E. *The Psychoneuroses and Their Treatment by Psychotherapy,* 2nd ed., tr. by Jelliffe, S.E., Lippincott, Philadelphia & London, 1915)

enteroptosis (en-tēr-op-tō'sis) See *habitus, ptotic.*

entheomania (en-thē-ō-mā'nē-à) Demonomania.

entitlement The special privileges which a narcissitic person feels are owed him; for instance, he expects that he will be treated as a *V.I.P.* (q.v.).

entoderm (en'tō-dērm) In medicine and embryology, this term designates either the second primitive germ layer which is developed in the embryo's didermic *gastrulation* (q.v.) and is also called *hypo-*

blast; or the primary tissues which are subsequently derived from this layer and, thus, are characteristically distinguished from the organs and tissues developed from the other primitive germ layers, the *ectoderm* and the *mesoderm* (qq.v.).

In contrast to the *ectodermal* tissues, which eventually take over protective and neural functions, the *entoderm* becomes further specialized to subserve chiefly trophic functions. The blastopore, or primitive mouth, marks the future site of the anus, while the definitive mouth develops at approximately the opposite end, as soon as the embryo has attained a bilateral symmetry.

The entodermal tissue derivatives mainly consist of the epithelium of the digestive tract and associated glands, including pancreas, liver and gall bladder; epithelium of the respiratory system, thyroid, middle ear and auditory tube; epithelium of the urinary bladder, female urethra, proximal part of the male urethra, and the prostatic and bulbo-urethral glands.

entomophobia (en-tō-mō-fō'bē-à) Fear of insects.

entropy (en'trō-pē) A measure of the unavailable energy in a thermodynamic system; a measure of the unavailable information in an information system, usually '. . . in terms of the number of a priori equiprobable states compatible with the macroscopic description of the state—that is, it corresponds to the amount of microscopic information missing in the macroscopic description.' (Goldstine, H.H. *Science 133:* 1395, 1961)

The term is used more loosely in psychoanalytic theory to refer to the affective cathexis unavailable for displacement in a psychodynamic system. Freud pointed out that as one grows older there is a 'striking diminution' in the movements of 'mental cathexes.' Some people lose mental plasticity prematurely, while others retain it far beyond the usual age-limit. 'So that in considering the conversion of psychical energy no less than of physical, we must make use of the concept of an *entropy,* which opposes the undoing of what has already occurred.' (Freud, S. *Collected Papers,* vol. 3, tr. by Strachey, A. and J., Leonard and Virginia Woolf and The Institute of Psychoanalysis, London, 1925).

enuresis (en-ū-rē′sis) In general, the involuntary passage of urine. It may be the result of some physical disorder or it may be psychically determined. According to psychoanalysis, enuresis may acquire the significance of nocturnal masturbation (Jones), of exhibitionism (Abraham), of penis-envy in women (Abraham). Freud believes there is a relationship between incontinence of the bladder and fire. Ferenczi noted that bed-wetting and incendiarism were often connected with one another. He regarded enuresis as a urethral-erotic trait.

C.M. Pierce *et al.* (*U.S. Armed Forces Medical Journal 7:* 208-219) suggest an organic basis for enuresis on the strength of their findings of a significant preponderance of abnormal electroencephalograms and high incidence of familial history of enuresis in known enuretics. They suggest that sleep disturbances may be characteristic of the enuretic and may be a direct and measurable result of an inherited gene pattern.

enuresis nocturna (-nok-tĕr′nȧ) Bed-wetting; nocturnal enuresis; technically, urinary incontinence at night. Enuresis nocturna is more often psychic than physical in origin, although it may be secondary to urinary tract pathology, spina bifida, or other spinal cord anomalies. See *enuresis.*

environment 'Those forces or situations, or more strictly those stimuli, which reach and affect the human beings from the outside.' (Young, K. *An Introductory Sociology,* American Book Company, New York, 1934)

Bernard classifies the social environments of man as: (1) *physico-social,* including tools, weapons, ornaments, machines, transportation and communication systems, household and office equipment; (2) *bio-social,* as domesticated plants and animals, and human beings performing services; (3) *psycho-social,* as the inner behavior of individuals with whom we come in contact, uniformities of behavior as customs, folkways, conventions, traditions, beliefs, mores, externalized language symbols, and inventions such as books, magazines, newspapers, motion pictures and radio; and (4) *institutionalized derivative control* environments, as economic, political, racial, esthetic, ethical, educational, cultural, nationalistic, regional, religious, revolutionary, conservative, masculine, etc.' (Bernard, L.L. *Introduction to Social Psychology,* Holt, New York, 1926)

environment, neutral A physical and social environment which aims to impose no specific or rigid limitations or make demands upon the patient. 'Psychological determinants for what appear to be the same maladjustments may be quite different, and because of that, they require different situations. Since a therapy group supplies a neutral environment, each member can take from it whatever his needs may be. The aggressive child finds relief from his anxiety . . . while the shy and withdrawn one overcomes his fears.' (Slavson, S.R. *An Introduction to Group Therapy,* The Commonwealth Fund, Oxford University Press, New York, 1943, p. 84)

environment, permissive A social and physical environment in which acting out and verbalization are allowed but not necessarily sanctioned or approved.

envy, penis In psychoanalysis, the girl's desire for a penis. 'Women go through an early phase in which they envy their brothers the token of maleness and feel themselves handicapped and ill-treated on account of the lack of it (really, on account of its diminutive form). In our view this "penis-envy" forms a part of the castration complex.' (Freud, S. *Collected Papers,* vol. 4, tr. by Riviere, J., Leonard and Virginia Woolf and The Institute of Psychoanalysis, London, 1924-25)

Freud says that when the little girl realizes she has no penis, she reacts either by hoping that some day she will have one or by denying that she does not have one. In the latter case she may be 'compelled to behave as though she were a man.

Penis-envy is responsible for 'a loosening of the girl's relation with her mother as a love-object,' because the girl blames her mother for the alleged loss. At this stage the girl is prepared for the further development of the Oedipus situation. The wish for the penis is transformed into the wish for a child, 'With this object in view, she takes her father as a love-object. Her mother becomes the object of jealousy.'

enzygotic Of the same egg; usually the term refers to identical (homozygotic) twins.

enzyme See *chromosome.*

eonism (ē'on-iz'm) The adoption of the female role by a male. See *transvestitism.*

eosophobia (ē-ō-sō-fō'bē-à) Fear of dawn.

ephialtes (ef-i-al'tēz) *Obs.* Nightmare.

ephialtes vigilantium (e-fē-àl'tās vē-gē-làn'tē-oom) (L. 'nightmare of those awake') Daymare.

epicritic sensibility (ep-i-krit'ik) The ability to appreciate light touch and its localization; point discrimination; discrimination of moderate variations; distinguished from protopathic. 'To test epicritic or gnostic sensibility the light touch is employed. . . . Either a wisp of cottonwool should be used or a fine camel-hair brush.' (Jelliffe, S.E. and White, W.A. *Diseases of the Nervous System,* 6th ed., Lea & Febiger, Philadelphia, 1935)

epidemiology In psychiatry, the study of the occurrence of mental disorder within a specified population; often expressed in terms of (1) *incidence:* the number of new cases that appear during a specified time period, such as the number of first admissions to mental hospitals during one year; and (2) *prevalence:* the number of cases of any mental disorder that exist currently within the population. *Point prevalence* is the number of cases that exist at a specific point in time, such as the number of schizophrenics in a population on 1 January 1970; *period prevalence* is the number of cases that exist within a defined period of time, such as a month or a year; *lifetime prevalence* is the number of persons who have had a mental disorder in their lifetimes.

epigenesis *Emergence* (q.v.).

epilempsis (ep-i-lemp'sis) Hippocratic term for epilepsy.

epilentia (-pē-len'tē-à) *Obs.* Epilepsy.

epilepsia corticalis continua (e-pē-lep'sē-à kôr-tē-kà'lēs kôn-tē'noō-à) See *epilepsy, continuous.*

epilepsia cursiva (koor-sē'và) *Obs.* A symptom of epilepsy with apparently aimless running about.

epilepsia dromica (drô'mē-kà) A term used by Semmola to denote a syndrome of epilepsy resembling chorea.

epilepsia gravior (grà'vē-ôr) (L. 'severer epilepsy') *Obs.* Grand mal epileptic seizure.

epilepsia mitior (mē'tē-ôr) (L. 'milder epilepsy') *Obs.* Petit mal form of epilepsy.

epilepsia partialis continua (pär-tē-à-lēs kôn-tē'noo-à) (L. 'partial continuous epilepsy') Kozhevnikoff originally described this 'doubtless somewhat rare' motor variant of epilepsy; 'it differs from the general myoclonic type in that the twitching is limited to one segment of the body, nearly always a peripheral part such as the wrist and fingers, is practically continuous between the paroxysmal fits, and on the whole partakes of the form less of movements than of irregular, individual muscular contractions.' (Wilson, S.A.K. *Modern Problems in Neurology,* Wood, New York, 1929) See *epilepsy, continuous.*

epilepsia trochaica (trô-kà'ē-kà) (L. 'trochaic [i.e. choreic] epilepsy') Epilepsia cursiva.

epilepsia vertiginosa (ver-tē-gē-nō'zà) (L. 'vertiginous epilepsy') Epilepsia mitior; also refers to the dizziness that occasionally precedes or replaces a grand mal attack.

epilepsie larvee (à-pē-lep-sē' lar-và') (F. 'masked epilepsy') Masked epilepsy; epileptic equivalent.

epilepsy (ep'i-lep-sē) A paroxysmal, transitory disturbance of brain function which develops suddenly, ceases spontaneously, and exhibits a conspicuous tendency to recurrence. The typical epileptic attack, or fit, or convulsion, consists of the sudden onset of loss of consciousness, with or without tonic spasm and clonic contractions of the muscles. There are many forms of epilepsy, which vary depending upon the site of origin, the extent of the area involved, and the nature of the etiological factors; at the present time the term also includes transient episodes of sensory or psychic disturbances. Epilepsy, in short, is not a disease but a symptom, consisting of recurrent episodes of changes in the state of consciousness, with or without accompanying motor or sensory phenomena. Epilepsy has also been called paroxysmal cerebral dysrhythmia.

The average frequency or expectancy of epilepsy in the general population is 1 in 200; but persons with one epileptic parent have a higher expectancy (1 in 35), and those with both parents epileptic have a much higher expectancy (1 in 10). For each person who develops seizures during his lifetime, it is said that there are 20 more with a predisposition to the affliction. There is no difference in incidence between the sexes, although epilepsy tends to begin earlier in the female.

Today it is customary to divide epilepsy into two major groups on the basis of etiology: (1) *genuine* or *idiopathic* or *cryptogenic epilepsy*, in which there is no known local, general, or psychologic cause; and (2) *symptomatic epilepsy*, in which an organic basis is demonstrable. Approximately 25 percent of all epileptics fall clearly within the symptomatic group. But as the horizons of neurology widen to include the more recent pathological, physiological, and biochemical advances, it can be anticipated that specific etiologic agents will be demonstrable in an increasing number of cases. Electroencephalograph studies, for example, show that epilepsy is an uncontrolled discharge of cortical and/or subcortical neurones, i.e. an abnormal conversion of the potential energy of the neurones into kinetic energy. Epilepsy can thus be considered a physiochemical disturbance, which could be produced by any number of agents.

Within the *symptomatic* group of epilepsies are those due to: (a) local causes —intracranial infection, brain trauma, congenital abnormalities, degenerative diseases such as Pick's disease, various circulatory disturbances of the brain, etc.; (b) general causes—exogenous poisons, anoxemia, endocrine disorders, metabolic disorders (uremia, hypoglycemia, alkalosis, eclampsia, and hypertension of pregnancy), etc.; and (c) psychogenic causes.

In regard to the psychogenic group: there is little evidence that epileptic seizures, as distinct from hysterical fits, are ever purely psychogenic, but it is well recognized that the individual attack may be precipitated by fear, excitement, or other strong emotions. In his article "Dostoevsky and Parricide," (1928) Freud

suggested that epilepsy was an organic discharge mechanism which could be brought into play by any number of factors, and that hystero-epilepsy represented an instance of the mechanism being called into play for impulse discharge in hysteria. See also *personality, epileptic; dementia, epileptic.*

The *idiopathic epilepsies* have no known local, general, or psychologic cause; this is a large and heterogeneous group which suffers from a predisposition to convulsions, the nature of which is not yet understood. This predisposition in some cases seems to be largely hereditary in origin, but not all workers would subscribe to the view that idiopathic epilepsy is essentially a hereditary disorder. What is inherited is not epilepsy itself, but rather a predisposition to the development of convulsions under certain conditions, i.e. the physical basis of a cortical dysrhythmia. And only a small proportion of those with this cortical dysrhythmia become epileptic.

Gibbs and Gibbs, and Lennox, feel that the cortical dysrhythmia is inherited as a Mendelian dominant; it often remains latent, however, and the condition appears only in a collateral line. Lilienfeld and Pasamanick, on the other hand, feel that epilepsy is a result of complications of pregnancy and delivery, and these writers postulate a continuum of reproduction casualty composed of a lethal component (stillbirths, neonatal deaths), a severe sublethal component (cerebral palsy), and a less severe sublethal component (epilepsy).

The onset of epilepsy is often difficult to determine, for minor attacks may not be recognized, and major attacks (25%) may be only nocturnal, especially in children. The first seizure occurs before the age of 20 in 75 per cent of cases.

Epilepsy is divided into types on the basis of etiology, as discussed above; it may also be subdivided on the basis of physical manifestations, and when considered in this way, three major seizure types are distinguished: (1) *major epilepsy, grand mal epilepsy;* (2) *minor epilepsy, petit mal epilepsy,* and (3) *psychomotor epilepsy* (also known as *psychic equivalents,* or *temporal lobe seizures*). Various types of prodromata may precede major attacks or a series of minor attacks, and an *aura* (q.v.) precedes grand mal attacks in 60 per cent of cases.

In *grand mal epilepsy,* the convulsion or

fit consists of a tonic spasm of all the limbs, rarely lasting longer than 30 seconds. This is followed by the clonic phase —a series of sharp, short, interrupted jerks which result from a series of interruptions of the tonic phase. Following cessation of these spasms, the patient may pass into a heavy sleep lasting for hours; some patients, in this 'post-ictal phase,' evidence post-epileptic automatism in which they wander, completely amnesic and disoriented, from the scene of attack (this may last for hours or days). Other patients become psychotic, maniacal, or even homicidal.

Petit mal epilepsy may be associated with major seizures or may occur without them. Laymen know them as faints, sensations, or spells. They consist of one or more of the following: mild attacks of dizziness, faintness, queer sensations, dazed states, hot flashes, pallor, vomiting, belching, temper tantrums, sudden relaxation of musculature (so that the patient drops anything in his hand and stops speaking for a moment), momentary confusion and change of color, dreamy sensations, sudden visual or auditory or gustatory sensations, peculiar rushing sensations through the body, sudden jerks and starts. Petit mal attacks are usually extremely brief in duration and often there is no memory of the loss of consciousness so that the patient is only dimly aware of the occurrence of a spell. These minor spells sometimes take the form of the patient's aura preceding his major attacks, as if the attack were incomplete; patients will often spontaneously label them their frustrated or incomplete spells. Petit mal epilepsy occurs typically in young people and only rarely begins after the second decade. Associated psychiatric symptoms are rare and there is almost never an aura. Usually there is immobility during an attack, and the patient is mentally clear immediately after the attack. Incontinence is infrequent in petit mal epilepsy.

Petit mal epilepsy is sometimes further subdivided into *myoclonic, akinetic* and *short stare types*. Petit mal is associated with a spike and wave complex (also known as dart and dome complex) in the electroencephalogram, usually at a frequency of three per second. Some workers use the term *pyknolepsy* (q.v.) synonymously with petit mal.

The group called *psychomotor epilepsy* includes a bewildering variety of recurrent periodical disturbances which usually take the form of some mental disturbance during which the patient carries out movements of a highly organized but semiautomatic character. These seizures are rare in children, and the attack itself is marked by confusion rather than loss of consciousness, and there is later amnesia. Psychomotor attacks last longer than petit mal attacks, with which they are easily confused; but incontinence and post-ictal confusion, which do not occur in petit mal, are seen frequently in psychomotor epilepsy. About two-thirds of the psychomotor group also have grand mal seizures, but only about 3 per cent also have petit mal attacks. There is general agreement that the great majority of psychomotor seizures are the epileptic manifestations of temporal lobe lesions.

Classification of psychomotor epilepsy is arbitrary. Lennox proposes the following subdivisions: (a) psychomotor seizures proper (43%), with an excess or absence of involuntary motor activity, combined with amnesia for the events that transpire during attack; (b) automatic seizures (32%), where activity of a purposeful or semi-purposeful nature is carried out, with amnesia for the event; these seizures are also known as primary automatisms, or primary ictal automatisms, so long as they are not preceded by an aura; and (c) psychic or subjective seizures (25%), including déjà vu or dream states, hallucinations, episodes of confusion or stupor, or feelings of depression or exaltation without motor components.

epilepsy, acoustico-motor See *epilepsy, reflex.*

epilepsy, affective This is an expression used by Bratz to designate a form of epilepsy characterized by exaggerated emotional responses, which generally culminate in an epileptiform seizure. Bonhoeffer referred to such states as *reactive epilepsies* and Kraepelin classified many of them as *epileptic swindlers.*

epilepsy, akinetic (à-kin-et′ik) A type of petit mal epilepsy. See *epilepsy.*

epilepsy, alcoholic This is an ill-defined clinical disorder, including a variety of manifestations associated with alcoholism and so-called epilepsy.

An alcoholic may experience an epileptiform seizure; or a person with the epileptoid personality may try to solve his personality difficulties through alcohol; or the alcoholism and epilepsy may be more or less independent of each other.

epilepsy, autonomic (aw-tō-nom'ik) Diencephalic epilepsy; sympathetic epilepsy; parasympathetic epilepsy. Autonomic epilepsy refers to symptoms of sudden, diffuse discharge of the autonomic nervous system in otherwise normal individuals. In some, symptoms are primarily of sympathetic discharge; in others, symptoms are primarily of parasympathetic discharge. Usually, however, symptoms are mixed.

Penfield, in 1929 under the name 'diencephalic autonomic epilepsy,' described predominantly sympathetic seizures consisting of fever, flushing, tearing, sweating, salivation, hiccoughing, and shivering. In this case, a ball valve tumor of the third ventricle had resulted in compression of adjacent hypothalamic nuclei.

Cushing, in 1932, reported on parasympathetic outbursts occurring in response to intraventricular injections of pituitrin and pilocarpine. Symptoms included profuse sweating, flushing, fall in blood pressure, lowering of temperature and basal metabolic rate, and increased peristalsis in the stomach and intestines.

epilepsy, centrencephalic Generalized (in contrast to focal) epilepsy, in which extensive areas of both hemispheres are simultaneously activated by epileptic discharge from some midline center (probably the thalamus). See *system, centrencephalic.*

epilepsy, continuous This is a form of epilepsy, including the polyclonia epileptoides continua of Choroschko, the epilepsia corticalis continua of Kozhevnikoff and the epilepsia partialis continua of Wilson, characterized by myoclonic attacks in single muscular groups; it is limited to one side of the body and consciousness is retained during the attacks.

epilepsy, co-ordinated 'Those cases where the movements seen during the attack are coördinated and seemingly purposive, exhibiting objectively to a large extent the features of "voluntary" movements. They may, however, be aimlessly repeated and in any case do not attain the end to which they may be supposed to be directed.'

(Wilson, S.A.K. *Modern Problems in Neurology,* Wood, New York, 1929)

epilepsy, cryptogenic (krip-tō-jen'ik) Epilepsy without known etiology and pathology.

epilepsy, diencephalic (dī-en-se-fǎl'ik) See *epilepsy, autonomic.*

epilepsy, digestive The commonest form of visceral epilepsy, manifested in gastrointestinal symptoms such as colic, eructation, nausea, vomiting, epigastric distention, meteorism, diarrhea and tenesmus.

epilepsy, erotic A type of epileptiform focal seizure in which the patient experiences spells of intense erotic sensation; first reported by T.C. Erickson (*Archives of Neurology & Psychiatry 53:* 226-231, 1945) in a 43-year-old housewife, in whom a small vascular tumor was later disclosed on the medial surface of the cerebral hemisphere, impinging upon the motor and sensory representation of the genitalia.

epilepsy, essential Idiopathic epilepsy.

epilepsy, gelastic (je-las'tik) A form of epilepsy in which laughter is a part of the seizure pattern, usually due to a lesion in the left temporal region.

epilepsy, genuine Same as *idiopathic epilepsy.*

epilepsy, hallucinatory A type of focal epilepsy in which complex hallucinations are the main part of the attack. The hallucinations are short-lived, paroxysmal, and irresistible in quality; they tend to be identical in each attack.

epilepsy, inhibition of See *epilepsy, reflex.*

epilepsy, inhibitory A rare form of petit mal epilepsy in which transitory loss of power occurs in a limb or on one side of the body without preceding tonic spasm or clonic movements; there may be an associated impairment of consciousness.

epilepsy, Jacksonian A variant of grand mal epilepsy described by John Hughlings Jackson. The convulsion begins with clonic movements which increase in severity and spread (the 'cortical march') to involve large segments of the limb, then the other limb on the same side, then the face, and finally sometimes the other side, at which point consciousness is usually lost. The spread is along anatomical and/or physiological lines, and this type of epilepsy almost always indicates organic disease of the precentral cortex. Jacksonian epilepsy usually begins in one of three foci: thumb and index finger; angle of the mouth; or the great toe.

epilepsy, larvated Epileptic equivalent.

epilepsy, major Grand mal epilepsy.

epilepsy, masked Epileptic equivalent.

epilepsy, minor Petit mal epilepsy.

epilepsy musicogenic (mū-si-ko-gen'ik) See *epilepsy, reflex.*

epilepsy, myoclonic (mī-ō-klon'ik) A type of petit mal epilepsy. See *epilepsy.*

epilepsy, myoclonus (mī-ō-klō'nus) A variant of grand mal epilepsy first described by Unverricht in 1891. This type of epilepsy is usually familial and occurs in several siblings. Symptoms usually begin between 6 and 16 years. Generalized epileptiform attacks with loss of consciousness appear first, often only at night. After several years, the characteristic myoclonic contractions develop; they involve simultaneously the symmetrical muscles on both sides of the body and are strong enough to produce movements of limb segments. The face, trunk, and upper and lower limbs are most commonly involved. The contractions disappear during sleep and are intensified by emotional excitement. They tend to increase in severity before a generalized epileptic attack; sudden contraction of the lower limbs may throw the patient to the ground. For a period of years, myoclonic contractions and epileptic attacks are associated; during this time, a progressive dementia develops and there is a passing into a third stage, where the grand mal attacks tend to disappear. Then dysarthria and dysphagia increase and death often follows progressive cachexia.

epilepsy, nocturnal Jelliffe and White state that 'the possibility of exclusively nocturnal attacks—*nocturnal epilepsy*—should be borne in mind. It is suspicious

if the patient awakes tired and lame, as if his muscles had been beaten, particularly if he shows conjunctival ecchymoses, a wounded tongue and flecks of blood on the pillow. A localized muscular weakness that passes off promptly would add certainty to the diagnosis.' (Jelliffe, S.E. and White, W.A. *Diseases of the Nervous System,* 6th ed., Lea & Febiger, Philadelphia, 1935)

Exclusively nocturnal attacks occur in approximately 25 per cent of known epileptics; both day and night attacks occur in another 25 per cent of patients. Exclusively nocturnal attacks are more common in children.

epilepsy, parasympathetic (pà-rà-sim-pa-thet'ik) See *epilepsy, autonomic.*

epilepsy, photic (fot'ik) See *epilepsy, reflex.*

epilepsy, post-traumatic Convulsions following brain trauma, i.e. a type of symptomatic epilepsy. Post-traumatic epilepsy develops in three to five per cent of cases with closed head injury, and in 30 to 50 per cent of cases with open head injury. Convulsions tend to occur (1) within a few seconds of injury; (2) within a day or two; or (3) within the first two years following injury. About half of early-appearing epilepsy disappears; in late-appearing epilepsy, there is a tendency to abatement of attacks within two years of onset, and in 30 per cent, convulsions disappear completely.

epilepsy, procursive An epileptic symptom, characterized by sudden, impulsive running forward.

epilepsy, psychic (sī'kik) The epileptiform convulsion may be replaced by any one of the many epileptic equivalents. 'These attacks of *psychic epilepsy* frequently take the form so-called *epileptic automatism* or *epileptic dream states.* In these conditions the patient may do almost anything and when he comes to himself he has absolutely no recollection of what has happened.' (Jelliffe, S.E. and White, W.A. *Diseases of the Nervous System,* 6th ed., Lea & Febige, Philadelphia, 1935) Other manifestations of psychic epilepsy are states of depression, excitement, delirium, stupor, paranoid reaction, etc.

epilepsy, psychomotor See *epilepsy*.

epilepsy, psychopathology of (sī-kō-path-ol′ō-jē) See *personality, epileptic.*

epilepsy, reactive Bleuler speaks of 'the rare "reflex epilepsy," whose attacks are set free by the irritation of a scar or some other pathological focus. . . .' (Bleuler, E. *Textbook of Psychiatry,* tr. by Brill, A.A. Macmillan, New York, 1930)

epilepsy, reading A type of reflex epilepsy in which the affected person has the sensation of his jaw snapping or opening when he reads; if he continues to read once the myoclonic jaw movements appear, a generalized convulsion is likely to occur. See *epilepsy, reflex.*

epilepsy, reflex Epileptic convulsions precipitated by some external stimulus, such as a sudden loud noise (acoustico-motor epilepsy), music (musicogenic epilepsy), visual (photic epilepsy) or cutaneous stimuli. Reflex inhibition of the fit is an allied phenomenon: if, for example, a focal convulsion begins with movement in one limb, a strong stimulus such as a firm grip applied to the limb will often abort the attack if this is begun immediately after onset of the attack.

epilepsy, reflex inhibition of See *epilepsy, reflex.*

epilepsy, regional See *epilepsy, myoclonic.*

epilepsy, residual This infrequently used expression, coined by Kraepelin, refers to a form of epilepsy characterized by recurring epileptiform seizures without such other phenomena as dementia, marked personality changes, etc.

epilepsy, retropulsive An epileptic symptom, characterized by sudden, impulsive running backward.

epilepsy, sensory A type of petit mal epilepsy consisting of paresthesiae involving part or the whole of one side of the body, often without loss of consciousness. Sensory epilepsy is usually due to a contralateral lesion in the parietal lobe.

epilepsy, short stare A type of petit mal epilepsy. See *epilepsy.*

epilepsy, sleep *Obs.* Narcolepsy.

epilepsy, sympathetic See *epilepsy, autonomic.*

epilepsy, symptomatic A condition in which the convulsions represent a symptom of an underlying organic disease process. This may occur in such conditions as congenital defects of the brain, intracranial hemorrhages, meningitis, brain abscess, senile degeneration, carbon monoxide poisoning, etc.

epilepsy, tetanoid (tet′à-noid) Pritchard introduced this expression to refer to the form of epilepsy in which the spasm is tonic only.

epilepsy, tonic Epileptic fits 'characterized by tonic contractions only, to the exclusion of the clonic element, have long been known.' (Wilson, S.A.K. *Modern Problems in Neurology,* Wood, New York, 1929)

epilepsy, traumatic See *epilepsy, posttraumatic.*

epilepsy, true Same as *idiopathic epilepsy.*

epilepsy, vertiginous (vĕr-tij′i-nus) A rare type of seizure pattern precipitated by vestibular stimuli, characterized by recurrent attacks of vertigo (of the rotatory type); associated often with short lapses of consciousness.

epilepsy, visceral (vis′er-al) A form of focal epilepsy in which the fit is manifested as visceral sensations, usually referable to the gastrointestinal tract, the cardiorespiratory system, or the genitourinary system. The principal loci of lesions in such cases have been found to be in the frontotemporal and mid-frontal parasagittal regions, indicating that the visceral sensations arise from some central location, probably the amygdalohippocampal portion of the temporal lobe.

epileptic character See *personality, epileptic.*

epileptic clouded states Psychotic reactions occurring in epileptics; in DSM-II, coded 293.2. At times, either preceding or following a convulsive attack, the epileptic may manifest a dazed reaction with deep confusion or excitement, anxiety, and bewilderment. Associated with this, there may be violent outbreaks, hallucinations, fears, or ecstatic moods with religious exaltation.

epileptic cry See *cry, epileptic.*

epileptic deterioration See *dementia, epileptic.*

epileptic equivalent See *equivalent, epileptic.*

epileptic psychopathic constitution See *constitution, epileptic psychopathic.*

epileptic, psychoses (sī-kō′ses) See *dementia, epileptic.*

epileptic, pyknic (pik′nik) One who has epilepsy and a physique of the pyknic type. The majority of persons having epilepsy are of the athletic or dysplastic type; the pyknic type is encountered the least often. Westphal analyzed a large group of epileptics from the standpoint of body type. According to this analysis the percentages of incidence were as follows: dysplastic type, 29.5 per cent; athletic type, 28.9 per cent; asthenic type, 25.0 per cent; pyknic type, 5.5 per cent; 11.1 per cent were unclassified. (Hoch, P.H., and Knight, R.P. *Epilepsy,* Grune and Stratton, New York, 1947)

epilepticism (ep-i-lep′ti-siz′m) *Obs.* Status epilepticus.

epileptoid (ep-i-lep′toid) Resembling epilepsy.

epileptoid, orthostatic (or-thō-stat′ik) Children who have fainting spells and occasional convulsions when forced to stand for a long time or after getting up in the morning are referred to as *orthostatic epileptoids* by Husler. (Husler, J. 'Bermerkungen zur genuinen Epilepsie im Kindesalter,' *Zeitschrift für Kinderheilkunde 66,* 237-50, 1920)

epileptoidism The state of being epileptoid. Some psychiatrists hold that epileptic patients show personality traits and behavior patterns which they believe are characteristic and indicative of a developing epileptic disorder. The presence of these mental manifestations is referred to as epileptic character (see *personality, epileptic*). These mental traits appear in some epileptics after the occurrence of epileptic fits. In some, however, they are present before the epilepsy occurs. If it is a forerunner of epileptic manifestations, it is called epileptoidism in the same sense as schizoidism is present in many before the appearance of schizophrenia, cycloidism before the development of manic-depressive psychosis. (Hinsie, L.E. *Understandable Psychiatry,* Macmillan, New York, 1948)

epileptology (-tol′ō-jē) The science or study of epilepsy.

epileptosis (-tō′sis) A term suggested by Southard to refer to the various manifestations of epileptic psychoses.

epiloia See *sclerosis, tuberous.*

epinephrine (e-pin-e′frin) The active principle of the medullary portion of the adrenal glands, $C_9H_{13}O_3N$, often referred to by its proprietary name, adrenalin. Epinephrine is the most powerful vasopressor drug known; it increases blood pressure, stimulates heart muscle, accelerates heart rate, and increases cardiac output.

Stimulation of sympathetic nerve fibers releases a substance similar to epinephrine which is known as sympathin. Sympathin is the chemical mediator of the excitatory processes initiated by sympathetic nerve impulses at neuroeffector junctions. Like epinephrine, sympathin has both excitatory and inhibitory effects; that released when excitatory responses are stimulated is sympathin E, and that released when inhibitory responses are stimulated is sympathin I.

It has been suggested that epinephrine or products in its metabolism may be involved in the natural occurrence of mental disorders. Some doubt is cast on this by the fact that epinephrine itself is present in the brain only in small quantities. A closely related substance, norepinephrine (noradrenalin, arterenol), which is also present in the adrenal medulla, is known to occur in significant amounts in the brain, particularly in the hypothalamus, and derivatives of this substance might therefore be more likely as possible precursors of clinical psychoses. For these same reasons, it seems more likely that norepinephrine is the central sympathetic neurohumor.

Both epinephrine and norepinephrine

are normally present in the blood only in low concentration, but in response to stress both increase markedly. When the stress agent is removed, the circulating blood level of these *catecholamines* falls quickly back to normal. This rapid disappearance might be achieved by storage in tissues or by enzymatic destruction, and evidence to date favors the latter mechanism. It is possible that one mechanism for in vivo inactivation of these catecholamines is breakdown by the particular enzyme monoamine oxidase (MAO, amine oxidase). See *ergotropic.*

epinosic, epinosis (e-pin-o'sik, -ō'sis) See *gain, epinosic.*

episodic disorders Impulse-disorders. See *disorders, episodic.*

epistasis (e-pis'tà-sis) A genetic mechanism by which the phenotypical expression of one hereditary factor masks, or prevents, the manifestation of another factor which concerns the same organ, although it is not allelic to the factor with the greater expressivity. The factor exercising the masking effect is called *epistatic,* while the factor which is hidden is said to be *hypostatic.*

The result of *epistasis* is similar to that produced by a *dominant* character. However, there is a significant difference between the phenomena of dominance and epistasis. While a dominant and a recessive factor are always alleles of each other, an epistatic and a hypostatic factor are merely related to the same trait or organ, but they are not the two members of an allelic pair (see *dominance*).

epistemophilia (ē-pis-tē-mō-fil'ē-à) The love of knowledge or the impulsion to inquire into things; said by psychoanalysts to receive its earliest important stimulation during the phallic phase, although preliminary preparation is gained through interests in other and earlier erotogenic zones, particularly the oral and the anal. Freud believed that during the stage of so-termed 'phallic primacy,' 'the epistemophilic impulses are now largely occupied with the new center of sexual sensations, the penis, and that the boy's interest is concentrated upon this organ.' (Healy, W., Bronner, A.F., and Bowers, A.M. *The Structure and Meaning of Psychoanalysis,* New York, 1930) The many subsequent

manifestations of the impulse to learn are regarded as sublimations of the several varieties of infantile sexuality.

epithalamus (e-pi-thal'à-mus) A zone of brain tissue above the thalamus composed of: (1) *habenular ganglion* or *trigone,* a depressed triangular area anterior to the superior colliculus; (2) *pineal body* which lies between the superior colliculi; (3) *posterior commissure,* some of whose fibers connect the two superior colliculi.

equation, personal The individual or 'personal' peculiarities or variations (in both the experimenter and the person experimented upon) which must be discounted or deducted in order to 'equate' or correct the results of an observation.

equilibrium, homeostatic (hō-mē-ō-stat'ik) See *instinct, aim of.*

equilibrium, narcissistic (när-si-sis'tik) A state of harmony between the demands of the superego and the capabilities of the ego; derived from the original harmony between the obedient child and its loving parents. 'Both ego and super-ego are made up of identifications. Where the latter are harmoniously integrated in the personality we have the state of narcissistic equilibrium. The super-ego does not demand of the ego more than it can produce. The ego is not terrified by the threat of the super-ego severity.' (Hart, H.H. 'Narcissistic Equilibrium,' *International Journal of Psychoanalysis 28,* 106, 1947)

equivalent, anxiety See *anxiety-attack, equivalent of.*

equivalent, epileptic The manifestations of genuine epilepsy are many. When an epileptic patient has an 'attack' that is neither of the grand or petit mal type, he is said to have an *equivalent,* that is, a 'substitutive' attack. For example, a twilight state may take the place of a grand mal attack. A patient about to have a major seizure developed a condition in which he believed that he was in heaven, curing all the ailments of the universe. 'More frequent are those with an anxious or angry affect which readily lead to brutal acts of violence against the individual himself and others; sexual excitements are the basis of Ripper murders or frequent exhibitionism. Besides fearful visions of hell and the devil, there occur much more rarely ecstasies which are completely beyond the reach of reality and blissful erotic-religious hallucinations of all the senses.' (Bleuler, E. *Textbook of Psychiatry,* tr. by Brill, A.A., Macmillan, New York, 1930)

Some authors use this term to refer to psychomotor epilepsy. See *epilepsy.*

equivalent, onanistic (ō-nan-is'tik) Ferenczi uses this expression to refer to a great variety of acts that act as substitutes for (manual) masturbation. For example, rhythmic movements of the legs, resulting in genital stimulation, constitute an onanistic equivalent.

'Transition stages are here discoverable between symptomatic acts and certain forms of *tic convulsif,* of which as yet we possess no psychoanalytic explanation. My expectation is that on analysis many of these tics will blossom forth as stereotyped onanistic equivalents.' (Ferenczi, S. *Further Contributions to the Theory and Technique of Psycho-Analysis,* tr. by Suttie, J.I., Leonard and Virginia Woolf and The Institute of Psychoanalysis, London, 1926) See *onanism, larval.*

equivalent, psychic (sī'kik) Psychomotor epilepsy. See *epilepsy.*

Erdheim's tumor Craniopharyngioma. See *tumor, intracranial.*

erectio deficiens (ā-rek'tē-ō dā-fē'kē-ens) (L. 'deficient erection') Absence of (genital) erection.

eremiophobia (ē-rē-mē-ō-fō'bē-à) Fear of a lonely place or solitude.

eremophilia (er-ē-mō-fil'ē-à) Morbid desire to be alone.

eremophobia Fear of being alone.

erethism (er'ē-thiz'm) Morbid excitability. Erethism is initiated generally through psychical influences. Ellis mentions that 'a medical friend tells me of a lady considerably past middle age who experienced sexual erethism after listening to a heated argument between her husband and a friend on religious topics.' (Ellis, H. *Studies in the Psychology of Sex,* vol. 3, Davis, Philadelphia, 1903, p. 143)

Erethism means an exaggerated degree of irritability or sensitivity in any part of the body. While the term refers to excitement or stimulation of any organ or tissue of the body, it more commonly relates to the organs of reproduction, when used in psychiatry nowadays.

The term, originally meaning excitement, used to be followed by some word indicative of the cause of the excitement. Hence *erethismus ebriosorum* meant excitation from drink; later it was used synonymously with delirium tremens. In constitutional medicine *erethism* denotes overactivity in general. Thus, Pende says: 'Generally, however, the animal nervous system shows erethism, great instability and a tendency to crises of exhaustion.' (Pende, N. *Constitutional Inadequacies,* tr. by Naccarati, S., Lea & Febiger, Philadelphia, 1928) When psychic reactions, for example, are exaggerated, the condition is sometimes known as *tachypragia.*

Sexual erethism may be displayed as nymphomania, satyriasis, erotomania, etc.

erethismus ebriosorum (e-re-thēz'moos ā-brē-ô-zō'room) (Mod. L. 'drunkards' irritability') Delirium tremens.

erethistic (er-ē-this'tik) Same as erethismic. See *erethism.*

erethitic (-thit'ik) Characterized by excitement.

erethizophrenia (er-ē-thiz-ō-frē'nē-à) Exaggerated cortical excitability.

erethizophrenic (-fren'ik) Pertaining to or suffering from erethizophrenia. A term introduced by Hunt, equivalent to *cycloid.* (Hunt, J.R. *American Journal of Psychiatry 12,* 475-92, 1932-33)

ereuthophobia (ē-rōō-thō-fō'bē-à) Same as *erythrophobia* (q.v.).

erg R.B. Cattell proposed this term to replace 'instinct' and defined it as 'an innate psychophysical disposition which permits its possessor to acquire reactivity to certain classes of objects more readily than others, to experience a specific emotion in regard to them, and to start on a course of action which ceases more completely at a specific goal activity than at any other.'

ergasia (ēr-gas'ē-à) This term, introduced into psychiatry by Adolf Meyer, is designed to express the total of functions and reactions of an individual, in contradistinction to the functions of individual organs or parts of the human organism. It embraces the concept known as *the personality as a whole* and refers to those responses of a person that represent the results of the activity of many of his parts. It stands for the action of the total organism.

ergasiatry (ēr-gas-ī′à-trē) Adolf Meyer's term for psychiatry.

ergasiology (-ē-ol′ō-jē) Psychology.

ergasiomania *Obs.* A morbid impulse to work, to keep busy. It is observed in pronounced form in the manic state of manic-depressive psychosis.

ergasiophobia Fear of functioning or acting generally associated with an underlying dread that if movement takes place something disastrous will happen. There is a strong sadistic component in the fear. When the sadism is turned outwardly, its unconscious meaning is the equivalent of injury or death to another; when directed inwardly upon the subject himself, it has the same motive. The fear is often associated with the castration phantasy of the Oedipus complex. It is related to the magical feeling that what happens to oneself also happens to the environment. A patient may believe that if he stops functioning or moving, the world will do the same.

ergasthenia (ēr-gas-thē′nē-à) *Obs.* A condition of fatigue or debility due to overwork or excessive functioning.

ergastic (ēr-gas′tik) Ergasic.

ergodialeipsis (ēr-gō-dī-à-lāp′sis) Action which ceases before it is completely carried out. It occurs most commonly in schizophrenia and appears to be a type of *blocking* (q.v.).

ergotropic Having the quality of turning to, predisposing toward, or preparing for action. Hess and others have applied this term to that portion of the diencephalic, subcortical system which integrates sympathetic with somatomotor activities and prepares the body for positive action. The other division of this system is called the trophotropic; the latter integrates parasympathetic with somatomotor activities and promotes protective and recuperative behavior patterns.

Much of the work of experimental psychiatry in the mid-twentieth century has been devoted to attempts to define more specifically the neurophysiological bases of emotion in the belief that this will open the way to a better understanding of emotional disorders. Hess's proposal that the reactions of the organism to environmental change are effected by a subcortical system co-ordinating visceral, somatic, and psychic functions is an example of one way in which the general problem has been attacked.

The significance of Hess's hypothesis depends upon recognition of the brain as a communication system, whose functional integrity is maintained by neural excitation and transmission, which in turn depend upon metabolic production of energy and its transformation into neural activity. If disordered or abnormal behavior is considered to be due, possibly, to some fault in this communication system, either because of defective transmission of the impulse or because of abnormal response of the nerve cells involved, the problem becomes one essentially of production and/or destruction of metabolites and the enzyme systems involved.

The drawback at present is that it is still uncertain what the normal scheme of functioning is, and what enzyme systems might be involved. There are various working models of normal functioning which in many respects appear compatible with the experimental data available. The following example is an outgrowth of Hess's conception of the functional organization of the diencephalon.

Emotions and emotional behavior depend upon the functional integrity of a subcortical co-ordinating system, which in turn depends on the balance and interaction of two opposing functional systems—the ergotropic, whose neurohumor may be *norepinephrine* (q.v.), and the trophotropic, whose neurohumor may be *serotonin* (q.v.). The 'functional' psychoses may be due to a shift in equilibrium, to one side or the other, by any number of possible mechanisms. Thus, one neurohormone might be underproduced, or overproduced, or faultily stored, or inadequately released, etc.; or metabolic breakdown of neurohormone might be aberrant, and/or abnormal intermediary metabolites might be formed in the course of neurohormone breakdown.

Psychotomimetic agents appear to produce ergotropic predominance— mescaline (and amphetamine) by stimulating the ergotropic division, LSD (and other indoles) by blocking the opposing trophotropic division.

Tranquilizers, on the other hand, appear to produce trophotropic predominance—reserpine by stimulating the trophotropic division, chlorpromazine by depressing the opposing ergotropic division. See *psychotropics*.

erogeneity (er-ō-jē-nē'i-tē) The state or quality of being erogenous. See *orality; anality*.

Eros (ē'ros, er'os) (Gr. *Eros*, Eros, the god of love) The life instinct or drive. See *instinct; instinct, death*.

erotic, anal See *anal-erotism*.

erotic-cathexis See *cathexis*.

erotic, organ See *organ-erotic*.

erotic seizure See *epilepsy, erotic*.

eroticism (ērot'i-siz'm) See *erotism*.

eroticism, olfactory (ē-rot'i-siz'm, ol-fak'tō-rē) The pleasurable sensations associated with smelling. Along with the sexual impulses of hearing and tasting, olfactory eroticism 'participates to a relatively great extent in the general orientation of the child.' Thus these senses are filled with pleasurable erotic excitement for the infant or, in Fenichel's words, 'are highly cathected with infantile sexuality.' Also they show a close relationship to pregenital eroticism as a whole. More specifically, phenomena of smell sexuality coincide, for the most part, with anal eroticism.

Owing to repressed pregenitality, the average adult's sense of smell is much duller than it was in childhood. Olfactory eroticism, however, that has undergone repression becomes revived in certain pathological states. 'Emotions which originally were connected with infantile sexuality may later be remobilized in a conflict situation around sensations of smelling, tasting, or hearing.' A revival of nasal eroticism will occur whenever there is a regression toward anal and respiratory eroticism, as happens, for example, in bronchial asthma. Also, conflicts concerned with smelling and hearing are particularly prominent in states of narcissistic regression. The hallucinations of paranoid schizophrenics are very frequently linked with offensive sounds and odors. (Fenichel, O. *The Psychoanalytic Theory of Neurosis*, Norton, New York, 1945)

eroticize (ē-rot'i-sīz), To charge with libidinal or erotic energy. Any part of an individual may be invested with the erotic instinct, that is, eroticized (libidinized).

erotism, eroticism (er'ō-tiz'm) A condition characterized by the instinctual quality called 'love' or Eros. Thus, one speaks of erotism relating to body zones, such as anal, oral, and genital erotism; or to psychic structures, such as ego-erotism (narcissism); or to objects outside of the body or mind such as alloerotism.

erotism, anal See *anal erotism*.

erotism, ego See *narcissism, ego-libido*.

erotism, muscle Pleasure associated with muscular activity (dancing, posturing, walking, etc.).

erotism, oral The pleasure and gratification derived from using the mouth above and beyond the utility value of taking in food and drink. In the child it means the pleasure experienced when close to the mother's warm body, when sucking her breast or the nipple of the bottle and thus feeling secure and protected.

erotism, organ See *organ-erotism*.

erotism, urethral See *urethra*.

erotization (ē-rot-i-zā'shun) Libidinization; the act of erotizing or state of being erotized. During infancy the body becomes erotized, notably those parts of the body called erotogenic zones. All forms of activity subsequent to the stage of infantile sexuality may and usually do undergo erotization. Character traits, ideas, actions of all sorts, hobbies, recreations, etc. are erotized.

erotocrat (ē-rō'tō-krat) A man of powerful sexuality.

erotodromomania (-drō-mō-mā'nē-à) Hirschfeld uses this term to denote the morbid impulse to travel as an escape from some painful sexual situation.

erotogenesis (-jen'ē-sis) The springing or origination of libidinal or erotic impulses. In *Three Contributions to the Theory of Sex*, Freud shows that the sexual instincts in man are complex and result from impulses coming from several sources, among them the oral, anal, and phallic zones.

erotogenetic (-jē-net'ik) Same as *erotogenic*.

erotogenic (-jen'ik) Relating to or having its origin in the libidinal or erotic instinct; commonly applied to libidinal impulses that are expressed through special body areas or erotogenic zones (genitals, mouth, anus, urethra). Freud says: 'The genitals are the latest of these *erotogenic* zones. ...' (Freud, S. *New Introductory Lectures on Psycho-Analysis*, tr. by Sprott, W.J.H., Norton, New York, 1933)

erotographomania (-graf-ō-mā'nē-à) A morbid impulse to write love letters. Usually love is expressed in sublimated terms, often having a vivid religious background. The letters are generally written anonymously. Magnus Hirschfeld cites the letters of the monk Abelard and the nun Heloise as classical examples of erotographomania.

erotolalia (-lā'lē-a) Sexually obscene speech, especially in reference to the use of such speech during sexual intercourse as a means of enhancing sexual gratification. This term emphasizes the sexual content of speech in contrast to the obscene or socially tabu speech of coprolalia, which term is more properly limited to verbal expression of excretory processes. (Mac-Dougald, D., in A. Ellis and A. Brandt, *Encyclopedia of Sexual Behavior*, Hawthorn Books, New York, 1959)

erotomania (-mā'nē-à) Inordinate or morbid inclination to love. Its usual implication is love of genital relations with members of the opposite sex. It is closely related, however, to unconscious homosexual impulses, which in turn stem from the stages of infantile sexuality, particularly those identified with the Oedipus situation.

'Many cases of erotomania might give an impression that they could be satisfactorily explained as being exaggerated or distorted heterosexual fixations, if our attention were not attracted by the circumstance that these infatuations invariably begin, not with any internal perception of loving, but with an external perception of being loved.' (Freud, S. *Collected Papers*, vol. 3, tr. by Strachey, A. and J., Leonard and Virginia Woolf and The Institute of Psychoanalysis, London, 1925). The quotation is taken from *A Case of Paranoia (Dementia Paranoides)*, which deals largely with the projection mechanism and homosexuality. See *paranoia*.

erotopathy (ē-ro-top'à-thē) Any abnormality of the sexual impulse.

error 'Errors of memory are distinguished from forgetting and false recollections through one feature only, namely, that the error (false recollection) is not recognized as such but finds credence. ... Back of every error is a repression. More accurately stated: the error conceals a falsehood, a disfigurement which is ultimately based on repressed material.' (Freud, S. *The Basic Writings of Sigmund Freud*, tr. by Brill, A.A., Random House, New York, 1938)

erythrism (ē-rith'ris'm) In medicine and anthropology this term denotes a condition characterized by the presence of red hair in certain regions of the body, notably in the beard and pubic zone, where it contrasts with the color of the remainder of the body hair. This condition attains its significance for constitutional medicine from the theory that in analogy to *flavism* (q.v.) it constitutes a stigma of the *asthenic, microsplanchnic* physique and its tendency to tuberculosis. See *type, asthenic*.

erythroblastosis fetalis (er-rith-rō-blas-tō'-sis fē-tal'is) See *icterus gravis neonatorum*.

erythroedema polyneuritis (er-rith-re-dē'-mà pol-ē-nū-rī'tis) *Acrodynia* (q.v.).

erythrophobia (ē-rith-rō-fō'bē-à) Fear of red. This is most commonly associated with blood, although, as with other fears, anything identified with the original fear may act as a substitute for it. For example, the fear of blood may be expressed as the fear of red, of anything that is red; the fear may then spread to all colors; the fear of colors may then give way to that of certain localities in which colors are prominent. Fears amass with great facility; moreover, as fears grow they tend to appear less associated with the original one, until finally the fear seems thoroughly illogical and unrelated to any previous experiences.

The conscious fear is symbolic of an unconscious and antithetic impulse. Thus, the fear of blood may be related unconsciously to a wish for it. The wish may be a sadistic expression connected with the castration phantasy or one of its many subsequent symbolic expressions.

Not infrequently *erythrophobia* appears as a fear of blushing. It is said that the latter is related to exhibitionism and that it means genitalization of the face or head. The individual fears the red face as if it were the penis.

escapism In psychoanalytic therapy, this term denotes the tendency to escape from reality functioning to the relative security of childhood, a tendency often manifested by an accentuation of neurotic symptoms. It is a form of resistance.

Eshmun complex See *complex, Eshmun.*

ESN Abbreviation for educationally subnormal.

esophoria (ē-sō-for′ē-à) See *heterophoria.*

E.S.P. Abbreviation for extra-sensory perception. See *perception, extra-sensory.*

esprit de corps (âs-prē′ dē kôr′) (F. 'group spirit, corporate feeling') Group feeling or group enthusiasm.

Esquirol, Jean Etienne Dominique (1772 - 1840) (es-kē-rôl′) French psychiatrist.

EST Abbreviation of electro-shock therapy. See *therapy, electric convulsion.*

esthesia (es-thē′z[h]ē-à) Sensibility; capacity for sensation. Used frequently as a combining form.

esthesiogenesis (es-thē-sē-ō-jen′ē-sis) The production of a reaction in a sensory zone.

estrangement, inner Federn used this term to refer to the feeling that external objects, even though well perceived, have a strange, unfamiliar or unreal quality. He considered estrangement to be characteristic, nosologically and clinically, of the depressive psychoses (while depersonalization is characteristic of the schizophrenias). Federn ascribed estrangement to a failure of cathexis of the external ego boundary, one of whose functions is to identify non-ego (external objects) as real and familiar. This failure is due to a primary disturbance in the bodily ego feeling, which is derived from the narcissistic libido (the sexual energy investing the ego).

estrangement, kinship Social workers' term for 'the state of being out of touch or not on friendly terms with one's relatives because of disagreement or indifference.' (Hamilton, G. *A Medical Social Terminology,* Presbyterian Hospital, New York, 1930)

estromania Oestromania; *nymphomania* (q.v.).

état marbré (ā-tà′ mà r-brā′) Status marmoratus. See *dystonia, torsion.*

eternity, fear of By this term Fenichel designates one in the group of fears of 'surroundings that imply the loss of the usual means of orientation,' such as fear of cessation of customary routine, fear of death, fear of uniform noises, etc. The patient who has such fears is particularly afraid of a loss of control over infantile sexual and aggressive impulses, and then projects onto the outside world his own fears of losing control. A concept such as eternity, in which the normal assessment of time loses its significance, is seen as a great threat to him, for it means a loss of the forces protecting him against his own unconscious unmastered sexual and aggressive impulses (Fenichel, O. *The Psychoanalytic Theory of Neurosis,* Norton, New York, 1945)

etheromania Ether-drinking; ether was drunk as an inebriant in many parts of the world in the early 13th century and in some European peasant communities rivalled alcohol in popularity. This form of inebriety is rare nowadays.

ethnology (eth-nol′ō-jē) The branch of *anthropology* which deals with the division of mankind into races and studies the origin, history, customs, and institutions of the various racial groups.

ethnopsychology See *psychiatry, comparative.*

ethology (ē-thol'ō-jē) When applied to man ethology refers to the study of group behavior as it is reflected in the mores and customs of the group. More commonly the term is applied to lower animal forms, in which case it indicates the study of the behavior of animals in their natural habitat. Some of the key concepts of ethology are *instinct* (q.v.), *imprinting,* and *social releaser.* See *releaser, social.*

etiology (ē-tē-ol'ō-jē) The division of medical science relating to the cause of disease. The cause of general paresis is the germ of syphilis; not all patients with syphilis develop general paresis. Etiological studies involve also investigations into the nature and response of the tissues of the host as well as of the response of the total personality to the results of the disease.

eu- (ū-) prefix meaning good, well, advantageous, from Gr. *eu,* well.

eudemonia, affective (ū-dē-mō'nē-à) Flight into mental illness as an escape from frustrating or frightening reality. The *Ganser syndrome,* certain cases of *hypochondriasis,* and *faxen-psychosis* (qq.v.) are instances of affective eudemonia. This term emphasizes secondary gains, which are particularly prominent in these cases.

euergasia (ū-ēr-gas'ē-à) Adolf Meyer's term for wholesome or normal mental functioning.

eugenic (ū-jen'ik) Properly used in its original sense, the term relates only to the ideology or methods of preventive medicine in *applying* genetic principles to human health conditions as postulated by eugenics.

eugenics This term was coined by Francis Galton to denote the systematically organized efforts of preventive medicine to improve average human qualities through the observation of *heredity.* Galton's introduction of the word 'study' into his final definition: 'the study of agencies under

social control that may improve or impair the racial qualities of future generations, either physically or mentally,' makes it clear that he was thinking of such studies as would be the foundation of plans. Eugenics is thus complementary to *euthenics,* which aims at the betterment of the human race by studying the *environmental* conditions of human beings and differs from *genetics,* which is the branch of natural science that studies the origin, transmission, and manifestation of hereditary characters.

Eugenic measures are (1) *positive,* to encourage reproduction by persons biologically most highly qualified ('aristogenic'), or (2) *negative,* for the reduction or stoppage of parenthood among those least qualified physically and mentally ('cacogenic'). While positive eugenic activities consist mainly of educational propaganda and practical help to biologically sound families, negative eugenic procedure is devoted to the restriction of marriage and birth rates in the lowest class of family stocks through eugenic advice, contraceptive birth control measures, and voluntary or compulsory sterilization.

Accordingly, the *positive* aim of eugenics is to improve the human capacity for responding favorably to contemporary standards of culture and civilization, in order to obtain a general stabilized level of resistance to the dysgenic and antisocial influences of inferior family stocks; whereas the chief task of *negative* eugenics is to determine and prevent biological incapacity to thrive even in a favorable environment.

eumorphic (ū-mor'fik) According to the classification of constitutional types by the Italian school, this term means 'built along normal lines' and refers to a type intermediate between *dolichomorphic* and *brachymorphic* and is equivalent to Viola's *normosplanchnic* type.

Etymologically the term eumorphic is derived from the structure or shape of the body, as a whole, whereas normosplanchnic is derived from the size of the viscera and their effect on the contour of the body. It is held nevertheless that there is a complete correspondence between the eumorphic build and the normosplanchnic visceral status.

eunuch In general usage as well as in medicine this term designates a man *castrated before puberty* and subsequently developing the secondary sexual characteristics of a female. See *castrate*.

In Oriental harems the male supervisors were *eunuchs*, to prevent their sexual relations. However, the belief that the removal of the testes after puberty necessarily prevents sex functioning is erroneous: in neither sex does removal of the gonads *after puberty* invariably produce such an effect. 'Eunuchs' may therefore have sex relations as other men whose testes are removed after puberty.

Real eunuchs may be recognized by not growing bald, since they do not produce the hormones which make other men susceptible to the genetic tendency to baldness.

eunuchism A medical term for the state of being eunuched or of being a eunuch, that is, a man castrated before puberty.

eunuchoid In constitutional medicine this term describes the physical appearance of a male whose secondary sexual characteristics resemble those of a female. See *type, hypogenital*.

eunuchoidism In the classificatory system of constitutional medicine, the concept of *eunuchoidism* applies to a male resembling a *eunuch*, that is, a man who develops after castration the secondary sexual characteristics of a female: large hips, narrow sloping shoulders, absence of beard and body hair, and high-pitched feminine voice.

Eunuchoidism sometimes results from early derangement of the sex glands without operative castration before puberty. It may even occur in mature men, especially in old age, following drastic changes in their glandular balance, and is easily recognizable by high-pitched voice. See *castration*.

euphoria (ū-fō'rē-à) In psychiatry, a morbid or abnormal sense of well-being. See *mania*.

'Euphoria is a generalized feeling of well-being, not amounting to a definite affect of gladness.' (Henderson, D.K. and Gillespie, R.D. *A Text-Book of Psychiatry*, 4th ed., Oxford University Press, London, 1936)

euphoria, indifferent Elation and cheerfulness which lack emotional depth. Bleuler applies this term to apparent euphoria in the schizophrenic, where seemingly marked euphoria is often expressed in the same sentence, side by side with marked depression or indifferent expressions. Indifferent euphoria is an instance of the lack of homogeneity of mood and of the dissociation between mood and verbal expression which are almost pathognomonic of schizophrenia.

euphoriants See *psycholeptica*.

eupraxia (ū-prak'sē-à) Normal ability to perform co-ordinated movements.

eurhythmia (ū-rith'mi-à, ū-riTH') In constitutional medicine, harmonious body relationships.

eurotophobia (ū-rō-tō-fō'bē-à) Fear of female genitals.

euryplastic (ū-ri-plas'tik) A type described by Bounak, corresponding to the *pyknic* type in Kretschmer's system, the *megalosplanchnic hypervegetative* constitution of Pende.

eusthenic (ū-sthen'ik) In comparison with the *oligosthenic* and *phthinoid* divisions of the *asthenic* type in Kretschmer's system of constitutional types, this denotes the asthenic variety which is relatively the most vigorous and the closest to the *athletic*.

eutelegenesis (ū-tē-lē-jen'e-sis) This term is used in genetics, synonymously with *artificial insemination*, to denote the technical process of artificially impregnating a female with the sperms of a male without any contact between the two.

euthanasia (ū-thà-nā'z[h]ē-à) This term applies mainly to the measures by which physicians alleviate, or seek to remove, the distress attending the approach of death in the course of a chronic disease. According to this concept, the removal of pain is regarded as essential for an 'easy death.'

In a more specific sense, the term implies not only an easy, painless death, but also the means of bringing one on by legally putting to immediate death every sufferer from an incurable disease who prefers this kind of death to being tormented for a lengthy period before an eventual, painful death. This particular procedure is commonly known as 'mercy killing' and has been advocated by small groups of physicians subscribing to the belief that, with adequate safeguards, euthanasia should be legalized 'to allow incurable sufferers to choose immediate death rather than await it in agony.' These advocates of euthanasia hold that most of the legal and religious arguments against mercy killing are founded on emotion rather than on reason.

Within the province of eugenics, it is the method of infanticide—that is the destruction of infants with marked congenital defects—which has at certain times been practiced as a form of euthanasia which seemed advisable for the particular purposes of race betterment. It was in Plato's Republic and in ancient Sparta —whose population was essentially military and had become accustomed to looking at marriage chiefly as a means of supplying new soldiers—that infanticide was urged for the first time and actually practiced, upon the decision of the ephors, when a child was unlikely to turn out a vigorous citizen (soldier). Following the pattern of Sparta, numerous tribes and nations have also contrived, at one time or another, to destroy their unfit, in order to prevent them from becoming a burden to themselves and to society.

At present and in all civilized countries, of course, any kind of euthanasia is contrary to ethical and humanitarian concepts and is punishable as a felony (see *eugenics*).

euthenics (ū-then′iks) In contrast to *eugenics*, which aims at improving the biological qualities of future human generations with the aid of data gained from the observation of heredity, the term *euthenics* relates to the study of environmental conditions tending to improve the human race (see *peristasis*).

euthymia (ū-thim′ē-à, ū-thī′mē-à) Joyfulness or mental tranquility; bienaise.

eutonia sclerotica (ū-tōn′ē-à skler-o′ti-kà) A feeling of intense physical well-being experienced by some patients with multiple sclerosis, even when the disease itself is far advanced. See *sclerosis, multiple*.

evaluation, false This term is used by Adler to include under-evaluation of other persons or objects and over-evaluation of personal achievement or aims.

As an example of under-evaluation, Adler presents the story of the 'fox and the sour grapes.' He states that, 'instead of realizing his own inferiority the fox deprives the grapes of their inherent value— and thus *retains his high spirits*. He is prepared for his *megalomania*. These types of psychical procedure primarily serve the maintenance of "free will" and of personal worth. The same purpose is served by the over-evaluation of *personal achievements* and aims caused by the individual's flight from the pessimistic feeling of his own inferiority. They are thus "arranged" and arise out of an *exaggerated safety-tendency* directed against the feeling of "being below."' (Adler, A. *The Practice and Theory of Individual Psychology*, tr. by Radin, P., Kegan Paul, Trench, Trubner, London, 1924)

evasion See *paralogia*.

event, traumatic A term that in the evolution of psychiatry and psychiatric terminology was introduced for the purpose of designating a special variety of the concept already included without a qualifying adjective under the undifferentiated broader term *trauma;* the physical or psychic injury specifically precipitating emotional or mental illness of the injury-caused type, i.e. the traumatic neuroses or psychoses. The illness may be caused by a single injury, as in the case of a workman caught in a construction cave-in, or by a series of traumatic incidents, as a soldier participating in protracted warfare. In any case, the designation *traumatic event* is reserved for denoting *the* injury that precipitates the illness and finds representation in its clinical picture.

'As soon as the organism encounters an unfamiliar stimulus in the effective environment, it must assay this stimulus, and a new adaptive maneuver must be set into motion. If the maneuver is successful, the organism continues to thrive and adds the new pattern to its armamentarium. The stimulus may, however, be too strong, or the time too brief, to permit a successful maneuver, e.g. a temperature of 160 degrees F., an exploding shell, or a plane with one wing shot off. In this case a series of events takes place within the organism which indicates its failure to adapt to the new conditions. Although sometimes the organism ceases to exist, more often it continues to exist, its reaction to the failure becoming the starting point for a new adaptation. An *event* which creates conditions to which the organism cannot adapt may be called *traumatic*, and the point at which the organism's adapted capacities fail may be called the breaking point. . . .

'The traumatic neurosis is the record of the lasting consequences of an abrupt change in the external environment to which the resources of the individual are unequal. This situation we designated as a trauma [traumatic event]. The neurosis is, therefore, the record of the disturbance created by the trauma on the previously established adaptations.' (Kardiner, A., and Spiegel, H. *War Stress and Neurotic Illness,* Hoeber, New York, 1947)

evil, St. John's An old term for epilepsy.

eviration (ev-i-rā'shun) Emasculation; feminization; sometimes used also to indicate a delusion in a male that he has become a woman.

evolutility (ev-ō-lū-til'i-tē) The capability of an organism to exhibit change in growth and other aspects of the physical structure as a result of nutrition.

evolution In biology it has become customary to limit the meaning of the term to the evolution of living forms, first placed on a scientific footing by the observations made independently but almost simultaneously by Charles Darwin and A.R. Wallace. From their study of fauna and fossils in many lands they were able to form a picture of the distribution of animal life in space and time which forced each to the conclusion that the more complex forms of living beings including man are descended from more primitive forms (see *Darwinism*).

The great reputation of Darwin for the demonstration of the biological facts underlying this *theory of evolution* was scarcely diminished by the subsequent discovery of his mistakes in interpreting the mechanism of this evolutionary process. From the present genetic standpoint it may be said that regarding Natural Selection acting through Survival of the Fittest as a mechanism bringing new types into existence, in addition to favoring the better-adjusted types already in exis-

tence, Darwin implied the heinous genetic heresy of the inheritance of acquired characters. Modern genetics has not only discredited this heresy but, in revealing the frequency of *mutations* has provided a substitute for Darwin's false notion. When a new type has arisen by mutation, the principles of natural selection and survival of the fittest can work to preserve or destroy it. See *mutation.*

exaltation, reactive See *mania, reactive.*

examination, mental See *mental status.*

examination, psychiatric social 'The psychiatric social examination has as its immediate end as complete an understanding as possible of the patient's personality and behavior. It approaches the problem from a developmental point of view, bringing together data concerning the individual's heredity, his physical and mental makeup, his social and material environment, the personalities in his family group and his reactions to them, from the time of his childhood to the present.' (*Vocational Aspects of Psychiatric Social Work,* Mental Hygiene, 1925)

examinations, psychometric Various psychological tests that are administered to the subject in order to test one, several, or all of the following factors in his mental make-up: intelligence, special abilities and disabilities, manual skill, vocational aptitudes, interests, and personality characteristics.

exanthropia (ek-san-thrō'pē-à) An old term for what was called the third stage of melancholia, namely, dislike for society.

excandescentia furibunda (eks-kàn-des-ken'tē-à foo-ē-boon'dà) (L. 'furious irascibility') Plattner's term for psychosis characterized by violent reactions.

exceptions See *type, 'the exceptions.'*

excitation, deflection of By this term Freud indicates the turning aside of a response to stimulation from the psychical sphere to the somatic. In discussing hysteria and anxiety-neurosis he states: 'In each of them there occurs a deflection of excitation to the somatic field instead of psychical assimilation of it.' (Freud, S. *Collected Papers,* tr. by Riviere, J., Leonard and Virginia Woolf and The Institute of Psychoanalysis, London, 1924-25)

excitation, somatic sexual With Freud this term means a continuous visceral excitation produced by pressure on the walls of the seminal vesicles, which are lined with nerve-endings.

excitation, subliminal See *summation.*

excitatory state, central See *summation.*

excitement, anniversary Bleuler used this term to refer to episodes of agitation which appear on specific calendar dates and which usually disappear after a few repetitions. He included anniversary excitements among the acute syndromes of the schizophrenias. On analysis it is found that the anniversary excitement is related to something which had happened to the patient on a certain day which had some connection with his complex or complexes.

excitement, catatonic (ka-ta-ton'ik) See *schizophrenia, catatonic.*

excitement, constitutional An older term used by Kraepelin for *manic temperament.* See *temperament, manic.*

exhaustion, combat See *shell-shock.*

exhaustion, nervous An older term for *neurasthenia.*

exhaustion psychosis See *psychosis, infective-exhaustive.*

exhaustion, stage of See *syndrome, general adaptation.*

exhibitionism During the infancy period the sexual instinct consists of several 'component' or partial impulses, one of which is exhibitionism. This impulse, manifested early in the form of genital exhibitionism, is later subject to all the modification that may take place with any of the instincts. It may be progressively displaced from the genital zone to the body as a whole, to the oral zone (the pleasure of speaking), to clothes, to dramatics, to the possession of material assets, etc. Or, it may be expressed in terms of reaction-formation, that is, there may be aversion to display of any kind.

Psychiatric patients express the exhibitionistic impulse in a variety of ways. In its severest form the genitals are exposed, usually to some person who represents to the patient the parent of the opposite sex. Exhibitionism is thus associated with the Oedipus complex.

'The *turning around* of an instinct *upon the subject* is suggested to us by the reflection that masochism is actually sadism turned round upon the subject's own ego, and that exhibitionism includes the love of gazing at the subject's own body.' (Freud, S. *Collected Papers,* vol. 4, tr. by Riviere, J., Leonard and Virginia Woolf and The Institute of Psychoanalysis, London, 1924-25)

existence, intra-uterine See *intra-uterine.*

existentialism A system of philosophy particularly associated with the names of Jean-Paul Sartre, Martin Heidegger, Karl Jaspers, and Sören Kierkegaard. Existential philosophy is essentially of European origin and is a reaction to the realization that technology and a belief in pure rationalism, Logical Positivism, or similar philosophies have only alienated man from society and from himself. Existentialism rejects the Hellenic view of man as a man of detached, logical reason and instead emphasizes the Hebraic view of man as a man of faith and a concrete, individual doer.

Philosophy in the Western world before the time of Kierkegaard tacitly accepted Parmenides' belief that if a thing cannot be thought, it cannot be real. Yet existence cannot be thought, it can only be lived; thus reason must ignore existence completely or reduce it to nothingness. For Kierkegaard, existence was not a matter of speculation but a reality in which the individual is personally and passionately involved; the decisive encounter with the Self is in the Either/Or of choice. For Heidegger, existence is a Being spread over a field or region which is the world of its care and concern. This field of being is called *Dasein* (q.v.). In the everyday world, none of us is a private Self confronting a world of external objects; we are simply one among many—'the One,' a fallen state in that we have not yet become a Self and recognized our mortal, feeble, impotent nature. Sartre and his followers, representing a small part of existential philosophy, emphasize the despair of a world from which God has departed, and their themes include: 'Alienation and estrangement; a sense of the basic fragility and contingency of human life; the impotence of reason confronted with the depths of existence; the threat of Nothingness, and the solitary and unsheltered condition of the individual before this threat.' (Barrett, W. *Irrational Man*, Doubleday, New York, 1958)

In psychiatry, existentialism forms the philosophic background for 'existential analysis,' which in the main is represented by Europeans trained originally as psychoanalysts. The existential group does not consider itself divorced from the body of orthodox psychoanalytic theory and method, but it looks to existentialism rather as a more extensive and practicable approach to the patient and his world. Existential analysis is considered to have appeared in reaction to existing inadequacies in the various schools of thought in psychopathology.

For example: 'The existentialists conceive of schizophrenic episodes as moments when it is impossible for the patient to conduct his own life within the stream of existence around him. The question is, how can one conduct a life impossible to conduct?—by substituting for the uninterrupted, objective sequence of experience a subjective sequence. Experience takes on a non-sequential character in the schizophrenic, who aims for misguided ideals which are contradicted by experience. Thus the sequential character of experience is shattered and the schizophrenic becomes embroiled in alternatives which are impossible to fulfill. This leads to masking, imitation, eccentricity and mannerisms. Not being able to cope with life gives rise to anxiety for the attempt at masking fails and the misguided ideals cannot be achieved. Existential analysis consists of looking behind the symptoms for the specific modes of existence which determine those symptoms, and guiding the patient from an uncharted existence into new roads which allow existence to proceed in an orderly sequence.' (Campbell, R.J. *Psychiatric Quarterly 32:* 318-34, 1958) See *neurosis, existential.*

exogenism (eko-oj'ē-niz'm) State of being generated or born or caused by conditions or factors outside of the body. Thus, general paresis is exogenic in the sense that the original cause, the spirochete, is transmitted to the body from an outside source.

exogenous, exogenetic, exogenic (eks-oj'ē-nus, ek-sō-jē-net'ik, -jen'ik) In modern medical classification, the term *exogenous* relates to physical or mental disorders which are caused predominantly by factors acting either from outside of the body or from another part of the body (outside of the system), which is the very seat of the morbid condition in question. See *endogenous.*

exogeny, exogenism, exogenesis (eks-oj'ē-nē, -niz'm, ek-sō-jen'ē-sis) Although the medical term *exogeny* relates originally to the pathogenetic process of only those morbid conditions which are caused by factors acting from *outside* of the body, it is used in psychiatry in a more specific sense. The psychiatric classification includes disorders which are at least predominantly due to influences of pathological processes outside of the nervous system, and are not inherent in its particular genetic constitution.

According to this definition, a '*symptomatic*' psychosis which originates within the body, but arises primarily from morbid factors outside of the nervous system, thus constituting merely a secondary symptom of an organic disease affecting parts of the body other than the nervous system itself, must similarly be classified as exogenous, as the more obvious cases of traumatic psychosis, alcoholic hallucinosis or reactive depression (see *endogeny*).

exophoria (ek-so-for'ē-à) See *heterophoria.*

exophthalmic dysostosis (eks-of-thal'mik dis-os-tō'sis) *Xanthomatosis* (q.v.).

exophtalmic goiter *Thyrotoxicosis* (q.v.).

expansiveness Lack of restraint in feelings and actions and especially overvaluation of one's own work. Sometimes used to refer to megalomaniacal trends; thus, delusions of grandeur and omnipotence are called expansive delusions. Horney uses the term to refer to a type of neurotic solution of inner conflicts based on identification with the idealized self and expressed in the form of narcissism, perfectionism, arrogance and vindictiveness, or as other qualities consistent with mastery.

expectancy, life The number of years that persons of a given age will, on the average, live beyond that age, is called the expectation of life at that age.

In the United States in 1964, the expectation of life at birth was 70.2 years (compared with a life expectancy of 69.6 years in 1954, and 65.2 years in 1944). The following table shows life expectancy at birth for selected countries:

COUNTRY	PERIOD	MALE	FEMALE
Australia	1953-55	67.1	72.8
Brazil	1940-50	39.3	45.5
Cambodia	1958-59	44.2	43.3
Canada	1960-62	68.4	74.2
Ceylon	1954	60.3	59.4
Denmark	1956-60	70.4	73.7
England and Wales	1961-63	68.0	73.9
France	1963	67.2	74.1
Haiti	1950	32.6	32.6
India	1957-58	45.2	46.6
Israel (Jewish)	1963	70.9	73.0
Italy	1954-57	65.7	70.0
Ivory Coast	1956-58	35.0	35.0
Mexico	1956	55.1	57.9
Morocco	1960	49.6	49.6
Puerto Rico	1960	67.3	72.1
Senegal	1957	37.0	37.0
Spain	1960	67.3	71.9
Switzerland	1959-61	69.5	74.8
United Arab Republic	1960	51.6	53.8
United States	1963	66.6	73.4
U.S.S.R.	1960-61	65.0	73.0
West Germany	1962-63	67.1	72.8

expectation, anxious 'A lurking sense of apprehension. This "anxious expectation" shows itself most intensely on all occasions that depart from what is usual, in regard to anything that involves something novel, unexpected, unexplained, uncanny.' (Freud, S. *Collected Papers,* tr. by Riviere, J., Leonard and Virginia Woolf and The Institute of Psychoanalysis, London, 1924-25) See *neurosis, expectation.*

expediter In social psychiatry and psychiatric ecology, a person (or mechanism) who routes a patient through the network of social subsystems with which he articulates and effects linkages between those systems, as part of the total treatment and rehabilitation plan. See *ecology; psychiatry, community.*

experience, accidental See *accidental.*

experience, corrective emotional One of the briefer and more direct techniques advocated by Alexander to expedite psychotherapy. In this technique, the therapist temporarily assumes some particular role to bring the patient more quickly to an awareness of transference relationships and to other personal insights and reorientations.

experiment of nature See *nature, experiment of.*

experimental neurosis See *neurosis, experimental.*

expiation (eks-pē-ā'shun) The act of atoning for, or making complete satisfaction for, a misdeed. Expiatory behavior (especially expiatory self-punishment) has been emphasized by Rado in his writings on obsessive behavior. According to him, obsessive attacks are derived from the temper (rage) tantrums of childhood, but in the obsessive patient the discharge of rage is slow and incomplete since it is always opposed by guilty fear. The latter, in turn, must be followed by expiatory behavior, just as in the child the mother's punishment and threats led to fearful obedience.

Such expiatory behavior would be considered by some an expression of moral masochism. See *masochism.*

explicit role See *role.*

exploiting type See *assimilation.*

explosion-readiness See *readiness, explosion.*

exposure, indecent See *exhibitionism.*

expressible Synonymous with *penetrant.* See *penetrance.*

expressive pattern See *psychodynamics, adaptational.*

expressivity See *penetrance; chromosome.*

extension, symbolic The investment (through extension) of new situations or objects with the same meaning and values as were engendered by experience with older situations or objects, to which the new ones bear no actual resemblance. The original connection is forgotten, so that meaning and values have become dissociated from the experiential material, which originally determined them, and are now associated with the new material, which only *stands for or symbolizes* the original. Thus the original conceptions are extended by their application to symbols, and the process itself is known as symbolic extension. For example, psychoanalysis has demonstrated that in some people a belief in God represents a symbolic extension of the original ideational material concerning the father.

exteriorization (eks-tē-rē-ō-rī-zā'shun) The act of objectivating one's interests and affects. While speaking of treatment of schizophrenic individuals, Henderson and Gillespie say that '. . . we must encourage, stimulate, explain and try to "exteriorise" those who tend to day-dream and to lead asocial seclusive lives.' (Henderson, D.K., and Gillespie, R.D. *A Text-Book of Psychiatry,* 4th ed., Oxford University Press, London, 1936)

externalization (eks-tern-al-ī-za'shun) In discussing the Thematic Apperception Test, Bellak (in Abt, L.E., and Bellak, L., *Projective Psychology,* Knopf, New York, 1950) defines externalization as '. . . those apperceptive processes which function on a preconscious level and can therefore readily be made conscious.' The writer thereby differentiates between, on the one hand, projection as an unconscious defense mechanism which leads to extreme and pathological distortion of reality, and, on the other, the apperceptive distortions which make up the subject's responses in 'projective' tests.

Horney uses the term externalization to refer to the experiencing of any intrapsychic process as occurring between oneself and others. In active externalization, the feelings toward oneself are experienced as feelings toward others; in passive externalization, feelings toward others are experienced as being directed by others toward oneself. (In Horney's system, projection is the shifting of responsibility or blame for one's own undesirable qualities onto others.) See *projection.*

extinction In neurophysiology, disappearance of excitability to a previously adequate stimulus. Immediately after application of a stimulus to a nerve, there occurs a progressive depression of excitability of that nerve; at the point at which the nerve or focus becomes completely inexcitable, extinction is said to have occurred.

Extinction for visual and tactile stimuli is found in occipito-parietal lesions; it is a defect of visual and tactile attention (and hence is also termed *inattention*). The subject is able to perceive stimulation in the affected sensory area when this is the only area stimulated; but if stimulated in some other area of the visual or tactile field he can not recognize the stimulus object in the affected area.

For the meaning of extinction in psychoanalysis, see *ego, extinction of.*

extinction, order of In genetic family studies, the statistical estimate of families dying out in a certain generation because of lack of reproduction.

extractive disorders See *psychodynamics, adaptational.*

extrapunitive See *intropunitive.*

extrapyramidal system A functional system of nerve tracts whose main action is concerned with automatic movements involved in postural adjustments and with autonomic regulation. It is usually considered to include three layers of integration: cortical, basal ganglia, and midbrain (tegmental). Parkinsonism, athetosis, chorea, and torsion spasms are all possible results of extrapyramidal dysfunction. The mechanisms involved in the production of these syndromes are only poorly understood, but many believe that they are a result of release from suppressor action. There is also evidence that extrapyramidal disorders, both naturally occurring and secondary to medication with phenothiazine compounds, are due to a deficiency of dopamine.

extrasensory perception See *perception, extrasensory.*

extraversion (eks-trá-vēr'shun) Disposition to turn one's interests upon or find pleasure in external things. Jung speaks of *active* extraversion, when the libido is 'deliberately willed,' and *passive* extraversion 'when the object compels it, i.e. attracts the interest of the subject of its own accord, even against the latter's intention.' (Jung, C.G. *Psychological Types*, tr. by Baynes, H.G., Harcourt, Brace, New York and London, 1923)

The act or process of extraverting is *exteriorization* (q.v.).

extraversion, active See *extraversion*.

extraversion, passive See *extraversion*.

extremity, phantom See *limb, phantom*.

extroversion, extrovert Less correct, but equally frequent spellings of *extraversion, extravert*.

eye movement, rapid See *dream*.

eyelash sign See *sign, eyelash*.

F

F In Rorschach scoring, a form response, i.e. a response determined solely by the shape or outline of the area in the blot to which it refers. The F responses indicate what is most conventional and socialized in the subject and are a measure of the capacity for consistent thinking. When the form response is of good quality, i.e. when it fits its area at least as well as the popular responses fit their respective areas, it is scored as F +. When the form response is of poor quality, i.e. when it is vaguely perceived and/or it corresponds only indefinitely to the area of the blot selected for interpretation, it is scored as F−. The F+% is a measure of the tenacity with which a task is pursued, the evenness of performance, the consistency of thinking, and the adequacy of reality testing. F− responses, on the other hand, indicate indecision and inability due to perceptual vagueness; they occur primarily in schizophrenia and in organic brain disorders.

f Frequency.

F minus Rorschach scoring symbol for a form response (see *F*) of poor quality.

F plus Rorschach scoring symbol for a good form response.

fabrication See *confabulation; psychosis, Korsakov.*

fabulation Adolf Meyer used this term in the sense of confabulation or fabrication. He spoke of 'forms of protracted deliria usually with numerous fabulations. . . .' (*American Journal of Insanity LX*, 439, 1904)

facial hemiatrophy See *hemiatrophy,' facial.*

facies, ironed-out (fā'shē-ēz) This expression is usually applied to the facial expression of patients with general paresis. The loss of tone of the muscles of expression gives the face the appearance as if it has been 'ironed-out,' flattened.

facilitation In neurophysiology, shortening of the central reflex time (the synaptic delay, i.e. that portion of the total latent period of a reflex that is due to passage of impulse through internuncial neurons) either by giving a second stimulus soon after the first, or by increasing the strength of the stimulus. Facilitation is to be differentiated from *summation* (q.v.).

The above definition refers to local facilitation. It is known that facilitation (or suppression) from a distance may also occur, especially in motor areas of the cortex. The existence of bands of facilitation and suppression in the cortex has been established by Dusser de Barenne et al.

In genetics, facilitation refers to that form of interaction between hereditary and environmental factors in which a genetic tendency to a particular malformation or abnormality becomes manifest only under conditions of gestational stress.

factor In genetics, practically identical with *gene*.

factor, intrinsic See *sclerosis, posterolateral.*

factorial (fak-tō'rē-al) Pertaining to a genetic factor or a combination of factors.

factorial design See *design, factorial.*

facultative Having the power to live or operate under other conditions; that is, non-obligatory. In psychiatry, most commonly applied to homosexuality, *faute de mieux* (q.v.), and to other cases in which homosexuality is symptomatic of specific neurotic conflicts. See *homosexuality; homosexuality, female; homosexuality, male.*

faculty, criticizing Freud says that '*conscience* is a criticizing faculty. In this disease [i.e. melancholia] . . . the most remarkable characteristic is the way in which the super-ego—you may call it, but in a whisper, the conscience—treats the ego. The melancholiac during periods of health can, like any one else, be more or less severe towards himself; but when he has a melancholic attack, his super-ego becomes over-severe, abuses, humiliates and ill-treats his unfortunate ego, threatens it with severest punishments, reproaches it for long forgotten actions which were at the time regarded quite lightly, and behaves as though it had spent the whole interval in amassing complaints and was only waiting for its present increase in strength to bring them forward, and to condemn the ego on their account.' (Freud, S. *New Introductory Lectures on Psycho-Analysis,* tr. by Sprott, W.J.H., Norton, New York, 1933)

faeces amicae in os proprium inicere (L.) The phrase (quoted from Stekel) refers to a form of sexual perversion, namely, the oral incorporation of rectal contents.

Fahr's disease Cerebral calcinosis, occasionally seen as a consequence of hypoparathyroidism. Most commonly the calcifications are in the basal ganglia. A hereditary form is recognized in which there is no demonstrable disturbance in the calcium metabolism.

faith-cure Improvement (much less frequently, cure) as a result of faith or confidence of the patient in the therapist and/or the therapeutic method. Usually, faith-cures occur in favorable responses to the supportive type of psychotherapy, and particularly in the types known as prestige suggestion and persuasion.

fallacia (fal-lä′kē-à) (L. 'deceit, trick, deception') An illusion or hallucination.

fallacia optica (ôp′tē-kà) (L. 'optical deception') *Obs.* Optical illusion or hallucination.

fallectomy (fal-ek′tō-mē) See *salpingectomy.*

falling sickness A popular term for epilepsy.

Falret, Jean-Pierre (1794-1870) (fàl-rā′) French psychiatrist; in 1854, Falret and Baillarger independently described recurring attacks of mania and melancholia in the same patient.

Falret, Jules Ph.J. (1824-1902) French psychiatrist; in 1879 described 'folie cir-

culaire' and 'mixed states,' which he considered to be transitory stages between attacks of mania and depression.

false recognition, illusions of See *syndrome, Capgras'.*

falsehood, unconscious A false or untrue statement made by a person without intention or without his being aware of its false nature.

falsification, memory See *confabulation; psychosis, Korsakov.*

falsification, retrospective The addition of false details and meanings to a true memory; especially common in paranoid schizophrenia, where past experiences may be related to conform with the delusional system.

falx cerebelli (falks se-re-bel′ī) See *meninges.*

falx cerebri (se′re-brī) See *meninges.*

fames bovina (fà′mes bô-vē′nà) (L. 'oxlike hunger') *Obs.* Bulimia.

fames canina (kà-nē′nà) (L. 'doglike hunger') *Obs.* Bulimia.

fames lupina (loo-pē′nà) (L. 'wolfish hunger') *Obs.* Bulimia.

familial A normal or morbid trait tending, or observed, 'to run in families.' As the hereditary origin of such a trait is not proved by the mere observation of its occurrence in several members of the same family, the use of the expression 'familial' is to be interpreted in the sense that in the particular case of a disease or another trait the genetic basis is either not to be stressed or as yet unknown. See *heredity.*

familianism (fà-mil′i-an-iz′m) A sociological and psychological term emphasizing the tendency to maintain strong intrafamilial bonds, ties, and demands, culturally transmitted and inherited, and making for intensely compact family life and solidarity. This phenomenon, pointed to by some authors as characteristic of Jewish cultural tradition, tends as a result of centuries of enforced isolation and persecution to make for neurotic over-attachments, emotional maladjustments, and relative difficulty in the establishment of independent, adult, emotional maturity of the individual scions. (Harms, E. *Handbook of Child Guidance*, Child Care Publications, New York, 1947)

famille névropathique (fa-mēy′ nā′vrô-patēk′) (F. 'neuropathic family') A group of degenerative diseases in which Charcot included hysteria, since heredity, he felt, was the unique originating cause.

family care The boarding out of chronic patients (usually schizophrenics, tractable mental retardates, or senile cases) with relatives or, more commonly, with unrelated guardians. The patient is absorbed not only into the guardian's home but into the life of the local community as well. Perhaps the best known organized system of family care is the Gheel colony in Antwerp (Belgium).

family group intake See *intake, family group.*

family group therapy See *therapy, family group.*

family social work See *social work, family.*

fanaticism Excessive, unreasonable zeal on any subject, such as religion; fanaticism, like litigiousness, is extremely frequent in paranoids, whose zealotry in the espousing of causes may approach the delusional.

fantasy See *phantasy.*

fantasying, active A psychotherapeutic procedure in which the patient is asked to relate his spontaneous imagery. An analysis of these fantasied images enables the physician to find out the roots of the patient's conflicts. If it becomes possible to show the patient these unconscious connections, he is in a position to recognize the source of his conflicts and is able to bring the conflict within the sphere of conscious insight and control. (Baynes, H.G. *Mythology of the Soul*, Williams and Wilkins, Baltimore, 1940)

F.A.P. Fixed action pattern; see *instinct.*

fasciculation See *tremor.*

fasciculus cuneatus (fà-sik′ū-lus koon-ā-á′tus) Tract of Burdach, located in the posterior white column of the spinal cord between the fasciculus gracilis and the posterior gray column. The fasciculus cuneatus carries proprioception and vibratory sensation fibers from the upper limbs. These fibers terminate in the nucleus cuneatus at the medulla, whence arise internal arcuate fibers, some of which proceed to the homolateral restiform body and most of which cross to form the medial lemniscus of the opposite side.

fasciculus gracilis (-grà′si-lis) Tract of Goll, located in the posterior white column of the spinal cord next to the posterior (dorsal) median septum. The fasciculus gracilis carries proprioception and vibratory sensation fibers mainly from the lower limbs. These fibers terminate in the nucleus gracilis at the medulla, whence arise internal arcuate fibers, some of which proceed to the homolateral restiform body and most of which cross to form the medial lemniscus of the opposite side.

fascination When a desire for mastery of some factor in the environment cannot be gratified, a partial mastery of it is sometimes achieved by means of identification with it. This reaction is called *fascination.* For example, if an infant is seen paying rapt attention to a rattle which the mother waves before it, a phase preliminary to mastery can be assumed. But if mastery is not possible because the rattle is beyond reach, or perhaps because the knack of reaching has not yet been learned, there still remains the rapt attention, which becomes greatly intensified. The infant, so to say, loses itself in the sight and sound of the rattle and thus becomes one with it, and, through identification, a partial mastery is achieved by way of fascination.

fascinum (fàs′kē-noom) (L. 'witchcraft') This concept involves the belief, carried from the ancients, that certain people possess 'the evil eye,' because of which they are capable of fascinating and injuring others by looking at them. Patients with the paranoiac form of schizophrenia often express such a belief.

Among the Romans it also meant the membrum virile, because images of it were hung round the necks of children as a preventive against witchcraft (Varro, died B .C .27, *De Lingua Latina*, 7, §97, Müll).

fashion Fashion refers to changes in dress, manners, the arts, literature, and philosophy 'based fundamentally on differentiation and emulation.' (Blumer, H.E., in Park, R.E. *Principles of Sociology*, Barnes & Noble, New York, 1939)

Styles set by the social elite with the object of differentiation are imitated by classes lower in the social structure, which in turn cause the upper class to make fresh innovations in fashion.

fastidium cibi (fàs-tē'dē-oom kē'bē) Loathing of food.

fastidium potus (pō'tōōs) Loathing of drink.

father-fixation See *fixation, mother*.

father-ideal A psychoanalytic term for the father component of the ego-ideal. Jones writes: 'If we inquire into the matter and origin of the ego-ideal, we discover that it is compounded of two constituents, derived from the Father and the Self respectively—the original (primal) narcissism of the infant becomes in the course of development distributed in four directions, the actual proportion in each of these varying enormously with different individuals. *One* portion remains in an unaltered state attached to the real ego; that is probably the one concerned in the genesis of hypochondria. A *second* portion is deflected from any direct sexual goal and becomes attached to the idea of the parent, leading to adoration, devotion, and general over-estimation. It is important to bear in mind that to begin with this process is much more a matter of narcissistic identification than of any form of object-love. A *third* is transferred on to an ideal ego, and is one of the constituents of the "ego-ideal." The *fourth* is gradually transformed into object-love. Now the second and third of these commonly fuse during the latency period of childhood or even earlier. The form assumed by the resulting ego-ideal is largely derived from the ideas and mental attitudes of the father, the bond being effected through the second portion of the narcissistic libido mentioned above—that attached to what may be called the *father-ideal*. On the other hand, the energy that gives the ego-ideal its significance is wholly derived ultimately from narcissistic libido. There are three routes for this: (1) directly from the original narcissism of the primary ego (third portion mentioned above); (2) via the attachment to the *father-ideal* (second portion); (3) via the regression of narcissistic identification with the father that often takes place after a disappointment at the lack of gratification of object-love (fourth portion).' (Jones, E.J. *Papers on Psycho-Analysis*, Williams and Wilkins, Baltimore, 1949) See *ego-ideal; superego*.

father-imago (-ē-mä'gō) See *image*.

father-substitute See *surrogate, mother*.

father-surrogate See *surrogate, mother*.

father, vaginal A motherly, unaggressive feminine kind of husband or father, who typically has significant conflicts revolving about unconscious identification with his own mother.

fatigue, battle See *shell-shock*.

fatigue, combat See *shell-shock*.

fatigue-state See *hypoglycemia*.

fatuity (fà-tū'i-tē) Feeblemindedness; sometimes used synonymously with dementia of any kind.

fatuous Stupid.

faunorum ludibria (fou-nor'oom loo-dē'-brē-à) An old term, sometimes meaning nightmare, at other times referring to epilepsy.

faute de mieux (fōt dē mew) (F. 'for want of anything better') In psychiatry, this term is ordinarily used to refer to so-called accidental homosexuality, in which a male chooses another male as a sexual object when no women are available.

faxen-psychosis (fak'sen-sī-kō'sis) The German psychiatric term, literally in its English equivalent *buffoonery-psychosis*. See *psychosis, buffoonery*.

FC Rorschach scoring symbol for a form response determined by the colored areas of the card.

Fc' In Rorschach scoring, a shading response to the light gray areas of the blots that is to some degree influenced by the form of the blot area. See *ShR.*

Fc In Rorschach scoring, a shading response to the black areas of the blots that is to some degree influenced by the form of the blot area. See *ShR.*

fear See *anxiety.*

fear, guilty Rado's term for the fear that dire consequences are in store for one because of a misdeed (or forbidden impulse). Guilty fear is thus a derivative of the dread of conscience. It is a prominent feature of the obsessive syndrome where it opposes the patient's defiant rage and leads, ultimately, to repression of the latter. See *attack, obsessive.*

fear-hypnosis See *hypnosis, father.*

fear, impulse An 'impulse-fear' is one that arises within the individual, more or less directly from an instinctual source. It is contrasted with real fear, which is associated with some real object in the environment. The fear of being in a dark place is a real or a 'reality' fear. The fear of imminent collapse and death, while in excellent health, is an impulse-fear.

fear of:
air: aerophobia
animals: zoöphobia
anything new: kaino(to)phobia; neophobia
bacilli: bacillophobia
bad men: pavor sceleris; scelerophobia
barren space: cenophobia; kenophobia
bearing a monster: teratophobia
bees: apiphobia; melissophobia
being alone: autophobia; eremiophobia; monophobia
being buried alive: taphephobia
being enclosed: clithrophobia
being locked in: claustrophobia; clithrophobia
being looked at: scopophobia
being touched: (h)aphephobia; haptephobia
birds: ornithophobia
blood: hematophobia; hemophobia
blushing: ereuthophobia
brain-disease: meningitophobia
bridge: gephyrophobia
burglars: scelerophobia
carriage: amaxophobia

cat: ailurophobia; galeophobia; gatophobia
change: kainophobia; kainotophobia; neophobia
childbirth: maieusiophobia
choking: anginophobia; pnigophobia
cold: cheimaphobia; psychrophobia
color(s): chromatophobia; chromophobia
comet: cometophobia
confinement: claustrophobia
contamination: molysmophobia; mysophobia
corpse: necrophobia
(crossing) street: dromophobia
crowds: demophobia; ochlophobia
cumbersome, pseudoscientific terms: hellenophobia
dampness: hygrophobia
darkness: achluophobia; nyctophobia; scotophobia
dawn: eosophobia
daylight: phengophobia
death: thanatophobia
definite disease: monopathophobia
deformity: dysmorphophobia
demons: demonia; demonomania; entheomania
depth: bathophobia
devil: demonophobia; satanophobia
dirt: mysophobia; rhypophobia; rupophobia
disease: nosophobia; pathophobia
dog: cynophobia
dolls: pediophobia
dust: amathophobia
eating: phagophobia
electricity: electrophobia
emptiness: kenophobia
everything: pamphobia (*obs.*); panphobia; panophobia; pantophobia
examination: examination phobia
excrement: coprophobia
eyes: ommatophobia
failure: kakorrhaphiophobia
fatigue: kopophobia
fearing: phobophobia
feathers: pteronophobia
female genitals: eurotophobia
fever: fibriphobia; pyrexeophobia
filth: mysophobia; rhypophobia; rupophobia
filth (personal): automysophobia
fire: pyrophobia
fish: ichthyophobia
flash: selaphobia
flogging: mastigophobia
floods: antlophobia
flute: autophobia
fog: homichlophobia

food: cibophobia; sit(i)ophobia
forest: hylophobia
frogs(s): batrachophobia
functioning: ergasiophobia
ghosts: phasmophobia
girls: parthenophobia
glass: crystallophobia; hyelophobia
God: theophobia
gravity: barophobia
hair: trichopathophobia; trichophobia
heat: thermophobia
heaven: uranophobia
height: acrophobia; hyposophobia
hell: hadephobia; stygiophobia
heredity: patroiophobia
high objects: batophobia
house: domatophobia; oikophobia
ideas: ideophobia
infinity: apeirophobia
injury: traumatophobia
innovation: neophobia
insanity: lyssophobia; maniaphobia
insects: acarophobia; entomophobia
jealousy: zelophobia
justice: dikephobia
knife: aichmophobia
large objects: megalophobia
left: levophobia
light: photophobia
lightning: astraphobia; astrapophobia;
    keraunophobia
machinery: mechanophobia
man: androphobia
many things: polyphobia
marriage: gamophobia
materialism: hylephobia
medicine(s): pharmacophobia
metals: metallophobia
meteors: meteorophobia
mind: psychophobia
mirror: eisoptrophobia; spectrophobia
missiles: ballistophobia
moisture: hygrophobia
money: chrematophobia
motion: kinesophobia
mouse: musophobia
myths: mythophobia
naked body: gymnophobia
name: onomatophobia
needles: belonephobia
Negro(es): negrophobia
night: noctiphobia; nyctophobia
northern lights: auroraphobia
novelty: kainophobia; kainotophobia;
    neophobia
odor (personal): bromidrosiphobia
odor(s): olfactophobia; osmophobia;
    osphresiophobia
open space(s): agoraphobia
pain: algophobia; odynophobia

parasites: parasitophobia
people: anthropophobia
place: topophobia
pleasure: hedonophobia
points: aichmophobia
poison: iophobia; toxi(co)phobia
poverty: peniaphobia
precipice(s): cremnophobia
punishment: poinephobia
rabies: cynophobia
railroad or train: siderodromophobia
rain: ombrophobia
rectal excreta: coprophobia
rectum: proctophobia
red: erythrophobia
responsibility: hypengyophobia
ridicule: catagelophobia
right: dextrophobia
river: potamophobia
robbers: harpaxophobia
rod: rhabdophobia
ruin: atephobia
sacred things: hierophobia
scabies: scabiophobia
scratch: amychophobia
sea: thalassophobia
self: autophobia
semen: spermatophobia
sex: genophobia
sexual intercourse: coitophobia
shock: hormephobia
sin: hamartophobia
sinning: peccatiphobia
sitting: thaasophobia
sitting down: kathisophobia
skin disease: dermatosiophobia
skin lesion: dermatophobia
skin (of animals): doraphobia
sleep: hypnophobia
small objects: microphobia; microbio-
    phobia
smothering: pnigerophobia
snake: ophidiophobia
snow: chionophobia
solitude: erem(i)ophobia
sounds: acousticophobia
sourness: acerophobia
speaking: lal(i)ophobia
speaking aloud: phonophobia
spider: arachneophobia
stairs: climacophobia
standing up: stasiphobia
standing up and walking: stasibasi-
    phobia
stars: siderophobia
stealing: kleptophobia
stillness: eremiophobia
stories: mythophobia
stranger(s): xenophobia
street: agyiophobia

string: linonophobia
sunlight: heliophobia
symbolism: symbolophobia
syphilis: syphilophobia
talking: (lal(i)ophobia
tapeworms: taeniophobia
taste: geumaphobia
teeth: odontophobia
thinking: phronemophobia
thunder: astra(po)phobia; brontophobia
time: chronophobia
travel: hodophobia
trembling: tremophobia
trichinosis: trichinophobia
tuberculosis: phthisiophobia; tuberculophobia
vaccination: vaccinophobia
vehicle: amaxophobia
veneral disease: cypridophobia; cypriphobia
void: kenophobia
vomiting: emetophobia
walking: basiphobia
water: hydrophobia
weakness: asthenophobia
wind: anemophobia
women: gynophobia; horror feminae
work: ponophobia
writing: graphophobia

fear, real See *fear, impulse; anxiety.*

febriphobia (fe-bri-fō′bē-à) Pyrexeophobia; fear of fever.

febris hysterica (fe′brēs hēs-te′rē-kà) Hysterical fever.

feces-child-penis concept See *concept, feces-child-penis.*

Fechner, Gustav Theodor (1801-87) (feK′nēr) German physicist, psychologist, philosopher.

feeblemindedness Mental deficiency; oligophrenia; hypophrenia. See *retardation, mental.*

feeblemindedness, affective When the affects are so vividly in the ascendancy as to give rise to general inhibition of thought, Ferenczi uses the expression *affective feeblemindedness.* For example, anxiety may be so overpowering in a person that he cannot think, nor do ideas occur to him. For the duration of the anxiety he seems to be feebleminded.

When the anxiety is relieved, his usual thinking capacity is restored. Depressed patients often complain that they cannot think owing to the intensity of their feelings.

feeblemindedness, epileptic (ep-i-lep′tik) Often during the course of epilepsy there is a steady decline of intelligence which may eventuate in a greater or lesser degree of feeblemindedness. See *dementia, epileptic.*

feeblemindedness, hallucinatory See *dementia paranoides gravis.*

feedback (fēd′bak) Communication to the sender of the effect his original message had on those to whom it was relayed. Feedback may alter or re-enforce the original idea; it is a function that is basic to correction and self-correction.

Auditory feedback is the hearing of one's own speech. When this is delayed (as by transmitting the subject's voice to him through special headphones after a temporal delay of 200 to 300 milliseconds), the normal person shows dramatic changes in speech. He begins to stutter, vocal intensity increases, words become slurred, pitch is distorted, speech slows, and various emotional disturbances and other psychophysiological changes occur. In contrast, *delayed auditory feedback (DAF)* often has no adverse effect on the speech of schizophrenic children, a finding that has been interpreted to mean that the schizophrenic child excludes hearing as a basis for continuing monitoring of his speech.

feeding, demand Feeding an infant when he gives evidence of being hungry rather than by a predetermined, rigid schedule; also known as self-demand schedule.

feeding problem A common type of behavior disorder in which the child will not eat at all, or only under certain conditions, or shows any number of untoward and unusual reactions if and when he does eat.

feeding, self-demand In infant feeding, the modern concept that the infant is a reacting human being and should be fed whenever he is hungry. Everything else being equal, the child will cry when hungry and at the time he should be fed.

This is opposed to the Spartan attitude which requires that the infant be fed every four hours, regardless of his physiological needs, and that, even when hungry, he should be made to wait until the scheduled feeding time. During the first two or three weeks of life, hunger stimuli make themselves apparent at rather irregular intervals, but thereafter the normal infant settles gradually into a time schedule of his own.

feeding, tube Feeding through a nasal catheter that terminates in the stomach.

feeling The term is used by many 'with special reference to one only of the three kinds of process into which mental life is now usually classified—that part which deals with "feeling" in the narrower sense as distinct from "knowing" or "wishing." In this sense it is sometimes also called "affection" and is contrasted with "cognition" and "conation."' (Flugel, J.C. *Encyclopaedia Britannica*, 14th ed., vol. IX, p. 143)

According to Burrow, the total, spontaneous response of the organism to stimuli naturally affecting the empathic system. The sensations arising as a spontaneous reaction within the organism as a whole. Contrasted with affect or projected feeling. Synonym: empathic reaction. (Burrow, T. *The Biology of Human Conflict*, Macmillan, New York, 1937, p. 160)

feeling-apperception Jung says: 'The nature of feeling-valuation may be compared with intellectual apperception as an *apperception of value*. An *active* and a *passive* feeling-apperception can be distinguished. The passive feeling-act is characterized by the fact that a content excites or attracts the feeling; it compels a feeling-participation on the part of the subject. The active feeling-act, on the contrary, confers value from the subject—it is a deliberate evaluation of contents in accordance with feeling and not in accordance with intellectual intention. Hence active feeling is a *directed* function, an act of will, as for instance, loving as opposed to being in love. This latter state would be *undirected,* passive feeling, as, indeed, the ordinary colloquial term suggests, since it describes the former as activity and the latter as a condition. Undirected feeling is *feeling-intuition.*' (Jung, C.G. *Psychological Types*, tr. by Baynes,

H.G., Harcourt, Brace, New York and London, 1923)

feeling, ataxic (à-tak′sik) See *ataxia, intrapsychic.*

feeling, bodily ego See *ego, body.*

feeling, directed See *feeling-apperception.*

feeling, discharge of See *discharge, affective; abreaction.*

feeling-into This is a literal translation of the German *Einfühlung.*

'Feeling-into, therefore, is a kind of perception process, distinguished by the fact that it transveys, through the agency of feeling, an essential psychic content into the object; whereby the object is introjected.' (Jung, C.J. *Psychological Types,* tr. by Baynes, H.G., Harcourt, Brace, New York and London, 1923, p. 359)

Worringer used 'feeling-into' and *empathy* as synonymous, (ibid., p. 358)

feeling-intuition See *feeling-apperception.*

feeling, oceanic See *omnipotence; nautomania.*

feeling-sensation 'Ordinary "simple" feeling is *concrete*, i.e., it is mixed up with other function-elements, frequently with sensation for instance. In this particular case we might term it *affective*, or (as in this book, for instance) *feeling-sensation,* by which a well-nigh inseparable blending of feeling with sensation elements is to be understood.' (Jung, C.G. *Psychological Types*, tr. by Baynes, H.G., Harcourt, Brace, New York and London, 1923)

feeling, superiority The boy's feeling that he is superior to a girl in the domain of sex. 'The amalgamation of the desire for a child with the epistemophilic impulse enables a boy to effect a displacement on to the intellectual plane; his sense of being at a disadvantage is then concealed and over-compensated by the superiority he deduces from his possession of a penis, which is also acknowledged by girls.' (Klein, M. *Contributions to Psycho-analysis,* 1921 - 45, Hogarth Press, London, 1948)

feeling, undirected See *feeling-apperception.*

feelings, insanity of the *Obs.* Synonymous with *moral insanity.*

fellatio (fel-lä'tē-ō) Fellatio is the apposition of the mouth to the penis. The mucous membrane of the lips and mouth are regarded by Freud as a primary erotogenic zone. 'An intense activity of this erotogenic zone at an early age thus determines the subsequent presence of a somatic compliance on the part of the tract of mucous membrane which begins at the lips.' The original object of the lips and mouth is the nipple. 'It then needs very little creative power to substitute the sexual object of the moment (the penis) for the original object (the nipple) or for the finger which did duty for it later on, and to place the current sexual object in the situation in which gratification was originally obtained. So we see that this excessively repulsive and perverted phantasy of sucking at a penis has the most innocent origin.' (Freud, S. *Collected Papers*, vol. 3, tr. by Strachey, A. and J., Leonard and Virginia Woolf and The Institute of Psychoanalysis, London, 1925)

In present-day common (although socially taboo) parlance, the act of fellatio is referred to as a 'blow job,' 'sucking off,' or 'going down' (although the last is sometimes used to refer to heterosexual intercourse).

fellation See *fellatio.*

fellator, self- See *auto-fellatio.*

fellatrice (fel-lå-trēs') A female who takes the oral part in fellatio.

feminine traits in male See *traits, feminine, in male.*

femininity In contrast to the concept of *femaleness* which is primarily related to the proper sex chromosome structure of XX individuals, *femininity* preferably means a female individual's possession of the typical and well developed *secondary* sex characteristics of a woman (see *sex determination*).

Féré phenomenon See *reflex, psychogalvanic.*

Ferenczi, Sandor (1873-1933) (fe'ren-sē) Hungarian psychoanalyst; 'active' analysis.

Ferri, Enrico (1856-1929) (far'rē) Italian forensic psychiatrist.

fertility, differential Exhibiting a difference in reproductiveness; used in genetics and eugenics to refer particularly to the difference in number of offspring between the mental retardate and the intellectually superior. Most studies find a negative correlation between intelligence and number of offspring, but why this should be is an unsettled question.

fertility, net In human genetics this statistical concept is used for determining the reproduction and survival in tainted families. It applies to the number of those children of the carriers of a certain trait who reach the age group assumed to be the manifestation period of the trait in question.

fertilization That creative process in sexual reproduction which brings a sperm and an egg into union and enables them to form one single cell, the fertilized egg or *zygote*. By a series of cell divisions, this new cell develops into an embryo and finally into an adult organism (see *reproduction*). The essential feature in fertilization is the fusion of the nuclei of the gametes.

festination (fes-ti-nā'shun) Involuntary inclination to hurry one's gait; typical of Parkinsonism. See *paralysis agitans.*

fetalism *Foetalism* (q.v.).

fetish (fē'tish) A fetish is a material object of any kind (idol, charm, talisman) which embodies mysterious and awesome qualities and from which supernatural aid may be expected.

In psychiatry, the love object of the person who suffers from the perversion called fetishism—usually a part of the body or some object belonging to or associated with the love object. The fetish replaces and substitutes for the love object, and although sexual activity with the love object may occur, gratification is possible only if the fetish is present or at least fantasied during such activity. Typical also is the ability of the fetishist to obtain gratification from the fetish alone, in the absence of the love object. The most common fetishes—shoes, long hair, earrings, undergarments, feet—are penis symbols or serve to avoid complete nudity of the female, and fetishism is thus considered to be a means of denying castration fears. Such denial of the woman's lack of a penis in the adult male (and almost all fetishists are male) presupposes a degree of splitting in the person's ego that ordinarily is found only in cases with a defective or severely limited ego.

fetishism, acoustic The pleasure of listening to sexual stories, when it has acquired the quality of fetishism.

fetishism, adherent Magnus Hirschfeld uses this expression to refer to the form of fetishism in which clothing is donned by the fetishist. See *fetishism, coherent.*

fetishism, beast Animals often exert an aphrodisiac influence over human beings. 'The transmitting medium of this fetishism may, perhaps, be found in a peculiar idiosyncrasis of the tactile nerves which, by touching furs or animal skins, produces peculiar and lustful emotions (analogous to hair-, braid-, velvet-, and silk-fetishism).' (Krafft-Ebing, R. v. *Psychopathia Sexualis,* Login, New York, 1908)

fetishism, coherent By this term Magnus Hirschfeld refers to 'the attraction which is exercised, for many people far more than is normal, by stuffs, and objects which are not donned or thrown over the body as clothing, but are brought into immediate contact with the body surface.' (Hirschfeld, M. *Sexual Pathology,* tr. by Gibbs, J., Emerson Books, New York, 1939)

fetishism, foot See *retifism.*

Feuchtersleben, Ernst von (1806-1849) (foiK′tērs-lā-ben) German psychiatrist; author of *Lehrbuch der aerztlichen Seelenkunde.*

fever, erotic The 'fever' accompanying erotomania.

fever, psychogenetic Fever induced by psychical means is called psychogenetic fever. Body temperature may be elevated by hypnotic suggestion and in certain susceptible individuals by suggestion without hypnosis. The condition is more easily produced in hysterical than in other subjects.

Fiamberti hypothesis (A.M. Fiamberti, contemporary Italian psychiatrist) The theory that schizophrenia is due to a deficiency of acetylcholine (which Fiamberti believes to be essential for normal psychic activity), perhaps secondary to toxic-infectious influences.

fibrillation (fi-bri-lā′shun) Slow, vermicular twitchings of individual muscle fibers or bundles, occurring anywhere in the body, without producing movements of muscles or joints; the condition is mainly indicative of slow degeneration of anterior horn cells (nuclear masses of motor cells).

fiction, autarchic (aw-tär′kik) The false belief of the child in its own omnipotence. At the beginning of extra-uterine life the infant is ignorant of any sources of pleasure other than those within itself: the infant even thinks of the breast as a part of its body. Ferenczi has called this the period of unconditional omnipotence. The infant tries to cling to this feeling of omnipotence and only unwillingly orients itself to objects. This is the basis for the frequency of masturbation in children when they are weaned: they turn to themselves for pleasure rather than recognize their dependency upon the environment.

fiction, directive This term is used by Adler to describe the phantasy or idea of superiority which a person originally conceives as a subjective compensation for a feeling of inferiority. This phantasy or idea he utilizes and reacts to as if it were an absolute truth.

fictions, guiding Adler's term for the principles by which one understands, categorizes, and evaluates his experiences.

fidgetiness Fidgety state. Increased motor activity, more frequently used in reference to children than to adults. Winnicott distinguishes three types of fidgetiness: common fidgetiness due to anxiety, tics, and chorea.

fidgets Vague uneasiness, usually accompanied by restless movements. Fidgets or creeps were colloquial terms for 'the disease or morbid symptom called dysphoria.' (Tuke, D.H. *A Dictionary of Psychological Medicine,* vols. 1-2, Blakiston, Philadelphia, 1892); dysphoria nervosa.

field defect The field of vision is the limit of peripheral vision, the area within which an object can be seen while the eye remains fixed on some one point. The normal visual field has a definite contour, any change in which from the normal constitutes a field defect.

The various visual field defects (with their common causes) are: (1) *circumferntial blindness or tubular vision* (hyseria, optic or retrobulbar neuritis), consisting of a concentric contraction of the visual fields; (2) *total blindness* in one eye (complete lesion of optic nerve on same side); (3) *hemianopia* or *hemianopsia,* loss of one-half of the visual field, which may be (a) homonymous, i.e. loss of vision in the temporal half-field on the same side as the lesion and loss of vision in the nasal half-field of the other eye (lesions posterior to optic chiasm i.e. optic tract or optic radiation); or (b) heteronymous with loss of vision in the same half-field (usually the temporal) of both eyes (chiasmal lesion); or (c) unilateral hemianopia with loss of vision in the nasal or temporal half-field of one eye (perichiasmal lesion); (4) *quadrantic hemianopia* or *quadrantanopia* (partial involvement of optic radiation), with loss of vision in one quadrant of the visual field, usually homonymous.

fields of Forel See *subthalamus.*

figure In psychoanalytic psychology particularly, this term, in combination with other nouns denoting familial or close interpersonal relationships (e.g. father-figure, mother-figure, authority-figure) is approximately equivalent to substitute, replacement, representative, or surrogate.

figure-ground See *ground.*

figure, helpful In the child's world of phantasy, a male or female fairy-creature with so much love, understanding, and sympathy that the child could turn to it for help in any need.

filicide Murder of one's child; if the child is less than 24 hours old, the term *neonaticide* is used.

finding, object The process of transferring and finally placing libido upon environmental objects. The libido, formerly invested in erotogenic zones, may exhibit externalization in various forms.

'Adult object-finding is frequently determined by fetishism; the love-object must possess certain colored hair, wear certain clothing, or perhaps have certain physical blemishes.' (Healy, W., Bronner, A.F., and Bowers, A.M. *The Structure and Meaning of Psychoanalysis,* Knopf, New York, 1930)

finger agnosia See *agnosia.*

finger-painting See *painting, finger.*

fingers, insane Stoddart says: 'The name *insane fingers* has been applied to a low form of whitlow to which the insane, especially general paralytics, are liable.' The condition appears to be less common than formerly, probably on account of improved hygienic surroundings and greater cleanliness on the part of the attendants.

firing *Discharge* (q.v.).

first admission See *admission, first.*

first attack See *attack, first.*

fit, cerebellar (ser-ē-bel'ēr) Tonic or cerebellar fits were originally described by Hughlings Jackson in connection with tumors of the vermis. The patient suddenly loses consciousness, falls to the ground, develops cyanosis; the pupils are immobile and dilated. There is no tongue biting or incontinence. The head is retracted, the back arched, upper extremities extended and adducted with forearm pronated, the wrist and hand flexed and everted. The lower extremities are extended and the toes plantar flexed. There is no clonic phase; the phenomenon is one of decerebrate rigidity.

fit, tonic See *fit, cerebellar.*

fit, uncinate (un'si-nat) A subjective disturbance (hallucination) of smell and taste, characteristic of deep, mesial lesions involving the tip of the temporal lobe, at times accompanied by champing movements of the jaw—due to lesion of uncinate gyrus.

fits of horrific temptation See *temptation, horrific.*

fixate (fik'sāt) In psychoanalysis: to retain excessive amounts of libidinal or aggressive energy in one or more of the infantile structures to which they were originally attached.

fixatio mononoea (fēk-sä'tē-ō mô-nô-noi'à) *Obs.* Melancholia.

fixation In psychoanalytic psychology, persistence of the libidinal or aggressive cathexis of an object of infancy or childhood into later life. Fixation generally implies pathology and this connotes that the amount of energy retained at the infantile level is greater than is seen in the normal person, who never fully abandons an object or mode of gratification that was strongly connected with psychic energy. In the normal, even though earlier levels persist along with or under higher levels of psychic development, most psychic energy is concentrated in the higher levels. When the energy retained at lower levels exceeds the amount to be expected in the normal, the term 'fixation' is applicable, and in a general way fixation is indicative of a weak spot in psychic structure that may predispose to neurosis.

Closely related to fixation is *regression* (q.v.), for when the latter occurs it is typically to an object or mode of gratification on which he was fixated that the patient regresses.

In social work, fixation is 'a form of aberrancy of affection in which there is exaggerated devotion to someone, usually in the parental role; as mother fixation.' (Hamilton, G. *A Medical Social Terminology,* Presbyterian Hospital, New York, 1930)

fixation, cannibalistic The fixation of the libido and/or aggressive energy at the late oral or biting phase. This may lead to later cannibalistic impulses, such as the phantasy of biting and eating, swallowing, and incorporating a hated object.

fixation, father See *fixation, mother.*

fixation, libido (li-bēd'ō) The retention of libido at an early level of psychic growth.

fixation, mother Inordinate attachment to the mother. See *fixation; complex, Oedipus.*

fixation-point It is the opinion of psychoanalysts that the different neuroses and psychoses are reflections of a fixation of psychic energy at given foci or *fixation-points.* Schizophrenia, for example, is believed to have its fixation-point at the auto-erotic stage of development; paranoia signifies fixation at the narcissistic and homosexual levels; melancholia at the oral sadistic phase; hysteria at the early genital level; obsessional neurosis at the anal stage.

'If you think of migrating people who have left large numbers at the stopping places on their way, you will see that the foremost will naturally fall back upon these positions when they are defeated or when they meet with an enemy too strong for them. And, again, the more of their numbers they leave behind in their progress, the sooner will they be in danger of defeat.' (Freud, S. *Collected Papers,* vol. 3, tr. by Strachey, A. and J., Leonard and Virginia Woolf and The Institute of Psychoanalysis, London, 1925)

fixity, social The plan in which the role and status of each individual are rigidly fixed or defined as in feudal and caste societies. Social fixity also appears in modern society and in social and other groups where the place of members is defined and fixed. See *mobility, social.*

flagellantism (flaj'e-lant-iz'm, flà-jel'ant-) Erotic pleasure or stimulation derived from whipping or being whipped.

flagellation (flaj-e-lā'shun) The act of whipping as a sexual excitant. 'As for erotic flagellation, pure and simple, we know that it has existed from a remote antiquity, and that it was a recognized part of the love ritual of the ancients, a preparation for the rites of Eros, and as such, known to every debauchee.' (Putnam, S. in *Encyclopaedia Sexualis,* edited by Robinson, V., Dingwall-Rock, New York, 1936)

A patient was capable of sexual excitation only when his wife whipped him to the point of bleeding. He owned a unique collection of whips, each of which was given a proper name by him.

flagellomania *Flagellantism* (q.v.).

flapping tremor *Asterixis* (q.v.).

flare, histamine See *histamine.*

flattening In psychiatry, this term is ordinarily used to refer to a disturbance of affectivity. Flattening of affect (or 'flat affect') is rarely seen outside the schizophrenic group, although affect-block, which is seen also in obsessive-compulsive patients, may be difficult to distinguish from flattening. Flattening of the affect consists of a general impoverishment of emotional reactivity or failure to react appropriately to affect-tinged stimuli. The affect-flattened patient is often described as emotionally bleak or dull, colorless, flat, unresponsive, cold, removed, apart, uninvolved, or unconvincing. The patient himself may complain that reality seems far away, that nothing has meaning for him or that his emotional responses seem forced, false, and unreal.

flavism (flā'viz'm) The presence of yellow hair in certain regions of the body in contrast with the stronger, darker hair on other parts of the body. This condition attains its significance for constitutional classification from the theory that, like the phenomenon of *erythrism,* it constitutes a stigma of the *asthenic, microsplanchnic* physique and its tendency to tuberculosis.

fletcherism (Horace Fletcher, 1849 - 1919, American dietitian) The doctrine, or the carrying out of the belief, that each bite of food must be masticated thoroughly before it is swallowed, and that liquids should be ingested only in small sips; often includes an injunction as to the specific number of times each mouthful should be chewed.

flexibility, waxy See *catalepsy.*

flicker Flutter; rapid change in frequency of stimulation (usually auditory or visual) producing corresponding periodic change in the visual or auditory perception. In the case of vision, for example, a flickering light will be perceived as such until brightness of the light and/or frequency of the flicker is increased to a certain point (critical flicker frequency); at this point, the stimulus will be perceived as a single, continuing stimulus (fusion).

flight Act of fleeing or running away, as to escape danger. See *fugue.*

flight into disease Same as *conversion;* the flight away from threatening reality by means of the conversion symptoms represents the paranosic or primary gain of the illness.

flight into health *Transference cure* or *improvement; transference;* a relinquishing of symptoms that occurs not because the patient has resolved his neurosis, but rather as a defense against further probing by the analyst into painful, unconscious material. In many instances, the flight into health depends upon the patient's passive-dependent relationship to the analyst, whom he endows with magical power and omnipotence.

flight of ideas A near-continuous flow of speech which is not disjointed or bizarre, but which jumps rapidly from one topic to another, each topic being more or less obviously related to the preceding or to adventitious environmental stimuli. Flight of ideas is characteristic of acute manic states; consequently, it is seen most commonly in the manic phase of manic-depressive psychosis but can also be seen in the acute manic syndrome of schizophrenia. Cameron terms flight of ideas 'topical flight': 'The manic makes rapid shifts from topic to topic, but the alert, attentive listener can keep up with the changes because they do not differ fundamentally from the changes in subject a normal elated person might make. The shifts in schizophrenic talk . . . are confused by the indiscriminate overinclusion of material belonging to both shared social and private fantasy contexts. The manic in his talk keeps to social trails of communication, even though he may change his direction on them at every moment; the schizophrenic does not keep to social paths, but makes his own trail as he goes.' (Cameron, N. *The Psychology of Behavior Disorders,* Houghton Mifflin, Boston, 1947)

flight, topical Cameron's term for *flight of ideas* (q.v.).

floccillation (flok-si-lā'shun) *Carphology* (q.v.); aimless picking or plucking.

flogger One who whips; flagellator.

fluctuating ego states See *dedifferentiation*.

FM In Rorschach scoring, a non-human (i.e. animal) movement response, characterized by movement or tension that is unnatural or physically impossible for a human being. According to Piotrowski, the FM reflect the action and behavioral potentials of the subject when he is in a state of diminished consciousness and/or self-control. (Piotrowski, S. *Perceptanalysis,* Macmillan, New York, 1957)

focusing disturbance A disturbance of adaptability that may occur in patients with organic brain disease: some tasks can be performed when approached one way, but not if they are approached in any other way.

foetalism (fē'tal-is'm) Penrose's term for the signs of *mongolism* (q.v.), many of which appear to be remnants of fetal existence.

folie (fō-lē') French term for insanity. The French distinguished *mental alienation* and insanity *(folie),* considering the former in a generic sense, while they used *folie* to denote a psychiatric condition acquired by a person who had previously been in good mental health.

folie à deux (à dü') (F. 'double insanity') Folie à deux has been known by a number of names: communicated insanity, induced insanity, double insanity (Tuke, D.H.), folie simultanée (Régis), folie imposée (Lasègue and Falret), folie induite (Lehmann). See *association, psychosis of.*

'Suggestibility plays a part, among other factors, in the genesis of folie à deux or "communicated insanity," which is the term applied when two persons closely associated with one another suffer a psychosis simultaneously, and when one member of the pair appears to have influenced the other. The condition is not of course necessarily confined to two persons, and may involve three or even more *(folie à trois,* etc.).' (Henderson, D.K. and Gillespie, R.D. A *Text-book of Psychiatry,* 4th ed., Oxford University Press, London, 1936)

'It happens that paranoid or paranoiac and rarely hypomanic patients not only can make those with whom they live close together believe in their delusions, but they so infect them that the latter under conditions themselves continue to build on the delusion. . . .' (Bleuler, E. *Textbook of Psychiatry,* tr. by Brill, A.A., Macmillan, New York, 1930)

folie à double forme (à dōō'bl' fawrm') (F. 'insanity in double form') An older term for what is now called manic-depressive psychosis.

folie à formes alternes (fawrm' àl-tern') (F. 'insanity in alternate forms') An older term for manic-depressive psychosis.

folie à quatre (fôlē' à kat'r) (F. 'quadruple insanity') The appearance of the same delusions in four members of a family. Bleuler cites the following case: 'At one time we had in Burgholzli four siblings (two brothers and two sisters) who all had the same persecutory and religious delusions. It turned out that one sister, the most intelligent of the four, was the first to become ill; she imposed her delusions on the others. She deteriorated severely and later developed catatonic symptoms. The second sister could eventually be released, but had to be readmitted later. The two brothers managed to maintain themselves outside the hospital. There was no doubt that the two sisters were really schizophrenic; and we had excellent reasons for believing that the two brothers were also schizophrenic, not only because they never recovered completely afterwards, but also because of their peculiar modes of life already before the acute attack.' (Bleuler, E. *Dementia Praecox or the Group of Schizophrenias,* International Universities Press, New York, 1950) Bleuler considers this a form of *induced schizophrenia.* See *association, psychosis of.*

folie à trois (trwà) (F. 'triple insanity') The appearance of the same delusions in three members of a family. See *schizophrenia, induced; association, psychosis of.*

folie ambitieuse (äN-bē-syēz') (F. 'pretentious insanity') An older generic expression, equivalent to 'insanity with grandiose ideas.'

folie avec stupeur (à-vek' stü-pēr') (F. 'insanity with stupor') Psychosis with stupor; the term included what is now considered advanced deterioration in schizophrenia.

folie circulaire (sēr-kü-lâr′) (F. 'cyclic insanity') Falret's term for the condition known today as manic-depressive psychosis, circular or alternating type.

folie communiquée (kô-mü-nē-kā′) (F. 'infectious insanity') Synonymous with folie à deux.

folie d'action (dȧk′syawN′) (F. 'madness of movement, action') Brierre de Boismont's term for moral and emotional insanity.

folie de la puberté (dē lȧ pü-ber-tā′) (F. 'insanity of adolescence') Dementia praecox; schizophrenia.

folie démonomaniaque (dā-mô-nô-mȧ-nē-ȧk′) (F. 'demonomaniacal insanity') *Demonomania* (q.v.).

folie dépressive (dā-pre-sēv′) (F. 'depressive insanity') Melancholy.

folie des femmes en couches (dā fam′ äN kōōsh′) (F. 'insanity of women in childbirth') Puerperal psychosis.

folie des grandeurs (dā gräN-dēr′) (F. 'insanity of greatness') Megalomania.

folie des persécutions (dā per-sā-kü-syawN′) (F. 'insanity of persecutions') Paranoid psychosis.

folie du doute (dü doot′) (F. 'insanity of doubt') *Doubting mania*, today usually subsumed under the heading of anxiety-neurosis or obsessive-compulsive reaction.

'The fear of responsibility expresses itself in the compulsion to examine repeatedly whether a match thrown away no longer burns, whether the doors of closets are locked, whether letters are sealed, or whether a mistake was made in calculating (doubting mania, *folie du doute*).' (Bleuler, E. *Textbook of Psychiatry*, tr. by Brill, A.A., Macmillan, New York, 1930)

Falret introduced the expression as a nosological entity, calling it *la maladie du doute*. At an earlier date Esquirol termed the same condition *monomanie raison-*

nante; Baillarger referred to it as *monomanie avec conscience;* at other times it was known as *alienation partielle;* Oscar Berger named the condition *Grübelsücht.*

folie du pourquoi (pōōr-kwȧ′) (F. 'craze of "why."') Question-asking insanity. This is a manifestation of the compulsive-obsessive form of psychoneurosis, in which the patient has the morbid urge to ask questions.

folie gémellaire (zhā-me-lâr′) (F, 'twin-insanity') Psychoses in twins occurring simultaneously.

folie hypocondriaque (ē-pô-kawN-drē-ȧk′) (F. 'hypochondriacal insanity') Neurasthenia.

folie hystérique (ēs-tā-rēk′) (F. 'hysteric insanity') Hysteria.

folie imitative (ē-mē-tȧ-tēv′) (F. 'imitative insanity') Folie à deux.

folie imposée (eN-pō-zā′) (F. 'imposed insanity') See *association, psychosis of; folie à deux.*

folie induite (eN-dwēt′) (F. 'induced insanity') See *folie à deux.*

folie instantanée (eN-stäN-tȧ-nā′) (F. 'momentary insanity') *Mania transitoria* (q.v.).

folie morale (maw-ral′) (F. 'moral insanity') See *insanity, moral.*

folie morale, acquired Some of those who are referred to as *psychopathic personalities* may eventually develop a well-defined psychotic condition. Kraepelin calls the psychotic state an acquired form of *folie morale* or *moral insanity.*

'Numerous patients, who on account of moral incapacity either become habitual criminals, or fall into prostitution, or who, become incapable of earning a living, drift into a vagrant life, are for many years disciplined and punished, if the more striking symptoms of dementia praecox are absent, till the appearance of more severe disorders, states of excitement and stupor, hallucinations of hearing, and delusions, makes clear the morbidity of their state.' (Kraepelin, E. *Dementia Praecox and Paraphrenia,* tr. by Barclay, R.M., Livingstone, Edinburgh, 1919)

folie paralytique (pà-rà-lē-tēk′) (F. 'paralytic insanity') General paresis.

folie pénitentiaire (pā-nē-täN-syâr′) (F. 'penitentiary insanity') Prison psychosis.

folie puerpérale (pwer-pe-ràl′) (F. 'puerperal insanity') Puerperal psychosis.

folie raisonnante (rā-zaw-näNt′) (F. 'reasoning insanity') See *insanity, reasoning.*

folie raisonnante mélancolique (me-läN-kaw-lēk′) (F. 'melancholic reasoning insanity') Griesinger's expression for what was called in his time hypochondriacal melancholia.

folie simulée (sē-mü-lā′) (F. 'feigned insanity') Feigned psychosis.

folie simultanèe (sē-mül-tà-nā′) (F. 'simultaneous insanity') See *folie à deux.*

folie sympathique (seN-pà-tēk′) Sympathetic insanity.

folie systématisée (sis-te-mà-tē-zā′) (F. 'systematized insanity') An old term, synonymous with *primary delusional insanity* and with *paranoia.*

folie utérine (ü-tā-rēn′) (F. 'uterine insanity') A general term, denoting psychiatric conditions supposedly associated with uterine disorders; also nymphomania.

folie vaniteuse (và-nē-tēz′) (F. 'conceited insanity') Megalomania.

folklore Folk-wisdom or folk-learning. A term suggested by Thoms, in 1846. In the present-day life of civilized peoples, folklore is the sum-total of meager, often fragmentary relics (that have survived, through tradition, from earlier primitive-culture stages) of cultural monuments in word and art: historical accounts, legends and myths, adages and sayings, beliefs, customs, magic practices, folk-remedies, household prescripts, fairy tales, fables and songs (words, music, dances).

Folklore occupies a position of great significance in the psychiatry of today. It is a subdivision of ethnological psychol-

ogy. Psychiatric patients, especially those who show deep regression, vividly produce psychic material that may be said to have intimate parallelism with folklore.

'It is scarcely possible to estimate too highly the value of these ideas to psychopathology. The extension of the field of individual psychology into that of racial psychology, the psychological analysis of the myths, fairy tales, and magic practices of primitive peoples and early societies opened up to the clinician a surprising perspective and gave rise to a multitude of new and stimulating problems.' (Storch, A. *The Primitive Archaic Forms in Schizophrenia,* tr. by Willard, C., Nervous and Mental Disease Publishing Company, New York and Washington, 1924)

folk soul See *soul, folk.*

folkways Group habits or customs; the whole system of behavior patterns characteristic of a group. Folkways 'are developed out of experience, reach a final form of maximum adaptation to an interest, are handed down by tradition and admit of no exception or variation, yet change to meet new conditions, still within the same limited methods, and without rational reflection or purpose.' (Sumner, W.G. *Folkways,* Ginn, New York, 1906) They are the accepted or expected ways of performing the nearly infinite number of minor rituals of normal social living.

folly The clinical syndrome known in the early part of the 19th century as *folly* was roughly the equivalent of what is today known as *schizophrenia;* Guislain (early 19th century) used the terms *folly* and *paraphrenia* interchangeably.

fomes ventriculi (fō′mes ven-trē′koo-lē) (L. [foreign body as] contagium-carrier of the stomach') Hypochondriasis.

force, anti-instinctual See *anti-cathexis; counter-cathexis.*

force, central In his book on the psychology of Jung, Dr. Jacobi refers to 'the central force out of which at one time the individual psyche has been differentiated. This central force goes through all further differentiations and isolations, lives in them all, cuts through them to the individual psyche, as the only one that goes absolutely unchanged and undivided through all layers.' (Jacobi, J. *The Psychology of C.G. Jung*, Kegan Paul, Trench, Truner London, 1942) This central force (which Jung calls primal libido) lies at the very bottom of the whole structure of an individual's total psychic system. It is synonymous with undifferentiated energy, is psychical in nature, and has the general meaning of a life force.

force, psychic Mental power, a force generated by thought or mental action, apart from energy or physical force.

forebrain Prosencephalon, from which develop the telencephalon (which forms the cerebral cortex, striate bodies, rhinencephalon, lateral ventricles, and the anterior portion of the third ventricle) and the diencephalon (which forms the epithalamus, thalamus, metathalamus, hypothalamus, optic chiasm, tuber cinereum, posterior lobe of hypophysis, mammillary bodies, and most of the third ventricle). See *ergotropic*.

foreconscious, fore-conscious See *co-conscious*.

fore-pleasure In psychoanalysis, the pleasure that precedes final genital pleasure or end-pleasure. During the phase of infancy libido is invested in many erotogenic zones, the mouth, anus, skin, muscles, eyes, nose, etc. During the so-called pregenital stage, stimulation of these zones constitutes an end-pleasure, but with the advent of genital stimulation which will eventually culminate in adult genital behavior, the pregenital zones are subordinated to the genital; hence, they later become a fore-pleasure. The many physical and psychical antecedents to final genital action are called fore-pleasure. 'The increment of pleasure which is offered us in order to release yet greater pleasure arising from deeper sources in the mind is called an "incitement premium" or technically "fore-pleasure."' (Freud, S. *Collected Papers*, vol. 4, tr. by Riviere, J., Leonard and Virginia Woolf and The Institute of Psychoanalysis, London, 1924-25)

Forel, fields of (Auguste Forel, Swiss psychiatrist, 1848-1931). See *subthalamus*.

forgetfulness, organic Memory disturbances based on organic disorders.

forgetting, mechanism of Freud has given the following outline for the mechanism of the normal process of forgetting. In general, all memory material falls under two influences, condensation and displacement. The memories to which little emotion is attached are those that easily 'merge into a process of condensation.' On the other hand, the memories that are more emotionally charged resist condensation and then succumb to distortion. However, 'the tendencies of distortion also feed on the indifferent material, because they have not been gratified when they wished to manifest themselves.' Since these processes are always at work, the memory content will continue to be transformed by fresh experiences as time goes on. In this way time will blur memory and make it uncertain and indistinct. When repressed memories are recovered as in analysis, however, 'it can be verified that they suffer no changes even in the longest periods.' Although impressions assume many different forms in their development in the course of time, none of these forms is lost, and each of them is retained, including the form in which the memory was originally received. (Freud, S. *Psychopathology of Everyday Life* in *The Basic Writings of Sigmund Freud*, Modern Library, Random House, New York, 1938)

forgetting, motivated In psychiatry, this term means forgetting that is motivated by the desire to avoid painful memories. There are many cases of forgetting in which the subject feels that the impression or experience is so well known that it should not have been forgotten at all. In these and other cases the thing forgotten is often one that would be painful to the person if remembered. As a defense against experiencing this pain, he forgets the experience in question. The capacity for forgetting disagreeable things is differently developed in different persons: the individual will therefore often find it impossible to rid himself of painful memories or emotions, hard as he might strive to do so. On the other hand, things that have associative connection with the disagreeable material may frequently be forgotten. (Freud, S. *Psychopathology of Everyday Life* in *The Basic Writings of Sigmund Freud,* Modern Library, Random House, New York, 1938)

formation, character See *formation, personality.*

formation, habit See *training, habit.*

formation, inhibition Inhibition-formation refers to the organization of inhibiting or restraining influences. Inhibition-formation is one type of mental activity that serves to restrain the appearance in consciousness of impulses unacceptable to it. Symptom-formation is a method by which the unacceptable impulses gain the level of consciousness, but in symbolic form.

formation, personality This expression, used extensively in psychoanalytic literature, refers to the structure or arrangement of the constituents of the personality. It possesses the same meaning in any of the schools of psychological thought.

Psychoanalysts employ *personality-formation* and *character-formation* synonymously.

formation, ready-made While writing on *The Psychology of the Dream-Processes,* Freud emphasizes that the unconscious division of the psyche contains preformed dream-content. 'As for the riddle of the superabundant dream-content compressed into the briefest moment of time, we have been able to contribute the explanation that the dream seizes upon ready-made formations of the psychic life.' (Freud, S. *The Interpretation of Dreams,* 3rd ed., tr. by Brill, A.A., Macmillan, New York, 1933)

formation, replacement An idea or set of ideas that serve to substitute for another or other ideas.

'The generalization can be safely hazarded that all members of the family group, from brother to grandfather, from sister to aunt, are all replacement-formations of the image of the original trinity of father, mother and child.' (Jones, E. *Papers on Psycho-Analysis,* 4th ed., Wood, Baltimore, 1938)

formation, reticular The primitive, diffuse system of interlacing fibers and nerve cells which forms the central core of the brainstem; also called the bulbotegmental reticular formation. The reticular formation projects to the thalamic intralaminar nuclei via the reticulothalamic, tegmentothalamic, and tectothalamic tracts. From the reticular nucleus of the thalamus, nonspecific fibers project to all parts of the cerebral cortex. It is believed that these fibers can activate the cortex independently of specific sensory or other neural systems, and the reticular formation is thus considered a part of the 'reticular activating system' (R.A.S.) or *alerting system,* which also includes subthalamus, hypothalamus, and medial thalamus. The R.A.S. seems to be essential for the initiation and maintenance of alert wakefulness, for alerting or focusing of attention, perceptual association, and directed introspection. Impaired function of the R.A.S. may be associated with anesthesia and comatose states. There is evidence to indicate that the primary site of action of certain of the so-called tranquilizing drugs is in the R.A.S.

formes frustes (fawrm' frust') (F. 'defaced, worn, blurred forms') Relating to indefinite or less significant or atypical symptoms or types of a disease.

formication (for-mi-kā'shun) An abnormal subjective sensation (referred to skin areas) of ants (or other small insects) creeping in or under the given skin area; while the condition may occur in the so-termed psychogenic mental states, it is perhaps most commonly seen in those patients in whom there is some organic agent, usually in the form of narcotic drugs (alcohol, cocaine, morphine, etc.). Also known as the *signe de Magnan.*

'Hallucinations of touch (haptic hallucinations) and other skin sensations are common (*formication*—the "cocaine bug").' (Henderson, D.K. and Gillespie, R.D. *A Text-Book of Psychiatry,* 4th ed., Oxford University Press, London, 1936)

fornication (for-ni-kā'shun) Sexual intercourse on the part of an unmarried person.

fornicator (for'ni-kā-tēr) A male person who participates in illicit sexual intercourse.

fornicatrix (-triks) A female person who engages in illicit sexual intercourse.

fornix (for'niks) An arched white fiber tract lying beneath the corpus callosum, extending from the hippocampus and terminating in the mammillary body.

Foster Kennedy syndrome (Foster Kennedy, New York neurologist, 1884-1955) See *nerve, olfactory.*

Fothergill's neuralgia (Samuel Fothergill, English physician, 19th century) See *tic douloureux.*

fouetteuse (fwà-tēz') A female flogger or flagellator.

Fournier tests (Jean Alfred Fournier, French dermatologist, 1832-1914) Occasionally an ataxic gait may be absent in normal walking; to overcome this, the Fournier tests may be utilized to verify the presence of equilibratory ataxia in walking; the patient is commanded to rise quickly from a sitting position; he is asked to rise and walk, then stop quickly on command; he is requested to walk and turn about quickly on sharp command.

Foville's syndrome (Achille L. Foville, French neurologist, 1799-1878) A form of *hemiplegia alternans* (q.v.) with contralateral hemiplegia and homolateral paralysis of the abducens and facial nerves.

fractional interpretation of dream See *dream, fractional interpretation of.*

Fragesucht (frà'ge-sookt) Compulsion to ask irrelevant questions even though not particularly interested in the answers.

fragmentation White defines this expression as 'molecular splitting of the psyche' and says that it is 'an obvious psychological characteristic of dementia praecox at the descriptive level.' See *thinking, fragmentation of.*

free will The term for the concept that man is free to dispose of his own will; that he can choose between alternatives in such manner that the choice is entirely uninfluenced by factors not consciously controlled by him.

Discussing the subject of free will and its opposite, determinism, Ernest Jones writes: 'One of the psychological arguments against the belief in a complete mental determinism is the intense feeling of conviction that we have a perfectly free choice in the performance of many acts. This feeling of conviction must be justified by something, but at the same time it is entirely compatible with a complete determinism. It is curious that it is not often prominent with important and weighty decisions. On these occasions one has much more the feeling of being irresistibly impelled in a given direction (compare Luther's "Hier stehe ich, ich kann nicht anders"). On the contrary, it is with trivial and indifferent resolutions that one is most sure that one could just as well have acted otherwise, that one has acted from non-motivated free will. From the psychoanalytical point of view, the right of this feeling of conviction is not contested. It only means that the person is not aware of any conscious motive. When, however, conscious motivation is distinguished from unconscious motivation, this feeling of conviction teaches us that the former does not extend over all our motor resolutions. What is left free from the one side receives its motive from the other—from the unconscious—and so the physical determinism is flawlessly carried through. A knowledge of unconscious motivation is indispensable, even for philosophical discussion of determinism.' (Jones, E.J. *Papers on Psycho-Analysis*, Williams and Wilkins, Baltimore, 1949) The interrelation of conscious and unconscious mental processes provides the key to the problem of psychological *determinism* (q.v.).

Fregoli's phenomenon See *syndrome, Capgras'.*

frenetic Phrenetic.

frenzy Obs. Extreme excitement and mental agitation; it was sometimes considered synonymous with *mania.*

frequency The number of subjects with a given character, for example, the number of persons aged 20-24 years, is termed its frequency. See *table, frequency.*

frequency, flicker (fusion) See *flicker.*

Freud, Anna (1895-   ) Vienna-born lay analyst, daughter of Sigmund Freud;

The Ego and the Mechanisms of Defence (1936); play therapy; psychoanalysis of children and adolescents; fled to London with her father in 1938.

Freud, Sigmund (1856-1939), Austrian psychiatrist; founder of psychoanalysis; concepts of the libido, regression, transference, repression, sublimation, id, ego, superego, Oedipus complex, etc.; psychopathology of dreams; evaluation of infantile experiences and impressions.

friction In social work, the term means 'conflicts arising out of unlike temperaments or emotional needs which, instead of resolving themselves in a constructive manner, continue on a level of chafing and irritation. *Family Friction*—a generalized tension or irritation in any combination of family life, excepting when otherwise distinguished; *Marital Friction* —the spouse being the patient; *Parental Friction*—between the parents of a minor child, the child being the patient; *Parent-Child Friction*—between parent and child, either being the patient.' (Hamilton, G. A *Medical Social Terminology,* Presbyterian Hospital, New York, 1930)

friction, wet mitten 'This is a friction given with a coarse burlap or loofah bath mitten moistened in cold water. . . . Small areas of the body are uncovered, rubbed, dried, and covered. Rubbing is started at the chest, then abdomen, arms, legs, back. Rub until a pink glow is obtained.' (Steel, K.M. *Psychiatric Nursing,* Davis, Philadelphia, 1937)

Friedmann's complex (Max Friedmann, German neurologist, 1858-1925). See *constitution, post-traumatic.*

Friedreich's ataxia See *ataxia, Friedreich's.*

fright The reaction to an unexpected danger. According to Freud, 'fright is the name of the condition to which one is reduced if one encounters a danger without being prepared for it; it lays stress on the element of surprise.' This element of surprise distinguishes fright from both fear and apprehension. 'Apprehension denotes a certain condition of expecting a danger and preparation for it, even though it be an unknown one; fear requires a definite object of which one is afraid.'

Also, the element of surprise appears to be the essential causal factor in the traumatic neurosis. Apprehension cannot produce a traumatic neurosis, 'in apprehension there is something which protects against fright and therefore against the fright-neurosis.' Apprehension prepares the organism for 'oncoming masses of excitation' and it can therefore defend itself, whereas in fright the organism, taken unawares, is overwhelmed by the excitation. (Freud, S. *Beyond the Pleasure Principle,* Boni and Liveright, New York, n.d.)

fright, magic *Susto* (q.v.).

frigidity, sexual (305.6) Inability of the woman to achieve orgasm through coitus; the analogous condition in the male is termed impotence. See *impotence, psychic; orgasm.* 'Frigidity may be total or partial, but whatever its degree it is not a disease entity in itself; rather, it is a symptom or manifestation of underlying neurotic conflict and, as such, can be traced to any number of psychological mechanisms. It is difficult to say how common frigidity is; some estimate that it affects as many as 90% of women . . . while others would put it closer to 50%. . . . But whatever the actual incidence, all agree that it is high, and certainly that frigidity is more common than impotence in the male, even though the symptom itself may be less commonly complained of because it does not interfere so directly or so disastrously with the mechanics of intercourse or with reproduction.' (Campbell, R.J. 'Frigidity and Impotence" in *Marriage: A Psychological and Moral Approach,* edited by Bier, W., Fordham, New York, 1964).

Total frigidity includes complete anesthesia; absence of sexual interest; vaginismus, with or without dyspareunia— and women so afflicted will generally tolerate intercourse only after some coercion.

More common than total frigidity is some type of *relative frigidity,* among the more frequent of which are the following: (1) *vaginal hypoesthesia,* with sensitivity limited to the clitoral area; (2) sudden abrupt cessation of excitement before orgasm, even though there has been pleasure during intercourse, during both clitoral stimulation and vaginal friction; some women of this group, in their search for satisfaction, appear insatiable in their sexual demands and may go from one partner to another hoping that each new experience will bring orgasm; (3) vaginal orgasm can be achieved, but only under certain conditions—such as concurrent beating or rape phantasies—or only with certain men; (4) whatever the degree of satisfaction obtained during intercourse, the sexual act is followed by anxiety, tension, insomnia, guilt feelings and depression, physical complaints, or any other kind of symptom, all of which point to some kind of unconscious conflict about sexuality, usually revolving about unsatisfied infantile wishes.

fringe A term used by Morton Prince, generally in the combination of *fringe of consciousness.* He says: 'If you were asked to state what was in your mind at a given moment it is the vivid elements, upon which your attention was focused, that you would describe. But, as everyone knows, these do not constitute the whole field of consciousness at any given moment. Besides these, there is in the background of the mind, outside the focus, a *conscious margin or fringe* of varying extent *(consisting of sensations, perceptions, and even thoughts) of which you are only dimly aware.* It is a sort of twilight zone in which the contents are so slightly illuminated by awareness as to be scarcely recognizable.' (Prince, M. *The Unconscious,* Macmillan, New York, 1916)

fringe, subliminal See *summation.*

Fröhlich's syndrome (Alfred Fröhlich, Viennese neurologist, b. 1871) Fröhlich's syndrome or *dystrophia adiposogenitalis* described in 1901 is caused by a chromophobe adenoma which destroys the anterior lobe of the pituitary gland occurring mainly in individuals in the pre- or postadolescent period. The syndrome is characterized by a eunuchoidal obesity, alteration of the secondary sex characters, metabolic disturbances, change in bodily growth—gigantism, hypoplastic genitals, polyuria, polydipsia, and increased sugar tolerance.

Froin's syndrome (Georges Froin, French physician, b. 1874) High protein content of the cerebrospinal fluid (0.5 per cent or more) associated with xanthochromia, massive coagulation, and pleocytosis. Froin's syndrome is seen mainly in chronic meningitis, especially syphilitic, in obstruction of the spinal subarachnoid space by cord tumor or epidural abscess, and in cases of polyneuritis and Landry's paralysis.

Fromm-Reichmann, Frieda (1890-1957) German-born psychoanalyst; to U.S. in 1934; director of psychotherapy, Chestnut Lodge Sanitarium; Washington School of Psychiatry and Psychoanalysis; psychotherapy of schizophrenia.

frottage (frot'ij) A form of sexual perversion in which the orgasm is induced by rubbing against the clothing of an individual of the opposite sex, as occurs when the subject is pressed close to others in a throng or crowded public conveyance. An individual so afflicted is a *frotteur* (q.v.).

frotteur (frô-tĕr') (F. 'one who rubs') One who gains sexual excitement through the sense of touch by rubbing up against somebody. The term usually implies that the act of touching or being touched is not directly or overtly of a genital character, or at least that there is some measure of disguise. For example, some individuals are sexually stimulated when they are pressed closely by others as often happens when they are in a crowd. Some authorities use the term to mean direct genital or sexual activity, not including the union of the genital organs.

frustration From the standpoint of instinctual psychology (psychoanalysis), *frustration* generally refers to the denial of gratification by reality. Sometimes it is spoken of as external frustration to distinguish it from the thwarting of impulses by forces in the unconscious or also in consciousness.

When in a mentally healthy person the environment is not prepared for the acceptance of a libidinal urge, the latter may be held in suspension until reality is suitably arranged or until some form of substitutive gratification may present itself. Frustration may be eluded by means of sublimation.

When the instinctual urge cannot be handled normally by the subject, he may summon all his energies to the satisfaction of the urge, disregarding the mores of his surroundings. Or he may regress, that is, the frustrated libido may be withdrawn from objects in reality and take 'refuge in the life of phantasy where it creates new wish-formations and reanimates the vestiges of earlier forgotten ones.' (Freud, S. *Collected Papers*, vol. 2, tr. by Riviere, J., Leonard and Virginia Woolf and The Institute of Psychoanalysis, London, 1924-25, p. 114)

Internal frustration means the checking of instinctual impulses by forces in the unconscious, chiefly by the superego. Jones says: 'The ego defends itself against external danger by repressing the genital impulses [the topic under discussion by Jones] directed towards the love-object. Regression to the anal-sadistic level ensues, but the relation of this process to the frustration and to the influence of the ego-instincts is not clear.' (Jones, E. *Papers on Psycho-Analysis*, 4th ed., Wood, Baltimore, 1938)

frustration tolerance The ability to withstand tension arising from a buildup in instinctual demand which is not immediately relieved or gratified. Development of tension or frustration tolerance is an essential for achieving active mastery by the ego; low frustration tolerance and/or the need for immediate instinctual gratification are indicative of severe ego weakness.

fugue A condition in which the patient suddenly leaves his previous activity and begins to wander or goes on a journey which has no apparent relation to what he has just been doing, and for which he has amnesia afterwards. In fugues of short duration, the patient is generally agitated and confused, but in those of long duration he may often appear completely normal to the observer. Fugues may occur as one type of epileptic twilight state, as a form of catatonic excitement, or as a form of conversion hysteria (dissociative reaction). As a psychogenic reaction, they appear often to be precipitated by a need to escape an intolerable situation; such fugues are typically "orderly," while epileptic fugues are typically "disorderly."

fulfillment, punishment Freud employs this term to indicate self-punishment.

fulfillment, wish See *wish-fulfillment.*

Fulton, John Farquhar (1899-1960)

American physician; neurophysiology (esp. hypothalamus, cerebellum, autonomic nervous system), history of science and medicine.

function From the psychic point of view the psyche has organization, that is, structure. The operation of the structure is called function. The ego, as a structure of the psyche, has capacities for working or functioning.

Jung says: 'By psychological function I understand a certain form of psychic activity that remains theoretically the same under varying circumstances. From the energic standpoint a function is a phenomenal form of libido, which theoretically remains constant, in much the same way as physical force can be considered as the form or momentary manifestation of physical energy.' (Jung, C.G. *Psychological Types*, tr. by Baynes, H.G., Harcourt, Brace, New York and London, 1923)

function, auxiliary See *function, principal.*

function-complex See *complex, function.*

function, directed See *intellect.*

function, dream See *dream-function.*

function-engram In Jung's analytical psychology an inherited, archaic residue. 'The symbol is always derived from archaic residues, or imprints engraven in the very stem of the race, about whose age and origin one can speculate much, although nothing definite can be determined. It would certainly be quite wrong to look to personal sources for the source of the symbol, as for instance repressed sexuality. At best such a repression could only furnish the libido-sum which activates the anchaic imprint. The imprint (engram) corresponds with a functional inheritance whose existence is not contingent upon ordinary sexual repression, but proceeds from instinct differentiation in general.' (Jung, C.G. *Psychological Types*, tr. by Baynes, H.G., Harcourt, Brace, New York and London, 1923)

function, Gestalt See *psychology, Gestalt.*

function, inferior See *function, superior.*

function, irrational See *irrational.*

function pleasure See *pleasure, function.*

function, principal Among the many aspects of *function*, Jung speaks of the *principal* and *auxiliary* functions. 'For all the types appearing in practice, the principle holds good that besides the conscious main function there is also a relatively unconscious, auxiliary function which is in every respect different from the nature of the main function. From these combinations well-known pictures arise, the practical intellect for instance paired with sensation, the speculative intellect breaking through with intuition, the artistic intuition, which selects and presents its images by means of feeling judgment, the philosophical intuition which, in league with a vigorous intellect, translates its vision into the sphere of comprehensible thought, and so forth.' (Jung, C.G. *Psychological Types,* tr. by Baynes, H.G., Harcourt, Brace, New York and London, 1923)

function, rational See *rational.*

function, superior In Jung's analytical psychology, there are four basic psychological types—thinking, feeling, intuitive, and sensational. Any one of the functional types may predominate as the means by which the person adjusts himself to the problems of living. The predominating is called the *superior* function, while the remaining three functions are *inferior* in ivarying degrees.

function-type The generic name for Jung's various types: feeling, thinking, intuitive, and sensation. The characters of introversion and extraversion are ways of regarding reality rather than methods of adaptation to reality; hence they are called attitude-types.

function-way, archaic In analytical psychology this expression designates thinking, acting, and feeling characteristic of the primitive type of mind. While discussing *regression* Jung says: 'The draining of libido involves their gradual relapse below the threshold of consciousness, their associative connection with consciousness gets loosened, until they sink by degrees into the unconscious. This is synonymous with a regressive develop-

ment; namely, a recession of the relatively developed function to an infantile and eventually archaic level. But, since man has spent relatively only a few thousand years in a cultivated state, as opposed to many hundred thousand years in a state of savagery, the archaic function-ways are correspondingly extraordinarily vigorous and easily reanimated. Hence, when certain functions become disintegrated through deprivation of libido, their archaic foundations begin to operate in the unconscious.' (Jung, C.G. *Psychological Types,* tr. by Baynes, H.G., Harcourt, Brace, New York and London, 1923)

functional Relating to performance or execution; in psychiatry, used to refer to disorders that are without known organic basis, thus often (incorrectly) equated with 'psychogenic' or emotional. A functional disturbance is one in which the performance or operation of an organ or organ-system is abnormal, but not as a result of known changes in structure. While it is true that psychogenic disorders are functional, in that their symptoms are not based upon any detectable alterations in the structure of the brain or psyche, it is not true that all functional disorders of the psyche are of emotional origin—no more so than functional heart murmurs are based on emotional conflict. A drug-induced, temporary disturbance in synaptic transmission, for example, may produce many alterations in thinking, affect, and behavior. Since such a disturbance does not depend upon structural changes in the brain, it is properly termed 'functional'; yet it can hardly be considered to be of psychogenic origin.

functional inferiority See *inferiority, functional.*

functions, seriatim (ser-ē-ä′tim) Organization or synthesis of skilled acts or thoughts into an orderly series; such organization requires ability to anticipate a goal and ability for temporal organization. The seriatim functions are generally disturbed in the schizophrenias.

Funkenstein test (Daniel Hertz Funkenstein, American psychiatrist, 1910 -   ) See *test, adrenalin-mecholyl.*

fureur génitale (fü-rēr′ zhā-nē-tàl′) (F.

'genital rage') *Obs.* Bruisson's term for nymphomania and satyriasis.

furibundus (fū-ri-bun'dus) *Obs.* Maniacal, mad, raging.

furiosi (foo-rē-ō'zē) (L. 'those full of madness, raging, fury') This is one of the the two subdivisions of the insane recorded in the old Roman laws. Those who were violent and maniacal were called *furiosi;* those exhibiting dementia or feeblemindedness were termed *mente capti.*

furor epilepticus (foo'rôr e-pē-lāp'tē-koos) (L. 'epileptic rage') 'While observed in association with exaltation, as just noted, and among the prodromata of various insanities, it [irritability] is particularly characteristic of a primary emotional state of congenital and acquired mental weakness, neurasthenic insanity, and the epileptic psychoses. In the latter it not infrequently becomes a true *furor epilepticus.*' (Church A. and Peterson F.

Nervous and Mental Diseases, 6th ed., 1916)

furor uterinus (oo-te'rē-noos) (L. 'uterine rage') *Obs.* Nymphomania.

fusion In psychoanalysis, the union of the instincts. Normally during the early infantile months the two primal instincts, life and death, are separated from one another, each operating alone. Later the two fuse to a greater or lesser extent. In psychiatric conditions there is often some defusion of the instincts.

For example, when the ego is threatened by an external danger associated with a genital impulse, the latter is repressed and regression to the anal-sadistic level follows. Several possibilities then occur regarding the redistribution of libido. 'A part regresses and fuses with the hate instincts to constitute sadism.' (Jones, E. *Papers on Psycho-Analysis,* 4th ed., Wood, Baltimore, 1938) See *instinct.*

fusion See *flicker.*

G

G Rorschach scoring symbol for a response that includes the entire inkblot. See *W.*

gain, epinosic (ep-i-nō'sik) Secondary advantages accruing from an illness, such as gratification of dependency yearnings or attention seeking. 'In the traumatic neuroses, *secondary gains* play an even more important role than in the psychoneuroses; there are certain uses the patient can make of his illness which have nothing to do with the origin of neurosis but which may attain the utmost practical importance. . . . Obtaining financial compensation or fighting for one creates a poor atmosphere for psychotherapy, the more so if the compensation brings not only rational advantages but has acquired the unconscious meaning of love and protecting security as well. . . . Perhaps the idea of giving one single compensation at the right time may be the best way out.' (Fenichel, O. *The Psychoanalytic Theory of Neurosis,* Norton, New York, 1945).

gain, morbid Synonymous with *gain, epinosic; illness, advantage by* (qq.v.).

gain, secondary See *gain, epinosic.*

gait, ataxic Tabetic gait, due to loss of proprioceptive sense in the extremities as a result of posterior column disease. The patient walks on a wide base, slapping his feet, and typically watching his legs and feet so he will know where they are.

gait, cerebellar (se-re-bel'ēr) In diseases of the cerebellum, the patient walks unsteadily with a 'drunken,' wobbly gait. There is lack of association between the movements of the legs and body, so that in walking, the body either lags behind, or is abruptly brought forward, and there is a tendency to reel to one side.

gait, clumsy See *gait, waddling.*

gait, drunken Staggering gait, seen not only in acute alcoholic intoxication but also in other drug intoxications, polyneuri-

tis, multiple sclerosis, general paresis, and brain tumors.

gait, festination See *gait, propulsion.*

gait, foot-drop See *gait, steppage.*

gait, hemiplegic (he-mi-plē'jik) In patients with hemiplegia, the lower extremity is held stiffly and circumducted in walking, and the patient leans to the affected side.

gait, myopathic (mī-ō-pa'thik) A waddling gait is characteristic of the myopathies. See *gait, waddling.*

gait, propulsion *Festination gait, march à petits pas;* characteristic of Parkinsonism. The patient leans forward and takes short, shuffling steps which begin slowly but accelerate as he continues to walk; he looks as though he must run to keep up with his head.

gait, scissors In patients with bilateral spastic limbs, there is crossed progression, in the process of walking; the legs cross in scissors fashion.

gait, spastic (spas'tik) The patient walks stiffly with legs extended and feet shuffling.

gait, stoppage Foot-drop gait due to paralysis of the anterior tibial group of muscles, as in alcoholic neuritis, peroneal nerve injuries, poliomyelitis, and progressive muscular atrophy. The patient raises his affected knee high, and the foot flops with the toe usually dragging along the floor.

gait, stuttering A disorder in walking, usually, though not necessarily, psychogenic. It is characterized by a hesitancy in walking analogous to that observed in speech stuttering. It is sometimes seen in hysterical and in schizophrenic subjects.

gait, tabetic See *gait, ataxic.*

gait, waddling Clumsy gait, seen in dislocation of the hips and in muscular dystrophies with hip weakness. The weakness necessitates use of the trunk muscles in walking, so that the patient rolls from side to side as he walks.

galactosaemia An autosomal recessive disorder (in which the patient is homozygous for the gene) consisting of an absence of the enzyme galactose-1-phosphate uridyl transferase, which is essential for the conversion of galactose-1-phosphate to glucose-1-phosphate. Galactose-1-phosphate accumulates in erythrocytes, liver and kidney tissue, brain, and lens, with resultant impairment of tissue metabolism. Mental retardation (31x.2) may in large part be prevented by early administration of a galactose-free diet.

galeanthropy (gā-lē-an'thrō-pē) The delusion that one is a cat.

galeophobia (gā-lē-ō-fō'bi-à) Fear of cats; also *ailurophobia, gatophobia.*

gallows humor See *humor, gallows.*

Galt, John Minson 2nd (1819-62) American psychiatrist; forensic psychiatry, psychiatric records research.

galvanic skin response See *reflex, psychogalvanic.*

game, hallucinatory In children, the same factors that are responsible for illusions may produce reactions which Stern called hallucinatory games. (Stern, W. *Psychologies der Frühen Kindheit,* 5th ed., Quelle und Meyer, Leipzig, 1928, p. 237) These hallucinations differ from real hallucinations in their being actively created by the child instead of being felt as something foreign and passive. The infant literally makes a *game* of deliberately creating objects out of phantasy and amusing itself thereby. It is at all times fully aware of the unrealness of these self-created objects and can easily banish them when tiring of them, or for any reason whatever. A very young child's 'playing store' is largely a hallucinatory game: the business of the 'store' is playfully transacted through pantomime and the use of hallucinated merchandise and money.

gamete (gam'ēt) Special sex-cell. In genetics, a specialized sexual cell which unites

with another germ cell to form a zygote. Among animals the male gametes are known as spermatoza and the female gametes as *eggs* or *ova.*

Gametes are always haploid and genetically pure, because they contain only one member of a given factor pair. Since the formation of a gamete involves a reduction of 50 per cent in the amount of genetic material carried, each gamete has only half of the factorial equipment of an ordinary body cell and never shows the hybrid character of the individual producing it. See *chromosome.*

gammacism (gam'à-siz'm) Common speech defect (the 'baby talk') of young children who replace the *velars (g,k)* with corresponding *dental (d,t).*

gamo- (gam'ō-) combining form meaning marriage, (sexual) union, from Gr. *gámos,* wedding, marriage.

gamonomania (ga-mo-nō-mā'nē-à) Morbid desire to marry.

gamophobia (gam-ō-fō'bē-à) Fear of marriage.

gang 'The gang, whether developed out of lawless crowd behavior of adults or from the neighborhood play groups of children, is always a conflict group at war with other groups or with the forces of organized society.' (Reuter, E.B., and Hart, C.W. *Introduction to Sociology,* McGraw-Hill, New York 1933)

The gang is an interstitial group originally formed spontaneously, and then integrated through conflict. It is characterized by the following types of behavior: meeting face to face, milling, movement through space as a unit, conflict, and planning. The result of this collective behavior is the development of tradition, unreflective internal structure, *esprit de corps,* solidarity, morale, group awareness, and attachment to a local territory.' (Thrasher, F.M. *The Gang,* University of Chicago Press, Chicago, 1927)

Boy groups in American cities are an important factor in juvenile delinquency, in the beginnings of criminal careers, in organized crime, and in political corruption.

ganglia, basal See *basal ganglia.*

Ganser syndrome (Sigbert Joseph Maria Ganser, German psychiatrist, 1853-1931) Syndrome of deviously relevant answers, popularly called the 'nonsense syndrome'; it is often observed among prisoners, who, it is held, hope to be treated leniently by the court in virtue of their malady. It is described by many investigators as a hysterical reaction. The patient seldom does anything correctly. When shown a watch, reading 3:30, the patient may say it reads 5:00; when shown a glove he says it is a hand; he designates a 50-cent piece as a dollar bill; calls a key a lock. But in addition to such approximate answers, which may be seen also in hysterical pseudodementia, behavior is bizarre, with episodes of excitement or stupor, as though the subject were acting out an artificial psychosis.

gargalesthesia (gàr-gal-es-thē'zhē-à) Sensation of tickling.

gargoylism (gargoil-iz'm) *Hurler's disease;* also known as Pfaundler-Hurler syndrome, dysostosis multiplex, lipochondrodystrophy; a rare disorder of phospholipid metabolism that usually manifests itself in the early months of life. The child resembles an achondroplastic dwarf and shows multiple skeletal deformities (short neck, dorsal kyphosis, deformed thorax and long bones, flexion deformities of all joints, and maldevelopment of the skull vault and facial bones), hideous features (thickened skin and soft tissues, large head with widely spaced eyes and flattening of the bridge of the nose, coarse lips, protruding tongue, stridulent mouth breathing, and an apathetic, bovine expression), hepatosplenomegaly, corneal clouding, mental retardation (31x.2). Cause is unknown but several features suggest an autosomal recessive gene: several siblings are often affected, but the parents are always normal, and parental consanguinity is frequent.

G.A.S. General adaptation syndrome. See *syndrome, general adaptation.*

gases, psychosis due to Poisonous gases, such as carbon monoxide found in illuminating gas and in exhausts from automobiles, may produce mental disturbances. There is usually a preliminary period of unconsciousness followed by more or less protracted delirium after which the patient may experience increased fatigability and difficulty in concentration. Sometimes the symptoms clear up entirely; a normal interval of many weeks may ensue, to be followed by symptoms of mental defect from which the person may not recover. These patients then remain in a chronic state of moderate or severe mental enfeeblement.

gastropaths, false (gas'trō-paths) Déjérine and Gauckler so designate those who express *food phobias.*

gastrulation (gas-troo-lā'shun) In embryological development of a human organism, the stage characterized by the conversion of the monodermic *blastula* into a didermic *gastrula.* The gastrulating process is effected by the invagination, in the form of a blind tube, of the vegetal pole into the segmentation cavity. The wall of this tubular invagination is constituted by the primitive *entoderm* while its opening, or primitive mouth, is known as the *blastopore.*

gatekeeper In community psychiatry, an extramural, non-professional person whose role in the community (e.g. bartender, policeman, playground worker, etc.) is such as to allow him to observe segments of a population for signs of stress, disharmony, disaffection, and discord. He may receive specialized training from the Community Mental Health Center (the current catchphrase for such training is 'orientation sessions') so that he can function as a liaison worker between the Center and the community.

gatophobia (gà-tō-fō'bē-à) Fear of cats; also *ailurophobia, galeophobia.*

Gaucher's disease See *disease, Gaucher's.*

Gayet-Wernicke's encephalopathy *Wernicke's encephalopathy* (q.v.).

gaze, fascinating In hypnosis this term refers to the fixation of the eyes of the hypnotist upon the subject.

gazing, crystal A technique used in hypnoanalysis consisting of having the hypnotized subject observe a glass ball or a mirror and then produce associations. The patient is instructed to look at the glass and told that he will see in it things that he will describe to the analyst afterward.

gelamus (jē-laz'mus) Spasmodic laughter, observed in hysteria and the schizophrenias, and in some organic (especially bulbar) diseases of the brain.

gelatio (ge-lä'tē-ō) *Obs.* Rigid state of the body in catalepsy, as though it were frozen.

Gélineau's syndrome (Jean Baptiste Édouard Gélineau, French neurologist, b. 1895.) Idiopathic narcolepsy.

gender role The behavior and appearance that one presents in terms of what the culture considers to be 'masculine' or 'feminine.' That the gender role and sexual identity are not wholly determined by genetic constitution is demonstrated by pseudohermaphrodites who were reared contrary to their chromosomal sex; in all such cases, the gender role and orientation are congruent with the assigned sex and rearing, rather than with the biological sex.

gene Morphologically a gene is best understood as a particular state of organization of the chromatin at a particular point in the length of a particular *chromosome* (q.v.). This state of organization is to be regarded as the physical basis explaining how a hereditary character passes as a unit from parent to offspring, while it is the parallelism between the behavior of chromosomes and genes which supports the assignment of a physical basis in the chromosomes to the Mendelian units.

Both chromosomes and genes behave in inheritance as though they were individual units, and the principles of segregation and independent assortment apply to chromosomes in precisely the same way in which they have been demonstrated to apply to genes. It is assumed that the genes always occur in pairs, and that one member of each pair is contributed by one parent and the other by the other parent. Owing to the phenomenon of *crossing over* it has even been possible not only to map each chromosome in certain organisms, but also to assign the genes to their relative positions on the chromosome, and to establish the fact of the *linear order* of the genes.

In accordance with these experimental findings, Morgan's *theory of the gene* is formulated as follows:

(1) The hereditary characters of the individual are referable to paired elements [the genes] in the germinal material [the chromosomes] which are held together in a definite number of linkage groups;

(2) In accordance with Mendel's first law, the members of each pair of genes separate when the germ cells mature and in consequence each ripe germ cell comes to contain one set only;

(3) The members of different linkage groups assort independently in accordance with Mendel's second law;

(4) An orderly interchange, or crossing over, also takes place between the elements in corresponding linkage groups;

(5) The frequency of crossing over furnishes evidence of the linear order of the genes in each linkage group and of the relative position of genes with respect to each other.

genealogy (jē-nē-al'ō-jē) Although in a sense identical with the actual pedigree of an individual or with the demonstration of such a pedigree in the form of a genealogical family tree, the term applies to the scientific study, or the proper historical account, of the biological descent of a person, or a group of persons, from a certain number of ancestors. These studies aim to provide a complete list of ancestors for as many generations as possible and to clarify the relationship of a person with the families of a given population group, rather than to investigate either the biological qualities of these families or the variations of certain hereditary family traits in successive generations.

general paralysis of the insane See *paresis, general.*

general paresis See *paresis, general.*

general paresis, juvenile See *paresis, juvenile.*

general systems theory 'A set of related definitions, assumptions, and propositions which deal with reality as an integrated hierarchy of organizations of matter and energy. General systems behavior theory is concerned with a special subset of all systems, the living ones.' (Miller, J.G. *Behavioral Science 10,* 193-237, 1965) General systems behavior theory is an attempt to develop an embracing general theory of the behavior of man by identifying the organized, interacting components that make up the system; by defining the controls that keep those subsystems or fields stable and in equilibrium; and by establishing the roles, relationships, inputs, outputs, and routes of flow within the hierarchy of subsystems that make up the whole. General systems theory thus provides a holistic approach to the study of human behavior and attempts to integrate the different conceptions of how each subsystem operates from a wide variety of disciplines and specialties in a search for the general truth inherent in all.

generalization Applying to a whole group or class of conclusions, ideas, judgments, etc. based upon experience with a limited number of the class. While generalization is an essential element of conceptualization in the processes of normal thought, it attains particular significance in psychiatry in that one of the many thought-disorders in schizophrenia is the tendency to over-generalize, and to treat the concrete as though it were abstract.

generation Even in the field of biology, this term has several meanings. It denotes the act of producing offspring, or the biological process by which reproduction is accomplished, or a group of offspring produced. In the last sense the term may mean that the given offspring are: (1) of the same genealogical rank, as a stage in the succession of natural descent; (2) a series of siblings within one family, as the offspring of the same parents; (3) a particular group of persons within the general population, living at the same time; or (4) people of the same period.
As a statistical concept the term refers to the average duration of life in a species or group.

generative (jen′ēr-ā-tiv) *Biol.* Having the function, or power, or reproducing.

generativity (jen-ēr-à-tiv′i-tē) The impulse for procreation, general in the human race. 'Generativity is primarily the interest in establishing and guiding the next generation or whatever in a given case may become the absorbing object of a parental kind of responsibility.' (Erikson, E. *Childhood and Society,* Norton, New York, 1950, p. 231)

generic (jē-ner′ik) *Biol.* Pertaining to a *genus,* as compared with *specific.*

genes, modifying All those genes which have some influence on the effect of any particular gene; for all practical purposes, the modifying genes are all the genes other than the one under specific study, for even genes which produce a single large effect are subject to modification and qualification by the entire remainder of the genetic constitution.

genetic, genetical (jē-net′ik, -′i-kal) While *genetical* is used exclusively in the sense of pertaining to the province of genetics, the term *genetic* has two meanings: (1) it is synonymous with *genetical;* and (2) it means: produced or predetermined by a gene or a combination of genes, and is then practically identical with *hereditary.*

genetic block See *disease, genetotrophic.*

genetic drift See *drift, genic.*

genetics Bateson introduced this term to designate that portion of biology which seeks to account for the resemblances and the differences in organisms related by descent. It is the science which simply *studies* in living organisms such genetic phenomena as heredity and evolution, development and variation, whereas the doctrinal movement which tries to anticipate or enforce the practical utilization of the scientific principles studied is eugenics.
Genetic investigation seeks the cause, the material basis, and the manners of maintenance of the specificity of the germinal substance: it strives to clarify the problems of how the characters of parents and offspring are related, how those of the adult, latent in the egg, become patent as development proceeds.
Population genetics is the study of hereditary traits and the distribution of genes in normal and abnormal populations. *Biogenetics* is the study of the biochemical and biophysical aspects of heredity; included herein is *cytogenetics* or *chromosomal genetics,* the study of anomalies in the number and structure of chromosomes. *Behavioral genetics* is the study of genetically determined patterns of behavior.

genetotrophic disease See *disease, genetotrophic.*

genial *Biol.* Pertaining to or having the

particular genetic quality or the individual manifestations of a *genius.*

genic (jen'ik) Pertaining to, or produced by, a gene or a combination of genes.

genic drift See *drift, genic.*

geniculate (jen-ik'ū-lät) **bodies** The medial and lateral geniculate bodies are part of the posterior nuclei of the thalamus. The medial geniculate body receives auditory fibers from the cochlear nuclei (via the lateral lemniscus) and from the inferior colliculus. It sends fibers to the temporal cortex (Heschl's gyrus) via the auditory radiation, which ascends through the internal capsule. The lateral geniculate body receives most of the fibers of the optic tract; it sends fibers to the visual cortex (around the calcarine fissure) via the optic or geniculocalcarine radiation, which ascends through the internal capsule.

genidentic (jen-i-den'tik) Having identical genes.

genital (jen'i-tal) Pertaining to the organs of reproduction.

genital love See *love, genital.*

genitality (jen-i-tal'i-tē) A general term referring to the genital components of sexuality, and sometimes used to refer to adult sexuality; but genitality is evident before genital primacy is complete, as in childhood and adolescent genital masturbation. 'Infantile sexuality differs from adult sexuality in several respects. The most impressive difference lies in the fact that the highest excitation is not necessarily located at the genitals, but that the genitals, rather, play the part of *primus inter pares* among many erogenous zones. The aims, too, are different; they do not necessarily lead toward sexual intercourse, but linger at activities that later play a role in forepleasure. . . . In time, however, the genitals begin to function as a special discharge apparatus, which concentrates all excitation upon itself and discharges it no matter in which erogenous zone it originated. It is called genital primacy when this function of the genitals has become dominant over the extragenital erogenous zones, and all sexual excitations become finally genitally oriented and

climactically discharged.' (Fenichel, O. *The Psychoanalytic Theory of Neurosis,* Norton, New York, 1945, p. 61) Unlike orality and anality, genitality probably cannot be sublimated, for the genitals represent an apparatus for achievement of a full, unsublimated orgastic discharge. See *character, genital; primacy, complete genital; ontogeny, psychic.*

genitalize (jen'i-tal-īz) To displace genital libido, as onto a non-sexual (but predisposed) organ in hysteria, where libido is discharged, but inadequately and incompletely.

genitals Organs of reproduction; sex organs.

genius (jēn'yus) (L. 'tutelar deity of a person or place; wit, talent, genius') A generic, non-specific term used loosely to denote an individual child or adult of markedly superior intellectual, emotional, volitional, affective, or creative abilities. At the present time, there exists no unanimity of opinion about the origin or development of such outstanding abilities. One school of thought emphasizes that so-called 'genius creative ability' appears as a symptom of, or alternative to, the development of neurosis or psychosis. Another school tends to emphasize that superior traits in varying degree appear as incident to and an index of normal development, as a concomitant to rounded superior health and endowment.

The term *superior individual* is more general, less controversial, and less emotionally charged than 'genius.' For purposes of classification, superiorly endowed children, or superior children, have been divided into the following four categories: (1) the bright child; (2) the gifted child; (3) the superior child; (4) the prodigy. In our present loose usage of the term (in both scientific and lay parlance) any individual child, in any of the four categories above, may aptly be called 'a genius child,' (Harms, E. *Handbook of Child Guidance,* Child Care Publications, New York, 1947) See also *child, bright.*

genome (jē-nōm') The special biological term proposed by von Wettstein for the genes in the nucleus to differentiate them from an alleged system of analogous entities in the cytoplasm, called *plasmons.*

genophobia (jen-ō-fō'bē-à) Fear of sex.

genotropism (jen-ō-trō'piz'm) Szondi's hypothesis that latent recessive genes determine instinctive or spontaneous choice reactions. This is manifested in one way by attraction of libido between persons possessing similar gene stock. The Szondi test (see *test, Szondi*) was constructed to demonstrate this hypothesis experimentally, and it is Szondi's belief that the test subject chooses a particular picture because the corresponding need-system within himself is in a state of tension.

genotype (jen'ō-tīp) The term was coined by the Danism botanist Johannsen in connection with his pure-line theory, in order to distinguish the factorial structure of an organism from its manifested *phenotype*. According to this theory, all individuals descended from a common ancestor by asexual reproduction have an identical *genotype* (q.v.) and will continue to breed true, regardless of environmental differences, forming lines genetically pure for all their characters.

Although originally the term meant the sum of all inherited predispositional characters of an individual, it has become customary to use it now in the sense of a particular *predisposition* (q.v.) underlying an individual morbid condition.

genotypical Pertaining to the *genotype*.

genus (jē'nus) (L. 'birth, descent, offspring, race, stock, species') In biology this term signifies a group of related *species* and classifies the group as ranking above a species and next below a subfamily (see *species*).

geography, psychological 'Psychological geography is the mapping of a whole community in which the interrelations of its inhabitants and the interrelations of its collectives or groups are depicted in respect to (a) its locality and (b) the psychological currents between them.' (Moreno, J.L. *Who Shall Survive?* Nervous & Mental Disease Publishing Company, 1934, p. 233)

geophagy (jē-of'à-jē) Dirt-eating.

gephyrophobia (je-fi-rō-fō'bē-à) Fear of (crossing a) bridge or river.

geriatrics (jer-i-at'riks) The science of curing or healing disorders and ailments of old age.

geriopsychosis (jer-ē-ō-sī-kō'sis) A term suggested by Southard for psychoses of the senescent period; senile psychoses.

germ cell See *cell, germ*.

germinally affected See *affected, germinally*.

germ plasm See *plasm, germ*.

gerontology (jer-on-tol'ō-jē) The study of old age.

gerontophilia (jer-on-tō-fil'ē-à) Love for old persons. Magnus Hirschfeld calls this 'an infantile fixation on elderly individuals.'

'Some of the resultants of the "grandfather-complex" may now be mentioned. The most striking is the tendency to gerontophilia—i.e., a special fondness for old people. This may also come about from the father being well over middle age when the child was born.' (Jones, E. *Papers on Psycho-Analysis,* 4th ed., Wood, Baltimore, 1938)

gerophilia (jer-ō-fil'ē-à) Same as *gerontophilia*.

Gerstmann syndrome (Josef Gerstmann, 1888-1969, American neurologist) A symptom complex described by Gerstmann in 1940 consisting of finger agnosia, right-left disorientation, acalculia, and agraphia. There may be various additional features, such as constructive apraxia, amnestic reduction of word finding, disturbed ability to read, impaired color perception, absence of optokinetic nystagmus, and disturbance of equilibrium. The agraphia often takes the form of dissociated dysgraphia.

Presence of the Gerstmann syndrome implies definite parietal lobe pathology, usually in the neighborhood of the angular gyrus.

Gesell, Arnold L. (1881-1961) Founder and director (for 37 years) of Yale Clinic of Child Development.

Gestalt (Ge-stalt') See *psychology, Gestalt*.

gesticulation, involuntary A parakinesis, suggestive of a posterior or postero-medial frontal lobe lesion on the contralateral side; often observed in conjunction with a grasp reflex.

geumaphobia (gū-mà-fō'bē-à) Fear of taste.

Gheel Colony A colony in Gheel, Beligum, which has existed since the 13th century for the treatment of a large number of psychotic patients residing in private homes in the community.

gibberish Unintelligible and incoherent language such as is seen in some patients with schizophrenia, who, as Storch and others have shown, often regress to the stage in which language is founded on the principles of primitive mentality. The language of the patient is gibberish to those who cannot understand it, in much the same sense that dreams are 'gibberish,' or that any mode of communication, foreign to one, is gibberish. The term was appropriate when the 'language' of the patient was undecipherable; it is not in use today because the language of schizophrenia is often recognizable and translatable.

'The tendency to silly plays on words and neologisms can get the upper hand in our patients to such an extent, that they fall into a wholly *incomprehensible gibberish*.' (Kraepelin, E. *Dementia Praecox and Paraphrenia*, tr. by Barclay, R., Livingstone, Edinburgh, 1919)

gifted As used in child psychiatry, this term is meant to refer to a child whose intelligence is in the upper 2 per cent of the total population of his age. Often, however, the term is used more loosely to refer to a child who shows outstanding ability in any single area. See *child, bright.*

gigantism (jī-gan'tiz'm) The constitutional anomaly is characterized by a stature greatly above the average (any height above 205 cm. in white population groups) and by a corresponding excess of body mass. It is due either to a heredito-constitutional hyperplasia of the entire endocrine system or to a particular form of hyperfunction in the anterior lobe of the hypophysis during the period of growth of the person affected. This condition

of hyperpituitarism may be primary or it may be secondary to genital hypofunction. Only in rare cases, glands other than the pituitary may be primarily implicated, for instance, the adrenal cortex or the pineal gland.

Among the various forms of gigantism are Berlinger's *gigantosomia premordialis,* Pellizzi's *precocious macrogenitosomia,* and *eunuchoid small gigantism.* The latter consists of excessive growth, especially of the lower extremities, which takes place just before puberty and is associated with a hypogenesis of the secondary sexual characteristics. It is often found in the phthisic or dolichomorphic types of constitution and may correct itself in later years, unless it leads to active pulmonary tuberculosis.

gigantism, eurhythmic (ū-riTH'mik) *Gigantosomia primordialis* (q.v.).

gigantosomia primordialis (gē-gan-tô-sō'-mē-à prē-môr-dē-ä'ēs) Berlinger introduced this term for the extremely rare syndrome best described as a well-proportioned form of *gigantism* with normal sex development. Some authors attribute this condition to the effect of an excessive idiopathic energy in the development of the entire organism, while others consider it as a special form of gigantism with similar etiology.

gigolette (ji-gō-let') Hirschfeld defines a gigolette as a young woman of 'easy virtue'; a woman who participates in promiscuous love affairs.

gigolism (ji'gōl-iz'm) This term refers to serving as a professional escort usually to members of the opposite sex. As a rule the escort is a male, a gigolo, defined by the French as a fop, a lounge-lizard, a dandy, with implications of sexual immaturity, often of homosexuality.

Gilles de la Tourette syndrome (Georges Gilles de la Tourette [jēl du là toor-et'] Paris physician, 1857 - 1904) A syndrome which usually has its onset in childhood, first described in 1885. It begins with facial movements and throat noises; the involuntary jerkings become more generalized and progressive, and later phrases or sentences may be ejaculated. Coprolalia and echolalia have also been reported.

Prognosis is unfavorable, and most of these patients are considered to fall within the schizophrenic group. The syndrome has also been reported as a residuum of rheumatic encephalitis.

girl, phallus The unconscious symbolic equivalence of girl with phallus. Such a situation arises most frequently in a perversion, such as transvestitism. The male transvestite has phantasied that the woman has a penis. Having thus overcome his castration anxiety, he identifies with this phallic woman. He himself represents the phallic woman under whose clothes a penis is hidden. Moreover, the female identification frequently represents an identification not with the mother but with a 'little girl,' for example, with a little sister. On the other hand, on a deeper level, the identification is with one's own penis. 'At deeper levels, fantasies of introjections are found in which the penis is equated with an introjected woman.' Thus, occasionally in these cases, 'girl' comes to have the symbolic meaning 'penis.'

Another example in which 'girl' has the symbolic significance of 'penis' occurs in the urethral-erotic perversion in which men have a sexual interest in female urination. As always in perversions, the interest in female urination is used to achieve reassurance against castration fears. In one case that was analyzed 'the perversion meant primarily an intense rejection of any idea of a penis.' As a child the patient had thought women had only one opening and urinated from the anus. 'The perversion was conditioned by a simultaneous prohibition against looking which enabled the patient to cling to the fantasy of women urinating through the anus and thus to avoid again being reminded of castration by the sight of a urinating woman.' On a deeper level, moreover, 'the interest in watching urinating women meant the hope of finding out that they, too, have a penis. The "urinating girl" herself had the significance of a "urinating penis."'

This equation may also occur in heterosexuals who are not overtly perverse. Certain narcissistic men who in childhood liked to think of themselves as girls may fall in love with more or less boyish 'little girls,' in whom they see the reincarnation of themselves. They treat these girls with the tenderness with which they would like to have been treated by their own mothers. They love them not for themselves but they love in them the feminine parts of their own ego. As a result of 'a castration anxiety, similar to that in cases of homosexuality . . . the narcissistically chosen girl "may represent" not only one's own person in adolescence but specifically one's own penis.' Here again we see the unconscious symbolic equation of girl with penis. (Fenichel, O. *The Psychoanalytic Theory of Neurosis*, Norton, New York, 1945)

Gjessing's syndrome (jes'ing) Recurrent episodes of catatonic stupor or excitement occurring in schizophrenics and associated with phasic variations in the nitrogen metabolism; first described by R. Gjessing in 1938. The syndrome is related to inadequate metabolism of dietary protein, leading to periods of nitrogen retention which are concurrent with hyper- or hypokinetic episodes. Dietary regulation is sometimes enough to control such patients; in others, thyroid administration increases nitrogen output with corresponding improvement in mental state.

glia (glē-à) *Neuroglia* (q.v.).

Glick effect Positive correlation between dropping out of school and subsequent marital instability ('marriage drop-out'); not observed in all studies.

glioma (glē-ō'mà) The generic name for one of the commonest types of brain tumor. The gliomata (gliomas) account for approximately 50 per cent of all intracranial tumors. They arise from glial cells and are composed predominantly of astrocytes or their embryonal precursors (medulloblasts, spongioblasts, astroblasts). By common usage, nearly all tumors of neuroepithelial origin are included in this term. In general, prognosis is unfavorable because gliomata tend to grow deep into the neural tissue; the more adult cell types (astrocytoma, oligodendroglioma, ependymoma) grow more slowly and are relatively benign, while the more immature cell types (medulloblastoma, spongioblastoma, or glioblastoma) tend to grow more rapidly, are more invasive, and are more malignant.

globus hystericus (glô'boos hēs-ter'ē-koos) (L. 'hysteric globe or ball') A term for the sensation of a ball or globe that arises in the stomach area and progresses upwardly, being finally felt in the throat where it produces the feeling of strangulation.

Globus hystericus and other 'esophageal neuroses' are often based on an unconscious rejection of incorporation secondary to aggressive impulses, which are often of a sexual nature (such as castration wishes) and which are connected with eating and swallowing. Disgust plays an important role and is probably a combination of temptation and rejection along with an ambivalent attitude toward incorporation.

globus pallidus (pa'li-doos) See *basal ganglia.*

glorified self *Idealized self* (q.v.).

gloss, metallic Tschisch's term for what he believed to be a characteristic facial expression in patients suffering from essential epilepsy.

glosso- combining form meaning speech, language, from Gr. *glōssa,* tongue, language.

glossodynia (glos-ō-din'ē-à) An itching, burning sensation in the tongue and buccal mucous membranes.

glossolalia (glos-ō-lā'lē-à) Neologisms which simulate coherent speech; despite the fact that they are expressed as unintelligible conglomerations of sounds, or written as series of unintelligible letters, such neologisms mimic normal speech by maintaining the distinctions of words, sentences, and even paragraphs. Glossolalia is most often seen in ecstatic and somnambulistic states, and, somewhat less commonly, in schizophrenia. If completely devoid of content, glossolalia is termed psittacistic, although certain writers use glossolalia and psittacism interchangeably. See *neophasia, polyglot.*

glossospasm (glos'ō-spaz'm) Rapid protrusion and retraction of the tongue; the spasm generally lasts for several minutes.

glossosynthesis (glos-ō-sin'the-sis) *Neologism* (q.v.).

glow, salt This is a procedure designed as a circulatory stimulant. 'About two pounds of coarse salt are moistened with cold water and allowed to stand for a short time. The treatment should be given in a wet room or bathtub. A towel is pinned about the waist and the patient stands in a tub in which water at 105 ° F. covers the ankles. Each section of the body as it is treated is moistened with water from the tub, or the entire surface may be moistened by immersion or spray at a temperature of 100 ° to 105 ° F. Standing in front of the patient, take a small amount of the wet salt in each hand, spread it evenly over the neck and chest, give vigorous alternate circular friction of the neck and cross-stroking to the chest, until the skin is in a glow.' (Bailey, H. *Nursing Mental Diseases,* 3rd ed., Macmillan, New York, 1935) The same procedure is followed with other areas of the body.

gluco-corticoid (gloo-kō-kor'ti-koid) See *syndrome, general adaptation.*

glucogenosis *Von Gierke's disease;* mental retardation due to a deficiency of glycogen-metabolizing enzymes, so that glycogen is deposited in the brain and other organs (31x.2).

gnostic (**sensation**) A term applied by the Dutch school of neurologists (Brouwer, Kappers) to designate the deep and epicritic sensations in contradistinction to the protopathic sensations which are considered as vital or *paleosensations.*

goal, life This term is used by Adler to describe the *secret* strivings of the individual, implicit in everything he thinks and does, for a superiority which compensates the chief inferiority. This phantasy of what he thinks he could be acts as a striving from 'below' (ideas of his own disadvantages) to 'above' (ideas of how to gain advantages).

'This constant striving from below to above . . . is the basis of all individual orientation. . . . Individuality itself, in the human sense, depends upon this fact that there is always inferiority, against which a goal of superiority is erected.' (Mairet, P. *ABC of Adler's Psychology,* Kegan Paul, Trench, Trubner, London, 1928)

'Whether he regards his suffering as the most important thing in the world to which everyone must show obeisance, whether he is chasing after unattainable ideals or old deities, over-stepping all limits and norms, at every part of his way he is guided and spurred on by his longing for superiority, the thought of his godlikeness, the belief in his special magical power.' (Adler, C. *The Practice and Theory of Individual Psychology,* tr. by Radin, P., Kegan Paul, Trench, Trubner, London, 1924)

gold curve See *Lange's colloidal gold reaction.*

Goldstein, Kurt (gôld'shtīn) (1878-1965) German psychiatrist and neurologist; aphasia.

Golem (gō'lem) According to the widespread medieval tradition among the Jews, the Golem is a huge, man-shaped brute created from clay by the supernatural power of the Shem, the 'ineffable name' committed to writing, through the agency of a human being. The first man credited with this achievement was Elijah of Chelm (middle of sixteenth century), hence known as the Ba'al Shem, i.e. master of 'the Name.' The best-known Golem was created by Rabbi Judah Löw ben Bezalel of Prague (end of sixteenth century). A modern Yiddish play built around this latter event represents the rabbi to have conceived the idea of making this Gargantuan mass of flesh and brawn as a bulwark for the Jews of Prague against a threatened pogrom and then taught the new monster how to use an axe. For a time the Golem was a passive obedient servant who did various kinds of minor chores. Later on, however, he began to show a sexual interest in the rabbi's niece and also insisted on joining the congregation in the synagogue—'the two most valued relations of the rabbi.' The aroused rabbi denied him entrance to the synagogue, and the enraged Golem seized an axe and started a pogrom on his own. The rabbi tried to regain mastery of the Golem by using his rabbinical knowledge and authority to invoke the magic powers of cabala, but all to no purpose. 'Not until he is driven by sheer necessity to meet the Golem with the whole force of his human passion can he gain the upper hand,' and lay low the fiend—an earlier Frankenstein's monster. (Baynes, H.G. *Mythology of the Soul,* Williams and Wilkins, Baltimore, 1940)

Goll, column of (Friedrich Goll, Swiss anatomist, 1829-1904) *Fasciculus gracilis* (q.v.).

gonad (gō'nad) A germ-gland; sexual gland.

gonadocentric (gō-nȧ-dō-sen'trik) Relating to the genitals as focal points. 'At puberty the sex urge becomes fully gonadocentric, with masturbation at the threshold and fringe of object love.' (Tenenbaum, J. *Encyclopaedia Sexualis,* edited by Robinson, V., Dingwall-Rock, New York, 1936)

good and evil test See *test, good and evil.*

good object See *object, good.*

Goodenough test See *test, Goodenough.*

Gordon Holmes, rebound phenomenon of (Gordon Holmes, British physician, b. 1876) A test for ataxia, specifically illustrating the loss of cerebellar 'check' on co-ordinated movement; if an attempt is made to extend the flexed forearm against resistance and suddenly let go, the hand or fist flies unchecked against the mouth or shoulder.

Gordon reflex (Alfred Gordon, American neurologist, b. 1869) Dorsal extension of the great toe, induced by compression of the calf muscle.

government, patient See *patient-government.*

Gowers' tetanoid chorea (Sir William R. Gowers, English neurologist, 1845-1915) See *degeneration, hepatolenticular.*

G.P.I. General paralysis of the insane. See *paresis, general.*

Graefe's disease (Albrecht von Graefe, German ophthalmologist, 1828-1870) See *nerve, oculomotor.*

Graftschizophrenia (grȧft-skiz-ō-frē'ni-ȧ) *Propfschizophrenia* (q.v.).

grand mal (grȧN mȧl') (F. 'great malady') See *epilepsy.*

grande attaque hysterique (grȧNd ȧ-tȧk ē-stȧ-rēk) See *hysteria.*

grande hysterie (gräNd ē-stä-rē′) (F. 'great hysteria') See *hysteria, major.*

grande nevrose (gräNd′ nē-vrōz′) (F. 'grand, great neurosis') *Obs.* French term for epilepsy.

grandeur See *megalomania.*

grandiose Characterized by showing feelings of great importance, delusions of wealth, etc.

Grantham lobotomy See *lobotomy, Grantham.*

grapho- (graf′ō-) Combining form meaning writing, from Gr. *graphein,* to write.

graphology The study of handwriting, especially in the sense of deducing some of the personality traits of the writer from a sample of his handwriting.

graphomania (graf-ō-mā′nē-à) Inordinate impulse to write. 'Many persecuted patients react with evasion, threats, scolding, insulting letters, and appeals to the authorities. Those suffering from grandiose delusions often use the press in a prolific manner. In general many paranoiacs actually become "graphomaniacs."' (Bleuler, E. *Textbook of Psychiatry,* tr. by Brill, A.A., Macmillan, New York, 1930)

graphophobia Fear of writing.

graphorrh(o)ea (-rē′à) 'The writing of the insane is disordered in exactly the same way as their speech. Garrulous, voluble patients, who are sometimes said to be suffering from "logorrhoea," often write many sheets of foolscap daily ("graphorrhoea").' (Stoddart, W.H.B. *Mind and Its Disorders,* 5th ed., Lewis, London, 1926)

grasping, forced See *lobe, frontal.*

gratification Satisfaction; in psychiatry, usually satisfaction of a person's needs or desires.

Graves's disease *Thyrotoxicosis* (q.v.).

Gray, John Perdue (1825-86) American psychiatrist.

gray-out A relatively mild or partial loss of consciousness due to anemia of the brain or anoxemia such as occurs in high-altitude flying. A more complete or total loss of consciousness is known as a *black-out* (q.v.).

Greenacre, Phyllis (1894-   ) U.S. psychoanalyst; *Trauma, Growth and Personality,* 1952; biography in depth.

Greenfield's disease Infantile metachromatic leukodystrophy; see *sclerosis, diffuse.*

gregariousness (gre-gâr′ē-us-nes) See *instinct, herd.*

grief See *mourning; melancholia.*

Grieg's disease *Hypertelorism* (q.v.).

Griesinger, Wilhelm (1817-68) German psychiatrist.

grimace (gri-mās′) A distorted facial expression or facial tic, often a result of organic neurologic disorder; in psychiatric syndromes, grimacing is most frequently seen in the catatonic group of the schizophrenias.

groping, forced Same as forced grasping, grasp reflex or instinctive grasp reaction. See *lobe, frontal.*

ground Background; the scenery, area, etc, on which the figures or objects in a picture appear to be superimposed. The figure is generally the part attended to, although the relationship of figure to ground may be reversed. Defective differentiation of figure and ground is common in the patient with organic brain disease, who as a result is almost always experiencing the uncertainty and instability that a normal person experiences only when confronted with ambiguous figures.

group 'Any group is constituted by the fact that there is some interest which holds its members together.' (Sapir, E. *Group; Encyclopaedia of the Social Sciences,* vol. 7, Macmillan, New York, 1932, p. 179)

A social group is a collection of persons capable of consistent action.' (Park, R.E., and Burgess, E.W. *Introduction to the Science of Sociology,* University of Chicago Press, Chicago, 1921)

Groups have been variously classified as: (1) *primary*, characterized by intimate face-to-face associations, and *secondary*, where the members, typically without presence, are formally and impersonally associated; (2) *in-groups* of which the person is a member and *out-groups* those to which he does not belong and with which his group is often in conflict; (Sumner, W.G. *Folkways*, Ginn, New York, 1906) (3) as *homogeneous* and *heterogeneous*; (4) *conflict* groups, e.g. nationalities, parties, reds, labor unions, and gangs, and *accommodation* groups, e.g. classes, castes, vocations, denominations.

group-analysis See *analysis, group; psychotherapy, group.*

group, blanket See *group, structured.*

group, closed A therapy group to which no new patients are added in the course of treatment or after treatment has proceeded for a time. See *group, open.*

group, continuous Same as *open group.*

group-feeling Same as *instinct, herd.*

group-formation See *instinct, herd.*

group, open A therapy group to which new patients are added at any time during the course of treatment. Sometimes this is referred to as a *continuous group.*

group, structured A term introduced by S.R. Slavson to emphasize the fact that the selection and combining of patients is essential for group psychotherapy, though some group psychotherapists pay little or no attention to it. Since in group psychotherapy the group is an important factor and the major therapeutic agency, it must be planned in such a way that, according to Slavson, the patients, individually and as a group, would have therapeutic effect upon every other constituent member. He has described some of the criteria for selection and grouping in his *Analytic Group Psychotherapy* (Columbia University Press, New York, 1950, Chapter XIV). This term is opposed to *blanket group,* in which no criteria for grouping are employed.

group, transitional A therapy group de-

vised for children (in latency period and puberty) who do not require intensive group psychotherapy but are unable to participate with confidence in ordinary social clubs. A form of 'protective groups' has been developed for these young patients. (Slavson, S.R. *An Introduction to Group Therapy,* The Commonwealth Fund, Oxford University Press, New York, 1943, pp. 327ff.)

group-work, social 'Social group-work may be defined as a type of educational process carried on in voluntary groups during leisure time and with the assistance of a group leader. It aims at the growth and development of individuals through the group experience, and at the use of the group by its members for social purposes which they consider desirable. . . . The use of the term group-work is increasingly coming to mean a kind of guided group experience in which individuals are helped to meet their needs and develop their interests along socially acceptable lines, with the assistance of a group leader.' (Coyle, G.L. *Social Work Year Book 1939,* edited by Kurtz, R.H., Russell Sage, Foundation, New York)

Grübelsucht (grü′bel-sookt) Brooding over trifles; seen most commonly in obsessive-compulsive psychoneurosis and in depressive psychoses.

Gruhle (groo′le), **Hans W.** (1880-1958) German psychiatrist and psychologist; phenomenology (especially schizophrenia and delusions) and social psychiatry.

grumbling mania See *mania, grumbling.*

Grundsymptoma Basic or fundamental symptoms. Bleuler used this term to refer to the primary or fundamental symptoms of *schizophrenia* (q.v.).

GSR Galvanic skin response. See *reflex, psychogalvanic.*

guidance A form of supportive psychotherapy in which the patient is counseled and instructed in ways to set and achieve specific goals and in ways to recognize and avoid areas of conflict and anxiety-provoking situations. Educational guidance refers particularly to helping the patient find the school or courses best suited to him on the basis of his intelligence, aptitudes, preferences, and available opportunities. Vocational guidance refers particularly to helping the patient find a job which is realistically suited to his capacities.

Guidance is a relatively superficial type of psychotherapy and makes little attempt to deal with the unconscious motivants of behavior. It is based upon an authoritarian relationship in which the patient often overvalues the therapist and in which he must suppress any doubts or hostility against the therapist.

guidance, child See *child-guidance.*

Guillain-Barré syndrome (gē-yaN'bàr-rā') (Georges Guillain and J.A. Barre, French neurologists) Acute infective polyneuritis; acute toxic polyneuritis; rheumatic polyneuritis; polyradiculoneuritis. An acute, diffuse disease of the nervous system, probably due to a virus, consisting of chromatolysis of the anterior horn cells and the posterior roots and of myelin degeneration of the peripheral nerves. Most cases occur in males between the ages of 20 and 50 years. Initial symptoms are headache, vomiting, fever, and pain in the back and legs. These are followed by sudden paralysis of the limbs, in all segments, and of the facial muscles. The paralysis is flaccid in type and the deep reflexes are lost. There is pain, numbness, and tingling in the limbs. Cerebrospinal fluid protein is markedly elevated, but there are few or no cells. In sporadic cases the prognosis is good, but in some epidemics the mortality (usually from respiratory paralysis) is high. No specific treatment is known.

guilt, guilt feelings Realization that one has done wrong by violating some ethical, moral, or religious principle. Associated with such realization typically are lowered self-esteem and a feeling that one should expiate or make retribution for the wrong that has been done.

As used in psychoanalytic writings, the term usually refers to neurotic, unreasonable, or pathologic guilt feelings that do not appear to be justified by the reasons adduced for the guilt. Such guilt is indicative of a conflict between the ego and the *superego* (q.v.); the latter acts as an internal authority which stands between ego and id, compelling the

person on his own to renounce certain pleasures, and imposing punishment (loss of self-esteem, guilt feelings, etc.) for violations of its orders. Often, of course, the superego's prohibitions are directed against impulses (and especially hostile and destructive ones) of which the subject is not consciously aware; but because the unconscious impulses have incurred the superego's wrath, the end result is guilt. It is because the reasons for the guilt feelings are unconscious that the incorrect term 'unconscious' feelings of guilt has come into being; Freud suggested that the phrase 'unconscious need for punishment' would be a more correct substitute.

Guilt feelings are thus seen to be a topically defined anxiety, the anxiety of ego toward superego. What is feared by the ego is that something terrible will happen within the personality (food, affection, love, and/or narcissistic supplies will be cut off) and that there will be a loss of certain pleasurable feelings, such as of well-being and security. In its most severe form, the loss of self-esteem characteristic of guilt feelings becomes a feeling of complete annihilation, such as is seen in depression.

In Adlerian psychodynamics, guilt feelings are the demonstration of good intentions which one does not have (or at least which one is unable to effect or exercise). They occur when past transgressions are blamed for a present unwillingness to behave as one feels he should.

Guislain (gē-lâN'), **Joseph** (1797 - 1860) French psychiatrist.

gumma, intracranial A rare form of cerebral syphilis. The predominating pathological process is the gumma or syphiloma. This is an irregular or round granulomatous nodular growth, varying in size from that of a pinhead to a walnut; it is generally multiple. Occasionally when single and of large size, it may produce symptoms of intracranial pressure with or without focal signs. The mental symptoms include the acute organic type of reaction, and consist of delirium, with a memory defect for recent events, and emotional lability. When there is evidence of increased intracranial pressure, a dull, stuporous state is common, with a loss of sphincter control. The blood and spinal fluid findings may be similar to those observed in cerebral syphilis, and response to antisyphilic treatment is fairly successful. See *syphilis, cerebral.*

Gunn's synkinetic syndrome See *synkinesis.*

Gunther-Waldenstrom syndrome *Porphyria* (q.v.).

gustatism (gus'tá-tiz'm) See *sensation, secondary.*

gymnophobia (jim-nō-fō'bē-á) Fear of a naked body.

gynander, gynandromorph (ji-nan'dér, -drō-morf) An individual of a bisexual species, exhibiting a 'sexual mosaic' of male and female characters as a result of the development of both types of sex tissue in the same organism.

Most specimens are *lateral* or *bilateral* gynandromorphs, male on one side of the mid-line of the body, and female on the other, with a sharp demarcation between the two kinds of tissue. In some instances the distribution is in a ration of about 1 : 3, or the head may be female and the rest of the body male.

It is assumed that on the male side there appear the sex-linked characters received from either the mother or the father; while the characters of the female parts show the presence in these parts of both the maternal and paternal X chromosomes, as though one of the X chromosomes had been eliminated from the male parts, leaving them XO, while the female parts are XX. 'Such a gynander appears to have begun development as an XX female and at some early cell division to have lost one of the X chromosomes from part of the tissues.' (Sinnott, E.W., and Dunn, L.D. *Principles of Genetics,* 3rd ed., McGraw-Hill, New York and London, 1939)

gynandrian A biological term relating to the class of *Gynandria* as classified in the Linean system of botany.

gynandroid, gynandromorphic, gynandrous (-'droid, -drō-mor'fik, -'drus) Usually in biology these terms refer to the *hermaphroditic* combination, or the resemblance to such combination, of male and female characteristics in the physical and mental make-up of one person. In a more specialized sense, in con-

trast to *androgynous,* they also indicate predominantly female features in a hermaphrodite with some male characteristics (see *androgynous*).

gynandromorphism (-drō-mor'fiz'm) This biological phenomenon is characterized by a 'mosaic' of male and female characters in the same individual of a bisexual species, and probably results from abberation in the distribution of the X chromosomes. It is assumed that if in the mating which produces a gynandromorph, sex-linked characters are involved and if the sex-linked characters of the two parents are dissimilar, then the sex-linked characters of the male parts are those either of the father or of the mother; whereas the sex-linked characters of the female parts are a combination of those of both parents.

If the gynandromorph starts life as a female, XX in constitution, and at some stage, during the early divisions of the fertilized egg, a daughter X chromosome fails to enter one of the daughter cells, then this cell, unlike its sister, will contain one X instead of two, becoming XO instead of XX. It will thus come to possess the sex-chromosome constitution of male tissue.

If the X chromosome of paternal origin is lost, the sex-linked characterization of the male part of the gynandromorph will be like that of the mother.

gynecomania (jin-ē-kō-mā'nē-á) Morbid desire for women.

gynephobia (jin-ē-fō'bē-á) Fear of women.

gyno- (jinō'-, jī'nō-) combining form meaning woman, female, from Gr. *gyne,* woman.

gynomonoecism (jin-ō-mō-nē'siz'm) A genetic female's capacity for developing spermatozoa in the ovary, at certain times. See *hermaphroditism.*

gynophobia (jin-ō-fō'bē-á) Morbid fear of women.

gyrectomy (jī-rek'tō-mē) One of the several surgical operations on the brain performed as a therapeutic measure in certain cases of mental illness. In the gyrectomy procedure bilateral symmetrical removals of frontal cortex are carried out along fissure lines in order to leave the normally functioning gyri. For a more detailed discussion of psychosurgical operations see *topectomy*.

gyrus, angular (jī-rus) The posterior portion of the lower parietal region; the left angular gyrus is associated with speech function.

gyrus cinguli *Cingulate gyrus* (q.v.).

gyrus, postcentral See *lobe, parietal.*

gyrus, precentral See *lobe, frontal.*

H

h In Rorschach scoring, human response, a measure of the subject's interest in the psychology of other people.

habenular ganglion (ha-ben'u-lär gang' glē-on) See *epithalamus*.

habit, accident See *proneness, accident*.

habit, act See *act-habit*.

habit, complaint Kanner's term for hypochondriasis in children. At various times and in connection with a variety of situations children are known to complain of various aches and pains which clearly are emotionally rather than physically caused. For example, one child may complain of severe headache the morning of a day on which a severe test is to be given at school; another may complain of stomach-ache when some particularly disliked kind of food is served. But these are *isolated*, not habitual, complaints.

The complaint habit refers to a *habitual* way of reacting by means of complaints of bodily disorder, according to definite patterns. In some instances the pattern has been set by the child himself, out of certain material from his own experience. If a real stomach-ache or a real cough has kept the child from school, which he happens to dislike, and has brought all sorts of kindly attentions, comforts, and privileges not ordinarily forthcoming, it may be found thereafter that a great desire for all this as a relief from some stress or other will be heralded by a stomach-ache or cough which, though felt and complained about, is *not* real. More often the pattern is suggested to the child by observation of his environment. If he notices that mother or father seems always to be relieved of this or that chore by reason of the complaint of headache or backache, the child, too, will be found feeling and complaining of headache or backache when the performance of some hated task is expected. (Kanner, L. *Child Psychiatry*, 2nd ed., Thomas, Springfield, Ill., 1948)

habit deterioration See *deterioration, habit*.

habit-disorder See *behavior disorders*.

habit-formation See *training, habit*.

habit-forming This term, when used with a drug, usually refers to the fact that the drug leads to *addiction* (q.v.).

habit, hysterical Kretschmer distinguishes two kinds of hysteria, *reflex hysteria* and *hysterical habit*. The latter is a hysterical reaction that begins as a conscious, voluntary process and gradually becomes automatic by repetition. See *hysteria, reflex*.

habit-residual, hysterical This is Kretschmer's expression for a reflex hysteria which continues because of the patient's lack of desire to get well. It is distinguished from simple reflex hysteria in that the latter usually occurs upon occasions when there is something to be gained by the reaction.

habit-training See *training, habit*.

habituation See *addiction*.

habitus (hab'i-tus) (L. 'condition, state, nature, character, disposition') In general medicine, 'constitutional disposition or tendency' to some specific disease, in the sense of the *habitus phthisicus* and *habitus apoplecticus* as described by Hippocrates.

Later the meaning of the term was extended also to the type of physique associated with such tendencies by different typological schools of constitutional medicine, and to the general characteristic appearance of the human body.

habitus, affective A person's organization or constitution from the standpoint of the affects. 'Many mere psychopaths have the same affective habitus as pronounced *epileptoid* or as the less correctly designated *epileptic* character. . . . (Bleuler, E. *Textbook of Psychiatry*, tr. by Brill, A.A., Macmillan, New York, 1930)

habitus apoplecticus (hä'bē-toos à-pô-plek'tē-koos) (L. 'apoplectic constitution') A thick-set, rounded physique, corresponding to Kretschmer's *pyknic type* and its equivalent in other systems.

habitus, asthenic See *type, asthenic*.

habitus phthisicus (fthē'zi-koos) (L. 'consumptive constitution') By this term Hippocrates denoted the tendency of certain persons to *pulmonary tuberculosis*. He ascribed a slender, flat-chested physique to such persons, and the term is used in a derived sense to indicate the type of physique corresponding approximately to Kretschmer's *asthenic type* and its equivalents in other systems.

habitus, ptotic ([p]tō'tik) In constitutional medicine, a special body type described by Stiller as associated with the constitutional anomaly *enteroptosis*—a sagging or a dropped condition of the intestines. According to Pende, enteroptosis exerts secondary effects on the digestive functions, and also—through lack of diaphragmatic support—on the respiratory and circulatory systems and on the configuration of the thorax, thus contributing to the production of the 'general *dolichomorphic-asthenic* constitution.' (Pende, N. *Constitutional Inadequacies*, tr. by Naccarati, S., Lea & Febiger, Philadelphia, 1928)

habromania (hab-rō-mā'nē-à) *Obs.* General term for morbid gaiety.

hadephobia (hā-dē-fō'bē-à) Fear of hell.

Haeckel's biogenetic law (Ernst Heinrich Haeckel, German naturalist, 1834-1919) According to this formula, 'the child is on a lower developmental level of mankind than the adult.' In other words, the child is 'universally criminal.' In the child all the criminal drives of humanity are latent. Following Haeckel's conception, Stekel asserts that 'phrases about purity and innocence in the child are empty.' Compulsive acts are protective measures against the evil of one's self. A neurosis arises when the instinctual criminal drives are too powerfully developed. (Stekel, W. *Compulsion and Doubt*, Liveright, New York, 1949) See *law, biogenetic mental*.

haem(at)o- See *hem(at)o-*.

hair pulling *Trichotillomania;* the hair is usually pulled from the head, less often from the pubic area, in an almost compulsive fashion. Hair pulling may be a masturbatory substitute, and/or it may be an expression of aggressive and exhibitionistic impulses, and a denial of castration.

'half-show' A modification of puppet show technique in psychotherapy of children in which the patient sees only that part of the puppet show which presents or states a problem in dramatic fashion. When the conflict is at its height, the show is stopped with the promise that it will be continued later. Then the subject or group is asked what should happen. The solutions suggested, of course, are colored by the child's own problems, and the child will try to unravel the conflict in terms of his own constitution, background, emotional involvement, and general level of maturity.

halfway house A specialized residence for mental patients who are not sick enough to require full hospitalization, but not well enough to function completely within the community without some degree of professional supervision, protection, and support.

Hall, G(ranville) Stanley (1844-1924) American psychologist and sexologist.

hallucinate (ha-lū'si-nāt) To have a sense perception for which there is no external reality (i.e. sensory stimulus).

hallucinatio hypochondriasis (hàl-loo-kē-nä'tē-ō hē-pô-kôn-drē-ä'zēs) An obsolete expression for *hypochondriasis*.

hallucination (ha-lū-si-nā'shun) An apparent perception of an external object when no such object is present. A paranoid patient, sitting alone in a quiet room, complains that his persecutors who are miles away speak directly to him in derogatory terms; moreover, he believes implicitly that he feels electrical stimuli over the entire body, the stimuli coming, he alleges, from a machine operated by his persecutors. The auditory and tactile stimuli have no source in the environment; rather they are sensations arising within the patient himself. A hallucination is a *sense perception* to which there is no external stimulus. In the instances cited the *sensations* are *hallucinations*. The *false beliefs* regarding persecutors are *delusions;* a delusion is a *belief* that is obviously contrary to demonstrable fact.

When the same paranoid patient, sitting alone in an otherwise quiet room, upon hearing the crackling of the floor-boards, is firmly 'convinced' that the crackling sounds like those of a telegraph ticker are messages from the persecutors to him (the patient), he misinterprets actual stimuli from the environment. An *illusion* is a false impression from a real stimulus. But the text he thereupon reads into these messages is a *delusion*. See also *illusion; delusion.*

Obs. Fallacia.

hallucination, auditory (aw'di-tō-rē) See *hallucination, haptic.*

hallucination, auditory peripheric (per-i-fer'ik) An auditory illusion (mainly hearing of voices) experienced as a result of auditory sensory stimulation, as the pouring of water, rumpling of paper, a person's walking, etc.

hallucination, blank A general term that includes the *Isakower phenomenon*, the *dream screen* of Lewin, and the *abstract perceptions* of Deutsch and Murphy; it refers to certain uncanny experiences of sensations of equilibrium and space, such as unclear rotating objects, rhythmically approaching and receding objects, sensations of crescendo and decrescendo, typically localized in the mouth, skin, and hands and at the same time in the space immediately surrounding the body. Most often such feelings occur in stress situations, when falling asleep, and in dreams. They are believed to be defensive repetitions of responses to early oral deprivation and to reflect the infant's subjective experience of being overwhelmed by excitation in the early traumatic situation. Their appearance in an analytic session suggests that primal scene material is approaching.

hallucination, diminutive visual *Hallucination, Lilliputian* (q.v.).

hallucination, elementary 'As *elementary hallucinations* in the optic field we designate such unformed visions as lighting, sparks, and cloudlike partial darkening of the visual field, and in the acoustic field, the simple noises such as murmurs, knocks, and shooting.' (Bleuler, E. *Textbook of Psychiatry*, tr. by Brill, A.A., Macmillan, New York, 1930)

hallucination, extracampine (eks'trä-kam'pīn) 'Remarkable are the "extracampine" hallucinations which are localized outside of the sensory field in question. In the nature of the thing one deals

mostly with visions, the patient sees with perfect sensory distinctness the devil behind his head, but it may also concern the sense of touch; thus the patient feels how streams of water come out from a definite point of his hand.' (Bleuler, E. *Textbook of Psychiatry*, tr. by Brill, A.A., Macmillan, New York, 1930)

hallucination, gustatory See *hallucination, haptic.*

hallucination, haptic (hap'tik) A haptic hallucination is one associated with the sensation of touch. A paranoid patient complained that his persecutors, operating an electrical apparatus hidden in the walls of the building, induced very disagreeable sensations over his body through the machine.

Alleged persecutors reach the patient's body through many avenues, among which are the sensory zones. In clear-cut cases of schizophrenia the persecutors aspire to tempt the patient to engage in homosexual practices. Indeed, they constantly stimulate him sexually through the several sense areas. 'He operates a machine that masturbates me' is a common expression among paranoid schizophrenic patients. The persecutors are said also to surround the patient with 'bad sexual odors' (olfactory hallucination); they put 'scum' (seminal fluid) in his food (gustatory or taste hallucination); they call him a sexual pervert with men (auditory hallucination); they grimace at him, meaning he is homosexual (visual hallucination).

hallucination, hypnagogic (hip-nà-goj'ik) Same as *imagery, hypnagogic.*

hallucination, induced A hallucination aroused in one person by another, such as may occur, for example, during hypnosis. See *association, psychosis of.*

hallucination, Lilliputian (lil-i-pū'shan) (From the six-inch-tall inhabitants of the island of Lilliput, in Jonathan Swift's (1667-1745) *Gulliver's Travels*) When hallucinated objects, generally persons, appear greatly reduced in size, it is said that the patient has Lilliputian or microptic hallucinations. The term should be used only when true hallucination is present, that is, when there is no object in the environment that stimulates the perception. When a real object is misinterpreted by a patient, the condition is called an illusion. Certain patients, notably those with idiopathic epilepsy, while actually looking at objects, may believe them to be extremely diminutive; this constitutes an illusion. See *Lilliputian; micropsia.*

As a rule Lilliputian hallucinations occur in psychiatric states associated with febrile or intoxicating conditions. They may be observed in the absence of recognizable organic disorders.

hallucination, macroptic (mak-rop'tik) See *macropsia.*

hallucination, memory When material repressed into the unconscious returns to consciousness in the form of a visual image, Freud calls the latter a memory-hallucination. He says: 'The paranoiac memory-hallucination undergoes a distortion similar to that of the obsessional neurosis—an analogous current image takes the place of the repressed one. . . .' (Freud, S. *Collected Papers,* vol. 1, tr. by Riviere, J., Leonard and Virginia Woolf and The Institute of Psychoanalysis, London, 1924-25)

hallucination, microptic (mǐ-krop'tik) See *hallucination, Lilliputian.*

hallucination, motor An older term for *hallucination, psychomotor* (q.v.).

hallucination, negative A *negative hallucination* is not a hallucination at all; the expression refers to the condition in which the subject fails to see an object while apparently looking at it. It is a phenomenon that can be induced through hypnosis.

hallucination, negative memory A denial (of a so-called hallucinatory character) of something that the patient really has experienced. 'Thus a patient, like all the others, received cigars for Christmas; he smoked them quickly and then began to scold, because cigars were given to all patients except to him.' (Bleuler, E. *Text-book of Psychiatry,* tr. by Brill, A.A., Macmillan, New York, 1930)

hallucination of conception See *hallucination of perception.*

hallucination of perception An auditory hallucination in which the patient hears the sound or noise as coming from outside himself, in contrast to hallucination of conception (or, in Baillarger's terminology, psychic hallucination), in which inner voices are heard.

hallucination, olfactory See *hallucination, haptic.*

hallucination, psychic (sī'kik) See *hallucination of perception.*

hallucination, psychomotor (sī-kō-mō'tēr) A patient's sensation that certain parts of his body are being transferred to body regions distant from their natural location.

hallucination, psycho-sensorial (sī-kō-sen-sō'rē-al) Baillarger distinguished two kinds of hallucinations—psycho-sensorial and psychic. He said that the first are the result of the combined action of the imagination and of the organs of sense, while the second are the result of the imagination without the interposition of a sensory stimulus.

hallucination, reflex A sensory impression induced through stimulation of a distant and different sensory area. 'An auditory sensation may in this way arise from irritation in the region of the inferior alveolar nerve (carious tooth).' (Henderson, D.K. and Gillespie, R.D. *A Text-Book of Psychiatry,* 4th ed., Oxford University Press, London, 1936.) The use of the term *hallucination* in this sense is obsolete.

hallucination, retroactive (ret-rō-ak'tiv) Same as *hallucination, memory* (q.v.).

hallucination, slow-motion The sensation of inordinate slowness of body motion. One of Lippman's patients described it as 'a sensation of "slowing down." All my motions seem very slow. I try to move faster, and seem to move even more slowly. At the same time, everything around me seems to move very fast.' (Lippman, C.W. 'Hallucinations in Migraine,' *American Journal of Psychiatry CVII,* No. 11, May 1951)

hallucination, space-motor The 'sensation of acceleration involving the entire body.' (Lippman, C.W. 'Hallucinations in Migraine,' *American Journal of Psychiatry CVII,* No. 11, May 1951)

hallucination, teleologic (tel-ē-ō-loj'ik, or

tē-lē-) When a patient is advised through a hallucination about what course he should take, it is said that he has a teleologic hallucination.

hallucination, unilateral (ū-ni-lat'ēr-al) A term used when 'the hallucination is unilateral and affects only one side of the bilateral sensorial apparatus. The patient is influenced only through one eye, one ear, or one side of the body.' (Magnan, V. 'Chronic Delusional Insanity of Systematic Evolution,' *American Journal of Insanity* LV: 44, 1895-96)

hallucination, vestibular (ves-tib'ū-lēr) (L. *vestibulum*, forecourt, our *vestibule*, anteroom, in Anat. the approach to the cochlea of the internal ear) False sensory perceptions that come from irritation of the vestibular apparatus. This form of hallucination is referred mainly to visual and tactile organs. Visual images (real or imaginary) are affected by vestibular function. Under vestibular irritation these images show changes such as occur when the subject is submitted to passive rotating movement. In such experimental circumstances, there are certain typical movements, or deviations of the optic image. In one experiment, related by Bibring-Lehner, the subject, while turning, imagines a child: this image seems to turn in the same direction as the subject under experiment. Sometimes a half of the image disappears and often the colors become gray during the turning, but the most remarkable features are the multiplication of the image, and its reduction in size. According to Schilder, this is very important, 'because it shows that turning induces the same changes in optic images as in optic vision.' In alcoholic hallucinations one may also observe vestibular phenomena. Indeed, Schilder describes the case of a patient who said: 'Sometimes I saw three or four people on the street instead of one. I saw three faces in glaring white; faces of Negroes and whites. They moved forwards and backwards and when I saw them they started to chase me. I felt them behind me.' In psychosis the vestibular influences are not related exclusively to the visual sphere, but one also encounters marked changes in the feelings that the patient has about his own body. It should be mentioned that sensations of the body's lightness or heaviness are closely related to vestibular

functions. (Schilder, P. *Mind Perception and Thought*, Columbia University Press, New York, 1942)

hallucination, visual See *hallucination, haptic.*

hallucinogen (ha-lū-sin'ō-jen) Any substance capable of producing hallucinations in an experimental subject. See *psychotomimetic; psychotropics.*

hallucinosis (ha-lū-si-nō'sis) The state of experiencing sensory stimuli to which there is no discoverable reality. Thus, a paranoid patient who hears voices, who feels the electricity that his persecutors send forth at him, who smells the bad odors that they force upon him and who tastes poison in the food, when there is no possible validity to any of these assertions, is said to be in a state of hallucinosis.

hallucinosis, acute Sudden appearance of hallucinations, usually in a clear intellectual field, without confusion or intellectual impairment; most commonly due to intoxication with alcohol or drugs, or following traumata such as surgical procedures and childbirth. Usually there is a slow return to normal within a period of weeks; if symptoms persist, the condition is generally considered to be a schizophrenic reaction. The most common form of acute hallucinosis is alcoholic hallucinosis. See *hallucinosis, alcoholic.*

hallucinosis, alcoholic (291.2) A form of acute hallucinosis that is seen typically in chronic alcoholics following an unusual excess of alcohol intake. Alcoholic hallucinosis is relatively rare in the female; it consists of auditory hallucinations and paranoid hallucinations, both usually of a derogatory or persecutory nature, in a clear intellectual field without confusion or intellectual impairment. During the period of acute hallucinosis, the patient may commit crimes of violence in response to his delusions. There is a slow return to normal within a period of weeks; recurrence is frequent. If the condition becomes chronic, it is considered to be a schizophrenic reaction.

hallucinosis, diabetic Hallucinatory state associated with diabetes.

hallucinosis, uremic Hallucinatory states associated with kidney disease.

halo, semantic See *dissociation, semantic.*

hamartophobia (hȧ-mär-tō-fō'bē-ȧ) Fear of error or sin.

Hand-Christian-Schüller's syndrome *Xanthomatosis* (q.v.).

hand-to-mouth reaction See *reaction, hand-to-mouth.*

handedness *Laterality* (q.v.).

handicap, collective life A term used in social work to refer to 'any disability (physical, mental, or emotional) which limits or threatens the patient's normal range of social intercourse, association, and enjoyment of fellowship.' (Hamilton, G. *A Medical Social Terminology,* Presbyterian Hospital, New York, 1930)

handicap, family life In social work this means 'any disability (physical, mental, or emotional) which definitely interferes with or limits either one's capacities for home making or for marriage.' (Hamilton, G. *A Medical Social Terminology,* Presbyterian Hospital, New York, 1930)

handicraft Manual art or trade, used as a means of treatment in occupational therapy.

hangover The after-effect ("morning after") syndrome following ingestion of alcohol or other sedatives, such as barbiturates. Symptoms include a bad taste, nausea, vomiting, tachypnea, pallor, irritability, sweating, conjunctival injection, etc. The syndrome may be a direct result of ethanol intoxication or due to effects of acetaldehyde, an intermediate metabolite that develops in the course of alcohol oxidation, and/or a result of toxic congeners contained in most forms of commercially available alcohol which extend and amplify the effects of alcohol itself.

Hans The patient on whom Freud reported in his 1909 paper, 'Analysis of a Phobia in a Five-Year-Old Boy.' The initial phobia of little Hans was directed to horses, and analysis revealed that the phobia represented the father, against whom Hans nourished jealous and hostile wishes because of rivalry for the mother. One interesting feature of this case is that the analytic treatment was carried out by the father, who corresponded with Freud and received the latter's suggestions about interpretation and technique by mail.

haphalgesia (haf-al-jē'zē-ȧ) See *aphalgesia.*

haphephobia (haf-ē-fō'bē-ȧ) See *haptephobia.*

haploid (hap'loid) In the maturation of a reproductive cell this genetic term refers to the stage in which the number of chromosomes is halved following the reduction division. This reduced number is called haploid as constrasted with the original or *diploid* number (see *diploid*).

haploidy (hap'loid-ē) The genetic process known as the reduction division of reproductive cells results in *haploidy* as the stage of meiosis at which the number of chromosomes per cell is reduced to half. Consequently, the haploid number of chromosomes in all daughter cells is just half as large as their original or *diploid* number in the cells from which they are derived (see *dipolidy*).

haplology (hap-lo'lō-jē) Omission of syllables in words because of speed in speech; seen often in mania and in schizophrenic syndromes in which there is pressure of speech.

haptephobia (hap-tē-fō'bē-ȧ) Fear of being touched.

haptophonia (hap-tō-fō-nē-ȧ) The hearing of noises or voices in response to tactile or haptic stimulation. One patient, for example, complained of hearing voices coming from his forearm, where there was the scar of an old injury.

harmatophobia (här-mȧ-tō-fō'bē-ȧ) A common misprint for *hamartophobia* (q.v.).

harmine (har'mēn) See *psychotomimetic.*

harpaxophobia (här-pak-sō-fō'bē-ȧ) Fear of robbers.

Harris's syndrome Hypoglycemic syndrome. See *hypoglycemia.*

Hartmann, Heinz (1894 -   ) Viennese-born U.S. psychoanalyst; ego psychology.

Hartnup disease A pellagra-like disorder caused by a genetic abnormality of tryptophan metabolism: instead of conversion into nicotinamid, tryptophan is converted into indican. A variety of mental symptoms may result, including anxiety, feelings of depersonalization, depression, delusions, hallucinations, delirium, confusion, irritability, apathy, emotional lability, and in many cases mental retardation (31x.2; if psychosis appears rather than retardation, 294.1; if non-psychotic, 309.5). See *nicotinic acid deficiency.*

hate See *aggression.*

hate, fetish *Antifestishism* (q.v.).

haut mal (ō màl') (F. 'high disease') Major (epileptic) attack; grand mal.

Hd Rorschach scoring symbol for a response of parts of the human figure.

headache, histamine See *histamine.*

headache, lead-cap In describing neurasthenic symptoms Church and Peterson write that 'one describes a sensation as if the head were splitting or the skull lifting; another has a terrible weight or a severe constriction about the head. This *lead-cap headache* is very common.' (Church, A. and Peterson, F., *Nervous and Mental Diseases,* 8th ed., Saunders, Philadelphia and London, 1916)

headaches, cluster Non-migrainous headaches, including histamine cephalalgia, ciliary neuralgia, sphenopalatine neuralgia (vidian neuralgia, Sluder's syndrome), and other atypical facial neuralgias. In contrast to migraine, cluster headaches rarely have prodromata, usually are located in the retro-orbital or orbito-temporal areas, and frequently occur daily in bouts lasting several months.

head-banging One of the many typical physical exertions commonly observed during a temper-tantrum in small children. The child works itself up to a pitch of excitement and by almost every conceivable physical or muscular movement literally 'throws itself all over the place.'

head-knocking A habit developed by some infants which consists of bumping the head against the crib sides or other objects. (Pearson, G.H.J. *Emotional Disorders of Children,* Norton, New York, 1949)

head-rolling Rhythmical, semi-circular movements of the head exhibited by some children before going to sleep. When sufficiently constant, this movement may be considered similar to tics in its nature. In some instances, the rolling of the head may be attributed to restraint of movement in the crib and, in other instances, to absence of play material (monotony). It seems that in other cases it may have as its origin the passivity of the foetus during intra-uterine life. In these cases the rolling of the head will represent a hyperactive function which serves as a balance for the intra-uterine inactivity. (Pearson, G.H.J. *Emotional Disorders of Children,* Norton, New York, 1949)

head trauma See *compression, cerebral; concussion; contusion, brain.*

health, flight into See *flight into health.*

health, mental 1. Mental hygiene, in which sense mental health is a field of endeavor based on knowledge contributed by the *behavioral sciences* (q.v.) and amplified with scientific, professional, and social applications. 2. Psychologic well-being or adequate adjustment, particularly as such adjustment conforms to the community-accepted standards of what human relations should be. Some of the characteristics of mental health are: reasonable independence; self-reliance; self-direction; ability to do a job; ability to take responsibility and make needed efforts; reliability; persistence; ability to get along with others and work with others; co-operation; ability to work under authority, rules, and difficulties; ability to show friendliness and love; ability to give and take; tolerance of others and of frustrations; ability to contribute; a sense of humor; a devotion beyond oneself; ability to find recreation, as in hobbies. (Appel, K.E. *Journal of the American Medical Association 172,* 1343-6, 1960). See *norm, psychic.*

hearing, color Color hearing is usually

believed to be a hallucinatory disturbance, characterized by a sensation of color when sounds are heard. A schizophrenic patient said that people talked to him in colors, meaning that colors occurred to him when he heard voices.

heart, soldier's See *neurasthenia, war.*

hebephrenia (hē-be-frē'nē-à) A symptom-complex now considered a chronic form of schizophrenia. In 1871 Hecker described hebephrenia and the heboid, and in 1896 Kraepelin included hebephrenia in the group dementia praecox. See *schizophrenia.*

hebephrenia, depressive Some patients with the hebephrenic form of schizophrenia run, for some time, a course that resembles the periodic changes observed in manic-depressive psychosis. When the constituents of a depression appear in hebephrenia, the state is known as *depressive hebephrenia.* When there is similarity to a manic phase, it is known as *manic hebephrenia.* Currently, most such cases are classified as the schizoaffective type of schizophrenia.

hebephrenia, insurance Maier's term for schizophrenia manifested initially as a compensation neurosis; in time, the patient's claims become increasingly absurd, illogical, and bizarre.

hebephrenia, manic See *hebephrenia, depressive.*

hebephrenic schizophrenia See *schizophrenia, hebephrenic.*

hebetude (hē'be-tūd) Emotional dullness of disinterest. It is most characteristically expressed in schizophrenia in which the pronounced withdrawal of interest from the environment and apparently, in late cases, from the patient himself causes the patient to appear thoroughly listless; unemotional, disinterested, apathetic. See *affectivity, disturbances of.*
'In the severer forms of schizophrenia the *"affective dementia"* is the most striking symptom. In the sanatoria there are patients sitting around who for decades show no affect no matter what happens to them or to those about them. They are indifferent to maltreatment; left to them-

selves they lie in wet and frozen beds, do not bother about hunger and thirst. They have to be taken care of in all respects. Toward their own delusions they are often strikingly indifferent.' (Bleuler, E. *Textbook of Psychiatry,* tr. by Brill, A.A., Macmillan, New York, 1930)
An older meaning of hebetude included listlessness or apathy from any cause, physical or mental. It is still sometimes used in this sense.

hebetudo animi (he-be-too'dô à'nē-mē) (L. 'dullness of spirit') *Obs.* Imbecility.

hebetudo mentis (men'tēs) (L. 'dullness of mind') *Obs.* Imbecility.

heboid praecox See *praecox, heboid.*

heboidophrenia (hē-boid-ō-frē'nē-à) This term, not too common today, was first used by Kahlbaum for the simple form of dementia praecox (schizophrenia).

Hecker, Ewald (1843 - 1909) German psychiatrist; known from his studies in hebephrenia, which term was coined by him.

-hedonia (-hē-dō'nē-à) combining form meaning pleasure, from Gr. *hēdonĕ,* delight, enjoyment, pleasure.

hedonic level See *psychodynamics, adaptational.*

hedonism (hē'don-iz'm) A philosophic doctrine in which pleasure or happiness is presented as the supreme good. In psychiatry, hedonism refers to the seeking of certain goals because they afford some type of gratification. Hedonism, then, is in opposition to the doctrine that goals may be sought as ends in themselves, irrespective of the pleasure or gratification they give the individual. See *hormism.*

hedonophobia (hē-don-ō-fō'bē-à) Fear of pleasure.

heel-to-knee test See *test, heel-to-knee.*

Heidenheim's disease *Jakob-Creutzfeldt's disease* (q.v.).

Heine-Medin disease (Jacob Heine, German physician, 1800 - 1879, and Karl Oskar Medin, Swedish physician, 1847 - 1928) *Poliomyelitis* (q.v.).

heir of the Oedipus complex See *superego*.

heliophobia (hē-lē-ō-fō'bē-à) Fear of sunlight.

hellenomania Impulse or tendency to use complicated, cumbersome, Greek or Latin terms instead of readily understandable English words. The impulse is rampant in the field of psychiatric writing, as witness the list of (generally undesirable) terms under *fear of* (q.v.).

Heller's disease (Theodore Heller, German neuropsychiatrist, early twentieth century) See *dementia infantilis*.

helmet, neurasthenic (nū-ras-thē-nik) A feeling of pressure over the entire cranium in certain cases of neurasthenia, as if from a tight-pressing helmet. See *headache, lead-cap*.

Helmholtz See *accommodation*.

helper, magic Fromm's term describing a particular form of interpersonal relationship. Man has today become aware of himself as a separate entity. The growing realization of his separateness gives him a sense of isolation and a longing to return to the earlier feeling of solidarity with others. So he uses certain irrational methods of relating back to the group, and these are termed mechanisms of escape. One method is to seek to lean on another for support. The other person represents a power or authority who can be used for that purpose. Sometimes the individual expects the other person to solve all his problems for him and endows the person with almost magical omnipotence. This other person is then termed the 'magic helper.' It is obvious that the person so endowed with magical power must himself be affected by it and to a degree be dependent on it. The power he has illustrates a form of *irrational authority* which is based not on competence but on a neurotic need for power. See *authority, irrational*.

helping relationship A type of relationship, as defined by Carl Rogers, in which one of the participants intends that there should come about, in one or both parties, more appreciation, expression, or functional use of latent inner responses. Examples include mother and child, and teacher and student, as well as therapist and patient.

helplessness, psychic The state that occasions the first expression of anxiety in early infancy. Freud describes anxiety as a state of unpleasure in which there is an increase of excitation relieved through physiologic discharge phenomena such as an increase in the respiratory and pulse rates, rise in blood pressure, etc. The prototype of this experience of anxiety is seen as the experience of birth, in which the above-described sensations and responses first occur. All later anxiety states are reproductions of this earliest experience. Anxiety as experienced in later life, however, is clearly a response to a danger-situation. Thus some type of danger is understood to be associated with the production of anxiety from the time of its earliest appearance.

Initially, in birth, this danger is merely the increased quantity and intensity of stimuli which necessitates a discharge through respiratory, cardiovascular, and other pathways. Later, this increase in unpleasurable stimuli will occur in the infant every time his needs for food, warmth, etc. are not gratified. The infant is psychically unable to cope with these needs and thus provide for their discharge. This is 'a situation analogous to the birth experience, a repetition of the danger-situation; what the two situations have in common is the economic disturbance brought about by an increase in stimuli demanding some disposition be made of them, this common factor hence being the very essence of the "danger." In both cases the reaction of anxiety appears . . .' Freud describes as psychic helplessness this anxiety-invested danger-situation in which the small infant is powerless to gratify his needs. Later on, as the infant experiences the fact that 'an external and perceptible object, i.e. the mother, may put an end to the danger-situation reminiscent of birth,' the content of the danger becomes object loss or loss of the mother. What is now dangerous for the infant is absence of the mother, who satisfies his needs. Without her, it is possible that he might again be swept with the unpleasurable stimuli reminiscent of birth and associated with nongratification.

As the child continues to develop, other danger-situations arise, such as castration threats and dread of the superego. The early danger-situation of psychic helplessness is important chiefly in the 'period of immaturity of the ego' and grows less important as the ego develops and the later danger-situations of object loss, castration, and others successively emerge. The earliest danger-situations such as psychic helplessness may persist, however, and cause the ego to react with anxiety at a later period. Freud suggests that the form of the neurosis that develops in a given patient may be closely related to the variety of danger-situation typical of that particular patient. (Freud, S. *The Problem of Anxiety,* Norton, New York, 1936)

hematidrosis (hem-à-ti-drō'sis) Bloody perspiration.

hemato- (hē'mà-tō-, hem'à-) combining form meaning blood, from Gr. *haima, -atos,* blood.

hemato-encephalic barrier See *barrier, blood-brain.*

hematophobia (hem-à-tō-fō'bē-à) See *hemophobia.*

hemeralopia (hem-ēr-à-lō'pē-à) Day-blindness; vision is poor by day, in bright light, and good in dim light; the opposite of *nyctalopia.*

hemeraphonia (-fō'nē-à) Voicelessness during daytime, usually a symptom of hysteria.

hemi- (hem'i-) a prefix meaning, *half-, semi,* from Gr. *hemi-,* half.

hemianopic, hemianopsia (ē-an-op'ē-à, -op'sē-à) See *field defect.*

hemianopsia, heteronymous (her-ēr-on'i-mus) Bitemporal or binasal loss of vision.

hemianopsia, homonymous (hō-mon'i-mus) Loss of vision in the similarly situated (*both right,* or *both left*) halves of one's eyes, i.e. in the nasal half of one eye and in the temporal half of the other.

hemianthropia (hem-ē-an-thrō'pē-à) *Obs.* Insanity.

hemiatrophy, facial (-a'tro-fē) Parry-Romberg's syndrome. A trophic disorder, perhaps due to disturbance of the sympathetic nervous system, in which there is progressive wasting of some or all of the tissues of one side of the face, which as a result looks old and wrinkled. The disorder usually begins during the second decade; it causes no disability.

hemiballism (-bal'iz'm) Violent, uncontrollable shaking, twisting, and rolling movements involving one side of the body, occurring as a result of hemorrhage into the subthalamic body.

hemichorea (-kō-rē'a) Chorea affecting one side of the body only.

hemichorea, paralytic (par-à-lit'ik) Hemichorea associated with hemiplegia.

hemichorea, post-hemiplegic (post-hem-i-plej'ik, -plē'jik) Hemichorea following an attack of hemiplegia.

hemichorea, preparalytic (prē-par-à-lit'-ik) A condition in which unilateral choreic movements precede an attack of hemiplegia.

hemicrania (-krā'nē-à) *Migraine* (q.v.).

hemiopia (ō'pē-à) Hemianopia; see *field defect.*

hemiparesis (-par'ē-sis) Slight paralysis or weakness of only one side of the body.

hemiplegia (-plē'jē-à) A symptom-complex and not a disease, characterized by paralysis of one side of the body.

hemiplegia alternans (al'ter-nans) Crossed paralysis; paralysis of one or more cranial nerves and paralysis of the arm and leg of the opposite side. Hypoglossal hemiplegia alternans involves the twelfth cranial nerve; Weber's syndrome involves the oculomotor (third cranial) nerve.

hemiplegia cruciata (hā-mê-plā'gē-à kroo-kē-ā'tà) (Mod.L. 'crossed hemiplegia') Paralysis of an upper extremity and of the lower extremity on the side opposite to that of the upper extremity.

hemiplegia, nocturnal See *paralysis, sleep.*

hemo- (hē'mō-, hem'ō-) Same as *hemato-.*

hemophobia, hematophobia (hē-mō-, hem-à-tō-fō'bē-à) Fear of blood.

hemorrhage, cerebral (hem-ēr-rēj) See *accident, cerebrovascular.*

hemothymia (hē-mō-thim'ē-à, -thī'mē-à) Passion for blood; morbid impulse to murder.

hepatolenticular degeneration Wilson's disease. See *degeneration, hepatolenticular.*

herbivorous (hēr-biv'ō-rus) While in zoology this term applies to animals (herbivora) subsisting on herbaceous plants or vegetables, in constitutional medicine it designates a type described by Bryant and corresponding roughly to Kretschmer's *athletic* type and its equivalents in other systems.

Herculeus morbus (her-koo'le-oos môr'-boos) (L. 'Herculean disease') An old term for epilepsy, supposedly because of the epileptic's Herculean violence and strength.

herd See *instinct, herd.*

hereditary, hereditarial (he-red'i-ter-ē, -târ'i-al) Referring to both the Mendelian mechanism by which physical or mental attributes are transmitted from one generation to another, and to the inherited attributes to which an organism is predisposed by the presence of a certain gene or combination of genes.
 'We usually call what is programmed in the chromosomes hereditary or genetic. The sum of what is biologically given (whether determined by genetics or intrauterine environment) is referred to as constitutional. . . . The unfolding of biologically given factors and their manifestation at critical periods in the life history are referred to as maturation, a somatically programmed schedule. The opposite of maturation is involution.' (Redlich, F.C. and D.X. Freedman, *The Theory and Practice of Psychiatry* Basic Books, New York, 1966)

hereditary cerebellar ataxia of Marie See *ataxia, Marie's hereditary cerebellar.*

hereditary spastic paraplegia See *paraplegia, hereditary spastic.*

heredito-constitutional (he-red'i-tō-kon-sti-tū'shun-al) Referring to those genetic elements in the individual constitution of an organism which have been derived from its original genotype (see *constitution*).

heredity (he-red'i-tē) As it has become customary to use the terms *inheritance* and *transmission* for designating the actual genetic process by which physical or mental traits are transmitted from parents to offspring, *heredity* has a more general and abstract sense—of classifying the process of inheritance as a biological phenomenon and identifying it with the forces responsible for the resemblance between an individual and his ancestors, insofar as this resemblance is due to the operation of predisposing gene units rather than to the similarity of environmental influences.
 The morphological equivalent of heredity is the *Mendelian* mechanism based on the integrity of the chromosomes and their continuity from one cell generation to the next, while the science dealing with the study of heredity is usually called *genetics.* See *Mendelism.*

heredo-familial essential microsomia (mī-krō-sō'mi-à) See *dwarfism.*

heritable (her'it-à-b'l) A general genetic term synonymous with *inheritable* (q.v.).

hermaphrodism (hēr-maf'rō-diz'm) *Hermaphroditism* (q.v.).

hermaphrodism, psychical Adler's term for the constant striving of the person to free himself from feelings of weakness, inferiority, and futility to attain self-confidence, superiority and self-gratification. It is the conflict between the masculine and feminine components.
 'The normal craving of the child for nestling, the exaggerated submissiveness of the neurotically-disposed individual, the feeling of weakness, of inferiority protected by hyper-sensitiveness, the realization of actual futility, the sense of being permanently pushed aside and of being at a disadvantage, all these are gathered together into a feeling of femininity. On the contrary, active strivings, both in the case of a girl as of a boy, the pursuit of self-gratification, the stirring up of instincts and passions are thrown challengingly forward as a masculine protest. On the basis of a false evaluation, but one which is extensively nourished by our social life, there thus develops a *psychical hermaphrodism* of the child, "logically" dependent upon its inward opposition. From within itself is then unfolded that frequently unconscious urge toward a reinforced masculine protest which is to represent the solu-

tion for the disharmony.' (Adler, A. *The Practice and Theory of Individual Psychology*, tr. by Radin, P., Kegan Paul, Trench, Trubner, London, 1924)

hermaphrodite (-dīt) One who has the reproductive organs of both sexes; a·bisexual organism.

hermaphroditism (hēr-maf'rō-dit-iz'm) State of being a hermaphrodite; bisexuality. This term signifies the biological phenomenon of *bisexuality* (q.v.) occurring either synchronously or heterochronously and originating in the production of both male and female gametes by the same organism. There are two types of hermaphroditism:
I. The *non-functional,* when both male and female germ cells are provided transiently or permanently, yet only one kind of germ cells functions. Of this type there are 3 forms:
   (1) *accessory,* when, in addition to the testis there is a *rudimentary ovary,* which, however, does not reproduce ova.
   (2) *accidental,* with sporadic occurrence of ova in the testis or of spermatic tissues in the ovary.
   (3) *teratological* (common in birds and mammals) when the reproductive system presents an intimate mixture of male and female structures.
II. The *functional,* when both male and female gametes, produced by one and the same individual, are functioning. Of this type, which is characterized by *monoecism* there are also 3 forms:
   (1) *unisexual monoecism,* when at certain times a genetic female develops spermatozoa in the ovary (*gynomonoecism*) or a genetic male develops ova in the testis (*andromonoecism,* less common), so that one sex becomes hermaphroditic, i.e. the individual previously functioning as (1) female (or male) now functions as (1) male (or female).
   (2) *consecutive monoecism,* when a male later functions as a female, or (less commonly) a female later becomes a male. Genetically these organisms are either males or neutrals.
   (3) *spatial monoecism,* manifesting real functional hermaphroditism is characterized by the presence of both male and female reproductive organs.

hermaphroditism, psychic (sī-kik) Bisexuality from the mental point of view. See *transvestism.*

herniation, lumbar disk (hēr-nē-ā-shun) See *disk, herniated lumbar intervertebral.*

hero-birth, primordial image of Jung says: 'We can be certain only that, when a man is identical with his persona, the individual qualities are associated with the soul. It is this association which gives rise to the symbol, so often appearing in dreams, of the soul's pregnancy; this symbol has its source in the primordial image of the hero-birth. The child that is to be born signifies the individuality, which, though existing, is not yet conscious. Hence in the same way as the persona, which expresses one's adaptation to the milieu, is as a rule strongly influenced and shaped by the milieu, so the soul is just as profoundly moulded by the unconscious and its qualities.' (Jung, C.G. *Psychological Types,* tr. by Baynes, H.G., Harcourt, Brace, New York and London, 1923)

hero-worship From the psychoanalytic point of view, hero-worship is a product of the need of the great majority of people 'for authority which they can admire, to which they can submit, and which dominates and sometimes even ill-treats them.' The need for such an authority is simply the longing of each person for the father, for a father figure, this longing having persisted since childhood days. As a result of this need it is possible for a great man to rise to extraordinary significance in the lives of large masses of people so that he is regarded as a hero. This hero will have in particular the traits that are characteristic of the father. 'The decisiveness of thought, the strength of will, the forcefulness of his deeds, belong to the picture of the father; above all other things, however, the self-reliance and independence of the great man, his divine conviction of doing the right thing, which may pass into ruthlessness. He must be admired, he may be trusted, but one cannot help also being afraid of him.' (Freud, S. *Moses and Monotheism,* Hogarth Press, London, 1939)

heroin See *opium.*

heroinomania (her-ō-in-ō-mā'nē-à) Morbid craving for heroin. See *addiction; dependency, drug; opium.*

Herrick, Charles Judson (1868-1960) American neurologist; comparative neurology; *The Evolution of Human Behavior.*

Herstedvester (hār'sted-ves-tēr) A town in Denmark, of importance in psychiatry because of the rehabilitation program in use in its Institution for Criminal Psychopaths. The program is a combination of group and individual treatment which provides a therapeutic community for the inmates. See *community, therapeutic.*

Hertwig-Magendie phenomenon (hert'-viK-mà-zhäN-dē') (Oscar Hertwig, German physiologist, 1849-1922, and François Magendie, French physiologist, 1783-1855) See *deviation, skew.*

Herxheimer reaction See *Jarisch-Herxheimer reaction.*

hetaera (hē-tē'rà) A classical synonym for mistress or concubine.

hetaerism (-'riz'm) *Rare.* Concubinage; a state of common law or natural, as opposed to civil marriage.

hetero- (het'ēr-ō-) combining form meaning *other, different,* from Gr. *heteros,* the other, one of two.

heterocentric (-sen'trik) Directed away from oneself; opposed to autocentric.

heteroclite (he'tēr-ō-klīt) A person who deviates from the common rule, as opposed to *homoclite,* a person who follows the common rule and is ordinary, normal, healthy, etc.

hetero-erotic (-e-rot'ik) Relating to the attachment of libido (Eros) to objects outside of oneself, and specifically to objects of the opposite sex.

hetero-erotism (-er'ō-tiz'm) The attachment (cathexis) of the energy of the libidinal drive to objects outside of oneself, and specifically to objects of the opposite sex. If one uses the term *libido* synonymously with *Eros,* then hetero-erotism is hetero-libido or object-libido.

Heteroeroticism is a phase in the development of object relationships (see *ontogeny, psychic*); its achievement constitutes the chief task of adolescence. At puberty, libidinal strivings that have been dormant during the period of *latency* (q.v.) reappear because of biological in-

tensification of sexuality. In childhood, the person had come to recognize his sexual impulses as dangerous; at puberty, he returns to just that point in his sexual development where he had abandoned it earlier, and the fears and guilt connected with the Oedipus complex reappear. But overt sexuality now has a physiologically mature genital discharge apparatus, and finally, at about 16 or 17, the adolescent desexualizes his relationship with all but one person of the opposite sex and the stage of heterosexuality is reached.

heterogamous (-og'à-mus) Relating to the structural and functional differences between the male and female gametes, as they appear in most animals and plants. See *syngamy.*

heterogeneity, heterogeny (-ō-jē-nē'i-tē, -oj'ē-nē) Dissimilarity in the genotypical structure of individuals originating through sexual reproduction. See *homogeneity.*

hetero-hypnosis (-hip-nō'sis) Hypnosis induced by another, in contradistinction to auto-hypnosis.

heterolalia (-lā'lē-à) The substitution of meaningless or inappropriate words for those meant or intended.

heteronymous hemianopia (het-er-on'i-mus hem-ē-an-op'ē-à) See *field defect.*

heterophasia (-fā'zhē-à) Heterolalia.

heterophemy (-of'ē-mē) The saying of one thing when another is meant.

heterophonia (-ō-fō'nē-à) Heterolalia.

heterophoria (-for'ē-à) Deviation of one eye because of muscular imbalance. Inward deviation is known as esophoria; outward deviation is exophoria; downward deviation is hypophoria; upward deviation is hyperphoria.

heterorexia (-rek'sē-à) Alibert's term for morbid appetite; dysorexia.

heterosexuality Sexuality (in all its manifestations, normal and morbid) directed to the opposite sex. See *character, genital; genitality.*

heterosis (het-ēr-ō'sis) The favorable influence of crossing on growth and other developmental properties of animals and plants, as exercised by an increase in heterozygocity in contrast to the decrease in vigor following inbreeding. *Genet.* The beneficial effect of heterosis is observed and utilized by breeders of animals and plants all over the world. It is best evidenced in the generation immediately following the cross, by: greater size, larger parts, increased longevity, and higher resistance to disease. Equally significant is the fact that any form of hybrid vigor disappears rapidly under inbreeding.

The mule is commonly cited as a hybrid animal whose vigor, hardiness, and resistance to disease are due to heterosis.

heterosociality (-sō-shē-al'i-tē) Social relationship between members of the opposite sex (J.C. Fluegel).

heterosome (het'ēr-ō-sōm) The sex chromosome, as distinguished from all other chromosomes (autosomes). See *chromosome; sex-determination.*

hetero-suggestibility The state of influencing another; the opposite of auto- or self-suggestibility.

hetero-suggestion See *auto-suggestion.*

heterotopia (-tō'pē-à) Congenital displacement of gray matter of the spinal cord into the white substance.

heterotropia *Strabismus* (q.v.); squint.

heterozygocity (-zī, zi-gos'i-tē) *Heterozygousness* (q.v.).

heterozygosis (-zī, zi-gō'sis) *Heterozygousness* (q.v.).

heterozygote (zī'gōt, -zig'ōt) A zygote which has been produced by the union of two dissimilar gametes and is heterozygous with respect to any pair of allelomorphs. In the case of a recessive factor, the heterozygotes transmit its predisposition to the offspring but the latter do not develop the character in question themselves.

heterozygousness (-zī'gus-ness) This term (identical with *heterozygosity* or *heterozygocity*) relates to the genetic condition of an organism whose two genes of a given factor pair are *different.*

Only dominant characters can appear in the state of heterozygousness, while the heterozygotic condition of a recessive trait affects the organism merely 'germinally.' A heterozygotic individual transmits the trait to the offspring but is not able to manifest the trait in his own phenotype. See *inbreeding; heterosis.*

heuristic (hū-ris'tik) Promoting investigation or favoring discovery.

hexafluorodiethyl ether (heks-à-floo-or-ō-dī'eth-il ē'thēr) A convulsant agent which has been used in psychiatric treatment in the same capacity as ECT. The trade name for this drug is Indoklon.

H.I. Hyperglycemic index. See *index, hyperglycemic.*

hibernation This term has been used to refer to prolonged sleep therapy, especially when this was accompanied by a lowering of the body temperature. High dosages of chlorpromazine, for instance, were used to keep patients in a continuous semi-somnolent state with a lowered body temperature; such treatment was called hibernation therapy.

hibernation (of ament) L. Down remarked that 'many cases of imbecility, particularly those of the Mongolian variety, lose a large amount of intellectual energy in the winter—go through, in fact, a process of hibernation, their mental power being always directly as the external temperature.' (Cited from Tredgold, A.F. *A Text-Book of Mental Deficiency,* 6th ed., Wood, Baltimore, 1937)

hiccough, hiccup A spasmodic myoclonous of the diaphragm producing a sudden inhalation of air which is interrupted by a spasmodic closure of the glottis, thus producing a sound which may simulate an ordinary cry or an unpleasant crow; also known as *singultus.*

hidden self See *personality, secondary.*

-hidrosis (-hi-drō'sis) Perspiration.

hieromania (hī-ēr-ō-mā'nē-à) *Obs.* Religious insanity.

hieronosus (-nō'sus) Linnaeus's term for epilepsy.

hierophobia Fear of sacred or religious things.

hindbrain Rhombencephalon, from which develop the metencephalon (cerebellum, pons, part of the fourth ventricle) and the myelencephalon (medulla oblongata and part of the fourth ventricle).

hindering, mania for Janet describes the symptom thus: 'Instead of simply resisting orders by refusing to perform the action which is commanded, the action which they dread, these patients try to check the activities of the persons with whom they come into contact, even when the latter ask nothing of them.' (Janet, P. *Psychological Healing*, vols. 1-2, tr. by Paul, E. and C., Macmillan, New York, 1925)

Hinkemann (hing′kē-män) This proper name is widely used in Germany for a castrated male. Hinkemann, the principal character of a play by the same name, written by Ernst Toller (1893-1939) lost his genitals as a result of injury sustained in the World War.

hippanthropy (hip-an′thrō-pē) A symptom in which a patient imagines he is a horse.

hippocampus (hip-ō-kam′pus) See *rhinencephalon*.

hippus (hip′us) A condition in which the pupil alternately contracts and dilates on stimulation with light.

Hirschfeld, Magnus (1868-1935) (hērsh′-felt) German sexologist.

histamine (his′ta-mēn) An amine occurring in all animal and vegetable tissues. Histamine dilates capillaries and arterioles, constricts the bronchioles, stimulates the smooth muscles of the uterus, and stimulates many glands of external secretion, especially the gastric glands. Intracutaneous injection of histamine produces focal erythema within 1-5 seconds, within 30-50 seconds a spreading flush (the histamine flare) and, later, a wheal. The flare reaction is dependent upon an intact arteriolar circulation and an intact axon reflex; hence it has been used in diagnosis of peripheral nerve lesions. Histamine has also been used in the determination of circulation time, in various gastric function tests, and in the diagnosis of histamine headache (histaminic cephalalgia, Horton's syndrome). The latter is a unilateral headache associ-

ated with redness of the eye, lacrimation, rhinorrhea or stuffiness of the nostril, swelling of the temporal vessels of the affected side, and dilatation of the vessels of the pain area (usually the orbital area).

Histamine has been used in the treatment of peripheral vascular disease, rheumatoid arthritis and Ménière's disease.

histiocytosis, lipid See *disease, Gaucher's; disease, Niemann-Pick*.

histrionic personality *Hysterical personality* (q.v.).

hoarding The practice of collecting any number of objects, generally of limited size and of no practical use. Hoarding is seen most commonly in deteriorated schizophrenics and in other organic cerebral disorders. Hoarding is one of the behavioral manifestations on which an opinion of *incompetency* (q.v.) may be based.

hoarding type See *assimilation*.

Hoch, August (1868-1919) (hōK) American psychiatrist.

Hoch, Paul Henry (1902-1964) Hungarian-born neuropsychiatrist, to U.S. in 1942; somatic treatment, mental hospital administration, community psychiatry.

Hoche, Alfred (1865-1943) (hō′Kē) German psychiatrist.

hodophobia (hod-ō-fō′bē-à) Fear of travel.

Hoffer, Willi (1897-1967) Austrian psychoanalyst; fled to London with S. Freud in 1938.

Hoffmann (or Tromner's) sign (Johann Hoffmann, 1857-1919, German neurologist.) In hemiplegia, due to organic brain disease, snapping of the index or ring finger produces flexion of the thumb.

hog A slang expression to describe a morphine or heroin addict who takes progressively increasing doses in order to be 'loaded.' See *user*.

holergasia (hol-ēr-gas′ē-à) A psychiatric disorder of such a nature as to involve the *whole* person. For example, schizophrenia and manic-depressive psychosis ordinarily are associated with a disorganization of the entire personality and the syndromes are, therefore, known as holergastic reactions.

holism (hō′liz′m) *Gestalt totality;* the thesis that the study of parts cannot explain the whole, because the whole is something different from the simple summation of its parts. The application of the holistic principle to the study of human beings has far-reaching implications. We have a number of sciences *relating to* the person, but no science *of* the person. Physiology, psychology, and sociology deal with artificially separated single aspects of the human organism, but at present there is no single science that studies the human person in its totality. From a holistic point of view the human being is more than a mere aggregation of physiological, psychological, and social functions: the person as a whole has attributes that cannot be explained by the attributes of its constituent parts. (Angyal, A. *Foundations for a Science of Personality,* The Commonwealth Fund, Oxford University Press, New York, 1941)

Adler particularly emphasized the need for the holistic approach in the understanding of personality; recognizing that the whole person cannot be understood by an analysis or dissection of his parts, he emphasized that he could be understood in term of the goals he sets for himself and towards which he moves.

Holmes, Gordon, rebound phenomenon of See *rebound.*

holophrastic (hō-lō-fras′tik) Expressing a complex of ideas in a single word, as in some primitive languages which require a completely new word for any slight change in the total situation. Schizophrenics, who typically demonstrate a reduction in their connotation ability and a relative overemphasis on denotation, can be described as manifesting holophrastic association defects. See *connotation.*

Homburger, August (1873-1930) (hôm′-boor-gēr) German psychiatrist; psychopathology of children.

home, loveless From the standpoint of mental hygiene, this term is used to describe those homes in which an inharmonious atmosphere is prevalent as the result of constant discord among the members of the family, and where the children are made buffers between quarreling parents who have 'fallen out of love.' This is the type of surrounding that breeds delinquency. In these loveless homes the children are constantly exposed to traumatic experiences which have a definite influence in the development of neuroses and other mental disturbances. Furthermore, it is an established fact that such loveless homes have a much more deleterious effect upon the children's mental development than have the so-called 'broken homes' which seem to play a rather secondary role in this respect. (Seliger, R.V., *et al. Contemporary Criminal Hygiene,* Oakridge Press, Baltimore, 1946)

homeostasis (hō-mē-os′tā-sis) The status quo; the tendency of an organism to maintain a constancy and stability of its internal environment; the result of the various autonomic mechanisms which adjust and adapt the body as a whole to changes in the external or internal environment. Homeostasis is Cannon's term for a steady, balanced, internal constitution; Claude Bernard's term for this was 'milieu interieur.' 'Autonomic adjustments, while allowing for necessary responses of the organism, must maintain a physiological state adequate for the needs of the tissues. . . . The physiological requirements of any tissue must be balanced against those of all others, and with minor fluctuations, a steady "internal constitution" maintained. . . . Forces pulling in opposite directions are equilibrated so as to give an appearance of rest.' (J.F. Fulton, *Physiology of the Nervous System,* 3rd ed., Oxford University Press, New York, 1949) In general, rapid adjustments are made by the autonomic nervous system while slower adjustments occur through chemical and hormonal influences.

homesickness An acute separation syndrome appearing in dependent persons when for any reasons they are removed from their usual sources of dependency gratification.

homichlophobia (hō-mik-lō-fō′bē-à) Fear of fog.

homicidomania (hom-i-sīd-ō-mā′nē-à) See *mania, homicidal.*

homilopathy Kraepelin's term for disease due to mental induction and persecution mania of the deaf.

homilophobia (hom-il-ō-fō-bē-à) Fear of sermons; also, fear that in a group of people the others in the group might find something wrong with one's appearance, attire, or demeanor.

homo- (hō'mō-) Combining form from Gr. *hómos*, one and the same, common; opposed to *hetero-*.

homoclite See *heteroclite*.

homocystinuria (31x.2) An inborn error of metabolism, transmitted as an autosomal recessive, associated with mental retardation and characterized by excretion of moderate amounts of the essential amino acid, methionine, and of an abnormal amino acid, L-homocystine, in the urine. The syndrome was first reported in 1962.

homoerotic Relating to or manifesting the erotic or libidinal instinct toward one of the same sex.

homoerotism, homoeroticism (-er'ō-tiz'm, -e-rot'i-siz'm) A general term for the objectivation of erotic or libidinal interests upon a member of the same sex. The impulse is subject to all the modifications of erotic impulses. It may be expressed directly (homogenitality); it may be sublimated (homoerotism or homosexuality); it may be severely repressed; if so, the impulses may be subjected to reaction-formation, that is, they may appear as aversions against the homoerotism; or they may be transferred into reality in symbolic form (delusions, hallucinations, etc.).
  Homoeroticism is also a phase in the development of object relationships (see *ontogeny, psychic*) and the term is generally applied to that period following the Oedipal phase and lasting until adolescence, when libidinal energies are repressed, and aggressive energies are redirected into elaborating a more effective web of defenses, including the superego, and into increasing mastery in the social sphere, in socially condoned and desirable competitiveness, conquest, and domination. See *latency*.

homogamy In contrast to *panmixia*, this genetic term applies to the *inbreeding* conditions in an isolated population group composed of organisms with the same hereditary characteristics.

homogeneity, homogeny (hō-mō-jē-nē'i-tē, hō-moj'ē-nē) Identical genotypical structure of two or more organisms of common descent, as found in the case of pure lines or in monozygotic sets of twins.

homogenital (-jen'i-tal) Relating to interest in the genital organs of one's own sex.

homogenitality (-jen-i-tal'i-tē) Interest in the genitals of one's own sex. See *homosexuality*.

homologous (hō-mol'ō-gus) Referring to gene units which belong to the same pairs of *homologues*. See *allelic*.

homologue (hom'ō-log) If one form or condition of a genetic character is contrasted with another form or condition of the same character, such as two eye colors or two color patterns, the genes which are responsible for these two conditions are said to belong to the same pair of *homologues*.
  'They are so related that in the reduction division of maturation they regularly go to different cells, each germ cell receiving one, but not both.' (Shull, A.F. *Heredity*, 3rd ed., McGraw-Hill, New York and London, 1938) See *chromosome*.

homonymous hemianopia (hō-mon'i-mus hem-i-an-op'si-à) See *field defect*.

homonymous quadrantic field defect See *field defect*.

homophile A lover of one's own kind; specifically, a homosexual, and a term used especially by organizations that purport or attempt to represent homosexuals as a group.

homosexual Relating to or directed toward one of the same sex.

homosexual panic An acute, severe episode of anxiety related to the fear (or the delusional conviction) that the subject is about to be attacked sexually by another person of the same sex, or that he is thought to be a homosexual by fellow-workers, etc. First described by Kempf in 1920 and hence sometimes known as *Kempf's disease;* symptoms include agitation, ideas or delusions of reference, conscious guilt over homosexual activity, hallucinations, ideas and threats of suicide, depression, and often perplexity.

The panic state is typically precipitated by loss or separation from a member of the same sex to whom the subject is emotionally attached, or by fatigue, illness, fears of impotence, failures in sex performance, homesickness, etc. It may appear as the first acute episode in schizophrenic disorders, and it is more frequent in males than in females.

Sometimes, instead of overt sexual material, the anxiety is related to fears of undue malignant influence, physical violence, or impending death. Such an episode is termed *acute aggression panic*.

homosexuality The state of being in love with one belonging to the same sex. Until the early part of the 20th century, this generally meant a form of sexual perversion. With the development of psychoanalysis, however, there came to be laid less emphasis on sex proper and a correspondingly broader connotation assigned to the term sexual. In current usage, overt homosexuality is used to refer to physical, sexual contact between members of the same sex, while latent homosexuality is used to refer to impulses and desires toward a member of the same sex which are unconscious or, if conscious, are not openly expressed. Some writers differentiate between homogenitality (genital relations); homosexuality (sexual relationship, but not expressed genitally); and homoerotism (erotic relationship which is well sublimated). See *homosexuality, female; homosexuality, male.*

In general, the term inversion is equivalent to homosexuality. When 'sex-role inversion' is used, however, it must be differentiated from homosexuality. Homosexuality refers to sexual desires and/or activity between members of the same sex, while sex-role inversion refers to adoption of the sex role and introjection of the psychologic identity of the opposite sex. Occasionally the two may co-exist, but more frequently one or the other is present alone.

homosexuality, female Erotic, sexual, or genital contact between females (see *homosexuality*). While it is generally believed that homosexuality is more frequent in the female than in the male, specific data on relative incidence do not support this belief (Bromley and Britten; Gilbert Youth Research; Hamilton; Kinsey). 'The incidences and frequencies of homosexual responses and contacts, and

consequently the incidences of the homosexual ratings, were much lower among the females in our sample than they were among the males on whom we have previously reported. Among the females, the accumulative incidences of homosexual responses had ultimately reached 28 per cent; they had reached 50 per cent in the males. The accumulative incidences of overt contacts to the point of orgasm among the females had reached 13 per cent; among the males they had reached 37 per cent. . . . Moreover, compared with the males, there were only about a half to a third as many of the females who were, in any age period, primarily or exclusively homosexual.

'A much smaller proportion of the females had continued their homosexual activities for as many years as most of the males in the sample.

'A much larger proportion (71 per cent) of the females who had had any homosexual contact had restricted their homosexual activities to a single partner or two; only 51 per cent of the males who had had homosexual experience had so restricted their contacts. Many of the males had been highly promiscuous, sometimes finding scores or hundrends of sexual partners.' (Kinsey, A.C., *et al. Sexual Behavior in the Human Female*, Saunders, Philadelphia, 1953)

'The institutions which have developed around male homosexual interests include cafés, taverns, night clubs, public baths, gymnasia, swimming pools, physical culture and more specifically homosexual magazines, and organized homosexual discussion groups; they rarely have any counterpart among females. Many of these male institutions, such as the homosexually oriented baths and gymnasia, are of ancient historic origin, but there do not seem to have been such institutions for females at any time in history. The street and institutionalized homosexual prostitution which is everywhere available for males, in all parts of the world, is rarely available for females, anywhere in the world. All of these differences between female and male homosexuality depend on basic psychosexual differences between the two sexes.' (ibid.)

Female homosexuality is often referred to as 'lesbian' or 'sapphic' after Sappho, a female homosexual who lived on the Isle of Lesbos in ancient Greece.

homosexuality, latent Often used interchangeably with 'unconscious homosexuality'; it denotes an erotic impulse toward a member of the same sex, present in the unconscious, though not felt or overtly expressed.

homosexuality, male Erotic or genital relationship between two (or more) males; see *homosexuality.*

Data on the frequency of male homosexuality are difficult to obtain. Havelock Ellis (1936) estimated the incidence at 2 to 5 per cent; Hirschfeld (1920) at 2 to 3 per cent; but these and many other estimates are biased by the belief that to qualify as a homosexual the individual must be exclusively homosexual. Kinsey's data are based on sexual contact resulting in orgasm; that is, his statistics do not include those who engage in sexual activity without coming to climax, or those who are erotically aroused by a homosexual stimulus without ever having overt relations. As thus defined, Kinsey found that 37 per cent of the male population has some homosexual experience between the beginning of adolescence and old age; and of unmarried males who are 35 years of age or over, almost 50 per cent have had a homosexual experience since the beginning of adolescence. Kinsey finds that 4 per cent of the white male population are exclusively homosexual throughout their lives.

Accidental homosexuality, the choice of a man as sexual object when no women are available (faute de mieux), indicates that most males are probably capable of a homosexual object choice. But the true homosexual must exclude women as his object choice for some other reason. Freud pointed out that fear of castration, intense Oedipal attachment to the mother, narcissism and narcissistic object choice, and identification with sibling rivals with secondary overcompensatory love for them are important etiological factors in male homosexuality. The sight of the female genitalia provokes castration anxiety by providing concrete evidence that castration is a reality and, through association with old oral anxieties, by perception of the genitalia as a castrating instrument. Such castration anxiety may make the boy retire from rivalry with the father by a denial and renunciation of all women. Castration anxiety is seen in non-homosexual neurotics, too; the decisive factor in the homosexual is the type of reaction

to the castration shock—refusal to have anything more to do with such frightening sights.

The non-homosexual neurotic also shows an Oedipal attachment to the mother; but in the homosexual, the castration anxiety makes the mother and the female genitalia disappointing as a love object. Following such a disappointment, there is regression from object love to identification, and the homosexual identifies with the frustrating mother in a particular aspect—like his mother, he loves men. Then, if his fixation is predominantly narcissistic, he will choose young men or boys as love objects who represent himself, and he loves them in the way he wanted his mother to love him. These are 'subject homoerotic' persons, one of whose conditions of love is often that the homosexual object be of the same age as the person himself when the change into overt homosexuality occurred. If, on the other hand, his fixation is predominantly anal (i.e. passive-receptive), he will choose the father or masculine father-substitutes as love objects and attempt to enjoy sex in the same way as his mother; such 'object homoerotics' cover with superficial passivity and submissiveness the unconscious idea of depriving the object choice of his 'secrets' or of his genitals. Narcissistic and anal fixations may, of course, occur in the same individual, in which case a combination of the above types would be seen.

F.J. Kallmann (*Heredity in Health and Mental Disorder,* Norton, New York, 1953) presents evidence that the major factors in such a development as outlined above are genetically determined.

Studies of the effect of rearing on sexual orientation, however, cast doubt on the thesis that sexual identity is largely determined by genetic constitution. Many pseudohermaphrodites and subjects with gonadal agenesis have been reared as females when their chromosomal sex is male (and vice versa); yet in every case the gender role and orientation was consistent with the assigned sex and rearing.

It would appear that homosexuality, like all other sexuality, can be a pathway for gratification of a diversity of infantile drives, including non-sexual ones, and that it can function as a defense against any drive or affect that threatens to disrupt the ego. Dependency needs and power strivings so frequently contribute to homosexual object choice that they have been termed *pseudohomosexual motivations* (Ovesey, L., Gaylin, W., and Hendin, H. *Archives of General Psychiatry* 9, 19-31, 1963). Recent studies have emphasized the intrafamilial relationships that favor development of significant conflicts in these areas, such as fathers who are detached, hostile, or in discontinuous contact so that they fail to protect the son from destructive maternal behavior. The latter is often expressed in the form of a 'close-binding-intimate' (CBI) relationship in which the mother interferes with heterosexual development by sexually overstimulating or inhibiting her son, by being demasculinizing, by interfering with her son's peer group participation, by interfering with the father-son relationship, and/or by blocking development of independence and self-assertiveness. (Bieber. I. *Homosexuality*, Basic Books, New York, 1962)

homosexuality, masked Unconscious homosexual impulses. For example, a marrried man, complaining that his wife was frigid, insisted on having solely anal intercourse with her, since this was much more gratifying to him than genital relations. The unique pleasure found exclusively in anal contact represented his masked homosexuality.

homosexuality, unconscious See *homosexuality, latent.*

homosociality A term coined by J.C. Fluegel to denote social relationship between members of the same sex.

homozygocity (hō-mō-zī-gos'i-tē) *Homozygousness* (q.v.).

homozygosis (-zī-, zi-gō'sis) Homozygousness.

homozygosity (-zī, zi-gos'i-tē) Homozygousness.

homozygote (-zī'gōt, -zig'ōt) A zygotic organism produced by the union of two similar gametes and therefore possessing two like genes of a given factor pair. In the case of *recessive* Mendelian inheritance, a hereditary character can be manifested only by those offspring who have inherited its predisposing factor from both parents and thus are homozygous for the character in question.

homozygousness (-zī'gus-nes) This rather obsolete term (identical with *homozygosity* or *homozygocity*) relates to the 'germinally pure' condition of a person who inherits the same gene factor from each parent, so that in his organism the two genes of the given pair are *alike*.

Homozygousness of a dominant anomaly is very rare, as it can be assumed only when both parents of a diseased person are also patients. In the case of a recessive anomaly which can only appear in the phenotype of a homozygote, all trait-carriers must be homozygotes. Consequently, the occurrence of such a recessive anomaly is not possible, unless *both* parents are either homozygotes or heterozygotes for the anomaly in question (see *recessiveness*).

Certain deleterious effects of inbreeding are now assumed to be due chiefly to the attainment of homozygousness rather than merely to the process of inbreeding itself. The frequent mating of persons closely related in descent must automatically result in a reduction of heterozygosity unless new mutations occur in these inbred lines. If the mutation rate is high, this may defer or prevent the attainment of homozygousness. See *inbreeding; heterosis.*

homunculus (hō-mung'kū-lus) (L. 'little man') According to Paracelsus (1493-1541), a tiny man produced artificially, and hence endowed with magic power; dwarf; manikin. Herbert Silberer wrote a monograph on 'Der Homunculus' (*Imago, III,* 37-79, 1914) in which he made an extensive survey of the concept from the standpoint of folklore and from that of the clinician. In folklore homunculus means a little man created artificially out of dung or gold. In folklore dung and gold are equated. The homunculus continues to gain magical power, until finally he is master of his creator.

According to psychoanalysts, the homunculus is related to onanism, in the sense that it is the result of onanism. The product of onanism is transformed (i.e. sublimated) into a little man. This concept appears frequently in dreams. Silberer cites the case of a girl who masturbated by rubbing the genitals against the edge of a wooden table; she then dreamed of wooden children.

Hooton, Ernest Albert (1887-1954)

American anthropologist; anthropometry; *Up From the Ape* (1931).

Hoover's sign (Charles F. Hoover, 1865 - 1927, American physician.) Observed in organic hemiplegia and used for differentiating organic from hysteric hemiplegia; if the patient, lying on his back, attempts to raise the paretic leg, he unconsciously presses down forcibly the heel of the healthy leg; this accentuation does not occur in hysteria.

hormephobia (hor-mē-fō'bē-à) Fear of shock.

hormism (hôr'miz'm) A term used in the writings of the school of psychology which holds that goals are sought for their own sake because of some intrinsic value, regardless of any pleasure attendant upon their attainment. McDougall believes that in man and animals there are present certain tendencies or urges which account for all forms of behavior, including abstract mental processes. Each tendency leads to a definite end, or purpose. Hormism is thus opposed to hedonism, which states that goals are sought only because they give pleasure or gratification to the person. See *hedonism.*

hormone (hor'mōn) In the higher organisms, this term designates a variety of internal chemical secretions which enter the blood from the ductless glands and provide a very important part of the *'internal environment'* in which biological development takes place through the actions of the genes.

Some hormones correlate the general processes of development, others regulate growth or are responsible for the attainment of normal maturity. 'A hormone itself may often be one channel through which a gene affects general characters; and there is undoubtedly a complex series of interactions between the genetic factors, the endocrine secretions, and the other agencies of the internal environment during development.' (Sinnott, E.W., and Dunn, L.D. *Principles of Genetics,* 3rd ed., McGraw-Hill, New York and London, 1939)

Horner's syndrome See *syndrome, Horner's.*

Horney, Karen (1885 - 1952) American

psychoanalyst; the Horney school emphasizes environmental and cultural factors in the genesis of neurosis. Horney and H.S. Sullivan represent the two chief branches within the 'dynamic-cultural' school of psychoanalysis.

horror feminae (hôr'rôr fā'mē-nī) 'The essential feature of this strange manifestation of the sexual life is the want of sexual sensibility for the opposite sex, even to the extent of horror, while sexual inclination and impulse toward the same sex are present.' (Krafft-Ebing, R.V. *Psychopathia Sexualis,* Login, New York, 1908)

horrors *Delirium tremens* (q.v.).

hospital, day or night See *day hospital.*

hospitalism See *depression, anaclitic.*

hospitalitis A humorous term coined to emphasize the complete hospital-conditioning (or dependency on the hospital) of a patient, who is usually an utterly helpless or incompetent person before his admission to the hospital. It may be difficult for him to leave the hospital, and each attempt to prepare the patient for discharge results in an aggravation of symptoms. See *disease, sanatorium.*

housewife's syndrome See *neurosis, housewife's.*

Hsieh-Ping (sē-ping') A trance-like state, seen in Formosa, characterized by tremor, disorientation, delirium, and ancestor identification, and often accompanied by visual or auditory hallucinations. The seizure may last from 30 minutes to several hours.

HTP See *test, House-Tree-Person.*

Hubner, Arthur (b. 1878) (hüb'nēr) German forensic psychiatrist.

humiliation Feeling of being disgraced, shamed, debased, or ignominiously dishonored; it may represent a frustration of narcissistic aspirations and disapproval or punishment by the superego. Such feelings are frequent concomitants to the dejection of clinically depressed patients (loss of self-esteem). Provocation of others into actions that appear to warrant feelings of humiliation is seen often in *masochism* (q.v.).

humor, gallows Galgenhumor; this is a term, infrequently used in psychiatry, to refer to humorous and comical behavior in the face of disaster or death. Gallows humor is seen most frequently in the organic psychoses, and particularly in delirium tremens cases.

hunger, affect Indiscriminate and insatiable demand for attention and affection, seen often in children who have suffered *emotional deprivation*. Affect hunger frequently takes the form of aggressive, hostile, antisocial behavior with an inability to accept limitations or recognize the needs of others. See *deprivation, emotional*.

hunger, nervous Urge to eat (orally incorporate) as a method of allaying anxiety or tension and of gratifying frustrated pleasure cravings. Obesity is frequently the secondary symptomatic result of such chronic and intense nervous hunger. Nervous hunger is an expression of intense dependence and stems back to the oral incorporative stage of infantile development.

Food addiction, as well as cigarette addiction, is a closely related phenomenon. Thumb-sucking, which is closely related to the use of 'pacifers' in infancy, with the thumb replacing the 'pacifier,' is an early infantile prototype of nervous hunger.

hunger, social 'The desire to be accepted by the group . . . which is one of the strongest drives in human beings. It is also the major incentive for improvement in a therapy group.' (Slavson, S.R. *An Introduction to Group Therapy*, The Commonwealth Fund, Oxford University Press, New York, 1943, p. 15)

hunger-strike, neurotic Adler thus denotes the fear of eating, occurring mainly in females at about the age of seventeen. There follows usually a rapid decrease in weight. The goal, to be inferred from the whole attitude of the patient, is the rejection of the female role.

'In other words, it is an attempt by means of an exaggerated abstinence—as is so generally the case—to retard the development of the female bodily form.' (Adler, A. *The Practice and Theory of Individual Psychology*, tr. by Radin, P., Kegan Paul, Trench, Trubner, London, 1924)

Huntington's chorea See *chorea, Huntington's*.

Hurd, Henry Mills (1843-1927) American psychiatrist.

Hurler's disease *Gargoylism* (q.v.).

hybrid (hī'brid) The inbred offspring of two parents who differ with respect to one gene factor or a combination of factors or even belong to different species. *Genet*. Used also as an adjective. The hybrids which constitute the first filial generation are heterozygotic individuals originating from the cross of parents who carry a given hereditary stock in a pure, unmixed form. When such hybrids differ with respect to only *one* character, they are called *monohybrid*. When they differ in two characters, they are *dihybrid*; analogously, other hybrids are *trihybrid* or *polyhybrid*.

'It is not always, not even usually, possible to cross species, for there is a strong tendency for species to be intersterile. Some of them will not mate, or their germ cells will not unite, or the hybrid does not reach maturity. Other species leap all these hurdles, cross, and yield offspring, but the hybrids are sterile. There are, however, many grades of interfertility between species, and some such crosses are as fruitful as matings within species.' (Shull, A.F. *Heredity*, 3rd ed., McGraw-Hill, New York and London, 1938)

The genetic mechanism leading to developmental disharmony in hybridization is still by no means well understood. It is assumed that in the case of unlike chromosomes of the two parents, normal pairing at meiosis cannot take place and gametes consequently fail to be produced. 'This may result from differences in the number or size of the chromosomes, in the character of the genes that they contain, or in the arrangement of these genes.' (Sinnott, E.W., and Dunn, L.D. *Principles of Genetics*, 3rd ed., McGraw-Hill, New York and London, 1939)

hybridization (hī-brid-i-zā'shun) Genetic term for the process of increasing the variability in a species or group of plants or animals through the production of *hybrids*. The increase in variability is reflected in the appearance of many new character combinations and enables the breeders of animals and plants, by practicing selection among them, to develop new and valuable types.

Hybridization also accounts for the well-known fact that 'hybrids or mongrels, whatever their own excellent qualities, do not breed true and hence are valueless for breeding purposes where uniformity of type is desired.' (Sinnott, E.W., and Dunn, L.D. *Principles of Genetics,* 3rd ed., McGraw-Hill Book Company, Inc., New York and London, 1939)

hydro- (hī'drō-) Combining form meaning water; hydrogen, from Gr. *hydor,* water.

hydrocephalus (hī-drō-sef'à-lus) An increase in the volume of cerebrospinal fluid within the skull. If cerebrospinal fluid pressure is normal, the condition is termed *compensatory hydrocephalus,* since the excess fluid compensates for brain atrophy, as in congenital cerebral hypoplasia and in acquired cerebral atrophy due to diffuse sclerosis, general paralysis, and senile or presenile degeneration. If pressure is increased, the condition is termed *hypertensive hydrocephalus,* which may be (1) obstructive, when an obstruction to the circulation of cerebrospinal fluid within the ventricles or at the outlet from the fourth ventricle prevents free communication between the ventricles and the subarachnoid space; or (2) communicating, when communication between ventricles and subarachnoid space is free and hydrocephalus is due to increased fluid formation (as in meningitis, certain toxic states, and after head injury), decreased absorption (as in compression of venous sinuses by tumor, products of infection, etc., or in impaired venous drainage secondary to increased intrathoracic pressure in cases of pulmonary neoplasm, aneurysm of the aorta, or severe emphysema) or to obstruction within the subarachnoid space (as in the case of tumor, adhesions following trauma, inflammation or hemorrhage, or congenital abnormalities such as platybasia or the Arnold-Chiari malformation).

Hypertensive hydrocephalus may be congenital or acquired. In congenital hydrocephalus, the most conspicuous symptom is enlargement of the head, which usually is slowly progressive. The cranial sutures are widely separated and the anterior fontanelle is greatly enlarged. Convulsions are common, and also optic

atrophy due to pressure on the optic nerves. Mental deficiency is seen in severe cases (31x.4). Most cases die by the age of four; in the survivors, mental deficiency, epilepsy, and blindness are the usual sequelae.

In acquired obstructive hydrocephalus, increased intracranial pressure causes headache, vomiting, and papilledema. In time, there is usually some mental deterioration, often with emotional lability, hallucinations, and delusions. Cranial nerve palsies may occur.

hydrocephalus, toxic See *pseudotumor cerebri.*

hydrodipsomania (-dip-sō-mā'nē-à) Periodic attacks of uncontrollable thirst often found in epileptic patients.

hydro-encephalocele (-en-sef'à-lō-sēl) A developmental anomaly of the brain in which the brain protruding through the skull contains a cavity which communicates with the cerebral ventricles.

hydromania (-mā'nē-à) *Obs.* Impulse to commit suicide by drowning.

hydromyelia (-mī-ē'lē-à) An increase of fluid in the dilated central canal of the spinal cord or elsewhere in the cord substance where congenital cavities may be present.

hydromyelocele (-mī'el-ō-sēl) The protrusion of a portion of the spinal cord, thinned out into a sac which is distended with cerebrospinal fluid, through a spina bifida.

hydrophobia (-fō'bē-à) Fear of water; rabies. The symptoms of rabies are: (1) in the premonitory stage, irritability, general malaise, anorexia, headache, insomnia; tingling, numbness, or pain in the course of the nerves radiating from the site of the wound; spasms of the muscles of the larynx and pharynx; huskiness; difficulty in swallowing; (2) in the stage of excitement there is exaggeration of the premonitory symptoms; intense excitement with terror; intense thirst, but every effort to drink is forthwith followed by choking and dyspnea; elevation of temperature and pulse. As the disease progresses, convulsions become generalized;

(3) in the stage of paralysis, restlessness abates, convulsions cease, the musculature becomes limp and paralytic.

hydrophobophobia (-fō-bō-fō'bē-à) Fear of hydrophobia; in severe cases, the symptoms of hydrophobia are actually paralleled.

hydropsychosis (-sī-kō'sis) Keen attraction to water. 'To the simple animisms of children water lives, sings, laughs, moans, beckons, and often talks in words and phrases of which Bolton collected many. . . . Youth works a sea change and the hydropsychoses strike inward.' The curve of runaways to go to sea rises steeply, and a sailor's life now makes its strongest appeal. (Hall, G.S. *Adolescence*, vol. 2, Appleton, New York, 1908, p. 196)

hydrorrhoea, nasal (-rē'à) A 'running nose.' 'This is a phenomenon which may be observed not only in hysterics, but also, much more frequently, under certain special circumstances, in the neurasthenic. The nasal secretion is, as a matter of fact, liable to be directly influenced by the psychism. And the latter, on the other hand, is capable of directly creating sensations identical to those which result from a real nasal secretion. It is so true, that, in an individual with the least tendency toward any neuropathic traits, it is only necessary for him to notice that he has forgotten his handkerchief in order to have this simple idea cause him the most intense and legitimate desire to use one.' (Déjérine, J. and Gauckler, E. *The Psychoneuroses and Their Treatment by Psychotherapy*, 2nd ed., tr. by Jelliffe, S.E., Lippincott, Philadelphia and London, 1915)

hydrotherapy (-ther'à-pē) 'The treatment of disease by water. This may be administered internally or externally. It may be given of the same temperature as that of the body, or of lower or higher temperature.' (Sands, I.J. *Nervous and Mental Diseases for Nurses*, 3rd ed., Saunders, Philadelphia and London, 1937)

hyelophobia (hī-ē-lō-fō'bē-à) Fear of glass.

hygiene, criminal The branch of mental hygiene of which the object is the 'study and investigation related to the causes, prevention and treatment of the social-medico-psychological illness known for centuries as crime.'
In taking into consideration the complexity of this problem in modern society, the science aiming at the study of crime has necessarily to deal with many aspects of the offender: heredity, environment, home, social, economical, and political factors, legal aspects, emotional and physical development, psychiatric investigation, etc. (Seliger, R.V., *et al. Contemporary Criminal Hygiene*, Oakridge Press, Baltimore, 1946)

hygiene, mental The science and practice of maintaining mental health and efficiency—for a twofold purpose: first, to develop optimal modes of personal and social conduct in order to produce the happiest utilization of inborn endowments and capacities; and second, to prevent mental disorders. See *orthopsychiatry*.

hygiene, social 'Social hygiene deals with problems which have a direct or indirect origin in the phenomena of sex. Its goal may be said to be a healthy sex life for individuals and a healthy and scientific attitude toward sex by society. It fosters every measure which has been devised to strengthen and preserve marriage and family relations. These measures may be roughly divided into three groups: medical and public health, educational, and legal and protective.' (Edwards, M.S. *Social Work Year Book*, edited by R.H. Kurtz, Russell Sage Foundation, New York, 1939)

hygrophobia (hī-grō-fō'bē-à) Fear of moisture or dampness.

hylephobia (hī-lē-fō'bi-à) *Obs.* Epilepsy.

hylophobia (hī-lō-fō'bē-à) Fear of forest.

hypacusia (hī-pà-kū'zē-à) Hypoacusia; partial deafness.

hypalgia, hysterical (hī-pal'jē-à) A psychogenically induced decrease in the normal sensitivity to pain in any body area. The psychogenic basis has two elements: (1) As in all hysterical symptoms, the hypalgia is a defense against unconscious instinctual demands. Sexual or aggressive sensations that would be painful—that is, would cause anxiety—are repressed. These anxiety-causing impulses are often linked to specific memories. Hypalgia helps suppress these memories by decreasing the sensitiveness to pain in the body areas connected with these particular memories. (2) The decrease in painful sensation permits this body area to be used for unconscious phantasies and thus the repressed material can be expressed without concomitant painful anxiety. (Fenichel, O. *The Psychoanalytic Theory of Neurosis*, Norton, New York, 1945)

hypapoplexia (hī-pà-pō-pleks′e-à) A mild form of apoplexy.

hypengyophobia (hip-en-jē-ō-fō′bē-à) Fear of responsibility.

hyper- (hī′pēr-) combining form meaning *over, above, beyond, more than* (the normal), from Gr. *hypér*, over, beyond.

hyperactivity Excessive muscular activity; *hyperkinesis* (q.v.). In psychiatry, the term most commonly refers to manifestations of disturbed child behavior and indicates the child whose movements and actions are performed at a higher than normal rate of speed and/or the child who is constantly restless and in motion. Hyperactivity may be: (1) physiologic, i.e. not integrally associated with any other pathology although it may secondarily produce disturbances in living; (2) based on organic brain damage, and typically showing additional symptoms such as educational deficits, short attention span, perceptual difficulties, perseverative tendencies, and sleep disturbances; (3) associated with mental retardation without evident brain damage; (4) a symptom of reaction or neurotic behavior disorder, usually with more or less devious motivational character as part of an attempt to cope with environmental stress and/or neurotic conflicts within the child; or (5) a symptom of childhood schizophrenia. (Chess, S. *New York State Journal of Medicine 60*, 2379-2385, 1960).

hyperactivity, purposeless A symptom seen often in organic brain disease: stimulation of a great enough intensity to provoke any reaction evokes an exaggerated emotional response or a prolonged bout of excessive activity that ful-

fills no purpose. Also known as *occupational delirium*. See *syndrome, organic*.

hyperacusia, hyperacusis (-à-kū-sē-à, -sis) Inordinate acuteness of the sense of hearing.

hyperadrenocorticism Cushing's syndrome; see *adenoma, basophile*.

hyperaldosteronism Aldosteronism (q.v.).

hyperalgesia (-al-jē′zē-à) Inordinate sensitiveness to pain.

hypercathexis (-kà-thek′sis) See *cathexis*.

hypercedemonia (-sē-dē-mō′nē-à) *Obs.* Excessive grief or anxiety.

hypercenesthesia (-sen-es-thē′z[h]-ē-à) A feeling of exaggerated well-being.

hyperechema (-ē-kē′mà) Auditory magnification or exaggeration.

hyperephidrosis (-ef-i-drō′sis) Excessive sweating.

hyperepidosis (-ē-pid′ō-sis) An abnormal or excessive growth of any part of the body.

hyperepithymia (-ep-i-thī′mē-à, -thim′ē-à) Inordinate desire.

hypereridic Characterized by excessive strife or violence. The term *hypereridic state* has been used to refer to attempted suicide triggered by acute interpersonal conflict that produced impulsive, uncontrolled rage.

hyperergasia The manic form of manic-depressive psychosis (A. Meyer).

hyperesthesia (-es-thē′zhē-à) Inordinate sensitiveness to a tactile stimulus.

hyperesthesia psychica (hē-per-es-thā′zē-à psē′kē-kà) *Obs.* Hypochondriasis.

hyperevolutism (e-vol′ū-tiz′m) In constitutional medicine, excessive morphological, physiological, and psychological development.

According to Pende, *hyperevolute* physiques result from an evolution of the individual constitution, which develops more rapidly than is normal or usual for the average person. Such a rapid evolution may be *general* or *local;* for instance, the structural and functional advance of the heart may exceed the development of the other organs of the body, or certain tissues within a single organ may evolve unequally, or the entire habitus may be hyperevolute. (Pende, N. *Constitutional Inadequacies,* tr. by Naccarati, S., Lea & Febiger, Philadelphia, 1928)

hyperfunction Activity or functioning above the subject's own or a standard group's average.

hypergenitalism (-jen′i-tal-is′m) Overdevelopment of the genital system.

hyperglycemic index See *index, hyperglycemic.*

hypergnosis (-gnō′sis) Exaggerated perception, such as the expansion of an isolated thought into a philosophical system that is seen in some paranoids. (Feigenbaum, Dorian. *Psychiatric Quarterly 5,* 307, 1936)

hyperhidrosis (-hi-drō′sis) Excessive sweating.

hyper-independence In social work: 'exaggerated desire to live one's own life in one's own way; extreme individualism and disregard of the advice of others or limitations imposed by the situation.' (Hamilton, G. *A Medical Social Terminology,* Presbyterian Hospital, New York, 1930)

hyperinsulinism, functional (-in′sul-is′m) See *hypoglycemia.*

hyperkalemia (hī-pēr-kal-ē′mē-à) Excessive blood potassium; hyperpotassemia.

hyperkinesis (-ki-nē′sis) Excessive muscular activity, observed in many disordered states, physical and psychical. For example, in epidemic encephalitis, due to definite organic changes, exaggerated motility is often observed. Excessive activity is likewise associated with functional disorders, such as manic-depressive and schizophrenic psychoses.

hyperkinetic impulse-disorder See *impulse-disorder, hyperkinetic.*

hyperlogia (-lō′jē-à) Morbid loquacity.

hypermanic (-man′ik) See *mania.*

hypermetamorphosis (-met-à-mor′fō-sis) An excessive tendency to attend and react to every visual stimulus; noted in monkeys by Bucy and Kluever following bilateral removal of the temporal lobes.

hypermimia (-mim′ē-à) Excessive mimetic movements.

hypermnesia (-mnē′zē-à) Exaggerated memory; ability to recall material that is not ordinarily available to the memory process. Hypermnesia as a psychopathologic phenomenon has been reported in the following conditions: (1) manic phase of manic-depressive psychosis; (2) schizophrenic disorders, where the remembered material is sometimes woven into the patient's hallucinations; (3) organic brain disorders, and particularly the acute confusional deliria; (4) hypnosis; (5) psychoanalytic reactivation; (6) during the seconds of shock and fright in situations that endanger life; (7) fever; (8) as an effect of certain drugs, and particularly amphetamines and other stimulants, and hallucinogenic agents; (9) during neurosurgery, especially when this involves stimulation of the temporal lobes; and (10) following some brain injuries.

hypernea, hypernoia (-nē′à, -noi′à) *Obs.* Exaggerated mental activity; hyperpsychosis

hyperontomorph (-on′tō-morf) One of the two constitutional types distinguished by Beu, characterized by long, lanky bodies with short intestines, in contrast to the *mesontomorph;* corresponds roughly to Kretschmer's *asthenic type.*

hyperopia (-ō′pē-à) Far-sightedness, longsightedness. As a result of an error in refraction or flattening of the globe of the eye, parallel rays are focused behind the retina. See *myopia.*

hyperorexia (-ō-rek′sē-à) Bulimia; excessive hunger.

hyperosmia (-oz'mē-à) Exaggerated sensitiveness to odors.

hyperpathia (-path'ē-à) Sensation of pain in a hypesthetic zone as may be observed in association with lesions of the thalamus.

hyperpathia, thalamic (thà-là'mik) See *thalamus.*

hyperphoria (-for'ē-à) See *heterophoria.*

hyperphrasia (-frā'zē-à) Hyperlogia; polyphrasia; excessive loquacity.

hyperphrenia (-frē'nē-à) (1) Excessive mental activity, such as occurs in the manic phase of manic-depressive psychosis or in the severe preoccupations associated with the psychoneuroses; (2) intellectual capacity far above the average. See *phrenalgia.*

hyperpituitary constitution See *constitution, hyperpituitary.*

hyperplasia (-plā'z[h]ē-à) Increase in the bulk of a part or organ of the body, due to an increase in the number of the individual tissue elements, excluding tumor formation.

Some pathologists make this increase in *number* the criterion for sharply distinguishing *hyperplasia* from *hypertrophy* (q.v.), which is defined by them as an increase in bulk due to the increase in *size* of the individual tissue elements. Others restrict the usage of the concept of hyperplasia to cases in which the proliferative changes mentioned are not occurring to meet a demand for increased functional activity or to compensate for an organic inferiority elsewhere, which would fall under their definition of hypertrophy.

hyperponesis (hī-pèr-pō-nē'sis) Increased invisible motor activity, measurable electromyographically, presumed to be due to hyperactivity of neurons of the motor portion of the nervous system. Hyperponesis is seen in patients with clincial depressions; increased invisible motor activity is also seen with increasing age.

hyperpragia (-prā'jē-à) Excessive mentation; the type of mental activity commonly observed during the manic phase of

manic-depressive psychosis, namely, an excess of thinking and feeling.

hyperpragic (-praj'ik) Relating to or characterized by excessive mental activity; in constitutional medicine, by excessive or increased activity of various systems and organs of the body, with a *miopragic* type.

hyperprosessis (-prō-ses'is) Exaggerated attention. Diminished attention is called *hypoprosessis.*

hyperprosexia (-sek'sē-à) Exaggerated attention.

hyperpselaphesia (-sē-là-fē'zhē-à) Eulenburg's term for tactile over-sensitiveness.

hyperpsychosis (-sī-kō'sis) Hypernoia; see *apsychosis.*

hypersensibility 'A degree of sensitivity, physical, or psychological, or both, which calls for simplification of environment and protection.' (Hamilton, G. *A Medical Social Terminology,* Presbyterian Hospital, New York, 1930)

hypersexuality A disturbance of sexuality in which there is a greatly or morbidly increased sexual activity. Since all neurotics are unable to attain complete sexual satisfaction, any neurotic may show this symptom. He might try to gain satisfaction through persistent repetition of the sexual act, yet never achieve that quelling of desire which comes with complete orgasm. Also he may boast about the frequency with which he can perform the sexual act, or behave in an 'oversexed' way, giving sexual connotations to many of his relationships or activities. This occurs for two reasons: (1) the dammed-up sexuality will come out 'in unsuitable places and at inconvenient times,' just because it cannot be satisfied with orgasm; (2) there is a narcissistic need to prove through such activity that the subject is not impotent or frigid.

In case the symptom of hypersexuality is so marked as to dominate the clinical picture, additional factors are at work. The genital apparatus is being used to discharge 'some nongenital, warded-off, and dammed-up need.' These needs might be various: (1) The primary purpose of the sexual activity might be to obtain self-esteem by contradicting an inner feeling of inferiority with erotic 'successes.' Whether the person is a Don Juan or a nymphomaniac, 'analysis shows that the condition depends on a marked narcissistic attitude, on a dependency on narcissistic supplies, on an intense fear over loss of love, and a corresponding pregenital and sadistic coloration of the total sexuality. . . . The sadistic attitude is manifest in the attempt to coerce the partner by violence into "giving" complete sexual satisfaction and therewith a re-establishment of self-esteem.' As soon as the sexual act has been performed, the patient is no longer interested in his partner, but must find another, both because his narcissistic needs demand that he continually prove his ability to excite other partners, and because this partner has failed to satisfy him completely. (2) Another source of hypersexuality which can be traced to nongenital needs is an unconscious homosexual inclination. Though aroused, the patient cannot, through increased heterosexual activity, obtain the satisfaction he seeks. (3) Still another source, operative in women, might be an intense penis-envy. Through nymphomanic activities the patient seeks to fulfill the wish phantasy of depriving the man of his penis. (Fenichel, O. *The Psychoanalytic Theory of Neurosis*, Norton, New York, 1945)

hypersomnia (-som'nē-à) Sleep of excessive duration as in lethargic encephalitis; sometimes used to refer to coma-vigil. See *mutism, akinetic*.

hypersthenic (-sthen'ik) In constitutional medicine, excessive tension and strength or a hyperfunction of the lymphatic elements and organs, in contrast to an 'asthenic lymphatic' condition.

In Pende's constitutional system, the term is used in connection with the *hypertonic* type to designate a sub-group of both the *megalosplanchnic hypervegetative* constitution and the *microsplanchnic hypovegetative* constitution.

In Mills's system, the term has a sense which corresponds roughly to the characteristics of the *pyknic* type of Kretschmer.

hypertelorism (-tel'ō-riz'm) Excessive distance between two parts or organs. D.M. Greig's term denotes a form of mental deficiency characterized by general mental and physical retardation, not very dissimilar to the essential features of mongolism (31x.4).

hypertension, essential Abnormally high blood pressure without known cause. In psychiatry, many consider essential hypertension to be a psychophysiologic (psychosomatic) cardiovascular disorder. Alexander believes that the specific dynamic pattern is the repression of all hostile, competitive tendencies which are intimidating because of fears of retaliation and failure; this general readiness for aggression is combined with a passive-receptive, dependent longing to be rid of the aggression. But these dependent longings arouse inferiority feelings and thereby reactivate the hostile competitiveness; this leads to anxiety and the need for further inhibition of aggressive, hostile impulses. This vicious circle is the basis for arterial hypertension, but the syndrome probably occurs only in those whose vasomotor system (and/or kidneys and/or endocrine constitution) is predisposed to instability, perhaps by virtue of inherited factors. Essential hypertension is probably so frequent in the American businessman because in business a great amount of aggression is necessary even though the culture as a whole greatly depreciates aggression.

'A fully consummated aggressive attack has three phases. At first there is the preparation of the attack in phantasy, its planning and its mental visualization. This is the conceptual phase. Second, there is the vegetative preparation of the body for concentrated activity: changes in metabolism and blood distribution. . . . Finally there is the neuromuscular phase, the consummation of the aggressive act itself through muscular activity. . . . If the inhibition takes place as early as the psychological preparation for an aggressive attack, a migraine attack develops. If the second phase, the vegetative preparation for the attack, develops but the process does not progress further, hypertension follows. And finally if the voluntary act is inhibited only in the third phase, an inclination toward arthritic symptoms or vasomotor syncope may develop.' (Alexander, F. *Psychosomatic Medicine, Its Principles and Applications*, Norton, New York, 1950) See *encephalopathy, hypertensive*.

hyperthymia (-thī'mē-à, -thim'ē-à) State

of overactivity, greater than average and less than the overactivity of the manic stage of manic-depressive psychosis.

'The hyperthymic types show exaggerated activities in the way of the usual business occupations, writing letters and the like.' (Jelliffe, S.E., and White, W.A. *Diseases of the Nervous System*, 6th ed., Lea & Febiger, Philadelphia, 1935)

Hyperthymia is a subdivision of cyclothymia. It is probably very close to hypomania, but occupies a position between normal overactivity and hypomania.

hypertonia (-tō′nē-à) Extreme tension of the muscles; spasticity or rigidity.

hypertrophy (hī-per′trō-fē) The process of overgrowth, or the kind of increase in the bulk of an organ or part of the body which is not due to tumor formation.

Some pathologists restrict usage of the term to denote greater bulk through increase in *size*, but not in *number*, of the individual tissue elements; it is then contrasted with *hyperplasia*.

Other pathologists limit the term *hypertrophy* to those cases in which the increase in size meets a demand for increased functional activity or compensates for an organic inferiority elsewhere. The other cases fall under their definition of hyperplasia.

In the field of constitutional medicine, the term is used by some typologists to indicate undue size of a body area relative to other parts of the body.

hypertropia (-trō′pē-à) A type of strabismus in which the affected eye deviates upward.

hyperuricemia Abnormally high blood content of uric acid; seen typically in gout, but it occurs also as an inborn metabolic disorder in children. In the latter case, symptoms include severe mental retardation, spastic cerebral palsy, choreoathetosis, and bizarre self-destructive behavior such as biting of the flesh—sometimes so deeply that the bones themselves are gnawed (31x.2).

hyperventilation Overbreathing. See *syndrome, hyperventilation*.

hypesthesia (hip-es-thē′zhē-à) Subnormal sensitiveness to a tactile stimulus.

hyphedonia (hif-ē-dō′nē-à) A state in which the subject experiences slight pleasure from what normally gives great pleasure.

hypnagogic (hip-nà-goj′ik) Inducing sleep; hypnotic. See *imagery, hypnagogic*.

hypnagogic intoxication See *intoxication, hypnagogic*.

hypnalgia (hip-nal′jē-à) Dream-pain.

hypnenergia (hip-nē-nēr′jē-à) *Obs.* Somnambulism.

hypnic (hip′nik) Relating to or causing sleep; hypnotic.

hypno- (hip′nō-) combining form meaning sleep, from Gr. *hypnos*, sleep.

hypnoanalysis (-an-al′i-sis) The use of hypnosis in psychoanalytic therapy as an aid to removing resistances that prevent awareness of unconscious material. Regression and revivification under hypnosis may open up pathways to memories which are not available to the patient at an adult, waking level. It is obvious, however, that no matter what material is elicited in the trance state, in order to be effective it must be integrated and incorporated into the more conscious layers of the psyche.

hypnobades (hip-nob′à-dēz) *Obs.* Somnambulist.

hypnobadicus (hip-nō-bad′i-kus) *Obs.* Pertaining to or affected by somnambulism.

hypnobadisis (-bad′i-sis) *Obs.* Somnambulism.

hypnobasis (hip-nob′à-sis) *Obs.* Somnambulism.

hypnobat (hip′nō-bat) A sleep walker; somnambulist.

hypnobatesis (hip-nō-bà-tē′sis) *Obs.* Somnambulism.

hypnobatia (-bat′ē-à) The performance, during sleep, of actions that take place in the waking stage.

hypnocatharsis (-kȧ-thär′sis) 'Essentially, this method consists of hypnotizing the patient and having the patient free-associate while in this state. Often memories will flow more easily under such circumstances. The difficulties, however, lie in the fact that all patients are not hypnotizable and that hypnosis casts a shroud of mystery about the process, making a "mystic" affair of that which one desires the patient to be very clear about.' (Kraines, S.H. *The Therapy of the Neuroses and Psychoses*, Lea & Febiger, Philadelphia, 1948)

hypnodia (hip-nō′dē-ȧ) Somnolence.

hypnogenic spot (hip-nō-gen′ik) See *spot, hypnogenic.*

hypnograph (hip′nō-graf) An instrument to measure sleep. The basic hypnograph consists of a recording pen attached to a coil of the sleeper's bed so that any movement of his is communicated to the instrument and traced in a graph. This gives a measure of the amount of gross motor activity during sleep. In the same manner other functions may be tested during sleep, and there are modifications of the hypnograph which will measure any or all of the following: blood pressure, pulse, temperature, respiration, metabolic rate, muscle tone, reflexes, urine volume, sweating, gastric secretion, lacrimal and salivary secretion, etc.

hypnolepsy (hip′nō-lep-sē) Narcolepsy.

hypnology (hip-nol′ō-jē) The science of sleep and hypnotism.

hypnonarcosis (hip-nō-när-kō′sis) Narcosis (a state of deep sleep) induced through hypnosis.

hypnonergia (-nēr′jē-ȧ) See *hypnenergia.*

hypnopathy (hip-nop′ȧ-thē) Hypnolepsy.

hypnophobia (hip-nō-fō′bē-ȧ) Fear of falling asleep.

hypnophrenosis (-frē-nō′sis) A general term, introduced by C.H. Schutze, for various forms of sleep disturbance.

hypnopompic (-pom′pik) Sleep-dispelling. Relating to or ushering out the semiconscious state between the stages of sleep and awakening.

hypnosigenesis (-si-jen′e-sis) Induction of hypnosis.

hypnosigenic (-si-jen′ik) Pertaining to the induction of hypnosis.

hypnosis (hip-nō′sis) The state or condition induced through hypnotism. The subject to be hypnotized usually lies in the recumbent position. He is commanded to fix his attention, usually by staring at an object, while the hypnotist keeps repeating in a monotonous manner that the subject is growing tired, drowsy, and sleepy. The purpose is to induce a trancelike state in which, in deep hypnosis, the conscious mind of the subject no longer functions, as in sleep, yet the subject is completely obedient to the commands of the hypnotist.

Therapeutic hypnosis or hypnotherapeusis may be of two degrees, superficial or deep. During the former 'he has not been asleep, and has heard all my words. He has felt fatigue and a heaviness in the limbs, but might have opened his eyes and moved about, had he wished. . . . This is the type of a very superficial hypnosis.' (Schilder, P. and Kauders, O. *Hypnosis,* tr. by Rothenberg, S., Nervous & Mental Disease Publishing Company, Washington, D.C., 1927) The same authors state that in deep sleep 'the outcome is the same, with the exception that the patient declares, after awaking, that she cannot remember what was said to her.'

As defined by the British Medical Association: 'a temporary condition of altered attention in the subject which may be induced by another person and in which a variety of phenomena may appear spontaneously or in response to verbal or other stimuli. These phenomena include alterations in consciousness and memory, increased susceptibility to suggestion, and the production in the subject of responses and ideas unfamiliar to him in his usual state of mind. Further, phenomena such as anesthesia, paralysis, and muscle rigidity, and vaso-motor changes can be produced and removed in the hypnotic state.'

hypnosis, catalyzing action of The accelerating influence of hypnosis upon the various phases of analytical proceedings. The hypnosis is induced as an adjunct to psychoanalysis, and then used in order to hasten the uncovering of unconscious material which might otherwise take a long time to come to the awareness of the patient. (Wolberg, L.R. *Hypnoanalysis*, Grune and Stratton, New York, 1945)

hypnosis, cathartic (kà-thär'tik) See *hypnotism.*

hypnosis, coaxing See *hypnosis, father.*

hypnosis, dependency in The patient under hypnosis may establish an exaggerated transference to the analyst based upon an overvaluation of the power and authority of the hypnotist. This exaggerated identification is called dependency in hypnosis. The patient plunges himself into a subordinate position in order to achieve his objectives, but such a position is incompatible with normal self-esteem. 'It tends to destroy assertiveness, to sap independence, and to vitiate activity and creative self-fulfillment. It may render the patient progressively more helpless—an automaton who lives without a self and is secure and confident only insofar as the omniscient hypnotist can shield him from harm and gratify his needs for him. Unable to achieve his goals through his own efforts, the patient may become increasingly hostile and finally may interrupt the therapy with a return to his neurotic symptoms.' (Wolberg, L.R. *Hypnoanalysis*, Grune and Stratton, New York, 1945)

hypnosis, father 'We could maintain that hypnotic submission is to be traced back to blind obedience, but this again to the transference of paternal fixation. There are only two kinds of hypnosis: father-hypnosis (that might also be called fear-hypnosis) and mother-hypnosis (in other words, coaxing-hypnosis).' (Ferenczi, S. *Further Contributions to the Theory and Technique of Psycho-Analysis*, tr. by Suttie, J.I., Leonard and Virginia Woolf and The Institute of Psychoanalysis, London, 1926)

hypnosi-therapeutics (hip-nō-sē-ther-à-pū'-tiks) *Obs.* Treatment by hypnosis.

hypnotherapeusis, hypnotherapy (-ther-

à-pū'sis, ther'à-pē) Treatment by means of hypnosis. See *hypnotism.*

hypnotism (hip'nō-tiz'm) The theory and practice of inducing hypnosis or a state resembling sleep induced by psychical means. It is also known as braidism (or Braidism) and induced somnambulism. 'Hypnosis may be applied therapeutically in many ways. We shall distinguish for the present between three such applications:
'1. The hypnotically induced sleep is used directly as a healing factor.
'2. The suggestion given in hypnosis is directed outright against the psychic or physical symptom which is to be eliminated.
'3. Forgotten experiences are brought back to memory in hypnosis and are made accessible to the consciousness (cathartic hypnosis).' (Schilder, P. and Kauders, O. *Hypnosis*, tr. by Rothenberg, S., Nervous & Mental Disease Publishing Company, Washington, D.C., 1927)

hypnotizability (hip-nō-tīz-à-bil'i-tē) Susceptibility to hypnosis.

hypnotization, collective (-ti-zā'shun) Simultaneous hypnosis of several subjects.

hypo- hyp- (hī'pō-, hip'ō-) A combining form meaning: under, below, less than (the normal), from Gr. *hypó*, under.

hypoaffective type See *type, hypoaffective.*

hypoalgesia (hī-pō-al-jē'zē-à) Lessened sensibility to painful stimuli.

hypoboulia, hypobulia (-bū'lē-à) Deficiency or inadequacy of the will or will power, seen primarily in schizophrenic patients. See *will, disturbances of; unforthcomingness.*

hypocathexis (-ka-thek'sis) See *cathexis.*

hypochondria (-kon'drē-à) *Hypochondriasis* (q.v.).

hypochondriac language See *speech, organ.*

hypochondriasis (hī-pō-kon-drī'à-sis) (300.7) Hypochondria; hypochondriacal neurosis; somatic overconcern; morbid attention to the details of body functioning and/or exaggeration of any symptom, no matter how insignificant. Although hypochondriasis may appear in the form of a specific neurosis, it may also occur in association with such disorders as anxiety neurosis, obsessive-compulsive neurosis, and most often with the initial states of any psychosis. The hypochondriacal patient is typically self-centered, seclusive, and sometimes almost monomaniacal in his attention to his body; his major environmental contacts are somatically colored and he seeks one consultation after another with his family physician or with as many specialists as will agree to re-examine him. In other cases, preoccupation with his own health leads the hypochondriac to seek a career in medicine; similarly, he may become a health faddist. If he uses reaction formation as a defense, hypochondriacal concern may ultimately be expressed in a total neglect of his health and well-being.

Psychodynamically, hypochondriacal anxiety is seen often to represent castration anxiety; further, it may represent an attempt to expiate for guilt feelings by the turning of hostility and sadism onto the self.

'Hypochondriasis is a chronic complaint habit. It may arise from a variety of sources. Imitation of observed adult patterns, the desire to retain privileges derived during a period of actual illness, unhappiness at home or at school, ill-treatment, overwork with no recreational outlets, solitary life, parental oversolicitude, feeling of insecurity, medical mismanagement, and fear of punishment may all contribute to the development of somatic complaint on a psychogenic basis.' (Strecker, E.A. and Ebaugh, F.G. *Practical Clinical Psychiatry*, 4th ed., Blakiston, Philadelphia, 1935)

Freud regarded hypochondriasis as an *actual neurosis*, as he does *neurasthenia* and *anxiety-neurosis*. He says: 'Hypochondria, like organic disease, manifests itself in distressing and painful bodily sensations and also concurs with organic disease in its effect upon the distribution of the libido. The hypochondriac withdraws both interest and libido—the latter specially marked—from the objects of the outer world and concentrates both upon the organ which engages his attention. A

difference between hypochondria and organic disease now becomes evident: in the latter, the distressing sensations are based upon demonstrable organic changes; in the former, this is not so. But it would be entirely in keeping with our general conception of the processes of neurosis if we decided to say that hypochondria must be right; organic changes cannot be absent in it either.' (Freud, S. *Collected Papers*, vol. 4, tr. by Riviere, J., Leonard and Virginia Woolf and The Institute of Psychoanalysis, London, 1924-25)

hypochondriasm, hypochondrism, hypocondriacism (-kon'dri-az'm, -'driz'm, -kon-drī'à-siz'm) *Obs.* Hypochondriasis.

hypochondrophthisis (-kon-drof'thi-sis) An infrequently used term for the wasting away of the body in hypochondriasis.

hypochoresis (-kō-rē'sis) Defecation.

hypodepression Simple depression, i.e. mild depression occurring as an episode in manic-depressive psychosis. This form of depressive episode may be difficult to distinguish from normal grief and from so-called psychoneurotic depressive reaction. As in all clinical depressions, however, lowering of the self-esteem and self-depreciatory, self-accusatory thought content are seen in hypodepression but do not occur in normal grief (mourning). For differentiation of hypodepression from psychoneurotic depression, see *depression, (psycho)neurotic; depression, reactive.*

hypoergasia (-ēr-gas'ē-à) The depressed type of manic-depressive psychosis.

hypoesthesia, vaginal See *frigidity, sexual.*

hypoevolutism (-ev'ō-lū-tiz'm) Deficient morphological, physiological, and psychological development. The term is applicable to the body as a whole, to particular systems, organs, and tissues, as well as to the psyche and aspects thereof. One usually distinguishes between *ontogenetic* and *phylogenetic* hypoevolutism.

hypofunction Reduced action or function.

hypogenitalism (hī-pō-jen'i-tal-iz'm) Various forms of underdevelopment of the genital system.

hypoglossal hemiplegia alternans (-glos'-sal) See *hemiplegia alternans*.

hypoglycemia (-glī-sē'mē-à) Concentration of blood sugar below the normal range. In psychiatry, hypoglycemia is of interest (1) in insulin coma treatment, where the blood sugar is deliberately lowered by injection of insulin; and (2) in functional hypoglycemia (functional hyperinsulinism), which is believed by some to be the psychophysiologic disturbance at the basis of many fatigue states. Franz Alexander (*Psychosomatic Medicine, Its Principles and Applications*, Norton, New York, 1950) believes that under the influence of emotional protest and regression, the vegetative functions may regress toward a state of passivity and relaxation characterized by a preponderance of parasympathetic tonus. The organism is then forced either by external pressure or by the internal voice of conscience to undertake activity, even though the person is physiologically in a state of relaxation. Alexander calls this 'vegetative retreat.' The specific psychodynamic constellation is the conflict between passive, dependent wishes and reactive aggressive ambition—a conflict, to be sure, almost universal in our civilization, but in fatigue states the following factors are more specific: little hope of success in a struggle against insuperable odds; no genuine incentive; the inconstancy of anxiety; and in many male cases a feminine identification which opposes aggressive, ambitious attitudes.

hypokinesis (-ki-nē'sis) Slow or diminished movement. It may be physically or psychically determined.
Depressed patients are generally hypokinetic.

hypolepsiomania (-lep-sē-ō-mā'nē-à) A general term, coined by Andral, to denote the various forms of monomania.

hypologia (-lō'jē-à) Reduction in speech, used usually to refer to cases of organic origin in which capacity for speech is limited.

hypomania (-mā'nē-à) See *mania*.

hypomelancholia (-mel-an-kō'lē-à) Mild case of the depressed form of manic-depressive psychosis.

hypomotility (-mō-til'i-tē) Diminished or slowed-down movement.

hyponoia (-noi'a) *Rare*. Deficient mental activity; hypopsychosis.

hyponoic (-nō'ik) Kretschmer's term for hysterical reactions that stem from the deeper psychic layers. 'If the stimulation of the experience is overstrong or the personality, as a result of degeneration, is dissociable with abnormal ease, the deeper psychic layers, which we have already begun to study in hysterical volitional processes, are not always laid bare by simple repression, but through a splitting of the personality. These deeper layers, now working separately, in the field of ideational content furnish us with *hyponoic formations* belonging to an early ontogenetic functional type. We recognize these hyponoic formations in mythology and the art of primitives; in the modern normal adult person, we can study them, above all in the dream, and, aside from hysteria, very frequently in the schizophrenias.' (Kretschmer, E. *Hysteria*, tr. by Boltz, O.H., Nervous and Mental Disease Publishing Company, New York and Washington, 1926, p. 98)

hypophoria (hī-pō-for'ē-à) See *heterophoria*.

hypophrasia Bradyphrasia; slowness of speech, such as is seen as a part of the generalized psychomotor retardation of depressed patients.

hypophrenosis (-frē-nō'sis) A term suggested by Southard for feeblemindedness.

hypophysial cachexia See *cachexia, hypophysial*.

hypoplasia (hī-pō-plā'z[h]ȳ-à) In pathology, the underdevelopment of a tissue or organ, whether due to deficient number or deficient size of the cells which constitute the body structure in question.
The usage of the term in constitutional medicine is somewhat different, and varies. Kretschmer applies it to underdevelopment of certain body areas; for in-

stance, to a hypoplastic condition of the midface. Other typologists distinguish between relative and absolute hypoplasia.

When hypoplasia is *uniform* and relates to an organism as a whole, it results in a manikin or dwarf. However, it occurs more frequently as a *selective* condition, and in this case it implies *dysplasia.*

hypoplastic (-plas'tik) Pertaining to the condition of hypoplasia or, in constitutional medicine, to a type characterized by Bartel's *status hypoplasticus* and equivalent to Rokitansky-Beneke's *habitus phthisicus* (qq.v.).

hypoprosessis (-prō-ses'is) See *hyperprosessis.*

hypopsychosis (-sī-kō'sis) Hyponoia; see *apsychosis.*

hyposomnia Lack of sleep; sleeping for shorter periods than usual.

hypostasis (hī-pos'tà-sis) The obstructive mechanism by which one hereditary factor is prevented by the manifestation of another factor from being phenotypically expressible. The masking effect itself is known as *epistasis,* while the factor which is hidden is called *hypostatic* (see *epistasis*).

hyposthenia (hī-pos-thē'nē-à) Deficient strength.

hyposthenic (-then'ik) Pertaining to or suffering from hyposthenia.

In the systems of constitutional types described by Mills and by Pende the term is used in a sense which contrasts the *hyposthenic* with the *hypersthenic* variety of constitution and corresponds roughly to the characteristics of Kretschmer's *asthenic* type.

hypotaxia (hī-pō-tak'sē-à) Durand introduced this term for the emotional rapport existing between the subject and the operator in a hypnotic setting. Ernest Jones refers to the relationship as *affective suggestion.*

hypotaxis (-tak'sis) Light, hypnotic sleep.

hypothalamotomy (-thal-à-mot'ō-mē) A psychosurgical procedure, employing the same technique as in *thalamotomy* (q.v.) and producing partial ablation of the hypothalamic area—performed subsequently in thalamotomy cases that have not responded to the original operation.

hypothalamus (-thal'à-mus) A phylogenetically old constellation of nuclei lying in the ventral part of the diencephalon just above the optic chiasm and sella turcica. 'It is the principal centre in the forebrain for integration of visceral functions involving the autonomic nervous system. The constituent nuclei may be divided into four groups: (1) anterior including the paraventricular and the supraoptic nuclei, (2) the middle including the tuber, dorsomedial and ventromedial hypothalamic nuclei, (3) the lateral area, and (4) the posterior group including the posterior hypothalamic nucleus and mammillary bodies. Pervading the whole area are ill-defined neurons, grouped under the general heading of "substantia grisea centralis."' (Fulton, J.F. *Physiology of the Nervous System,* 3rd ed., Oxford University Press, New York, 1949)

Functions of the hypothalamus include regulation of sexual activity, water, fat, and carbohydrate metabolism, and heat regulation. The posterior hypothalamus is concerned primarily with the sympathetic system, the middle and anterior nuclei with the parasympathetic system; but all levels of the structure are subject to regulation from thalamic, striatal, and cortical levels.

The following hypothalamic syndromes are recognized: hypothermia, hypersomnia, the adiposogenital syndrome, diabetes insipidus, and autonomic epilepsy.

hypothesis, Fiamberti See *Fiamberti hypothesis.*

hypothesis, mediumistic (hī-poth'ē-sis, mē-di-um-is'tik) Baynes puts forth the hypothesis that the schizophrenic patient is closer than others to the collective unconscious and is strategically in a position to recognize forthwith the early signs of his own disintegration: *eo ipso* he is able to foresee the unconscious trend of events better than can those whose firm clinging to existing forms and conditions renders them insensible for discerning such signs.

hypothesis, structural See *id.*

hypothesis, topographic See *id.*

hypothymia (hī-pō-thī'mē-à, -thim'ē-à) Diminution in the intensity of the affective or emotional state.

hypotonia (-tō'nē-à) Subnormal tension of the muscles; flaccidity.

hypovegetative (-vej'ē-tā-tiv) In contradistinction to the *hypervegetative* (q.v.) biotype of Viola and Pende, this term designates the constitutional type in which the 'animal system' (muscular, nervous, and skeletal systems) predominates in forming contact with the external world, over the organs in the trunk, which represent the nutritional system and are associated with the vegetative life of an individual.

The biotype thus described corresponds exactly to the *dolichomorphic* and *microsplanchnic* types and approximately to Kretschmer's *asthenic.*

hypovigility (-vi-jil'i-tē) Pathological subnormal awareness or response, or complete lack of it, to external stimuli. Hypovigility is the opposite of exaggerated distractibility. Although exaggerated distractibility sometimes occurs in catatonic excitement, hypovigility is more characteristic of the schizophrenic group as a whole. 'The [schizophrenic] patients converse only rarely with those around them even when they are talking a great deal. The incitement to speech as well as its content originates for the most part autistically from inner sources.' (Bleuler, E. *Dementia Praecox or the Group of Schizophrenias,* International Universities Press, New York, 1950) Bleuler considers this an important point in the differential diagnosis of manic schizophrenia and true mania.

hypsarrhythmia (hip-sà-rith'mē-à) An EEG pattern associated with certain infantile spasms of epileptic origin; also known as *major dysrhythmia* and *myoclonic encephalitis.* It affects children, usually under the age of one year, and appears in the form of generalized, symmetrical flexion spasms lasting a few seconds. Between attacks, the EEG shows a diffuse dysrhythmia of the delta-wave type. Psychomotor regression with loss of motor skills and mental deterioration is typical; complete recovery is unusual. Treatment

is unsatisfactory; benefit is sometimes achieved with corticotropin.

hypsophobia (hip-so-fō'bē-à) Fear of a high place.

hysteria (his-tēr'ē-à) Currently, the term is used in several ways: (1) to describe a pattern of behavior, the *hysterical personality* (q.v.); (2) to refer to a conversion symptom, such as hysterical paralysis; (3) to refer to a psychoneurotic disorder, such as conversion hysteria or *anxiety-hysteria* (q.v.); (4) to refer to a specific psychopathologic pattern in which repression is the major defense; and (5) loosely, as a term of oppobrium.

Conversion hysteria appears clinically as (1) a physical manifestation without accompanying structural lesion, or as a peripheral physiologic dysfunction; (2) a calm mental attitude (called 'la belle indifference' by Janet) that is specifically limited to the physical symptom and not generalized to include the entire life of the patient; and (3) episodic mental states, in which a limited but homogeneous group of functions occupies the field of consciousness, often to the complete exclusion of the usual contents of consciousness—fugues, somnambulisms, dream-states, hypnotic states, etc. There is, in other words, a dissociation of the mental or bodily functions, and the dissociated functions may operate in co-existence with normal consciousness, or they may operate to the exclusion of the other functions. In conversion hysteria, the split-off function is ordinarily a unity and the splitting is seldom into more than two parts; thus it is commonly said that in schizophrenia the splitting is molecular or fragmentary, while in hysteria it is molar or massive.

There are no physical symptoms in hysteria that cannot be produced by volition or by emotion, although it may ordinarily be possible to maintain these symptoms for only a short time. Further, the physical symptoms correspond strikingly with the usual lay concepts of disease. Thus hysterical paralysis shows an exact delimitation and an excessive intensity, and it is more frequently accompanied by sensory disturbances than organic paralysis.

The *motor symptoms* include paralysis with or without contracture, tics, tremors, etc. The *sensory symptoms* include anesthesiae, paresthesiae, and hyperesthesiae;

their distribution is rarely according to
anatomical lines; they vary at different
examinations; and they are susceptible to
suggestions. Blindness and deafness are
also seen. The *visceral symptoms* include
anorexia, bulimia, vomiting, hiccough or
respiratory tic, various abdominal complaints, flatulence, etc.

The *mental symptoms* include amnesiae,
somnambulisms, fugues, trances, dream-
states, hysterical 'fits' or 'attacks,' etc.
The amnesia is commonly for a circumscribed series of events and occasionally is for the entire period of life up
to a certain recent point. In a fugue, the
patient suddenly leaves his previous
activity and goes on a journey which has
no apparent relation to what he has just
been doing, and for which he has amnesia
afterward. Somnambulisms are fugues
which begin during sleep and are usually
of shorter duration than fugues. The
movements of the somnambulist are in
response to the manifest or latent content
of the dream; the meaning may be an
escape from the temptation of the bed, or
a movement toward a positive goal which
represents gratification or reassurance. In
double or multiple personalities, there is
further elaboration so that the groups of
dissociated functions when fully conscious
and in charge of the motor apparatus can
at least superficially appear as a complete
personality. Hysterical spells are a pantomimic expression of (mainly Oedipal)
phantasies; in them can be seen condensation, displacement, representation by
the opposite, exaggeration of details
which represent the whole, reversal of the
sequence of events, multiple identification, and suitability for plastic representation. Dream-states are similar to these,
but here the pantomimic discharge is
lacking; dream-states may represent repression, or orgasm, or death-wishes
turned against the ego, or the blocking of
any hostile impulse.

Until Freud advanced his theory of
hysteria, there had been few attempts at
explanation. Charcot had described the
'grande attaque hysterique' with its four
phases: (1) epileptoid phase; (2) large
movement phase; (3) phase of 'attitudes
passionelles'; (4) the 'délire terminal.'
Janet's theories of restriction of the field
of consciousness and the hereditary tendency to dissociate at moments of great
emotion did not explain what it was that
brought the dissociation to pass. Freud's

earlier theory was that the hysterical attack was a symbolic representation of a
repressed sexual trauma. He believed that
the patient had undergone a passive sexual experience in childhood, but that this
psychical experience could not find adequate discharge because the nervous system was incapable of dealing with it at
that time; the experience was forgotten,
but with puberty the memory of it was
reawakened. But adequate discharge ('abreaction') was still not possible, because
the memory conflicted with the conscious
strivings of the personality and/or his
culture. Instead, the strong affect associated with the memory is diverted into the
wrong somatic channels (conversion) and
the hysterical symptom results. Freud and
Breuer found that 'catharsis'—reactivation of the childhood memory, at that time
by means of hypnosis, and allowing abreaction—removed the hysterical symptom.
This theory was later revised when it was
discovered that the sexual traumata uncovered in hysterical patients were really
fictitious memories designed to mask the
autoerotic activities of childhood.

The hysterical attack itself may be
aroused (1) associatively, if the content
of the complex is stirred by a conscious
occurrence; (2) organically, if for any
reason the libidinal cathexis exceeds a
certain amount; (3) in the service of the
primary tendency (paranosic gain) as an
expression of 'flight into illness' if reality
becomes painful or frightening; (4) in the
service of the epinosic gain, to achieve
some end through an attack. To the hysterical patient, all sexuality represents infantile incestuous love, so he cannot love
fully if the genitals are present because
of Oedipal fears. The conversion symptom
is a distorted substitute for sexual (and/or
aggressive) gratification; but because of
the effectiveness of repression, the symptom leads to suffering rather than gratifi-
catory pleasure.

The choice of the afflicted region is
determined by (1) the unconscious sexual
phantasies and the corresponding erogeneity of the area; (2) somatic compliance
('locus minori resistentiae'); (3) the situation in which the decisive repression occurred; (4) the ability of the organ to
symbolize the unconscious drive in question.

Since Freud, many investigators have
stressed pregenital determinants of conversion hysteria, and particularly oral

conflicts arising from intense frustration of oral-receptive needs or excessive gratification of those needs by one or both parents.

Conversion symptoms have also been viewed as unconsciously simulated illnesses, with the patient enacting a sick role as a way to reduce, mask, avoid, or deny a variety of other psychological disturbances (such as anxiety from any cause, identity problems, depression, and incipient schizophrenia). The disorder may be monosymptomatic or may involve many symptoms; these will sometimes be crude and transparent imitations, but equally often they can be accurate simulations of disease or exaggerations of symptoms of genuine physical problems. (Ziegler, F.J., Imboden, J.B., and Rodgers, D.A. *Journal of the American Medical Association 186*, 307-311, 1963)

hysteria, anxiety See *anxiety-hysteria*.

hysteria, artificial *Obs.* Hypnosis.

hysteria, combat See *shell-shock*.

hysteria, conversion *Hysteria* (q.v.).

hysteria, degenerative See *psychosis, degenerative*.

hysteria, epidemic Hysteria or hysteroid disturbances apparently acquired by association with hysterical patients.

hysteria, fixation That form of conversion hysteria (300.13) in which the area or function affected is one that had previously been, or is presently, the site of some organic disorder. An example is conversion paralysis of an area that had been wounded in an accident. Closely allied to fixation hysteria is *pathohysteria*, wherein a chronic disease process is itself productive of hysterical symptoms. A more general term for the latter phenomenon is *pathoneurosis*.

hysteria, major The expression major hysteria (grande hystérie) refers to a clinical syndrome of hysteria, perhaps first described at length by Charcot, later by Richer. It is characterized by several stages: first, the aural stage; second, the stage of epileptoid convulsions; third, the phase of tonic, then clonic spasms; fourth,

the phase of intense and dramatic emotional expressions; fifth, the stage of delirium. The total attack lasts from several minutes up to half an hour. There are many modifications in the form and order of the above-enumerated states.

Some authorities use the expression *major hysteria* synonymously with *hystero-epilepsy* (q.v.).

hysteria, masked *Obs.* A form of hysteria in which the symptoms resemble those of organic disease.

hysteria, reflex Kretschmer uses this expression for a hysterical sign in which an automatic nervous process, that is, a reflex, plays a dominant part, while the will plays a minor role. Examples of reflex hysteria are: simple spasm, tremors, and tics.

hysteria, retention Freud says that the splitting of consciousness is not a primary process in hysteria; according to J. Breuer, the basis is in the hypnoid state. In certain forms of hysteria 'the splitting of consciousness plays an insignificant part, or perhaps none at all. These are the cases in which all that had happened was that the reaction to traumatic stimuli had failed to occur, so that they are accordingly dissolved and cured by "abreaction" —they are the pure "retention" hysterias.' (Freud, S. *Collected Papers*, vol. 1, tr. by Riviere, J., Leonard and Virginia Woolf and The Institute of Psychoanalysis, London, 1924-25)

hysteria, traumatic (traw-mat'ik) A neurotic illness developing in consequence of an injury (a traumatic neurosis). 'The traumatic or accident neuroses rarely occur when the victim of the injury must bear the brunt of the financial responsibility for the accident, as in the case of injuries in sports. There is usually an incubation period between the injury, which may be quite slight, and the appearance of the mentally determined symptoms. This interval before the development of the chronic disabilities is of value in excluding an organic source. It is usually occupied with vague ruminations which tend to be of an imaginative, affective, wish-determined and suggestive nature.' (Noyes, A.P. *Modern Clinical Psychiatry*, Saunders, Philadelphia and London, 1940)

hysteria vaga (hēs-te'rē-à và-gà) (L. 'rambling hysteria') *Obs.* Hysteria.

hysterical personality (301.5) Also known as *histrionic personality;* includes any or all of the following: vain, egocentric, attention-seeking, dramatic description of past symptoms and illnesses with a multiplicity of vaguely described complaints and overtalkativeness during the psychiatric interview; suggestibility; soft, coquettish, graceful, and sexually provocative, although frigid and anxious when close to attaining a sexual goal; easily disappointed, excitable, emotionally labile, and often unaware of inner feelings; dependently demanding in interpersonal situations; history of excessive operations and hospitalizations.

Such a manipulative adaptational pattern occurs in those with a tendency toward rigid repression of dysphoric emotion and a denial of threatening stimuli; hence it has also been termed *repressive personality.* Conflicts in such patients are often centered around genital incest strivings and/or oral disappointments. See *defense, character.*

hysterical psychosis In current usage, an acute situational reaction consisting of sudden onset of hallucinations, delusions, depersonalization, bizarre behavior, and volatile affect. It rarely lasts beyond three weeks and is sealed off without residua; such reactions typically occur in those of the hysterical or histrionic personality type. Hysterical psychosis includes such entities as amok, latah, imu, whitiko, pibloktoq (Arctic hysteria), Puerto Rican psychosis, miryachit, olonism, etc. See *lata.*

hystericism (his-tēr'i-siz'm) *Obs.* Tendency or predisposition to hysteria.

hysterics (his-tēr'iks) A popular term for a mild hysterical reaction.

hysteriform (his-ter'i-form) Resembling or having the character of hysteria.

hysteriosis (his-tār-ē-ō'sis) A term used mainly by Russian investigators to refer to greatly exaggerated responses of the organism to various stimuli if the latter follow prolonged (and, presumably, exhausting) stimulation of some other part of the organism. When, for example, the tibial nerve of an experimental animal is tetanized for several hours and loses its capacity to respond, mild inflation of a segment of intestine (which ordinarily has little effect on blood pressure, pulse, etc.) may prove fatal to the animal so exaggerated is the response. The conclusion which has been drawn from such data is that the effects of internal stimuli are highly dependent upon the current functional state of the brain which receives the signals.

hystero-demonopathy (his'tēr-ō-dē-mon-op'à-thē) *Obs.* Demonomania in a hysterical person.

hystero-epilepsy (-ep'i-lep-sē) 'The clumsy name *hystero-epilepsy* originated at a period when epileptiform attacks were still looked upon as neuroses, and when they could not be differentiated. Besides the ordinary epilepsies with lesser striking hysterical symptoms, there are such who in addition show hysteroid attacks. Furthermore, there are hysteriacs, though they are extremely rare, who can imitate or produce an epileptiform attack. . . . *What is usually called hystero-epilepsy is hysteria with severe motor attacks,* which were falsely added to the side of epilepsy.' (Bleuler, E. *Textbook of Psychiatry,* tr. by Brill, A.A., Macmillan, New York, 1930)

hystero-erotism (-er'ō-tiz'm) *Obs.* Erotism in hysteria.

hysterofrenic, hysterofrenatory (-fren'ik, -fren'à-tō-rē) Aborting or arresting a hysterical attack. For example, when digital pressure is applied to some part of the body to check a hysterical episode, the pressure is called hysterofrenic.

hysterogenic spot (-je'nik) See *spot, hysterogenic.*

hysteromania (-mā'ni-à) The term is not in common use today. It is sometimes used synonymously with nymphomania and metromania. It has also been used to describe states of psychomotor overactivity in hysteria.

hystero-neurasthenia (-nū-ras-thē'nē-à) *Obs.* A state characterized by 'a mixture

of symptoms showing shades of both dis-
eases, which naturally occurs frequently.'
(Bleuler, E. *Textbook of Psychiatry*, tr. by
Brill, A.A., Macmillan, New York, 1930)

hysteropathy (his-tēr-op'ȧ-thē) Hysteria.

hysterophilia (his'tēr-ō-fil'ē-ȧ) Lewandow-
sky applies the term to certain clinical
conditions resembling hysteria, such as
migraine, epileptiform attacks, asthma,
membranous   enteritis,   occupational
cramps, etc.

hysteropnix (his-tēr-op'niks) *Obs.* Same
as *globus hystericus.*

hysterosyntonic (-sin-ton'ik) A special
personality type which represents a mixture of the hysterical personality type
and the syntonic personality type. See
syntone.

I

'I'-complex See *'I'-persona*.

'I'-persona (ī-pēr-sō'nȧ) By this term Burrow denotes the identity- or personality-constellation that synthesizes man's socially interfunctioning symbol-exchange. The 'I'-persona represents the systematized sum of the organism's cortical, partitive, or symbolic processes, but not the primary co-ordination of functions motivating the organism as a whole in its total bionomic adaptation. With man's attempt, by means of the cephalic segment, to symbolize or project feelings and sensations that are intrinsic to the organism as a whole, there has resulted the artificial conversion of these total sensations into partitive and divisive 'feelings' or affects. It is through this mechanism that the 'I'-persona has become a purely partitive, affective identity throughout man's interrelations. Contrasted with organic persona. Synonyms: Social substantive 'I,' pseudo-persona. (Burrow, T. *The Biology of Human Conflict*, Macmillan, New York, 1937, p. 390)

'I,' social substantive See *'I'-persona*.

iatrogeny (ē-ȧ-troj'e-nē) Production or inducement of any harmful change in the somatic or psychic condition of a patient by means of the words or actions of the doctor. The physician may tell the patient that he has an enlarged heart, for example, or low blood pressure, or a glandular disturbance, and such information may provide a nucleus around which the patient builds a neurosis or psychosis.

I.B. See *body build, index of*.

ICD Abbreviation for *International Classification of Diseases* (q.v.).

ichthyophobia (-ik-thē-ō-fō'bē-ȧ) Fear of or aversion to fish.

iconomania (ī-kon-ō-mā'nē-ȧ) Morbid impulse to worship and/or collect images.

ictal emotions (ik'tal) See *emotions, ictal*.

icterus gravis neonatorum (ik'ter-oss grȧ'-vis nē-ō-nȧ-tō'room) Kernikterus; a manifestation of erythroblastosis fetalis in which the infant becomes jaundiced two or three days after birth and, if untreated, develops convulsions, rigidity, and coma. Mortality is high (75%) in untreated cases, and those who survive manifest residua such as mental defect, epilepsy, chorea, or athetosis (*bilirubin encephalopathy*, 31x.0). Treatment is exchange transfusion with Rh-negative whole blood. Those in whom jaundice is severe, however, even when so treated show some degree of mental deficiency; follow-up studies indicate that such children have an I.Q. which averages 23 points below that of their siblings (Day, R., and Haines, M.S., *Pediatrics 13:* 333-338, 1954)

ictus (ik'tus) (L. 'blow, stroke') An acute apoplectic stroke; epileptic seizure.

ictus epilepticus (e-pē-lep'tē-koos) *Obs.* (L. 'epileptic stroke') An epileptic seizure with sudden onset and no premonitory aura.

id In psychoanalytic psychology, one of the three divisions of the psyche in the so-called *structural hypothesis* of mental functioning; the other two are the ego and the superego. (In Freud's earlier theory, usually referred to as the *topographic hypothesis*, the psyche was divided into the three systems—Conscious, Pre-Conscious, and Unconscious.) The id is completely unconscious and hence partakes of the same processes that characterize the latter; viz., the pleasure principle and the primary process (see *process, primary*). It is the reservoir of the psychic representatives of the drives and of all the phylogenetic acquisitions. Freud assumed that the id comprised the total psychic apparatus at birth, and that the ego and superego were later differentiated from what had originally been id. At present, however, many psychoanalysts believe that the id itself is differentiated from the totally undifferentiated psychic apparatus and does not give rise to the ego and superego; but all agree that the id precedes, chronologically, the ego and the superego.

It is the obscure inaccessible part of our personality; the little we know about it we have learned from the study of dream-work and the formation of neurotic symptoms, and most of that is of a negative character, and can only be described as being all that the ego is not. We can come nearer to the id with images, and call it chaos, a cauldron of seething excitement. We suppose that is is somewhere in direct contact with somatic processes, and takes over from them instinctual needs and gives them mental expression, but we cannot say in what substratum this contact is made. These instincts fill it with energy, but it has no organization and no unified will, only an impulsion to obtain satisfaction for the instinctual needs, in accordance with the pleasure-principle.' (Freud, S. *New Introductory Lectures on Psycho-Analysis*, tr. by Sprott, W.J.H., Norton, New York, 1933) 'Instinctual cathexes seeking discharge, — that, in our view, is all that the id contains.' (ibid.)

idea Any mental content, especially imagining or thinking; often the term connotes a mental process that originates endogenously, rather than in response to any specific external stimulus. In psychoanalytic psychology, an idea is conceived of as existing in two parts, the mental representation of the thing being thought about and an accompanying affective charge; the latter, especially when the idea is 'painful,' may be split off or dissociated from the mental representation and attached to another idea (whose affective charge then appears inappropriate or excessive).

idea, autochthonous (aw-tok'thō-nus) A psychic disturbance of a delusional character in the sphere of judgment, characterized by the existence of a persistent idea which the patient believes is put into his mind by an influence foreign to him. The idea seems to exist by itself, beyond the control of the patient, who, most of the time, attributes the existence of such ideas to some malevolent cause. See *delusion, autochthonous.*

idea, by See *by-idea.*

idea-chase *Flight of ideas* (q.v.).

idea, co-conscious See *unconscious,* as viewed by Morton Prince.

idea, determinative The goal or end-re-sult towards which thoughts progress. One of the schizophrenic's disturbances of associations is an inability to keep to the determinative idea or to focus his attention on a central goal. See *associations, disturbances of.*

idea, dominant *Obs.* Obsessive thought.

idea, fixed See *idée fixe.*

idea, imperative Obsession.

idea, obtrusive An obsessive idea that persistently repeats itself in the patient's mind and disturbs the normal flow of his thoughts. The patient considers the obtrusive idea as foreign to his ego and vainly attempts to renounce it.

idea of reference A morbid impression that the conversation, smiling, or other actions of other persons have reference to oneself.

idea, overcharged A dreamer's central idea or conflict which has been exceptionally endowed with inner repressed psychic energy and consequently appears in the dream in the form of various symbols and several identifications. (Stekel, W. *The Interpretation of Dreams,* Liveright, New York, 1943)

ideal ego See *ego, ideal.*

ideales (ē-de-ä'lās) (pl. of L. *idealis,* existing in idea, ideal) Linnaeus formulated three subdivisions of mental disorders, one of which he termed the ideales — disturbances of the intellectual faculties.

idealization (ī-dē-al-i-zā'shun) Process or act of idealizing. Freud says that idealization is 'sexual over-estimation' of the love-object. It is 'the origin of the peculiar state of being in love.' Emphasis is placed upon the object rather than the aim. As Freud maintains, the love-object 'is aggrandized and exalted in the mind.'

Idealization is to be distinguished from *sublimation* and *identification.* The process of sublimation involves the *deflection* of the sexual *aim,* whereas idealization concerns the *object,* not the aim. Identification necessitates a partial alteration of the ego, in the sense that the ego is patterned after the love-object, whereas idealization constitutes 'an impoverishment of the Ego in respect of libido' in favor of the love-object.

Idealization may be related to object-libido, as stated above, or to ego-libido. In the latter case 'some of the self-love which in childhood is directed to the Ego (primary narcism) is transferred or displaced onto a substitute [ego-ideal, superego] which now instead of the infantile Ego is looked upon as "the possessor of all perfections."' (Healy, W., Bronner, A.F., and Bowers, A.M. *The Structure and Meaning of Psychoanalysis*, Knopf, New York, 1930)

idealize (ī-dē'al-īz) To transfer an inordinate quantity of libido from the ego to a love-object. The latter is hypercathected, over-evaluated.

idealized image See *idealized self.*

idealized self In Horney's terminology, grandiose overestimation of the self based on identification with the idealized image. The identification is a defense against recognition of the gap between the person as he really is and the person which his neurotic pride says he should be (*idealized image*).

ideas, complex of '. . . the elemental ideas which make up the experiences of any given moment tend to become organized (i.e., synthesized and conserved) into a system or complex of ideas, linked with emotions, feelings and other innate dispositions, so that when one of the ideas belonging to the experience comes to mind the experience as a whole is recalled. We may conveniently term such a system, when in a state of conservation, an *unconscious complex or neurogram, or system of neurograms.*' (Prince, M. *The Unconscious*, Macmillan, New York, 1916)

ideas, concatenated (kon-kat'ē-nāt-id) Interconnected or interdependent ideas.

ideas, flight of See *flight of ideas.*

ideas, insanity of irrepressible Kraepelin's expression for what is now called the compulsive-obsessive form of psychoneurosis.

ideas, overproductive See *mania.*

idée fixe (ē-dā' fēks') A delusion, i.e. an

unfounded or unreasonable idea that is staunchly maintained despite evidence to the contrary. In contrast is an *imperative idea*, an obsessive thought that is recognized as unreasonable but cannot be resisted. An *authochtonous idea*, on the other hand, is an imperative idea that is attributed to some malevolent influence.

identical In genetics, *monozygotic*, arising from one egg, as opposed to *dizygotic* or *fraternal*, twin pairs arising from two eggs. It is incorrect, therefore, to speak of 'almost identical' twins.

identification (ī-den'ti-fi-kā'shun) Literally, the process of making (or considering to be) the same. In psychoanalytic psychiatry it carries a similar connotation. When a person incorporates within himself a mental picture of an object and then thinks, feels, and acts as he conceives the object to think, feel, and act, the process is called identification, but the process is largely an unconscious one.

It is a common misconception that conscious emulation can somehow lead to unconscious identification. That this is not primarily true can easily be seen from a consideration of the events that lead to identification in the first place. In the beginning of extra-uterine life, the infant is ignorant of any sources of pleasure other than in himself. The mother's breast is thought of as a part of the child's body. This is probably the first identification and represents no emulation of a pleasure-giving object but a reluctant admission of frustrating reality. When hungry the infant is not fond of the mother's breast but angry with it because the breast has allowed him to become hungry. Frustration at the hands of this object is mastered by identification with the object. 'Identification is the most primitive method of recognizing external reality; it is, in fact, nothing less than mental mimicry. Its necessary preconditions are an unbroken narcissism, which cannot bear that anything should exist outside itself, and the weakness of the individual, which makes him unable either to annihilate his environment or to take flight from it.' (Balint, A. 'Identification,' *The Yearbook of Psychoanalysis I*, 317, 1945) The child, then, uses identifications to transform what is strange and frightening in the external world into what is familiar and enjoyable. The same process holds true in identification at the Oedipal stage. Balint says: 'According to the schematic formula of the Oedipus complex, a small boy should love his mother and identify himself with his father. And, in general, this is the case. The boy's mother is after all the source of gratification and his father is the powerful rival against whom he cannot defend himself successfully either by attack or by flight, so that he is eventually obliged to resort to identification . . . What I have said applies also, *mutatis mutandis*, to little girls.' In other words, the male identifies with his father not because he emulates him, but because his father is to him a source of frustration in reality. And later in life, the sensitive person protects his self-esteem and can continue to love himself by identification with his frustrating and humiliating environment. This is the basis for the well-known mechanism of 'identification with the aggressor.' Identification, then, operates in the interest of and clings to the defense of narcissism.

According to Balint: 'After we have taken mental possession of a portion of the external world by means of identification, mental material which has thus been assimilated can itself serve as a basis for further identifications. So there would seem to be no essential distinction between ego-identification (i.e. identification of the ego with an object) and object-identification (i.e. identification of one object with another). For it is only objects which have already been identified with ourselves that can become the starting-point for further identifications.'

From the psychoanalytic point of view there are two forms of identification, *primary* and *secondary*. The *primary* form, arising during the oral phase, represents 'oral mastery of the object.' (Freud) It is first associated with the erogenous zones. Thus, the child identifies itself with the parent on the oral, then the anal, and still later on the genital basis, depending upon the area in which reality frustrations operate. Subsequently the child identifies itself with the character traits of the parents, and this leads to the formation of the superego. These early identifications with the parent or parents are called primary identifications. The energy of the child flows out to the real object. It is a manifestation of object cathexis, of object identification. Balint says: 'The out-

come of the struggle round an individual's narcissism is one of the most important events of his development. As a result of identification with the various commands and prohibitions, his ego undergoes a decisive transformation. Since obedience takes place not through understanding but through identification, the command becomes a part of the child's ego, which he defends henceforward just as much as his own will . . . The consequence is a splitting of the ego into two parts, of which one is the vehicle of the original instinctual wishes, while the other is the vehicle of the wishes that have been incorporated by means of identification. This second, transformed part of the ego, is called by Freud the "super-ego."'

Secondary identification is the consequence of incorporating the object within the psyche of oneself. The psychic energy now becomes attached to the object as it is represented in the mind of the person. The libido (psychic energy) is withdrawn from the object as it exists in reality. 'The Ego itself becomes the Id's libidinal-object.' (Healy, W., Bronner, A.F., and Bowers, A.M. *The Structure and Meaning of Psychoanalysis as Related to the Personality and Behavior*, Knopf, New York, 1946) It is as if the instinctual impulses were asked to take a substitute (namely, the introjected object) for the real object. Secondary identification serves the purpose of detaching libido from an object outside of oneself; it makes it easier for an object to be given up.

It seems that *secondary identification* and *introjection* are synonymous in psychoanalysis; Freud himself interchanges them. During the early stages of introjection, however, an introjected object is apparently recognized by the person as foreign to his ego, whereas an object of identification is regarded as an original, not a borrowed, expression of his ego. Prolonged introjection, as in depressed states, may eventually bring about the quality of identification. It would be technically more correct to say that introjection (incorporation) is the mechanism whereby identification takes place; but this distinction is often not carefully drawn in present-day writings. See *incorporation*.

identification, cosmic Belief that one is the universe and a failure, on the part of the patient (usually a schizophrenic), to differentiate between himself and the outside world.

identification, multiple Identification with more than one model or object, seen most commonly in hysterical seizures wherein the patient simultaneously or serially plays the part of various persons with whom he has identified. Such seizures may even represent the enactment of a whole drama. Multiple identification is also seen in cases of multiple personality.

identify To incorporate an object into one's ego system and to act toward the object as if it were originally one's own self and not something borrowed from the environment. See *identification.*

identity, body See *image, body.*

identity crisis Social role conflict as perceived by the person himself; loss of the sense of personal sameness and historical continuity, and/or inability to accept or adopt the role the person believes is expected of him by society. Identity crises are frequent in adolescence, when they appear to be triggered by the combination of sudden increase in the strength of drives with sudden changes in the role the adolescent is expected to adopt socially, educationally, or vocationally.

identity diffusion, malignant See *crime and mental disorder.*

identity, ego That sense of identity which 'provides the ability to experience one's self as something that has continuity and sameness, and to act accordingly.' (Erikson, E. *Childhood and Society,* Norton, New York, 1950, p. 38) The term refers particularly to the degree to which the boundaries of the physical and the mental self are clearly delineated; those whose ego-identity is confused are believed by many to be especially vulnerable to schizophrenia.

'Identity is the unconscious directional pattern or sensing apparatus whereby the individual orients himself to others and to his environment. In part it consists of identifications and representations of relationships with primary love-objects. . . . Ultimately it must represent a temporally persistent, co-ordinate system whereby the self is located. *Identification,* by contrast, should probably be used to describe the process whereby external objects and the exchanges with them are partially or totally represented in the psychic apparatus, and subsequently subjectified or equated or correlated with the representations of the self.' (Suslick, A. *Archives of General Psychiatry 8,* 252, 1963)

identity, organic See *persona, organic.*

ideogenetic (ī-dē-ō-je-net'ik) Relating to mental processes in which images of sense-impressions are employed, rather than ideas that have reached the form or stage of being ready for verbal expression.

ideoglandular (-glan'jū-lēr) Relating to the effect of mental impression on glandular functions.

ideographic See *nomothetic.*

ideology (ī-dē-ol'-jē, id-ē-) A systematic scheme of ideas.

ideometabolic (ī-dē-ō-met-à-bol'ik) Relating to the effect of emotional impressions on the metabolic processes.

ideophobia (-fō'bē-à) Fear of ideas.

ideophrenia (-frē'nē-à) Guislain's term for delirium, characterized by ideational disorders.

ideoplastic See *stage, ideoplastic.*

ideoplasty (ī'dē-ō-plas-tē) Durand's term for the process of molding, making plastic, the subject's mind by means of ideas suggested by the hypnotist. It is called *verbal suggestion* by Ernest Jones.

ideosynchysia (-sin-kis'ē-à) *Obs.* Delirium.

idio- (id'ē-ō-) Combining form meaning own, private, personal, distinct, from Gr. *idios,* one's own, private, personal.

idioctonia (id-ē-ō-ktō'ni-à) *Obs.* Suicide.

idiocy, absolute 'In this condition we see humanity reduced to its lowest possible expression. Although these unfortunate creatures are, indeed, the veritable offspring of *Homo sapiens,* the depth of their degeneration is such that existence—for it can hardly be called life—is on a lower plane than even the beasts of the field, and in many respects may almost be described as vegetative. They come into the world without even the hereditary instinct of sucking. As they grow up they have to be fed, and would die of inanition amid abundance of food were it not put into their mouths. They respire, assimulate, and excrete, but they have no sexual instinct.' (Tredgold, A.F. *A Text-Book of Mental Deficiency*, 6th ed., Wood, Baltimore, 1937)

idiocy, amaurotic family See *amaurotic family idiocy.*

idiocy, developmental Idiocy due to arrested brain development.

idiocy, eclamptic (ek-lamp'tik) Idiocy associated with convulsions in children.

idiocy, genetous, congenital (jen'e-tus, kon-jen'i-tal) See *amentia, primary.*

idiocy, hydrocephalic (hī-drō-sē-fal'ik) Idiocy due to congenital or acquired hydrocephalus.

idiocy, hypertrophic (hī-per-trof'ik) Idiocy associated with hypertrophy of the brain.

idiocy, inflammatory See *idiocy, hypertrophic.*

idiocy, Kalmuk (kal'muk) (Kalmuk, member of a nomad Tartar tribe.) Mongolism.

idiocy, moral See *insanity, moral.*

idiocy, plagiocephalic (plā-jē-ō-sē-fal'ik) Idiocy due to cranial distortion.

idiocy, scaphocephalic (skaf-ō-sē-fal'ik) A form of idiocy in which the head is boat-shaped.

idiocy, sensorial Intellectual deficiency due to abnormality in a sense organ.

idiogamist (id-ē-og'à-mist) 'One who is capable of coitus only with his own wife, or with a few individual women, but is impotent with women in general.' (*Encyclopaedia Sexualis*, edited by Robinson, V., Dingwall-Rock, New York, 1936)

idioglossia *Idiolalia* (q.v.).

idiokinesis (id-ē-ō-ki-nē'sis) This obsolete term refers to the 'spontaneous' origin of a new hereditary character by means of *mutation* (q.v.), or more specifically, by mutation which takes place without determinable cause.

idiolalia (-lā'lē-à) Development of one's own language, such as is seen with some children who suffer from auditory aphasia (word-deafness).

idioneurosis (-nū-rō'sis) *Obs.* Neurosis.

idiopathic (-path'ik) When the etiology of a disease or disorder is undetermined, but its *functional* phenomena are known, it is said that the condition is idiopathic. The National Conference on Nomenclature of Disease refers to 'diseases due to unknown or uncertain causes, the functional reaction to which is alone manifest.' For example, the syndrome called *narcolepsy* is well-known, but its etiology is unknown; hence, the symptom complex is named *idiopathic narcolepsy.*

idiophrenia (-frē'nē-à) *Obs.* A psychiatric disorder associated with an organic brain disease.

idiophrenic (-fren'ik) Originating in one's own mind, psychogenic.

idioplasm, idioplasma (-plaz'm, id-i-ō-plaz'mà) This term was introduced into biology by Naegeli, to distinguish from the nutritive parts of the protoplasmic substance that portion of a cell upon which its specific qualities depend. Genetically it corresponds closely to the *germ plasm* of a germ cell while its more general meaning embraces all the special hereditary equipment of an organism. See *plasm, germ.*

From the genetic standpoint, the transmission of hereditary characters from parents to offspring depends on the fact that the latter have, entirely or partially, the same idioplasmic structure as the parents, while all the genetic variations among adult individuals must be primarily the outcome of structural or chemical differences in the idioplasm. Minute idioplasmic differences between two ova many produce, in the course of their individual processes of development, a whole series of differences in various parts of the adult organism.

idiosome (id'ē-ō-sōm) This term denotes the idioplasmic unit as the theoretically ultimate element of living matter carrying hereditary characteristics. See *idioplasm.*

idiosyncrasia olfactoria (ē-dē-ō-sēn-krä'-zē-à ŏl-fàk-tō'rē-à) Perversion of the sense of smell.

idiot In ancient times, the differentiation between mental illness and mental retardation was not clear-cut, and often not made at all. For the ancients, 'idiot' referred to any person who lived as a recluse in a private world; the term thus included all exceptional children (such as those who nowadays would be termed 'autistic') who were unable to adapt themselves satisfactorily to the community. See *amentia, degree of; retardation, mental.*

idiot-savant (-sà-väN', -sav'ant) (F. *savant,* man of learning, scholar) 'These are rare cases, who, although idiots, still have some special faculty wonderfully developed. It may be music, calculation, memory for some certain variety of facts, etc.

'The calculators can name the answer to mathematical problems almost instantly; the musical prodigies often play well and even improvise; one of my cases could instantly name the day of the week for any date for years back.' (White, W.A. *Outlines of Psychiatry,* 12th ed., Nervous & Mental Disease Publishing Company, Washington, D.C., 1929)

idiotism (id'i-ut-iz'm) State of being an idiot. Pinel divided insanity into four subdivisions, namely, mania, melancholia, dementia and idiotism. By the last term he meant 'advanced dementia.'

idiotropic (id-ē-ō-trō'pik) Introspective; egocentric.

idiovariation (id-ē-ō-vā-ri-à'shun) This biological term covers the genetic phenomenon of *mutation* and signifies a constant change in the genotypical structure of an organism. Mutated genes necessarily lead to the appearance of new hereditary

characters and, thus, to the origin of hereditarily distinct new groups of a species and new races (see *mutation*).

idolism, sexual (ī'dul-iz'm) Sexual fetishism.

idolum (ē-dō'lum) *Obs.* A false idea, illusion, or hallucination.

Illinois Test of Psycholinguistic Abilities A diagnostic test of language abilities which yields language ages for nine specific psycholinguistic areas; precise areas of disability can thereby be identified and an appropriate remedial program be planned that provides special training in the problem areas. Often abbreviated *ITPA.*

illness, advantage by Epinosic gain. 'Psycho-analysis recognized early that every neurotic symptom owes its existence to a compromise. Every symptom must therefore in some way comply with the demands of the ego which regulates repression, must offer some advantage, admit of some profitable utilization, or it would undergo the same fate as the original impulse itself which is being kept in check.' (Freud, S. *Collected Papers,* vol. 1), tr. by Riviere, J., Leonard and Virginia Woolf and The Institute of Psychoanalysis, London, 1924-25) See *gain, epinosic.*

illness as self-punishment See *resistance, superego.*

illuminism (i-lū'mi-niz'm) A state of mental exaltation in which the subject's hallucinations generally assume the form of conversations with imaginary, especially supernatural, beings.

illusio sensus (ēl-lōō'zē-ō sen'sōōs) (L. 'illusion of sense') Hallucination.

illusion (i-lū'zhun) An erroneous perception, a false response to a sense-stimulation; but in a normal person this false belief usually brings the desire to check or verify its correctness, and often another sense or other senses may come to the rescue and satisfy him that it is merely an illusion.

When a small ball or bead is rolled on the table between the tips of the crossed middle finger and index finger, one has the tactical illusion of rolling *two* balls instead of one. But our own eyes convince us that our tactile sensations are misleading, that *two* balls are but an illusion.

If a straight glass tube is lowered into a tumbler of water, we have the visual illusion that the submerged portion of the tube has bent and forms an angle with its free upper part. This unexpected sight impels us to pull the tube out and convince ourselves that there is nothing the matter with the tube, merely our eyes have misinterpreted the situation into an illusion: it merely looks, but actually is not bent.

Similarly a line-segment with > < at its ends (>————<) appears to us definitely longer than an equal segment with < > at its ends (<————>). But the simple application of a ruler dispels this visual illusion.

But the fact that in all these illusions the stimulus and the illusion (i.e. the reaction) involve the identical sense and can be disproven, makes it so much harder to realize that it is not an illusion when, sitting alone in a room, we suddenly start because we have 'heard' somebody else in the room, only to convince ourselves that we are still alone in the room and that no sound had actually been heard.

This absence of a sense-stimulus places the reaction in a different class from those cited above—it is a *hallucination* (q.v.). *Obs.* Fallacia.

illusion, memory Ascribing to oneself the experiences of others and believing implicitly that the experiences are one's own.

'Whoever considers himself Christ, believes that he had been crucified, and, under certain conditions can delude himself into remembering the details of it with perceptible acuteness . . .' shows memory illusions. (Bleuler, E. *Textbook of Psychiatry*, tr. by Brill, A.A., Macmillan, New York, 1930) See *appersonification*.

illusion, necessary A literary term used in psychoanalytic literature in reference to a person's special character defenses as they make for healthy and effective adjustment in the practical and real-life world. In their functioning in relation to the real world these character defenses will make for illusional, private evaluations of what is important and unimportant, what is of great value and of little

value—evaluations that represent private predilections in private lives. It is important that an analyst be free of the tendency to confuse his private predilections, and his own unconsciously determined illusions, with the aims and goals of his patient's needs.

E.F. Sharpe (*Collected Papers on Psycho-analysis*, Hogarth Press and The Institute of Psychoanalysis, London, 1950) states: 'We may privately prefer beech trees to cedars, that type of character to this, and have our private evaluations of what a worthy life really is. . . . But these things, eminently useful as they are to us as individuals and to our necessary illusions, are of small importance to the world outside us, and most assuredly they are of no use in the consulting-room.'

illusion, proofreader's Failure to detect an error in spelling, punctuation, construction, etc. because of familiarity with the subject matter; a tendency to see things 'as they ought to be' rather than as they are.

illusions of doubles See *syndrome, Capgras*.

image, imago (im'ij, i-mā'gō) In psychoanalysis, the image or likeness of someone, usually not of the subject himself, constructed in the unconscious and remaining therein. The commonest imagos are those of the parents and of those who stand for the parents. Jones defines *imago* as 'an image preserved indefinitely in the unconscious and often identified with persons other than the original one.' (Jones, E. *Papers on Psycho-Analysis*, 4th ed., Wood, Baltimore, 1938)

'The mother-child relation is certainly the deepest and most penetrating one we know; the child in fact for a long time is, so to speak, a part of the maternal body! Later it is really a continuum of the psychic atmosphere of the mother for years, and in this way, all that is primordial in the child, so to speak, indissolubly fused with the mother image.' (Jung, C.G. *Psychological Types*, tr. by Baynes, H.G., Harcourt, Brace, New York and London, 1923)

Jung speaks of *primordial images*. 'Thus there naturally exists in the archetype, in the collectively inherited mother-image, that extraordinary intensity of relationship which first impels the child instinctively to cling to its mother.' (ibid.) 'Her inclination towards elderly married men (always platonic) is also traceable to her father *Imago.*' (Stekel, W. *Frigidity in Women*, vols. 1-2, tr. by van Teslaar, J.S., Boni & Liveright, New York, 1926)

Sometimes the person whose image is mirrored in the unconscious is spoken of as the *imago.* This use of the word is not encouraged.

image agglutinations See *agglutinations, image.*

image, body The concept which each person has of his own body as an object in space, independently and apart from all other objects. The body is always in space and experiences are not possible without this conception of our body, or body image, since we live as human beings with a body.

The body image or *body identity* is the conceptualization of the body's structure and functions that grows out of the awareness of the self and one's body in intended action. Schizophrenic children are often deficient in the ability to localize, discriminate, or give pattern and meaning to body perceptions. 'Thus, they lack body images that are integrated, stable in time, and clear in form. One child walked about all day feeling her body. Another observed the motions of her hand in fascination and addressed it as a baby.' (Goldfarb, W. *International Psychiatry Clinics 1*, 821-845, 1964) See also *limb, phantom.*

L.C. Kolb ("The Body Image in the Schizophrenic Reaction," Chapt. 4 in Auerback, A. *Schizophrenia, An Integrated Approach*, Ronald, New York, 1959) distinguishes between *body percept* (or *body schema*) and the *body concept*. The body percept is the postural image on has of one's body as it functions outside of central consciousness; it is organized over the years, mainly on the basis of incoming kinesthetic and tactile perceptions. The body concept, or conceptual image, includes the perceptions, thoughts, and feelings which the ego has in reference to viewing its own body.

image, conceptual See *image, body.*

image, idealized The defense of having

a false picture of one's virtues and assets. The more unrealistic (idealized) this image is, the more vulnerable is the person amid the vicissitudes of life.

The term was introduced by Horney, who was among the first to give a detailed description of the role of cultural pressures in producing neurosis. Though constituting the base from which attitudes toward authority in general develop, the early attitude toward the father is added to and modified by subsequent experiences with father figures. In the relationship to the father, or to subsequent father figures, difficulties often arise, and to circumvent them, neurotic defenses may be developed. For instance, if the patient adjusts to a difficult father by becoming submissive, submissiveness itself becomes a problem. Thereupon, some sort of periodic aggressiveness may be developed to circumvent the problem of submissiveness. This new difficulty, in turn, produces new defenses and the adult patient now presents a complicated defensive system. Thus the patient is sick because of what happened to him and also because, in coping with it, he establishes goals which lead him to pursue false values.

image, memory Anticipation of the recurrence of a past experience, immediately before its recurrence, as in conditioning experiments when the subject anticipates a repetition of the electric shock. According to Reik, 'the past situation returns in the service of the present,' and it can even be reproduced with hallucinatory vividness. In such cases the memory image may be said to be a part of the conditioned reflex in Pavlov's sense, that is, the memory image is an ingredient of the inner preparedness for the stimulus, and is part and parcel of the individual's total reaction.

image, percept See *percept-image.*

image, personal 'A *personal* image has neither archaic character nor collective significance, but expresses contents of the personal unconscious and a personally conditioned, conscious situation.' (Jung, C.G. *Psychological Types*, tr. by Baynes, H.G., Harcourt, Brace, New York and London, 1923)

In contrast is a *primordial image*; 'I speak of its archaic character when the image is in striking unison with familiar mythological motives. In this case it expresses material primarily derived from the collective unconscious, while, at the same time, it indicates that the momentary conscious situation is influenced not so much from the side of the personal as from the collective.' (ibid.)

image, primary memory Eidetic image. See *imagery, eidetic.*

image, primordial (prī-môr'di-al) 'The primordial image is a mnemic deposit, an *imprint* ("engramm"—Semon), which has arisen through a condensation of innumerable, similar processes. It is primarily a precipitate or deposit, and therefore a typical basic form of a certain ever-recurring psychic experience. As a mythological motive, therefore, it is a constantly effective and continually recurring expression which is either awakened, or appropriately formulated, by certain psychic experiences.' (Jung, C.G. *Psychological Types*, tr. by Baynes, H.G., Harcourt, Brace, New York and London, 1923)

Also known as *archetype.* See *image.*

'The most immediate primordial image is the mother, for she is in every way the nearest and most powerful experience; and the one, moreover, that occurs in the most impressionable period of a man's life. Since the conscious is as yet only weakly developed in childhood, one cannot speak of an "individual" experience at all. The mother, however, is an archetypal experience; she is known by the more or less unconscious child not as a definite, individual feminine personality, but as the mother, an archetype loaded with significant possibilities. As life proceeds the primordial image fades, and is replaced by a conscious, relatively individual image, which is assumed to be the only mother-image we have.' (Jung, C.G. *Contributions to Analytical Psychology,* tr. by Baynes, H.G. and C.F., Kegan Paul, Trench, Trubner, London, 1928)

image, social Burrow's term for an affective impression representing crystallized opinions, beliefs, and prejudices which are deeply ingrained in the individual and in society but for which there is no objective, demonstrable correspondence in actuality. These emotionally toned impressions have no direct relation to the object or situation upon which they are projected. The social image is wishfully determined and is not based upon demonstrable reality. See *affect; partitive; 'I'-persona; semiopathic.* (Burrow, T. 'Social Images Versus Reality,' *The Journal of Abnormal and Social Psychology, XIX,* 230 -35, 1924)

image, unconscious See *memory, unconscious.*

imagery, eidetic The general meaning of this term applies to a psychological phenomenon which is intermediate between the ordinary visual memory-image and the after-image. This phenomenon attains its significance for constitutional medicine from the observation of E.R. Jaensch that although it occurs in 60 per cent of children under 12, it persists after adolescence only in two types, the *Basedow* type and the *tetany* type, or, as they are usually called, the B type and the T type.

The eidetic image differs from the ordinary memory-image by the following details: (1) it possesses a pseudo-perceptual quality; (2) it is superior in clearness and richness of detail, and this clearness is less dependent upon the organization of its content; (3) it is more accurate (mimetic) in its reproduction of detail; (4) it is more brilliant in coloration; (5) it requires more rigid fixation for its arousal; and (6) it shows a greater degree of coherence with the projection ground. It differs from the after-image by the following characteristics: (1) it may be aroused by a more complicated and detailed object; (2) it is superior in clearness and continues longer in the visual field; (3) it is subject to voluntary recall, even after the lapse of considerable time, as well as to voluntary control; (4) it requires a shorter length of exposure and less rigid fixation for its arousal; and (5) it is more dependent upon factors of interest.

The B type is nearer to the memory-image and has been observed only in persons with Basedow's disease or the tendency to it. The T type, in which the imagery approaches the after-image, has been found in subjects whose blood calcium and potassium show either definite evidence of tetany or changes in the direction of it. These differences in imagery, referable to the different biochemical conditions in Basedow's disease and tetany, are thought to be symptomatic of two contrasting types of mind, the integrated and the disintegrated, respectively. According to the studies of W. Jaensch, characteristic capillary loops of the nail beds are an additional item of difference in these two distinctive psychosomatic types.

imagery, hypnagogic (hip-nà-goj′ik) Imagery, occurring during the stage between wakefulness and sleep, that is, just before sleep has set in.

imagery, hypnopompic (hip-nō-pom′pik) The visions or mental pictures that occur just after the sleeping state and before full wakefulness. The phenomenon is analogous to hypnagogic imagery, save for the time at which the images occur.

imagery, spontaneous Augusta Jellinek's term for visual images which can be produced at will when the eyes are closed. Spontaneous imagery is not a pathological phenomenon and is seen more commonly in children, probably because most children have a positive eidetic disposition. Spontaneous imagery is sometimes misinterpreted as visual hallucinations.

imaginarii (ē-mä-gē-nä′rē-ī) One of Linnaeus's three subdivisions of mental disorders, characterized by disturbances of the sensory faculties.

imagination Synthesis of mental images into new ideas; the process of forming '. . . a *mental representation* of an *absent* object, an affect, a body function, or an instinctual drive,' the results of which process are images, symbols, phantasies, dreams, ideas, thoughts, and/or concepts. (Beres, D., *International Journal of Psycho-Analysis XLI*, 327, 1960) Imagination is not, then, the obverse of reality, but affords, rather, a means of adaptation to reality. 'Only with the development of the imaginative process, the capacity to create a mental representation of the absent object, does the child progress from the syncretic sensori-motor-affective immediate response to the delayed abstract, conceptualized response that is characteristically human.' (ibid.)

imagination, creative The terms *creative imagination* or *creative work* designate the process in which dormant, unrelated contents of the unconscious become associated with the organized labor of consciousness and accomplish something new.

imago See *image.*

imbalance, intellectual 'The state of an individual with special abilities or disabilities, markedly competent in some respects and deficient in others, but not well integrated or compensated.' (Hamilton, G. *A Medical Social Terminology*, Presbyterian Hospital, New York, 1930)

imbalance, sibling A situation in which 'the number or distribution of children in a family contributes to a problem of spoiling, or economic insufficiency; e.g., only boy in female setting, hyper-large family, etc.' (Hamilton, G. *A Medical Social Terminology*, Presbyterian Hospital, New York, 1930)

imbecile (im′be-sil) See *amentia, degree of; retardation, mental.*

imbecility, moral (im-be-sil′i-tē) See *insanity, moral.*

imbecillitas (ēm-bā-kēl′lē-tàs) Weakness, feebleness, imbecility. 'It is often taken for a disease, but generally means a debilitated state of the habit, and sometimes the word *arrhostia* is made use of to express imbecility.' (Motherby, G. *A New Medical Dictionary*, 5th ed., forJ. Johnson, St. Paul's Church-Yard, etc., London, 1801)

imitation In sociology, 'the tendency, under the influence of copies socially presented, to build up mechanisms of habits, sentiments, ideals, and patterns of life.' (Park, R.E., and Burgess, E.W. *Introduction to the Science of Sociology*, University of Chicago Press, Chicago, 1921)

imitation, hysterical The ability of a hysterical patient to imitate all the symptoms that impress him when they occur in others. The psychological mechanism at work in hysterical imitation is identification: the patient (unconsciously) identifies himself with a person who has the same unconscious needs as he, who is 'just like' him. As a result, the patient reproduces the symptom shown by the person with whom he identifies. Through this hysterical imitation 'patients are enabled to express in their symptoms not merely their own experiences, but the experiences of quite a number of other persons; they can suffer, as it were, for a whole mass of people, and fill all the parts of a drama with their own personalities.' For example, one girl in a school may react to a love letter with a fainting spell. Some of the other girls then may also get fainting spells. Unconsciously the other girls also wanted love letters, and having had the same unconscious wish they had to suffer the same consequence—they, too, had fainting spells through hysterical identification. (Freud, S. *The Interpretation of Dreams* in *The Basic Writings of Sigmund Freud*, Modern Library, Random House, New York, 1938)

immobilization-paralysis See *paralysis, immobilization.*

immorality, maniacal An older term for the preponderance of overt and uncontrollable sexuality in cases of simple mania.

immortality This concept is encountered with great frequency in psychiatric patients. It is expressed directly by some schizophrenics, who believe that they have always existed and always will. The belief is intimately associated with delusions of omnipotence, omniscience, timelessness and ubiquity. Other patients, notably those with a psychoneurosis, express the same God-like qualities but in a highly symbolized manner. The concept gains frequent expression in dream form.

Jones believes that wish-fulfillment plays an important role in this belief. He holds that 'salvation betokens a joyful reunion with the parents against whom the unconscious sinful thoughts were directed.' (Jones, E. *Papers on Psycho-Analysis*, 4th ed., Wood, Baltimore, 1938)

impediment, speech Any disorder of speech, but especially stammering or *stuttering* (q.v.). See *speech disorders.*

imperative, authoritative The pressing directives emanating from the superego which subconsciously direct behavior; the commanding voice of parental or social rule in the subconscious mind. According to Stekel, a compulsion is always a substitute for an imperative. The current (adult) imperative is always a resonance of infantile imperatives. 'One may say that neurotics run after their infantile imperatives. The imperative

apparently leads to an action which, however, in reality consists only of an inhibition.' (Stekel, W. *Compulsion and Doubt*, Liveright, New York, 1949)

imperative, categorical In psychoanalysis, the equivalent of *blanket demand.* The superego, for instance, is said to exercise its duties by the rigid 'yes' or 'no' rule, by the 'all or none' law.

imperative, ethical The inexorable disciplinary power of moral principles exerted upon one's mental life and behavior. It represents 'the wish of the moral self, the endeavor of the nobler side of man leading the ego to higher and better things in life.' One may also speak in terms of 'the upward aspiration of man,' which in fact constitutes the admonitions of the moral consciousness in the life of an individual. (Stekel, W. *The Interpretation of Dreams*, Liveright, New York, 1943)

imperative, immoral The antisocial unconscious impulses that compel the person to desire the occurrence of events, or the performance of actions, considered unethical or antimoral. This mental mechanism is often observed in the compulsive-neurotic. It is a compulsion to act against the rules of society, an impulsive subconscious rebellion against moral principles. The destructive aims of the immoral imperative are often directed against religious priciples, precisely because religion is one of the most powerful barriers controlling man's instinctual life. (Stekel, W. *Compulsion and Doubt*, Liveright, New York, 1949)

impetus (im'pe-tus) In psychoanalytic psychology, one of the parameters defining a *drive* (q.v.). The impetus of a drive is its force, or strength, or energy, and in all likelihood is genetically determined. The other parameters by which a drive (or, in older terminology, an instinct) is customarily defined are: source (the physiological disequilibrium or organ system through which the drive becomes manifest), and the *aim* and *object* (qq.v.) of the drive.

implant, dynamic Introduction or instillation of a significant idea into consciousness. The term is used mainly in connection with *psychic driving*, one of whose values is said to be long-lasting action on the part of the patient as a result of one or more dynamic implants. The latter bring the patient to focus on specific behavior or action tendencies; this usually leads to intensified activity in the form of tension and anxiety and thus to greater efforts to free himself of such intensification. As a result, the patient tends to ruminate over and to reorganize his reactions to the material in question. This would appear to be a mechanistic description of one type of insight. See *driving, psychic.*

implicit role See *role.*

impostor A type of pathological liar who seeks to gain some advantage by means of imposing on others fabrications of his attainments, position, or worldly possessions. Phyllis Greenacre (*Psychoanalytical Quarterly 27*: 359-82, 1958) has noted the compulsive, pressured aspect to the impostor's urge to seek the limelight and 'put something over' on his audience. This writer outlines the following features which appear to be of psychodynamic significance: the typically ambivalent and over-possessive mother creates so intense a maternal attachment in the child that he is unable to develop a full sense of separate identity. At the same time his ability to assume an uncontested supersedence over the father as far as the mother is concerned intensifies infantile narcissism and favors a reliance on omnipotent phantasy to the exclusion of reality testing. Imposture is an outgrowth of the oedipal conflict and represents an attempt to kill the father and/or to rob him of his more adequate penis. Success of this mechanism as evidenced by belief in the impostor by his audience (the mother) furnishes a powerful incentive for endless repetition of the fraudulent behavior.

impotence, impotency (im′pō-tens, -ten-sē) The male's inability to perform sexual intercourse; the corresponding condition in the female is termed frigidity. See *frigidity, sexual; impotence, psychic.*

impotence, anal A term describing certain types of constipation in which the analogy to cases of neurotic genital sexual impotence in males is emphasized. In this type of constipation, anxiety concerning the injurious or filthy aspect of the fecal mass to be ejected or parted with is of central importance. This is analogous to the anxiety of many orgastically impotent men concerning the poisonous or sullying effect of the seminal ejaculation. Thus, constipation in the anorectal area is the result of inhibitions against *offending,* but they result in emissive and ejaculatory impotence in the seminal vesical or prostatic areas.

At military induction centers it is a frequent experience that many candidates cannot void (produce a urine specimen) in the presence of others. This is also commonly seen in boys' camps where certain boys find it impossible both to urinate and to defecate unless they have absolute privacy. Fundamentally such symptoms stem back to the early infantile developmental conflicts concerning soiling and toilet training. These symptoms can be thought of as the adult neurotic residues of conflicts between desires for co-operative regularity, giving, and cleanliness, on the one hand, and desire for the maintenance of continued stubborn autonomy, spite, defiance, soiling, and direct stool pleasure on the other. (Weiss, E., and English, O.S. *Psychosomatic Medicine,* 2nd ed., Saunders, Philadelphia and London, 1949)

impotence, cerebral Magnus Hirschfeld postulates four types of impotence: (1) cerebral, due to cerebral causes; (2) spinal, associated with difficulties of erection and ejaculation, of spinal origin; (3) genital, connected with genital defects; and (4) germinal. (Hirschfeld, M. *Sexual Pathology,* tr. by Gibbs, J., Emerson, New York, 1939)

impotence, genital (jen′i-tal) See *impotence, cerebral.*

impotence, germinal (jēr′mi-nal) See *impotence, cerebral.*

impotence, orgastic (awr-gas′tik) The incapacity for achieving the orgasm or acme of satisfaction in the sexual act. Many neurotics cannot achieve adequate discharge of their sexual energy through the sexual act. For example, the neurotic 'may attempt to achieve satisfaction by persistent repetitions of the sexual act.' Although he thus gives the impression of being very vigorous genitally, in reality he never achieves genuine satisfaction and cannot lose his desire. Also, as a result of their inability to attain genuine end-pleasure, many neurotics lay more stress on the fore-pleasure mechanisms.

'In other cases the physiological course of the sexual act may seem to be normal; but if a person whose sexuality actually has remained infantile tries to ward off a contradicting anxiety by ungenuinely performing acts of adult sexuality these acts can never bring full gratification.' The sexual behavior is rigid and, although a certain narcissistic functional pleasure is felt, this is not the complete relaxation of a full orgasm. In this 'pseudo-sexuality,' narcissistic aims are disturbing the true sexuality.

Finally, in the neurotic there may be a diminution of conscious sexual interest. This reflects his constant struggle with his repressed sexuality which 'diminishes his disposable sexual energy.' In some cases, however, the amount lacking is rather small, so that the patient's sexual life appears superficially undisturbed and he feels subjectively as if his sexuality were satisfactory.

According to Fenichel, an important concomitant of orgastic impotence is that such patients are incapable of love. Their need for self-love, for self-esteem, overshadows their capacity for object love. In further elucidating the mechanism of orgastic impotence, Fenichel quotes Reich's analysis of the course of sexual excitement. According to Reich, in order to obtain an 'economically sufficient discharge in orgasm, the full development of the latter part or "second phase" of sexual excitement in which there are involuntary convulsions of the muscles of the floor of the pelvis is necessary. The climax of pleasure occurs at the climax of sexual excitement in this second phase and coincides with a loss of ego. In orgastically impotent egos this climax of pleasure does not occur. Indeed it is at this very point that the pleasure turns into anxiety and loss of ego control.' (Fenichel, O. *The Psychoanalytic Theory of Neurosis*, Norton, New York, 1945)

impotence, psychic (305.6) Functional inability of the male to perform sexual intercourse in spite of sexual desire and the presence of intact genital organs. There may be erective impotence (inability to achieve or maintain erection), ejac-

ulatory impotence (inability to expel seminal fluid), or orgastic impotence (inability to achieve full orgasm). Premature ejaculation, *ejaculatio retardata*, the separation of the tender and sensual components of the sexual act so that intercourse is possible only with prostitutes, and the need for fixed and specific conditions to be operative before sexual intercourse can be performed are all types of psychic impotence. Depression following the sexual act *(post-coitum triste)* is a type of orgastic impotence.

E. Bergler (*Psychiatric Quarterly* 19, 412, 657, 1945) classified psychic impotence on the basis of etiology into three main groups: (1) potency disturbance arising from phallic (hysterical) mechanism; (2) potency disturbance arising from anal mechanisms (obsessional, hypochondriacal, and masochistic types); (3) disturbance arising from oral mechanisms. Impotence based on phallic mechanisms results from an unresolved attachment to the mother of the Oedipal period; castration fears lead to subsequent repression of sexual desire for the mother, but finally all sexual objects become identified with her. Persistence of castration fears leads to potency disturbances. In the second group, in an obsessional neurotic, potency disturbances result from the association of sexuality with dirt and filth, which must be avoided at all costs, and from the need to ward off the aggressive and sadistic impulses which are aroused by the sexual act. Erective impotence is rare in the obsessional group, but *ejaculatio retardata* is common. The latter has the significance of anal retention pleasure combined with sadistic pleasure in harming the woman through prolonged intercourse. Potency disturbance arising from oral mechanisms is commonly expressed as either premature ejaculation or psychogenic *aspermia*. The former signifies: 'I do not want to refuse the woman anything; indeed, I give immediately.' Psychogenic aspermia (ejaculatory impotence) signifies: 'I deny you my semen just as mother denied me her milk.'

impotence, spinal (spī'nal) See *impotence, cerebral.*

impotentia coeundi (ĕm-pô-ten'tē-à kô-e-oon'dē) Inability to cohabit.

imprinting Called *Pragung* by the German

ethologists who originally described the phenomenon, imprinting is 'the process by which certain stimuli become capable of eliciting certain "innate" behavior patterns during a critical period of the animal's behavioral development.' (Jaynes, J. *Journal of Comparative and Physiological Psychology 49*, 201, 1956) In the mallard duck, for instance, the first moving object the duckling sees during a critical period shortly after hatching is thenceforward reacted to as ducklings usually behave toward the mother duck. The degree to which imprinting determines or affects learning and behavioral patterning in the human has not been established, although it has been hypothesized that some forms of mental retardation are due to lack of appropriate stimulation or opportunity when the child is in a critical or sensitive period for the acquisition of specific skills. See *instinct; releaser, social; retardation, mental.*

improvement, transference Amelioration of neurotic symptoms on the basis of the transference relationship. The physician is perceived unconsciously as a reincarnation of the parents, and as such he is thought of as providing love and protection, or as threatening with punishments. So-called 'flight into health' is an instance of transference improvement.

impuberism (im-pū′bēr-iz′m) The state of not having reached the age or stage of puberty. While, strictly speaking, the term denotes the life-period before puberty and thus embraces the stages of infantilism and childhood, generally it means, nevertheless, that the mental and physical characteristics of childhood or occasionally of infancy run into and continue during the chronologically later and distinct adolescent or even adult life.

impulse A stimulus that sets the mind in action. The stimulus may originate in (1) the objective world, or (2) the subject himself: (a) his soma—within or any part of the body; (b) his psyche—its conscious or its unconscious part. In psychoanalysis the term impulse most commonly refers to the instincts; a basic impulse is an instinct, the source of which is a 'somatic process in an organ or part of the body.' (Freud, S. *Collected Papers,* vol. 4, tr. by Riviere, J., Leonard and Virginia Woolf and The Institute of

Psychoanalysis, London, 1924-25) See *drive.*

impulse, component Any of the various pregenital or pre-adult manifestations of drive and particularly, in the case of the libidinal drive, those infantile activities and impulses that will later become subordinate to the adult genital organization. Among the component impulses are sucking, biting, touching, defecating, urinating, looking (voyeurism), exhibiting, sadism, masochism, etc.—all of which although they may be detectable in adulthood, will generally be expressed as forepleasure activities and will remain subservient to genital primacy. See *genitality; impulse, sexual component; organization, pregenital.*

impulse, cross An impulse that crosses the path of another impulse and in so doing checks the further development of the latter.

'The side impulses which at first bring about only flourishes in action may gradually become cross impulses which lead to complete derailment of volition.' (Kraepelin, E. *Manic-Depressive Insanity and Paranoia,* tr. by Barclay, R.M., Livingstone, Edinburgh, 1921)

impulse-disorder, hyperkinetic (hī-pēr-ki-net′ik) A type of childhood behavior disorder, believed to be due to diencephalic dysfunction, characterized by hyperactivity, short attention span, poor concentration, and irritability.

Other symptoms include: specific learning deficits (e.g. dyslexia, 306.1), perceptual-motor deficits, defective coordination, impulsivity and/or antisocial acts, and emotional lability. In addition, neurological examination of such children often uncovers 'equivocal' abnormalities (e.g. transient strabismus, mixed and confused laterality, speech defect) and borderline EEG records.

The above symptom picture has also been termed the brain-damage behavior syndrome, minimal brain dysfunction (MBD), central nervous system deviation, Strauss syndrome, post-encephalitic behavior disorder, infantile hyperkinetic syndrome, and choreatiform syndrome. (309.x).

impulse-disorders A varied group of personality disorders with the following characteristics: (1) the impulse or symptom is ego-syntonic; (2) there is a pleasurable component; (3) there is minimal distortion of the original impulse, and (4) the impulse possesses a quality of irresistibility.

Frosch and Wortis (*American Journal of Psychiatry 3:* 132-138, 1954) differentiate two groups of impulse-disorders, the discrete symptom type (including what others call the impulse neuroses, perversions, and catathymic crises) and the diffuse character type, with low frustration tolerance and a tendency to explosive reactions to deprivation.

Some of these patients show rather typical epileptoid records on encephalography, often with indications of pathologic discharge in the temporal lobe.

impulse, epistemophilic (e-pis-te-mō-fil'-ik) *Epistemophilia* (q.v.).

impulse, fundamental social Desire to check the sprouting manifestations of evil. Influenced by Jung's investigations, Baynes thinks that this impulse expresses itself in various social rituals (such as coronation, marriage, ordination of priests, and other forms of social rites) brought into being by this single fundamental necessity, all of them merely elaborations of the same pattern, their symbolic elements remaining relatively constant with both savage and civilized people all over the world. (Baynes, H.G. *Mythology of the Soul,* Williams and Wilkins, Baltimore, 1940)

impulse, irresistible See *responsibility, criminal.*

impulse-life The instinctual life. See *drive; impulse.*

impulse, sexual component 'The sexual instinct is not at first a unit. It consists of various components, emanating from manifold organic sources. These components at first function quite independently of one another, each as it were blindly seeking for organic pleasure and satisfaction, and it is only later that they combine in the function of reproduction. They at first begin in conjunction with the activity of ego instincts, for instance hunger, with which they have a common source, aim and object, and only gradually

do they emancipate themselves from this association to achieve an existence of their own. An infant sucks its food before it sucks its thumb and long before it uses its lips for kissing.' (Jones, E.J. *Papers on Psycho-Analysis,* Williams and Wilkins, Baltimore, 1949)

This same conception of the nature of the sexual instinct is expressed by Fenichel: 'The small child is an instinctual creature full of polymorphous perverse sexual drives or, to put it more correctly, full of a still undifferentiated total sexuality which contains all the later "partial instincts" in one. Reality seems to be judged at first only as to whether it is compatible with instinct satisfaction. Reality, as conceived of by the primitive ego, is colored by the status of its sexual aims. Every kind of excitation in the child can become a source of sexual excitement: mechanical and muscular stimuli, affects, intellectual activity, and even pain. In infantile sexuality excitement and satisfaction are not sharply differentiated, although there are already orgasm-like phenomena, that is, pleasureful sensations that bring relaxation and the end of sexual excitation. In time, however, the genitals begin to function as a special discharge apparatus, which concentrates all excitation upon itself and discharges it no matter in which erogenous zone it originated.

'It is called genital primacy when this function of the genitals has become dominant over the extragenital erogenous zones, and all sexual excitations become finally genitally oriented and climactically discharged.' (Fenichel, O. *The Psychoanalytic Theory of Neurosis,* Norton, New York, 1945)

impulse, side An impulse that exists by the side of another impulse. Kraepelin says that the condition is common in dementia praecox (schizophrenia). Often the side or secondary impulse interrupts the primary one, producing irrelevant action or speech.

impulse, wandering Drapetomania; dromomania; ecdemomania; *wanderlust* (q.v.).

impulse, wish See *wish-impulse.*

impulsion (im-pul'shun) Blind obedience

to internal drives, such as is seen typically in children, whose interpersonal relations and superego have not yet formed an organized defense against the drives. Impulsion is seen in adults whose defensive organization is weak; the obsessive-compulsive patient, for example, may be a miser, a hoarder, or a cruel moralizer, yet he considers his impulses right and follows them openly. In adults, impulsion tends to be much more symbolic than in children. (Schilder, P. *Psychotherapy*, Norton, New York, 1938)

impulsive Relating to, characterized by, impulse. In psychoanalysis, *impulsive* and *instinctive* are generally used interchangeably as equivalent terms. In general psychiatry, impulsive usually applies to swift action without forethought or conscious judgment.

'In most cases this word refers to the impulses for actions, which are accomplished unexpectedly, without real reflection, or with inconsistent reflection, or without the assent of the whole personality.' (Bleuler, E. *Textbook of Psychiatry*, tr. by Brill, A.A., Macmillan, New York, 1930)

impulsiveness See *impulsive*.

Imu A psychoreactive phenomenon seen among the Ainu, consisting of hyperkinesia, catalepsy, echolalia, echopraxia, and command automatism. Imu occurs almost exclusively in adult females. See *hysterical psychosis*.

inaccessibility Inability to be reached; unresponsiveness. Used most commonly to refer to the autism and withdrawal of the schizophrenic.

inadequacy, constitutional Any inborn defect; the term, which is vague and no longer in common use, often implies some hereditary defect and/or some physical or mental abnormality that is largely unmodifiable. In constitutional medicine, the term refers to anatomical and physiological imbalance between two or more of the systems (physical and mental).

inadequacy, intellectual See *retardation, mental*.

inadequate personality See *personality pattern disturbance*.

inappetence (in-ap′ē-tens) Absence of appetite or desire.

inattention See *extinction*.

inattention, selective Inattention to or disregard of by choice, contingent on keeping out of the sphere of a child's awareness (during the development of his self-system) the attributes which, for the time being, are neither 'good' nor 'bad' in the eyes of the significant people in a child's milieu.

According to Sullivan, the self is finally formed out of a great number of potentialities. The child tends to develop and enhance those of his traits that are pleasing or acceptable to the significant adults, and to block out of awareness and disassociate those attributes that meet with their disapproval. Obviously there are some attributes that are neutral in the estimation of the significant people. Since no special attention is paid to these attributes, the child may or may not be aware of them, and it may be said that 'selective inattention' has been at work. Unlike disassociated material, disavowed because it has been disapproved by the significant adults, the material on which selective inattention acts can, without great difficulty, be incorporated into the *self-system* (q.v.) if such behavioral attributes should later become important in the eyes of others. The difference between selective inattention and disassociation is not clear cut, however, and is merely one of degree.

in-between A literal translation of Hirschfeld's *Zwischenstufe*, meaning an in-between stage or homosexualist.

inbred Produced by inbreeding. Pertaining to the origin and qualities of animals which originate from the breeding from types of the same parentage, or in the more general sense of human genetics, relating to the descent and biological conditions of individuals descended from common ancestors, that is, from ancestors who frequently or persistently intermarried among themselves, thus creating a particular population group (see *intermarriage*).

inbreeding In genetics, the special form of reproductive conditions which prevail in a rather isolated and relatively homogeneous group of individuals, exclusively and persistently selecting their marriage partners from their own group. Such selective reproduction gradually leads to the formation of more or less pure-bred stocks and counteracts the normal effects of propagation, consisting of the continuous creation of new combinations of hereditary or non-hereditary differences (see *variation*).

In the reproduction of a species in which *hybridization*, or even *panmixia*, has been the rule, the results of *inbreeding* are almost invariably disadvantageous. The worst effects are caused by the increased production of homozygotic carriers of *recessive* traits, which under normal reproductive conditions would appear only rarely.

Another disadvantage of inbreeding is that, for unknown reasons, inbreeding weakens the offspring and reduces the capacity for reproduction. This weakening always progresses until, sooner or later, a stable minimum is attained. 'The vital efficiency of the offspring decreases at first rapidly generation after generation, but eventually the decrease slackens, and in the end a condition is reached wherein further inbreeding does no more harm. The minimal efficiency thus reached varies greatly from one organism to another.' (Baur, E., Fischer, E. and Lenz, F. *Human Heredity*, Macmillan, New York, 1931)

A doubtful kind of dysgenic inbreeding effect may be due to the fact that inbreeding, when of a marked degree, tends to make mutations more frequent. It must be taken into consideration, however, that the majority of mutations are recessive, so that inbreeding may only facilitate their easier discovery.

incendiarism (in-sen'di-à-riz'm) *Pyromania* (q.v.).

incest Sexual congress between male and female who are blood related, such as between mother and son, father and daughter, brother and sister, or among cousins. As a real act, incest is believed to be relatively rare, although the impulse toward it at least in psychiatric patients is frequent.

incest-barrier See *barrier, incest*.

incidence The number of new cases of any disorder that develop in a given population in a given period of time. Incidence rates are usually expressed per year, per 100,000 population:

$$\text{incidence rate of illness} = \frac{\substack{\text{number of new cases} \\ \text{developing during one year}}}{\substack{\text{number of persons exposed,} \\ \text{during the year, to the risk} \\ \text{of developing the disease}}} \times 100,000$$

The exposed population may be the entire population or, particularly when the illness in question begins only during a limited period of years or is confined to one sex, it may be specifically limited to an age group or sex within the total population. See *epidemiology; prevalence; rate*.

incipient Beginning, inchoate, threatening, not fully formed; used often to modify the word schizophrenia by those reluctant to make such a diagnosis in the absence of secondary or accessory symptoms.

incoherence (in-kō-hēr'ens) Disorganization; used most commonly to refer to speech that is disconnected and unintelligible.

incompetence, incompetency (in-kom'petens, -ten-sē) A legal term referring primarily to defects in intellectual functioning such that comprehension of the nature of a transaction is interfered with or otherwise inadequate. The term, thus, refers to intellectual capacity and takes no note of temperament, emotions, or the like which may also interfere with a person's capacity to function. Ordinarily, incompetence implies an interference with thinking which gives rise to defects in judgment and leads to behavioral abnormalities such as squandering, hoarding, or gullibility. Competence bears little or no relationship to underlying psychiatric diagnosis and will vary in degree according to the magnitude or significance of the action under consideration. Thus a person of low intelligence might be considered competent to handle and manage a weekly allowance of twenty dollars, but he might be considered incompetent to manage a trust fund of $20,000.

incongruity Lack of consistency or appropriateness; used most commonly to refer to the disharmony between speech and affect so characteristic of the schizophrenic. The term is also applied to inconsistency in the informational interaction between the organism and environmental circumstances; i.e. the discrepancy between incoming information of the moment and information already stored and coded within the brain in the course of previous encounters with the category of circumstances concerned. There appears to be an optimal amount of incongruity (or 'novelty,' *uncertainty, cognitive dissonance*, etc.) for each organism at any given moment, in all probability determined largely by experience. When a situation is too incongruous, the organism withdraws; where it offers too little incongruity, boredom results and the organism seeks another situation offering more incongruity, stimulus change, novelty, dissonance, or uncertainty. (Hunt, J. McV. *American Scientist 53*, 80-96, 1965)

inco-ordination (in-kō-or-di-nā'shun) Ataxia.

incorporation (in-kor-por-ā'shun) The earliest instinctual aim directed toward objects and the most primitive method of recognizing external reality by assimilating external objects. Everything that is pleasurable is something to swallow and becomes ego; thus incorporation is the prototype of instinctual satisfaction, and all sexual aims are derivative of incorporation aims. Incorporation is also the prototype of regaining the omnipotence previously projected onto adults. But what is incorporated and taken in is also destroyed, so that the ego later uses incorporation in a hostile way to execute destructive impulses. Any instinctual aim may regress to incorporation or introjection.

Some writers use incorporation synonymously with *identification* and *introjection* (qq.v.); others equate incorporation with introjection and define both as the mechanism by which identification takes place. Others differentiate between them on the basis of the phase or level of psychic organization and development at which the assimilation of the object takes place. Thus incorporation refers to assimilation of external objects at the phase of primary narcissism, when there is no distinction between subject and object; introjection takes place during the phase of differentiation between the I and the not-I; while identification can occur only when the distinction between subject and object is solidly established. Unlike introjection, identification is a purely intrapsychic process.

incubus (in'kū-bus) (L. 'nightmare, evil demon') *Obs*. Nightmare; specifically, a woman's nightmare that a man or evil demon has entered her bed during the night to lie upon her (i.e. to have intercourse with her). See *succubus*.

incubus, family In social work, 'a person who, because of mental or physical incapacity or difficult personality creates a problem distinctly burdensome or depressing to others.' (Hamilton, G. *A Medical Social Terminology*, Presbyterian Hospital, New York, 1930)

index-case In genetics a person disclosing clinical evidence of the trait under investigation.

index, cephalic (se-fal'ik) A measure of head size obtained by dividing the maximal breadth of the head by its maximal length and multiplying by 100. Medium heads (mesocephaly) have an index number from 76.0 to 80.9. Long heads (dolichocephaly) have an index below 76.0; broad or short heads (brachycephaly) have an index of 81.0 or over.

index, homeostatic (hō-mē-ō-sta'tik) Any measure of the capacity to resist alteration of the status quo; the higher the homeostatic index, the more rapidly will an organism 'recover' from any disturbing situation and return to normal balance.

index, hyperglycemic (hī-pēr-glī-sē'mik) Often abbreviated H.I. The hyperglycemic index is a measurement used by McGowan as a prognostic indicator in various psychoses.

The index is computed as follows:

$$H.I. = \frac{\text{2-hour blood sugar level} - FBS}{\text{maximal blood sugar level} - FBS} \times 100$$

A high index is considered unfavorable and is seen in melancholia, and in catatonic and depressive stupors, but is usually low in mania. McGowan considers the hyperglycemic index to be a measure of the emotional tension under which a patient labors.

index of body build See *body build, index of.*

index of sexuality An index proposed by Linhares and De Oliveira:

$$I.S. = \frac{\text{urine 17 ketosteroids (in mg.)} \times 10}{\text{urine phenol} = \text{steroids (in microgm.)}}$$

Normal values are 2.6 to 4.3 for men, 0.6 to 1.0 for women. The index is low in hypogenital men and high in climacteric women.

index, skelic (ske'lik) A measurement used in anthropometry; the ratio between the length of the legs and the length of the trunk.

indicator, complex Any stimulus that arouses an emotion because it has touched off some unconscious complex is termed complex indicator. 'In group therapy . . . despite subject matter, which is probably quite involved for the average patient, it is significant how often "complex indicators" are uncovered concerning which the patients will evidence far more comprehension than they might be credited with.' (Klapman, J.W. *Group Psychotherapy*, Grune and Stratton, New York, 1946)

indigenous worker See *caregiver.*

indigestion, nervous Symptoms of gastrointestinal dyspepsia, the origin of which is assumed to be psychological (emotional).

indirect method of therapy See *therapy, indirect method of.*

individual Jung defines the psychological individual as 'unique-being.' 'The psycho-logical individual is characterized by its peculiar, and in certain respects, unique psychology. The peculiar character of the individual psyche appears less in its elements then in its complex formations. (Jung, C.G. *Psychological Types*, tr. by Baynes, H.G., Harcourt, Brace, New York and London, 1923)

'The psychological individual, or individuality, has an *a priori* unconscious existence, but it exists consciously only in so far as a consciousness of its peculiar nature is present, i.e. in so far as there exists a conscious distinctiveness from other individuals.' (ibid.)

'Everything is individual that is not collective, everything in fact that pertains only to one and not to a larger group of individuals. Individuality can hardly be described as belonging to the psychological elements, but rather to their peculiar and unique grouping and combination.' (ibid.)

individual psychology See *psychology, individual.*

individual response See *popular response.*

individuation (in-di-vij-ū-ā'shun) 'The process of forming and specializing the individual nature; in particular, it is the development of the psychological individual as a differentiated being from the general, collective psychology. Individuation, therefore, is a *process of differentiation*, having for its goal the development of the individual personality.' (Jung, C.G. *Psychological Types*, tr. by Baynes, H.G., Harcourt, Brace, New York and London, 1923)

Individuation is often used to refer to therapy by the methods of Jungian psychology.

Jung's method of treatment in psychiatry involves a procedure which he termed *individuation*. 'The process of individuation is an intense analytical effort which concentrates, with strictest integrity and under the direction of consciousness, upon the internal psychological process, eases the tension in the pairs of opposites by means of highest activation of the contents of the unconscious, acquires a working knowledge of their structure, and leads through all the distresses of a psyche that has lost its equilibrium, hacking through layer upon layer, to that center which is the source and ultimate ground of our psychic existence—to the inner core, the Self.' (Jacobi, J. *The Psychology of C.G. Jung,* Kegan Paul, Trench, Trubner, London, 1942)

Jacobi states further that 'the course of individuation has been roughly plotted and exhibits a certain formal regularity. Its sign posts and milestones are various archetypal symbols, whose form and manifestation vary according to the individual. To describe the archetypal symbols of the individuation process in all the manifold forms in which they appear would require a thorough knowledge and consideration of the different mythologies and of symbolic accounts of human history.' (ibid.) There exist, however, certain archetypes that seem to be universally identified with and characteristic of the four principal stages of the individuation process. They are, in chronological order: (1) the archetype of the shadow; (2) the archetype of the soul-image; (3) the archetype (in men) of the old wise man or of the Magna Mater (in women); (4) the archetype of the self.

indole A class of biogenic amines that includes lysergic acid (LSD), bufotenin, dimethyltryptamine, and *serotonin* (q.v.). The indole amines derive from the essential amino acid tryptophan; monoamine oxidase inhibitors elevate the levels of indole amines by delaying their breakdown. See *amine.*

Indoklon (in'dō-klon) Trade name for hexafluorodiethyl ether, which has been used as a form of convulsant therapy in psychiatric patients.

induction, dream The production of a dream through hypnotic stimulation. Such dreams may be 'artificially stimulated on command during hypnosis or they may be posthypnotically suggested, to appear later during spontaneous sleep.' Both the induction and the interpretation of this type of dream play an important part in the technique of hypnoanalysis. (Wolberg, L.R., *Hypnoanalysis,* Grune and Stratton, New York, 1945)

induction, psychological (in-duk'shun, sī-kō-loj'i-kal) A psychological charging; psychological irradiation.

industrial psychiatry See *psychiatry, industrial.*

inefficiency, family In social work, 'the state of a "shiftless" family chronically without financial margin or unable to manage its own affairs without assistance.' (Hamilton, G. *A Medical Social Terminology,* Presbyterian Hospital, New York, 1930)

inefficiency, general In social work, 'a broken-down state, physical, mental or both; an enfeebled condition; decay; not necessarily due to old age but to wasting diseases, infections, overwork, etc.' (Hamilton, G. *A Medical Social Terminology,* Presbyterian Hospital, New York, 1930)

inertia, psychic (in-ēr'sha, sī'kik) Fixation; resistance. Jung says that a peculiar psychic inertia which opposes any change and progress is a basic condition of a neurosis. Freud holds that 'this inertia is in fact most peculiar; it is not a general one, but is highly specialized; it is not even all-powerful within its own scope, but fights against tendencies towards progress and reconstruction which remain active even after the formation of neurotic symptoms.' He adds: 'This specialized "psychic inertia" is only a different term, though hardly a better one, for what in psychoanalysis we are accustomed to call a *fixation.'* (Freud, S. *Collected Papers,* vol. 2, tr. by Riviere, J., Leonard and Virginia Woolf and The Institute of Psychoanalysis, London, 1924-25)

infancy The period from birth until the beginning of the sixth year.

'This period of life, during which a certain degree of directly sexual pleasure is produced by the stimulation of various cutaneous areas (erotogenic zones), by the activity of certain biological impulses and as an accompanying excitation during many affective states, is designated by an expression introduced by Havelock Ellis as the period of auto-erotism.' (Freud, S. *Collected Papers,* vol. 2, tr. by Riviere, J., Leonard and Virginia Woolf and The Institute of Psychoanalysis, London, 1924-25)

infanticide (in-fan'ti-sīd) The killing of an infant or child. See *euthanasia.*

infantile (in'fan-til) Of or belonging to the period of *infancy* (q.v.). The term is used particularly in reference to those who are adults chronologically but whose behavior, or psychic organization, betrays more of its childhood background than is ordinarily accepted as 'normal.' See *infantilism.*

infantile hyperkinetic syndrome See *impulse-disorder, hyperkinetic.*

infantile paralysis *Poliomyelitis* (q.v.).

infantilism (in-fan'ti-liz'm) In psychoanalysis, the state of infancy.

'With the extension of the concept of the Ucs [unconscious], infantilism is still regarded as one of the main characteristics of this system, and the term now seems to refer not only to the content, but also to the unconscious mode of functioning.' (Healy, W., Bronner, A.F., and Bowers, A.M. *The Structure and Meaning of Psychoanalysis,* Knopf, New York, 1930)

In constitutional medicine, the term means anomalous type of hypoevolute constitution characterized by the persistence of certain constitutional (psychological, physiological, morphological) features of childhood up to an age which is no longer infantile. This anomaly may concern the body mass as well as the proportions, the soma as well as the psyche (although in different degrees) and cause the individual who has either reached or passed the puberal crisis to be left in the psychosomatic condition of an infant or child.

According to Pende, the ordinary form of infantilism is to be differentiated from such other forms of *hypoevolutism* as *microsomia, hypogenitalism, juvenilism,* and *persistent puberism.*

infantilistic (in-fan-ti-lis'tik) Referring to or characterized by *infantilism* or a particular form of *dwarfism* (q.v.).

infantilization (in-fan-ti-li-zā'shun) 'The performance of activities in the case of a child beyond the time when such activities usually occur.' (Levy, D. 'Maternal Overprotection,' *Psychiatry* 2, 99, 1939)

infection, familial mental Sequin's term for psychosis of association. See *association, psychosis of.*

infection, psychic (sī'kik) The 'induction' of a mental syndrome in another person. 'It happens that paranoid or para-

noiac and rarely hypomanic patients not only can make those with whom they live close together believe in their delusions, by they so infect them that the latter under conditions themselves continue to build on the delusions.' (Bleuler, E. *Textbook of Psychiatry,* tr. by Brill, A.A., Macmillan, New York, 1930). See *folie à deux; association, psychosis of.*

infectious disease, psychosis with Acute disease such as influenza, pneumonia, acute rheumatic fever, typhoid fever, etc. may give rise primarily and predominantly to psychosis, especially during the febrile period. (294.2) The psychosis is characterized by delirium, with or without motor excitement or hallucinations. Frequent shifts in the levels of consciousness may be observed and the attacks may be followed by amnesia for the period. The mental picture usually improves with improvement in the physical disease. Such psychoses are today classified as organic brain syndrome associated with systemic infection. See *organic brain syndrome associated with systemic infection.*

inferiority In general, any type of adaptation of a lower order than normally expected.

Adler is known chiefly for the stress he placed upon feelings of inferiority. He believed that everyone is born with an inferiority—organic or psychical—and that the manner in which the inferiority is handled determines the 'style of life' led by the individual. Psychiatric states are the result of faulty management of the inferiority characterizing the individual.

From the psychoanalytic point of view perhaps the most important contribution to what is called the *inferiority complex* stems from the early Oedipus situation. 'The irreconcilability of these [Oedipus] wishes with reality and the inadequacy of the childhood stage of development lead to a narcistic scar that constitutes the basis of the inferiority feeling.' (Healy, W., Bronner, A.F., and Bowers, A.M. *The Structure and Meaning of Psychoanalysis,* Knopf, New York, 1930)

inferiority, constitutional psychopathic (sī-kō-path'ik) Psychopathic inferiority; psychopathy; psychopathic state. The term is rarely used today.

inferiority, feeling of By this term Adler

indicates that through the whole period of development, the child possesses a feeling of inadequacy in its relation both to parents and the world at large.

'Because of the immaturity of his organs, his uncertainty and lack of independence, because of his need for dependence upon stronger natures and his frequent and painful feeling of subordination to others, a sensation of inadequacy develops that betrays itself throughout life.' (Adler, A. *The Practice and Theory of Individual Psychology*, tr. by Radin, P., Kegan Paul, Trench, Trubner, London, 1924)

inferiority, functional Adler includes this as a sub-group of organ inferiority. 'Its [functional inferiority's] characteristic quality is, briefly stated, a quantity or quality of work insufficient to satisfy a standard of required effectiveness.' (Adler, A. *Study of Organ Inferiority and its Psychical Compensation*, tr. by Jelliffe, S.E., Nervous & Mental Disease Publishing Company, New York, 1917)

inferiority, general In social work, 'a lack of efficiency rather than a wasting process. This phrase refers to one who constitutionally does not have average physical or mental equipment or energy.' (Hamilton, G. *A Medical Social Terminology*, Presbyterian Hospital, New York, 1930)

inferiority, morphologic (mor-fō-loj'ik) As used by Adler a sub-group of organ inferiority characterized by a deficiency in the shape of an organ, or in its size, its individual portions of tissue, its individual cell complexes, of the whole apparatus or of limited parts of it.

inferiority, organ Adler maintained that 'inherited inferiorities' of gland or organs, if they made themselves felt psychically, were conducive to a neurotic disposition, i.e., they caused a child with some 'inherited stigma' to feel a sense of inferiority in relation to his environment. This feeling of humiliation and inferiority induced by some constitutional or organ defect produces psychic compensatory and hyper-compensatory strivings.

inferiority, psychic constitutional (sī'kik) This expression, used by Healy, refers to a state of permanent abnormal social and mental reaction to the usual conditions of living on the part of those who are called borderline cases.

inferiority, psychopathic (sī-ko-pa'thik) *Obs. Psychopathic personality* (q.v.).

inferiority, simultaneous co-ordinate Adler thus indicates simultaneous manifold inferiority of organs due to reciprocal embryonic influence, or embryonic connection of many organs. As an example, he cites gastro-intestinal affections in diseases of the lungs, in emphysema, and particularly in tuberculosis. He does not feel that these gastro-intestinal affections are dependent upon a primary lung disease, but are due to simultaneous inferiority of both systems.

information theory Study of the transmission of messages or the communication of information. Information science and technology are concerned with the structure and properties of scientific information and the techniques for information handling, the characteristics of information processing devices, and the design and operation of information handling systems. See *communications unit; cybernetics*.

informational under-load See *deprivation, sensory*.

inhalation, carbon dioxide See *therapy, carbon dioxide inhalation*.

inheritable (in-her'it-à-b'l) Capable of being transmitted from parents to offspring—as applied to a physical or mental trait. *Genet.* The English term most closely approximating the German term *erbfest*, 'fixed in heredity' and contrasting the hereditary qualities of an individual with those which are acquired by the phenotype during its own lifetime and do not become transmissible by heredity. See *Mendelism*.

inheritance This specifically genetic term has two meanings: (1) the *process* of transmission of inheritable attributes from parent to offspring—being then equivalent to *hereditary transmission;* (2) more commonly, the *trait* transmitted. In the second sense it is frequently modified by an adjective or phrase, as *Mendelian* inheritance, *cytoplasmic* inheritance, inheritance of *acquired characters*. See *chromosome*.

inheritance, archaic The realization of racial influences operating in the development of the individual psyche (see *phylogenesis*).

As a figurative concept, archaic inheritance rests upon the old theory that 'morbid mental conditions presenting themselves as a reflection of a disease of the organism, are rendered more comprehensible, if we look upon them as the reappearance of a peculiar form of life which is normal for a lower level of organic development.' On this theory, propounded by Carus early in the 19th century, Jung based and built his doctrines of the 'racial unconscious' and 'archetypes,' but he makes it clear that the archetypes are *literally* inherited.

Dreams are believed to give best evidence of the primitive elements in the individual minds of modern man. According to Freud, they 'preserve for us an example of the manner in which the primitive apparatus worked, a mode that has now been abandoned as useless.'

inhibition (in-hi-bish'un) 1. In psychoanalysis, an unconscious confining, hemming in, checking, or restraining of an instinctual impulse or some manifestation of it. The force of the superego inhibits the impulse, prevents it from crossing the boundary-line between the id and the superego. 'All manifestations of neurotic *inhibition* rest upon the schematic procedure of the super-ego.' (Alexander, F.)

2. In Pavlovian conditioned-reflex psychology, inhibition refers to the active restraining of response by the experimental subject during the latent period of delayed reaction. Inhibition can itself be inhibited by any extraneous stimulus administered during the latent period, and the result will be a release of the response from its original inhibition.

inhibition-formation See *formation, inhibition*.

inhibition, occupational An inhibition in the field of the work or vocation of a patient. This can be 'evidenced in diminished pleasure in work, or in its poor execution or in such reactive manifestations as fatigue (vertigo, vomiting) if the subject forces himself to go on working.'

In general, inhibitions 'represent a limitation and restriction of ego functions, either precautionary or resulting from an impoverishment of energy.' In some cases, there is a widespread impoverishment of energy, a general inhibition in all the ego functions, of which occupation is only one. This occurs when the ego must use all of its energy for some particularly difficult task such as mourning, the suppression of rage, etc. As a result of concentrating all its energies on this particular task the ego is unable to perform many of its other usual functions such as the sexual function, eating, work.

In other cases of occupational inhibition, there is a specific inhibition, that is, a precautionary limitation of the work function. The inhibition is carried out in order to prevent a conflict with the superego. The strict superego has forbidden that any advantage or success accrue to the patient. Thus the patient must insure inadequate functioning in the work area, i.e. he inhibits his behavior in this area. In Freud's words, occupational inhibitions 'subserve a desire for self-punishment.' (Freud, S. *The Problem of Anxiety*, Norton, New York, 1936)

inhibition, prenefarious (prē-nē-fâ'rē-us) 'With guilt there is first what we have termed the *prenefarious inhibition*, the function of which is to assist the early fear reaction and which in effect is hardly to be distinguished from it, and, secondly, the stage of guilt proper, the function of which is to protect against the external dangers.' (Jones, E. *Papers on Psycho-Analysis*, 4th ed., Wood, Baltimore, 1938)

inhibition, specific An inhibition in some particular function of the ego, e.g. of eating, of sexual function, of locomotion, etc. An inhibition of eating would most frequently be expressed as anorexia; sexual inhibition as various forms of impotency or frigidity; inhibitions of locomotion as an antipathy to and weakness in walking. These specific inhibitions (e.g. of writing) are renunciations of functions which if exercised would give rise to a severe anxiety or built. Under analysis this type of inhibition—that is, of functions involving the use of the fingers—reveals an excessive erotization of the fingers. Writing acquires the significance of a sexual activity; and allowing fluid to flow out from a tube upon a piece of white paper might have the symbolic meaning of coitus.

initiation, individual and collective An individual initiation is a ritual that takes place 'under the command of heaven.' It indicates a dedication to an individual goal that demands the utmost intensity of purpose and unreserved lifelong devotion. In such cases the libido is transformed from its original objective into a cultural one, usually in the framework of a religious idea. The coronation of a king and the ordination of a priest illustrate such an initiation. Initiation also takes place in some ethnic groups in a collective way, where, for instance, adolescents are initiated into manhood with appropriate ceremonies. The purpose of these ceremonies is to direct the infantile libido into mature objectives. (Baynes, H.G. *Mythology of the Soul,* Williams and Wilkins, Baltimore, 1940)

inner language See *test, Lichtheim's.*

innervation, antagonistic inversion of the (in-ēr-vā'shun) In his general remarks on hysterical attacks, Freud states: 'A particularly effective form of distortion is *antagonistic inversion of the innervation,* which is analogous to the very usual changing of an element into its opposite by dream-work. For instance, in an hysterical attack an embrace may be represented by the arms being drawn back convulsively until the hands meet above the spinal column. Possibly the well-known *arc de cercle* of major hysterical attacks is nothing but an energetic disavowal of this kind, by antagonistic innervation of the position suitable for sexual intercourse.' (Freud, S. *Collected Papers,* vol. 2, tr. by Riviere, J., Leonard and Virginia Woolf and The Institute of Psychoanalysis, London, 1924 - 25)

innervation, expressive The nervous pathways of emotional behavior such as weeping, laughing, and sexual excitement. The expressive innervations are involuntary, even though they can be influenced, up to a point, by volition.

inquiry Questioning or asking about; in Rorschach testing, a review of the subject's responses to the ink blots in order to define as accurately as possible the exact nature of each response and thus facilitate scoring, and also to collect additional data such as elaborations on the original responses and/or further responses which were not given during the performance proper.

insane Of or pertaining to one who is of unsound mind. See *insanity.*

insane, criminally See *crime and mental disorder.*

insania cadiva (ēn-sä-nē-á ká-dē'vá) *Obs.* Epilepsy.

insania gravidarum (grá-vē-dä'room) *Obs.* Insanity of pregnancy or gestation.

insania lactantium (lák-tán'tē-oom) (L. 'insanity of those giving the breast') Lactational insanity.

insania lupina (loo-pē'ná) (L. 'wolfish insanity') *Lycanthropia* (q.v.).

insania post partum (pôst pàr'toom) (L. 'after-birth insanity') Post-partum psychosis.

insania puerperarum (poo-er-pe-rä'room) (L. 'insanity of women in childbirth') Puerperal psychosis.

insaniola (in-sá-nē-ō'lá) Eccentricity.

insanity (in-san'i-tē) 'Unfortunately, the word has no technical meaning either in law or in medicine, and it is used by courts and legislators indiscriminately to convey either of two meanings: (1) any type or degree of mental defect or disease, or (2) such a degree of mental defect or disease as to entail legal consequences (i.e., as to require commitment to an insane institution, or the appointment of a guardian, or to avoid a contract or relieve from responsibility for crime).' (Weihofen, H. *Insanity as a Defense in Criminal Law,* Commonwealth Fund, New York, 1933)

'The test of insanity as laid down in the law centers about three matters; namely, the knowledge of right and wrong, the existence of delusion, and the presence of an irresistible impulse. . . . Insanity is purely a legal concept and means irresponsibility, or incapacity for making a will, or for entering into a contractual relationship, or for executing a conveyance or what not as the case may be. The tests are essentially medical in character.' (White, W.A. *Insanity and the Criminal Law*, Macmillan, New York, 1923) See *responsibility, criminal*.

Singer and Krohn define insanity as 'a disorder of the mind due to disease, characterized by more or less prolonged departure from the individual's usual method of thinking, feeling or acting.' (Singer, H.D. and Krohn, W.O. *Insanity and Law*, Blakiston, Philadelphia, 1924)

insanity, adolescent *Obs.* Hebephrenia. See *schizophrenia*.

insanity, affective *Psychosis, affective* (q.v.).

insanity, alternating See *psychosis, manic-depressive*.

insanity, amenorrhoeal (ā-men-o-rē'al) ('due to absence of the menses') See *insanity, uterine*.

insanity, apathetic (ap-à-thet'ik) *Obs.* 'A form of insanity simulating dementia, but in which the memory is not wholly impaired, and the mind is in a state of torpor.' (Tuke, D.H. *A Dictionary of Psychological Medicine*, vol. 1 - 2, Blakiston, Philadelphia, 1892)

insanity, atheromatous (ath-ēr-om'à-tus) *Obs.* Psychosis with cerebral arteriosclerosis. See *arteriosclerosis, cerebral*.

insanity, attonic (a-ton'ik) *Obs.* Catatonia.

insanity, circular See *psychosis, manic-depressive*.

insanity, climacteric (klī-mak-ter'ik) *Obs.* Equivalent to *psychosis, involutional* (q.v.).

insanity, collective Ireland's term for psychosis of association. See *association, psychosis of*.

insanity, communicated See *folie à deux; association, psychosis of*.

insanity, constitutional An early 19th-century psychiatric term referring specifically to a concept of etiology or causation

of certain mental disorders. To the observers of that time it appeared that these disorders were of an inborn nature, predetermined by congenital, hereditary, or 'constitutional' peculiarities, defects, or deviant trends. In our newer terminology the old term 'constitutional insanity' would be equated with mental disorders with outstanding phylogenetic or genotypic hereditary etiological factors, in contrast to the ontogenetic, postnatal, environmental, experiential causes.

insanity, criminal sexual The state of Michigan has recognized a condition of insanity termed criminal sexual insanity. The statute states: 'Any person who is suffering from a mental disorder and who is not insane or feebleminded, which mental disorder has existed for not less than one year and is coupled with criminal propensities to the commission of sex offenses is hereby declared to be a sexual psychopathic person.' (*Michigan State Annotations XXV, XXVIII*, 967 (2) (3) (4) (5) (6) (7), 1942.) (Abrahamsen, D. *Crime and the Human Mind*, Columbia University Press, New York, 1944)

insanity, cyclic (sī'klik, sik'lik) See *psychosis, manic-depressive*.

insanity, delusional A rarely used term for 'acute conditions in which delusions and hallucinations or even only one of the two symptoms dominate the picture. . . .' (Bleuler, E. *Textbook of Psychiatry*, tr. by Brill, A.A., Macmillan, New York, 1930)

insanity, deuteropathic (dū-tēr-ō-path'ik) This was one of the large subdivisions of insanity under the classification arranged by Bucknill and Tuke. (Bucknill, J.C., and Tuke, D.H. *Manual of Psychological Medicine*, 3rd ed., Churchill, London, 1874.) It comprised "Insanity caused by Disorder of, or Developmental Changes occurring in other Organs than the Encephalic Centres' and included such classifications as pubescent insanity, masturbatic insanity, uterine and ovarian insanity, tubercular insanity, syphilitic insanity, etc.

insanity, dissolute Dissolute insanity, or the insanity of dissolution, includes those forms of psychiatric syndromes characterized by regression and the symptoms thereof. The terms are not in common use today.

insanity, double Tuke's term for folie à deux. See *association, psychosis of.*

insanity, hysterical (his-tēr'i-kal) An infrequently used general term for 'severe' forms of hysteria.
'It is possible that sometimes through a certain treatment the affective relation to the environment may resemble an insanity.' (Bleuler, E. *Textbook of Psychiatry,* tr. by Brill, A.A., Macmillan, New York, 1930) See *hysterical psychosis.*

insanity, idiopathic (id-i-ō-path'ik) See *insanity, symptomatic.*

insanity, impulsive An older term for those psychiatric states in which 'in addition to the ordinary symptoms of nervous fatigue, abnormal impulses, phobias, and various other psychical disturbances form part of the clinical picture.' (Patton, S. *Psychiatry,* Lippincott, Philadelphia and London, 1905)

insanity, induced See *folie à deux; association, psychosis of.*

insanity, infectious Ideler's term for psychosis of association. See *association, psychosis of.*

insanity, intellectual Prichard's term, now obsolete, for the forms of insanity known in the 19th century as monomania, mania, and dementia.

insanity, intelligential (in-tel-i-jen'shal) Noble and Mones (19th century) used this term for the large class of mental disorders known today as *organic dementias.*

insanity, intermittent Manic-depressive psychosis.

insanity, interpretational See *interpretation, delirium of.*

insanity, involute (in'vō-lūt) 'Insanity of underdevelopment' (Mercier, C.A. *A Text-Book of Insanity,* George Allen & Unwin, London, 1914); feeblemindedness.

insanity, melancholic (mel-an-kol'ik) See *melancholia, paranoid.*

insanity, moral The condition of those 'in whom the feeling tone of all ideas concerned in the weals and woes of others is stunted *(moral imbeciles)* or is entirely absent *(moral idiots);* both groups together would be designated as *moral oligophrenics.* Sympathy with others, instinctive feelings of the rights of others (not one's own) is absent, or is inadequately developed. At the same time the other kinds of emotional feelings can be perfectly retained. . . .' (Bleuler, E. *Textbook of Psychiatry,* tr. by Brill, A.A., Macmillan, New York, 1930)
Prichard stated that patients of this group showed 'uncontrollable violence and depravity of the instincts and emotions, without any impairment of the intellectual faculties.'
Henderson and Gillespie say: 'His (Prichard's) "moral insanity" was what would now be called in England "moral imbecility," and priority is claimed for his description of it.' (Henderson, D.K. and Gillespie, R.D. *A Text-Book of Psychiatry,* 4th ed., Oxford University Press, London, 1936) See *psychopathic personality.*

insanity, normal For Jung the difference between insanity and what he terms 'normal insanity' is in degree—that is, the extent to which unconscious autonomy has overcome and supplanted conscious autonomy. Jung states that 'the lunatic is an individual completely overcome by the unconscious. The same condition may exist to a less degree in the case of a person whom we cannot characterize as lunatic. We then hate to deal with a man who is only partially overcome by his unconscious. He is not entirely "beside himself," but only partially or metaphorically. Or, the condition may be temporary. Such a case can be a matter of ordinary panic or some other emotional upset. In such a state of violent emotion one says or does things out of proportion, things one regrets afterward when reason is restored. Even the most normal individual is not proof against this danger. Under suitable conditions he will "jump out of his skin" and temporarily imitate the insane, with more or less success. Not much is needed; love, hatred, joy, or sadness is often strong enough to reverse the relation between the ego and the unconscious.
'On such occasions, strange ideas may seize upon otherwise sound individuals. Groups and societies, even whole peoples

may have seizures of a similar kind; these are mental epidemics. In such a case only malevolent critics speak of a psychosis, while others speak of an "ism." The ordinary lunatic is generally a harmless, isolated case; since everyone sees that something is wrong with him, he is quickly taken care of. But the unconscious infections of groups of so-called normal people are more subtle and far more dangerous, although they derive from the autonomy of unconscious processes just as much as does insanity.' (Jung, C.G. *The Integration of the Personality,* Farrar and Rinehart, New York, 1939)

insanity, notional A 19th century diagnostic division of mental disorders, suggested by Noble and Mones; it included roughly what today is known as the schizophrenias and the psychoneuroses.

insanity of childhood An older diagnostic term for any type of mental disorder occurring before the age of puberty.

insanity of negation Psychosis with nihilistic delusions. See *Cotard's syndrome.*

insanity of pregnancy See *psychosis, puerperal.*

insanity-panic, neurotic (nū-rot'ik) Severe anxiety arising from the fear of becoming insane.

insanity, partial This expression, usually of medico-legal import, is sometimes synonymous with *monomania;* it was so regarded in the M'Naghten case. It is also defined as a borderline type of mental unsoundness.

Partial insanity 'means a mental impairment which is not so complete as to render its victim irresponsible for his criminal acts.' The law speaks of 'limited responsibility.' 'There are, as we have seen, two types of cases in which, this concept of "limited responsibility" may be called into play: (1) cases in which, though there is evidence of mental disorder which probably was a contributing cause in the criminal conduct, the disorder is not of such a type as to come within the legal test, so as to render the person irresponsible; (2) cases in which, by reason of mental disorder, the person was incapable of deliberation, premeditation, malice, or

other mental state usually made a requisite for first degree offenses, and in which, therefore, a lesser offense than that charged was in fact committed.' (Weihofen, H. *Insanity as a Defense in Criminal Law,* Commonwealth Fund, Oxford University Press, New York, 1933)

insanity, periodic Manic-depressive psychosis.

insanity, presenile (prē-sē'nīl) See *senium praecox.*

insanity, primary delusional An old term, synonymous with *folie systématisée* and with *paranoia.*

insanity, primary traumatic (traw-ma'tik) *Obs.* The symptoms that directly follow head injury, such as delirium, coma, stupor, insomnia, somnolence, headache, dizziness, etc.

insanity, progressive systematized *Obs.* Magnan's term for *paranoia* (q.v.).

insanity, protopathic (prō-tō-path'ik) Bucknill and Tuke speak of protopathic insanity as 'Insanity or Mental Deficiency caused by Primary Disease or Defective Development of the Encephalic Centres.' They subsumed *congenital or infantile deficiency, traumatic insanity, general paresis, paralytic insanity, epileptic insanity* and *senile insanity* as protopathic forms. (Bucknill, J.C. and Tuke, D.H. *Manual of Psychological Medicine,* 3rd ed., Churchill, London, 1874)

insanity, pubescent (pū-bes'ent) ('reaching puberty') An older term for *hebephrenia.*

insanity, reciprocal Parsons' term for psychosis of association. See *association, psychosis of.*

insanity, saturnine (sat'ēr-nīn) *Obs.* Chronic encephalopathy due to *lead poisoning* (q.v.).

insanity, secondary *Obs.* The schizophrenic syndrome which allegedly follows a phase of acute mental excitement.

insanity, secondary traumatic (traw-ma'-tik) When a mental syndrome, resembling one of the formal mental disorders, such as schizophrenia, manic-depressive disorder, neurasthenia, hysteria, etc. is superimposed upon an injury.

insanity, stuporous (stū'pēr-us) Old term for *anergic stupor.*

insanity, sympathetic *Obs.* Insanity for which the primary cause or seat was believed to be in an organic part of the body (as, e.g., the large intestine) biologically unconnected with the cerebrum.

insanity, symptomatic (simp-tō-mat'ik) *Obs.* Organic psychosis in contradistinction to those psychiatric syndromes, termed *idiopathic insanity* by Mercier, which are not to be identified with an organic substratum and which are called psychogenic disorders.

insanity, syphilitic (si-fi-li'tik) Obsolete term for chronic brain syndrome associated with central nervous system syphilis.

insanity, toxic (tok'sik) Bucknill and Tuke classified insanity into three groups: (1) protopathic; (2) deuteropathic; and (3) toxic, as examples of which they included alcoholic insanity, pellagrous insanity and cretinism. (Bucknill, J.C. and Tuke, D.H. *Manual of Psychological Medicine*, 3rd ed., Churchill, London, 1874)

insanity, traumatic (traw-ma'tik) See *psychosis, traumatic.*

insanity, uterine (ū'tēr-in) *Obs.* Clouston expressed the feeling that 'insanity in some few cases actually results *de novo* from this [amenorrhoea] as an exciting or predisposing cause . . . Most of them, two-thirds at least, are melancholic in character, the mental symptoms following the amenorrhoea and passing away when regular menstruation occurs.' (Clouston, T.S. *Clinical Lectures on Mental Diseases*, 6th ed., Churchill, London, 1904)

insanity, volitional (vō-lish'un-al) An older term synonymous with the present compulsive-obsessive form of psychoneurosis.

insanorum paralysis generalis (ēn-sä-nō'-room på-rá'lē-zēs ge-ne-rä'lēs) (L. general paralysis of the insane.) General paresis.

insecurity A feeling of unprotectedness and helplessness against manifold anxieties arising from a sort of all-encompassing uncertainty about one-self: uncertainty regarding one's goals and ideals, one's abilities, one's relations to others, and the attitude one should take toward them. The insecure person does not or dares not have friendly feelings in what seems to him an unfriendly world. He lives in an atmosphere of anticipated disapproval. He has no confidence today in yesterday's belief, no faith tomorrow in today's truth.

'Children are unable to form the certainties which arise from *consistent* patterns, if they experience unpredictable fluctuations in which there is no cohesion. Frequent changes of residence and schools break constantly into any attempt at forming friendships, belonging to a neighborhood group, cementing the concept of "home," getting accustomed to a method of instruction. The child's need of *consistency* rests chiefly for its gratification on parental attitudes and parental behavior. If you can predict what you can do tomorrow from what you have been permitted to do through a series of yesterdays, you acquire confidence in foresight and faith in your ability to "get along." If what you are permitted to do today depends, not on what you were permitted to do yesterday, but on parental indigestion, the stock market, the number of last night's highballs, or the latest article on child training published in the Sunday paper, then, as long as you live, you may never know where you stand in relation to any other human being.' (Kanner, L. *Child Psychiatry*, Thomas, Springfield, Ill., 1948)

insemination (in-sem-i-nā'shun) *Biol. Obs.* The act of impregnating or fertilizing.

The technical expression for *artificial insemination* is *eutelegenesis* (q.v.).

insight The patient's knowledge that the symptoms of his illness are abnormalities or morbid phenomena. For example, when a patient who fears crowds realizes that the fear is a symptom of abnormality within his own mind but is unfounded in reality, he is said to have insight. When, on the other hand, a patient affirms that his body is composed of many other human beings, that God, Napoleon, Mithras, and others are actually within his organs, he is described as having no insight. Insight is further defined from the standpoint of knowledge of the factors operating to produce the symptoms. When a patient says he understands the explanation regarding the origin and development of his symptoms, it is said that he possesses insight.

'With perfect insight there is recognition of the abnormality through which the patient has passed.' (MacCurdy, J.T. *The Psychology of Emotion*, Harcourt, Brace, New York, 1925)

Intellectual insight is knowledge of the objective reality of a situation, but without the ability to utilize that knowledge in the mastery of or successful adaptation to that situation. It is generally conceded that intellectual insight alone is ineffective in producing therapeutic change, and that the quest for it may even constitute a resistance to the therapeutic process.

insight, derivative Insight arrived at by the patient himself without interpretation by the therapist — characteristic of activity therapy groups.

insight, imaginative See *empathy*.

insipientia (ēn-sē-pē-en'tē-à) *Obs.* Dementia.

insolation (in-sō-lā'shun) Sunstroke.

insomnia (in-som'ni-à) (L. 'sleeplessness') Sleeplessness.

instigator (in'sti-gā-tēr) Any member in a therapy group who stimulates others toward activity or verbalization. See *agent, catalytic; isolate; neutralizer.*

instinct 'An organized and relatively complex mode of response, characteristic of a given species, that has been phylogenetically adapted to a specific type of environmental situation.' (Warren, H.C. *Dictionary of Psychology*, Houghton Mifflin, Boston, 1934)

'Every instinctive process has the three aspects of all mental processes, the cognitive, the affective, and the conative. Now, the innate psychophysical disposi-

tion, which is an instinct, may be regarded as consisting of three corresponding parts, an afferent, a central, and a motor or efferent part, whose activities are the cognitive, the affective, and the conative features respectively of the total instinctive process.' (McDougall, W. *An Introduction to Social Psychology*, 15th ed., Luce, 1923) McDougall says that the primary emotions, such as anger, fear, and disgust are instinctive, while what he calls secondary emotions, such as jealousy, hatred and admiration, that is, those compounded of two or more primary emotions, are not.

'An instinct may be described as having a source, an object and an aim. The source is a state of excitation within the body, and its aim is to remove that excitation; in the course of its path from its source to the attainment of its aim the instinct becomes operative mentally. We picture it as a certain sum of energy forcing its way in a certain direction.' (Freud, S. *New Introductory Lectures on Psycho-Analysis*, Norton, New York, 1933)

An instinct, according to Freud, is a primal trend or urge that cannot be further resolved. Jealousy can be resolved into love and hate; therefore, it is not an instinct; it is a 'part-instinct' or an 'instinct-component.' From the Freudian standpoint there are two primal instincts, those of *life* and of *death.*

In present-day psychoanalytic psychology, the term *drive* (q.v.) is generally preferred to what Freud termed 'instinct.' An 'instinct' is considered to be an innate capacity or necessity to react in a sterotyped way to a particular set of stimuli; it is a lower-level, automatic response (such as the reflexes). The term 'drive,' on the other hand, ordinarily does not refer to the organism's response but instead emphasizes the state of central excitation; unlike the instinct, the response to the drive is not automatic but requires the functioning of the ego and depends on learning and experience.

In *ethology* (q.v.), an 'instinct' is an inherited system of co-ordination, made up of an 'internal drive,' which builds up as 'specific action potential' until it is released, and one or more 'inherited releasing mechanisms' (I.R.M.) which release the specific action potential and produce the instinctive act or fixed action pattern' (F.A.P.). The specific action patterns are species-specific, uniform, and generally rigid, although (especially as one goes up the vertebrate scale) some links of the instinctual action are subject to modification by learning. Such learning, when it occurs, can be conceived of as a replacement of innate, instinctual links by learned behavior patterns—a phenomenon called 'instinct-training interlocking.' In man, instinctive behavior patterns are rudimentary, and most genetically determined, instinctual behavior is replaced by learned, plastic, purposive, adaptive behavior—that is, by the ego. (Schur, M. *International Journal of Psycho-Analysis, XLI*, 275, 1960) See *imprinting; releaser, social.*

The two instincts are constant psychic forces, arising from the organism itself; their sources are in the soma and represent the biological needs of the body. Somatic processes create the need, which acts through the psyche in order to secure specific forms of motor discharge for the relief of the 'tension' set up in the original source. Successful gratification of the instinctual needs can be attained only through contact with the outer world.

The two primal instincts are (1) Eros or life instinct, the function of which is to maintain life; its aim is constructive. It is composed of three principal manifestations; (a) the uninhibited sexual or organ-gratifying impulses; (b) sublimated impulses derived from those originally associated with organ-satisfaction; and (c) self-preservative impulses, which strive to protect and preserve the body and the mind.

(2) The second primal instinct is Thanatos, the death or destruction instinct. Freud says that the tendency of the instinct is 'to re-establish a state of things which was disturbed by the emergence of life.' The death instinct is said to be composed of (a) impulses that tend toward regression, that is, toward a reinstatement of an earlier level of personality development; (b) impulses that aim to injure or destroy the individual, and (c) those that possess the aim of (b) with regard, however, to objects outside of oneself. Freud has emphasized that the death instinct does not exist literally as such in the unconscious; rather it is expressed as complete passivity toward which the organism instinctively strives. See *instinct, death.*

One of the basic theses upon which psychoanalysis rests assumes that the process of life is a conflict and a compromise between the two primal instincts.

Jung says that 'the collective unconscious consists of the sum of the instincts and their correlates, the archetypes.'

instinct, aggressive See *instinct, death.*

instinct, aim of In all cases, the aim of an instinct is the reestablishment of that state of relative total organismal balance which existed before the instinct was aroused, through either external or internal stimulation. The state of instinct arousal in an organism is a state of tension or unpleasure in that organism 'driving' the organism, as a whole, in the direction of 'finding' and 'applying' the appropriate means for relieving the arousal tension—or dissatisfaction through gratification. The Boston physiologist Cannon coined the phrase 'homeostatic equilibrium' for this state of relative harmony and balance, and used the term 'homeostasis' for the multiplicity of forces that interact within the organism and react to internal or external stimulation in the directional trend of equilibrium.

The *aim* of an instinct must be sharply discriminated from the *object* of that instinct. Water is the object of the instinct of thirst, while the aim of thirst is gratified through the imbibition and absorption of water by the tissues—namely, the disappearance of the unpleasurable state of thirstiness or 'thirst.' The process of gratifying the instinctual aims is heralded in consciousness by the sensation of pleasure. (Sterba, R. *Introduction to the Psycho-analytic Theory of the Libido,* Nervous and Mental Disease Monographs, No. 68, New York, 1942)

instinct, antipathic sexual (an-ti-path'ik sek'shoo-al) 'Great diminution or complete absence of sexual feeling for the opposite sex, with substitution of sexual feeling and instinct for the same sex (homosexuality, or antipathic sexual instinct).' (Krafft-Ebing, R.v. *Psychopathia Sexualis,* Login, New York, 1908)

instinct, complementary The tendency of all infantile sexual instincts with an active aim to be integrally associated with, or accompanied by, the antithetical instinct drive with a passive aim. In infancy and childhood, the separation or *defusion* (q.v.) of these equal and opposite active and passive instinctual aims is marked. On the other hand, in adult life, with the achievement of emotional maturity at the so-called genital level, this persistence of antagonistic instinctual trends toward the same object tends to drop out or disappear. In childhood, side by side with the wish to beat, there exists the wish to be beaten; the wish to eat co-exists with the wish to be eaten, etc. In adult life one frequently finds, as an infantile remnant, the wish to be loved by a person and, simultaneously, the wish to love that person. See *ambivalence.*

instinct-component (-kom-pō'nent) *Part-instinct* (q.v.). See also *impulse, component.*

instinct, conscience *Superego* (q.v.).

instinct, curiosity *Epistemophilia* (q.v.).

instinct, death The destructive or aggressive or ego instinct(s). In psychoanalytic psychology, two basic instincts or drives are recognized: those under the control of the pleasure-unpleasure principle (the life instincts, the sexual instincts, Eros); and those instincts under the control of the repetition-compulsion principle (the death instincts, destructive instincts, ego instincts, aggressive instincts, destrudo, Thanatos).

It was not until 1920, in *Beyond the Pleasure Principle,* that Freud first recognized the death instincts as an independent drive. During the earlier years of psychoanalysis Freud occupied himself largely with the libidinal or erotic instinct and later conceived of an aggressive or destructive instinct which in its primary form he considered to be non-sexual. He came to believe that not all mental processes were subject to the pleasure-pain (pleasure-unpleasure) principle, and that there was a phylogenetically older principle, the repetition-compulsion principle. The latter operates to restore a previous condition of pleasure and harmony, whenever noxious stimuli cannot adequately be handled by the pleasure-pain principle. Since the repetition-compulsion tends to restore the status quo, Freud reasoned that it must ultimately

tend to return the organism to the earliest state of all, namely that of inanimate existence; thus the manifestations of the repetition-compulsion principle were called the death instinct, and it was presumed that deflection of the death instinct onto objects in the external world constituted the aggressive instinct.

Because Freud's consideration of the death or destructive drives came relatively late in the development of his psychology, the term *libido,* which technically refers only to the energy of the sexual instinct, is often used as a general term to refer also to the energy of the death instinct. The term *destrudo* was suggested for the energy of the death instinct, but this has not been widely accepted.

The death instinct strives for a state of complete and eternal rest, is averse to new experiences, seeks to return to the past, and is essentially conservative in nature. As a rule, neither the life nor the death instinct is seen in pure and completely independent form; rather, there is fusion of the two. The death instinct goes through approximately the same ontogenetic development as does the sexual instinct, but the death instinct is not as intimately related to the erogenous body zones as is the sexual. It is not known if the discharge of destructive or aggressive drives brings pleasure; Freud believed that it did not, but many contemporary psychoanalytic writers believe that it does.

The death instinct is a biological tendency to self-destruction which, although always operative, is ordinarily deeply hidden; in its earliest developmental stage it is known as *primal masochism.* By union with the narcissistic libido (that part of the sexual libido which has the ego as its object, as is seen in purest form in the narcissistic phase of development, when the libido has not yet come to know or cathect objects in the external world) the death instinct acquires an erotic tinge and becomes pleasurable; it is then known as *actual masochism.* The aggressive or death instinct aims at destroying the outside world which is the source of disturbing stimuli; but disturbing stimuli may also come from within by means of an increase in (sexual) libido. As the sexual instincts develop, this increase in libido is accompanied by a transformation of narcissistic libido into object libido. The primal masochism, directed originally against the narcissistic libido, is now projected onto the objects of the libido in the outside world as *sadism*.

Just as the genital is the executive organ of the sexual instinct, so is the musculature (both striated and smooth) the executive organ of the death instinct.

The death instinct operates in the oral phase, which thus is often termed the cannibalistic stage; for gratification of hunger also destroys the object. In the anal phase, the destructive instinct appears as soiling, retention, and other means of defiant rejection of the disturbing external world. In the phallic phase, phantasies of piercing, penetration, or dissolution of the object betray the operation of the destructive instinct. Genital sadism appears in the form of hatred, which normally is restricted by love and persists only as the activity involved in taking possession of the love object. In the genital phase, there is fusion of the destructive instinct with the sexual instinct, and the destructive instincts, if not completely paralyzed by the sexual instincts, are at least restrained by them. In certain psychiatric conditions, however, there is a greater or lesser defusion of the instincts; this is seen particularly in depressive psychoses and in certain forms of schizophrenia.

Freud's hypotheses about the death instinct have by no means achieved universal acceptance in psychoanalytic circles, and many feel that although destructiveness may accompany any response pattern, it is not an instinct or drive in itself but is rather a '. . . maladaptive or misdirected expression of the single instinct to live. The only aim of instinct is to reduce the physiological stimulus or disequilibrium, and maintain optimal tension, i.e. life.

'Drives, on the other hand, arise only with the development and operation of psychic structure. They should be conceptualized as a psychological rather than a biological phenomenon—the product of a highly specialized bodily system which is a different level of organization from biological instinctual activity patterns.' (Pleune, F.G. *International Journal of Psycho-Analysis XLII*, 479, 1961)

instinct, destruction See *instinct, death*.

instinct-eruption See *thrust*.

instinct, herd Group feeling; group-formation; the desire to be with others and to take part in social activities; gregariousness. From the psychoanalytic point of view this is not an instinct; rather, social and group phenomena are explained as results of *identification*, the origin of which is to be found in the jealousy and hostility of childhood. It is said that the first child is jealous of his successors and desires to get rid of them. He realizes, however, that his animosity cannot be maintained without injury to himself. If the jealousy is maintained he will lose the admiration and love of his parents. He is eventually compelled to unite (to identify himself) with his brothers and sisters.

When identification takes place it is followed by reaction-formation, that is, sympathy with the rival replaces hostility. The identification with the leader is of the same order as the earlier identification with the father. The leader is a new ego-ideal.

MacCurdy says: 'It is possible and convenient to group instincts (or interests) under three great headings, ego-activities (self-preservation and aggrandizement), sexual proclivities (mating and parenthood) and herd or social functions.' (MacCurdy, J.T. *The Psychology of Emotion*, Harcourt, Brace, New York, 1925)

instinct, mastery According to Fenichel, mastery means the ability to handle outer demands and inner drives, to postpone gratification when necessary, to assure satisfaction even against hindrances.' There exists, however, no instinct bent on mastering. Mastery 'is a general aim of every organism, but not of a specific instinct.' (Fenichel, O. *The Psychoanalytic Theory of Neurosis*, Norton, New York, 1945) See *mastery, oral*.

instinct-need See *need*.

instinct, partial Part-instinct; see *organ-pleasure*.

instinct, passive When Freud speaks of a passive instinct, he refers to the aim of the instinct and not to its state of activity or inactivity. 'Every instinct is a form of activity; if we speak loosely of passive instincts, we can only mean those whose aim is passive.' (Freud, S. *Collected Papers*, vol. 4, tr. by Riviere, J., Leonard and Virginia Woolf and The Institute of Psychoanalysis, London, 1924-25) For example, an instinct may be reversed into its opposite; an active instinct (e.g., sadism) may be reversed and appear as a passive one (e.g., masochism).

It appears that the *aim* of a passive instinct is the same as that of an active one. The difference rests in the object. When oneself is the object, the instinct is passive, while it is active when the instinct is directed away from oneself.

instinct, possessive The drive for power, the primitive urge to conquer and retain the love-object. In the infant, the possessive instinct manifests itself in the acts of sucking and swallowing, and in the stubbornness with which the child holds on to the nipple of the mother. It is also shown in the capacity to control the anal sphincter and thus retain the feces. The possessive instinct is partly responsible for the child's excessive need of having exclusively for himself the parent's undivided love. Later the infant's crude possessive urge is transformed into a more socialized form; it becomes, one may say, 'civilized,' in order to be approved by the community and accepted by the person himself. In this more socialized form, the possessive instinct may express itself in stinginess, punctuality, the habit of collecting things, even the search for intellectual knowledge, and in many other character traits. In the adult, the crude possessive urge is sublimated under the constant exigencies of the superego (a code of moral behavior) and acquires a constructive quality, a proper intensity, and an acceptable direction toward admissible goals. (Schilder, P. *Psychotherapy*, Norton, New York, 1938)

instinct-presentation The mode by which an instinct is expressed.

instinct-ridden Beset by or characterized by aggressive and/or libidinal impulses that are only inadequately modified or controlled by the superego; the instinct-ridden character typically keeps his superego '. . . actively and consistently at a distance. Experience with the persons whose incorporation created the superego have made it possible for the ego to feel the conscience in one place or at certain

periods (and for the most part in very distorted forms), but to be relatively free from the inhibiting influences of the superego, when tempted by the irresistible urge of strivings for instinctual gratification and for security.

'An isolation of this kind is fostered if the ego has previously experienced both intense erogenous pleasure and intense environmental frustrations, especially if experiences of this kind were encountered by a person already characterized by an oral regulation of self-esteem and an intolerance of tensions, developed under the influence of early traumata or orally fixating experiences.' (Fenichel, O. *The Psychoanalytic Theory of Neurosis*, Norton, New York, 1945)

instinct, self-preservative See *instinct; instinct, death.*

instinct-training interlocking See *instinct.*

institution 'The established forms or conditions of procedure characteristic of group activity.' (McIver, R.M. *Society, Its Structure and Changes*, Macmillan of Canada, Toronto, 1931)

Typical social institutions in the broader sense are the family, the school, the church, the economic system, and the state. Each institution has its particular function to play in its service to its members and to society.

instrumentalism (in-stroo-men'tal-iz'm) 'An extreme form of *Self-Extension* in which one makes use of people for pleasure or profit; exploitation of others.' (Hamilton, G. *A Medical Social Terminology*. Presbyterian Hospital, New York, 1930)

insufficiency, apperceptive (ap-ēr-sep'tiv) In his studies of the vitally important psychic process of symbolism (the indirect representation of objects or ideas by means of symbols), Silberer originated this term for the essential cause of symbolism — an incapacity of the apperceptive faculty of the mind. Because of this incapacity the mind cannot truly and correctly apperceive the nature of some hitherto unencountered object by appraising the attributes of this object *sui generis*, so to speak, but only by appraising similarities and/or dissimilarities of the new object in association with some old (known) object. The new object then becomes synonymous with the old object and is given the same name. One is the other: the other is the one. This is the origin of symbolism.

Silberer recognizes two types of apperceptive insufficiency: (1) of purely intellectual origin; (2) of affective origin. In the first type apperception is insufficient by reason of mental incapacity inherent in the organism (or by reason of a capacity *as yet undeveloped*), or by mental incapacity of functional nature, i.e. as induced by sleep, fatigue, drugs,'etc. In the second type apperception is insufficient because of psychopathology existing in the interplay of affective (emotional) components attaching to the apperceiver or to that which is to be apperceived.

insufficiency, segmental In Adlerian psychology, inferiority of a body segment (using the term segment in its embryological, developmental sense); the inferiority of the internal organs is typically betrayed by some disorder of the skin of that segment—nevi, angiomata, telangiectasiae, neurofibromata, etc., all of which Adler termed the *external stigmata.*

insular sclerosis See *sclerosis, multiple.*

insularity, psychological The quality or state of being narrowminded or circumscribed in outlook, mentality, and character. 'The most important value to character formation of group experiences is the modification or elimination of egocentricity and psychological insularity.' (Slavson, S.R. *An Introduction to Group Therapy.* The Commonwealth Fund, Oxford University Press, New York, 1943)

insulin treatment See *treatment, insulin.*

insurance, narcissistic (när-si-sis'tik) 'It is the narcissistic satisfaction derived from the fulfilling of an ideal which benumbs the critical judgment of the ego, and secures gratification of the forbidden aggressive tendencies. This economic mechanism may be described as a kind of *narcissistic insurance.*' (Rado, S., *International Journal of Psychoanalysis IX,* 222, 1928)

intake The initial face to face contact between the patient (or, in the case of a child, a member of the patient's family) and the therapist (or any member of the psychiatric team); the initial interview, usually in reference to a patient who is admitted into a psychiatric clinic or a mental hospital.

intake, family group An initial interview technique, devised by the Riley Child Guidance Clinic (Indianapolis, Indiana), that substitutes the family unit (usually the child and his parents) for the usual single informant and a psychiatric team (consisting of a psychiatrist, a psyhologist, and a social worker) for the usual single interviewer. One member of the team acts as the principal interviewer and opens the way to a discussion by the family of the presenting problems as they see them. The other team members later enter into the discussion as active participants. Interaction between family members is interrupted only if one member is too aggressively attacked (verbally or physically) by another.

The major objectives of such a technique are . . . '(1) clarification of the presenting problems for all persons involved, including the child, (2) observation of the family interaction, and (3) information which will lead to tentative hypotheses about the relationship between the family dynamics and the child's symptoms.' (Tyler, E.A., et al. *Archives of General Psychiatry 6,* 46, 1962)

integration (in-te-grā'shun) Act of bringing together the parts into an integral whole. In early infancy the components of the mind operate independently, as separate entities. One component does not influence another by any so-called combination of forces. The singleness of individual parts remains a characteristic of the mind during the greater part of the infantile period. From the psychoanalytic point of view, for example, oral, anal, and genital factors remain essentially discrete for a considerable period; gradually, however, through various mechanisms the individual parts begin to act in co-operation with one another; it is the harmonizing of separate parts that is called integration.

During the infantile period, extending approximately through the fifth year of life, integration is relatively simple, being manifested chiefly in the form of knowledge on the part of the child that its body and mind are distinct from the environment. The integration at this stage of development is call *primary*. Subsequent integration that co-ordinates individual components into unified and socialized action is termed *secondary integration*.

When integration, having once been established, breaks down into its component parts, that is, when there is a reversal of the processes of integration, the condition is known as *disintegration*.

When disintegration is followed by a reorganization of the individual parts into a harmonious whole, the process is called *reintegration*. Hence, it is said that a manic-depressive patient is disintegrated during the illness and reintegrated following it.

integration, primary See *integration*.

integration, secondary See *integration*.

intellect (in'te-lekt) From the standpoint of Jung (analytical psychology) intellect is 'directed thinking.' He adds: 'The faculty of passive, or undirected, thinking, I term *intellectual intuition*. Furthermore, I describe directed thinking or intellect as the *rational* function, since it arranges the representations under concepts in accordance with the presuppositions of my conscious rational norm. Undirected thinking, or intellectual intuition, on the contrary, is, in my view, an *irrational function*, since it criticizes and arranges the representations according to norms that are unconscious to me and consequently not appreciated as reasonable.' (Jung, C.G. *Psychological Types*, tr. by Baynes, H.G., Harcourt Brace, New York and London, 1923)

intellectual inadequacy See *retardation, mental*.

intellectualization (in-te-lek-chū-al-i-zā'-shun) See *brooding*.

intelligence (in-tel'i-jens) According to Thorndike, there are three distinctive types of intelligence: *abstract, mechanical* and *social*.

The capacity to understand and manage abstract ideas and symbols constitutes abstract intelligence; the ability to understand, invent and manage mechanisms comprises mechanical intelligence; and the capacity to act reasonably and wisely as regards human relations and social affairs constitutes social intelligence.

Tolman's pragmatic viewpoint regards intelligence as the interrelated capacities of an organism (a) to perceive its environment through its various sensory modalities ('discriminanda'); (b) to integrate these sensations into total configurations ('Gestalt apperceptions'); (c) to attribute meaning and personal reference ('symbolization' and 'value') to them in terms of retained past experiences ('memory'), and (d) to respond to such differentiated apperceptions by internal and external reactions of various degrees of finesse, versatility, and efficiency ('manipulanda' capacities).

Spearman's 'g' is an overall index of general intelligence, made up of: 'p' (perseveration factor); 'f' (fluency factor); 'w' (will factor); and 's' (speed factor).

intelligence quotient See *quotient, intelligence*.

intelligence, subconscious Morton Prince asks whether 'a subconscious process can perform the same functions as are ordinarily performed by conscious *intelligence* (as we commonly understand that term); that is to say memory, perception, reasoning, imagination, volition, affectivity, etc.?' He cites clinical material at great length, concluding that 'in the quality of the functions performed they [i.e. subconscious processes] frequently exhibit that which is characteristic of *intelligence*.' (Prince, M. *The Unconscious*, Macmillan, New York, 1916)

intensity, displacement of psychic According to Freud, the affects associated with an idea or impulse are frequently shifted onto ideas or impulses that seem inconsequential.

'This product, the dream, has above all to be withdrawn from the censorship, and to this end the dream-work makes use of the *displacement of psychic intensities*, even to the transvaluation of all psychic processes; thoughts must be exclusively or predominantly reproduced in the material of visual and acoustic memory-traces, and from this requirement there proceeds the *regard of the dream-work for representability*, which it satisfies by fresh displacements.' (Freud, S. *The Interpretation of Dreams*, 3rd ed., tr. by Brill, A.A., Macmillan, New York, 1933) See *displacement*.

intensive care syndrome See *syndrome, intensive care*

intent, criminal 'Criminal intent is a knowing disregard of criminal law (bearing in mind that ignorance of a law is no defense as knowledge of the law itself is presumed). Any person manifesting this disregard is an outlaw, that is to say, he is a criminal in the eyes of the law.' The authors add: 'intent is often wrongly confused with motive; motive is merely that which impels.' (Singer, H.D. and Krohn, W.O. *Insanity and Law*, Blakiston, Philadelphia, 1924) Years ago Sir FitzJames Stephen wrote that 'intention is the result of deliberation upon motives, and is the object aimed at by the action caused or accompanied by the act of volition. Though this appears to me to be the proper and accurate meaning of the word it is frequently used and understood as being synonymous with motives.'

intention 'An impulse for action which has already found approbation, but whose execution is postponed for a suitable occasion.' Freud stresses the forgetting of intentions, saying that they can 'invariably be traced to some interference of unknown and unadmitted motives—or, as may be said, they [are] due to a *counterwill*.' (Freud, S. *The Basic Writings of Sigmund Freud*, tr. by Brill, A.A., Random House, New York, 1938)

intention tremor See *tremor*.

interaction theory of personality See *chronograph, interaction*.

intercalated Internuncial; see *reflex*.

inter-cortical (in-tẽr-kor′ti-kal) A term applied by Burrow to the interrelationship among individuals by means of the sign, word, or symbol. In man's inter-cortical functioning only the restricted, cortical segment of one person is brought into contact with the cortical segment of another. Contrasted with intra-se, intra-organismic. Synonymous: inter-individual, inter-se, social, symbolic, semiotic, linguistic. (Burrow, T. *The Biology of Human Conflict*, Macmillan, New York, 1937, pp. 219-20)

intercourse, buccal (buk′al) Act of applying the mouth to the genitals.

interego (in-tẽr-ē′gō) Stekel's proposed substitute for the Freudian term superego. According to Stekel, the Freudian *superego* (q.v.) should be considered not as a simple 'watchman' (the vigilant moral part of the ego), but rather as an intermediary between our inner crude impulses and the final conscious aims of those impulses. For this reason Stekel prefers to call the superego an interego—a structure functioning as a compromiser between crude subconscious trends and the moral principles. (Stekel, W. *The Interpretation of Dreams*, Liveright, New York, 1943)

interest To interest is to attract and hold the attention, to occupy and engage a person's concern to the extent of employing his time. This is one of the basic principles upon which occupational therapy is applied.

interest, social Adler's term for the desire to belong, to be a part of a social group, a desire that he felt was basic to all human beings.

interest, stimulation See *occupation, stimulating*.

interference pattern of discharge See *attack, obsessive*.

interlocking, instinct-training See *instinct*.

intermarriage In genetics, marriage between two blood-relations, especially in the sense of a *cousin marriage*, or the union between two individuals belonging to different racial groups of a mixed population.

Cousin marriages are of particular genetic significance in the case of *recessive* Mendelian inheritance (see *recessiveness*).

intermediate In genetics the type of Mendelian inheritance characterized by the fact that the expressivity of a dominant character is not always complete, but is to a certain extent modifiable by the recessive member of a given pair of contrasting characters. The term denotes both this 'blended' kind of inheritance and the particular hybrids who resemble neither parent exactly, but are *intermediate* in several respects between the original characteristics of the two parent types. For instance, pink hybrids would be intermediate when they have one red and one white parent. See *dominance*.

Within the intermediate mode of heredity, many cases are known in which one and the same genetic factor has a dominant effect on one set of characters, but a recessive effect on others.

Another modification is constituted by those cases in which each member of a contrasting pair of factors produces its own effect independently, so that the heterozygote is neither a blend nor an intermediate, but a *mosaic*.

intermediate brain syndrome due to alcohol See *black-out*.

intermission When a psychiatric syndrome ends in a disappearance of symptoms for a temporary period, only to reappear at a subsequent time, the interval between attacks is called an *intermission*. When after an attack it is not known that the symptoms will reappear, the term *remission* (q.v.) is used. A patient in a state of remission may never have another attack.

internal capsule See *basla ganglia*.

International Classification of Disease (ICD) The official list of disease categories issued by the World Health Organization. DSM-II (Diagnostic and Statistical Manual, second edition) is based upon the eighth revision of the ICD, prepared in 1966. See *nomenclature, 1968 revision*.

internuncial Intercalated; see *reflex*.

interoception The Pavlovian concept that the cerebral hemispheres analyze and synthesize not only impulses entering from the external world but also impulses arising from changes taking place within the organism itself. Russian neurophysiologists have investigated extensively the presence of receptors in internal organs.

interpenetration (in-tēr-pen-e-trā'shun) A speech or writing defect in which the intensity of the patient's preoccupations reduces his ability to respond directly to questioning and instead every now and then will be interjected a few fragments of the topic suggested by the question. Interpenetration is also used to refer to intrusion of the patient's complexes and preoccupations into any direct response he may give to a question. Interpenetration is seen frequently in the schizophrenias but occurs in other disorders as well; it is, therefore, considered an accessory schizophrenic symptom.

interpretation (in-tēr-pre-tā'shun) The description or formulation of the meaning or significance of a patient's productions and, particularly, the translation into a form meaningful for the patient of his resistances and symbols and character defenses. Interpretation consists of seeing beyond the facade of manifest thinking, feeling and behavior, into less obvious meanings and motivations. Involved in interpretative activities are different degrees of directiveness. The lowest degree consists of waiting for the patient to interpret things for himself, giving him as few cues as possible. Next, the patient is enjoined to attempt the interpretation of representative experiences. Of greater degree, is a piecing together of items of information, and of seemingly unrelated bits, so that certain conclusions become apparent to the patient. Leading questions are asked to guide the patient to meaningful answers. More directive is the making of interpretations in a tentative way, so that the patient feels privileged to accept or reject them as he chooses. Finally, the therapist gives the patient strong authoritative interpretations, couched in challenging, positive terms.' (Wolberg, L.R. *The Technique of Psychotherapy*, Grune & Stratton, New York, 1954)

interpretation, action S.R. Slavson defines this as 'the non-verbal reaction of the therapist of the group to the statements or acts of the patient. Action interpretation is employed almost exclusively in activity group psychotherapy.'

interpretation, allegoric (al-e-gor'ik) 'A view which interprets the symbolic expression as an intentional transcription or transformation of a known thing is *allegoric*.' (Jung, C.G. *Psychological Types*, tr. by Baynes, H.G., Harcourt, Brace, New York and London, 1923) See *semiotic*.

interpretation, anagogic (an-à-goj'ik) This

is an expression used by H. Silberer to denote a form of dream interpretation. He says that every dream is capable of two different interpretations. The first he calls the *psychoanalytic*, referring particularly to interpretations from the standpoint of infantile sexuality; the second, the *anagogic*, 'reveals the more serious and often profound thoughts which the dream-work has used as its material. . . . The majority of dreams require no overinterpretation, and are especially insusceptible of an anagogic interpretation.' (Freud, S. *The Interpretation of Dreams*, 3rd ed., tr. by Brill, A.A., Macmillan, New York, 1933)

interpretation, deep An ambiguous term that usually refers to any interpretation concerned with early developmental levels (e.g. pregenital as opposed to genital levels) and/or with earliest repressed material. The terms 'deep' and 'depth' belong to an early phase of psychoanalytic theory, when description of the psyche was mainly in topographical terms—Cs (consciousness), below which is Pcs (preconsciousness), and below that the Ucs (unconscious).

interpretation, defense Ego and superego interpretation; in psychoanalytic therapy, an interpretation that brings to consciousness the kind and sources of defensive resistances used by the patient.

interpretation, delirium of (dē-lir'i-um) Sérieux and Capgras suggest that there are but two forms of paranoia; one is the *delirium of interpretation*, characterized by delusions of persecution; the other is the *delirium of revindication*, the central theme of which has to do with a delusional organization based upon the urgency to gain justice for alleged offenses perpetrated against the patient. The term *delirium* in this sense signifies a delusional, not a delirious state.

interpretation-delusion See *delusion, interpretation.*

interpretation, ego See *interpretation, defense.*

interpretation, id See *interpretation, impulse.*

interpretation, impulse Id interpretation; in psychoanalytic therapy, an interpretation that overcomes a defense and permits certain painful thoughts or feelings to come into consciousness.

interpretation, mutative Any interpretation productive of change; specifically, an interpretation that produces a breach in the neurotic vicious circle. J. Strachey (*International Journal of Psychoanalysis* 15, 127-159, 1934) outlines the nature of such an interpretation as follows: first, the analyst in his role of auxiliary superego allows a particular quantity of the patient's Id-energy to become conscious (e.g. in the form of an aggressive impulse); secondly, such Id impulses will be directed onto the analyst; thirdly, the patient '. . . will become aware of the contrast between the aggressive character of his feelings and the real nature of the analyst, who does not behave like the patient's "good" or "bad" archaic objects.' This is the point at which the vicious circle of the neurosis is breached, and, with the patient's recognition of the distinction between the archaic phantasy object and the real external object, the way is opened to the recovery of further infantile material which is being re-experienced by the patient in his relationship to the analyst.

interpretation, serial This term applies to the elucidation of a consecutive number of dreams taken as a group. The interpretation of a series of dreams taken as a group gives the analyst important psychic material which no study of a single, individual dream can bring forward. In other words, when the patient describes a dream, the analyst should not confine himself to the interpretation of the individual dream, but should rather consider this dream in relation to previous dreams and also wait for the occurrence of further dreams before he reaches a conclusion. This is the only way to elucidate deeply repressed material which expresses itself only in part in sundry dreams. After such a serial study the analyst can reconstruct the jigsaw puzzle of the whole conflict with the aid of the various pieces. 'Serial interpretation is of great advantage. Should a symbol whose meaning seems inexplicable turn up, we can tranquilly await its reappearance in later dreams. It will recur often, until its meaning grows plain.' (Stekel, W. *The Interpretation of Dreams*, Liveright, New York, 1943)

interpretation, superego See *interpretation, defense.*

inter-psychology (in-tēr-sī-kol'ō-jē) A term used by Tarde, Janet, and others for interpersonal relationships.

intersex (in'tēr-seks) A sexually intermediate individual that has developed as a male (or female) up to a certain point in its life-history and thereafter has continued its development as a female (or male).

Owing to the supersession of one type of sex tendency by the other, intersexes usually show a mixture of male and female parts and are almost invariably sterile. They are *not* gynandromorphs, because their structures are not definitely and clearly male or female.

In cattle, an intersex which 'is made so by action of hormone of the opposite sex' is called a *freemartin*. According to Shull, all freemartins are modified females.

intersexuality Incomplete sex reversal, which leads to the production of individuals intermediate between the sexes, as the final result of a competition between opposed male and female tendencies, in which supremacy is gained at the 'turning point' by the formerly less developed tendency. The time at which this switch-over takes place determines the degree of intersexuality. Intersexuality is thought to be of common occurrence, even if it may not yet be exactly recognizable.

A special form of intersexuality, occurring in man as well as in domesticated mammals, is probably caused by delayed or deficient hormone production and results in modifications of both internal and external sex organs and secondary characteristics.

Intersexuality is sometimes used to refer to severe trans-sexualism or *transvestism* (q.v.).

interstimulation (in-tēr-stim-ū-lā'shun) Modification of behavior in response to the presence of others. In the case of a child, for instance, his general conduct is altered by the presence of one or more other children. Interest is stimulated or diminished, activity is intensified or decreased, and anxiety is heightened.

interview, Amytal (am'i-tal) See *narcotherapy.*

intimidate To frighten or cow; to make another fearful that one will attack him verbally or physically or that one will shame or embarrass him. Intimidation is sometimes used as a defense against anxiety proceeding from conflicts over passive homosexual impulses.

intoxication, alcoholic Alcohol poisoning; the state resulting from excessive ingestion of alcohol. Psychiatrically, alcoholic intoxication generally refers to an acute brain syndrome which develops as a result of overdose of alcohol. This syndrome may be of two varieties: (1) acute intoxication, or (2) pathologic intoxication (also known as mania à potu).

Acute intoxication (291.4 or 309.13): Alcohol is a physiological depressant, but the release of higher control as a result of this depression leads to an initial heightening of physical and mental activities and to a greater psychomotor speed; during this initial period, organic tremors may be decreased. With increasing depression, however, there soon appear generalized muscular weakness, impairment of intellectual functions, and, because the cerebellar system is attacked early, ataxia, reeling gait, and coarse inco-ordination of the upper extremities. The marked loss of inhibition typically gives rise to many medico-legal problems. Walking a chalk line, repeating certain paradigmata, and chemical analysis of the breath, urine, and blood have all been used to determine the degree of intoxication, but none of these is completely valid because of the adaptation of the central nervous system to alcohol. Tolerance to alcohol varies greatly; the epileptic, the hysteric, many schizophrenics, and some psychopaths have a low tolerance, as do patients following a head injury.

Pathologic intoxication (291.6) or mania à potu: This occurs predominantly in people with a low tolerance to alcohol. Usually the syndrome lasts several hours, although it may continue for a whole day. It is characterized by extreme excitement ('alcoholic fury') with aggressive, dangerous, and even homicidal reactions. Persecutory ideas are common. The condition terminates with the patient falling into a deep sleep; there is usually complete amnesia for the episode.

intoxication, hypnagogic (hip-nà-gōj'ik) *Obs.* A rare condition in which a rough or stormy waking generates a dream and induces motility before the dream disappears; 'in rare cases something clumsy is then performed, indeed, under the influence of terrifying ideas an attack or murder may be perpetrated.' (Bleuler, E. *Textbook of Psychiatry*, tr. by Brill, A.A., Macmillan, New York, 1930) 'Hypnopompic intoxication' would be the more correct term for this condition.

intoxication, pathological See *intoxication, alcoholic.*

intracranial tumor See *tumor, intracranial.*

intralaminar system See *system, intralaminar.*

intrapsychic, intrapsychical (in-trȧ-sī'kik, -sī'ki-kal) Situated, originating, or taking place within the psyche.

intrauterine Within the uterus or womb; the intrauterine 'theme' occurs in many dreams, and schizophrenic patients may express directly a desire to return to the womb, often as part of a more elaborate rebirth phantasy.

intrinsic factor See *sclerosis, posterolateral.*

introitus (in-trō'i-tus) The entrance into a canal or hollow organ, most often the vagina.

introject (in-trō-jekt') To withdraw psychic energy (libido) from an object and direct it upon the mental image of the object; to incorporate.

introjection (in-trō-jek'shun) The act of introjecting or state of being introjected. When one incorporates into his ego system the picture of an object as he conceives the object to be, the process is known as introjection. Libidinal and aggressive cathexis are then transferred from the object in the environment to the mental picture of the object. For example, when a person becomes depressed due to the loss of a loved one, his feelings are directed to the mental image he possesses of the loved one. He acts toward the image as if it were the loved one in reality.

The term introjection is sometimes used as if it were identical with *secondary identification* and perhaps also with

secondary narcissism. 'The replacement of object-cathexis by identification brings about a profound change in the libidinal situation. The image thus incorporated into the (super-) ego serves itself as an object to the libidinal impulses proceeding from the id, so that more of them are directed towards the ego as a whole than previously; this constitutes what Freud terms "secondary narcissism."' (Jones, E. *Papers on Psycho-Analysis* 4th ed., Wood, Baltimore, 1938) See *identification; incorporation.*

From the point of view of analytical psychology, introjection is 'psychologically ... a process of assimilation, while projection is a process of dissimilation. Introjection signifies an adjustment of the object to the subject, while projection involves a discrimination of the object from the subject, by means of a subjective content transveyed into the object.' (Jung, C.G. *Psychological Types*, tr. by Baynes, H.G., Harcourt, Brace, New York and London, 1923)

'A *passive* and an *active* introjection may be discriminated: to the former belong the transference-processes in the treatment of the neuroses and, in general, all cases in which the object exercises an unconditional attraction upon the subject; while "*feeling-into,*" regarded as a process of adaptation, should belong to the latter form.' (ibid.)

intropunitive (-pū'ni-tiv) Having the quality of turning anger against the self, as in the self-pejorative, demeaning, and belittling trend of the depressed patient. This is in contrast to extra-punitive, which refers to externally directed anger.

introversion (-ver'shun) Turning of the instincts inwardly upon oneself. 'The libido in introversion is directed toward the inner world, the world of representation, instead of the world of reality. With object-love there is a desire for motor discharge, a going out toward the object, but with introversion there is no desire for motor expression: satisfaction is found in imagined response, in dwelling on phantasied activities in connection with images and ideas of external objects.' (Healy, W., Bronner, A.F., and Bowers, A.M. *The Structure and Meaning of Psychoanalysis*, Knopf, New York, 1930)

Introversion is often used synonymously with *phantasy-cathexis.* Both imply a loss of contact with reality and because of it, they differ from *narcissism,* which does not imply such loss.

Freud's definition of introversion differs from Jung's. Freud says that introversion does not mean that erotic relation with reality has been severed but that the subject 'has ceased to direct his motor activities to the attainment of his aims in connection with real objects.' (Freud, S. *Collected Papers,* vol. 4, tr. by Riviere, J., Leonard and Virginia Woolf and The Institute of Psychoanalysis, London, 1924 -25) 'Introversion means a turning inwards of the libido, whereby a negative relation of subject to object is expressed. Interest does not move towards the object, but recedes towards the subject. Everyone whose attitude is introverted thinks, feels, and acts in a way that clearly demonstrates that the subject is the chief factor of motivation while the object at most receives only a secondary value.' (Jung, C.G. *Psychological Types,* tr. by Baynes, H.G., Harcourt, Brace, New York and London, 1923)

introversion, active 'Introversion is *active,* when the subject *wills* a certain seclusion in face of the object; it is *passive* when the subject is unable to restore again to the object the libido which is streaming back from it.' (Jung, C.G. *Psychological Types,* tr. by Baynes, H.G., Harcourt, Brace, New York and London, 1923, p. 567)

introversion, passive See *introversion, active.*

introvert (in'trō-vĕrt) One whose psychic energy (libido) is turned inwardly upon himself.

intuition (in-tū-ish'un) A literary and psychological term with no exact scientific definition or connotation. It refers to a special method of perceiving and evaluating objective reality. Intuition differs from foresight and conscious perception and judgment in that it relies heavily on unconscious memory traces of past and forgotten experiences and judgments. In this way, a storehouse of unconscious wisdom which had been accumulated (in unconscious memory) in the past is used in the present.

Intuition is characterized by accurate 'predictability' in the engineering and mathematical sense. It is also character-

ized by the fact that people will feel and say 'I don't know just how I know that, but I know it's correct,' and it often is. The wisdom of the sum total of all past experiences, which have registered in some way or another in the individual, albeit these past experiences may be unremembered, is the generally accepted concept of what is meant by intuition.

E.F. Sharpe (*Collected Papers on Psycho-analysis,* Hogarth Press, Ltd., and The Institute of Psychoanalysis, London, 1950) states: '. . . the scientist who understands without having to learn to understand is working with and not against intuitive powers in the same way as the artist. He projects intuition which, when it works in reality to the discovery of real facts, must be initially based upon his own real bodily and psychical experiences.'

intuition, intellectual See *intellect.*

invalid, nervous An unscientific term used by the laity to designate a person who is mentally upset or emotionally disturbed, yet in ordinary parlance is not regarded as a 'mental' case.

invalidism (in'vȧ-lid-iz'm) Condition of being a chronic invalid. From the standpoint of the social worker: 'the habit of preoccupation with one's health not justified by one's actual condition.' (Hamilton, G. *A Medical Social Terminology,* Presbyterian Hospital, New York, 1930).

invalidism, psychological (sī-kō-loj'i-kal) The mental state of a patient who, though he has been cured of his physical illness, refuses to accept this fact. He repudiates the idea of getting well and gives a thousand reasons why he should continue to live as he was compelled to live during the height of his physical illness.

Through this unrealistic attitude toward a physical illness, the patient 'accepts all the restrictions placed upon him; so much so that as he starts to recover, he resists any attempt to remove them.' Such an attitude is observed particularly among children. 'The child will not hear any encouragement to the effect that he is better and can do more now. Instead of recovering, he becomes a chronic invalid. When the situation is studied, it is found that he has learned that there are many benefits from being an invalid—extra attention, marked concern by his parents, extra food and toys, and frequent excuse from duties.' The mechanism is largely an unconscious one, however; most children who suffer from chronic invalidism are not aware that they are using their disability as a means of gaining benefits. (Pearson, G.H.J. *Emotional Disorders of Children,* Norton, New York, 1940)

inversion (in-vĕr'shun, -ver'zhun) See *inversion, sexual.*

inversion, absolute Freud speaks of those who are 'absolutely inverted; i.e., their sexual object must always be of the same sex, while the opposite sex can never be to them an object of sexual longing, but leaves them indifferent or . . . may even evoke sexual repugnance.' (Freud, S. *The Basic Writings of Sigmund Freud,* tr. by Brill, A.A., Random House, New York, 1938)

inversion, amphigenous (am-fij'e-nus) Psychosexual hermaphroditism; i.e. the sexual object may belong indifferently to either the same or to the other sex.

inversion, occasional Accidental homosexuality, or homosexuality faute de mieux. See *homosexualty, male.*

inversion, sexo-esthetic (sek-sō-es-thet'ik) Eonism; *transvestitism* (q.v.).

inversion, sexual Homosexuality. Freud distinguished three types of sexual inversion: *absolute, amphigenous* and *occasional* (qq.v.).

inversion, sleep Somnolence by day and insomnia at night; seen most commonly in organic brain disorders and in the schizophrenias.

invert (in'vĕrt) A person who is a homosexual.

invest To cathect; see *cathexis.*

investment The affective charge given to an idea or object. See *cathexis.*

involution See *hereditary.*

involutional period *Climacterium* (q.v.).

involutional psychotic reaction See *psychosis, involutional.*

iophobia (ī-ō-fō'bē-à) Fear of poison.

ipsation (ip-sā'shun) An infrequent term for *autoerotism* (q.v.).

I.Q. Abbreviation of intelligence quotient. See *quotient, intelligence.*

iridoplegia (ir-i-dō-plē'gē-à) Paralysis of the iris muscle; failure of the pupil to react to light. The Argyll Robertson pupil is a special form of reflex iridoplegia. Reflex iridoplegia may be caused by optic nerve lesions, optic tract lesions, lesions in the upper part of the midbrain, and lesions in the motor path (oculomotor nerve). The condition is occasionally seen in alcoholic polyneuritis and in diabetes.

I.R.M. Inherited releasing mechanism. See *instinct.*

irradiation (i-rā-dē-ā'shun) Illumination; more specifically, in medicine, exposure to rays (heat, light, X-rays, etc.) for diagnostic or therapeutic purposes. In neurophysiology, a spreading of the neural impulse within the central nervous system and, by analogy in psychodynamics, the spread of energy or tension outside the system in which the tension was originally generated. In conditional stimulus experiments (see *conditioning*) irradiation refers to elicitation of the conditional response by a stimulus other than the one to which conditioning has been established; ordinarily, such irradiation occurs only when the other stimulus is of the same general class as the original condition stimulus.

irradiation, ultrasonic (ul-tra-so'nik) Ultrasonic irradiation of the prefrontal areas of the brain has been used as a substitute for lobotomy; it is said to cause less variable and less severe cerebral damage than the surgical procedure, to entail minimal risk, and to give comparable results. Irradiation is applied through bilateral trephine openings, using a frequency of 1000 kc. per second and an average intensity of 7 watts per sq. cm. for 4 to 14 minutes.

irrational (ir-rash'un-al) Though commonly this term means unreasonable, Jung says: 'As I make use of this term it does not denote something contrary to *reason,* but something outside the province of reason, whose essence, therefore, is not established by reason.' 'Elementary facts belong to this category, e.g., that the earth has a moon, that chlorine is an element, that the greatest density of water is found at 4.0 centigrade. ... Both thinking and feeling as *directed functions* are rational,' while sensation and intuition are irrational. (Jung, C.G. *Psychological Types*, tr. by Baynes, H.G., Harcourt, Brace, New York and London, 1923) See *rational.*

irregular Social workers' expression 'covering unlegalized unions, unconventional love affairs, and adultery.' (Hamilton, G. *A Medical Social Terminology*, Presbyterian Hospital, New York, 1930)

irreminiscence Amnesia; inability to remember; more specifically, a type of agnosia with inability to form a mental picture of objects.

irresistibility (ir-re-sist-i-bil'i-tē) See *responsibility, criminal.*

irresponsibility See *responsibility, criminal.*

irritability, acoustic (ir-i-tà-bil'i-tē, à-kōōs'tik) Auditory hypersensitivity. A generalized, diffuse irritability is one of the common characteristics of the traumatic neurosis. 'From the point of view of distribution, irritability is present in every case of traumatic neurosis. It chiefly concerns auditory stimuli, but in some instances there may be abnormal sensitivity to temperature, pain, or sudden tactile stimuli. From the physiologic point of view there exists a lowering of the threshold of stimulation; from the psychologic point of view—a state of readiness for fright reactions. This is intimately connected with the general hypertensity of these cases. Auditory hypersensitivity is the most common symptom, being occasioned by the most widely distributed sudden stimulus, perceived by the oldest sense organ which establishes contact with its environment, and the most intimately connected with fright.' (Kardiner, A., and Spiegel, L. *War Stress and Neurotic Illness*, Hoeber, New York, 1947)

irrumation (i-rōō-mā'shun) Fellatio.

I.S. *Index of sexuality* (q.v.).

Isakower phenomenon See *hallucination, blank.*

ischnophonia (isk-nō-fō'ne-à) Stammering; *stuttering* (q.v.).

ischophonia (is-kō-fō'nē-à) Stammering.

iscortex (ī-sō-kor'teks) The most commonly found type of cortex of the cerebral hemispheres, composed of 6 layers of cells which have their embryologic origin in the mass of gray matter surrounding the ventricles—the outermost molecular layer, external granular layer, external pyramidal layer, internal granular layer, ganglionic layer, and the innermost fusiform layer. The isocortex is also known as the neocortex.

isogamous (ī-sog'à-mus) *Genet.* Pertaining to or characterized by gametes which are equal in size and similar in structure in both sexes (see *syngamy*).

isolate (ī'sō-lāt, is'ō-) A term suggested to describe, in the therapy group, any one who does not participate in group activities or make contact with other members of the group. See *instigator; neutralizer.*

isolate (is'ō-, ī'sō-lāt) From the psychoanalytic point of view, 'to separate experiences or memories from their affect.'

isolation (is-ō-, ī-sō-lā'shun) In psychoanalysis, the separation of an idea or memory from its affective cathexis or charge, 'so that what remains in consciousness is nothing but an ideational content which is perfectly colorless and is judged to be unimportant.' (Freud, S. *Inhibitions, Symptoms and Anxiety*, tr. by Strachey, A., Leonard and Virginia Woolf and The Institute of Psychoanalysis, London, 1936.) For example, a patient remembered the many occasions on which he made ineffectual attempts to murder his father. The recollections were entirely without affect.

Isolation may also be observed in the motor sphere. There is a pause 'in which nothing is to happen, no perception is made, no action carried out.' (Freud, S. *Inhibitions, Symptoms and Anxiety*, tr. by Strachey, A., Leonard and Virginia Woolf and The Institute of Psychoanalysis, London, 1936)

Freud distinguishes between *isolation* and *undoing*. Isolation implies a kind of foresight that tries to check the appearance of something unpleasant; it is a rational process, according, to Freud, whereas *undoing* is 'irrational or magical in nature.'

As a therapeutic regimen *isolation* has been practiced for centuries. P. Janet writes: 'The chief difficulties in life arise in connection with social relationships, and it has long been felt that social activities are more exhausting than any other kind. On this recognition has been based a method of treatment which is often associated with the rest cure of nervous diseases, namely, treatment by isolation.' (Janet, P. *Psychological Healing*, vols. 1 - 2, tr. by Paul, E. and C., Macmillan, New York, 1925)

In 1895 Déjérine inaugurated a particularly strict plan of isolation. He kept his patients continuously in a bed completely surrounded by white curtains.

In sociology isolation is the separation of the person or group from social contacts.

'Isolation means a limitation of the opportunity for stimulus and response.' (Young, K. *An Introductory Sociology*, American Book Company, New York, 1934)

isolation, action in With this expression P. Janet designates independent initiative. He spoke of one of his patients, Lydia, who tried to conceal her distress when she was separated from her sister. 'Now the art of living alone, of taking the initiative in isolation, is an art of a very special kind, one which stands at a high level, one which has developed slowly, and which has played an important psychological part by becoming the starting-point of ideas of unity and freedom.' (Janet, P. *Psychological Healing*, vols. 1 - 2, tr. by Paul, E. and C., Macmillan, New York, 1925)

isolation, perceptual (per-sep'chu-al) See *deprivation, sensory.*

isolation, psychic (sī'kik) Carl Jung's term for the sense of estrangement from one's fellows which is immediately felt upon experiencing material communicat-

ed from one's collective unconscious. Under certain conditions material from this area of the psyche irrupts into consciousness. 'Such irruptions are uncanny, because they are irrational and inexplicable to the individual concerned. They signify a momentous alteration of the personality in that they immediately constitute a painful, personal secret that estranges the human being from his environment and isolates him from it. It is something that "you can tell to no one," except under fear of being accused of mental abnormality, and with some justification, for something quite similar befalls the insane. It is still a long way from an intuitively sensed irruption to pathological overthrow; but a layman does not know this.

'The result of the *psychic isolation* through a secret is, as a rule, the vivifying of the psychic atmosphere as a surrogate for the lost contact with the individual's fellow beings.' (Jung, C.G. *The Integration of the Personality*, Farrar and Rinehart, New York, 1939) Emphasizing and explaining the comparative rarity of such revelations of the unconscious, Jung writes: 'The resistance of consciousness to the unconscious, as well as the underestimation of the latter, is a historic necessity of human psychic development, for otherwise consciousness could never have differentiated itself from the unconscious at all points. The consciousness of modern man, however, has withdrawn somewhat too far from the reality of the unconscious. We have forgotten that the psyche does not correspond to our conscious intention, but is for the most part autonomous and unconscious. For this reason, the approach of the unconscious arouses a panic fear in civilized man, not least of all because of the threatening analogy to insanity. There is nothing questionable to the intellect in describing the unconscious as a passive object; on the contrary, such an activity would correspond to rational expectations. But to let the unconscious happen and to experience it as a reality—this exceeds the courage as well as the powers of the average Occidental. He prefers simply not to understand this problem. It is also better so for the weak in spirit, since this thing is not without its danger. The experiencing of the unconscious is a personal secret communicable only to the very few, and that with difficulty. *It isolates the individual to whom it happens*. But isolation effects a compensatory animation of the psychic atmosphere, and this is uncanny.' (ibid.)

isolation, psychological (sī-kō-loj'i-kal) Disinclination, aversion to, or fear of making contact with another member of the group.

isolation, sensory (sen'sor-ē) See *deprivation, sensory.*

isophilic (ī-sō-fil'ik) H.S. Sullivan's term for affection or liking for others of the same sex, such affection lacking the genital element characteristic of homosexual-ity. Isophilic is approximately synonymous with homoerotic.

isozyme A genetically determined variant of a normally occurring enzyme. Isozymes catalyze similar processes as their normal counterparts, but because they differ slightly in protein linkage they differ also in optimal conditions for function.

it The same as *id.*

itching See *craving, autonomic-affective.*

ITPA *Illinois Test of Psycholinguistic Abilities* (q.v.).

J

Jack the Clipper The designation given to any person with a morbid propensity to clip hair or braids of girls; the name was first used in reference to a man in Chicago who for several years carried on the practice.

Jack the Ripper A London physician, an epileptic, who over a period of years committed brutal murders, presumably while in a post-ictal fugue state.

Jackson, John Hughlings (1834-1911) British neurologist.

Jacksonian epilepsy See *epilepsy, Jacksonian.*

Jackson's syndrome A bulbar syndrome due to involvement of the vagus, spinal accessory, and hypoglossal nerves. Symptoms are: homolateral paralysis of the soft palate, pharynx, and larynx; homolateral paralysis of the sternocleidomastoid and trapezius muscles; and homolateral paralysis and atrophy of the tongue.

jactatio capitis nocturna (yak-tä'tē-ō ka'-pi-tis nôk-toor-na) (L. 'nocturnal head-tossing or head-shaking') A disturbance of sleep sometimes observed in children: it consists in rhythmical rolling of the head from side to side—which hinders normal sleep. See *head-rolling.*

jactation (jak-tā'shun) See *jactitation.*

jactitation (jak-ti-tā'shun) Extreme restlessness or tossing about.

Jakob-Creutzfeldt's disease (290.0; 309.6) Presenile dementia with dysarthria and a syndrome of amyotrophic lateral sclerosis. Also known as Heidenheim's or Kraepelin's disease. See *degeneration, cortico-striato-spinal.*

jamais (zha-mā') A paramnestic phenomenon consisting of the erroneous feeling or conviction that one has "never experienced or seen anything like that before." Such a *denial* (q.v.) produces a fragmentation or break in continuity of memory.

James, William (1842-1910) American philosopher and psychologist.

James-Lange theory See *theory, James-Lange.*

Janet's disease (Pierre Janet, French psychiatrist, 1859-1947) Psychasthenia.

jargon, organ (jär'gon) Adler applies this term to the 'somatic language' (symptoms) which the neurotic uses to express a masculine protest. According to Adler, the child's ego-consciousness is in conflict with the facts of his environment. Thus, he wishes to be big and powerful but actually he is small and weak. The child therefore constructs all its aggressive attitudes into one of masculine protest against all symptoms of weakness (femininity) such as tenderness, subordinacy, and, most important, manifestations of organ inferiority. The neurotically predisposed child, however, endeavors further to gain an effective weapon by associating with his organ inferiority such character-traits as originate in his ego-consciousness—i.e. obstinacy, need of affection, exaggerated cleanliness, pedantry, covetousness, ambition, etc. Thus, in order to gain attention and affection a psychogenic epileptic managed so that most of his 'attacks' were preceded by obstipation, thereby worrying his family—all this to offset his degradation. In this way the masculine protest makes use of a 'somatic language' or organ-jargon to gain expression. As one of Adler's patients expressed it in a dream, 'my disease has its origin in my feeling of inferiority.' (Adler, A. *The Neurotic Constitution,* tr. by Glueck, B. and Lind, E., Moffat, Yard, New York, 1917)

Jarisch-Herxheimer reaction (ya'rish herks'hī-mer) (Adolf Jarisch, Austrian dermatologist, 1850-1902; Karl Herxheimer, German dermatologist, b. 1861) An inflammatory reaction in syphilis, involving skin, mucosae, viscera, and/or nervous system, often precipitated by antisyphilitic treatment and possibly due to an allergic reaction to liberated toxic products. Such reactions are much less common with penicillin than with older anti-spirochetal agents and rarely consist of more than transient fever during the first 24 hours of treatment. Some workers advise a course of bismuth and iodide before instituting penicillin treatment in an attempt to minimize such reactions.

Jaspers, Karl (1883-1969) German philosopher and psychiatrist; existentialism.

jaw-jerk A deep reflex. The patient opens his mouth so that the lower jaw hangs a little; the examiner places his finger on the side of the lower jaw, and strikes it with a percussion hammer; this results in contraction of the masseter muscle and raising of the jaw.

jealousy According to Freud, normal jealousy is compounded of (1) grief, which is the pain caused by the thought of losing the loved object; this being associated with (2) narcissistic injury, i.e. a loss of self-esteem; (3) feelings of enmity against the successful rival; and, finally (4), self-criticism which blames the person himself for his loss. This reaction is not completely rational, for it is disproportionate to the real circumstances, not completely under the control of the conscious ego, and not derived from the actual situation. Rather it is rooted in the Oedipus complex. Frequently jealousy is experienced also bisexually: for example, a man will feel both 'the suffering in regard to the loved woman and the hatred against the male rival,' and 'grief in regard to the unconsciously loved man and hatred of the woman as a rival.' (Freud, S. *Certain Neurotic Mechanisms in Jealousy. Paranoia and Homosexuality* in *Collected Papers*, vol. 22, Hogarth Press, London, 1924)

jealousy, projected The type of jealousy that is derived from the person's own actual unfaithfulness or from repressed impulses toward it. In this type of jealousy, the person who is being tempted in the direction of infidelity alleviates his guilt by projecting his own impulses onto the partner to whom he owes fidelity. Now, social conventions permit a certain amount of latitude to the married woman's desire to attract, and the married man's desire to possess, members of the opposite sex. Through these social flirtations the person exercises his tendency to unfaithfulness and the desire now awak-

ened is gratified by a turning back to the marital partner. The jealous person, however, does not recognize these conventions of tolerance: having projected onto his partner his own impulses toward infidelity, he will interpret as actual infidelity this behavior that covers such unconscious impulses in his partner. (Freud, S. *Certain Neurotic Mechanisms in Jealousy. Paranoia and Homosexuality* in *Collected Papers*, vol. 2, Hogarth Press, London, 1924)

Jelliffe, Smith Ely (b. 1866) American psychiatrist and neurologist; psychodynamics, psychotherapy, psychosomatic medicine.

Jendrassik reinforcement (yen′drȧ-sēk) (Ernest Jendrassik, 1858-1922, Slovakian physician) A weak response of the knee-jerk may often be reinforced, that is, strengthened, by having the patient grasp his own hands and pull vigorously on them.

jerk, elbow See *reflex, triceps.*

jerk, knee Patellar reflex; the leg is flexed at the knee joint and the quadriceps tendon is tapped just below the patella; this results in extension of the leg with visible and palpable contraction of the quadriceps muscle. The femoral nerve contains both the afferent and the efferent pathways for the patellar reflex, whose spinal center is at L_{2-4}

jerk, patellar Knee-jerk.

jerk, pendular knee When tapping the patellar tendon, several oscillations of the leg occur before it comes to a stop; observed in disease of the cerebellum.

joint, Charcot See *arthropathy.*

Joint Commission on Mental Illness and Health Authorized by the U.S. Congress' Mental Health Study Act of 1955; a multidisciplinary study group that included 36 national agencies in the mental health and welfare fields; its final report, *Action for Mental Health,* was instrumental in the legislation and federal funding that made possible the development of community mental health centers for the mentally ill and mentally retarded. See *psychiatry, community.*

Jones, Ernest (1879 - 1958) British psychoanalyst; one of the original group who gathered around Freud in the early days of psychoanalysis; first to introduce psychoanalysis into English-speaking world (England, 1906); one of the founders of American Psychoanalytic Association (1911) and British Psychoanalytic Society (1913); honorary life-president of International Psychoanalytic Association; 3-volume biography of Freud.

judgment Of the many definitions of judgment, the one most commonly used in psychiatry has to do with the ability to recognize the true relations of ideas. This involves what is called *critical judgment.* 'But if we speak in psychiatry and jurisprudence of the capacity to judge, we mean the ability to form judgments, that is, the capacity to draw correct conclusions from the material acquired by experience.' (Bleuler, E. *Textbook of Psychiatry,* tr. by Brill, A.A., Macmillan, New York, 1930)

Some authorities distinguish between *critical* and *automatic* judgment, meaning by the latter the performance of action as a reflex. When a patient with good vision walks directly into a wall, instead of stopping or turning, it is said that his automatic judgment is impaired.

jumps See *epilepsy, myoclonic.*

junctim (junk'tim) 'Purposive connection of two thoughts and affect-complexes that have in reality little or nothing to do with one another, in order to strengthen the affect. For example, a patient with agoraphobia, in order, by a complicated mechanism, to raise his prestige at home and force his environment into his service and to prevent himself likewise from losing, while on the street or in open places, the "resonance" so fervently desired, unites unconsciously and emotionally into a

"junktim," the thought of being alone, of strange people, of purchases, search for the theatre, society, etc., and the phantasy of an apoplectic stroke, a confinement on the street, disease infection through germs on the street.' (Adler, A. *The Practice and Theory of Individual Psychology,* tr. by Radin, P., Kegan Paul, Trench, Trubner, London, 1924)

Jung, association test See *association.*

Jung, Carl Gustav (1875 - 1961) (yoong) Swiss psychiatrist; originally associated with Freud, later founded own school of *analytic psychology* (q.v.).

jus primae noctis (ūs' prē'mē nôk'tēs) (L. 'right to the first night') The 'right to the first night' or 'right of the lord' *(droit du seigneur)* is usually described as 'a lascivious tribute levied by feudal lords upon their vassals, in accordance with which the lord enjoyed the first embrace of the vassal's bride.' (From Putnam's translation of Paolo Mantegazza's *Gli amori degli uomini.*) It was also called *virginal tribute.* Among certain primitive tribes the 'right to the first night' belonged to the father of the bride and was supposedly symbolical of his authority.

juvenile (joo'vē-nīl) The juvenile period extends from the beginning of the phase of puberty to the end of the stage of adolescence; that is, juvenilism includes the phases of puberty and adolescence.

juvenile general paresis See *paresis, juvenile.*

juvenile tabes See *tabes, juvenile.*

juvenilism (joo'vē-ni-liz'm) A constitutional condition characterized by a persistently youthful appearance of the body in a mature individual exhibiting all the signs of having passed the puberal crisis.

K

Kahlbaum, Karl Ludwig (1828-99) (käl'-boum) German psychiatrist; catatonia.

Kahlbaum-Wernicke syndrome *Presbyophrenia* (q.v.)

kainophobia (kī-nō-fō'bē-à) See *neophobia; kainotophobia.*

kainotophobia (kī-no-tō-fō'bē-à) Fear of change or novelty.

kakergasia (kak-ēr-gas'ē-à) See *merergasia.*

kakidrosis (kak-i-drō'sis) Perspiration with disagreeable odor. 'Perspiration is diminished and sometimes transformed in character, so as to give a peculiar and often extremely disagreeable odor (kakidrosis).' (Church, A. and Peterson, F. *Nervous and Mental Diseases,* 8th ed., Saunders, Philadelphia and London, 1916)

kakorrhaphiophobia (kà-kō-raf-ē-ō-fō'-bē-à) Fear of failure.

Kalinowsky, Lothar B. (1899-   ) German-born neuropsychiatrist; in U.S. since 1940; electroconvulsive and other somatic treatments.

Kallmann, Franz J. (1897-1965) German-born psychoanalyst and geneticist; genetics of human behavior, especially schizophrenia, manic-depressive psychosis.

Kandinsky-Clérambault Complex See *complex, Clérambault-Kandinsky.*

karyotype (ka're-ō-tīp) The chromosomal arrangement of tissue cells. See *chromosome.*

katalepsia (kat-à-lep'sē-à) *Obs.* Same as *catalepsy.*

katasexual (ka-ta-seks'ū-al) Necrophiliac.

katatonia See *catatonia.*

kathisophobia (kà-this-ō-fō'-bē-à) Fear of sitting down.

Kayser-Fleischer ring (Berhard Kayser, German ophthalmologist, b. 1869, and Richard Fleischer, Munich physician, 1848-1909) See *degeneration, hepatolenticular.*

Keeler polygraph See *detector, lie.*

Kempf's disease See *homosexual panic.*

kenophobia (ken-ō-fō'bē-à) Also spelled *cenophobia;* fear of barren or empty space, of voids.

keraunoneurosis (kē-raw-nō-nū-rō'sis) This term introduced by H. Oppenheim, refers to traumatic neuroses associated with electric shocks.

keraunophobia Fear of lightning. It is related to the fear of strong and superior forces and as such it appears to stem from the fear of the father, arising during the stage of phallic primacy. It is, therefore, closely allied with the fear of castration.

kernal complex Oedipus complex. See *complex, Oedipus.*

kernicterus, kernikterus (kēr-nik'ter-us) See *icterus gravis neonatorum.*

key-concept Arnold Gesell and his co-workers at the Yale Clinic òf Child Development have formulated the idea that in all psychological studies of the preschool child the interpretation of individual differences should be governed by one key-concept: that a child's abilities are all relative to one inclusive ability, his ability to grow. 'Growth, therefore, becomes a *key-concept* for the interpretation of individual differences. There are laws of sequence and of maturation, which account for the general similarities and basic trends of child development. But no two children grow up in exactly the same way.' (Gesell, A., *et al. The First Five Years of Life,* Harper, New York, 1940)

The tempo and style of growth is different in every child and is characteristic of its individuality. Gesell holds that 'mental growth is a patterning process: a progressive morphogenesis of patterns of behavior,' and that 'envisagement of the mind as a growing system puts us in a better position to observe and comprehend the determinants of the child's behavior.'

kibbutz (ki'boots) A form of collective education and upbringing of children, in use in Israel, in which the rearing of the child by his parents is replaced by upbringing in communal houses under the direction of specially trained 'metapelets' or mother substitutes.

kinephantom (kin'e-fan-tum) An illusory phenomenon: the movement of an object that actually occurs is perceived as being different from what the movement really is. An example is perceiving the wheels of an automobile as moving in a counterclockwise direction when they are, in fact, moving in a clockwise direction.

kinesalgia (kin-es-al'je-a) Pain induced by movement. A common phenomenon when organic lesions are present. Very vivid pain of psychical origin (psychalgia) may also be experienced in the absence of organic pathology, usually as a conversion symptom.

kinesics The study of movement and action, particularly as a part of communication; see *method, linguistic-kinesic.*

kinesis (ki-ne'sis) Generic term for motion.

kinesitherapy (ki-nes-i-ther'a-pe) See *therapy, physical.*

kinesophobia (ki-ne-so-fo'be-a) Fear of motion.

kinesthesia (kin-es-the'ze-a) Perception of one's own movement; proprioception. The receptors for kinesthesia are located in the muscles, tendons, and joints. The cell bodies of these peripheral sensory neurons are in the spinal root ganglia. The central processes pass via the dorsal roots into the spinal cord and brain stem and, uncrossed in the posterior columns of the spinal cord, ascend to the gracilis and cuneate nuclei. Here they make synaptic connections with their second-order neurons, which cross and enter the medial lemniscus of the opposite side, and thence pass to the thalamus. Synaptic connections are made here with third-order neurons which

ascend to the sensory projection center in the postcentral gyrus of the cortex (areas 3, 1, 2 of Brodmann).

kinetic (ki-net'ik) Relating to movement.

Kinsey, Alfred Charles (1894-1956) American biologist; director of Indiana University's Institute for Sex Research; *Sexual Behavior in the Human Male* (1948), *Sexual Behavior in the Human Female* (1953).

kinship *Genet.* The blood-relationship among individuals belonging to the same stock by common descent. See *consanquinity.*

Kirchhoff, Theodor (1853-1922) (kirK'-hof) German psychiatrist; historian of psychiatry.

Kirkbride, Thomas Story (1809-83) American psychiatrist; one of the 13 founders of the Association of Medical Superintendents of America (the forerunner of the American Psychiatric Association); mental hospital construction.

klazomania (kla-zo-ma'ne-a) Compulsory shouting; usually a motor discharge phenomenon based on mesencephalic or other central nervous system irritation.

Klebedenken (kla'be-den-ken) Adhesive, sticky, perservative thinking. Klebedenken is one of the associational disturbances seen in the schizophrenias.

Klebenleiben (kla'ben-bli-ben) A type of language disturbance occurring in schizophrenic patients in which the speaker remains glued to the same topic; he restates the topic in different words, elaborates it, qualifies it, explains it, but cannot leave it.

Klein, Melanie (1882-1960) Psychoanalyst (British Psychoanalytic Society-Institute); child analyst; a controversial figure whose theories of early psychic development (e.g. the ubiquity of 'internal objects,' the 'depressive' and 'paranoid positions,' and her direct clinical application of the death instinct) were at variance with orthodox psychoanalytic theory.

Kleine-Levin syndrome See *syndrome, Kleine-Levin.*

kleptolagnia (klep-tō-lag′nē-à) A morbid desire to steal. A psychiatric term devised by J. C. Kiernan to designate 'theft associated with sexual excitement'—on the analogy of 'algolagnia.' In 1896 La Cassague (and others later) had stressed that sex and kleptomania were often associated, but the prevailing view that 'cleptomania was a syndrome of irresistible and motiveless impulses to theft based on constitutional "degeneration"' persisted. 'In 1908, Stekel observed that irresistible and apparently motiveless thefts were substitutive forms of sexual gratification [consequent to sexual deprivation or repression]. Ellis's concept of kleptolagnia represented the theft as a means of generating fear and anxiety to "reinforce" the "feeble sexual impulse" in its drive for gratification. Lacking understanding of the psychodynamics which comes from clinical training and experience, Ellis could not appreciate that the states of anxiety which to him appeared to "overflow into the sexual sphere" are in actuality, as in the theft itself, a form of defense of the ego against sexual impulses which threaten to overwhelm it. Ellis separated his concept of kleptolagnia from essentially similar cases of other investigators and the fundamental conclusions of Stekel. But his observations were influential in ending the obscurantism regarding cleptomania. The understanding of pyromania, for which Ellis in a footnote proposed "pyrolagnia," following Kiernan, must also have been indirectly furthered by this study, although not comparably with observations by Stekel on the subject.' (Freedman, B. *Psychoanalytic Quarterly 11*, 416-17, 1942)

kleptomania (klep-tō-mā′nē-à) Morbid impulse to steal; pathological stealing. From the psychoanalytic standpoint it is believed that obsessive stealing stems from the period of infantile sexuality. The thief steals objects that possess libidinal value to him (or should we say 'her,' for stealing is regarded by Staub as essentially a female problem). It is held that stealing is rooted in penis-envy. When one steals from those in superior position, it is said that the theft traces back to original penis-envy and active castration of the superior (father).

Abraham and Alexander believe that the motive for stealing arises at the suckling stage, when the mother refuses to give the child the breast. Abraham further maintains that obsessive stealers are those who were emotionally starved during the infancy period; they become anti-social, because they were not loved. The narcissistic injury gives rise to revenge.

Adler says: 'Lies, thefts and other crimes committed by children are manifestly attempts to extend the limits of power in this way' [i.e. toward superiority]. (Adler, A. *The Neurotic Constitution*, tr. by Glueck, B. and Lind, J.E., Moffat, Yard, New York, 1917)

kleptophobia (klep-tō-fō′bē-à) Fear of stealing or becoming a thief.

Klinefelter's syndrome See *syndrome, Klinefelter's.*

Klippel-Feil syndrome See *syndrome, Klippel-Feil.*

klon See *clone.*

klopemania (klō-pē-mā′nē-à) *Obs.* Kleptomania.

Klumpke-Déjerine syndrome See *syndrome, Klumpke-Déjerine.*

Klüver-Bucy syndrome See *syndrome, Klüver-Bucy.*

knee, wobbly Laxness of the knee joint, indicative of lowered muscular tonus. The wobbly knee sign, elicited by shaking the knee, is seen in the cerebellar and pseudocerebellar syndromes and is probably indicative of disturbed proprioception.

knowledge-test See *responsibility, criminal.*

knowledge, unconscious See *unconscious.*

Köhler, Wolfgang (1887-1967) U.S. psychoanalyst, born in Estonia; author of the classic work *Gestalt Psychology* (1929).

Kohnstamm maneuver See *test, Kohnstamm.*

koinotropy (koi-not′rō-pē) The state of being identified with the common interests of others or the public (Adolf Meyer).

kolyphrenia (ko-li-frē'nē-à) Cortical inhibitability.

kolytic (hō-lit'ik) Inhibitory. J.R. Hunt has used this term in a way which is approximately equivalent to 'schizoid.'

kopophobia (kō-pō-fō'bē-à) Fear of fatigue.

Koro (kōr'ō) An acute delusional syndrome seen in Malaya and Southern China in which the patient suddenly comes to believe that his penis is shrinking into his abdomen. Elaborate measures are taken to prevent such an end result, such as tying a red string around the penis or clamping a wooden box around it.

Korsakov psychosis See *psychosis, Korsakov.*

Krabbe's disease (Korud H. Krabbe, contemporary Copenhagen neurologist) See *sclerosis, diffuse.*

Kraepelin, Emil (1856 - 1926) (krā'pe-lin) German psychiatrist; psychiatric nosology and systematization; attempted to sort out definite disease entities and differentiated between manic-depressive psychosis and dementia praecox (schizophrenia), and between endogenous and exogenous psychoses; prognostic approach, by correlating basic symptoms with course of illness.

Kraepelin's disease *Jakob-Creutzfeldt's disease* (q.v.).

Krafft-Ebing, Richard (1840 - 1903) (kräft-ā'bing) German sexologist.

Kretschmer, Ernst (1888 - 1964) (krech'-mēr) German psychiatrist; somatotyping and relationship of physique to character, personality, and mental illness.

Kronfeld, Arthur (b. 1886) (krōn'-felt) German psychiatrist; psychotherapy.

Kuf's disease See *amaurotic family idiocy.*

kuru (kōō'rōō) A neurologic disorder, reported in Australia and the South Pacific, consisting of progressive motor inco-ordination and mental changes, particularly in the affective sphere. The disease is often fatal within 6 to 9 months after onset. Major pathological changes include widespread neuronal atrophy, with shrinking and vacuolation of cells, most marked in the cerebellum and cerebellar pathways and in the thalamus, corpus striatum, globus pallidus, and the precentral gyrus of the cerebral cortex. Etiology is unknown; hereditary factors may be involved, or it may be the result of a slowly progressive microbial or viral infection (292.3, 309.0).

L

la belle indifference (la bel äN-dē-fā-räNs) See *hysteria*.

labile (lāb′il) Characterized by free and usually uncontrolled expression of the emotions. See *lability*.

lability (lā-bil′i-tē) Volatility; instability. Emotional lability refers to emotions that are inordinately mobile and hence not under adequate control; seen most commonly in the organic brain syndromes and in the early stages of the schizophrenias.

labyrinthine (lab-ē-rin′thēn) A type of schizophrenic speech based upon association defects. Labyrinthine speech wanders aimlessly, from one topic to another, without obvious connection between the various topics. Certain topics may be elaborated tangentially, others appear to be an outgrowth of circumstantiality; the overall effect on the listener is to produce a massive, vague, hazy maze of words, made all the more remarkable by the fact that typically the patient is able to return to the initial topic of conversation and appears to think that his incomprehensible ramifications have been appropriately related to that topic.

laceration, cerebral (la-ser-ā′shun, ser′e-bral) A cerebral contusion of sufficient severity to cause a visible breach in the continuity of the brain substance. This may occur either directly below the site of the blow to the head, or by contre-coup on the opposite side of the brain. See *contusion, brain*.

lachschlag-anfall (läK′shläK än′fȧl) (G. 'attack of short loss of consciousness due to laughter') A condition described by Herman Oppenheim (German neurologist, 1858-1919) in which the patient falls unconscious in violent laughing.

lacunae, superego Defects in the superego of delinquents and psychopathic personalities that are believed to originate from similar defects in the parents. Viewed in this way, some antisocial behavior would appear to be an acting out of unconscious wishes and impulses of the parents. (Johnson, A.M. and S.A. Szurek *Psychoanalytic Quarterly 21*, 323-343, 1952)

Laehr, Henrich (1820-1905) (lär′) German psychiatrist; bibliography.

lagneia furor (lȧg-nā′ȧ foo′rôr) Mason Good's expression for *erotomania* (q.v.).

lagnesis (lag-nē′sis) *Obs.* Erotomania.

lagneuomania (lag-nū-ō-mā′nē-ȧ) Sadism in the male.

-lagnia (-lag′nē-ȧ) Combining form meaning lust, from Gr. *lagneís*, act of coition, salaciousness, lust.

lagnosis (lag-nō′sis) Satyriasis.

lagophthalmos, lagophthalmus (lȧg-of-thal′mus) A condition in which the upper lid fails to move down when the patient attempts to close the eye. It is one of the signs of affection of the seventh, or facial nerve.

Laignel-Lavastine, Maxine (b. 1875) (lā-ñel′-lȧ-vȧ-stēn′) French psychiatrist.

-lalia (-lā-lē′ȧ) combining form meaning talk(ing) from Gr. *laliá*, talk(ing), chat, loquacity.

laliophobia (lā-lē-ō-fō′bē-ȧ) Fear of talking (and possibly stuttering).

lallation, lalling (la-lā′shun, lal′ing) Unintelligible speech, such as infantile babbling; often used more specifically to refer to substitution of *l* for more difficult consonants such as *r*.

lalo- (lal′ō-) Combining form meaning talk(ing), from Gr. *lálos*, talkative, babbling, loquacious.

laloneurosis (lal-ō-nū-rō′sis) Nervous speech-disorder.

laloneurosis, spasmodic (spaz-mod′ik) Stammering.

lalopathy (lȧ-lop′ȧ-thē) Any form of speech-disorder.

lalophobia (lal-ō-fō′bē-ȧ) Fear of speaking.

laloplegia (-plē'gē-à) Inability to speak because of paralysis of speech muscles other than the tongue muscles.

lalorrhea (-rē'à) See *tachylogia.*

lambitus (lam'bi-tus) Cunnilinction.

Landry's paralysis (Jean Baptiste Octave Landry, French physician, 1826 - 1865) Acute ascending paralysis; a disorder of unknown etiology (?infectious; ?toxic) consisting of flaccid paralysis beginning in the lower limbs and spreading upward to the bulbar and respiratory muscles. Males account for 80 per cent of cases, and most cases occur during the third decade of life. Between 50 per cent and 80 per cent die by the fifteenth day; in the remainder, recovery is usually complete within three months.

Lange, Carl Georg (1834 - 1900) (läng'ē) Danish pathologist.

Lange's colloidal gold reaction (Carl Lange, German physician, b. 1883) A diagnostic test whose theoretical basis is only incompletely understood; it depends upon the fact that cerebrospinal fluid in certain diseases is able to precipitate a preparation of colloidal gold. The test is performed using 10 test tubes, each with the same amount of gold solution but with progressively smaller concentrations of cerebrospinal fluid. The unchanged gold solution is cherry red in color; the changes caused by precipitation are expressed numerically, 0 signifying no change and the figures 1 to 5 denoting progressive degrees of alteration. Normal fluids cause no precipitation; the normal curve is thus reported as 0000000000. The 'paretic' curve (seen in general paralysis, meningovascular syphilis, tabes, and in about half of multiple sclerosis cases) is 5555321000. The 'luetic' or 'tabetic' curve (seen in tabes and meningovascular syphilis) is 1233210000. The 'meningitic' curve (seen usually in meningitis) is 0012344310.

language, artificial Bleuler speaks of the artificial language of schizophrenic individuals, meaning neologistic language.

language, gestural-postural A method or form of communication between persons by means of gestures and/or postures without resorting to the use of words. Communication of this kind is better known by the more inclusive expression 'communication by means of non-verbal language,' and gestural-postural language is but one form of this. See *language, non-verbal.*

language, hypochondriac (hī-pō-kon'dri-ak) See *speech, organ.*

language, irrelevant Words, phrases, utterances that have meaning only for the speaker and for *no other person.* In listening to schizophrenic patients, the psychiatrist commonly encounters instances of irrelevant language. In the course of an otherwise wholly intelligible utterance, the patient has said a word, phrase, or even a sentence which conveys or communicates nothing to the psychiatrist. The patient has a clear understanding of what his utterance means to *himself,* for it is his own creation—he has made it up. According to Kanner, instances of irrelevant language occur in 'the language of schizophrenia and early infantile autism.' He points out that the irrelevant utterances, 'though peculiar and out of place in ordinary conversation, were far from meaningless. Some words or phrases were metaphoric substitutions.' Kanner cites the following example where an irrelevant utterance of an autistic child was traced to an earlier source: 'Jay S., not quite four years old, referred to himself as "Blum," whenever his veracity was questioned by his parents. This was explained when Jay, who could read fluently, once pointed to the advertisement of a furniture firm which said in large letters: "Blum tells the truth." Since Jay had told the truth, he *was* Blum.' (Kanner, L. *Child Psychiatry,* Thomas, Springfield, Ill., 1948)

language, metaphoric (met-à-for'ik) The term metaphoric language is used in psychiatry in a sense rather different from the one it has in rhetoric and, for that matter, in ordinary speech. *Metaphor* means the use of a word (or phrase) literally denoting one kind of object (or idea), instead of another word (or phrase) through suggested likeness (e.g. a *stream* of words). In the case of a psychiatric patient's metaphoric language, that other object (or idea) (by which the metaphor has suggested itself to the speaker through likeness or similarity) remains an unrevealed entity and *eo ipso* makes the metaphor incomprehensible to the listener, though perfectly logical and legitimate for the speaker. Hence, the term *irrelevant* for the language of psychiatric patients — often framed in this kind of 'meaningless metaphoric configuration.'

language, nonverbal Communication by gestures, sounds, facial expressions, posturings, and so forth. In psychiatry, especially in child psychiatry, communication between doctor and patient by way of nonverbal language often tells more than any words that may be spoken.

language, primitive psychosomatic (sī-kō-sō-mat′ik) A phrase used by L.E. Hinsie to characterize the expression of feelings or thoughts by means of bodily movements rather than by words.

This primitive psychosomatic language can be easily observed in schizophrenics and in latent schizophrenics. Children who later in life develop catatonia often exhibit rather early a 'tendency to stubborness manifested through postures, gestures, immobility or exaggerated movements of the body. These children speak more with their muscles than with their mouths.' For example, when they do not want to see anything they shut their eyes tightly, or they close the lips tightly when they do not want to talk. In advanced schizophrenics body movements often express specific beliefs or delusions. A patient may sway to and from in the belief that this movement is necessary to keep the universe going or may drop his outstretched hand repeatedly in the belief that he thus destroys the universe. (Hinsie, L.E. *Understandable Psychiatry,* Macmillan, New York, 1948)

lapse Same as *petit mal.* See *epilepsy.*

lapsus calami (lăp′soos kă′lă-mē) A slip of the pen.
'A lady once told me that an old friend in writing to her had closed the letter with the curious sentence, "I hope you are well and *unhappy.*" He had formerly entertained hopes of marrying her himself, and the slip of the pen was evidently determined by his dislike at the thought of her being happy with some one else. She had recently married.' (Jones, E. *Papers on Psycho-Analysis,* 4th ed., Wood, Baltimore, 1938). See *act, symptomatic.*

lapsus linguae (lin′gwī) Slip of the tongue. See *act, symptomatic.*

lapsus memoriae (me-mô′rē-ī) Lapse or slip of the memory. See *act, symptomatic.*

lascivia (lăs-kē′vē-ă) (L. 'jollity, wantonness, lewdness) Nymphomania.

lasciviency (la-siv′i-en-sē) Lasciviousness; lewdness.

lascivus (lăs-kē′voos) (L. 'wanton, frisky, lewd, lustful, lascivious') Paracelsus' term in describing chorea, to denote the unrestrained character of the motor symptoms.

Lasègue sign (la-sâg′) (Ernest Charles Lasègue, French physician, 1816-83) The Lasègue sign is significant of disease of the sciatic nerve. Pain and resistance are caused by extending the leg on the thigh and flexing the thigh at the hip joint.

Lashley, Karl Spencer (1890-1958) U.S. psychologist, bacteriologist, and geneticist; psychology of learning; *Brain Mechanisms and Intelligence* (1929), numerous monographs in psychology, neurology, and the biology of behavior; director of Yerkes Laboratory of Primate Biology.

lata, latah, lattah (lă-tă) A behavioral pattern seen among the Malays, usually precipitated by sudden fright or tickling, consisting of imitative behavior (echopraxia), automatic obedience and coprolalia. It is seen more often in women and usually in middle or older age; it does not occur before late adolescence. Some authorities consider latah and related states, such as the miryachit or olonism of Siberian tribes, the inu of the Ainu, and the Jumpers of New England (a nineteenth century Shaker sect), as acute forms of schizophrenia. Others classify latah as a hysterical reaction or a startle pattern, and among the Malays themselves it is considered as a behavioral quirk rather than a disease.

'It has been traditional in much of the medical literature to treat *maladie des tics* as though it were identical with latah and its cognate disorders. This is almost certainly incorrect. Tics, the earliest and often the most striking manifestation of Gilles de la Tourette's disease, are unknown in latah, whereas the imitation phenomena, which are the core of latah reactions, are often totally lacking in *maladie des tics.* The coprolalia in latah always follows provocation and is never preservative. Latah reactions (with the significant exception of "jumping") are far more common in females, *maladie des tics* in males (L. Eisenberg, E. Ascher, and L. Kanner. *American Journal of Psychiatry 115*, 715-723, 1959) See *Gilles de la Tourette syndrome.*

latency In psychoanalysis, the period of one's life extending from the end of the infantile to the beginning of the adolescent stage. In point of years it normally begins at about the age of five and terminates at about the age of puberty.

Freud employed the term latency at a time in the development of psychoanalytic psychology when attention was focused largely on the sexual drive and libido; later work in the area of ego psychology has made it abundantly clear that the drives are by no means inactive during this period. Instead, what has happened is that the dangers of the Opedipus relationship have necessitated a strong blockade against libidinal impulses. The ego achieves this by mobilizing aggressive energies against the id. In effect, then, libidinal energies are repressed, and aggressive energies are redirected into elaborating a more effective web of defenses, including the superego, and into increasing mastery in the social sphere, in socially condoned and desirable competitiveness, conquest, and domination. Mental development, in other words, has occurred in spurts. In the infantile years, libidinal forces are more in evidence as they are deployed in various areas in accordance with physiologic growth. With the appearance of the Oedipus, these forces must be held in check, and the aggressive forces of the ego acquire greater prominence. They are used as front line combatants to prepare the way for the reappearance of libidinal strivings during adolescence.

latent Not visible or apparent; dormant, quiescent. Latent homosexuality, for example, refers to homosexual tendencies or conflicts that have never been manifested overtly and/or are unrecognized by the subject. Latent psychosis refers to an existing disorder that has not erupted into full-blown or florid psychotic symptoms; sometimes also termed prepsychotic, borderline, or incipient, and almost always referring to an underlying

schizophrenic disorder. See *schizophrenia, latent.*

laterality Handedness; preferential use of one side of the body for such acts as writing, eating, sighting, and listening. See *dominance, cerebral.*

lateropulsion (lat-ēr-ō-pul'shun), Rapid running sidewise with short steps, in paralysis agitans.

laughter, compulsive Inappropriate laughter, as seen in the hebephrenic form of schizophrenia.

'Among the affective disturbances [in schizophrenia] compulsive laughter is especially frequent; it rarely has the character of the hysterical laughing fit, but that of a soulless mimic utterance behind which no feeling is noticeable. It may often be provoked by allusion to a complex. Sometimes the patients feel only the movements of the facial muscles (the "drawn laughter").' (Bleuler, E. *Textbook of Psychiatry,* tr. by Brill, A.A., Macmillan, New York, 1930)

laughter, drawn See *laughter, compulsive.*

Laurence-Moon-Biedl syndrome See *syndrome, Laurence-Moon-Biedl.*

law, autonomic-affective According to Kempf, 'all the autonomic-affective cravings, whether they compel an acquisitive or an avertive course of behavior or attitude toward the environment, follow the same two laws:

1. When an autonomic-affective craving is aroused, either to compensate for the deficiencies due to metabolism (as in hunger) or through the influence of an exogenous stimulus (as in fear), it compels the projicient (striped muscle) apparatus to shift the exteroceptors about in the environment so that they will acquire such stimuli as are necessary to counterstimulate and neutralize the autonomic derangement so that the segment will assume comfortable tensions.

2. The projicient apparatus that shifts the receptors about so as to expose them to appropriate stimuli is organized and coordinated so as to bring a *maximum of affective gratification with a minimum expenditure of energy.*' (Kempf, E.J. *Psychopathology,* Mosby, St. Louis, 1921)

law, biogenetic mental (bī-ō-jen-e'tik men'tal) According to the biogenetic law of the mind, 'the history of the development of the species repeats itself in the embryonic development of the individual. Thus to a certain degree in his embryonic life man passes through the anatomical forms of primordial times. The same law is valid for the mental development of mankind. Accordingly, the child develops out of an originally unconscious and animal-like condition to consciousness; first to a primitive, and then slowly to a civilized consciousness.' (Jung, C.G. *Contributions to Analytical Psychology*, tr. by Baynes, H.G. and C.F., Kegan Paul, Trench, Trubner, London, 1928)

law, Briggs' A law of Massachusetts named after L. Vernon Briggs; the law provides that a person indicted for a capital offense, or one indicted by the grand jury who has previously been convicted of a felony or who is known to have been indicted for any other offense more than once, will be examined by a psychiatrist-expert appointed by the State Department of Mental Health. The examiner is not asked to determine whether the accused can distinguish between right and wrong or whether the accused acted because of an irresistible impulse; instead, the psychiatrist is asked whether the accused suffers from a mental illness severe enough to affect his responsibility and to require treatment in a mental hospital. See *responsibility, criminal.*

law, Jackson's According to Hughlings Jackson's concept of the hierarchic development of mental functions, when there is organic brain disease the higher (i.e. the more complex and most recently developed) centers will be paralyzed or affected first, and the lower centers will resist deterioration the longest.

law, Pitres' (Pē-tres') This law states that the first language to return in polyglottic patients with aphasia is the one which is easiest for the patient, usually the mother tongue.

law of avalanche Law of the distribution of energy in the nervous system as framed by Cajal. Sensory stimuli reaching the central nervous system normally gain release through a number of paths of discharge, which take the form of reflex arcs. When some of these reflex arcs are closed, so to speak, as avenues of release for nervous energy, the energy is forced to flow through the remaining arcs. It is possible, as, for instance, in epilepsy, that, when discharged, the dammed-up energy produces a condition likened by Cajal to an avalanche.

'Such a conception would apply equally well to the "idiopathic" or "genuine epilepsy" with Ammon's horn gliosis and the typical character traits, and to the epilepsies associated with marked developmental defects (idiocy) in which it may be conceived that the wider paths for avalanche discharge have not been laid down.' (Jelliffe, S.E. and White, W.A. *Diseases of the Nervous System*, 6th ed., Lea & Febiger, Philadelphia, 1935)

law of retrogenesis See *retrogenesis.*

laws, Mendelian (men-dē'li-an) The Mendelian law relating to the mechanism of inheritance, accounts for the results of Mendel's breeding experiments in terms of the segregation, independent assortment, and recombination of the individual gene factors, which he postulated as existing in the gametes as independent units for every inherited character. This system consists of at least two different principles.

First, segregation, or clear separation of genetic factors during the formation of the gametes: the various characters of hybridized organisms are transmitted separately and distributed to the reproductive cells independently of each other so that they may form every possible combination. Every known hereditary trait operates in accordance with segregation, and this principle is to be regarded as the basic aspect of the Mendelian system of heredity. Although it was evolved frome examples with both dominant and recessive characters, dominance is not an essential feature of Mendelian inheritance, as is demonstrated by many intermediate hybrids. While dominance alone does not necessarily presuppose the existence of unit characters, this element is essential to the law of segregation.

Second, the *independent* assortment of the genetic factors and their recombination. It is demonstrated by the 9:3:3:1 ratio in the redistribution of the four gene factors involved in the crosses with two different pairs of allelomorphic characters (see *Mendelism*). According to the same principle, the ratio 27:9:9:9:3:3:3:1 results, on the average, in the F2 generation of a 'trihybrid' mating, that is, one involving three pairs of allelomorphs, one member of each pair being dominant.

The simplest formulation of the entire Mendelian law seems to be as follows: When we cross two organisms unlike with respect to any character, the offspring of the first generation will be apparently like one of the parents in regard to the character in question. The parent who impresses a trait upon the offspring in this manner is called *dominant*, while the one who fails to be visibly represented is *recessive*. When, however, the hybrids of this first generation are in turn crossed with each other, they will produce a variety of offspring. One fourth of them will be like the dominant grandparent, one fourth like the recessive one, and the remaining half like the parents who resembled the dominant grandparent, yet failed to breed true to it. See *dominance; recessiveness*.

lay analyst See *psychiatrist*.

layers, cortical See *isocortex*.

lead pipe rigidity See *rigidity, lead pipe*.

lead poisoning Plumbism; although more common in children, it occurs also in adults, as in painters and workers with lead pipes (e.g. plumbers), and it may result from use of some cosmetics and abortifacients and from too close contact with lead-containing petrol. Poisoning is more frequent in summer, because the greater amount of vitamin D_3 formed in the skin by the sun's radiation increases absorption of lead from the gut.

Lead produces a selective degeneration of ganglion cells, especially in the spinal cord, to a lesser extent in the cortex. Among the various syndromes of lead poisoning are: (1) acute encephalopathy—with convulsions, delirium, coma; (2) chronic encephalopathy (294.3; 309.14)—with mental changes, convulsions, and occasionally optic atrophy; (3) neuritis—which is really a myopathy, affecting chiefly the extensors of the wrists and fingers and thus producing wrist-drop; (4) progressive muscular atrophy, due to anterior horn cell degeneration.

Prognosis is worsened if convulsions appear, and chronic encephalopathy responds little to treatment. As many as 35 per cent of affected children die, and girls have a higher mortality than boys. Severe residua are common: epilepsy, cerebral atrophy, paresis, blindness, speech defects, tremor.

Treatment includes high calcium diet to promote storage of lead in bones, followed by a high acid-low calcium diet to promote gradual elimination; and BAL (British anti-lewisite) or EDTA (ethylene-diamine-tetra-acetic acid, or versenate) to form a stable, non-toxic, excretable compound with the lead.

leadership Leadership 'may be broadly defined as the relation between an individual and a group built around some common interest and behaving in a manner directed or determined by him.' (Schmidt, R. *Leadership; Encyclopaedia of the Social Sciences*, vol. 9, Macmillan, New York, 1933, p. 282)

Two types of leadership are 'representative or symbolic and dynamic or creative.' (ibid) Max Weber has emphasized the importance of the *charismatic* form of leadership, where the leader is thought to have divinely instilled or at least extraordinary qualities. (Weber, M. *Wirtschaft und Gesellschaft*, Tübingen, 1925)

leadership, dual See *psychotherapy, multiple*.

leaping ague *Choreomania* (q.v.).

learning, accretion See *accretion*.

Leber's disease See *disease, Leber's*.

lecanomancy (lek′a-nō-man-sē) 'A method of divination by means of a suitable person looking into a bowl half-filled with water, on the surface of which the indefinite images of candle flames are reflected . . .' Herbert Silberer used free association to find the meanings of the visions reported. This showed 'how the divination[s] are merely the results of the medium's own complexes' and the close relation between the visions and dreams was well brought out. (*Psychoanalytic Review I*, 348, 1913-14, reporting Herbert Silberer's 'Lakenomantische Versuche,' pp. 566-87, *Zentralblatt fur Psychoanalyse II,* 10-11, Wiesbaden, 1912)

lécheur (lā-shĕr′) One who applies the mouth to the genitals of others, that is, practices fellatio; cunnilingus.

left-handedness See *dextrality-sinistrality.*

leipolalia (lip-ō-lā′lē-à) Elision; ellipsis.

lengthening reaction See *rigidity, decerebrate.*

Lennox, William Gordon (1884-1960) U.S. neurologist; epilepsy.

-lepsia (-lĕp′sē-à) Combining form meaning seizure, attack, from Gr. *-lepsia,* as in *epilepsia, epilepsis,* epilepsy.

leptomeninges (lep-tō-men-in′jēz) See *meninges.*

leptomeningitis (-men-in-jī′tis) See *meningitis.*

leptoprosopia (-pros-ō′pē-à) In anthropology and constitutional medicine, a condition characterized by a narrow face and an elongated cranium.

leptosomal, leptosomic (-so′mal, -so′mik) Identical with *asthenic.* In coining the term Kretschmer wanted to describe the main structural characteristics of the anthropological type in question rather than a secondary and not universal property of the type. See *type, asthenic.*

leptosome (lep′tō-sōm) A person of the asthenic body type.

lerema, leresis (le-rē′mà, -′sis) *Obs. n.* Garrulity; childish speech observed in patients with senile dementia.

lesbianism (lez′bi-an-iz′m) *Sapphism,* lesbian love. Aristophanes (*Frogs,* 1308) uses the word *lesbiázein,* 'to do like the Lesbian women,' translated in the Greek dictionary by L. *fellare.* See *homosexuality, female.*

leschenoma (les-kē-nō′mà) Garrulity; see *leresis.*

lethal (lē′thal) Deadly, fatal. This describes a hereditary character which in its homozygous condition produces an extreme modification that is *fatal* to the organism affected.

Lethal factors occur quite frequently in all kinds of animals and plants and are always recognizable by their drastic effect only in the form of homozygosity. 'In the heterozygous condition they may be carried with impunity by perfectly normal individuals, but that portion of the offspring of such individuals in which segregation has brought two lethals together is killed.' (Sinnott, E.W. and Dunn, L.D. *Principles of Genetics,* 3rd ed., McGraw-Hill, New York and London, 1939)

lethe (lē′thē) *Obs.* Total loss of memory.

letheomania (lē-thē-ō-mā′nē-à) Morbid longing for narcotic drugs.

leucomoria (lū-kō-mō′rē-à) *Obs.* Agitated melancholia.

leucotomy; leucotomy, frontal (lū-kot′ō-mē) See *lobotomy, prefrontal.*

leukodystrophy (lū-kō-dis′trō-fē) See *sclerosis, diffuse.*

leuko-encephalopathia myeloclastica primitiva (lū-kō-en-cef-à-lō-pà′thē-à mē-ē-lō-klas′tē-kà prē-mē-tē′và) See *sclerosis, diffuse.*

level, confidence See *confidence, level of.*

level, hedonic (hē-don′ik) See *psychodynamics, adaptational.*

level, maintenance The dosage of therapeutic agent which must be repeated at stated intervals in order to sustain the desired effect. In subacute combined degeneration of the spinal cord, for example, maintenance level of vitamin B$_{12}$ is commonly 4 micrograms weekly for 6 months; in various psychiatric patients, maintenance level of chlorpromazine hydrochloride may be 600 mg. per day for an indefinite period of time.

level of confidence See *confidence, level of.*

level of risk See *confidence, level of.*

levels, mental From the standpoint of analytical psychology (Jung) there are three mental levels: '(1) consciousness; (2) the personal unconscious; (3) the collective unconscious. The personal unconscious consists of all those contents that have become unconscious, either because, their intensity being lost, they were forgotten, or because consciousness has withdrawn from them, i.e., so-called repression. Finally, this layer contains those elements—partly sense perceptions—which on account of too little intensity have never reached consciousness, and yet in some way have gained access into the psyche. The collective unconscious, being an inheritance of the possibilities of ideas, is not individual but generally human, even generally animal, and represents the real foundations of the individual.' (Jung, C.G. *Contributions to Analytical Psychology*, tr. by Baynes, H.G. and C.F., Kegan Paul, Trench, Trubner, London, 1928)

level of development See *developmental levels.*

levophobia (lē-vō-fō′bē-à) Fear of objects to the left; opposite of *dextrophobia.*

Lewis, Nolan D.C. (1889-) American psychiatrist; research in schizophrenia, history of psychiatry; Director, New York State Psychiatric Institute, 1936-1953.

lex talionis (leks′ tà-lē-ō′nēs) (L. 'law of retaliation, retribution') See *talion.*

liaison psychiatry See *consultant.*

liar, pathological (path-ō-loj′i-kal) The pathological liars and swindlers are often grouped under the category of 'psychopathic personality.' 'The pathological liars and swindlers are among the most interesting examples of the "charming scamps." They are extremely imaginative and champion tellers of "tall tales," in which they invariably play the leading role. They make social contacts easily and build up their stories by proper accessories, such as accents, uniforms, forged documentary evidence, and other items. From time to time newspapers report the exposure of a bogus nobleman, officer, diplomatic agent, or some other impostor. Their activity sometimes takes the form of sexual conquests, and they may obtain

money under false pretenses, either on the promise of marriage or after a bigamous marriage.' (Lowrey, L.G. *Psychiatry for Social Workers,* Columbia University Press, New York, 1946) See *impostor.*

libidinal, libidinous (li-bid′i-nal, -nus) (1) Relating to psychic energy; (2) relating to the erotic instinct.

libidinal-cathexis (-kà-thek′sis) See *cathexis.*

libidinization (li-bi-di-ni-za′shun) See *erotization.*

libidinize (li-bid′i-nīz) See *eroticize.*

libido (li-bē′dō) In psychoanalysis, the energy of the sexual drive; but because Freud's consideration of the death or destructive drive came relatively late in the development of his psychology, the term libido is commonly used in a more general sense to refer also to the energy of the death or aggressive drive. See *instinct, death.*

'I have advocated calling the energy concept used in analytical psychology by the name "libido."' (Jung, C.G.)

McDougall suggests the term *hormé* for libido. He adds that it is the equivalent of Bergson's *élan vital.*

libido, asexual 'If we go back to the earliest possible manifestations of libido, we must admit that they probably have very early beginnings in the unicellular animal, and that as such, the libido is in itself asexual, and it may be that we shall have to come to the conclusion that the libido is always asexual, and that it only becomes sexual because it flows through sexual channels. (Bousfield, P. *Psychoanalytic Review 12,* 142-3, 1925)

libido-binding See *activity, immobilizing.*

libido deficiens (lē-bē′dō dà-fē′kē-ens) (L. 'failing libido') Lack of sexual urge.

libido, displaceability of A psychoanalytic concept pertaining to one aspect of the 'libido theory' of sexual development from infancy to childhood. In order of their appearance and development, the libidinal phases are usually considered as: (1) the oral, (2) the anal, (3) the phallic, (4) the genital.

Sexual excitations and gratifications are specifically related to the erogenous zones, characteristic of each specific phase of libidinal development, and have been called 'partial' impulses, since they tend to form or contribute partial components to the total final pattern of fully achieved adult sexuality. These partial impulses are usually discernible in adult sexual life, in what is called 'fore-play' or fore-pleasure activities or perversion traits.

These partial impulses can substitute for and replace one another in both excitation and gratification. Dissatisfaction at one zone may make for earlier or later increased activity at another zone. This gives the metaphorical impression that the total sexual instinct energy, or libido, is fluid in nature, subject to metaphorical hydrostatic and hydrodynamic forces. From this impression are derived such psychoanalytic terms as 'block,' 'recanalization,' 'displacement,' implying the shunting of excitation and gratification from one area of outlet to another. (Sterba, R. *Introduction to the Psychoanalytic Theory of the Libido,* Nervous and Mental Disease Monographs No. 68, New York, 1942)

libido-fixation See *fixation, libido.*

libido, mobility of The libidinal energy's characteristic ease of transfer from one object to another. Freud defines the libido as the total energy available to the love instinct, Eros. This instinct drive is one of the two sources of all human activity and it aims at the satisfaction of its need, which is 'to establish ever greater unities and to preserve them thus—in short, to bind together.' The other instinct, which likewise aims at the satisfaction of its need, is the death instinct, whose final aim is to destroy, 'to reduce living things to an inorganic state.' Basically the two instincts (both of 'somatic origin) represent the physiological demands of the human organism. The interaction of the two basic instincts with and against each other gives rise to the whole variegation of the phenomena of life.' For example, the biological function of eating both destroys the object and unites with it by incorporation.

Initially, all libido is stored up in the ego 'and serves to neutralize the destructive instincts which are simulta-neously present.' This is the state of *primary narcissism.* Later, as the infant begins to discern an outside world, he begins to invest the objects of the outside world with libidinous energy, with the energy of the love instinct. He 'begins to cathect the presentation of objects with libido—to change narcissistic libido into object libido.' The aim of uniting is directed toward objects. Throughout life, moreover, libidinous energy can be sent out toward different objects and withdrawn with ease. This ease with which libidinous energy can be shifted from one object to another is termed 'mobility of libido.' Freud contrasts the mobility of libido with the fixation of libido, in which the libido attaches itself to particular objects and often the attachment persists through life. (Freud, S. *An Outline of Psychoanalysis,* Norton, New York, 1949)

libido, object See *ego-libido.*

libido, plasticity of That specific quality of the libido which makes for the adaptability of the sexual instincts (or the partial impulses of the libido) to modified discharge of tensions through indirect rather than direct avenues of gratification.

The general fate of instinctual energy that cannot be overtly or directly discharged in instinct gratification has been described under the general term of 'the vicissitudes of the instinct.' The four major vicissitudes, or indirect avenues for partial gratification and discharge of instinct, are: (1) repression with subsequent symptom and dream formation; (2) sublimation; (3) transformation of the instinct aim into its opposite; (4) transformation of the direction of the instinctual aim from an external object onto the self. R. Sterba (*Introduction to the Psycho-analytic Theory of the Libido,* Nervous and Mental Disease Monographs No. 68, New York, 1942) states: 'We owe our culture to the plasticity of the sexual instinct, which is manifested in its vicissitudes. See *libido, displaceability of.*

libido, primal See *force, central.*

libido-quantum (-kwon'tum) See *ego-libido.*

libido-theory See *theory, libido.*

libido, traumatization of the (traw-mà-ti-zā'shun) Injury of instinctual energy. 'The author contends that any depletion of the heterosexual constituent of the libidinous urge by virtue of psychic trauma in the moral sphere, or traumatization must divert the libido's energy so as to augment the other components; homosexuality, narcism and the perversions are enlarged, at the expense of heterosexuality . . . The word "trauma" is applicable to material injury, the ultimate result of action. In the neologism "traumatization" action takes place, but it is not final: it continues in a state of metamorphosis.' (London, L.S. *Libido and Delusion,* 2nd ed. enlgd., Mental Therapy Publications, Washington, D.C., 1946)

libido, viscosity of (vis-kos'i-ti) A psychoanalytic term carrying still further the metaphorical idea concerning the fluidity of the libido. The concept of the libido's viscosity is apt because of the following two characteristics of the libido: first, the slow pace of emotional growth from infancy to maturity; second, the tendency of the libido to remain fixed at or return, at slight provocation, to earlier phases of infantile sexual gratification.
   The forward movement of libidinal development is apparently more oscillatory than direct, with many strong reactionary expressions of a kind of stubborn inertia, as well as a tendency toward the maintenance and reactivation of old or earlier phases of libidinal development. This makes for an instability and undependability of the newer or more recently acquired phases of developmental maturity. See *libido, displaceability of.* (Sterba, R. *Introduction to the Psycho-analytic Theory of the Libido,* Nervous and Mental Disease Monographs No. 68, New York, 1942)

libido-wish See *wish, libido.*

Liebeault, Ambroise-August (1823 - 1904) (lē-bō') French psychiatrist; hypnotism.

liebestod (lē'bes-tōt) J.C. Flugel's term for phantasies involving dying with a loved one. Such phantasies may signify a wish to become pregnant by the partner and/or an attempt to deny the possibility of death by phantasying eternal union with the mother.

lie detector See *detector, lie.*

lie, life Adler uses this term for the tendency of the neurotic to include in his lifeplan the idea that he will fail because of the fault of others or owing to events beyond his control.
   'It is a categorical command of his lifeplan that he should fail either through the guilt of others and thus be freed from personal responsibility, or that some fatal trifle should prevent his triumph.' (Adler, A. *The Practice and Theory of Individual Psychology,* tr. by Radin, P., Kegan Paul, Trench, Trubner, London, 1924)

lie, white A harmless and condonable untruth, as contrasted with the lie that is told with malicious intent or habitually, just for the sake of lying.

life-course See *closure, law of and life-course.*

life-goal See *goal, life.*

life-lie See *lie, life.*

life, mental See *mentality.*

life, noon of A figure of speech denoting the dividing line between the first and second halves of a person's life: used by Jacobi in his book on the psychology of Jung. Referring to Jung's 'functional' and 'attitudinal' types he writes: 'This opposition of the functions and of the conscious and unconscious attitude intensifies itself into a conflict in the individual, as a rule, only toward the second half of life; indeed, it is just that problem which indicates an alteration of his psychological situation in that portion of life. Often it is precisely the capable persons, well adjusted to the environment, who, once past their forties, suddenly find that they are, in spite of their "brilliant mind," perhaps not equal to domestic difficulties or are, for example, insufficiently suited to their professional position. If this phenomenon is correctly understood, it must be taken as a sign and warning that the inferior function, too, now demands its rights and that a confrontation with it has become a necessity. The latter, therefore, plays in such cases the greatest role at the beginning of an analysis.
   'Just as the differentiation and isolation of that function which is constitu-

tionally destined in the individual to enable him most surely to find food and meet the demands of the external world is the most important psychic task in youth, the differentiation of the other functions can only be taken up after the successful accomplishment of this task. For before the individual has firmly anchored his consciousness in reality—and that occurs only in adulthood, often only after a certain amount of experience in later life—the way into the unconscious cannot and should not be ventured upon unless absolutely necessary. It is the same with the attitudinal habitus. The constitutionally given habitus must take the lead in the first half of life, because the individual can in all likelihood best find his place in the world with the help of his naturally given attitude. The task of letting the opposite habitus come into its own only emerges during the second half of life. That it will be easier for the born extravert than for the born introvert to accomplish the external adjustment that the first half of life above all requires needs no further explanation. Perhaps one may then venture the assertion: the born extravert gets along in the world more easily in the first, the born introvert in the second half of his life; with which justice is done at least approximately. The danger threatening both types is one-sidedness. An efficient person can be so far driven into the world by his extraversion that he never finds his "way home." His most personal, inner being has grown strange to him. He is continually in flight from it, until one day he can go no farther. Or he may have relied too much upon his reason, have exercised and strengthened only his intellectual function, and now he perceives that he has estranged himself from his own living core. No feeling reaches from him even to the nearest of his fellow-men. Not only for him who is open to the world, but also for the introvert difficulties arise in the course of life from his one-sided orientation. The neglected functions and the unlived attitude revolt—as it were, demand their place in the sun—to be seized by means of a neurosis if not otherwise. For the goal is always totally—the ideal solution, in which all four psychological functions and both forms of attitudinal reactions are at the person's command in as nearly the same degree of consciousness and

disposability as possible. And once, at least, must a certain approximation to this ideal be attempted. If it does not make itself felt earlier as a demand, then the *noon of life* signifies the last summons to attain it now or never and thereby to "round out" the psyche, so that it may not go toward life's evening unfinished and incomplete.' (Jacobi, J. *The Psychology of C.G. Jung*, Kegan Paul, Trench, Trubner, London, 1942)

life-organization See *organization, life.*

life-plan See *plan, life.*

life style See *constancy.*

Lilliputian (lil-i-pū'shan) (From *Lilliput*, an imaginary kingdom of 6 inch pygmies in Jonathan Swift's (1667-1745) *Gulliver's Travels.*)

'In Lilliputian or microptic hallucinations, the objects seen appear much reduced in scale.' (Henderson, D.K. and Gillespie, R.D. *A Text-Book of Psychiatry*, 4th ed., Oxford University Press, London, 1936). See *micropsia.*

Lilliputian hallucinations have been reported in intoxication from alcohol, chloral, ether, trichlorethylene, cholera, typhoid, scarlet fever, cocainism, tumors of the temporal or temporosphenoidal lobe, and in some cases of petit mal epilepsy.

limb, phantom The feeling that an extremity which has been lost is really present. Fenichel points out that phantom extremity phenomena are closely associated with what is termed the *body image.* In its development the infant is first able to discern self from non-self because its own body can be distinguished from all other parts of the universe, or the rest of the world, by the fact that the body is perceived through two types of sensation simultaneously: external tactile sensations and internal sensations of depth sensibility. Thus the first idea of self consists of the sum total of the mental representations of the body and its organs, the so-called body image. The nucleus of the ego is this body image. 'Freud stated that the ego is primarily a bodily thing, that is, the perception of one's own body.'

In phantom extremity phenomena, the basic importance of the body image is underlined. For, indeed, the patient finds great difficulty in correlating with his body image the objective fact of the absence of the extremity. In the body image, which is the basic mental representation of the body, and the nucleus of the ego, the extremities are of the greatest importance. Thus a phantom extremity can be included in the body image. (Fenichel, O. *The Psychoanalytic Theory of Neurosis*, Norton, New York, 1945)

Appearance of the phantom is the expected physiologic reaction to amputation, if this takes place after early childhood, and admission of the phantom is a healthy psychological response. In time, the amputee slowly reorganizes his body image, accepts the defect, resumes his social and occupational role, and uses his prosthesis appropriately. Failure in any of these steps is indicative of coexistent personality disturbance. In all patients with phantom limb, there occur mild tingling sensations which probably depend upon the sensorimotor cortex; but the term 'painful phantom' refers to patients who in addition complain of twisting, burning, pulling, or itching sensations in the non-existent limb. Such pain seems to represent an emotional response to the loss of an important part of the body which had significance to the patient in terms of his relationships with others. Amputation produces an upsurge of anxiety related to the resultant distortion of the concept of the body and the self. Hostile feelings typically emerge toward those with whom the amputee identifies as having been similarly mutilated and toward those on whom he is dependent and whose rejection he anticipates Sometimes patients are further threatened by guilt feelings related to the upsurge in hostility. While typically the phantom tends to shrink and eventually disappear into the stump, such reorganization may not occur in those whose self esteem is dependent on a high evaluation of the part lost. Some patients deny their loss, and this is especially common after amputation of the breast or penis. Still others project their loss and tend to see those around them as suffering in a similar way. (Kolb, L.C. *The Painful Phantom*, Springfield, Illinois, 1954)

limbus See *rhinencephalon.*

limitation, sex See *sex-limitation.*

limophoitas (lī-mō-foi'tas) Psychosis induced by starvation.

limophthisis (lim-of'thi-sis) Emaciation from insufficient nourishment.

limosis (lī-mō'sis) Mason Good's term for mental disorders associated with abnormal appetites.

Lindau's disease (Arvid Lindau, contemporary Swedish pathologist) Angioma of the brain occurring in connection with angiomatosis of the retina, occasionally familial and hereditary.

line, pure This biological term was introduced by the Danish botanist Johannsen, to characterize the identical *genotypical* equipment of an autogamous stock of organisms descended from a common ancestor by self-fertilization. According to the pure line theory, these organisms will continue to breed true regardless of environmental differences, forming lines genetically pure for all their characters. Whenever such genetic purity has been attained, all differences except newly occurring mutations must be caused by environmental influences and, therefore, cannot be hereditarily transmitted.

linguistics The study of words and language; see *method, linguistic-kinesic.*

lingula (lin-gū'lä) See *cerebellum.*

linkage Act of linking, or state of being linked. This is an important exception to the Mendelian principle of independent assortment and is the foundation of the modern chromosome theory of inheritance as formulated by Morgan, in 1910, from his famous Drosophila experiments. It is characterized by the tendency of genes located in the same chromosome to remain in their original combinations and to be inherited as a 'block,' rather than independently of one another.

Apart from the assumption that *linked* genes must be located in the same chromosome, in order to permit such a *coupling*— the mechanism of linkage has been partly explained by the discovery that 'the gametes of a plant or animal which is heterozygous for two linked traits are not formed in equal numbers, but that the gametes with the parental combinations of genes are always more numerous than the gam-

etes with the new combination of genes. '
(Sinnott, E.W. and Dunn, L.D. *Principles
of Genetics*, 3rd ed., McGraw-Hill, New
York and London, 1939)
Because of the frequent occurrence
of *crossing over* (q.v.), most of the known
instances of linkage are *incomplete*. Although it is theoretically possible that
two linked genes may never separate,
because they are so close together in the
chromosome that a break cannot occur
between them, actual cases of *complete*
linkage are exceedingly rare.

linkage, sex See *sex-linkage.*

linonophobia (li-nō-nō-fō'bē-à) Fear of
string.

lipochondrodystrophy *Gargoylism* (q.v.).

lip-pursing See *Schnautzkrampf.*

lisping A type of defective articulation
in which the sounds 's' and 'z' (sibilants)
are not pronounced perfectly, by pressing
the tip and next narrow part of the blade
of the tongue to the alveoli (the sockets
where upper front teeth are rooted), but
are pronounced by carelessly pushing the
tip of the tongue forward and touching
the edges of the upper front teeth as
when uttering the sound of 'th.' Like all
speech disorders, lisping is more common
in boys than in girls. Lisping may be based
on any or all of the following etiological
factors: (1) local conditions, secondary
to congenital or acquired organic defects;
(2) mental retardation; (3) faulty training,
especially as a result of parental ignorance or carelessness and the use of 'baby
talk.' It is this last factor that is the most
important and the most common, and
when it is operative lisping is often found
to be a behavior reaction acquired in the
interest of some personal or social goal.
Treatment is directed to the removal or
correction of organic defects and to re-
education of parents and child. Speech
classes are normally helpful in removing
the defect.

Lissauer's dementia paralytica (dā-men'-
tē-à pà-rà-lē'tē-kà) (Heinrich Lissauer,
German neurologist, 1861-91) An atypical syndrome of general paresis characterized by (1) unusually well-retained

intellectual functions and (2) severe focal
symptoms, such as apoplectiform attacks,
hemiplegia, aphasia, etc.

lithiasis, hysterical (li-thī'à-sis, his-ter'i-
kal) In the nine cases (eight of whom were
women) of the disturbance labeled hysterical lithiasis in the Mayo Clinic's report,
the 'hysterical lithiasis' was neither *hysterical* nor *lithiasis*, but simply a disease
picture faked for a definite purpose. These
patients made use of foreign bodies that
would appear as kidney stones. One patient placed a bag of pebbles in the kidney
region at the time of the x-ray exposure.
Another patient manufactured a renal
colic to obtain morphine, to which she
was addicted. (Dunbar, F. *Emotions and
Bodily Changes*, Columbia University
Press, New York, 1946)

lithic diathesis See *diathesis, lithic.*

lithium A naturally occurring element,
number 3 on the periodic table (1 is hydrogen, 2 is helium), and the lightest metal
known; of interest to psychiatry because
it appears to provide an effective treatment for manic states and may be an effective prophylactic agent against recurrent
manic or depressive episodes. Mechanism of action is unknown; lithium may
interfere with sodium retention within
brain cells. Usually lithium is administered
as lithium carbonate; side effects with
overdosage include nausea, diarrhea,
tremor, muscular heaviness, hypersensitivity to sights and sound, and irritability.

Litten's sign (Moritz Litten, German physician, 1845-1907) In paralysis of the
diaphragm—non-projection of shadow by
the diaphragm x-rayed during respiration.

Little Hans See *Hans.*

Little's disease (William John Little,
1810-94, English surgeon) Congenital
diplegia; cerebral palsy; atrophic lobar
sclerosis; congenital spastic paralysis;
spastic diplegia. A congenital disorder,
probably due to in utero degeneration,
consisting of a bilateral symmetrical
atrophy of the nerve cells and gliosis,
mainly of the pyramidal tracts. As a result
the limbs (particularly the lower) become
weak and spastic. Other symptoms include
involuntary movements and ataxia and,

usually, some degree of mental deficiency. Predominant symptoms are spastic in 65 per cent of cases, athetoid in 25 per cent, and ataxic in 10 per cent. Few cases survive beyond the early adult years.

L-K Linguistic-kinesic; see *method, linguistic-kinesic.*

LMT Lowenfeld Mosaic Test. See *test, mosaic.*

load, case In psychiatric social work, a term for the number of 'clients,' as well as for the intensity of service being given.

lobar sclerosis, atrophic (lo′ber skle-ro′ sis, at′ro-fik) *Little's disease* (q.v.).

lobe, flocculonodular (flo-ku-lo-nod′u-ler) See *cerebellum.*

lobe, frontal That portion of the cerebral hemisphere which lies in front of the central sulcus and above the lateral fissure. The principal areas of the frontal lobe, as designated by Brodmann, are: area 4 (precentral gyrus; principal motor area); immediately in front of 4 is area 6 (premotor area; a part of the extrapyramidal tract circuit); in front of this, area 8 (which is concerned with eye movements and pupillary changes); and in front of this, at the frontal poles and continuing along the inferior surface of the frontal lobe, areas 9, 10, 11, and 12 (which are frontal association areas).

Cells of the precentral gyrus (Betz cells) control voluntary movements of skeletal muscle on the opposite side of the body via the pyramidal tracts; irritative lesions in this area may give convulsive seizures (Jacksonian epilepsy). Destructive lesions in area 4 produce flaccid paralysis; spasticity will occur if area 6 and intermediate cortex is also involved. Forced grasping is often seen following destructive lesions of area 6. Destruction of the frontal association areas (9, 10, 11 and 12) may produce facetiousness (Witzelsucht), change in moral and social behavior, loss of interest, intellectual deterioration, and distractibility.

lobe, limbic (lim′bik) See *rhinencephalon.*

lobe, occipital (ok-sip′i-tal) The posterior lobe of the cerebral hemisphere; it is pyramidal in shape and lies behind the parieto-occipital fissure. Visual function is localized in the occipital lobe, primarily in the calcarine cortex (area striata, area 17 of Brodmann). Neurons from the retina project to the external geniculate body, whence 2nd-order neurons project to the calcarcine cortex. Fibers from the nasal half of each retina cross in the optic chiasm and so are projected onto the visual cortex of the opposite side; fibers from the temporal half of the retina remain uncrossed. The posterior occipital poles are mainly concerned with macular (central) vision; the more anterior parts of the calcarine area are concerned with peripheral vision. The human loses both object vision and light perception when the calcarine cortex is removed.

The calcarine cortex (area 17) projects to area 18 (parastriate lobule), which in turn projects to area 19 (preoccipital area). Areas 18 and 19 are visual association areas; lesions here cause disturbances in spatial orientation and visual word-blindness (alexia). Area 19 receives projections from all parts of the cortex and then co-ordinates visual with other reflexes.

lobe, parietal (par-ie′tal) That portion of the cerebral hemisphere which extends from the central sulcus to the parieto-occipital fissure and laterally to the level of the Sylvian fissure. The postcentral gyrus (areas 3-1-2, the somesthetic area), the supramarginal gyrus, and the angular gyrus are portions of the parietal lobe. The postcentral gyrus receives projections from the relay nuclei of the thalamus; the latter receive the great ascending somatosensory tracts of the spinal cord and the trigeminal lemniscus. Areas 5 and 7, which make up the posterior parietal lobule, are sensory association areas. Experimental studies indicate that the body surface is projected dermatome by dermatome on the postcentral gyrus. It appears that taste is also a function of the sensorimotor area and is localized at the inferior end of the lobe, possibly on the opercular surface of the Sylvian fissure.

lobe, temporal That portion of the cerebral hemisphere which lies below the Sylvian fissure and extends back to the level of the parieto-occipital fissure. The temporal lobe receives auditory projections from the medial geniculate body, and ablation of the temporal lobe in man results in partial deafness, contralateral disturbance in auditory localization, and disturbance in memory for auditory impressions. The temporal lobe also receives vertibular projections, but the source of these is unknown.

Symptoms of temporal lobe tumors include visual field defects, auditory and speech defects, and minor seizures known as dreamy states (see *states, dreamy*). If the uncus is implicated, there may be hallucinations of smell and taste (uncinate seizures).

lobotomy, Grantham Lobotomy performed by means of electrocoagulation of the ventromedial quadrant of the prefrontal lobe of the brain.

lobotomy, prefrontal (lō-bot'ōmi) A psychosurgical procedure consisting of ablation of the prefrontal area of the frontal lobe. The prefrontal area is that portion of the frontal lobe anterior to Brodmann's area 6, the premotor area. As a psychosurgical procedure, the operation is ordinarily performed bilaterally. In contrast to frontal lobectomy, which is an open procedure in which tissue is excised and, therefore, more direct cortical damage is caused, the lobotomy procedure is 'blind.' A hole is drilled through the skull and a leukotome is inserted to cut white nerve fibers connecting the frontal lobe with the thalamus. Thus, in lobotomy, there is less cortical damage than in lobectomy. This procedure interrupts frontothalamic and thalamofrontal fibers and also the association systems of the frontal lobe.

Prefrontal lobotomy was among the first psychosurgical procedures used in the United States. It seems to reduce anxiety feelings and introspective activities; and feelings of inadequacy and self-consciousness are thereby lessened. Lobotomy reduces the emotional tension associated with hallucinations and does away with the catatonic state. Because nearly all psychosurgical procedures have undesirable side effects, they are ordinarily resorted to only after all other methods have failed. The less disorganized the personality of the patient, the more obvious are post-operative side effects. For this reason, bilateral prefrontal lobotomy is employed more commonly in schizophrenia than in any other disorder.

Prefrontal lobotomy is of value in the following disorders, listed in a descending scale of good results: affective disorders, obsessive-compulsive states, chronic anxiety states and other non-schizophrenic conditions, paranoid schizophrenia, undetermined or mixed types of schizophrenia, catatonic schizophrenia, and hebephrenic and simple schizophrenia. Good results are obtained in about 40 per cent of cases, fair results in some 35 per cent, and poor results in 25 per cent or thereabouts. The mortality rate probably does not exceed 3 per cent. Greatest improvement is seen in patients whose premorbid personalities were 'normal,' cyclothymic, or obsessive-compulsive; in patients with superior intelligence and good education; in psychoses with sudden onset and a clinical picture of affective symptoms of depression or anxiety, and with behavioristic changes such as refusal of food, overactivity, and delusional ideas of a paranoid nature.

Convulsive seizures are reported as sequelae of prefrontal lobotomy in 5 to 10 per cent of cases. Such seizures are ordinarily well controlled with the usual anti-convulsive drugs. Post-operative blunting of the personality, apathy, and irresponsibility are the rule rather than the exception. Other side effects include distractibility, childishness, facetiousness, lack of tact or discipline, and post-operative incontinence.

Prefrontal lobotomy has also been used successfully to control pain secondary to organic lesions. In this case, the tendency has been to employ unilateral lobotomy, because of the evidence that a lobotomy extensive enough to relieve psychotic symptoms is not required to control pain.

Since the introduction of prefrontal lobotomy and prefrontal lobectomy various other psychosurgical procedures have been initiated—transorbital lobotomy, thalamotomy, cortical undercutting, and topectomy. The present trend is toward selective operation, the particular procedure being chosen on the basis of the nature of the disease, its duration and extent, the patient's age, etc. Also called *frontal lobotomy; prefrontal leukotomy; frontal leukotomy.*

lobotomy, transorbital (trans-or'bi-tal) A psychosurgical procedure consisting of partial ablation of the prefrontal area. The approach is through the superior conjunctival sac, and the operation is usually performed bilaterally. The plane of section corresponds roughly to that of *topectomy* but, like prefrontal lobotomy, the procedure is a 'blind' one and white matter rather than gray matter is destroyed. The incision interrupts the frontothalamic and thalamofrontal radiations and also the frontal lobe association fibers. Some surgeons prefer the transorbital approach to classical prefrontal lobotomy, because they feel that incontinence, apathy, and other undesirable side effects are less frequent. See *lobotomy, prefrontal.*

locomotor ataxia (lō-kō-mō'ter à-tak'sē-à) See *tabes.*

Loeffler's syndrome See *syndrome, Loeffler's.*

logagnosia (log-ag-nō'zhē-à) Sensory aphasia.

logamnesia (log-am-nē'zhēa) Forgetting words; nominal or amnestic aphasia.

-logia, -logy (-lō'jē-à, -'lō-jē) Combining form meaning (1) speaking, speech; (2) science, doctrine, theory, from Gr. *-logía* (in composition), from *lógos,* word, speech, discourse.

logoclonia (log-ō-klō'nē-à) Logospasm.

logodiarrhea (-dī-à-rē'à) See *tachylogia.*

logomania (-mā'nē-à) See *tachylogia.*

logomonomania (-mon-ō-mā'nē-à) *Obs.* An abnormal mental state characterized only by great loquacity. It is difficult today to name a psychiatric state of which volubility is the only symptom.

logoneurosis (-nū-rō'sis) *Obs.* Any neurosis associated with a speech defect; by some, used synonymously with *stuttering* (q.v.).

logopathy (lō-gōp'à-thē) A general term for any type of speech disorder.

logopedics (log-ō-pē'diks) The study of speech and its disorders.

logophasia (-fā'zhē-à) A form of aphasia, characterized by loss of ability to use articulate language correctly.

logoplegia (-plē'jē-à) *(Obsnt)* Aphasia.

logorrhea (-rē'à) See *tachylogia.*

logospasm (log'ō-spaz'm) Explosive speech; stuttering.

logotherapy Existential analysis (see *existentialism*). Logotherapy is a type of psychotherapy based on a system of spiritual values rather than on a system of psychobiologic laws. Logotherapy emphasizes the search for the meaning of human existence; lack of assurance in any meaning is believed to be one of the main causes of frustration in the present era.

Lombroso, Cesare (1836-1909) Italian criminologist and psychopathologist.

longeval (lon-jē'val) *Rare.* Longevous.

longevity (lon-jev'i-ti) Length of life. In its medical and statistical sense, this term refers to the phenomenon of a long duration, or great length, of life, and hence to a biological concept with important implications in medical statistics as well as in constitutional medicine and genetics.

The existence of *genetic* factors operating in human longevity has been conclusively demonstrated by a number of family studies, although the details of the genetic mechanism involved have not yet been elucidated. Certain experiments of Pearl have shown *longlivedness* to be dominant over *shortlivedness* in Drosophila. A number of cases of short lifespan may thus be accounted for by single-recessive mechanisms. There is also the possibility of *lethal* (q.v.) genes which merits consideration as a factor influencing life-span, although the present evidence is to the effect that the significant role of lethal genes is in the fairly early (prenatal) stages.

According to Pearl's theories, it is 'the total genetic constitution of the individual, rather than any particular genes lethal or other, that is most important as a factor in determining length of life.' (*Human Biology,* volume 3). However, Scheinfeld advances as a speculative opinion the notion that if there are genes producing a fatal breakdown at early stages of life, there might also be genes 'timed' to bring death at later periods. On this theory rests the belief that there may be sets of genes, collectively inherited in given families, which in a general way make some of them potentially long-lived and others short-lived. (Scheinfeld, A. *You and Heredity*, Book of the Month Club, New York, 1939)

Concerning the constitutional aspect of longevity it has been shown by Pearl that the long-lived are more asthenic and the short-lived more pyknic, that women have a decided biological advantage over men, and that in youth all individuals below average height have a greater mortality, while overweight means greater mortality in individuals over 40 years of age.

Studies on the factor of *marital status* in longevity have demonstrated an advantage for the married over the unmarried in general, but this is mainly due to selective factors rather than to environmental benefits conveyed by marriage. Longevity is also positively correlated with a favorable *social* and *economic* status, and with professional work as opposed to manual occupations, although the question of the relative influence of genetic factors determining simultaneously low grade occupation and a poor constitution on the one hand, and the environmental disadvantages of manual occupations on the other has not been carefully worked out.

As regards the *physico-chemical* basis of longevity there is Meggendorfer's interesting hypothesis that it is not duration of life as such that is hereditarily determined, but only longevity in the sense of a definite quantity of life energy. Environmental influences such as temperature and light may affect longevity by altering the speed of metabolic processes and hence the rate of consumption of the fixed available supply of energy.

longevous (lon-jē′vus) Living a long time or being of great age.

longilineal (lon-ji-lin′ē-al) In constitutional medicine, this term refers to one of the two constitutional types distinguished by Manouvrier on the basis of the configuration of the body as a whole. Persons of this type are built on lines that tend to be long rather than broad, and are to be contrasted with the *brevilineal* (q.v.) type.

The *longilineal* type corresponds roughly to the *asthenic* type of Kretschmer, and the *dolichomorphic* type of Pende.

longitypical (-tip′i-kal) Identical with *longilineal* and *dolichomorphic*.

look, amphetamine Many patients on

long-continued administration of amphetamine or its derivatives are said to show a characteristic facial appearance—a pale, pinched, serious facial expression with dark circles or hollows under the eyes. This appearance is termed the 'amphetamine look.'

look, metallic See *gloss, metallic.*

look, paranoid (par′à-noid) The facial appearance of a paranoid schizophrenic when he thinks about certain of his complexes. 'In a few patients, this phenomenon can be evoked or made to disappear again momentarily by changing the subject of conversation. I do not know on what it is based. Often it remains perfectly recognizable even if a mask leaves nothing but the eyes visible.' (Bleuler, E. *Dementia Praecox or the Group of Schizophrenias*, International Universities Press, New York, 1950)

Lorr scale See *MSRPP.*

love In psychiatry the most commonly accepted definition of *love* is contained in the word *pleasure*, particularly as it applies to gratifying experiences between members of the opposite sex. The manifestations of love are almost legion, ranging from those of the infantile period up to those of sublimated maturity.

Love is pleasure; when the pleasure is directed to oneself it is self-love; the word is annexed by a hyphen to the particular part of oneself that pleases; it may be oral, anal, genital, muscular, dermal, psychic (with all its subdivisions). When love is directed away from oneself it becomes object-love, which has as many manifestations as self-love.

In general it may be said to correspond to *eros* and *libido*. Freud defines libido as 'the energy . . . of those instincts which have to do with all that may be comprised under the word "love."'

According to Freud the choice of a love-object may be based upon (1) the narcissistic type, with four possibilities: one may love (a) a person like himself; (b) a person resembling him as he once was; (c) a person who meets the requirements of being what one would like to be; and (d) someone who was once part of himself.

The love-object, (2) patterned after the anaclitic type, may be: (a) the woman who tends or (b) the man who protects.

love, anal-sadistic That type of ambivalent object relationship characteristic of the anal-sadistic period. See *anal-erotism; sadism, anal.*

love, Dorian (dō′ri-an) Love for boys. Stekel refers to the works of the philologist E. Bethe: 'The author proves that boy love in Hellas was introduced by the Dorians. Although traces of the custom are found also among the Ionians, boy love, like knighthood, became fashionable in Greece through the Dorians.' (Stekel, W. *The Homosexual Neurosis,* tr. by van Teslaar, J. S., Badger, Boston, 1922)

love, genital (jen′i-tal) The type of object love characteristic of the genital or adult stage; adult, mature, non-ambivalent object love.

love, monkey A literal translation of the German term *Affenliebe.* It refers to inordinate maternal love in which the mother caters unqualifiedly to all the wishes and whims of the child.

love, mother The feeling of affection, devotion, possessiveness, and the need of protecting the child born to a woman. 'Mother love is frequently called an instinct, a proclivity that appears in a woman, because she becomes a mother and for no other reason. There may be something to this idea, but . . . "instinct" is not all that is involved. In general, people love those for whom they have to make sacrifices, and babies demand sacrifices. Not only "instinct" but many other types of pressures—social mores, the expectancy of the family for her to act in a motherly way, her husband's pride in her motherhood, pity for the helpless infant— are also involved in setting up the pattern of feeling and action we recognize as mother love.' (Lemkau, P. V. *Mental Hygiene in Public Health,* McGraw-Hill, New York, 1949)

love-object See *object-love.*

love, passive object See *narcissism.*

love, phallic (fa′lik) The type of object love characteristic of the phallic period.

love, pregenital (prē-jen′i-tal) Abraham thus terms the behavior of the child toward the mother in particular, during the pregenital phase. Although the infant is relatively, if not completely, indifferent to the welfare of the object in the early suckling phase, it shows the first signs of caring for the mother during the biting stage. 'We may also regard such a care, incomplete as it is, as the first beginnings of object-love in a stricter sense since it implies that the individual has begun to conquer his narcissism.' (Abraham, K. *Selected Papers,* tr. by Bryan, D. and Strachey, A., Leonard and Virginia Woolf, Hogarth Press, London, 1927)

love, smother A phrase sometimes applied to the mother who overprotects her child so that he has little opportunity to develop independence, overindulges him so that he becomes unable to tolerate frustrations, dominates and controls his every action, and ultimately engenders multiple fears in him and doubts about his own adequacy and ability. Smother love predisposes to passive dependent types of mastery and is seen often in obsessive or phobic mothers.

L.P. Lumbar puncture. See *puncture, lumbar.*

LSD See *psychotomimetic.*

lucidity From the legal point of view 'a lucid interval is not a perfect restoration to reason, but a restoration so far as to be able, beyond doubt, to comprehend and do the act with such perception, memory and judgment as to make it a legal act.' (Frazer *v.* Frazer, 2 Del.Chi., 263)

ludic (lū′dik) Unreal, play-like, quasi, pseudo. See *activity, ludic.*

lues (lū′ēz) Originally, plague or pestilence; in current usage, syphilis.

lues deifica (loo′es de-ē′fe-kȧ) (L. 'sacred plague,' epilepsy) *Obs.* Epilepsy.

lues divina (dē-vē′nȧ) (L. 'divine plague') *Obs.* Epilepsy.

luetic curve (lū-e′tik) See *Lange's colloidal gold reaction.*

lumbar puncture See *puncture, lumbar.*

lunacy (lū′na-sē) *Obs.* Mental abnormality of such degree as to render the patient incompetent and bring him under the guardianship of the state.

lunacy commission A committee, usually of qualified psychiatrists, appointed by judicial order to determine the mental state of an individual whose case the court has under consideration.

lunacy, moral An old psychiatric term emphasizing social and moralistic attitudes toward symptomatic behavior disorders, for which the present-day synonyms are (1) psychopathic personality; (2) constitutional psychopathic inferiority; (3) the impulse neuroses and perversions.

lunatic (lū'nȧ-tik) One possessing a mental disorder.

lunatismus (lōō-nȧ-tēz'moos) (G. 'somnambulism') An old expression given to those somnambulists who only walk about at the time the moon shines.' (Tuke, D.H. *A Dictionary of Psychological Medicine,* vols. 1 - 2, Blakiston, Philadelphia, 1892)

lune (lūn) *Obs.* A fit of insanity.

lust dynamism Sullivan's term for clearly expressed feelings of sexual interest and ability, such as the wish of the adolescent boy to reach orgasm.

Luys, body of (Jules Bernard Luys, French physician, 1828 - 98) See *subthalamus.*

lycanthropy (lī-kan'thrō-pē) The belief that one can change himself or others into a wolf or some other animal.

The *delirium of metamorphosis* or transformation into some form of animal (lycanthropy) . . . is met with much more rarely today than in past centuries, including even the first half of the nineteenth century.' (Bianchi, L. *A Text-Book of Psychiatry,* tr. by MacDonald, J.H., Bailliere, Tindall & Cox, London, 1906)

lycomania (lī-kō-mā'nē-ȧ) Lycanthropy.

lycorexia (lī-kō-rek'sē-ȧ) Bulimia.

lygophilia (lī-gō-fil'ē-ȧ, lig-ō-) Longing for dark or gloomy places.

lying, pathological (pa-thō-loj'i-kal) 'Pathological lying is falsification entirely disproportionate to any discernible end

in view, engaged in by a person who, at the time of observation, cannot be definitely declared insane, feebleminded or epileptic. Such lying rarely, if ever, centers about a single event; although exhibited in very occasional cases for a short time, it manifests itself most frequently by far over a period of years, or even a lifetime. It represents a trait rather than an episode.' (Healy, W. and Healy, M.T. *Pathological Lying, Accusation, and Swindling.* Little, Brown, Boston, 1915.) Pathological lying is also known as mythomania or pseudologia fantastica.

lypemania (lip-ē-mā'nē-ȧ; lī-pē) Esquirol, the pupil of Pinel, divided mental disorders into five classes:
1. Lypemania or melancholia.
2. Monomania, in which 'the disorder of the faculties is limited to one or a small number of objects, with excitement and predominance of a gay and expansive passion.'
3. Mania, characterized by 'delirium' extending 'to all kinds of objects' and accompanied by excitement.
4. Dementia, 'in which the insensate utter folly, because the organs of thought have lost their energy and the strength requisite for their functions.'
5. Imbecility or idiocy, 'in which the conformation of the organs has never been such that those who are thus afflicted can reason justly.'

lypothymia (lī-pō-thī'mē-ȧ, -thim'ēȧ; lip-ō) Melancholy.

lysatotherapy (lī-sa-tō-ther'ȧ-pē) A form of treatment for clinical depression reported by Timopheyev which uses a lysate of the anterior hypophysis. Lysatotherapy is based on the assumption that hypophyseal hypofunction is of etiologic significance in the pathogenesis of pure depression or cyclothymia.

lysergic acid diethylamide (lī-ser'jik a'sid dī'eth-il-am-id) See *psychotomimetic; psychotropics.*

lyssa (lis'ȧ) *Obs.* Insanity.

lyssophobia (lis-ō-fō'bē-ȧ) Fear of becoming insane.

lytic cocktail See *cocktail, lytic.*

M

M In Rorschach scoring, a human-movement response, i.e. a response in which human figures are seen in movement or in a position of tension, or one in which animals behave physically like humans. According to Piotrowski the M responses reveal the subject's prototypal role in life, such as activity or passivity, aggressiveness or submissiveness, etc. M indicate an interest in people and are positively correlated with creative imagination and the level of intelligence. Absence of M is frequent in deterioration secondary to intracranial pathology. (Piotrowski Z. *Perceptanalysis*, Macmillan, New York, 1957) See *type, M*.

m In Piotrowski's perceptanalytic scoring system, a response of movement or prevention of movement in reference to inanimate, inorganic, or insensate matter. Such responses are believed to indicate roles in life which are desired and pleasant, but unrealizable, and thus to some extent they are a measure of motor restraint. (Piotrowski, Z. *Perceptanalysis*, Macmillan, New York, 1957)

M.A. Acronym for mental age; see *quotient, intelligence*.

machlaenomania (mak-lē-nō-mā′nē-à) Masochism in women.

machlosyne (mak-lōs′i-nē) Nymphomania.

macro- (mak′rō-) combining form meaning large, enlarged, extended, exaggerated, from Gr. *makrós*, long, large.

macrobiotic (mak-rō-bī-ot′ik) Longevous.

macrocephaly (-sef′à-lē) Abnormally large size of the head.

macrogenitosomia (-jen-it-ō-sō′mē-à) A syndrome occurring in children before the age of puberty, due to tumors of the pineal gland. The condition is also known as *pubertas praecox* (precocious puberty). The sexual development is precocious with early ejaculation or menstruation and the growth of prematurely large genitals. The secondary sex characters occur early with gruff voice, facial, pubic, and axillary hairs, and mammary gland development.

macrogenitosomia, precocious Pellizzi introduced this term for a particular form of gigantism (q.v.) occurring in children and characterized by premature, rapid, and exaggerated development of the entire organism, including the sexual organs. In addition to the overgrowth of stature and body mass, which may reach the dimensions of the adult in a few years, there are frequently dissociations and partial hypoevolutisms of the sexual characteristics, and also adiposity and a certain degree of mental deficiency.

This syndrome is caused either by tumors of the adrenal cortex, the testicle, or the pineal gland, or in rare cases by dyspituitarism and, in female children, sometimes by constitutional hypothyroidism.

macroglobulinemia, Waldenstrom's Described by Waldenstrom in 1944; a disease of unknown origin characterized by a serum globulin of very large molecular size, lymphocytosis, thrombopenia, weight loss, weakness, and often splenomegaly and a hemorrhagic tendency. The illness is fatal within two to ten years of onset, and approximately 25 per cent of cases have central nervous system symptoms (which cases are termed *Bing-Neel syndrome*) such as progressive encephalopathy, polyneuritis, polyradiculitis, strokes, subarachnoid hemorrhage, delirium, coma, convulsions and other focal central symptoms, loss of hearing and any number of mental disturbances such as depression. (294.8,309.9)

macrology (mak-rol′ō-jē) Long speech with little reasoning.

macromania (mak-rō-mā′nē-à) *Obs.* 'That form of insanity in which the insane person conceives things, especially parts of his own body, to be larger than they in reality are.' (Tuke, D.H. *A Dictionary of Psychological Medicine*, vols. 1-2, Blakiston, Philadelphia, 1892)

macropsia, macropsy (mak-rop′sē-à,

mak'rop-sē) Visual sensation of objects as larger than they really are.

macroskelic (mak-rō-skel'ik) In Manouvrier's system of constitutional types, that type characterized by excessive length of the legs; it corresponds roughly to Kretschmer's asthenic type. See *type, asthenic.*

macrosomatognosia (mà-krō-sō-mà-tognō'sē-à) See *somatognosia.*

mactation (mak-tā'shun) Murder of a sacrifical victim, a concept occasionally observed among psychotic patients.

madbrain A popular expression denoting rashness, ungovernability.

madcap A popular term for a rash, wild, reckless person.

madman A popular expression for one mentally unbalanced.

madness A popular term for mental disorder.

maenad (mē'nad) *Obs.* A mentally sick woman.

maenas (mē'nas) *Obs. Mania.*

magic See *thinking, magical.*

Magna Mater (mag'nà mā'tēr, màg'nà mä'ter) (L. '(the) Great Mother') Cybele, whose cult as a goddess originated in Asia Minor (Phrygia), later known to the Romans most commonly as the Great Mother of the Gods, the symbol of universal motherhood, the parent of gods and every living being, particularly wild creatures. In her reputed nocturnal wanderings over wooded mountains, the religious retinue of semi-demonic Corybantes attended her with noisy music and armed dances. Her festivities were celebrated by eunuch priests (wearing women's attire), the Galli, headed by the chief Archigallus, together with the priestesses, amid rites of raving excitement and dancing (to the tunes of wild music), until they collapsed in utter exhaustion. The term designates one of Jung's archetypes. See *archetype; archetype, mother.*

Magnan's sign *Fornication* (q.v.).

magnetism The property of mutual attraction or repulsion possessed by magnets; such a force was once believed to be the principal factor in hypnosis, which was thus called animal magnetism.

magnus morbus (màg-noos môr'boos) (L. 'great disease,' epilepsy) *Obs.* Epilepsy.

magrums (mā'grumz) *Obs.* Chorea.

Mahler, Margaret Schoenberger (1897 -) Hungarian-born U.S. psychoanalyst; symbiotic psychosis, childhood schizophrenia.

maid *Obs.* A virgin man, one who has not had sexual intercourse.

maieusiomania (mā-ū-sē-ō-mā'nē-à) *Obs.* Puerperal psychosis.

maieusiophobia (mā-ū-sē-ō-fō'bē-à) Fear of childbirth.

mainliner A slang expression for addicts who take narcotics by intravenous injection.

Main's syndrome See *syndrome, Main's.*

maintenance-level See *level, maintenance.*

maitre de plaisir (mâtr' dē plâ-zēr') (F. 'master of pleasure') One who derives satisfaction from arranging for the sexual pleasures of others.

make-up, mental Character or personality structure. See *character.*

make-up, personality The constitution of the personality; see *constitution, personality.*

mal d'orient (màl' dô-ryäN') (F. 'oriental evil') Homosexuality. It is said that the practice spread to Europe through the influence of the Crusaders. In some countries a homosexual is called a Turk or a Bulgar; hence, the French term *bougre* and the English *bugger*, both denoting a homosexual.

maladaptation, common See *psychodynamics, adaptational.*

maladie des tics (mà-là-dē' dä tēk') *Gilles de la Tourette syndrome* (q.v.).

maladie du pays (mà-là-dē' dü pā-ē') (F. 'homesickness') Nostalgia.

maladjustment, simple adult Adult situational reaction. See *transient situational personality disorders.*

malady, English *Obs.* Hypochondriasis.

malignant identity diffusion See *crime and mental disorder.*

malinger (mà-ling'gēr) To feign or protract one's illness; to simulate, with intent to deceive.

malingering Simulation of symptoms of illness or injury with intent to deceive. Malingering occurs, usually, in one of the following situations: (1) in criminal cases, when psychosis or mental deficiency is advanced as a defense; (2) in personal injury actions and compensation cases; and (3) in military service or similar special situations where nervous or mental disease might afford an escape from hazardous or arduous duty. The diseases most likely to be malingered are amnesiae, psychoses, psychoneuroses, and mental deficiency. Detection in the latter case is relatively simple with available psychometric tests.

malleation (mal-ē-ā'shun) Convulsive-like movements of the hands, as if in the act of hammering.

malum caducum (mà'loom kà-dōō'koom) (L. 'falling evil or sickness') *Obs.* Epilepsy.

malum minus (mē'noos) (L. 'minor evil') Petit mal form of epilepsy.

mammalingus (mam-à-lin'gus) Sucking on the breast. 'The fellatio conception of coitus, in fact, would seem to be only one-half of the story. One finds also the complementary idea that the father not only gives to the mother, but receives from her; that in short she suckles him. And it is here that the direct rivalry with the father is so strong, for the mother is giving him just what the girl wants (nipple and milk). ... When this "mammalingus" conception, as it may be called, gets sadistically cathected, then we have the familiar feminist idea of the man who "uses" the woman, exhausts her, drains her, exploits her,

and so on.' (Jones, E. *Papers on Psycho-Analysis,* 4th ed., Wood, Baltimore, 1938)

man, effeminated (e-fem'i-nāt-id) Passive homosexual male.

manager disease A type of occupational neurosis (300.13) occurring in overworked employers and leading officials who are overburdened with responsibility. The symptoms most commonly complained of are those relating to the heart and cardiovascular system.

mandala (man'dà-là) Jung's term for the magic circle that symbolizes total unity of the self.

mania (mā'nē-à) 1. *Obs.* Any mental disorder, "madness," especially when characterized by violent, unrestrained behavior. 2. When used as a suffix, a morbid preference for or an irrepressible impulse to behave in a certain way, such as *kleptomania* (q.v.). 3. One of the two major forms of manic depressive illness; see *psychosis, manic-depressive.*

The manic-form of manic-depressive psychosis is characterized by (a) an elated or euphoric, although unstable, mood; (b) increased psychomotor activity, restlessness, agitation, etc.; and (c) increase in number of ideas and speed of thinking and speaking, which in more severe forms proceed to *flight of ideas* (q.v.), often with a grandiose trend.

In mania, the main disturbances in the ideational sphere are: *overproductivity, flight of ideas,* that is, a rapid shifting from one topic to another; of which *distractibility* is a part, the patient changing from topic to topic in accordance with the stimuli from without and from within; the shifting may be occasioned by what is called *clang association*—stimulation of a new train of thought by some external sound; *leveling of ideas,* that is, essentially all topics have about the same value to the patient; *ideas of importance, grandiose ideas,* the patient expressing delusions of greatness perhaps in all fields; the feelings of well-being are expressed also in the sphere of *physical excellence.* Often the ideas are reproductions of those relating to *infantile sexuality.*

The principal modifications in the emotional field are: exaggerated feelings of gaiety, well-being, extreme happiness—in consonance with the ideas expressed.

The expression *psycho-motor overactivity* refers to physical overactivity. In extreme states it is incessant throughout the waking hours; the patient attempts to motorize, that is, to put into physical execution all the ideas that occur to him; this tendency, therefore, leads to a shifting of physical activity paralleling that in the mental sphere.

Depending upon the degree of mania, there are three types: *hypomania*, which is a less intense form; *mania*, which is presumably the common or usual type; *hypermania*, or a more intense expression of the manic reaction.

Some authors use the term *acute mania* synonymously with *mania*, and *hypermania*, is often referred to as *delirious mania*, *Bell's mania*, *typhomania*, *delirium grave*, or *collapse delirium*, with partial or complete disorientation as the rule.

When a patient has a succession of manic attacks the condition is known as *recurrent* or *periodic mania*. When manic and depressive episodes alternate, the condition is called *alternating* or *circular psychosis* or *insanity*.

Periodic mania is to be distinguished from *chronic mania*, a form described by Schott in 1904 in which manic symptoms continue uninterruptedly for an indefinite number of years (in Schott's series, for 30, 25, 21, and 17 years). In all such cases which have been reported, the particular episode which becomes chronic has begun after the age of 40.

A patient in a manic phase may not talk; his state is then known as *unproductive* or *stuporous mania;* he is said to be in a condition of *manic stupor*.

When a patient presents the symptoms of mania, but does not move, his condition is called *akinetic mania*. Follow-up studies suggest that akinetic mania and manic stupor and all of Kraepelin's 'mixed' or 'intermediate' states are really schizophrenic.

The psychoanalytic point is one which several analytic investigators have already formulated in so many words, namely, that the content of mania is no different from that of melancholia, that both the disorders are wrestling with the same "complex," and that in melancholia the ego has succumbed to it, whereas in mania it has mastered the complex or thrust it aside.' (Freud, S. *Collected Papers*, vol. 4, tr. by Riviere, J., Leonard and Virginia Woolf and The Institute of Psychoanaly-

sis, London, 1924-25) In mania, the ego for a time has thrown off the yoke of the superego and protests, 'I don't need control any more.' The removal of inhibition allows all those impulses (mainly oral) which had been kept down to come to the fore. But the freedom from the superego is not a real one, and the ego must deny its fear of the superego by overcompensation. The cramped nature of the symptoms is due to the fact that they are of a reaction-formation type and deny opposite attitudes. Mania is not a genuine freedom from depression but rather a cramped denial of dependencies.

mania a potu (mả'nē-ả ả pō'tōo) (L. 'madness from drink(ing)') A state, produced by alcohol, characterized by extreme excitement and sometimes leading to homicidal attacks. The attack is usually brought on, in a susceptible person, by the ingestion of comparatively small amounts of alcohol. See *intoxication, alcoholic*.

mania, absorbed Manic stupor; see *mania*.

mania, acute See *mania*.

mania, akinetic (ak-i-net'ik) See *mania*.

mania, ambitious *Obs.* Delirium grandiosum; megalomania; folie ambitieuse.

mania, anxious A mixed form of manic-depressive psychosis. 'If in the picture depression takes the place of cheerful mood, a morbid state arises, which is composed of flight of ideas, excitement, and anxiety. The patients are distractible, absent-minded, enter into whatever goes on round them, take themselves up with everything, catch up words and continue spinning out the ideas stirred up by these. . . .' (Kraepelin, E. *Manic-Depressive Insanity and Paranoia*, tr. by Barclay, R.M., Livingstone, Edinburgh, 1921) See *mania*.

mania, Bell's (Luther V. Bell, American physician, 1806-62) Acute mania; see *mania*.

mania, brooding Morbid impulse to meditate long and anxiously; obsessive doubting.
'We have already mentioned the impor-

tant part played by the sadistic instinctual components in the genesis of obsessional neuroses. Where the epistemophilic instinct is a preponderating feature in the constitution of an obsessional patient, brooding becomes the principal symptom of the neurosis.' (Freud, S. *Collected Papers*, vol. 3, tr. by Strachey, A. and J., Leonard and Virginia Woolf and The Institute of Psychoanalysis, London, 1925) See *folie du doute.*

mania, Caesar *Obs.* 'A feeling of being absolute master of life and death among savages.' (Bleuler, E. *Textbook of Psychiatry*, tr. by Brill, A. A., Macmillan, New York, 1930)

mania, chattering *Obs.* Uncontrollable urge to talk gibberish; pressured speech.

mania, chronic Term first used by Schott for the manic type of reaction that is more or less permanent.

mania, chronic intellectual *Obs.* 'A general disturbance of the intellect characterized by the existence of varying unsystematized delusions, accompanied by periods of mental excitement or depression, with more or less incoherence and mental weakness.' (Foster. F.P. *Medical Dictionary*, Appleton, New York, 1892-4)

mania, classification of See *depression, classification of; mania.*

mania(co)comium (mä-ni-à-[kō]-kō'mē-um) Psychiatric hospital.

mania, collecting The morbid impulse to collect. It is seen in one of its most vivid forms in patients with schizophrenia, who often collect all sorts of articles, most of them useless; they stuff their clothing with trash. The collecting mania is often clearly representative of anal erotism. The symptom is also frequent in senile dementia. See *soteria.*

mania concionabunda (mà'nē-à kôn-kī-ô-nà-boon'dà) *Obs.* Mania for addressing the public. (*Lancet*, 1176, 1886)

mania, depressive Anxious *mania;* See *mania.*

mania, doubting An obsessive doubting in which the patient finds it necessary to say 'no' to everything. This patient will raise objections to whatever comes into his mind from within or without. For example, the names of people known intimately for years may become uncertain to the patient. He may realize intellectually that what he objects to is correct, but his emotions deny the fact. Usually, under analysis, it emerges that unconscious instinctual demands are being denied through the doubting-mania. (Hinsie, L. E. *Understandable Psychiatry*, Macmillan, Ne York, 1948)

mania, ephemeral (e-fem'ēr-al) See *mania transitoria.*

mania errabunda (mà'nē-à er-rà-boon'dà) *Obs.* Impulsive wandering from home, apparently without aim; occurs frequently in senile states.

mania, grumbling 'The patients, indeed, display exalted self-consciousness, are pretentious and high-flown, but by no means of cheerful mood; they rather appear dissatisfied, insufferable, perhaps even a little anxious. They have something to find fault with in everything, feel themselves on every occasion badly treated, get wretched food, cannot hold out in the dreadful surroundings, cannot sleep in the miserable beds, cannot have social intercourse with the other patients.' (Kraepelin, E. *Manic-Depressive Insanity and Paranoia*, tr. by Barclay, R.M., Livingstone, Edinburgh, 1921)

mania, homicidal *Obs. Homicidomania.* Any kind of mental disease where there is an attempt or desire on the part of a patient to kill. 'But, as you have seen, the homicidal desire may occur in melancholia, and is often associated with the suicidal feeling. As we shall see, it may occur as an uncomplicated impulse, not accompanied by depression or exaltation of mind, and it then stands as one of the varieties of impulsive insanity.' (Clouston, T. S. *Clinical Lectures on Mental Diseases*, 6th ed., Churchill, London, 1904)

mania, incendiary Pyromania.

mania, inhibited One of Kraepelin's 'mixed states,' characterized by flight of ideas, cheerful mood, and psychomotor inhibition; see *mania.* 'The patients of this kind are of more exultant mood, occasionally somewhat irritable, distractible, inclined to jokes; when addressed they easily fall into chattering talk with flight of ideas and numerous clang associations, but remain in outward behaviour conspicuously quiet, lie still in bed, only now and then throw out a remark or laugh to themselves. It appears, however, as if a great inward tension, as a rule, existed, as the patients may suddenly become very violent. Formerly I classified this "inhibited mania" with manic stupor; I think, however, that it may be separated from that on the ground of the flight of ideas which here appears distinctly.' (Kraepelin, E. *Manic-Depressive Insanity and Paranoia,* tr. by Barclay, R.M., Livingstone, Edinburgh, 1921)

mania, metaphysical *Obs. Folie du doute* (q.v.); insanity of doubt.

mania mitis (mà'nē-à mē'tēs) (L. 'mild madness') This is an older term, designating what is today called *hypomania.* 'The slightest forms of manic excitement are usually called "hypomania," mania mitis, mitissima, also, but inappropriately, *mania sine delirio.*' (Kraepelin, E. *Manic-Depressive Insanity and Paranoia,* tr. by Barclay, R.M., Livingstone, Edinburgh, 1921)

mania, muscular (mā'nē-à) *Obs.* 'Automatic coördinated movements that are ordinarily voluntary, but result evidently from morbid exaltation of function in the highest motor centres in the convolutions. It is a *muscular mania,* the intellectual and volitional power being comparatively intact, but the highest ideo-motor centres being paralysed.' (Clouston, T. S. *Clinical Lectures on Mental Diseases,* 6th ed., Churchill, London, 1904) He refers to the exaggerated motor activity characteristic of *mania* (q.v.).

mania, periodic See *mania.*

mania phantastica infantilis A rare syndrome of childhood consisting of exaltation states, fugues, confabulations or *pseudologia fantastica* (q.v.), immaturity, and retardation of mental development. The syndrome may occur as part of the delirious state following infectious diseases, and also as a psychogenic or autochthonous reaction.

mania, puerperal (mā'nē-à) *Obs.* 'People very often speak of "puerperal mania" in the sense of a particular form of insanity produced exclusively by the puerperium, but this view can only be maintained today within very narrow limits. Where mania really appears in the puerperal state, it is, like every other kind of mania, only a link in the chain of attacks of maniacal-depressive insanity. The puerperium cannot therefore be regarded as the cause, but only as the last impulse to the outbreak of the disease.' (Kraepelin, E. *Lectures on Clinical Psychiatry,* 3rd ed., revised and edited by Johnstone, T.H., Ballière, Tindall & Cox, London, 1913) A variety of *puerperal psychosis.*

mania, reactive Bleuler says that there is no condition known as *reactive mania,* though a milder state akin to it, *reactive exaltation,* is described. The latter state, resembling that of *hypomania,* is induced by some external cause and ceases when the cause is removed. See *reactive.*

mania, recurrent See *mania.*

mania, religious *Obs.* An acute psychotic episode, usually schizophrenic or organic in origin, characterized by generalized hyperactivity, agitation, restlessness, and many hallucinations with a religious coloring. See *ecstasy.*

mania senilis (mà'nē-à se-nē'lēs) (L. 'old-age madness') See *melancholia senilis.*

mania sine delirio (mà'nē-à sē'ne dā-lē'rē-ō) (L. 'mania without delirium') *Mania mitis* (q.v.).

mania, stuporous See *mania.*

mania transitoria (mà'nē-à tràn-zē-tō'-rē-à) (L. 'passing, temporary madness') *Obs.* 'This term is used to describe a somewhat rare form of maniacal exaltation, which comes on suddenly, is usually sharp in its character, and is accompanied by incoherence, partial or complete unconsciousness of familiar surroundings, and sleeplessness. An attack may last from an hour up to a few days.' (Clouston, T.S. *Clinical Lectures on Mental Diseases,* 6th ed., Churchill, London, 1904) It was also called *ephemeral mania.*

mania, tropical (mä'nē-à) A general term for a variety of psychiatric disorders occurring in the tropics; save in specific instances, such as heat stroke, it is not known what role, if any, heat plays in the disorders.

mania, wandering See *wanderlust.*

maniaphobia (mä-nē-à-fō'bē-à) Fear of insanity.

manic-depressive See *psychosis, manic-depressive.*

manie de perfection (mà-nē' dē per-fek-syawN') (F. 'perfection mania') Compulsive perfectionism; *scrupulosity* (q.v.). For the person affected with such a symptom, everything must be 100 per cent good, moral, clean, efficient, or otherwise perfect.

manie de rumination (rü-mē-nà-syawN') (F. 'rumination mania') Janet's term for the morbid tendency to recall to mind and consider past events again and again; seen commonly in obsessive-compulsive neurosis and in some involutional psychoses.

maniodes (man-ē-ō'dēz) *Obs.* Maniacal; ferine, brutal, beastly.

manipulanda (mà-nē-poo-làn'dà) See *intelligence.*

manipulative Exploitative; skillful in getting what one wants from others, and able to control or manage others in gaining one's own ends. Most commonly the term is used in a pejorative sense to refer to patients whose artful maneuvers in getting their own way border on the fraudulent; therapists are likely to use the term when they feel they have been made to feel foolish or out-smarted by their patients. Manipulative behavior may be seen in anyone, but it is particularly characteristic of some children, of personality types labelled hysterical, and of some schizophrenic patients—all of whom may use threats of throwing a tantrum, of suicide, or of other behavior that plays on the guilt of others in order to achieve their own goals of the moment. See *syndrome, Main's.*

mannerism A gesture or other form of expression, usually peculiar to a given subject; sometimes used interchangeably with *stereotypy* (q.v.), although generally a mannerism is less insistently and less monotonously repeated, and more in keeping with the subject's personality.

manustupration (man-ū-stū-prā'shun) An older term for *masturbation* (q.v.).

MAO *Monoamine oxidase* (q.v.).

maple syrup urine disease (31x.2) A cerebral degenerative disorder due to a genetically induced defect in the metabolism of the branched-chain aminoacids leucine, isoleucine, and valine. Clinical manifestations are poor feeding, developmental retardation, hypertonicity, convulsions, and a urine odor resembling that of maple syrup. The latter is due to increased plasma level of the above-named amino acids, whose keto-derivatives are excreted in increased amounts in the urine. Central nervous system pathology includes defective myelin formation within the white matter of the entire brain, areas of edema and spongy change, an associated astrocytosis, and a decrease in oligodendroglia. Although genetically induced, the disease does not manifest itself clinically until after birth; death usually occurs within two years after onset of symptoms, which may be partially controlled on a diet low in the amino acids involved.

marasmic state See *detachment, somnolent.*

marasmus nervosus (mà-ràz'moos nervō'zoos) (Neo L. 'nervous emaciation') *Obs.* Neurasthenia; *anorexia nervosa.* (q.v.).

marche a petits pas (màrsh á pē-tē-pà') (F. 'short-step walking') A disturbance in gait in which the patient takes very short steps. The condition may be observed in cerebral arteriosclerosis and striatal rigidity. See *gait, propulsion.*

Marchiafava-Bignami disease A rare neuropsychiatric syndrome associated with alcoholism; the essential pathology is central necrosis of the corpus callosum and sometimes of the anterior commissure. This syndrome appears most typically in chronic alcoholics who are addicted to Italian red wine; when the central necrosis begins, the patient develops an acute psychotic picture consisting of excitement, ataxia or apraxia, disorientation, and confusion. With progression (and presumably due to spread of the process to the cingulate gyri), the clinical picture changes markedly: the patient becomes totally apathetic, aboulic, quiet, and completely inattentive; he appears devoid of all conation, shows akinetic mutism, and may develop hemiplegia or hemiparesis. Once this stage is reached, death is the usual end-result. It is generally believed that alcohol per se is not the cause of this syndrome, but rather that it is due to metallic impurities found in wine as a result of processing and/or that it is a manifestation of vitamin deficiency.

Marcus Gunn sign (Marcus Gunn, contemporary British surgeon.) The raising of a ptosed lid on opening the mouth and moving the jaw to the opposite side.

margin, conscious See *fringe.*

Marie's ataxia See *ataxia, Marie's hereditary cerebellar.*

Marie's disease (Pierre Marie, French physician, 1853-1940) See *acromegaly.*

marihuana, marijuana (mä-rē-hwä′nä) A variety of cannabis sativa obtained from the flowering tops of the Indian hemp plant, which grows freely in all parts of the United States and Mexico; other forms are kief, ma, ganja, dagga, charas, hashish and bhang. Marihuana is most commonly taken in the form of 'reefers' (known also as pot, tea, weed, hay, grass, charge, joints, and sticks)—shorter and thicker than the usual cigarette and wrapped in brown paper. Smoking two or three reefers gives the desired effect: a dreamy state of partial consciousness, in which ideas are disconnected, uncontrollable, and plentiful; at times, euphoria and an excited joyousness, at other times a moody reverie or panic and fçar of death; imagination runs riot, and perception is crowded and disturbed; a peculiar distortion of time, so that minutes seem to be hours, and of space, which is broadened so that near objects seem far away; vivid, pleasant hallucinations, often with a sexual coloring; loss of discrimina-

tory ability so that a three-piece honkytonk band may seem like a symphony orchestra. Under the influence of marihuana behavior is impulsive, mood is elevated, and random ideas are quickly translated into action. Prolonged use in those with a psychopathic personality may result in a certain degree of mental deterioration, but no positive relationship between violent crime and the use of drug has ever been demonstrated. Marihauna, as also cocaine and peyote, does not produce physical dependence; hence there is not the great drive to get these drugs as is seen with opiates. These drugs, like alcohol, merely release inhibitions and thereby expose the basic inadequate personality of the habitual user (in DSM-II, termed marihuana dependency, 304.5). Treatment consists of abrupt withdrawal.

Marin Amat syndrome See *syndrome, Marin Amat.*

marketing type See *assimilation.*

marriage counseling See *counseling, marriage.*

marriage, psychiatric aspects of Nearly one-half of the United States have laws whose interest is to prevent persons with mental disorder to marry. In some cases, issuance of a license is interdicted; in others, performance of the ceremony is forbidden. Most states afford no means of enforcing such laws, however, and the question of legality of marriage typically arises only when one of the parties concerned seeks annulment of the marriage contract. The validity of the marriage can be questioned by the 'incompetent' spouse on the ground that he was incapable of understanding what he was doing. By statute in England, and in most of the United States, marriage may be voided on the ground of mental unsoundness. Similarly, England and more than half of the United States consider 'incurable insanity' as grounds for divorce.

marriage, therapeutic (ther-à-pū′tik) As an adjunct to their treatment certain probably well-intentioned, but misguided, physicians actually advise marriage for their patients. Generally, this is rationalized in the following fashion: it functions as an impetus or catalyzer for the patient, forcing the emergence of emotional maturity. As a rule, these patients have presented themselves for treatment for the symptomatic physical expression of disorders of neurotic psychogenic origin, usually centering around various forms of psychogenic impotence in the male, and frigidity and sexual aversion in the female. When such people, upon the well-meant advice of physicians, actively carry out the counsel to marry, the specific character-testing intimacies of the marital situation, particularly in the sexual sphere, soon precipitate the symptoms of their characterological emotional inadequacies. As a therapeutic medium the advice 'to marry' is commonly either contraindicated or unnecessary.

The best guarantee for the development of marital problems is for two immature personalities to 'fall in love' and marry. Contrariwise, when two mature people find each other attractive and marry there is the best chance for marital happiness. One of the criteria of minimal maturity for marriage is for people to assume the responsibility of their own choice, and to marry 'under their own steam.' (Weiss, E., and English, O.S. *Psychosomatic Medicine*, 2nd ed., Saunders, Philadelphia and London, 1949)

marriage therapy See *therapy, marriage; counseling, marriage.*

masculine attitude in female neurotics Adler uses this term to indicate the masculine protest against feminine or apparently feminine stirrings and sensations occurring in the female neurotic. She manifests unconscious tendencies to play the masculine (domineering, active, cruel) role with the use of all available means.

masculine protest See *protest, masculine.*

masculinity While *maleness* primarily relates to the proper sex chromosome structure of XY individuals, *masculinity* is preferably understood as a male's possession of the typical and well developed *secondary* sex characteristics of a man (see *sex determination*).

mask Stekel uses this term to mean characterological disguise: 'Less known are other masks of homosexuality which I now mention. The love of old women (gerontophilia) and passion for children often covers a homosexual tendency.'

(Stekel, W. *Bi-Sexual Love*, tr. by van Teslaar, J.S., Badger, Boston, 1922) See *persona.*

masochism (maz'ok-iz'm) (From Leopold von Sacher Masoch (1836-95), an Austrian novelist, whose characters indulge in all kinds of sex perversions, deriving sexual pleasure from being cruelly treated) When sexual satisfaction depends upon the subject himself 'suffering pain, ill-treatment and humiliation' (Freud), the condition is known as masochism (302.7).

Krafft-Ebing defined masochism as 'a peculiar perversion of the psychical *vita sexualis* in which the individual affected, in sexual feeling and thought, is controlled by the idea of being completely and unconditionally subject to the will of a person of the opposite sex, of being treated by this person as by a master, humiliated and abused. This idea is colored by sexual feeling; the masochist lives in fancies in which he creates situations of this kind, and he often attempts to realize them.' (Krafft-Ebing, R.v. *Psychopathia Sexualis*, Login, New York, 1908, p. 115)

Havelock Ellis notes that Stefanowsky termed it *passivism.*

Freud originally believed that masochism was always secondary and represented a turning of sadism against the ego under the influence of guilt. Later, however, applying his theories of Thanatos or the Nirvana principle, he differentiated three types of masochism:

1. *erotogenic* or *primary masochism,* when masochism is a requisite condition for sexual gratification. The self-destructive tendencies arising from the death instinct are to a large extent disposed of early in life by displacement onto objects in the outer world; this is the origin of mastery, the will to power, and true sadism. The part which is not so disposed of remains as the original erotogenic masochism, elements of which can be traced through all the developmental stages of the libido: oral (fear of being devoured), anal (desire to be beaten by the father), phallic (castration phantasies), and genital (in situations characteristic of womanhood, the passive part in coitus and the act of giving birth).

2. *feminine masochism,* as an expression of feminine nature.

3. *moral masochism,* when there is a need for punishment arising from uncon-

scious needs relating to re-sexualization of the parental introjects and reactivation of the Oedipus complex. The basic desire is to have intercourse with the father passively, and through regressive distortion this becomes a desire to be beaten by the father. The moral masochist must act against his own interests, even to the point of destroying himself, in order to provoke punishment from authority figures. Asceticism is related to moral masochism, for the mortification is sexualized and the act of mortifying becomes a distorted expression of the blocked sexuality.

Wilhelm Reich agreed that behind the masochist's behavior lay a desire to provoke authority figures, but he disagreed that this was in order to bribe the superego or to execute a dreaded punishment. Rather, he maintained, this grandiose provocation represented a defense against punishment and anxiety by substituting a milder punishment and by placing the provoked authority figure in such a light as to justify the masochist's reproach, 'See how badly you treat me.' Behind such a provocation is a deep disappointment in love, a disappointment of the masochist's excessive demand for love based on the fear of being left alone.

More recently, B. Berliner has emphasized the role of the infantile love object in the genesis of masochism; he regards the masochistic attitude as a bid for the affection of a hating love object. 'Masochistic suffering represents in the unconscious the original personal love object that once gave suffering. Masochism is the sadism of the love object fused with the libido of the subject.' ('The Role of Object Relations in Moral Masochism,' *Psychoanalytical Quarterly* 27: 38-56, 1958)

masochism, actual See *instinct, death.*

masochism, erotogenic (ē-rō-tō-jen'ik) Of the three types of masochism described by Freud, erotogenic masochism is 'the lust of pain.' It is the form commonly implied by the term masochism. See *masochism.*

masochism, ideal Mental, psychic, or moral masochism; when the masochistic injury is mental or psychical, rather than physical, Freud termed it *ideal.* See *masochism.*

masochism, mass By this term Reik denotes 'the mixture of (a) renunciation of one's own power and (b) enjoyment of its being used by proxy,' such as may be seen in the enthusiasm and devotion shown by the masses to a dictator, who demands hardships and sacrifices of the masses, which they would be unable to bear if they did not consider him to be their own idealized image. (Reik, T. *Masochism in Modern Man,* Farrar and Rinehart, New York, 1941)

masochism, mental See *masochism, ideal.*

masochism, primal See *instinct, death.*

masochism, psychic (sī'kik) See *masochism, ideal.*

masochism, secondary During growth the main part of sadism or the death-instinct is directly outwardly; the portion that remains in the individual is called primary sadism or (now being directed inward upon the subject himself) masochism. Under given conditions, for example, in states of deep depression the objectivated sadism is withdrawn from objects and redirected onto the subject himself; that is, it is introjected. This involves the process of regression to its earlier condition. 'It then provides that secondary masochism which supplements the original one.' (Freud, S. *Collected Papers,* vol. 2, tr. by Riviere, J., Leonard and Virginia Woolf and The Institute of Psychoanalysis, London, 1924-25) See *masochism.*

masochism, social A characteristic subordinate attitude toward life, forcing the person into submissive and passive behavior, which enables him to stand defeats, privations, and misfortune. Such a situation can be described as a 'giving up' attitude. (Reik, T. *Masochism in Modern Man,* Farrar and Rinehart, New York, 1941)

masochism, verbal The condition in which a person craves to hear insulting or humiliating words and derives sexual excitement by imagining himself abused or insulted verbally. A certain choice, succession, or emphasis of words and sentences seems important for the sexual excitement. Dialogues during the masochistic phantasy are quite frequent. These imagined situations 'are frequently maintained for years with little or no change, and yet remain exciting. Alterations are usually restricted to trifling displacements and substitutions of persons, times and places, while the main theme, if it may be called so, is adhered to.' (Reik, T. *Masochism in Modern Man*, Farrar and Rinehart, New York, 1941)

massa intermedia (màs′à ēn-tēr-mād-ē-à) See *thalamus*.

massotherapy (mas-ō-ther′à-pē) Treatment by massage.

mastery, oral Domination by means of the mouth. Mastery is a technique which the infant utilizes in adapting itself to its environment when seeking to control (master) it. 'In the fourth month of life the mastery technique consists of seeing an object, grasping it, and directing it to the mouth. This may be called the phase of oral mastery.' (Kardiner, A., and Spiegel, L. *War Stress and Neurotic Illness*, Hoeber, New York, 1947) See *instinct, mastery*.

mastigophobia (mas-ti-gō-fō′bē-à) Fear of flogging.

mastodynia (mas-tō-din′ē-à) A type of intercostal neuralgia in which there is pain and tenderness of the breast and often hyperesthesia of the nipples.

masturbation (mas-tēr-bā′shun) Direct self-manipulation of the genitals, most commonly by the hand, accompanied by phantasies that are usually of a recognizably sexual nature, and having as its aim the discharge of sexual excitation. '*Psychic masturbation*' is also recognized, where phantasy alone is sufficient to effect sexual discharge without any direct physical manipulation. The masturbatory act, then, has two aspects—form (the physical manipulations) and content (the nature of the accompanying or provoking phantasy).

As thus defined, masturbation first occurs in the phallic period, although auto-erotic activity that includes the genitalia and any other areas of the body can certainly be observed from the earliest days of life. But in the phallic period, the major portion of psychic energy is invested in the genital area, and autoerotic activity at that time comes to be associated with oedipal phantasies and so can be termed true masturbation.

'It is recognized that all children masturbate during the infantile period, most do during adolescence, and some do during the latency period. Masturbation, then, can be considered psychologically normal during childhood, and is a major avenue for the discharge of instinctual tension. Under present cultural conditions, masturbation can also be considered psychologically normal during adolescence, and to some extent even in adulthood when gratification of a physical and emotional relationship with a member of the opposite sex is not possible.

'Kinsey finds that masturbation occurs in 92 per cent of American males, and these figures are in line with other surveys and estimates both in this country and in Europe.

'Those adolescents who do not masturbate during puberty show regularly in analysis an especially deep repression of infantile masturbation, threats about which have overwhelmed them with guilt and fear; such patients, incidentally, have a poor prognosis in psychotherapy.

'Certainly sexual gratification is important to the individual, yet the healthy person can tolerate a temporary lack within certain limits and can find substitute gratification along the line of sublimation; it is only the disturbed, neurotic patient who is unable to tolerate any diminution in or postponement of gratification without becoming depressed, and such patients use masturbation to prevent potential depression and to remove already existing depression. The conflicts which the adolescent has over his masturbatory activity are often solved by reaction formations; if he is successful, these contribute to the formation of valuable character traits; if unsuccessful, he must find substitutes for masturbation, or the masturbation itself becomes a neurotic symptom. Thus the control and inhibition of instinctual impulses, at least within certain limits, may well be salutary for the development of character and personality.

'Probably the most important consequence of masturbation is the guilt which typically accompanies it, and the struggle to defend oneself against it which may last for years and adsorb onto itself all the energy of the psychic system. And it is surprising to note how very incompletely the adolescent can be reassured about the dangers of masturbation, to which he ascribes almost every conceivable ill — pimples, insanity, stooped shoulders, weakness, loss of manly vigor, weak eyes, ulcers, impotence, feeblemindedness, cancer, to name only a few. Freud tended to the view that neurasthenia could follow upon excessive masturbation; it is nowadays felt that it would be more correct to say that neurasthenia is an outcome of insufficient orgasm — that is, if anxieties and guilt disturb the satisfactory character of the masturbation.

'It appears, then, that harmful physical consequences may possibly follow masturbation, but that these effects and the likelihood of their occurrence have been greatly exaggerated, and that the chief harmful consequence is in the psychic sphere and pertains to the feeling of guilt over masturbation. When one deals with the adolescent in conflict about the practice, however, he is soon aware that the young boy is unable to accept this benign approach. Instead, he has a deep need to believe that masturbation is a terrible thing and he strongly resists enlightenment about its harmlessness. This is because the conscious masturbatory phantasies are distorted derivatives of unconscious Oedipus phantasies, and if the adolescent did indeed believe that masturbation is harmless he would have to resurrect these phantasies and would have to face the Oedipal desires which are responsible for the guilt.' (Campbell, R.J. 'Sexual Development and Pathology in the Second Decade,' *Proceedings*, 2nd Institute for Clergy on Problems in Pastoral Psychology, Fordham University, New York, 1957)

masturbation, compulsive An ill-defined term used with various meanings by different authors. Some use it synonymously with habitual masturbation or pathological masturbation, i.e. when masturbation is preferred to sexual intercourse or when masturbation is used, not occasionally to relieve sexual tension, but so frequently as to indicate a disturbed capacity for sexual satisfaction. Others apply the term to the constant impulse to masturbate which is seen in some children, who stimulate their genitals frequently, without regard to their environment, and usually without accompanying sexual erotic phantasies. More properly, the term is confined to repetitive masturbatory activity performed without adequate sexual feelings or without any accompanying sexual feelings. 'Symptoms that were created for the purpose of warding off masturbation, through penetration by the warded-off forces, eventually may be replaced by masturbation. A masturbation of this kind does not bring pleasure. The lack of satisfaction increases the striving for satisfaction. The protection-forgiveness of the gods, which would make a relaxing satisfaction possible, may be sought with the same aggressive fury by masturbating, with which it is sought by the gambler in his gambling. And like gambling, masturbation also may be performed for the purpose of punishment, being thought of as an equivalent of castration. The ego demonstrates its self-destruction equivalent to its superego, asking for forgiveness by ingratiation and by stubbornness. And the superego behaves as the gods did who punished King Midas' greediness by ruining him through the fulfillment of his wishes. The sexuality the ego wanted is granted, but in a painful and devastating manner. . . . Instinctual behavior of this kind may also represent a desperate and inadequate attempt to discharge, in a sexual way, tensions of any kind. The act is carried out not only to obtain pleasure or to achieve punishment but also to get rid of an unbearable painful tension and to be relieved of a state of depression. In the same way that the drug may become insufficient in addictions and an ever increasing amount of the drug is needed, so the orgastic impotence in such cases may require more and more of the pseudosexual acts. In severe cases of "sexual addictions," sexuality loses its specific function and becomes an unsuccessful nonspecific protection against stimuli.' (Fenichel, O. *The Psychoanalytic Theory of Neurosis*, Norton, New York, 1945)

Used in a more general sense as synonymous with habitual, pathological, or overfrequent masturbation, or masturbatory pseudo-sexuality, the term compulsive masturbation implies a disturbance in capacity for satisfaction. Such cases are often based on: (1) conflicts over hostility and aggressiveness, especially in those who are afraid to manifest overt defiance; or (2) conflicts over the expectation of punishment, for which masturbation may represent a substitute; or (3) conflicts over 'perverse' sexual impulses, where masturbation is felt to afford a higher pleasure than can be achieved in reality; or (4) attempts to forestall threatened depression or to remove existing depression, which typically is related to unsatisfied yearnings for love and narcissistic supplies; or (5) use of masturbation to withdraw from reality in those who are neurotically inhibited, shy and afraid of interpersonal relationships. (Campbell, R.J. 'Habitual Masturbation,' *Proceeds,* 2nd Inst. for the Clergy on Problems in Pastoral Psychology, Fordham University, New York, 1957)

masturbation, habitual See *masturbation, compulsive.*

masturbation, larval See *onanism, larval.*

masturbation, passive An older expression for fellatio.

masturbation, pathological (pa-thō-loj′i-kal) See *masturbation, compulsive.*

masturbation, psychic See *masturbation.*

masturbation, symbolic The displacement of thinly disguised masturbatory activity upon bodily parts and organs which function as symbolic objects substituting for the phallus-clitoris, or penis, even if they give no direct orgastic gratification. Such symbolic masturbation can consist of nail-biting, playing with hangnails, pulling the cuticle, twisting the coat sleeve or handkerchief corners, pulling at buttons, twisting and plucking hairs or hair strands, fingering nose, ear-lobe, or inserting of finger into nose, mouth, or ear.

materialization, hysterical (ma-tēr-ē-al-i-zā′shun, his-ter′i-kal) Somatization; Ferenczi's term for that type of conversion hysteria in which unconscious conflicts are expressed as alterations of physical functions. See *hysteria.*

The particular alterations occurring in physical functions symbolize certain specific memories and phantasies, determined by the patient's history and centering around the repressed instinctual demands and the anxieties they cause. Sometimes the conversions can be analyzed in the same way as dreams and the

underlying phantasies uncovered, for often the same distortion mechanisms are used. (Fenichel, O. *The Psychoanalytic Theory of Neurosis,* Norton, New York, 1945)

mathematical biology See *biology, mathematical.*

mating, assortative The mating of individuals who resemble one another in some particular, such as intelligence or hair color. Since for any such quality there is likely to be some genetic basis, assortative mating implies also the mating of genetically similar people; but the term *inbreeding* (q.v.) is used to refer to the mating of related people.

matronism, precocious In constitutional medicine, this term refers to a dysgenital syndrome in young girls, which owes its name to the physical and sexual forms of a mature woman (matron's body) occurring in them at such a very early age. The particular characteristics of this condition apply to the size and form of the pendulous breasts, the breadth of the shoulders, pelvis and thighs, and the adiposity of the legs and ankles. The face also has an adult expression, the menstruation appears prematurely, and the temperament is vivacious and irritable.

The morphological basis of this anomaly probably consists of a pluriglandular unbalance, in which follicular hyperovarism and cortical hyperadrenalism predominate.

mattoid (mat′oid) A person of erratic mind, a compound of genius and fool. Eugenio Tanzi used the term for that subgroup of paranoia characterized by abstract delusions, garrulousness, and feelings of persecution. These patients have no hallucinations, but are erotic and ambitious types. G. Lombroso used the term mattoid for cranks, eccentrics, etc. who are not overtly psychotic but are rather on the borderline of a psychosis.

maturation (mach-ū-rā′shun) In genetics, the cell process (in sexual reproduction) which leads to the formation of gametes in the gonads. See *hereditary.*

Following the multiplication of the reproductive cells by repeated cell division of the ordinary duplicating type, some of these cells cease to divide by ordinary division and become the *primary spermato-cytes* and *primary oöcytes* in the respective sexes. When these cells mature, they grow in size, and the homologous chromosomes pair in them.

Two cell divisions follow to complete maturation: (1) the *equation* division in which the chromosomes are duplicated as in ordinary cell division, (2) the *reduction* division, in which the chromosomes are merely separated so that the number of chromosomes per cell is reduced to half (see *meiosis*).

maturation, anticipatory, principle of Carmichael uses this term in proposing a tentative generalization that almost all functions in a wide variety of organisms can be elicited by experimental means at some time prior to the spontaneous appearance of the function in the normal life cycle of the organism. This principle intimates that such functions are fully developed before they are needed by the organism.

mature *Genet.* The term describes the reproductive cells which have undergone the process of *maturation* or *meiosis*.

MBD Acronym for minimal brain dysfunction. See *impulse-disorder, hyperkinetic.*

McDougall, William (1871-1938) American psychologist and psychiatrist.

McNaughton See *responsibility, criminal.*

MCR Acronym for *mother-child relationship* (q.v.).

mean Arithmetic average.

mechanism (mek'à-niz'm) In psychiatry the mode of action performed by a psychic structure. For instance, repression is called a mental mechanism; it refers to functions of psychic structures and to the forces that give rise to them. One of the functions of the ego is to repress unconscious elements that are unwanted in consciousness. The various activities involved in the repression, from the time that the unwanted impulse makes itself felt or known in consciousness until the ego represses, constitute a mechanism.

Healy, Bronner, and Bowers list 17 dynamisms or mechanisms: displacement,

transference, symbolization, condensation, unconscious phantasy, repression, reaction-formation (reversal-formation), projection, isolation, undoing, conversion, introjection, identification, sublimation, rationalization, idealization, and dream-work. See *defense.*

'The fundamental regulating mechanisms of mental processes are the tendencies to seek pleasure by bringing about a relief from psychical tension, and to avoid pain by preventing accumulation of psychical energy.' (Jones, E. *Papers on Psycho-Analysis*, 4th ed., Wood, Baltimore, 1938)

The term mechanism is also used in a less specialized sense to refer to the way in which any machine or system operates; it is also used to refer to the philosophical doctrine that human behavior is wholly explicable in terms of the laws of physical mechanics.

mechanism, compensatory 'These persons [psychoneurotics] who are intolerant of themselves often develop a compensatory attitude of intolerance of others. It is very common to find that persons who are overbearing, over-certain, almost offensive in manner, are underneath shy, sensitive, and fearful of their own inadequacies. Frequently they will criticize harshly in others the very faults which they themselves display.' (Kraines, S.H. *The Therapy of the Neuroses and Psychoses*, Lea & Febiger, Philadelphia, 1948)

mechanism, flight The ego's (or psychic structure's) mode of procedure to escape from unbearable suffering. 'I pointed out one or two other methods by which the ego attempts to escape from the sufferings connected with the depressive position, namely either the flight to internal good objects (which may lead to severe psychosis) or the flight to external good objects (with the possible outcome of neurosis).' (Klein, M. *Contributions of Psycho-analysis, 1921-1945*, The Hogarth Press, London, 1948)

mechanism, homogenic (hō-mō-jen'ik) A mechanism described by Burrow in which *part-impressions* of an object are substituted for the actual contact with the object itself, and *part-feelings* or *affects* are substituted for the total feelings with which the organism natively responds to the object as a whole. This mechanism has to do with the picture-forming processes associated with inter-individual affects. Contrasted with central constant, orthogenic mechanism. Synonyms: graphogenic system, graphonomic system, index-system. (Burrow, T. *The Biology of Human Conflict,* Macmillan, New York, 1937, p. 297)

mechanism, mote-beam Ichheiser's term for that distortion of social perception wherein the person is exaggeratedly aware of the presence of an undesirable trait in a minority group although oblivious to its presence in himself.

mechanism, orthogenic (or-thō-jen'ik) The organism's total co-ordinative function. It preserves the balance of the organism as a whole in its relation to the total environment. Contrasted with homogenic mechanism. (Burrow, T. *The Biology of Human Conflict,* Macmillan, New York, 1937, pp. 296-7)

mechanism, scapegoat A term used to denote the mental state of a patient who has strong antisocial feelings and looks for incidents on which he can displace, project, and rationalize his hostilities. (Burton, A., and Harris, R.E. eds., *Case Histories in Clinical and Abnormal Psychology,* Harper, New York, 1947)

mechanophobia (mek-à-nō-fō'bē-à) Fear of machinery.

median (mē'di-an) If all items constituting a series with respect to any measurable character are arrayed from smallest to largest, in order, the median is that value which will divide the total frequency in half, with just as many below as there will be above.

Example: five subjects are aged 15, 20, 22, 25 and 26 years, respectively. The median age is 22, since 2 are younger and 2 are older.

medical model See *psychiatry, community.*

medicine, constitutional That branch of medical science which occupies itself with the study of the heredito-constitutional elements governing the biological equilibrium of human organisms and controlling their resistance or susceptibility to disease (see *constitution*).

Its aim is a most comprehensive and synthetic conception of the natural history of Man, while its research procedure consists mainly of devising methods for classifying human beings according to both their disease potentialities and capacities for adaption, and of establishing correlations between types of human morphology and the success or failure of these types in the struggle for existence. 'The evidence of the outcome of this reaction between individual and environment is expressed in terms of health, physical disease, insanity, criminality, and other less sharply defined inadequacies both physical and mental.' (Draper, G. *Disease and the Man,* Macmillan, New York, 1930)

Another definition of the main purpose of constitutional medicine is that of Pende, stressing the evaluation of *correlational principles,* 'according to which the various combinations of organs and organic fluids and the special relationship or anatomical and functional correlations between the parts of the body, which determine the different physical and mental constitutions, *vary* according to the characteristics that are dominant in the interorganic equilibrium.' (Pende, N. *Constitutional Inadequacies,* tr. by Naccarati, S., Lea & Febiger, Philadelphia, 1928)

The four basic categories or 'panels,' which are distinguished by Draper as the primary objects of constitutional investigation, are 'the hereditary unit characters found in the domains of anatomy, physiology, psychology, and immunity.' See *panels, personality.*

medicine, physical See *physical medicine.*

meditatio mortis A feeling of impending death; frequent in anxiety states.

medulla oblongata (me-doo'là ob-lon-gà'-tà) The pyramid-shaped portion of the brain-stem lying between the spinal cord and the pons. The ventral portion contains the pyramidal decussation; the lateral portion contains the olive; the dorsal portion contains the funiculus gracilis and the funiculus cuneatus. The medulla also contains the nucleus of the hypoglossal nerve, the nucleus ambiguus (somatic motor nucleus of glossopharyngeal, vagus, and spinal accessory nerves), the dorsal motor nucleus, and the sensory nucleus of the vagus nerve, and the dorsal and ventral cochlear nuclei. The medulla oblongata is sometimes called the bulb; syndromes resulting from lesions of the medulla are therefore known as bulbar syndromes, whose characteristic symptoms are due to involvement of the various tracts passing through the medulla and particularly to involvement of the nuclei of cranial nerves IX, X, XI and XII.

Meduna, Ladislas J. (1896-1964) Hungarian-born U.S. psychiatrist; developed Metrazol therapy, carbon dioxide therapy.

megalo- (meg′à-lō-) combining form meaning big, large, great, from Gr. *mégas, -álon,* big, great, akin to L. *magnus.*

megalomania (meg-à-lō-mā′nē-à) A type of delusion in which the subject considers himself possessed of greatness. He may believe himself to be Christ, God, Napoleon, etc. He may think that he is everybody and everything. He is lawyer, physician, clergyman, merchant, prince, generalissimo, ace athlete in all divisions of sports, etc.

'The question arises: What is the fate of the libido when withdrawn from external objects in schizophrenia? The megalomania characteristic of these conditions affords a clue here. It has doubtless come into being at the expense of the object-libido. The libido withdrawn from the outer world has been directed on to the ego, giving rise to a state which we may call narcissism.' (Freud, S. *Collected Papers,* vol. 4, tr. by Riviere, J., Leonard and Virginia Woolf and The Institute of Psychoanalysis, London, 1924-25)

The ideas in megalomania are called *delusions of grandeur.*

megalophobia (-fō′bē-à) Fear of large objects.

megalopia hysterica (me-gà′lō′pē-à histe′rē-kà) See *macropsia.*

megalosplanchnic (meg-à-lō-splangk′nik) In Viola's classification of the constitutional forms of body build, the type which has the abdominal portion of the body relatively large in proportion to the thoracic, owing to the large size of the abdominal viscera. This type is further characterized by a predominance of the trunk over the extremities.

megrim (mē′grim) *Obs.* Migraine.

meiosis (mī-ō′sis) See *miosis.*

meiotic (mī-ot′ik) Relating to or manifesting miosis.

melancholia, melancholy (mel-an-kō′lē-à, mel′an-kol-ē) A morbid mental state characterized by *depression* (q.v.). 'The distinguishing mental features of melancholia are a profoundly painful dejection, abrogation of interest in the outside world, loss of the capacity to love, inhibition of all activity, and a lowering of the self-regarding feelings to a degree that finds utterance in self-reproaches and self-revilings, and culminates in a delusional expectation of punishment. This picture becomes a little more intelligible when we consider that, with one exception, the same traits are met with in grief.' (Freud, S. *Collected Papers,* vol. 4, tr. by Riviere, J., Leonard and Virginia Woolf and The Institute of Psychoanalysis, London, 1924-25) The one exception is the loss of self-esteem, which is not seen in grief or normal mourning.

According to Freud, normal mourning is to melancholia as normal fear is to morbid anxiety. Briefly stated, the loss of a love-object leads to withdrawal of libido from reality and the introjection of the libido upon the mental picture of the lost love-object. The self-reproaches of the melancholic patient are understood to be directed toward the lost love-object. Abraham has shown that in these states libido regresses to the oral stage (see *psychosis, manic-depressive*).

melancholia, abdominal A rarely used term for depressions (mainly the agitated, involutional type) characterized by a delusional fixation on the gastro-intestinal tract, with vociferous complaints of dyspepsia, eructation, flatulence, constipation, etc.

melancholia activa (me-làn-kō′lē-à àktē′và) (L. 'active melancholy') *Melancholia agitata* (q.v.).

melancholia agitata (me-làn-kō′lē-à à-gētä′tà) (L. 'agitated melancholy') Agitated depression; usually the term refers to involutional psychosis, although in the 19th century it was used to refer to catatonic excitement.

melancholia, alcoholic (mel-an-kō′lē-à)

'Not very rarely alcoholics suffer from depressive conditions which cannot be distinguished symptomatologically from a melancholia of manic-depressive insanity, even though the delusions remain merely rudimentary. But they do not last long, only about two weeks.' (Bleuler, E. *Textbook of Psychiatry*, tr. by Brill, A.A., Macmillan, New York, 1930)

melancholia, amenorrhoeal (ā-men-o-rē'-al) *Obs.* 'Melancholia associated with the organic disturbances that have produced amenorrhoea, and that is erroneously attributed to the latter.' (Quain, R., ed. *A Dictionary of Medicine*, Appleton, New York, 1899)

melancholia anglica (me-làn-kô'lē-à ang'-glē-kà) *Obs.* English melancholy, or suicidal insanity.

melancholia attonita (me-làn-kō'lē-à àt-tô'nē-tà) *Obs.* The morbid state, common in the catatonic form of schizophrenia, characterized by immobility and muscular rigidity.

melancholia canina (kà-nē'nà) (L. 'canine, doggish melancholy') *Obs. Lycanthropy* (q.v.).

melancholia, cataleptic (mel-an-kō'li-à, kat-à-lep'tik) A form of stuporous depression in which there are cataleptic manifestations.

melancholia, climacteric (klī-mak-ter'ik) Melancholia developing at the climacteric period of life. See *psychosis, involutional.*

melancholia complacens (me-làn-kô'lē-à kôm-plà'kens) (L. 'complacent melancholy') Melancholy with complacency.

melancholia, convulsive (mel-an-kō'li-à) *Obs.* Melancholia associated with Jacksonian epilepsy.

melancholia, excited *Motor melancholia;* agitated depression. See *psychosis, involutional.*

melancholia, fantastic *Obs. Melancholia gravis* (q.v.).

melancholia flatuosa (me-làn-kô'lē-à flà-too-ô'zà) (L. 'flatuous melancholy') *Obs.* Hypochondriasis.

melancholia gravis (grà'vēs) (L. 'severe melancholy') Kraepelin's term for the depressive syndrome in which 'the patients see figures, spirits, the corpses of their relatives; something is falsely represented to them, "all sorts of devil's work." Green rags fall from the walls; a coloured spot on the wall is a snapping mouth which bites the heads off children; everything looks black. The patients hear abusive language ("lazy pig," "wicked creature," "deceiver," "you are guilty, you are guilty"), voices which invite them to suicide; they feel sand, sulphur vapour in their mouth, electric currents in the walls.' (Kraepelin, E. *Manic-Depressive Insanity and Paranoia*, tr. by Barclay, R.M., Livingstone, Edinburgh, 1921)

melancholia, homicidal (mel-an-kō'lē-à) See *mania, homicidal.*

melancholia, hypochondriacal (hī-pō-kon-drī'à-kal) A symptom complex consisting of depressive affect, inhibition of thinking and acting, and hypochondriacal delusions. When not organic, this symptom complex is almost always schizophrenic in nature. Monoideism, in contrast to the simple melancholias, may here be almost absolute. For long periods there seem to be no thoughts other than the constantly repeated wishes, complaints, or maledictions. Even though the affect seems to dominate the entire personality, it is typically stiff, superficial, and exaggerated. In this condition, ideas of grandeur may co-exist with appalling fears and terrors in spite of logical contradictions involved.

melancholia, intermittent (in-tēr-mit'ent) Recurrent melancholia.

melancholia, involutional (in-võ-lū'shun-al) See *psychosis, involutional.*

melancholia, motor *Obs.* See *melancholia, excited.*

melancholia nervea (me-làn-kô'lē-à ner'-ve-à) *Obs.* Hypochondriasis.

melancholia, panphobic (pan-fō'bik) *Obs.* Melancholia in which there is dread of everything.

melancholia, paranoid (par'à-noid) 'The depressive attack [of manic-depressive disorder], also, because of the increase of the hallucinations or the thought disturbance, may assume a paranoid or delirrious appearance *(melancholic insanity).'* (Bleuler, E. *Textbook of Psychiatry,* tr. by Brill, A.A., Macmillan, New York, 1930)

melancholia, paretic (pa-ret'ik) *Obs.* Melancholia that may be the prodrome or concomitant of paresis.

melancholia, passive *Obs.* 'Melancholia that develops slowly with a gradual failure of physical health, restless worry or jealousy being the first objective sign.' (Quain, R., ed. *A Dictionary of Medicine,* Appleton, New York, 1899)

melancholia, periodic See *neurasthenia, periodic.*

melancholia, religious *Obs.* Melancholia with delusions of a religious nature.

melancholia, resistive *Obs.* Melancholia with unreasoning active or passive resistance as its characteristic feature.

melancholia simplex (me-làn-kô'lē-à sēm' pleks) (L. 'simple melancholy') Simple depression, according to Kraepelin.

melancholia, sympathetic (mel-an-kō'li-à) *Obs.* Melancholia that arises from some organic disturbance other than that of the brain.

melancholia vera (me-làn-kô'lē-à vā'rà) (L. 'true melancholy') See *anxietas praesenilis.*

melancholia zoanthropia (zō-àn-thrō'pē-à) (L. 'zooanthropic melancholy') *Lycanthropy* (q.v.).

melancholy (mel'an-kol-i) In current psychiatry the term is synonymous with *melancholia* (q.v.). In the literature of the 19th century melancholy was distinguished from melancholia 'in that there are no morbid sense perversions, no irrationality of conduct, no morbid loss of self-control, no sudden or determined impulse towards suicide or homicide, and where surrounding events and occurrences still afford a certain amount of interest, though lessened in degree, and where the power of application to ordinary duties is still present.' (Tuke, D.H. *A Dictionary of Psy-*

chological Medicine, vols. 1-2, Blakiston, Philadelphia, 1892)

melissophobia (me-lis-ō-fō'bē-à) Fear of bees.

Melkersson-Rosenthal syndrome See *syndrome, Melkersson-Rosenthal.*

melomania (mel-ō-mā'nē-à) *Obs.* Psychosis characterized by incessant singing.

mem-element (mem'-el'e-ment) See *system.*

memory The ability, process, or act of remembering or recalling, and especially the ability to reproduce what has been learned or experienced. Memory is more than mere registration, retention, and recall. It is a complex mental function that includes at least the following:

1. primary response—perception, apperception, recognition, and often some degree of understanding of the significance of what is to be learned; the primary response is affected by many factors, such as previously learned responses, set, fatigue, etc.

2. short-term retention—a transient holding of information which decays rapidly with time.

3. long-term retention, subdivided into a. secondary elaboration, in accord with other memories, needs, wishes, etc. b. consolidation—memory traces become increasingly well established with the passage of time; c. inhibition—blocking out of unessential memories, even though these may be brought back on demand; d. extinction—eradication of previously re-enforced but no longer useful memories.

4. retrieval—bringing stored material into consciousness at will (and in some early dysmnesias, the first symptom is having to wait excessively long before the information can be retrieved—"It will come back to me in a moment').

5. activation or read-out—decoding retrieved material, a process that is affected by the rest of the mental apparatus so that what is finally reproduced is different from what was actually laid down as a memory trace.

Such fine differentiation can rarely be made at the clinical level, however; instead, memory is usually subdivided into *immediate memory* (the ability to recall or reproduce material that has been presented within the past few seconds, corresponding to what is termed 'short term retention' above), *recent memory* (the ability to remember what has been experienced within the past few hours or days or weeks), and *remote memory* (the ability to remember what was experienced in the distant past).

Defects in memory *(dysmnesia)* are characteristic of many organic brain disorders, where immediate and recent memory tend to be disturbed first, while remote memory may be relatively well retained for some time. See *syndrome, organic.*

Even small lesions in the inferomedial portions of the temporal lobes—and especially in the amygdala, hippocampus, fornix, mammillary bodies, and medial dorsal nucleus of the thalamus, the area comprising the *limbic lobe*—can produce a permanent dysmnesic syndrome with little disturbance in other aspects of mental functioning. The importance of this area of the brain in memory is further attested to by the symptom of *panoramic memory*, a well-recognized temporal lobe aura. There is general agreement that bilateral hippocampal lesions produce deficits in learning ability and in remote memory (or habit retention). Short-term memory, on the other hand—a transient holding of information which decays rapidly with time and forms no permanent trace—seems not to be affected by such lesions.

It is possible that memory is at least a two-stage procedure insofar as the cerebral hemispheres are concerned: an initial focal process of registration and consolidation within a localized area; and a subsequent dispersal through large portions of the hemispheres by means of binding or linkage with other traces. Such an hypothesis would at least explain why remote memory tends to be better preserved in organic lesions.

How memories are formed and stored remains as much a mystery as where the processes occur. Many present-day investigators subscribe to a molecular theory of the substrate for memory; viz., that learning depends on alterations in the molecular structure of intracellular chemicals, and that the neurons involved in memory become fully functional only after chemi-

cal structural changes. Most recently, RNA (ribonucleic acid) has been suggested as the template which carries information acquired during training, in much the same fashion that it carries genetic information from DNA to amino acids (see *chromosome*). Some experimenters have reported that RNA isolated from the brains of trained animals transmits training to a recipient animal when the RNA is injected intraperitoneally or intracisternally. Many subsequent attempts to replicate those results have failed, however. Others have been only partially successful and would favor a polypeptide, rather than RNA, as the information-bearing molecule that adheres to pre- and postsynaptic membranes in the recipient's brain.

memory, automatic Reactivation of an affective state or emotional complex by means of an associative link to the original situation, even though the subject is not himself aware of the association. The term, used by Morton Prince, is rare, although the phenomenon itself is well-known; one type of automatic memory, at least according to Freud, is *déjà vu* (q.v.).

memory, biological Inherited knowledge of how to react; inherited engram. Instincts, for example, may be an expression of such biological memories or inherited engrams. The collective unconscious of Jung probably springs from biological memories in that the motives and images which he includes in the term collective unconscious are not dependent upon the acquisitions of personal existence, but originate in the inherited brain structures. See *memory, physiological.*

memory, cover See *memory, screen.*

memory, dislocation of Holland's term for complete but temporary forgetfulness or amnesia.

memory-hallucination See *hallucination, memory.*

memory, hyperesthetic (hī-per-es-thet′ ik) Oversensitive memory, especially one that is too easily aroused according to the laws of association. Breuer and Freud hypothesized that the provocation of hysterical attacks was in large part due to associative reactivation of hyperesthetic memories.

memory, liquidation by Assimilation or incorporation of experiences in the sphere of memory or intellect. 'A situation has not been satisfactorily liquidated, has not been fully assimilated, until we have achieved, not merely an outward reaction through our movements, but also an inward reaction through the words we address to ourselves, through the organization of the recital of the event to others and to ourselves, and through the putting of this recital in its place as one of the chapters in our personal history.' (Janet, P. *Psychological Healing*, vols. 1 - 2, tr. by Paul, E. and C., Macmillan, New York, 1925, p. 662)

memory, panoramic See *absent state*.

memory, physiological Morton Prince's term for the process of registration, retention, and reproduction of a somatic experience outside the field of conscious awareness; conditioning of autonomic system reactions would be an example of physiological memory.

Since 1950, when Katz and Halstead hypothesized that memory depends upon structural chemical changes in a nucleoprotein template, it has been learned that ribonucleic acid (RNA) is probably the substance involved in storing memory traces in the brain, and that deoxyribonucleic acid (DNA) comprises the genes and carries a code of chemical information that is the basis for the phylogenetic memory of the species. Both personal and phylogenetic memory, in other words, are mediated through the same chemical systems. As a result of such knowledge, the terms *biological memory* and *racial memory* are sometimes used to refer to the DNA and RNA chemical systems, rather than to the older senses of the terms.

memory, psycho-physiological (sī-kō-fiz-i-ō-loj′i-kal) 'Still another variety of memory is *psycho-physiological.* This type is characterized by a combination of psychological and physiological elements and is important . . . because of the conspicuous part which such memories play in pathological conditions. Certain bodily reactions which are purely physiological, such as vaso-motor, cardiac, respiratory, intestinal, digestive, etc., disturbances, become, as a result of certain experiences, linked with one or another psychical element (sensations, perceptions, thoughts) and, this linking becoming conserved as a "disposition," the physiological reaction is reproduced whenever the psychical element is introduced into consciousness.' (Prince, M. *The Unconscious*, Macmillan, New York, 1916.) See *memory, physiological.*

memory, racial The part of mental life that a person brings with him at birth, the archaic heritage of fragments of phylogenetic origin. This archaic inheritance consists, first of all, of the ability and tendency of all human organisms 'to follow a certain direction of development and to react in a particular way to certain excitations, impressions, and stimuli.' The differences among organisms in this respect are the constitutional element in the individual.

Freud states, however, that ideational contents, memory traces of the experiences of former generations, as well as these dispositions to react in the particular ways mentioned above, are included in the archaic heritage. The study of the reactions to early traumata has shown that these reactions 'do not keep strictly to what the individual himself has experienced, but deviate from this in a way that would accord much better with their being reactions to genetic events and in general can be explained only through such an influence. The behavior of a neurotic child to his parents when under the influence of the Oedipus and castration complex is very rich in such reactions which seem unreasonable in the individual and can be understood only phylogenetically, in relation to the experiences of earlier generations.'

A particular memory becomes part of the racial memory when the experience is either important enough or repeated often enough or both. Such a memory will become conscious again (though in an altered and distorted form) when an actual repetition of the remembered event has recently occurred. The obsessive character of religious phenomena in particular demonstrates the altered and distorted return (to consciousness) of memory-traces of experiences that had occurred in the distant past and remained in the racial memory. (Freud, S. *Moses and Monotheism,* Hogarth Press, London, 1939)

memory, replacement The substitution of one memory for another. 'Of especial interest is the fact that the repressed complex, which was responsible for the forgetting, betrayed itself in the replacement-memory, which was, as is always the case, a compromise-formation.' (Jones, E. *Papers on Psycho-Analysis,* 4th ed., Wood, Baltimore, 1938)

memory-romance See *romance, memory.*

memory, screen When a memory, a real thought, not a fantasied one, is used as a shield to conceal an allied memory, it is called a screen-memory or cover-memory. Thus, when a patient recalls playing in the basement, but does not remember the nature of the play, he is said to be providing a screen-memory.

memory-symbol See *symbol, memory.*

memory-system See *system.*

memory-trace See *trace, memory.*

memory, unconscious Retention of mental impressions of an event, even though, in ordinary circumstances, they are not subject to recall into consciousness. Freud first applied the concept to his studies of hysteria. He found that certain events, usually sexual, occurred to the patient, but were so unbearable that they were actively put out of consciousness by being repressed. In the process of *repression* (q.v.), the ideational content as well as its affective component is relegated to the unconscious and kept there as an unconscious memory or unconscious image. 'At puberty, when the sexual drive is stronger, this unconscious mental impression, under certain conditions, is reactivated. Because of the increased capacity for sexual feeling, the repressed memory acquires new force. It now produces the same result as an actual event in the present, an effect which the original experience itself lacked. Such a memory is not conscious. When, at puberty, it is reawakened, there is a liberation of affect, although the ideas associated with it remain repressed.' (Thompson, C. *Psychoanalysis, Evolution and Development,*

Hermitage House, New York, 1950) In such instances, the goal of therapy is to bring back into consciousness the unconscious ideational content as well as the associated affect.

mendacity As used in psychiatry, pathologic lying.

Mendel, Abbot Johann Gregor (1822-84) an Augustinian monk (and later abbot) at Brünn, published in 1865 his *Experiments on Plant Hybrids,* the result of his experiments on peas and honeybees in the monastery garden. In 1910 his findings and theories were rediscovered simultaneously by Correns, von Tschermak, and De Vries, and thus *Mendelism* (q.v.) became the new science of *genetics* (q.v.).

Mendelian law See *law, Mendelian.*

Mendelism (men'del-iz'm) The biological phenomena underlying the distributive mechanism of organic inheritance as discovered by Mendel.

The problem of how true-breeding varieties within a species are related was attacked by him from its simplest side by concentrating his attention upon the genetic mode of inheritance of sharply contrasted pairs of characters: he crossed round peas with wrinkled ones, or a yellow species with a green one, and was thus able to determine that all hybrids of the first filial generation (F_1) resembled each other, but exhibited only one of the two alternative characters distinguishing the parents. In the crosses of round and wrinkled peas all the offspring were round, and this 'prevailing' member of a pair of individual characters was called *dominant,* while the other member which was 'repressed' was called *recessive.*

If the round F_1 plants were allowed to become self-fertilized and the seeds were harvested separately and sown separately, producing the second filial generation (F_2), the wrinkled form reappeared in this generation in the proportion of one wrinkled to three round. By inbreeding, in turn, the wrinkled F_2 individuals it was found that they constantly produced wrinkled peas while the round form completely failed to reappear; genetically speaking, every individual exhibiting the recessive character bred true. Of the autofertilized round *(dominant)* individuals one-third likewise produced only round offspring. The remaining two-thirds propagated themselves in the same proportion as the uniform first generation, one-quarter wrinkled to three-quarters round, and similarly in all the subsequent generations.

These phenomena are explained by Mendel's theory that the hybrid does not produce any hybrid gametes, but merely pure gametes of various kinds, some of which bear dominant and others recessive characters. The hybrids of the first filial generation with round seeds contain the factor for wrinkled as well as the factor for round, but the former is hidden and suppressed by the latter. Since the recessive character reappears in the next generation, the dominant and the recessive characteristics must necessarily separate at the moment when the hybrid forms its gametes. See *law, Mendelian.*

mendicancy, pathological (men'di-kan-sē, path-ō-loj'i-kal) A syndrome characterized by the necessity on the part of the patient to beg, regardless of whether or not he has any real financial need.

meninges (men-in'jez) The membranous coverings of the brain and spinal cord. The outermost meninx is the *dura mater;* the middle one is the *arachnoid;* the innermost is the *pia mater.* The dura mater is known as the *pachymeninx;* fibrous processes of the dura mater form the falx cerebri (which separates the two cerebral hemispheres), the tentorium cerebelli (which forms a partition between the posterior and middle fossae of the skull), the falx cerebelli (which separates the cerebellar hemispheres) and the diaphragma sellae (which forms a roof to the sella turcica and through which passes the infundibulum). The arachnoid and pia mater are known as the *leptomeninges;* the space between them is the subarachnoid space, which contains the cerebrospinal fluid.

meningismus (men-in-giz'mus) Meningeal manifestations closely simulating those of meningitis, but in which no actual inflammation of the meninges is present.

meningitic curve See *Lange's colloidal gold reaction.*

meningitis (men-in-jī'tis) Any inflammatory process involving the cerebrospinal lepto-meninges, producing mental symptoms of the organic reaction type, in its acute form, with severe headache, delirium, somnolence, or stupor. Localized or generalized convulsions, generalized rigidity, twitching, and monoplegia or hemiplegia may also occur.

meningitis, aseptic (à-sep'tik) Meningitis without identifiable organisms in the gram stain or bacterial culture of the spinal fluid; usually due to virus infection.

meningitis, serous (ser'us) See *pseudotumor cerebri.*

meningitis, tuberculous A condition in which the tubercle bacillus infects the meninges of the central nervous system and produces mental symptoms of the organic reaction type. The disease is always secondary to a tuberculous focus elsewhere in the body, and without treatment the course is usually slowly progressive toward a fatal termination. Headache, delirium, stupor, and convulsions occur. The neck is rigid; often the tubercle bacillus can be demonstrated in the spinal fluid.

meningitophobia (men-in-ji-tō-fō'bē-à) A hysterical presentation of meningeal symptoms; morbid dread of brain disease.

meningocele (mē-ning'-gō-sēl) A developmental anomaly in which there is a protrusion of the membranes of the brain or spinal cord through a defect in the skull or spinal column respectively.

Menninger, William Claire (1900-1966) American psychoanalyst.

menopause Climacterium; the period of natural cessation of menses; the involutional period; known popularly as 'change of life.' See *psychosis, involutional.*

mens rea (mens' rē'à) (L. 'criminal mind') 'It is a general principle of our [English] law that there must be as an essential ingredient in a criminal offense some blameworthy condition of mind. Sometimes it is negligence, sometimes malice, sometimes guilty knowledge, but as a general rule there must be something of that kind which is designated by the expression *mens rea.*' (Cave, J.: Chisholm *v.* Doulton (1889) 22 Q.B.D. 736)

menses (men'sēz) Flow of blood, normally recurring every month, from a woman's uterus.

mensuration (men-shoo-rā'shun) Measurement of areas and distances on the surface of the body. 'Mensuration has been used rather more extensively within the past few years, though limited rather sharply to the matter of total height vs. span and trunk-extremity relationship.' (Draper, G. *Disease and the Man*, Macmillan, New York, 1930)

mental deficiency See *retardation, mental.*

mental disorders, classification of See *nomenclature, 1968 revision.*

mental health See *health, mental.*

Mental Health Center See *psychiatry, community.*

mental hygiene See *hygiene, mental.*

mental make-up See *character.*

mental science Psychology.

mental status The psychological and behavioral appearance of a person; in clinical psychiatry this term is commonly used to refer to the results of the mental examination of a patient. The written report of the mental status usually contains specific references to the following areas (adapted from N.D.C. Lewis. *Outlines for Psychiatric Examinations*, State Hospitals Press, Utica, New York, 1943):
I. Attitude and General Behavior
  A. General health and appearance (?weak ?prematurely aged ?immature)
  B. General habits of dress (?overmeticulous ?slovenly)
  C. Personal habits (toilet and eating habits)
  D. General mood (elation, excitement, calm, apathy, dejection)
  E. Use of leisure time
  F. Degree of sociability
  G. Speech (productivity; disorders of speech such as stuttering; topics of conversation)
II. Attitude and Behavior During Interview
  A. Co-operativeness
  B. Poise (?stilted ?poised ?boisterous ?uncontrolled)
  C. Facial Expression (pain, grief, anxiety, distrust, bewilderment, anger, defiance, contempt, exaltation, preoccupation, apathy)
  D. Motor activity (gestures, co-ordination, retardation, or acceleration)
  E. Mental activity (flow of speech; flow of thought; loss of continuity or alterations of language and speech structure)
  F. Emotional reactions (appropriateness, harmony)
  G. Trend of thought (persecutory, hypochondriacal, unreality, nihilism, dejection, grandiosity, hallucinations, delusions, illusions, obsessions, compulsions, fears)
III. Sensorium, Mental Grasp, and Capacity
  A. Orientation
  B. Memory and retention
  C. School and general knowledge
  D. Estimate of intelligence
  E. Abstraction ability
  F. Tests of absurdity, interpretation of proverbs
  G. Judgment

mentales (men-tä'lās) Linnaeus, in 1763, divided mental disorders *(mentales)* into three classes: *ideales, imaginarii,* and *pathetici.*

mentalia (men-tä'li-à; L. -tä'lē-à) *Psychalia* (q.v.).

mentalism (men'tal-iz'm) The primitive tendency to personify, in spirit form, the forces of nature and the motions of things on the earth and in the heavens; the endowment of inert matter with the quality of 'soul'—this synonymous with *animism* (q.v.). This philosophical concept implies the existence of spiritual or mental forces completely different from the somatic structures, and denotes the subjective, mental, or mind approach to psychiatry in contrast to the behavioristic approach, which stresses objective physiological activities.

mentality (men-tal′i-tē) Mental action or power—the psyche in action. In pychiatry mentality is considered from two points of view: (1) of intellectuality and (2) of the instincts. The former refers to the intellectual capacity, such as superior, average, or inferior intelligence.

The second (instinctual) aspect of mentality forms the basis of personality structure and function. Since the introduction of the formulations of Freud the mind or psyche has been conceived in the light of an organ of the body, with its own structures and functions, and with its correlative action with other body organs and with the environment.

According to such conceptions, the psyche is the central organ that expresses mentality from the instinctual point of view, while the brain occupies an analogous position with regard to the intellectual aspects of mentality.

mente capti (men′tā kåp′tē) (L. 'out of their senses, out of mind, mad') See *furiosi.*

menticide (men′ti-sīd) 'An organized system of psychological intervention and judicial perversion, in which a powerful tyrant synthetically injects his own thoughts and words into the minds and mouths of the victims he plans to destroy by mock trial.' (Meerloo, J. *American Journal of Psychiatry 107*, 594, 1951) Menticide is popularly known as 'brainwashing.'

mentiferous (men-tif′ĕr-us) Telepathic.

mentism (men′tiz′m) *Rare.* Mental derangement.

Mercier, Charles Arthur (1852 - 1919) British psychiatrist; forensic psychiatry.

mere-, -mere (ēr′) Combining form meaning *part,* portion, partial, from Gr. *méros,* part, share.

merergasia (mer-ēr-gās′ē-à) Partial ability to work, function. Term used by Adolf Meyer to designate a clinical psychiatric syndrome that causes only a partial disorganization of the personality. In general it may be stated that the psychoneuroses and neuroses constitute the merergastic reactions.

mergent, partial (mēr′jent) Burrow thus denotes the inter-verbal conditioning that occurs reflexly among individuals and is socially systematized within groups or communities. By virtue of this reflex community-reaction coincident with the employment of words or symbols, two phenomena which are completely disparate and unrelated outside the organism may become united or merged socially (inter-cortically) into a common motivation or 'meaning' within the organism. Through this mechanism the organism's primary total feelings have been socially replaced by mere reflex partial affects. The partial mergent represents a false mergent in contrast to the organism's total or true mergent. Contrasted with total mergent. (Burrow, T. *The Biology of Human Conflict,* Macmillan, New York, 1937)

mergent, total Burrow's term for the organism's response as a whole to the total environmental situation. Contrasted with partial mergent. (Burrow, T. *The Biology of Human Conflict,* Macmillan, New York, 1937)

merogony (me-rog′ō-nē) The process in which the egg cytoplasm comes from one parent and the nucleus, through the sperm, from the other, thus making possible a comparison of their effects. Boveri fertilized enucleated eggs of one species with sperm from a markedly different one. The merogonous embryos resembled the species from which the sperm was derived.

Thus development seems to be controlled by the nucleus, even if it is surrounded by cytoplasm from a very different source. However, since there is evidence that the nuclear material may not have been removed from the egg entirely, the resemblance to the male parent may be explained on other genetic grounds (see *nucleus*), and the question is still open.

merycism (mer′i-siz′m) 'Merycism is a voluntary regurgitation, moderate in degree and slow, but rather pleasant, of food from the stomach to the mouth, in which it is masticated and tasted a second time, as in rumination. This remarkable habit is special to certain idiots and dements of a very low type.' (Tanzi, E. *A Text-Book* *of Mental Diseases,* tr.. by Robertson, W.F. and Mackenzie, T.C., Rebman, New York, 1909)

mescaline (mes'ka-lin) The active principal of the cactus from which peyote is obtained. See *peyotism.*

Mescaline is used today as one of the two chief agents to produce an experimental or model psychosis (the other agent is lysergic acid). The major effects are personality disturbances and an increase in sympathetic tension in the experimental subject; the former include visual (and sometimes auditory) hallucinations, illusions, distortions of the body image, altered time sense, thought-language changes, and an increase in self-observation sometimes to the point of complete withdrawal and feelings of unreality and detachment.

The mode of action of mescaline is not fully understood. It is a powerful synaptic inhibitor, and its sympathomimetic effects may be due to inhibition of the opposing parasympathetic system. It seems more likely, however, that its effects are due to stimulation of the sympathetic system by reason of imitation of norepinephrine at the latter's receptor sites, this leading to arousal, sympathetic outflow, increased psychomotor activity, and enhancement of sensitivity to external stimuli. It has also been suggested that the mescaline psychosis is due to formation of a protein-bound mescaline compound in the liver, which then acts as a toxic agent to sensitive areas in the brain.

mesencephalon (mes-en-sef'à-lon) *Midbrain* (q.v.)

mesenchyme, mesenchyma (mes'eng-kim, -'ki-mà) Although this term was introduced in embryology by O. and R. Hertwig to denote the part of the *mesoderm* (q.v.) which separates from the original mesothelium as a loose mass of anastomosing cells to form the connective tissues, it has lost some of its precise meaning. It is now generally assumed that the mesenchymal tissue, occupying practically all the intervals between the epithelial layers, does not arise from the middle germ layer alone, but probably from certain parts of the *entoderm* and *ectoderm* also (qq.v.), and that it forms not only the various forms of connective tissue, but also the

skeletal system, the smooth muscular tissue, the stroma of the iris and the ciliary body, the cartilages and ligaments of the larynx, and, especially, the blood and blood vessels.

In constitutional medicine, Viola's ontogenetic law contrasts *ponderal* evolution, or increase of mass due to the mesenchyme with *morphological* evolution, or change of proportion due to the *parenchyme* (q.v.), and holds that these two evolutionary types are in inverse proportion to one another. It is believed by Viola that, when there is evolutionary disharmony, one system preponderates over the other, giving rise to the two great antithetic types of deviation from the average human constitution, namely the *megalosplanchnic* and the *microsplanchnic* (qq.v.).

Godin's *law of alternations* is a corollary to Viola's. It also identifies the mesenchyme with mass, and the parenchyme with morphological differentiation, and stresses the fact that, in normal growth, phases of growth in width alternate with phases of growth in length.

Mesmer, Franz (or **Friedrich**) **Anton** (1733 - 1815) An Austrian who first gave a demonstration of hypnotism (animal magnetism) in Vienna about 1775.

mesmerism (mez'mēr-iz'm) Hypnotism; animal magnetism.

mesmeromania (-ō-mā'nē-à) *Obs.* Misguided faith in the power of mesmerism.

meso- (mes'o-) Combining form meaning middle, intermediate, from Gr. *mésos,* middle.

mesocephaly (mes-ō-sef'a-lē) See *index, cephalic.*

mesoderm (-dērm) The middle or third germ layer which is developed in the tridermic stage of the embryo called *notogenesis* (q.v.), or the fundamental tissues subsequently derived from this layer.

The *medial* portions of the original mesoderm, the paraxial or segmental mesoderm, become subdivided into blocks of tissue, the mesodermic segments or *somites,* while the *lateral* plates develop a split-like cavity, the *celom.* The connections between somites and lateral plates are collectively known as the *intermediate cell mass*, the primordium of the urogenital system.

The main tissue derivatives developed from the primitive middle germ layer include all muscular, connective, and vascular tissues, with blood and lymph vessels and all lymphoid organs; the cortex of the suprarenal gland and the sex cells; the epithelium of uriniferous tubules, renal pelves, and ureters, of the seminiferous tubules and the associated excretory ducts of the testis; of oviduct and uterus; and of pleurae, pericardium and peritoneum.

mesomorphic (-mor'fik) In W.H. Sheldon's system of constitutional types, the type characterized by a predominance of its third component (bulk), that is, the structures of the body that are developed from the *mesodermal* layer of the embryo (q.v.). Persons of this type are contrasted with the *ectomorphic* or *endomorphic* (qq.v.) types and correspond roughly to Kretschmer's *athletic* type. See *type, athletic*.

mesontomorph (mes-on'tō-morf) According to Beau's system of constitutional medicine, this general constitutional type is to be distinguished from the *hyperontomorph*, characterized by broad, stocky body with long intestines. See *type, pyknic*.

mesopallium Limbic lobe; see *rhinencephalon*.

mesoskelic (mes-ō-skel'ik) Possessing legs of normal length.

In Manouvrier's system of constitutional types this describes a type which is intermediate between the *brachyskelic* and the *macroskelic* types (qq.v.). See *type, athletic*.

messenger RNA See *chromosome*.

meta- (met'à-), **met-** (before vowels) Prefix meaning change, transformation; after next; trans-, beyond, over, from Gr. *metá-*, together with, after, behind, change.

metabolic-nutritional model See *psychiatry, community*.

metabolism (me-tab'ō-liz'm) The bio-physiological processes by which the living cells and tissue systems of an organism undergo continuous chemical changes in order to build up new living matter and to supply the energy necessary for the life of an individual.

The morphological effect of *metabolism* can be *anabolic* or *catabolic* (qq.v.), according to whether it is of a constructive or destructive nature.

metabolism, destructive Catabolism; see *metabolism*.

metabolism, mental 'An increase in "mental metabolism"' was the phrase used by Abraham to describe the condition characteristic of mania in which the patient is continuously 'hungry for new objects.' In general, manic phenomena arise out of an immense increase in self-esteem or, what is the same thing, a decrease in conscience. There are no longer any inhibitions: all the impulses formerly inhibited now seek discharge, and the energies themselves, formerly used to restrain these impulses, are now released. Henceforth, these energies as well as the now uninhibited impulses 'flow out, using any available discharge.' As a result the patient is 'hungry for objects' in order 'to get rid of the now uninhibited impulses that seek discharge.'

Fenichel notes that most of these uninhibited impulses are oral in nature. The manic's object relationships aim unconsciously at incorporation of the object. Accordingly, it is particularly appropriate to describe this condition as an increase in mental metabolism since the manic, in effect, continually consumes new objects in order to discharge his intensified uninhibited oral instinctual impulses. (Fenichel, O. *The Psychoanalytic Theory of Neurosis*, Norton, New York, 1945)

metaerotism (met-à-er'ō-tiz'm) S. Radó stresses the idea that intoxicants [e.g. morphine] effect changes principally 'in the abode of the libido.' He says: 'The whole peripheral sexual apparatus is left on the one side as in a "short circuit" and the exciting stimuli are enabled to operate directly on the central organ. I propose to term this phenomenon, which deserves to be distinguished by a special name, "metaerotism."' He adds in a footnote that he prefers 'to use this term rather than the obvious "paraerotism," which I think should be reserved for the less questionable scientific designation of the perversions.' (*International Journal of Psychoanalysis VII*, 402, 1926)

metagnosis The changing of one's mind or attitude.

metalanguage The rules for use of a language (e.g. grammar, syntax); or any language system that can explain, relate, or unite two or more subsystems.

In communications theory, the specific instructions that accompany the spoken word to insure correct interpretation. Such instructions are typically expressed by voice tone, gestures, sentence construction, etc.

metallophobia (mē-tal-ō-fō′bē-à) Fear of metals.

metalloscopia (-skō′pē-à) An obsolete method of treatment in hysteria by the application of metals to anesthetic areas.

metals, psychosis due to Persons with prolonged exposure to metallic poisoning, such as lead, mercury, and arsenic, may show psychotic reactions (294.3; if nonpsychotic, 309.14). Early symptoms may include gastro-intestinal disturbances and peripheral nerve toxic symptoms, followed possibly by delirium with marked prostration. There may be recovery from these mental symptoms or the patient may present a residual intellectual and emotional defect, based on the neurological changes associated with these toxins. The clinical picture occasionally resembles the Korsakov syndrome. According to the 1952 revision of psychiatric nomenclature, these psychoses are classified as acute or chronic brain syndromes due to poisons.

metamorphopsia Faulty perception of objects, which appear to be distorted; seen most often in parietal lobe lesions and as a type of illusion in intoxication with *mescaline* (q.v.).

metamorphosis, delirium of See *lycanthropy*.

metamorphosis sexualis paranoica (me-tà-môr-fō′zēs sek-soo-ä′lēs pà-rà-nô′ē-ka) *Rare*. Delusion, often seen in paranoid

patients, that one's sexuality has been changed into that of the opposite sex.

metapelet See *kibbutz*.

metaphase (met′à-fāz) *Biol.* The second stage of the division of a cell by mitosis. (See *division, cell.*)

metaphor A type of comparison in which one object is equated with another and qualities of the first are then ascribed to the second — "He was a tiresome psychoanalytical turnkey with a belt full of rusty complexes." Metaphorical language is a form of primary process thinking.

metaphoric paralogia *By-idea* (q.v.).

metapsychology That branch or extension of *psychology* (q.v.) which deals with the philosophical significance of mental processes, the nature of the mind-body interrelationship, the origin and purpose of the mind, and similar speculations that are beyond the reach of empirical verification.

metatropism (me-tà-trō′pizm) See *transvestism*.

metempsychosis (met-em-sī-kō′sis) Migration of the soul or rational spirit at death into another body; the doctrine of metempsychosis is part of the Hindu religion, which further teaches that the soul carries with it the memories of former existences for a thousand years. It then induces forgetfulness by drinking of Lethe and begins all over again.

metencephalon (met-en-sef′à-lon) See *hindbrain*.

meteorophobia (mē-tē-or-ō-fō′bē-à) Fear of meteors.

methadone A dependence-inducing, synthetic, narcotic-analgesic with morphine like-effects; at the present time its chief use is as maintenance therapy for heroin addicts according to the method advocated by V.P. Dole and M.E. Nyswander (hence called the *Dole-Nyswander program*). Methadone maintenance differs from other methods in that the successive peaks of elation obtained by repeated intravenous or subcutaneous injections of heroin are replaced by a sustained and uniform drug action without notable elation, abstinence symptoms, or demand for escalation of dose. Because maintenance is not considered a wholly satisfactory answer to the drug abuse problem, the Dole-Nyswander program is still to be considered in the experimental stage.

Cyclazocine is another synthetic narcotic antagonist which prevents the actions of large doses of narcotics. Since it prevents the development of physical tolerance, it controls the factors that ordinarily lead to compulsive build-up in heroin dosage. Published reports to date, although few in number, are promising in their results, and both Cyclazocine and Methadone may become pharmacologic mainstays in the fight against addiction. See *dependency, drug; addiction; opium.*

methilepsia (meth-i-lep'sē-à) Morbid craving for intoxicants.

method, concentric (kon-sen'trik) A concept of stratification of the personality employed by Laignel-Lavastine. Five concentric (i.e. having a common center) zones of personality are recognized: psychic, nervous, endocrine, visceral, and morbific. Personality difficulties and psychiatric symptòmatology result from abnormalities in any zone, or in any combination of zones.

method, co-twin control A method of study developed by Gesell and Thompson for use in medical genetics. In this method, observational twin data are obtained from a few selected one-egg pairs, whose aptitudes or adjustments under different life conditions are then compared.

method, cross-cultural Comparison of different cultures or societies to determine the effect of a particular variable on behavior.

method, linguistic-kinesic An approach to the study of disordered behavior as it manifests itself in disturbances of communication. Linguistics, the study of words and language, and kinesics, the study of movement, are methods designed to isolate and study infracommunicational systems and thereby reduce the data of interactional behavior to objective, significant, measurable and manipulatable units. This approach is often referred to as the L-K method.

method, need-press A technique of analysis of the TAT used by Murray (one of the originators of the test); in this method, each sentence of the subject's story is analyzed as to the needs of the hero and the press (environmental forces) he is exposed to. Each need and press is given a weighted score and a rank-order system of the needs and press is then tabulated. The method is not widely used clinically because it is too time-consuming to be practical.

method, pedigree Study of the family history to determine the frequency with which a familial trait occurs in the members of an affected family. This method does not ordinarily afford conclusive proof of heredity and is largely restricted to rare pathological traits which are fairly constant in penetrance and expressivity.

method, projective As distinguished from the direct, question-and-answer method in psychiatric examination, the projective method seeks to gain information indirectly, through the use of certain test techniques specifically designed to provide opportunity for self-expression without direct verbal accounting.

'Thus, an essential characteristic of projective techniques is that they are unstructured in that cues for appropriate action are not clearly specified and the individual must give meaning to (interpret) such stimuli in accordance with his own needs, drives, defenses, impulses—in short, according to the dictates of his own personality. Whether the stimuli are inkblots (the Rorschach test) or ambiguous pictures (the TAT), the patient's task is to impose or project his own structure and meaning onto materials which have relatively little meaning or structure and which, in a purely objective sense, are only inkblots or ambiguous pictures.' (Carr, A.C. *International Psychiatry Clinics 1*, 773-798, 1964)

method, sibship (sib'ship) A method devised by Weinberg for use in psychiatric genetics. In this method, the blood relatives of a statistically representative number of probands or index cases are studied to determine whether or not a particular trait occurs more frequently in them than it does in the general population (or in a group of persons not related to the carriers by blood).

method, Turkish-bath A type of treatment based on transference relationship in which the therapist applies threats and reassurances one after the other—one day hot, the next day cold.

method, twin-study One of the two principal methods used in psychiatric genetics for differentiation between genetic and environmental influences in relation to specific forms of adjustment or maladjustment. In this method, the dissimilarities of one-egg twins, genotypically identical organisms, are compared with the behavioral variations seen in ordinary sibs or two-egg twins.

methodology The study of the systems and procedures that are used in scientific investigation. Methodology attempts to devise a set of rules or guidelines that will govern or at least influence the choice of procedures to be used in a particular study. When the study in question has, in fact, used procedures in accord with such rules, it can be said that 'the procedures of the study were selected and applied in accordance with sound principles of methodology.' In current writings this cumbersome sentence is typically abbreviated to 'the methodology was sound.' As a result, methodology and method are often used interchangeably.

methomania (meth-ō-mā′nē-à) *Methilepsia* (q.v.).

metonymy (me-ton′i-mē) A disturbance of language seen most commonly in the schizophrenias in which an approximate but related term is used in place of the more precise, definite, or idiomatic term which would ordinarily be used. A young schizophrenic patient, for example, spoke in a labyrinthine, circumstantial manner for many minutes during a psychotherapy session, but suddenly became blocked. He recovered spontaneously after 5 - 10 seconds, and said: 'Now let's see. What was I saying? I seem to have lost the piece of string of the conversation.' The phrase, piece of string, would be considered a metonymic substitution for the idiom, to lose the thread of conversation.

metrazol (met′rà-zol) Cardiazol. See *treatment, metrazol.*

metromania 1. Mania for incessant writing of verses. 2. *Obs.* Nymphomania.

Meyer, Adolf (1866 - 1950) American psychiatrist; 'the mind in action,' psychobiology.

Meynert, Theodore (1833 - 92) (mī′nērt) German neurologist and psychiatrist.

micro- (mī′krō-) Combining form meaning small, minute, diminished, from Gr. *mikrós,* small, little.

microbiophobia (mī-krō-bī-ō-fō′bē-à) *Microphobia* (q.v.).

microcephaly (-sef′à-lē) Smallness of the head; a condition in which there is defective development of the whole brain and premature ossification of the skull.

microcosm (mī′kro-koz′m) See *words, microcosm of.*

microgeny (mī-krà′je-nē) The sequence of the necessary steps inherent in the occurrence of any psychological phenomenon; psychodynamic formulations, for example, are a statement of the microgeny of the patient's symptoms or behavior.

microglia (mī-krog′lē-à) See *neuroglia.*

micromania (mī-krō-mā′nē-à) *Obs.* Delusion of belittlement; the delusion or conviction that one's body, or some part of it, is or has become abnormally small. Such delusions are most often found in organic depressions, but the *small penis complex* is also an example. See *délire d'énormite.*

micromelia Small limbs, associated with achondroplasia; seen in various types of mental retardation. See *syndrome, de Lange.*

micro-orchidism See *syndrome, Klinefelter's.*

microphobia (-fō′bē-à) Fear of small objects.

microphonia (-fō′nē-à) Weakness of the voice.

micropsia, micropsy (mī-krop′sē-à, mī-krop′sē) Perception of objects as smaller than they really are. This may be occasioned by organic or psychic causes. When the latter prevail the condition may also be known as Lilliputian hallucination (see *Lilliputian*).

micropsychia (mī-krō-sī'kē-à) *Obs.* Feeblemindedness.

micropsychosis (mī-krō-sī-kō'sis) See *schizophrenia, pseudoneurotic*.

microsomatognosia (mī-krō-sō-mà-tog-nō' sē-à) See *somatognosia*.

microsome, microsoma (mī'krō-sōm, -sō'-mà) In biology, one of the minute granules found in vegetable protoplasm; this should not be confused with the concept of *microsomia* used in constitutional medicine.

microsomia (mī-krō-sō'mē-à) See *dwarfism*.

microsplanchnic (-splangk'nik) According to Viola's classification of the constitutional forms of body build, this term refers to the type which has the abdominal portion of the body relatively small in proportion to the thoracic portion, owing to the small size of the abdominal viscera. It is further characterized by the overdevelopment of the vertical diameters of the body in comparison with the horizontal diameters, so that the body presents an elongated appearance.

This *microsplanchnic* type corresponds to the *hypovegetative* biotype of Pende, the *asthenic* (q.v.) type of Kretschmer.

Midas punishment See *masturbation, compulsive*.

Midas syndrome Increased sexual desire in the female associated with diminished desire and capacity in her male partner. The Midas syndrome typically appears in intellectuals, about the thirtieth year. (Bruyn, G.W., and U.J. DeJong *American Imago 16*, 251, 1959)

midbrain Mesencephalon; that portion of the brain lying between the pons and the cerebral hemispheres, containing thg *corpora quadrigemina* (q.v.), the cerebral peduncles and the aqueduct of Sylvius. The base of each peduncle contains the homolateral corticospinal, corticobulbar, and corticopontile tracts. The substantia nigra is a broad layer of pigmented

gray substance occupying the central portion of the peduncle. The roof or dorsal portion of the base is the tegmentum, which contains: lateral and medial lemnisci, median longitudinal fasciculus, red nucleus, spinothalamic and spinotectal tracts, superior cerebellar peduncle, the nuclei of the trochlear and oculomotor nerves, and the nucleus of the mesencephalic root of the trigeminal nerve.

Lesions of the corpora quadrigemina cause paralysis of upward eye movements; of the cerebral peduncle, spastic contralateral paralysis; of the red nucleus, substantia nigra, or reticular substance, involuntary movements and rigidity. In cats, destruction of portions of the tegmentum produces cataleptic manifestations similar to cerea flexibilitas.

mignon delusion See *romance, family*.

migraine (mī'grān) A syndrome of periodic, unilateral headache with photophobia, vomiting, nausea, and various prodromata such as scotomata, occasional paresthesiae, and speech difficulties (305.3). After the attack there is often a marked sensation of well-being. Between 50 and 80 per cent of patients have a directly homologous heredity; the mother to daughter transmission is the most common, mother to son is next common. There is a close relation between migraine and epilepsy, and they may be clinical manifestations of the same disorder; 60 per cent of epileptic patients have a migrainous heredity, but only 17 per cent of the general population. Epilepsy occurs more frequently in migraine patients, and migraine more frequently in epileptics, than in the general population. The same patient may have alternate periods of epileptic attacks and migraine attacks, one affliction replacing the other for a considerable time. Puberty is the most usual time of onset, and 50 per cent of cases begin before the thirtieth year. It affects females two and a half times more frequently than males. Individual attacks may be precipitated by a variety of conditions; mental and emotional excitement are common precipitants.

The headaches usually appear at irregular intervals; several attacks a month are common. The headache has a crescendo type of intensity; it may be dull, boring, pressing, throbbing, vise-like, lancinating, or hammering in character. It may begin at any point on the head and spread to involve the entire side. Because of the frequency of associated gastro-intestinal symptoms, migraine is often called sick headache or bilious headache. The headache rarely lasts longer than 12 to 24 hours. The present-day conception is that migraine is a result of functional disturbances in the carotid cranial vascular tree; these occur in response to various etiologic agents which apparently vary greatly in different cases.

Migraine is usually considered to be a psychosomatic (psychophysiologic autonomic) disorder. Psychodynamically, destructive and hostile impulses are the important feature, and migraine in a sense is a hostile attack. Alexander considers migraine the result of inhibition of the phase of psychological preparation for an aggressive attack. See *hypertension, essential.*

migrateur (mē-gra-tēr′) (F. 'migratory, migrant') A wanderer; vagrant.

milieu (mē-lyē′) Environment; surroundings. In psychiatry, the *social setting,* emphasis being placed upon the setting from the emotional point of view. To a psychiatrist a most important milieu is the home. Other environments—scholastic, recreational, industrial, religious, etc.—play a leading role in the growth of the personality. See *therapy, milieu.*

Millard-Gubler syndrome (August L.J. Millard, French physician, 1830-1915, and Adolphe Gubler, French physician, 1821-79) Paralysis of the external rectus on one side and supranuclear paralysis of the bulbar muscles and limbs on the opposite side.

Milligan annihilation method A type of regressive electroshock therapy (REST) in which 3 treatments are administered the first day, and 2 treatments are given daily thereafter until the desired regression is obtained.

-mimesis (-mi-mē′sis) Combining form meaning imitation, mimicry, from Gr. *mímēsis,* imitation, from *mimeisthai,* to mimic, imitate.

-mimia (-mim′ē-à) Combining form meaning imitation, mimicry, gesture, from Gr. *mimía,* imitation.

Minamata disease (294.3, 309.14) An unusual form of toxic neuropathy and/or encephalopathy seen in fisherman in Minamata Bay (Japan); cause is presumed to be eating of fish contaminated by a chemical (probably organic mercury) in the effluent from a nearby fertilizer plant. Pathology consists of widespread neurone degeneration most marked in the granular layer of the cerebellum and in the cortex. Symptoms indicate involvement of the peripheral nervous system, cerebellum, hearing, and vision, and in some cases there are signs of progressive brain damage. Mental symptoms include impairment of intelligence, of which the patient is often aware, and changes in disposition and personality in that patients are often testy, irritable, bashful, unsociable, etc.

mind *Psyche* (q.v.).

mind, miniature *Psycho-infantilism* (q.v.); 'a symmetrical retardation in all aspects of mental life, in contradistinction to mental deficiency. The psycho-infantile person is regarded as one with a *miniature mind,* a mental midget.' (Lindberg, B.J. *Psycho-Infantilism,* Ejnar Munksgaard, Copenhagen, 1950.)

mind-reading See *telepathy.*

mind-stuff See *psychology, atomistic.*

mineralo-corticoid (min-er-a-lō-kor′ti-koid) See *syndrome, general adaptation.*

minimal brain dysfunction See *impulse-disorder, hyperkinetic.*

minus complementarity See *complementarity.*

miolecithal (mī-ō-les′i-thal) Referring to the human type of *cleavage* (q.v.) in the development of an embryo.

miopragia (mī-ō-prā′jē-à) In constitutional medicine, diminished functional activity of an organ. For example, subjects of asthenic habitus may possess a small, immature, and functionally diminished cardiovascular apparatus. Thus, Lewis, in *Constitutional Factors in Dementia Praecox* reported, among other things, a hypoplastic heart with lessened functional capacity.

miosis (mī-ō'sis) A. Contraction of the pupil.
B. In genetics, that particular kind of cell division in sexual reproduction which occurs in the sex glands immediately preceding gametic formation and results in a *reduction* of the chromosomes from the double or *diploid* number, characteristic of all somatic cells, to the halved or *haploid* number characteristic of gametes. This 'reduction division' leads to the separation of the two elements of each chromosome pair and provides the necessary basis for the segregation of genetic factors. Miotic divisions are thus genetically *segregation divisions*. See *chromosome*.
According to A.F. Shull, the following features of miosis are most essential to the processes of heredity:
1. The pairing of the homologous maternal and paternal chromosomes;
2. The separation of these paired chromosomes and their passage to different cells in the reduction division;
3. The consequent separation of the genes of each pair to different germ cells;
4. The independence of the several pairs of chromosomes in this separation;
5. The resultant assembling of various combinations of maternal and paternal chromosomes in the different mature germ cells;
6. The variety of combinations of genes thus produced in the different germ cells;
7. The reduction of the number of chromosomes in the mature germ cells to half that found in the reproductive cells before maturation.

miriasha (mē-ryä'shà) A person affected with *miryachit* (q.v.).

mirror-imaging In genetics, reversed *asymmetry*, quite frequent in twins, with respect to handedness, hair whorl, dental irregularities, fingerprints, and other symmetrical characters including certain morbid traits based on heredity. The presence of *mirror-imaging* is confirmatory evidence of *monozygotic* twins, though monozygosity is not excluded by its absence (see *twin*).

mirror sign See *sign, mirror*.

miryachit (mē-ryà'chēt) 'This is the term applied in Russia and Eastern Siberia to a morbid condition, which, however, is met with under different names in various parts of the world. The term itself is part of a verb meaning "to fool" or "play the fool," and the victim of the disease, if he may be so named, has a desire, apparently irresistible, to imitate whatever action is carried out in his presence, and also to repeat whatever is said to him or in his hearing.' (*A Dictionary of Medicine*, ed. by Quain, R.D. Appleton & Company, New York, 1899.) See *echolalia; echopraxia; lata*.

misanthropy (mis-an'thrō-pē, miz-an'-) Hatred of, or aversion to, mankind. A profound morbid distrust of human beings individually and collectively.

misidentification, amnesic (am-nē'zik) The inability of a subject to identify the person confronting him, due to impairment of the memory or to clouding of consciousness.

misidentification, delusional A failure to recognize well-known objects as such, due to the delusion that the objects have been transformed; e.g. a patient may believe that a woman has been transformed into a man; or that a young person has been changed into an old one; or a new coat into a shabby one, etc.

misidentification, hyperbolic (hī-per-bol'-ik) A condition sometimes found in manic states in which the patient flippantly calls a person by someone else's name. This misidentification is rarely clung to with conviction.

miso- (mis'ō-) Combining form meaning hate, hatred, from Gr. *mīsos*, hate, hatred.

misocainia (-kī'nē-à) Hatred or fear of anything new or strange, sometimes expressed as an obsessive desire for preservation of the status quo. See *autism, early infantile*.

misogamy (mi-sog'à-mi) Hatred of marriage, often based upon an unresolved Oedipus complex. To some patients, and especially schizophrenics, marriage is equated with incest and misogamy is their defense against it.

misogyny (mi-soj'i-nē) Hatred of women When the hate of women is part of a morbid mental state, it may be associated with a wide variety of nosologic entities. The most common explanation for the condition has to do with the events of childhood, particularly those relating to the parents (see *complex, Oedipus*).

Abhorrence of women is expressed alike by women and men and is often a reflection of a homosexual conflict. A hysterical woman detested all women and all things effeminate; she had always wanted to be a male; indeed, throughout her childhood her father chided her because she was female; since early childhood she detested effeminacy and did as much as possible to become masculine.

Passive homosexual males may hold women in severe contempt, as a reaction to disappointment with their own masculinity. A paranoid, homosexual patient killed a woman in order to gain her femaleness. Thereafter he denied that he had any attributes, physical or mental, of masculinity.

misologia, misology (mis-ō-lō'je-à, mi-sol'ō-jē) Hatred of speaking or arguing. One patient with catatonic schizophrenia, for example, remained mute lest the world be destroyed through her speaking.

misomania *Obs.* The syndrome characterized by delusions of persecution.

misoneism (mis-ō'-nē'iz'm) Hatred of innovation, *misocainia* (q.v.).

misopedia (-pē'dē-à) Morbid hatred of children. A patient had an obsession to kill all children, because they were produced through the intervention of the male sex. He devoted his life to the Doctrine of Immaculate Conception.

Behind the hatred of children is often the idea of incest, the parent unconsciously viewing the child as the consequence of incestuous relations.

misopsychia (-sī'kē-à) *Obs.* Hatred or weariness of living; synonymous with the obsolete terms *misozoeticus* and *misozoia*.

mistakes, basic See *basic mistakes*.

Mitchell, S(ilas) Weir (1829-1914) American neurologist and psychiatrist; *rest cure* (q.v.).

mitissima (mē-tēs'sē-mà) Mania mitis; paraphrosyne; hypomania. See *mania*.

mitosis (mi-tō'sis) Originally meaning the division of the *nucleus* of a cell, the term is now often used for the entire process of cell division, involving all radical changes in the structure of a cell which are of utmost significance in inheritance (see *division, cell*).

mitten pattern An abnormal electroencephalographic complex, so-called because it consists of a slow spike-and-wave resembling the thumb and hand portion of a mitten. The pattern is found almost solely in adults and occurs significantly more frequently in psychotic patients than non-psychotic controls; e.g. near 40% of adult schizophrenics and epileptics with psychosis, but near 3% in non-psychotic epileptics and other unselected controls. (Gibbs, F.A., et al. *Journal of Neurology, Neurosurgery and Psychiatry 5*, 6-12, 1964)

mixoscopia (mik-sō-skō'pē-à) A form of sexual perversion in which orgasm is reached by watching the act of coition between the desired one and another person.

mixovariation (-và-ri-ā'shun) This genetic term is synonymous with *combination*, signifying hereditary variations between related individuals, due to the sorting out and recombining of separate factors in the generations following crosses of mates with unlike hereditary equipment (see *combination*).

mixture, Cloetta's (Max Cloetta, Swiss pharmacologist, 1868-1940) A combination of paraldehyde, amylene hydrate, chloral hydrate, alcohol, barbituric acid, digitalin and ephedrine hydrochloride which is usually administered per rectum in continuous sleep treatment. (See *treatment, continuous sleep*).

MMPI See *test, Minnesota Multiphasic Inventory*.

M'Naghten rule See *responsibility, criminal*.

mneme (nē'mē) Memory-trace or *engram* (q.v.).

mneme, phylogenetic (fī-lō-jē-net'ik) The racial ancestral memory present in the deep unconscious of the individual. See *memory, racial.*

mnemic (nē'mik) Pertaining to or characterized by memory.

mnemism (nē'miz'm)` Mnemic hypothesis that cells possess memory. See *mneme.*

-mnesia, -mnesis ([m]nē'z[h]ē-a, -[m]nē'-sis) Combining form meaning memory, recollection, from Gr. *mnēsi-* only in composition, from unrecorded Gr. *mnēsis,* memory, from *mnāsthai,* to remember.

mob 'A highly excited form of the crowd.' (Bernard, L.L. *Mob; Encyclopaedia of the Social Sciences,* vol. 10, Macmillan, New York, 1933, p. 552)
The mob is 'the crowd that acts.' (Thrasher, F.M. *The Gang,* University of Chicago Press, Chicago, 1927)

mobility (mō-bil'i-tē) 'A change of movement in response to a new stimulus or situation.' (Park, R.E. and Burgess, E.W. *The City,* University of Chicago Press, Chicago, 1925)
Examples of mob behavior are riots, lynchings, and mutinies.
Mobility 'measures not merely the social contacts that one gains from travel and exploration, but the stimulation and suggestions that come to us through the medium of communication, by which sentiments and ideas are put in social circulation.' (Park R.E. and Burgess, E.W. *Introduction to the Science of Sociology,* University of Chicago Press, Chicago, 1921)

mobility, social The free interactions among, and the changing roles and status of, members in a group. This term is used in contrast to social fixity. (See *fixity, social.*)

modality Any method or technique of treatment; a class or group within the therapeutic armamentarium. Also any class or subdivision of sensation, such as vision or smell.

mode The value in a frequency curve at which the height of the curve is greatest; i.e. the most frequently recurring score in a distribution. The mode is a very unstable measure.

models, treatment See *psychiatry, community.*

modification In genetics, the term is limited to variations in the phenotype which are caused by environmental influences and modify the individual appearance without affecting the idioplasm. Drastic effects of the environment of living beings may lead to profoundly modified developments, but it is generally assumed that they do not become inheritable.
Of the modifying factors which interact to produce a human phenotype, the physiological effects of nutrition, light, and climate seem just as important as social, cultural, and psychological influences. These various environmental modifications can be best observed in identical co-twins reared apart under different life conditions (see *variation*).

modifier In accordance with the genetic principle that of the several hereditary factors which interact to produce a given phenotype, some contribute a greater share than others to the total effect, this term is used to denote those factors which appear merely to modify the effect of another factor, having little or no effect when the main factor is not present.
A modifier is called *specific* when its effects are produced only upon a specific genotype. See *variation.*

Moebius, Paul Julius (1853 - 1907) (mē'-bi-oos) German neuropathologist and sexologist.

mogigraphia (moj-i-graf'ē-à) Writer's cramp. See *neurasthenia, professional.*

mogilalia (moj-i-lā'lē-à) Hesitancy or difficulty in speaking, and particularly the kind that appears as a type of resistance in psychotherapy.

Moira (moi'rà) Moira in Greek mythology was the goddess of fate and was sometimes identified with the supreme power *anánkē* to which even the gods were subject, the destiny which even they could not escape. (Baynes, H.G. *Mythology of* *the Soul,* Williams and Wilkins, Baltimore, 1940)

molar Massive or gross, as contrasted with molecular, nuclear, minute, or discreet.

molilalia (mol-i-lā′lē-à) *Mogilalia* (q.v.).

molimen (mō-lē′men) Distress, malaise; specifically, the labored or difficult performance of a normal function or of a task that could ordinarily be performed with ease. *Molimen virile* was formerly used to refer to fatigue symptoms associated with the male climacterium; *menstrual molimen* is still used to refer to premenstrual tensions.

molimina, premenstrual (mo-lim′i-na, prē-men′stroo-al) Premenstrual tension; the term includes both physical and psychic symptoms referable to the premenstrual period.

molysmophobia (mol-iz-mō-fō′bē-à) Fear of contamination.

mongol (1) One belonging to the Mongolian race. (2) One who presents the clinical syndrome of mental deficiency called *mongolism* (q.v.).

mongolism (mong′gol-iz′m) Mongolian idiocy; variously called the Mongolian, Kalmuck, Khirghiz, or Tartar type of mental retardation, although *none* of the foregoing terms is acceptable as a designation of the syndrome. Preferable terms are *autosomal trisomy of Group G, trisomy 21, Langdon-Down disease* or *syndrome, Down's syndrome,* or *congenital acromicria.* Yet because there has been no agreement on which of the preferable terms to use, and because the unpreferred term has been in widespread use for almost a century, the syndrome is described here, under its objectionable appellation.

Trisomy 21 (31x.5) is an autosomal anomaly, due most frequently to non-disjunction of the twenty-first chromosome, this resulting in three, rather than two, G-chromosomes (number 21 or 22), or a total of 47 chromosomes rather than the normal total of 46. The first report of an extra chromosome in this syndrome was made by the French workers, LeJeune, Gautier, and Turpin in 1959, and numerous studies since have confirmed that report. In the usual non-disjunction

type of trisomy-21, the 21st (or 22nd) pair of chromosomes (for reasons not yet known) fails to separate during meiosis; this produces a germ cell with 24 instead of 23 chromosomes. When such a germ cell is united with a normal germ cell during fertilization, the resulting organism tains 47 rather than 46 chromosomes.

In a less frequent type of Down's syndrome, extra genetic material does not remain in position 21 as an extra chromosome, but instead attaches itself to one of the other chromosomes—usually to a chromosome in the 13-14-15 group, and thus the process is termed *15/21 translocation.* In such cases, the normal chromosome count of 46 is retained, but the chromosome receiving the excess of genetic material is abnormally elongated.

Inherited Down's syndrome is rare, and obvious familial aggregation of cases would be expected only in the translocation type. It has been reported in both monozygotic twins and in both dizygotic twins (but not in twins of different sex). The conditions that generate excess genetic material from chromosome 21 are undetermined; ionizing radiations, viruses, and senescence have been suggested as possible factors, and it has long been known that increased frequency of the syndrome is positively correlated with advanced parental age.

The syndrome was first described by J. Langdon-Down in 1866. Data accumulated since that time suggest that the general frequency of the disorder is about 1 in 600 births. Probably not more than 10 per cent of these are of the translocation type, although in young mothers (who contribute only a small proportion of cases to the total group) translocation may be the responsible mechanism in as many as 25 per cent.

Pathologically, the brain is small, and there are widespread defects in the cortical cell layers and in the number of ganglion cells. Whole gyri may be faulty in development. The process apparently is stationary, for regressive changes are not seen. There are many signs characteristic of trisomy 21, but not all are seen in each case. In one reported series, the signs appeared with the following frequencies; slanting of the palpebral fissures (88%), hyperextensible joints (88%), flabby hands (84%), brachycephalic skull with flat occiput (82%), ear anomalies or small lobules (80%), diastasis recti (76%), high-arched palate (74%), irregular alignment of teeth (68%), flat nipples (56%), epicanthus (50%), speckling of the iris (30%), heart murmurs (28%), double-zoned iris (22%) and pathologically open fontanels (16%). (Levinson, A., Freidman, A., and Stamps, F. 'Variability of Mongolism,' *Pediatrics 16:* 43-54, 1955)

Mentally, the patient is usually docile and tractable and may give an appearance of higher mental capacity than is really present because of imitativeness. The majority have a mental age of 4 to 7 years, although there are variations from moronity to pronounced idiocy. A few are hyperactive and sometimes destructive.

Because of associated defects, probably less than 60 per cent live more than five years.

monitor To supervise, invigilate; especially, to watch carefully so as to give warning should anything go wrong.

Moniz, Ega (1874-1955) Pen name for Antonio Caetano deAbreu Freire, Portuguese neurologist; development of cerebral angiography and of frontal leukotomy (the first psychosurgical procedure), for which he received the Nobel Prize for medicine in 1949.

mono- (mon'ō-) Combining form meaning one, only, single, from Gr. *mónos,* alone, only, single, unique.

monoamine oxidase (mon-ō-am'ēn oks'i-dāz) Also known as MAO; an enzyme, discovered by Hare in 1928, which has since been shown to be able to oxidize (and thus inactivate) various amines, including serotonin, the catecholamines and their methoxy derivatives. Of interest clinically is that fact that many inhibitors of monoamine oxidase are psychic energizers.

monobulia (mon-ō-bū'lē-à) *Obs.* A wish, desire, drive, thought, obsession, etc., which dominates the psychic life and inhibits or eliminates all other forms of mental activity.

monoecism (mō-nē'siz'm) See *hermaphroditism.*

monohybrid Differing with respect to only *one* hereditary character (in a hybrid individual). See *hybrid.*

monohybridity, monohybridism (mon-ō-hī-brid'i-ti, -hī'brid-iz'm) The state of a hybrid whose parents differ in a single character, or the character of belonging to a type of individual heterozygous for a single pair of genes.

monoideism (mon-ō-ī-dē-iz'm) 'The theory according to which an idea detached from other ideas will exercise an unusually powerful force in the mind. This notion was formulated long ago both by Descartes and by Condillac. The magnetisers were well aware that suggestion was more powerful when the subjects were "isolated," that is to say when they were apparently unable to perceive any phenomena except the personality of the magnetiser and his utterances.' (Janet, P. *Psychological Healing* vols. 1-2, tr. by Paul, E. and C., Macmillan, New York, 1925)

The term is also used to refer to the symptom of harping on one idea, seen frequently in the senile group and in the schizophrenias.

monomania *Rare.* Partial insanity, in which the morbid mental state is restricted to one subject, the patient being of sound judgment and appropriate affect on all others.

In older psychiatry there were such expressions as *intellectual monomania* (e.g. paranoia); *affective monomania,* which corresponded with *manie raisonnante,* characterized by emotional deviation; *instinctive monomania,* which in general is the equivalent of the compulsive-obsessive syndrome of modern psychiatry.

When monomania or partial insanity was associated with depressive states, Esquirol suggested that the term *lypemania* be used, to distinguish the monomania with exaltation of mood.

monomania, affective An obsolete expression, used by Esquirol, most likely the equivalent of the manic phase of manic-depressive psychosis.

monomania, instinctive See *monomania.*

monomania, intellectual See *monomania.*

monomanie boulimique (mô-nô-mà-nē' boo-lē-mek') (F. 'bulimic impulse') Bulimia; insatiable hunger.

monomanie du vol (dü vôl′) (F. 'impulse to steal') Kleptomania.

monomanie érotique (ā-rô-tēk′) (F. 'erotic obsession') Erotomania.

monomanie expansive (ek-späN-sēv′) (F. 'cheerful obsession') Amenomania; manic phase of manic-depressive psychosis.

monomanie incendiaire (eN-säN-dē-âr′) (F. 'incendiary impulse') Pyromania.

monomanie meurtriere (mēr-trē-âr′) (F. 'murderous impulse') Morbid impulse to kill.

monomanie orgueilleuse (or-gē-yēz′) (F. 'obsession of haughtiness') Megalomania.

monomoria (mon-ō-mō′ri-à) *Obs.* Melancholia.

mononoea (-nē′à) Concentration on a single subject, as in monomania.

monopagia (-pā′jē-à) Clavus hystericus.

monopathophobia (-path-ō-fō′bē-à) Fear of a single, specific organic disease.

monophobia Fear of being alone.

monoplegia (mon-o-plē′jē-à) Paralysis of one limb or single part of the body, such as one arm, one leg, or the face alone, or only the fingers.

monopsychosis (-sī-kō′sis) *Obs.* Term, coined by Clouston, synonymous with *monomania.*

monosymptomatic (mon-ō-simp-tō-mat′-ik) Manifested by a single symptom. When a disorder is presented in the form of a single symptom it is said to be monosymptomatic.
'Hysterias in children without marked change of character are mostly monosymptomatic.' (Bleuler, E. *Textbook of Psychiatry,* tr. by Brill, A.A., Macmillan, New York, 1930)

monozygosity, monozygocity (-zi, zī-gos′i-ti) Both terms are used in genetics with reference to the origin from one egg of *monozygotic* or *identical* twins.

monozygote (-zī′got) One of the *monozygotic* (identical) co-twins.

monozygotic (-zī-got′ik) Referring to twins developed from a single egg and exhibiting extreme resemblances because of their identical genotypes. These *monozygotic,* or *identical,* or *one-egg* twin pairs are to be distinguished from the *dizygotic, fraternal,* or *non-identical* twin pairs produced by two eggs. See *twin.*

mood Feeling-tone, particularly as experienced internally by the subject; *affect* (q.v.) is generally used to refer both to mood and to external manifestations of the subject's feeling or emotional reactions.

mood, manic (man′ik) See *disposition, constitutional manic.*

mood, melancholic (mel-an-kol′ik) See *disposition, constitutional depressive.*

mood-swings The oscillation between periods of the feeling of well-being and those of depression or 'blueness.' All people have mood-swings, blue hours or blue days. Mood-swings are somewhat more marked in the neurotic than in the normal. In the manic-depressive patient, the swings are of much greater intensity and much longer duration.

moodcyclic disorders See *psychodynamics, adaptational.*

Mooney Problem Check List A questionnaire, used often as part of a rapid screening battery for high school and college students, in which the subject is asked to indicate which ones of a list of symptoms are frequent or troublesome to him.

moonstruck A popular term, meaning insane.

morality, sphincter Ferenczi's term for those forerunners of the superego that arise from introjection of parental (usually maternal) prohibitions and demands having to do with toilet training.

moral treatment In psychiatry, humane treatment of the mentally ill. It was French psychiatrists who spearheaded the late 18th century move toward humane treatment of the insane, culminating in their dramatic release from chains by Philippe Pinel in 1793. The unleashing of the mentally ill did not occur without severe resistance from the medical profession, from the politicians of the day, and from the Paris populace, and Pinel was more than once accused of harboring traitors in his hospital. One day he was set upon by a menacing crowd who threatened to lynch him for his 'crimes.' He escaped death only because his bodyguard, Chevigne, was able to fight off the mob—the same Chevigne who had been of the first group of patients to be released from their fetters.

Pinel's next step was to train hospital personnel in adequate care of the mentally ill, and it was his organization of mental hospitals that first demonstrated the value of hospital research and prepared the way for moral treatment and psychotherapy.

In the United States, Dr. Benjamin Rush (1745-1813) was a part of the movement towards humanization of treatment methods, including the abolition of mechanical restraint and the betterment of physical care. The period of moral treatment and humane care is the historical antecedent of the modern therapeutic community. See *social therapy*.

moramentia (mor-à-men'shē-à) *Obs.* Absolute amorality.

morbus astralis (môr'boos às-trä'lēs) (L. 'disease pertaining to the stars') *Obs.* Epilepsy.

morbus attonitus Celsi (àt-tô'nē-toos kel'sē) (L. 'Celsus's disease,' from Aurelius Cornelius Celsus, a Roman compiler of a medical encyclopedia, about 25 A.D.) *Obs.* Catalepsy.

morbus comitialis (kô-mē-tē-ä'lēs) (L. 'disease, pertaining to the comitia or elections,' as its occurrence on the day of the comitia was an ill omen and postponed the elections) *Obs.* Epilepsy.

morbus eruditorum (ā-roo-dē-tô'room (L. 'disease of the learned') Hypochondriasis.

morbus foedus (foy'doos) (L. 'foul, loathsome disease') Epilepsy.

morbus hypnoticus (hip-nô'tē-koos) (L. 'hypnotic disease') Drosdow introduced this term for a form of narcolepsy resembling the hypnotic state.

morbus infantilis (ēn-fàn'tē-lēs) (L. 'infantile disease') Epilepsy.

morbus interlunis (ēn-ter-lōō'nēs) (L. 'new-moon disease') Epilepsy.

morbus mirachialis (mē-rà-kē-ä'lēs) (L. 'abdominal disease') *Obs.* Hypochondriasis.

morbus popularis (pô-poo-lä'rēs) (L. 'people's disease') Epilepsy.

morbus publicus (poob'lē-koos) (L. 'public, common, disease') Epilepsy.

morbus puerilis (poo-ē'rē-les) (L. 'disease of childhood') Epilepsy.

morbus resiccatorius (rā-sēk-kà-tō'rē-oos) (L. 'drying, exhausting disease') Hypochondriasis.

morbus sacer (sà'ker) (L. 'sacred disease') Epilepsy.

morbus Sancti Joannis (sangk'tē yô-àn'-nēs) (L. 'Saint John's disease') Epilepsy.

morbus Sancti Valentini (và-len-tē'nē) (L. 'Saint Valentine's disease') Epilepsy.

morbus scelestus (ske-les'toos) (L. 'wicked, infamous disease') Epilepsy.

morbus sonticus (sôn'tē-koos) (L. 'dangerous, critical, disease') Epilepsy.

Morel, Benedict A. (1809-1873) French psychiatrist and physiologist; introduced the term *dementia praecox* (q.v.).

mores (mō'rēz) 'The popular habits and traditions, when they include a judgment that they are conducive to a societal welfare, and when they exert a co-ercion on the individual to conform to them, although they are not co-ordinated by any authority.' (Sumner, W.G. and Keller, A.G. *The Science of Society*, Yale University Press, New Haven, 1927-28)

'When the conviction arises that certain folkways are indispensable to the welfare of society, that they are the only "right" ways and that departure from them will involve calamity, i.e., when philosophical and ethical generalizations are developed about them, they are called mores.' (Davis, M.R. *Folkways; Encyclopaedia of the Social Sciences,* vol. 6, Macmillan, New York, 1931, p. 294)

mores, social Codes of manners and morals imposed by tacit authority (of 'unwritten' law) upon the individual to guide his social behavior in a given society, culture, or ethnical group and varying with the shift from one group, society, or culture to another.

moria (mō′rē-à) A morbid impulse to joke. Sometimes used synonymously with gallows humor or, more commonly, to refer to any dementia (usually of the exogenous-organic type) characterized by silliness. See *humor, gallows.*

morning after See *hangover.*

moron A person with mild mental retardation (I.Q. 52-67); in England, called *dullard.*

morosis (mō-rō′sis) *Obs.* Fatuity; also idiotism.

-morph (-morf) Combining form meaning one endowed with (specific) form or shape. From this are further formed *-morphic, -morphous, -morphy.*

morphinism (mor′fin-iz′m) Morphinomania. See *addiction; opium.*

morphinomania, morphiomania (mor-fi-nō-mā′nē-à, -ō-mā′nē-à) Morbid craving for morphine. See *addiction; opium.*

morphology The study of form and structure; anatomy.

mort douce (mawr′ doos′) (F. 'sweet death') Some authorities (e.g. Hirschfeld) use this expression to refer to the phenomena attendant upon the completion of the sexual act to those of 'sweet death.'
 Other authorities make the phrase synonymous with *euthanasia* (q.v.).

mortido (mor-tēd′ō) Federn's term for the destructive instinct; *destrudo* (q.v.).

morula (mor′oo-là, -ū-là) The embryological stage of a human organism, comprising the segmenting process of *cleavage* of a fertilized egg up to the 32-cell stage and the formation of the *blastula.*

Morvan's disease (Augustin Marie de Lannitis Morvan, French physician, 1819-97) See *syringomyelia.*

mosaic (mō-zā′ik) See *intermediate; test, mosaic.*

mother-child relationship (MCR) The reciprocal emotional interactions between mother and child, used particularly in reference to the effects of the mother's attitude on the emotional development of the child. Punitive mothers, for example, often have disobedient, hostile children; inconsistent mothers have children with temper problems; critical, depreciatory mothers have children who lie and are destructive.

mother, complete A term used by Federn to refer to the ideal type of mother that every schizophrenic seeks both in phantasy and in reality. The complete mother loves her child unselfishly, for himself alone, and does not use him as a means of gratifying her own psychological needs. She shows a conspicuous and admirable absence of certain characteristics of "typical" mothers of schizophrenics, viz., a sense of resentful obligation and reluctant duty in regard to the mother's responsibilities toward her child, or sensual gratification in her relationship with her offspring.

mother-fixation See *fixation, mother.*

mother, great See *Magna Mater.*

mother-hypnosis (-hip-nō′sis) See *hypnosis, father.*

mother-image See *image.*

mother, phallic The phantasy, which occurs early in the male's psychic development, that the mother has a phallus. In the course of his development, the male child reaches a stage in which his interest is concentrated on his genitals. Because this organ is so valuable and important to him, he believes that it is also present in other persons. Having seen no other type of genital formation, he will perforce assume that women also possess genitals like his. As part of the erotic activity developing around his genitals, the child manifests an intense desire to see the genitals of other persons, probably in order to compare them with his own. This erotic desire is very strong with regard to his mother, on whom his most intense feelings are concentrated at this age. He wishes to see the penis which he believes his mother possesses, and thus is developed the phantasy of the phallic mother in the male child.

This phantasy or belief may leave ineradicable traces in the child's subsequent psychic life. When he finds later that women, indeed, have no penis, his longing to see his mother's penis 'often becomes transformed into its opposite and gives place to disgust which in the years of puberty may become the cause of psychic impotence, of misogyny, and of lasting homosexuality.' And in fetishism the object which the patient reveres is 'a substitutive symbol for the once revered and since then missed member of the woman.' In mythology, too, 'this revered and very early fancied bodily formation of the mother' is retained. It is personified in those maternal deities appearing in many cultures in which the goddess is represented as having, in addition to breasts, a phallus. (Freud, S. *Leonardo da Vinci.* Kegan Paul, French, Trubner, London, 1922)

mother, schizophrenogenic A term used by those who believe that the attitude of the mother toward her child is the basic determinant of schizophrenia. By those who would subscribe to this viewpoint, the term usually includes (1) the overtly rejecting mother, who is domineering, aggressive, critical, and overdemanding (especially in regard to cleanliness and the observance of social forms); and (2) the covertly rejecting mother, who smothers her child with overprotectiveness. See *love, smother.*

Adherents of the schizophrenogenic mother hypothesis for the most part ignore that fact that of all the mothers who could be classified as fulfilling the above criteria, only a small percentage have schizophrenic children. Also ignored are the many studies indicating that there is no uniform pattern of family dynamics in the families of schizophrenic patients.

mother-substitute See *surrogate, mother.*

mother-surrogate See *surrogate, mother.*

motility disorder Any abnormality of motion or movement; used by many in a more specific sense to refer to the abnormal postures, gestures, etc., seen in catatonic schizophrenics and/or in childhood schizophrenics.

motility, unconscious Movements that are dissociated from consciousness, such as hysterical convulsions and spasms which are the unconscious and distorted physical expression of repressed instinctual demands.

motivation The force or energy that propels an organism to seek a goal and/or to satisfy a need; striving, incentive, purpose. Sullivan termed *conjunctive* those strivings directed to long-range satisfaction of real needs, and *disjunctive* those substitute strivings that afford only immediate gratification.

motivation, unconscious An aim or goal that is not recognized consciously by the subject, and especially any such aim that is the basis for a symptom, slip of the tongue or pen, or dream. Hysterical vomiting in a pregnant woman, for example, may be determined by her desire to rid herself of the fetus, a desire of which she is not consciously aware.

Freud's early work with hypnosis in hysterical patients led him to the conclusion that the symptoms afford a release of excitation in response to certain events, usually sexual, which are so unbearable that they are actively put out of consciousness and relegated into the unconscious portion of the psychic structure. But even though there is no longer any conscious awareness of these events, it does not mean that they cease to affect the individual: they nonetheless produce excitation which seeks for discharge, yet cannot operate within the field of awareness, and, therefore, finds *abnormal* discharge in symptoms, slips of the tongue, and dreams.

motive, lay See *tendency, final.*

motor cortex (kor'teks) That area of the cerebral hemisphere which controls movement; sometimes used synonymously with *precentral convolution,* although this is inaccurate, since movements can be excited from other areas as well.

motor-neurosis See *neurosis, motor.*

motorium (mō-tor'ē-um) 1. The motor cortex. 2. That faculty of the mind which has to do with volition (as the function of the sensorium is perception and of the intellect, thinking).

Mott, Frederick Walker, Sir (1859-1926) British neurologist.

mourning Normal grief, as contrasted with *melancholia* or *depression* (qq.v.), which are pathological.

movements, hypermetamorphotic (hī-pēr-met-à-mor-fot'ik) Wernicke's term for 'touching.'

MSRPP Multidimensional Scale for Rating Psychiatric Patients; often called the *Lorr scale.*

Much-Holzmann reaction (Hans Much; W. Holtzmann, German physicians) The alleged property of the serum from a person with schizophrenia or manic-depressive psychosis to inhibit hemolysis by cobra venom.

multidetermination *Overdetermination* (q.v.).

multiple sclerosis See *sclerosis, multiple.*

multiplication of personality See *personality, multiplication of.*

multiplicity, target A term suggested by S. R. Slavson to indicate the multiple possibilities existing in a group for projecting or displacing hostility on other patients, who replace the therapist as the target.

multipolarity (mul'ti-pō-lar'i-tē) A term introduced by S.R. Slavson to stress the fact that in group psychotherapy transference is directed toward more than the one person of the therapist. The inter-patient (sibling and identification) transference produces a state of multipolarity in transference.

mumbling Muttering; indistinct speech; asapholalia; mussitation. Continuous mumbling without apparent signs of excitation may be an outstanding manifestation of the terminal state in schizophrenia.

The mumbling consists of inarticulate, indistinct, and incoherent phrases, usually uttered in low tones so that the patient appears to be talking to himself.

Munsterberg, Hugo (1863-1916) (mün'-stēr-berk) American psychologist and psychotherapist.

musicomania (mū-zi-kō-mā'nē-à) *Obs.* 'A variety of insanity in which the passion for music has been fostered to such an extent as to derange the mental faculties.' (Tuke, D.H. *A Dictionary of Psychological Medicine,* vols. 1-2, Blakiston, Philadelphia, 1892)

musicotherapy (-ther'à-pē) Treatment of nervous and mental disorders by means of music, such as David's harp playing, which is said to have cured King Saul of his depression.

musomania (mū-zō-mā'nē-à) See *musicomania.*

musophobia (mū-sō-fo'bē-à) Fear of mice.

mussitate (mus'i-tāt) To mutter.

mussitation Movement of the tongue or lips as if in speech, without the production of articulate sounds.

mutant, mutational, mutated Pertaining to new hereditary characters originated by mutation.

mutation (mū-tā'shun) In genetics, that kind of *variation,* in the biological make-up of individual members of a species, which is the outcome of a permanent change in their idioplasmic equipment. Whether these mutational variations are minor or more conspicuous, it is their clear distinction from the parental type and their ability to reproduce the new type which distinguish them from other forms of variation. See *chromosome.*
  Mutant characters arise suddenly, breed true from the beginning, and give rise to a new and distinct race. They seem to occur in each species, usually with irregular frequency and more or less 'spontaneously.' This means that very little is known about the real cause, although it has been possible experimentally to produce various mutations by such external

influences as high temperatures, radium, or chemicals.

In human beings we find most frequently the so-called *factor mutations* brought about by a change in one of the chromomeres. These mutated genes produce more or less *pathological* types which often have a restricted viability (lethal factors). It may be assumed that the majority of hereditary malformations are caused by such factor mutations. Other kinds of mutation arise from changes in the chromosome equipment or in the position of genes.

Although all present evidence indicates that mutations are relatively common in nature and probably the starting point for every form of evolutionary development, it is clear that more differences among individuals are derived from combination than from changes of genes. As soon as a multiplicity of unlike genes have originated by mutation, the genes are brought together in ever new combinations as rapidly as crosses are effected between individuals differing with respect to them. In the last analysis, however, mutations must underlie the origin of each new stock, race, or species.

mutative Relating to or productive of change, variation, alteration, etc. See *interpretation, mutative.*

mutinus, mutunus (mōō-tē'noos, mōō-tōō'noos) Priapus; penis.

mutism (mūt'iz'm) The state of being mute, dumb, silent; voicelessness without structural alterations; silence due to disinclination to talk, as the 'vows of silence' in anchorites or monastics of various religious creeds or people who will not tell the reason for their mutism: they can, but they will not speak.

By usage the term *stupor* is often a synonym for *mutism.* The condition is frequently observed in the catatonic form of schizophrenia, in the stupor of melancholia, and in states of hysterical stupor.

'Dora had a very large number of attacks of coughing accompanied by loss of voice. Could it be that the presence or absence of the man she loved had had an influence upon the appearance and disappearance of the symptoms of her illness? . . . I asked her what the average length of these attacks had been. "From three

to six weeks, perhaps." How long had Herr K's absences lasted? "Three to six weeks, too," she was obliged to admit.' (Freud, S. *Collected Papers,* vol. 3, tr. by Strachey, A. and J., Leonard and Virginia Woolf and The Institute of Psychoanalysis, London, 1925).

mutism, akinetic (-,à-ki-ne'tik) A syndrome which is usually associated with tumors of the third ventricle; voluntary movements are limited and slow, and affective display is so reduced as to be barely discernible. Typically, the patient lies inertly in bed; he may follow the movements of the examiner but remains mute or answers in whispered monosyllables. He has to be fed, although swallowing is not impaired, and usually he is incontinent of urine and feces. The syndrome is believed to be due to interference with the reticular activating system so that response to environmental stimuli is defective.

One variant of akinetic mutism is *coma vigil* (also known as hypersomnia or parasomnia); this condition is characterized by a total absence of movements, except for respiration, but when the patient is stimulated by mechanical or auditory means he may blink his eyes with some degree of alertness and/or show some purposive reaction to nociceptive stimulation.

Akinetic mutism was first described by H. Cairns in 1941 and hence is often referred to as *Cairns' stupor.*

mutism, elective A term coined by M. Tramer, a German psychiatrist, in 1934 to describe children who were silent in all interpersonal contacts except for a small circle of close friends and relatives. Elective mutism is a selective refusal to speak, independent of intellectual endowment and/or neurologic status; it is often a part of *school phobia* and may first manifest itself in relation to separation from the family.

myasthenia (mī-as-thē'nē-à) Weakness of the muscles; fatiguability; seen often in schizophrenia and depression.

myasthenia gravis (grà'vis) A chronic disorder of conduction at the myoneural junction, due possibly to a toxic (?autoimmune) factor from the thymus gland that interferes with transmission at this site. The disorder shows a marked tendency to remissions and exacerbations; females are more commonly affected than males; and onset is usually between the ages of 20 and 50 years. The characteristic symptom is muscular fatigability; this begins in the ocular muscles (producing ptosis and diplopia) and eventually leads to the other common disturbances: snarling smile, nasal speech, difficulty in swallowing and articulation, etc. The upper limbs are more affected than the lower. Sooner or later, permanent paralysis of the affected muscles develops.

Management relies mainly on anticholinesterase compounds (neostigmine, pyridostigmine, ambenonium), which ameliorate weakness (but do not cure the disease). Thymectomy may be indicated in severe cases, although its value in male patients has not been firmly established.

mydriasis Dilation of the pupil. Mydriatics include *parasympatholytic* agents (such as atropine, scopolamine) and *sympathomimetic* drugs (such as cocaine, epinephrine). The former are *cycloplegic* (i.e. they relax ciliary muscles); the latter are not.

myelasthenia (mī-el-as-thē′nē-à) *Obs.* Neurasthenia of the spinal region.

myelencephalon (mī-el-en-sef′à-lon) See *hindbrain.*

myelinoclasis, acute perivascular (mī-el-in-ok′la-sis, à-kūt per-i-vas′kū-lar) See *encephalomyelitis, acute disseminated.*

myelitis (mī-e-lī′tis) Inflammation of the spinal cord.

myelo- (mī′el-ō-) Combining form meaning marrow; spinal cord, from Gr. *myelos,* marrow.

myelocystocele (mī-el-ō-sis′tō-sēl) Spinal cord substance contained in a *spina bifida* (q.v.).

myelogram An X-ray of the spine following injection of a suitable contrast medium (usually Pantopaque®) into the spinal subarachnoid space by means of spinal puncture. Myelography is most commonly used to demonstrate herniations of the intervertebral discs.

myelomeningocele (mī-el-ō-me-ning′gō-sēl) Spina bifida with protrusion of both the cord and its membranes.

myo- (mī′ō-) Combining form meaning muscle, from Gr. *mys,* gen. *myós,* mouse, muscle.

myoclonia (mī-ō-klōn′-ē-à) Any disorder characterized by spasmodic muscular contractions, as in infectious myoclonia, or chorea.

myoclonic epilepsy A type of petit mal epilepsy. See *epilepsy.*

myoclonus (mī-ok′lō-nus) A sudden, regular or irregular contraction of a muscle which does not usually produce movement of the part supplied by the muscle; it occurs oftenest in the limbs, but may be seen in the body and face.

myoclonus epilepsy See *epilepsy, myoclonus.*

myodynia, hysterical (mī-ō-dīn′e-à) Muscular tenderness, usually over the ovarian region, observed occasionally in hysteria.

myo-edema (-ē-dē′mà) Swelling of muscle; on tapping a muscle with a percussion hammer, a localized swelling appears and persists for a few moments; a sign of hyperirritability of atrophic muscles.

myokmyia (-kīm′ē-à) A transient quiver of a muscle, occurring in weak, anemic subjects.

myoneurasthenia (-nū-ras-thē′nē-à) Muscular weakness associated with neurasthenia.

myopathy, menopausal A pseudomyopathic polymyositis that appears in women during the menopausal years; proximal muscles are affected, and pathology consists of muscle neurosis without cellular infiltration.

myopia Short-sightedness or nearsightedness, caused by an elongation of the globe of the eye so that parallel rays are focussed in front of the retina. Farsightedness is the reverse condition and is known as *hyperopia.* See *ametropia.*

myopsychopathy (-sī-kop′à-thē) *Obs.* A tremor, paralysis, or other muscular disorder associated with the presence of mental weakness or change.

myopsychosis (-sī-kō′sis) See *myopsychopathy.*

myotonia atrophica (-tō′ni-à a-trof′i-kà) *Dystrophia myotonica* (q.v.).

mysophilia (mī-sō-fil′ē-à) Pathologic interest in, and desire for, filth or dirt; the desire to become unclean or polluted by contact with dirty or filthy objects—the opposite of *mysophobia* (q.v.). Mysophilia is commonly associated with *coprophilia* and *urophilia* and related to *paraphilias* (q.v.). Mysophilia is demonstrated in the following statement of a patient: 'I get more sex thrill from the idea of a dirty wench than I do from a clean one.'

mysophobia Fear of contamination. It is commonly observed in the form of incessant handwashing. Some patients spend the greater part of their waking hours washing their hands. They may exhibit the dread of uncleanliness by many other actions. Some refuse to touch anything unless they wear gloves; others must constantly wash everything in their surroundings.

mystic union See *union, mystic.*

mystical participation See *participation.*

mythomania (mith-ō-mā′nē-à) A morbid interest in myths and propensity for incredible stories and fabrications, a condition sometimes seen in psychiatric patients.

mythophobia Fear of stories or myths.

myxoneurosis (mik-sō-nū-rō′sis) A neurosis affecting the mucous membranes, marked by a mucous discharge from the respiratory or intestinal mucous membrane, unaccompanied by signs of active inflammation.

MZ Abbreviation for *monozygotic* (q.v.).

N

Nachmansohn, D. (Contemporary neurophysiologist) See *process, elementary.*

nail biting Onychophagia.

N-allylnormorphine (en-al-il-nor-mor'-fēn) See *psychotomimetic.*

naming A disturbance in association, peculiar to schizophrenia, in which the only recognizable association to external stimuli consists in naming them. Thus, in a word-association test, even though the patient understands its purpose, his only responses may be an enumeration of the furniture in the examining room. This 'naming' does not appear only in response to visual impressions. When asked to do something, the patient may name the act: 'Now he is sitting down.' Such patients appear to be completely dependent upon, and at the mercy of, external impressions. This seems to be related to the lack of a goal-concept, to the lack of directives and aims. See *touching.*

nanism (nā'niz'm, nan'iz'm) Paltauf's term for a special form of *dwarfism* (q.v.), which is of dysglandular origin and may best be classified as partial hypo-evolutism affecting especially the skeletal growth. A conspicuous exception to this underdeveloped skeleton is a very large skull, with which a normal development of brain and intelligence may be associated, although the face (saddle-nose) usually takes on a cretinoid aspect. Since the genitals also may be sufficiently developed, these dwarfs can procreate others of the same type.

nanism, senile See *progeria.*

nanosomia (nā-nō-sō'mē-à, nan-ō-) See *dwarfism.*

nanosomia, primordial Hansemann's term for a rare form of *dwarfism* (q.v.) with regular physical proportions of the dwarfed body and normal mental development. It seems to be hereditary, is more common in the male sex and is transmitted from the father. Although small from birth, these dwarfs accomplish their puperal crisis regularly and are able to reproduce.

This is practically identical with the other special forms of *microsomia* called *pygmeism* by the French school and *heredo-familial essential microsomia* (q.v.) by E. Levi.

Napalkov phenomenon See *phenomenon, Napalkov.*

narce (när'sē) Hippocratic term for mental torpor.

narcema (när-sē'mà) *Obs.* Narcosis.

narcism (när'siz'm) A shortened (and incorrect) form of *narcissism.*

narcissism (nar-sis'iz'm) This term was first used by Nacke to indicate the form of auto-erotism characterized by self-love, often without genitality as an object. Not infrequently, however, narcissism is associated with genital excitation: Krafft-Ebing cited the instance of a man who masturbated before a mirror.

In psychoanalytic psychology, narcissism is a stage in the development of object relationships in which the child's estimation of his capacities is heightened to the degree of omnipotence. At the narcissistic stage, which follows the auto-erotic or somatogenic stage, the infant is still in the primary undifferentiated phase of consciousness; he is ignorant of any sources of pleasure other than himself and does not differentiate between the breast (or other objects) and the self. The breast is thought of as a part of his own body, and since his slightest gestures are followed by satisfaction of his instinctual nutritional needs, he develops the 'autarchic fiction of false omnipotence.' This is the stage of *primary narcissism.* The ego believes itself to be omnipotent, but this is disproved by experience and frustration; the infant then comes to believe that the parents are the omnipotent ones, and he partakes of their omnipotence by introjection (the 'primary identification'). Even though reality has destroyed the feeling of omnipotence, the longing for this primary narcissism remains—the narcissistic needs—and self-esteem is the awareness of how close the individual is to the original omnipotence. The desire to partake of the parental omnipotence, even though it arose originally from the basic desire for the satisfaction of hunger, soon becomes differentiated from the hunger itself, and the child craves affection in a passive way ('passive object-love'); he is even willing to renounce other satisfactions if rewards of affection are promised. Thus the narcissistic needs are developed in relation to the ego and superego (and the term *secondary narcissism* refers to such love of the ego by the superego); the sexual needs, on the other hand, are developed in relation to the object.

When applied to the adult, the term narcissism implies a hypercathexis of the self and/or a hypocathexis of objects in the environment and/or a pathologically immature relationship to objects in the environment. Because the concept of narcissism was developed before Freud had formulated his last theory of the instincts (i.e. the dual-instinct theory of the sexual and aggressive instincts), it is not clear how Freud would have incorporated the aggressive instinct into his formulation of narcissism as described above; the formulation given refers only to the sexual drive. See *narcissism, primary.*

narcissism, disease Ferenczi used this expression to describe narcissism associated with an organic disease, in a soldier 'whose lower jaw had been almost entirely blown away by a shell. His face was horribly deformed by the injury. The only striking thing about his behaviour, however, was his naive narcissism. He requested that the nursing sister should manicure him thoroughly every day; he would not eat the hospital food, since much finer fare was due to him, and he reiterated these and similar requests unceasingly, after the fashion of querulants —a case, therefore, of true "disease-narcissism."' (Ferenczi, S. *Further Contributions to the Theory and Technique of Psycho-Analysis*, tr. by Suttie, J.I., Leonard and Virginia Woolf and The Institute of Psychoanalysis, London, 1926)

narcissism, negative An exaggerated underestimation of oneself. It is particularly expressed in states of melancholia, characterized by ideas of inadequacy, unreality and self-accusation.

narcissism, primary According to Freud, the whole available amount of libido is at

first stored in the ego. "We call this state of things absolute, primary narcissism. It continues until the ego begins to connect the presentations of objects with libido—to change narcissistic libido into object libido." (*International Journal of Psychoanalysis XXI*, 33, 1940) But in later writings (*The Ego and the Id*, London, Hogarth Press, 1949), Freud stated that in the beginning all libido is stored in the id and is drawn into the ego as narcissism only secondarily. "Part of this (original) libido is sent out by the id into erotic object cathexes, whereupon the ego, now growing stronger, attempts to obtain possession of this object libido and to force itself upon the id as a love object. The narcissism of the ego is thus seen to be secondary, acquired by the withdrawal of the libido from objects."

Thus it would seem that there is no such thing as primary narcissism, although Freud (and most of his followers) continued to refer to it despite the above quoted denial of it. And there are further contradictions in Freud's theory in that at various times he considered object love to be the primary and most primitive type of relationship to the environment, while at still other times (as discussed above) it was narcissism that was considered the most primitive type of relationship.

narcissism, secondary The narcissism once attached to external objects but now withdrawn from those objects and placed in the service of the ego (and not to objects in phantasy) is called secondary narcissism. This means that object-libido is transformed into ego-libido. 'The narcissism which arises when libidinal cathexes are called in away from external objects must be conceived of as a secondary form, superimposed upon a primary one that is obscured by manifold influences.' (Freud, S. *Collected Papers*, vol. 4, tr. by Riviere, J., Leonard and Virginia Woolf and The Institute of Psychoanalysis, London, 1924-25) For example, when a schizophrenic patient regresses, he withdraws libido from reality. The libido becomes attached, for instance, to ideas of grandeur and is called secondary narcissism. It is closely related, as Freud says, to infantile manifestations of megalomania.

Secondary narcissism is not introversion, as Freud describes the latter. In introversion libido goes into the service of phantasies of real objects.

narcissistic (när-si-sis′tik) Relating to self-love or narcissism.

narcoanalysis (när-ko-à-nal′i-sis) See *narcotherapy.*

narcocatharsis (-kà-thär′sis) See *narcotherapy.*

narcolepsy (när′kō-lep-sē) Friedmann's disease; Gelineau syndrome; a clinical syndrome consisting of cataplexy on emotion (i.e. sudden, transient loss of muscle tone in the extremities or trunk) and recurrent paroxysms of uncontrollable sleep lasting minutes or hours. The latter can often be controlled by amphetamines, but the condition itself usually persists throughout life.

narcolepsy, idiopathic (id-i-ō-path′ik) A disorder characterized by narcolepsy and cataplectic attacks; it is also known as the Gélineau syndrome.

narcomania A morbid desire to gain relief from painful stimuli usually through pharmacologic agents (morphine, opium, etc.), but also occasionally through psychic measures (for example, hypnosis).

narcosis, continuous (när-kō′sis) See *treatment, continuous sleep.*

narcosuggestion (när′kō-su (g) -jes′chun) See *narcotherapy.*

narcosynthesis See *narcotherapy.*

narcotherapy A form of treatment used extensively in the war neuroses of World War II. As a general group term it includes narcosuggestion, narcocatharsis, narcoanalysis, narcosynthesis, Amytal interview, Pentothal interview, 'truth serum.' The treatment consists of injecting a barbiturate drug intravenously, either sodium Amytal or sodium Pentothal. When slowly injected intravenously in a 5 to 10 per cent solution in doses of from 0.2 to 0.5 gram, either of these two drugs induces a state of complete relaxation and a feeling of well-being and serenity, with a desire to communicate thoughts and a capacity to verbalize easily. Previously repressed memories, affects, and conflicts are expressed and the therapist then guides the patient along the lines of narcosuggestion, narcoanalysis, or narcosynthesis.

Narcosuggestion implies the active utilization of suggestion and reassurance while the patient is in a state of complete relaxation in the process of receiving sodium Amytal or sodium Pentothal intravenously. Narcocatharsis or narcoanalysis (the two words are used interchangeably) implies either free association or direct questions by the therapist to uncover repressed memories and affects while the patient is under the effects of sodium Amytal or sodium Pentothal given intravenously. At the end of the narcoanalysis, after the effects of the drug have worn off, the therapist explains to the patient the significance of what he recalled. Narcosynthesis uses free association, dreams, and transference material obtained during the Amytal or Pentothal interview, but a day or so later the material is discussed with the patient, who is guided by the therapist to conative and emotional reintegration, behavioral adjustments, and social rehabilitation. Although this method is also known as 'truth serum' treatment, a patient who does not wish to tell the truth cannot be made to do so by the intravenous injection of Amytal or Pentothal. Consequently, this method is of limited value in medico-legal work.

narcotic blockade Total or partial inhibition of the euphoriogenic action of narcotic drugs through the use of other drugs, such as Methadone ®, which can then be used for maintenance treatment without producing the peaks of elation, abstinence symptoms, or demand for escalation of dose that characterize addiction to opiates.

narcotism (när′kō-tiz′m) The state of being under the influence of narcotic drugs. As commonly used, the term refers to the condition in which the drug is present in amounts great enough to be toxic, or, in any event, sufficient to alter behavior. See *addiction; dependency, drug.*

naturalia (nä-tōō-rä′lē-à) The sexual organs.

nature, experiment of A term frequently used in the field of objective psychobiology. Adolf Meyer emphasizes the study and treatment of stressful situations and the ways in which an individual reacts to such stresses. He refers to 'experiment of nature,' meaning the reaction to real environmental situations, and in particular to stressful ones.

nautomania (naw-tō-mā′ni-à) Seaman's mania. Not infrequently sailors are affected by a morbid fear of a ship or water.

-nea (-nē′à) Same as *-noea;* see *-noia.*

necro- (nek′rō-) Combining form, meaning *dead (body),* from Gr. *nekrós,* dead.

necromania (nek-rō-mā′nē-à) Morbid desire for a dead body, the interest in the corpse usually being of a sexual character.

necromimesis (-mi-mē′sis) The delusion in which the patient believes himself to be dead and acts as though he were.

necrophilia (302.8) A sexual perversion, whose condition is that the love object, whether heterosexual or homosexual, must be dead before orgasm can be achieved. Although a rare perversion overall, it is claimed by some that morticians, undertakers, etc., contribute a relatively high proportion of subjects who have the perversion in either a grossly overt or an attenuated form.

necrophilism (ne-krof′i-liz′m) 1. A morbid desire to be in the presence of dead bodies.
2. *Necrophilia* (q.v.).

necrophobia (nek-rō-fō′bi-à) Fear of a corpse or of death.

need Any stimulus of instinctual origin.

need, aboriginal See *psychodynamics, adaptational.*

need, acculturated (a-kul′chĕr-ā-ted) See *psychodynamics, adaptational.*

need, affiliative The desire to be associated with or allied with others in order to promote gratification of love, sexual desires, dependency, etc.

need, neurotic In Horney's terms, a demand or insistence that others behave toward the subject in a certain, specific way.

need for punishment See *criminal from sense of guilt.*

need-press See *method, need-press.*

needle-spray See *spray, needle.*

needs, narcissistic (när-sis-is′tik) See *narcissism.*

negation (ne-gā′shun) *Denial* (q.v.).

negation, delusion of Denial of the existence of externality and/or of oneself; often associated with *depersonalization* (q.v.).

negation, insanity of An older term introduced by J. Cotard as *délire des négations* for the syndrome known as *depersonalization* (q.v.).

negative period, first *Negativism* (q.v.) that normally occurs in children between the ages of two and four.

negative therapeutic reaction See *resistance, superego.*

negativism (neg′à-tiv-iz′m) Negative attitude or behavior. In psychiatry *negativism* is equivalent to *resistance,* as when a person, aware of stimuli from without, actively or passively opposes conformation with the stimuli. It is sometimes called contrasuggestibility or contrariety, though the latter terms are used more frequently in psychology than in psychiatry. It is also called command negativism.

Negativism is said to be *active* when the subject does the opposite of what he is asked to do. For example, when a catatonic patient closes his fists tightly upon being requested to open his hands, he presents active negativism.

He is said to exhibit *passive negativism* when, without prompting, he does not do things he is expected to do. He remains passive to his physiological urges; he does not get out of bed in the morning, nor dress, nor eat. Bleuler calls this *inner negativism.*

Some authorities use the expression intellectual *negativism* when a patient always expresses an opposite to a thought. Thus, a patient thought: 'I must go; I must not go. I am a man; no, I am a woman; I will tell him; I will not tell him.' This is more properly termed *ambivalence* (q.v.).

negativism, sexual Hirschfeld thus denotes absence of sexual interests, due, he believes, to deficiency 'in the sexual glands.' Synonymous with *anerotism*.

negrophilia (ne-grō-fil'ē-à) Love for the Negro.

negrophobia Fear of the Negro.

neighborhood The 'first grouping beyond the family which has social significance and which is conscious of some local unity [as the result of factors] such as topography and original vegetation, nationality bonds, religious purpose, the migration from a common place of residence and economic and social purposes.' (Kolb, J.H. *Rural Primary Groups*, Research Bulletin 51, Agricultural Experiment Station, University of Wisconsin)

The neighborhood is not only to be found in rural districts, but also 'in towns and cities, especially in residential areas which are not overdensely settled and which possess a population for the most part homogeneous and exhibiting a low rate of mobility.' (Carpenter, N. *Neighborhood; Encyclopaedia of the Social Sciences*, vol. 11, Macmillan, New York, 1933, p. 356)

neo- (nē'ō-) Combining form meaning new, recent, from Gr. *néos*, new, novel.

neoatavism (nē-ō-at'à-viz'm) The recurrence, in a descendant, of characters of traits of a near or immediate ancestor. See *paleoatavism*.

neocortex (-kor'teks) See *isocortex*.

neographism (nē-og'rà-fiz'm) The graphic equivalent of neologism, i.e. the writing of new words. See *neologism*.

neography (nē-og'rà-fē) Neologistic writing.

neolalia (nē-ō-lā'lē-à) Neologistic speech; frequent use of neologisms in patient's speech.

neologism (nē-ol'ō-jiz'm) '*Neologisms* are words of the patient's own making, often portmanteau condensations of several other words, and having originally had a special meaning for the patients.' (Henderson, D.K. and Gillespie, R.D. *A Text-Book of Psychiatry*, 4th ed., Oxford University Press, London, 1936)

'A paranoid female "is a Billy-goat," i.e., she is united with her beloved minister: minister = Christ = lamb = billygoat.' (Bleuler, E. *Textbook of Psychiatry*, tr. by Brill, A.A., Macmillan, New York, 1930)

'In another dream the same patient imagined she was called "Hokerring," a neologism produced by fusing the two words "smoked herring". . . . The term smoked herring reminded her of bloater, and of a rather vulgar word in her native language meaning nude, pronounced bloat.'* (Jones, E. *Papers on Psycho-Analysis*, 4th ed., Wood, Baltimore, 1938)

*In Dutch *bloot* means 'bare, naked'; cf. G. *bloss*, bare, naked, mere, and Scotch *blate*, bare, naked.

neomimism A type of stereotypy, analagous to neologisms, consisting of a seemingly senseless gesture that has a particular meaning to the patient.

neomnesis (nē-om-nē'sis) Memory for the recent past.

neonate The new-born infant; see *developmental levels*.

neonaticide See *filicide*.

neophasia, polyglot (nē-ō-fā'zhē-à) A type of neologism formation in which one or more languages are devised by the patient, sometimes with full vocabulary, grammar, and syntax. Polyglot neophasia is rarely seen except in expansive paranoiacs and, to a lesser extent, in manic states.

neophobia Fear of anything new or unfamiliar.

neophrenia (nē-ō-frē'nē-à) In 1863 Kahlbaum classified psychiatric conditions (then called insanity) in accordance with the patient's age: neophrenia (the insanity of childhood), hebephrenia (the insanity of adolescence) and presbyophrenia (the insanity of old age).

neopsychic (-sī'kik) Of recent psychic development.

neo-sleep See *dream*.

neostriatum (nē-ō-strē'à-toom) See *basal ganglia*.

nephelopsychosis (nef-e-lō-sī-kō'sis) *Obs.* Intense interest in clouds.

nerve, abducens (ab-dū-senz) The sixth cranial nerve. The abducens nerve arises in the lower portion of the pons and supplies the external rectus muscle of the eye. For symptoms of abducens nerve lesions, see *nerve, oculomotor.*

nerve, acoustic The eighth cranial nerve. The acoustic nerve is a sensory nerve with two separate portions, the cochlear or auditory nerve (hearing) and the vestibular nerve (orientation in space). First-order neurons pass from the receptor cells in the spiral organ of Corti to the cochlear nuclei; from here, second-order neurons proceed through the trapezoid body and lateral lemnisci to the medial geniculate bodies. From here, auditory radiations are projected to the auditory cortex. First-order neurons of the vestibular nerve pass from the receptor cells in the vestibular ganglion (Scarpa's ganglion) to the vestibular nuclei, and thence to the cerebellum.

Symptoms of cochlear nerve involvement include tinnitus, deafness, and, in the case of supranuclear disorders, auditory aphasia or word-deafness. Symptoms of vestibular nerve involvement include vertigo and nystagmus.

nerve, cochlear (kok'lē-ēr) See *nerve, acoustic.*

nerve, facial The seventh cranial nerve. The facial nerve is primarily a motor nerve which originates in the posterior pons and supplies the stapedius muscle of the middle ear and the superficial musculature of the face and scalp. Parasympathetic fibers supply the glands and mucous membranes of the pharynx, palate, and nasal cavity. The facial nerve also has some sensory fibers which carry taste from the anterior tongue. Lesions of the facial nerve may be peripheral (Bell's palsy or prosoplegia), nuclear, or supranuclear. In peripheral facial paralysis, the following signs will be seen on the affected side: drooping mouth, inability to whistle or wink or wrinkle forehead, tearing of eye, loss of deep facial sensation; food collects between cheek and gum, paralysis is of the flaccid (lower motor neuron) type. In the nuclear type of facial palsy, the above signs are also seen and, in addition, contralateral hemiplegia due to pyramidal involvement. In the supranuclear type of facial palsy, the paralysis is of the spastic (upper motor neuron) type, the frontalis muscle is spared because of its bilateral cortical innervation, and reflexes and emotional responses are retained. Supranuclear facial paralysis is often associated with homolateral hemiplegia or monoplegia.

nerve, glossopharyngeal (glos-so-far-in'-ge-al) The ninth cranial nerve. The glossopharyngeal nerve is motor to the stylopharygeus muscle and sensory to the pharynx, soft palate, posterior tongue, and to the carotid body (for reflex control of respiration, blood pressure, and heart rate). The glossopharyngeal nerve also supplies taste buds in the posterior third of the tongue. Symptoms associated with lesions of this nerve include loss of gag reflex, loss of taste in posterior tongue, and deviation of uvula to the unaffected side.

nerve, hypoglossal (hī-pō-glos'sal) The twelfth cranial nerve. The hypoglossal nerve is motor to the muscles of the tongue. Peripheral paralysis results in homolateral flaccidity, paralysis and atrophy, and the tongue deviates to the side of the lesion. Supranuclear paralysis results in contralateral hemiplegia, contralateral spastic paralysis of the tongue, and deviation of the tongue to the side opposite the lesion.

nerve, oculomotor (ok-ū-lō-mō'tēr) The third cranial nerve. The oculomotor nerve arises at the level of the superior colliculus and is the motor nerve to the following eye muscles: internal rectus, superior rectus, inferior rectus, inferior oblique, and levator palpebrae. Parasympathetic fibers originate in the Edinger-Westphal nucleus and proceed via the nasociliary branch of the oculomotor nerve to the ciliary ganglion, whence the short ciliary nerves pass to the sphincter muscle of the iris.

The other muscles of the eye are supplied by the trochlear and abducens nerves, which functionally are considered together with the oculomotor nerve. Symptoms of involvement of these three cranial nerves include: lid drop (ptosis), nystagmus, double vision (diplopia), squint (strabismus), and conjugate deviation, in which both eyes are turned to the same side. Strabismus may be internal, in which case the visual axes cross each other, or external, in which case the visual axes diverge from each other.

J.G. Chusid and J.J. McDonald (*Correlative Neuroanatomy and Functional Neurology*, 8th ed., Lange, Los Altos, California, 1956) suggest the following classification of disorders of these three cranial nerves:

A. Opthalmoplegias (paralyses)
  1. Oculomotor paralysis
    a. external ophthalmoplegia—divergent strabismus, diplopia, ptosis
    b. internal ophthalmoplegia—dilated pupil, loss of light and accommodation reflexes
    (Total ophthalmoplegia refers to a combination of external and internal ophthalmoplegia.)
    c. Argyll Robertson pupil—miosis with loss of light and cilio-spinal reflexes, and preservation of accommodation reflex (pretectal lesion)
    d. Paralysis of convergence (central lesion)
  2. Trochlear paralysis (rare)—slight convergent strabismus and diplopia
  3. Abducens paralysis (most common) —convergent strabismus and diplopia
  4. Chronic progressive ophthalmoplegia (Graefe's disease)—usually involves all three nerves
B. Myasthenic States
C. Spasmodic Ocular Disorders (supranuclear lesions)
  1. conjugate deviation spasm
  2. lateral or ventral association spasm
  3. central nystagmus: rhythmic (vestibular origin) or undulating (cerebral or cerebellar origin)

nerve, olfactory (ol-fak'to-rē) The first cranial nerve. The olfactory nerve is structurally a fiber tract of the brain; it is a sensory nerve which transmits olfactory (smell) stimuli. Symptoms due to olfactory nerve lesions include: anosmia (loss of sense of smell), hyperosmia, parosmia (perverted sense of smell), cacosmia (sensation of unpleasant odors), and olfactory hallucinations. The Foster Kennedy syndrome, caused by tumors at the base of the frontal lobe, includes anosmia with atrophy of the optic and olfactory nerves, blindness, and contralateral papilledema.

nerve, optic (op'tik) The second cranial nerve. The optic nerve is structurally a fiber tract of the brain; it is a sensory nerve which transmits visual stimuli. The rods and cones of the retina of the eye are the first-order neurons; they connect with the bipolar cells of the retina, which in turn connect with the ganglion cells. These form the optic nerve-fibers, which proceed to the optic chiasma, form the optic tracts, and then pass to the lateral geniculate bodies, the superior colliculi, and the pretectal region. From the geniculate bodies, fibers pass (as the geniculo-calcarine tract) to the occipital cortex. Fibers from the superior colliculi pass to various cranial and spinal nuclei (for involuntary oculoskeletal reflexes); fibers from the pretectal region pass to the Edinger-Westphal nuclei (for the simple and consensual light reflexes).

Visual defects include scotomata (abnormal blind spots in the visual fields), amblyopia (reduction of visual acuity), amaurosis (complete blindness), *field-defects* (q.v.), hemeralopia (day blindness), nyctalopia (night blindness), color blindness, and optic agnosia or word blindness.

nerve, spinal accessory The eleventh cranial nerve. The spinal accessory nerve is motor to the trapezius and sternocleidomastoid muscles. Unilateral paralysis results in inability to rotate head to unaffected side, atrophy of sternocleidomastoid, inability to shrug affected shoulder, and drooping of affected shoulder. Bilateral paralysis results in difficulty in rotating head or lifting chin, and in a dropping forward of the head.

nerve, trigeminal (trī-gem'in-al) The fifth cranial nerve. The trigeminal nerve has both motor and sensory components. Motor fibers arise from the motor nucleus in the pons and supply the muscles of mastication (masseter, temporal, internal and external pterygoids). Sensory fibers are in three divisions: the ophthalmic division supplies the forehead, eyes, nose, temples, and meninges; the maxillary division supplies the upper jaw and hard palate; the mandibular division supplies the lower jaw and tongue. Symptoms of trigeminal nerve lesions include: pain, loss of sensation, paralysis of muscles of mastication with deviation of the jaw to the affected side, loss of jaw jerk, sneeze, lid reflex, conjunctival reflex and corneal reflex, and various trophic changes in the nose, face, and jaw.

nerve, trochlear (trok′lē-ēr) The fourth cranial nerve. The trochlear nerve arises at the level of the inferior colliculus and is the motor nerve to the superior oblique muscle of the eye. For symptoms of trochlear nerve lesions, see *nerve, oculomotor.*

nerve, vagus (vā′gus) The tenth cranial nerve. The vagus nerve is motor to the muscles of the soft palate and pharynx, sends parasympathetic fibers to the thoracic and abdominal viscera, and is sensory to the pharynx, larynx, trachea, esophagus, and the thoracic and abdominal viscera. Symptoms of vagus nerve lesions include: aphonia, dysphagia, paralysis of the soft palate with loss of the gag reflex, cough, bradycardia (with irritative lesions), or tachycardia (with vagus palsies).

nerve, vestibular (ves-tib′ū-lēr) See *nerve, acoustic.*

nerves A colloquialism, meaning general excitability, uneasiness and fearfulness; it is often said that one 'has a bad case of nerves,' that one is 'jittery' or has the 'jitters.'

nervosism (nēr′vō-siz'm) An old doctrine which maintained that all morbid mental phenomena were due to variations in nerve force.

nervosismus (nēr-vô-ziz′moos) *Obs.* Neurasthenia.

nervosity (nēr-vos′i-ti) Kraepelin used this term in about the same sense that *nervousness* is used today. It includes a wide variety of psychic manifestations that do not substantially handicap a person in his daily activities, but which stamp him as temperamentally unstable, nervous, eccentric, etc. In his reactions he stands between mental health and the more formal psychiatric states. See *nervousness.*

nervous (nēr′vus) 1. Relating to a nerve or the nerves.
2. Easily excited or agitated; suffering from instability or weakness of nerve action.

nervous system, autonomic See *autonomic nervous system.*

nervous system, conceptual Any model whose operation is in accordance with known mechanisms of central nervous system functioning and which is capable of producing responses comparable to or identical with the behavior of the living organism. The value of the conceptual nervous system is primarily heuristic in that it affords a simplified and manipulatable analogy of the nervous system itself and thus stimulates hypotheses about how the nervous system operates. Often, however, it is accepted uncritically as an exact reproduction of the nervous system and then used incorrectly as a way to verify theories about the nervous system.

nervous system, parasympathetic See *autonomic nervous system.*

nervous system, sympathetic See *autonomic nervous system.*

nervous system, third See *third nervous system.*

nervous system, vegetative See *autonomic nervous system.*

nervousness A popular term, generally referring to a mild mental indisposition, not having the significance of a mental 'disease.' See *neurosis; neurosis, character.*

net fertility See *fertility, net.*

networks, psychological 'Psychological networks are formed when certain parts of social atoms link themselves with parts of other social atoms and these again with parts of other social atoms, thus forming complex chains of interrelations. On the other hand, numerous parts of social atoms remain isolated or buried between individuals.
'Some individuals comprising certain links of a network are unacquainted with those in more distant links, but can exert influence by indirection. The older and

wider the network as it spreads the less significant becomes the individual position within it. The function of the networks is to shape social tradition and public opinion.

'The changing psychological currents in a network tend to maintain a natural level as long as they are made up by spontaneous determinants only, or, the feelings and ideas which arise solely from the individuals themselves. Through the use of modern technological methods for the dissemination of propaganda artificial or mechanical determinants enter into the development of psychological currents. They denaturalize their spontaneous unfoldment and degenerate, by retroaction, the feelings of the individuals themselves. One of the chief objectives of sociometric techniques has been the control of network formation.' (Moreno, J.L. *Sociometry 1*, 213, 1937)

neuradynamia (nū-rad-i-nā'mē-à) Neurasthenia.

neural plate (tube) (nū'ral) See *cephalogenesis*.

neuralgia, Fothergill's (nū-ral'ji-à) See *tic douloureux*.

neuralgia, trifacial (trī-fā'shal) See *tic douloureux*.

neuralgia, trigeminal (trī-gem'in-al) See *tic douloureux*.

neurämie (noi-rā-mē') *Neurasthenia* (q.v.).

neurasthenia (nū-ras-thē'nē-à) Neurasthenic neurosis (300.5); nervous debility. The concept *neurasthenia* was introduced in America in 1869 by G.M. Beard; it had been outlined by Bouchut as *nervosisme* in 1860. During the second half of the 19th century it was more of a generic than a nosologic term. In Tuke's *Dictionary of Psychological Medicine*, Arndt said that neurasthenia 'represents to a certain degree the starting point of all the more severe nervous disorders, and the soil from which they grow.' (Vols. 1-2, Blakiston, Philadelphia, 1892). Thus it was the forerunner to hysteria, epilepsy, locomotor ataxia, general paralysis, etc. For a number of years neurasthenia was regarded as a syndrome associated with a more fundamental disorder.

Until modern times the expression *neurasthenia* was taken literally to mean weakness or exhaustion of the nervous system. Bleuler says: 'A general decline of strength is no neurosis. People who toil hardest, who with a few hours of sleep and at that frequently interrupted through attention to the children, regularly do a day's work of 16 or more hours, year in and year out, only exceptionally become neurasthenic.' (Bleuler, E. *Textbook of Psychiatry*, tr. by Brill, A.A., Macmillan, New York, 1930)

The clinical syndrome is characterized by a wide variety of symptoms, including easy fatigueability, feeling of physical and mental weakness, aches, pains, paresthesias, and a number of other pathological physical sensations; inadequate functioning of any organ or organic system of the body; insomnia, etc. While some subjects run the gamut of symptoms, usually complaints center upon some particular organ or system.

The fatigue state is a defense against some intrapsychic conflict, and is itself defended against by a search for some physical cause to explain the fatigue. The emotional basis is sometimes wholly and always at least partially outside conscious awareness. Fatigue may be a symbolic expression of or a defense against consciously disowned needs or wishes. Unresolved anger may lead to hidden resentment, which in turn provokes fear of punishment or disapproval, and the latter fear is expressed as being tired, and not feeling well. Such fatigue states are often found in conjunction with feelings of failure, frustration, and disappointment. Neurasthenic patients are typically narcissistic, self-centered, and manifest strong dependency needs.

In DSM-I, neurasthenia was classified as a psychophysiologic nervous system reaction. According to Freud's early theory, 'Neurasthenia arises whenever a less adequate relief (activity) takes the place of the adequate one, thus, when masturbation or spontaneous emission replaces normal coitus under the most favorable conditions.' (Freud, S. *Collected Papers*, vol. 1, tr. by Riviere, J., Leonard and Virginia Woolf and The Institute of Psychoanalysis, London, 1924-25) The foregoing was written in 1894. Four years later he said that neurasthenia was looked upon by him as an *actual neurosis*. 'Psychoneuroses appear under two kinds of conditions, either independently or in the wake of actual neuroses (neurasthenia and anxiety-neurosis).' (ibid)

'If we separate out from the cases of illness hitherto designated as neurasthenia everything that should be relegated to other, more natural nosological classifications, there remain behind a well-characterized group in which there predominate, pressure in the head, spinal irritation, constipation, paraesthesias, diminished potency, and from the effect of these conditions, a depression of the spirits.' (Ferenczi, S. *Further Contributions to the Theory and Technique of Psycho-Analysis*, tr. by Suttie, J.I., Leonard and Virginia Woolf and The Institute of Psychoanalysis, London, 1926)

neurasthenia, aviator's 'A chronic functional nervous and psychic disorder occurring in aviators and characterized by gastric distress, nervous irritabilities, minor psychic disorders, fatigue of the higher voluntary mental centers, insomnia, and increased motor activity.' The principal exciting etiological factor is emotional stress. This condition is also known as *aeroneurosis* (q.v.), *staleness*, and *flying sickness*. (Sladen, F. J. (ed). *Psychiatry and the War*, Thomas, Springfield, Ill., 1943)

neurasthenia, periodic 'Many cases which on superficial examination would be regarded as ordinary (neurasthenic) hypochondria belong to this group of obsessional affects; so-called "periodic neurasthenia" or "periodic melancholia" in particular appears to be reducible with unexpected frequency to obsessional affects and obsessional ideas—a recognition that is therapeutically by no means unimportant.' (Freud, S. *Collected Papers*, vol. 1, tr. by Riviere, J., Leonard and Virginia Woolf and The Institute of Psychoanalysis, London, 1924-25)

neurasthenia, post-infectious (309.14) A syndrome that may occur after any severe physical illness or during its later stages; it is a frequent sequel to influenza, typhoid, dysentery, Weil's disease, and infectious hepatitis. First described by Bonhoeffer under the name 'hypersensitive emotional debility,' its symptoms include: malaise, headache, feelings of weakness and fatigue, hypersensitivity to

light and noise, frightening hypnagogic hallucinations, lack of concentration, listlessness, and often depression with retardation and hypochondriacal trends. Recovery is usually gradual, over a period of months.

neurasthenia, professional Nervous prostration manifested principally in the patient's total or almost total inability to use the organ(s) habitually employed in the course of his profession or occupation.

'Writing for a long time causes fatigue of the nervous mechanism specialized for this function. In such a case, every time the subject prepares to write he is seized, even from the very start or after he has written a few lines, by a painful feeling of fatigue in the arm, or by a spasm that prevents him continuing (mogigraphia).' (Bianchi, L. *A Text-Book of Psychiatry*, tr. by MacDonald, J.H., Baillière, Tindall & Cox, London, 1906) See *neurosis, occupational.*

neurasthenia, traumatic (traw-mat′ik) A neurasthenic reaction pattern which develops in response to physical trauma, such as those caused by automotive or industrial accidents. Trauma is here considered to have precipitated an acute exacerbation of an underlying neurotic potentiality. See *neurasthenia.*

neurasthenia, tropical A diagnosis made on soldiers invalided in the tropics who manifested low blood pressure, peripheral congestion, dizziness, marked weakness fainting, even shock. It is doubtful whether this constitutes a true entity. Removal to a temperate climate relieved all symptoms. See *mania, tropical.*

neurasthenia, war A more recent and simpler psychiatric term for neurocirculatory asthenia as observed in soldiers in time of war. Neurocirculatory asthenia, or effort-syndrome, is a frequently observed disorder in civilian neuropsychiatry. When the disorder was met with and recorded in military neuropsychiatric casualties, its name took on a military flavor. Neurocirculatory asthenia became war neurasthenia, and effort-syndrome became soldier's heart.

As for the condition itself, however, most observers agree that neither of these names is really suitable. 'In other words, neurocirculatory asthenia is psychoneurosis with cardiac manifestations and while it may have special coloring in military life, it is still primarily a neurosis and should be looked upon and treated as such. If special evidences of vasomotor instability are present, they are only another phase of the disordered constitution and do not invalidate the principle that the neurotic element is the more important from the standpoint of management.' (Weiss, E., and English, O.S. *Psychosomatic Medicine.* W.B. Saunders Company, Philadelphia, 1943.) See *asthenia, neurocirculatory.*

neurasthenic, arrived *Obs.* Déjérine and Gauckler speak of 'neurasthenics who have arrived.' In them 'the intellectual fatigue is real, and in direct proportion to the emaciation and weakness of the subject, who may at the same time be physically as well as morally depressed. In these patients a very curious phenomenon sometimes occurs which resembles a periodic psychosis. It is not at all rare among such subjects to find that for short periods of time intellectual work becomes almost too easy for them.' (Déjérine, J. and Gauckler, E. *The Psychoneuroses and Their Treatment by Psychotherapy,* 2nd ed., tr. by Jelliffe, S.E., Lippincott, Philadelphia and London, 1915)

neurasthenoid (nū-ras'then-oid) Resembling neurasthenia.

neuraxon See *neuron.*

neuremia (nū-rē'mē-à) Laycock's term for functional disorders of the nervous system.

neuriatry, neuriatria (nū-rī'à-trē, -rē-at'-rē-à) Treatment of nervous diseases.

neurilemma See *neuron.*

neurinomatosis (nū-rin-ō-mà-tō'sis) A tendency toward new growth of primitive neuro-epithelial cells. See *diathesis, glial.*

neuritis, optic (nū-rī'tis, op'tik) An inflammatory process affecting the head of the optic nerve, or that part within the bulb of the eye. The condition is usually bilateral, and early loss of vision is characteristic. Ophthalmoscopically, there is blurring of the margins of the disk with congestion, dilatation of the veins, and

narrowing of the arteries. The retina may show hemorrhages, pigment deposits, exudates, connective tissue changes, and atrophic spots. Optic neuritis may occur in severe renal disease, syphilis, leukemia, carbon monoxide poisoning, diabetes, anemia, and other constitutional diseases.

neuro- (nū'rō) Combining form meaning nerve, from Gr. *neuron,* nerve.

neuroarthritism (nū-rō-är'thri-tiz'm) A condition with a predisposition to nervous and rheumatoid or gouty disorders.

neuro-central See *constant, central.*

neurofibromatosis (-fi-brō-ma-tō'sis) Neurofibroblastomatosis; von Recklinghausen's disease. A congenital, hereditary disorder, transmitted as a Mendelian dominant, consisting of café-au-lait pigmentation of the skin and the formation of tumors in various tissues (e.g. cutaneous fibromas or mollusca fibrosa, and perineural fibroblastomas of the peripheral and cranial nerves). The tumors are often associated with overgrowth of the skin and subcutaneous tissues. Of the cranial nerves, the eighth nerve is the most commonly involved. The disorder is sometimes progressive, but it does not always shorten life. It may be associated with varying degrees of mental retardation (in DSM-II, 31x.3). Treatment is palliative; the painful tumors may be excised or irradiated with X-ray.

neurogenic (-jen'ik) Caused or produced by, born of, springing from, or engendered by nerves or a nerve.

neuroglia (nū-rog'lē-à) A fine web of supporting tissue in the nervous system, composed of modified ectodermal elements in which are enclosed the neuroglia (or glia) cells: astrocytes, oligodendroglia and microglia.

neurogram (nū'rō-gram) 'Whatever may be the exact nature of the theoretical alterations left in the brain by life's experiences they have received various generic terms; more commonly "brain residual," and "brain dispositions." I have been in the habit of using the term *neurograms* to characterize these brain records. Just as telegram, Marconigram, and phonogram precisely characterize the form in which the physical phenomena which correspond to our (verbally or scripturally) thoughts, are recorded and conserved, so neurogram precisely characterizes my conception of the form in which a system of brain processes corresponding to thoughts and other mental experiences is recorded and conserved.' (Prince, M. *The Unconscious,* Macmillan, New York, 1916) See *memory, physiological.*

neurohumor A chemical substance which transmits the nerve impulse at the synapse. See *process, elementary; epinephrine; serotonin.*

neurohypnology (nū-rō-hip-nol′ō-jē) The study of 'magnetic sleep.' (Braid)

neurohypnosis (-hip-nō′sis) Braid's original term (now obsolete) which means literally sleep of the nervous system; later Braid dropped the first part of the word, and used hypnosis instead, 'for the sake of brevity.'

neuroinduction (-in-duk′shun) Suggestion.

neurokym (nū′rō-kim) *Psychokym* (q.v.).

neuroleptic Referring to a specific effect of a pharmacologic agent on nervous system; the terms ataraxic and tranquilizer, in contrast, are merely descriptive of a sedative effect. See *tranquilizer; psycholeptica.*

neurology (nū-rol′ō-ji) The branch of medicine that devotes itself to the study of the organization and function of the nervous tissue. The diseases of the peripheral nerves of the spinal cord and the brain, as far as they are based on organic pathology, are in the realm of neurology.

neurometadrasis (nū-rō-met-à-drā′sis) *Obs.* Animal magnetism or the influence of one body upon another.

neuromimesis (-mi-mē′sis) *Obs.* Mimicry of disease or disorder of a mental or nervous character.

neuromyelitis optica (-mē-e-lē′tis op′tē-ka) *Devic's disease* (q.v.).

neuron, neurone The unit of the central nervous system; the nerve cell, consisting

of cell body, dendrites, and neuraxon. Conventional descriptions of the neuron usually follow that of Ramón y Cajal (1911), even though his morphological description has long been inadequate in terms of neuron function. This inadequacy is related primarily to his inclusion of the cell body as the focal point of functional polarization of the neuron, a view no longer tenable if recent advances in neurophysiology and cytology are to be taken into consideration.

In the classical description, the dendrons or dendrites are described as receptor portions of a neuron which arise from the nucleated cell body or perikaryon; they conduct nerve impulses toward the cell body. The axon is a nerve-cell process which also arises from the cell body but it conducts nerve impulses away from the cell body.

D. Bodian (*Science 137,* 323, 1962) has proposed the following redefinition of structure in terms of function:

Dendrites—neuron processes with response generator function; the dendritic zone is 'the receptor membrane of a neuron, either consisting of a set of tapering cytoplasmic extensions (dendrites) which receive synaptic endings of other neurons or differentiated to convert environmental stimuli into local-response-generating activity.'

Nuclear cell body or *perikaryon*—consists of an internal portion (the chromidial neuroplasm) and an external membrane; it is located in a variety of positions in various nerve cells. The membrane alone is involved in synaptic transmission; the chromidial neuroplasm is a separate functional component of the cell and is a cytoplasmic zone related primarily to the trophic aspect of nerve cell function. Its position within the neuron 'is related to the outgrowth and metabolic maintenance of processes rather than to the conducting polarization of the neuron.' 'It may be located in the dendritic zone or within the axon, or it may be attached to the axon.'

Axon—'a single, often branched and usually elongated, cytoplasmic extension morphologically and perhaps uniquely differentiated to conduct nervous impulses away from the dendritic zone. It is characteristically uniform in caliber and ensheathed by neuroglial or neurilemma cells.' Functionally, 'the axon may be said to arise from any response generator structure, such as receptor terminal, dendrite, cell body, or axon hillock. . . . According to this view, axons do not arise from "cell bodies" which are separated from the response generating region.'

Axon telodendria—'the usually branched and variously differentiated terminals of axons which show membrane and cytoplasmic differentiation related to synaptic transmission or neurosecretory activity. Mitrochondrial concentrations, "synaptic vesicles," or secretory granules are commonly present in bulblike terminals. . . . They transmit electrical or chemical signals capable of producing generator potentials in the dendritic zone of other neurons and in muscle, and stimulatory effects in innervated glandular cells or in distant cells via the humoral route (neurohormones).'

The above revisions of classicial descriptions 'make it possible to relate basic functional aspects of neuron function to general aspects of neuron structure, as follows: response (spike) generation, to the "dendritic zone" (transducer and synaptic surfaces); impulse origin, at or near the axon origin (the initial axon segment or axon "neck"); impulse conduction, to the axon; and synaptic transmission or neurosecretory emission, to the axon telodendria.'

neuropathy (nū-rop′à-thē) Any (organic) disease of the nervous system; any disorder involving neural tissue. Formerly the term included disorders that currently would be termed neurotic or psychoneurotic.

neuroplasm, chromidial See *neuron.*

neuropsychiatry (nū-rō-sī-kī′à-trē) Sometimes used as a synonym for psychiatry; the term emphasizes the somatic substructure on which mental operations and emotions are based, and the functional or organic disturbances of the central nervous system that give rise to, contribute to, or are associated with mental and emotional disorders.

neuropsychosis (-sī-kō′sis) *Obs.* This term used to mean what *psychosis* means today. It is not interchangeable with *psychoneurosis.*

neurosal (nū-rō′sal) *Obs.* Pertaining to neurosis.

neuroses, class differences in Neuroses are considered by many authorities as consequences of the specific social and economic circumstances of a particular class. For example, some have felt that poverty and social misery are the chief conditions for the development of neurosis. Others, on the contrary, have said that only the idle and privileged classes have had the time to develop neuroses and that the hard-working lower classes are protected from neuroses by their all-absorbing preoccupation with keeping fed and sheltered.

Fenichel denies both views, pointing out that neuroses are equally widespread in all socio-economic groups. Further, he remarks on the negligible differences between types of neuroses prevalent in different classes. This 'illustrates the fact that morality is not too different in different classes of the same society,' for the particular type of neurosis found within a society or group depends on the specific repressions that society imposes upon biological instinctual demands—in other words, on the society's morality. (Fenichel, O. *The Psychoanalytic Theory of Neurosis*, Norton, New York, 1945)

neurosis (nū-rō′sis) As used today, this term is interchangeable with the term *psychoneurosis.* At one time it was used to refer to any somatic disorder of the nerves (the present-day term for this meaning is neuropathy) or to any disorder of nerve function. In psychoanalytic terminology, neurosis often is used more broadly to include all psychical disorders; thus Freud spoke of actual neuroses (neurasthenia, including hypochondriasis, and anxiety-neurosis); transference or psychoneuroses (anxiety-hysteria, conversion-hysteria, obsessional and compulsive neurosis; and Fenichel adds to this group organ neuroses, pregenital conversions, perversions, and impulse neuroses); narcissistic neuroses (the schizophrenias and manic-depressive psychoses); and traumatic neuroses.

In DSM-II, neuroses (300) are classified as follows:

300.0 *Anxiety neurosis* (q.v.)
300.1 Hysterical neurosis (see *hysteria*)
        300.13 conversion type
        300.14 dissociative type
300.2 Phobic neurosis (see *anxiety-hysteria*)

300.3 *Obsessive compulsive neurosis*
      (q.v.)
300.4 Depressive neurosis (see *depres-*
      sion; depression, classification
      of; depression, [*psycho*]*neurotic*)
300.5 Neurasthenic neurosis (see
      neurasthenia)
300.6 Depersonalization neurosis (see
      depersonalization)
300.7 Hypochondriacal neurosis (see
      hypochondriasis)
300.8 Other neurosis

Using the term in its more restricted
sense, as being synonymous with psychoneurosis, the following may be said about
neurosis and neurositic phenomena:

The distinctions between neurosis and
psychosis are symptomatic, psychopathological, and therapeutic. In the neuroses,
only a part of the personality is affected
(Meyer's 'part-reaction'), and reality is
not changed qualitatively although its
value may be altered quantitatively (i.e.
diminished). The neurotic acts as if reality had the same kind of meaning for him
as the rest of the community. Psycho-
pathologically, the psychotic change in
reality is partly expressed as projection,
and of a type which does not occur in the
neuroses. In the neuroses, language as
such is never disturbed, while in the
psychoses language is distorted and the
unconscious may come to direct verbal
expression. In the neuroses, the unconscious never attains more than symbolic
expression and regression to primitive
levels (e.g. soiling and wetting) is not
found in the presence of clear consciousness. Symptoms of neurosis include sensory, motor, or visceral disturbances and
mental disturbances such as anxieties,
specific fears and avoidances, memory
disturbances, trance-states, somnambulisms, troublesome thoughts, and the like.

Charcot was the first to make a systematic study of the neuroses; he formulated a group of clinical pictures which
he called hysteria, which was considered
to be an outcome of hereditarily determined degeneration. Pierre Janet was the
first to attempt a grouping of neuroses
on the basis of their dynamics. He theorized that there are two kinds of psychological operations—easy ones, requiring
the co-operation of only a few elements;
and difficult ones, requiring the systematization of an infinite number of elements, involving a very new and intricate
synthesis in each operation. When the
'nervous tension' or psychological force
is lowered (by puberty, disease, fatigue,
emotion, etc.) there is a general lowering
of the mental level and only the simpler
acts can be performed. Psychasthenia
(including obsessions, compulsions, fears,
and feelings of fatigue) results from a
generalized lowering of the mental level;
in hysteria, the lowering is localized in
one particular function, which disappears
(is dissociated) in consequence from the
rest of the conscious personality.

Since Janet, there have been many
other attempts at dynamic formulation of
the neuroses, but Freud's concepts are
probably the most widely accepted and
the most complete explanations at the
present time. They developed out of his
clinical experience with hysteria, where
Freud and Breuer found that hysterical
symptoms disappear when the patient recalls, under hypnosis, previous experiences which have been forgotten. These
experiences were found to be traumatic
and sexual in nature, and this led Freud
to pursue an investigation of sexuality.
He described the various stages of development, from auto-erotism to object love,
and he noted that the various erotogenic
zones, which originally are autonomous,
are finally subordinated to the primacy
of the genitals and reproduction. Not all
of the instinctual energy associated with
these various zones is useful for procreation, however, and normality as defined
by our culture is achieved when these
component instincts are repressed and
diverted into sublimation. There are
three stages in cultural development
which correspond with this development
of the sexual instinct: a stage in which
the sexual impulse is allowed free rein
regardless of its usefulness in procreation;
a stage in which the whole of the sexual
impulse is repressed except for that portion which subserves procreation; and a
third stage in which procreation itself
is limited by various factors. It is this
latter which is our current civilized sexual
morality. But constitutionally, not all
people are capable even of the second
stage and there thus arise two forms of
deviation from normal sexuality—the perversions and the inversions (homosexuality). In the perversions, there has been
fixation on an infantile aim; in the inversions, the sexual aim has been deflected
from its normal object onto one of like
sex. In both cases, those tendencies which

conflict with the cultural norms may be completely repressed, but such repression requires all of the energy which would otherwise be used in cultural activities. If such repression is not achieved, the individual may remain in conflict with his culture (the overt perversions), or repression may be only partially successful. In the latter case, the inhibited sexual impulses (and the painful memory of infantile sex experiences) are not expressed as such but reappear in a disguised form (symptoms of neurosis). Thus the neuroses are seen to be the negative of the perversions. If this disguise takes the form of somatic symptoms, the clinical picture is that of conversion hysteria; if conversion is not achieved, the conflict between the repressed material and the ego leads to conscious fear which is bound to some specific and apparently indifferent content, and the clinical picture is that of anxiety hysteria; if the material is allowed to remain in consciousness but is deprived of its affective cathexis, the clinical picture is that of obsessive-compulsive neurosis.

The above represents Freud's earlier theory of neurosis. He later came to recognize that aggression as well as the sexual instinct is important in the etiology of the neuroses, and he elaborated his theory of the death instinct (Thanatos or Nirvana principle). At the present time, it is believed that the neurotic conflict is essentially between the id (sexual and/or aggressive instincts) and the ego, with the superego taking either side. The external world may represent temptation or punishment so that the conflict may appear to be between the world and the ego. The ego attempts to defend itself against the instinctual impulses and does so successfully in the case of sublimation; but if the defense is unsuccessful, the warding-off process must be maintained at a high level of counter-cathexis. To excape the defenses, the impulses attempt indirect discharge through substitute impulses—the 'derivative.' The defensive system requires a damming up of tension and an inhibition of impulses; what then happens is that the original impulse manages to break through, in which case a symptom will be formed, or intensification of the defense will in itself constitute a symptom, or both of these may occur and the impulse will find a substitute outlet which helps to ward off the re-

mainder of the impulse. Thus, three main types of precipitating factors can be recognized in the neuroses: (1) an increase in the warded-off drive; (2) a decrease in the warding-off forces; and (3) an increase in the warding-off forces. An increase in the instinctual energy may be absolute, as in puberty and the climacteric; or relative, as in the case of exposure to temptation, or devaluation of other drives whose energy is then displaced onto the warded-off drive, or blocking of instinctual satisfaction which has hitherto been obtainable, or blocking of any activity which has supplanted instinctual satisfaction. A decrease in the warding-off forces is seen in fatigue, intoxication, and when the ego is strengthened at one point and in its false confidence allows some of its censorial activities to lapse. An increase in warding-off forces is found in instances of increase in anxiety or guilt feelings, when any means of support or reassurance are lost, and, finally, a reactive increase is ordinarily seen after any temporary diminution.

The type of defense mechanism (i.e. the *choice of neurosis*) depends on the nature of the warded-off impulse, the age of the patient when the decisive conflict was experienced, the intensity and nature of the frustrating factors, the availability of substitute gratifications at the time of the frustration, and, particularly, the specific historical situation, which forces certain types of reaction.

General symptoms of the neurotic conflict include: (1) specific avoidances; (2) inhibitions of partial instincts (such as smoking and eating), of aggressiveness, of sexualized functions, and of emotions; (3) sexual disturbances such as impotence, premature ejaculation, and frigidity; (4) lack of interest in the environment and general impoverishment of the personality due to the constant drain of energy necessary to maintain counter-cathexes, and awareness of this impoverishment gives rise to inferiority feelings; (5) use of emergency discharges for the relief of tension, and (6) sleep disturbances, because of the many dreams and because of the fear of the ego to relax its guard during sleep.

neurosis, actual In Freud's terminology, a true neurosis, i.e. symptoms which develop as a result of actual, true, or real disturbances of the sexual economy.

Forced abstinence, frustrated sexual excitement, incomplete or interrupted coitus, sexual efforts which exceed the psychical capacity, sexual outlet rendered inadequate by guilt-feelings or other conflicts, the need to revert to more primitive and/or less satisfactory means of sexual expression—these are the common 'present-day' disturbances of sexuality which give rise to actual neurosis. Psychoneurosis, on the other hand, is determined by infantile and childhood experiences, and present-day occurrences are significant only in that they represent or repeat earlier events. Freud considered neurasthenia (a form of which is hypochondriasis) and anxiety-neurosis as true or actual neuroses.

neurosis, alternation of This is an older expression 'calling attention to the fact that nervous disorders are frequently relieved by acute bodily disease, so that persons suffering from insanity may be temporarily or even permanently cured by the occurrence of some acute bodily ailment. . . .' (Tuke, D.H. *A Dictionary of Psychological Medicine*, vols. 1-2, Blakiston, Philadelphia, 1892) The more usual present-day term for this phenomenon is *pathocure* (q.v.).

neurosis, analytic (an-à-lit'ik) A neurosis that develops subsequently to, and as a result of, interminable analysis. Stekel is of the opinion that after a too lengthy analysis, conducted over a period of many years, the patient, even if cured of his neurotic symptoms, 'loses his natural attitude toward life, and what should have cured him becomes his illness.' In this manner, after maintaining an emotional dependency for several years the patient develops toward analysis and analysts a special attitude which is called analytic neurosis. Similarly, the harmful effects upon psychic life produced by an analysis that is carried out without the necessary skill are also known as analytic, or post-analytic, neurosis. (Stekel, W. *Compulsion and Doubt*, Liveright, New York, 1949)

neurosis, anxiety See *anxiety-neurosis*.

neurosis, artificial See *neurosis, experimental*.

neurosis, association See *psychosis, association*.

neurosis, cardiovascular (kar-di-ō-vas'kū-lēr) A neurosis characterized by symptoms and signs of cardiovascular disorder without any evidence of pathological changes in the structure of the cardiovascular apparatus.

neurosis, character The expression *neurotic character* is used by most authorities to refer to the person who shows abnormalities in the sphere of personality. The abnormalities may be mild or severe. See *personality disorders*.

In psychoanalysis the expression has acquired a nosologic implication. A neurotic character is one which in point of mental deviation occupies a position between the healthy and the clear-cut neurotic personality. Apparently the difference is largely one of degree. Alexander says that the neurotic character is one who suffers 'from no very definite symptoms of illness, but whose behavior in life is in the highest degree impulsive and frequently even compulsive.' Jones claims that the neurotic character exhibits 'manifestations intermediate between normal character traits and neurotic symptoms.' (Jones, E. *Papers on Psycho-Analysis*, 4th ed., Wood, Baltimore, 1938)

The neurosis is, as Jones expresses it, 'built into the character'; character traits acquire the significance of symptoms. Hence, the neurotic character is said to have a *character neurosis*. For example, a person presenting no formal symptoms, but excessively pedantic, meticulous, and cruel in an intellectual way, is said to be a neurotic character and to exhibit a character neurosis (of the obsessive-compulsive type). See *defense, character*.

neurosis, choice of See *compliance, somatic; neurosis*.

neurosis, circulatory See *neurosis, cardiovascular*.

neurosis, combat See *shell-shock*.

neurosis, compensation (1) Kempf classifies as a *compensation neurosis* one in which there is 'persistent striving to develop potent functions and win social esteem initiated by fear of impotence or loss of control of asocial cravings.' (Kempf, E. J. *Psychopathology*, Mosby, St. Louis, 1921)

(2) A form of traumatic neurosis induced by desire of monetary recompense.

It is believed that some people after sustaining an injury may develop a neurosis in the hope of gaining financially (and otherwise) as a result of the injury. See *neurosis, indemnity.*

Compensation neurosis has been defined as 'a state of mind, born out of fear, kept alive by avarice, stimulated by lawyers, and cured by verdict.' The degree and duration of the neurosis are often inversely proportional to the extent of injury. See *hebephrenia, insurance.*

neurosis, compulsion A mental disorder, characterized by an irresistible impulse to perform a morbid act or an act considered morbid by the subject. See *obsession; obsessive-compulsive psychoneurosis.*

In every compulsion-neurotic, Adler states, 'there inheres the function of withdrawing from external compulsion, so that he may obey only his own compulsion. In other words, the compulsion-neurotic struggles so definitely against the will of another and against every foreign influence, that, in his fight against these, he comes to the point of positing his own will as sacred and irresistible.' (Adler, A. *The Practice and Theory of Individual Psychology,* tr. by Radin, P., Kegan Paul, Trench, Trubner, London, 1924)

neurosis, compulsive-obsessive See *neurosis, compulsion; neurosis, obsessional.*

neurosis, contagiousness of The alleged but generally disputed capacity of a person's neurosis to affect another through contagion. In cases of hysteria and traumatic neurosis, there is a tendency for the patient to pick up additional symptoms from other patients who may be in the same ward. Of this concept Kardiner writes: 'Some authors have emphasized too much the fact that these symptoms were acquired in hospitals as a result of suggestion, that is, from seeing other patients in the same condition. This cannot be, for in almost every persistent case of this type the condition is kept alive eight years or more after the traumatic event by a distinct group of dynamic forces which no suggestion can set in motion. Furthermore, parts of the original traumatic experience are attached to or become a part of the symptom itself. The fact that the symptoms of a traumatic neurosis make their appearance sometime after the traumatic experience can be verified

without question. For this reason, attributing them to the contagiousness of the condition in hospital wards is somewhat exaggerated.' (Kardiner, A., and Spiegel, L. *War Stress and Neurotic Illness,* Hoeber, New York, 1947)

neurosis, covetous Compensation neurosis.

neurosis, desire *Compensation neurosis* (q.v.).

neurosis, dissociation Kempf says that in this neurosis 'the uncontrollable cravings dominate the personality despite efforts of the ego to prevent it.' The symptomatology constitutes 'distressing visceral tensions, with or without functional distortions, with or without eccentric defenses or compensations.' (Kempf, E.J. *Psychopathology,* Mosby, St. Louis, 1921)

neurosis, ego Traumatic neurosis. This neurosis 'differs in mental content from the non-traumatic psychoneuroses in that the conscious ego is more vividly disordered than are the unconscious parts of the mind.' There may be, for example, disturbances of orientation and memory, even delirious states and extreme fatigue and weakness, throwing out of gear almost all of the ego. For that reason the traumatic neurosis has been termed an ego-neurosis. (Hinsie, L.E. *Understandable Psychiatry,* Macmillan, New York, 1948) See *neurosis, traumatic.*

neurosis, esophageal (ē-sō-faj′ē-al) Psychogenic disturbances of the swallowing functions of the esophagus, usually manifested by choking on food, inability to 'get it down,' or the sensation of a foreign body in the upper region of the esophagus, the *globus hystericus.* The major unconscious emotional basis for the symptom is the rejection of, or defense against, the process of, 'incorporation,' which represents a guilty oral aggressive (castrative) wish.

A patient prone to cunnilingus, associated with phantasies of oral castration (eating off the female phallus, i.e. clitoris), developed frequent severe choking spells while voraciously eating symbolic foods such as asparagus or melon at meals, following such sexual activity. 'Kronfeld, on the basis of a systematic psychiatric study, distinguished two forms of esophageal neurosis, a sensory hyperalgetic and a reflectory spastic form.' (Alexander, F.

Psychosomatic Medicine, Norton, New York, 1950)

neurosis, existential Chronic meaninglessness, apathy, and aimlessness, which typically arise within a person who sees himself as nothing more than an embodiment of biologic needs and a player of social roles. See *existentialism.*

neurosis, expectation *Obs.* Anxiety that develops over the anticipated performance of an act. Such anxiety is a symptom, not a neurosis, and the term is thus a misnomer.

neurosis, experimental *Artificial neurosis.* Disorganized behavior which appears in the experimental subject in response to inability to master the experimental situation. Such behavior was noted by Pavlov in his dogs; when the animals were unable to discriminate between sounds of similar pitch or test objects of similar shape, they 'went to pieces.' Experimental neuroses have been induced in other animals as well—monkeys, chimpanzees, cats, goats, pigs, etc.

Neurotic symptoms are based on insufficiencies of the normal control apparatus and can be understood as involuntary emergency discharges which supplant the normal ones. The insufficiency may be brought about in two ways (which are not mutually exclusive)—too much excitation may be presented so that it cannot be mastered, as in traumatic neurosis; or a previous blocking or inadequacy of discharge may lead to an accumulation of tensions within the organism so that previously innocuous stimuli may release them and thus operate as though they were traumatic. The experimental neurosis is an example of this second type. 'Some stimulus which had represented pleasant instinctual experiences or which had served as a signal that some action would now procure gratification is suddenly connected by the experimenter with frustrating or threatening experiences, or the experimenter decreases the difference between stimuli which the animal had been trained to associate with instinct gratification and threat respectively; the animal then gets into a state of irritation which is very similar to that of a traumatic neurosis. He feels contradictory impulses; the conflict makes it impossible for him to give in to the impulses in the

accustomed way; the discharge is blocked, and this decrease in discharge works in the same way as an increase in influx: it brings the organism into a state of tension and calls for emergency discharges.' (Fenichel, O. *The Psychoanalytic Theory of Neurosis.* Norton, New York, 1945.)

neurosis, fate Failure in one's career as a result of unconscious need for punishment; a type of moral masochism. See *masochism.*

neurosis, holiday See *neurosis, Sunday.*

neurosis, housewife's Also called *housewife's psychosis;* a compulsion-neurosis characterized by constant preoccupation with cleaning, washing, and dusting the house. Though justified by the patient, who explains that these exaggerated domestic activities are necessary in view of the danger inherent in the lack of hygiene in the place where she lives, in reality they constitute an external disguise of obsessive ideas concealed by the patient. According to Stekel, the inner 'compulsions are covered up for many years until the decrease of the patient's working capacity, or the danger of complete isolation force the patient to confess her illness to other people.' (Stekel, W. *Compulsion and Doubt,* Liveright, New York, 1949) This is often the personality type of the woman who later develops an involutional psychosis.

More recently, the term *housewife's disease* or *housewife's syndrome* has been applied to a state of acute or chronic dissatisfaction and frustration that appears in some women as a type of mental stagnation secondary to marriage, motherhood, and separation from the stimulation of employment and free movement among people. Typical symptoms are loss of libido and fatigability at age 24-30, backache at age 30-35, and general somatic overconcern at age 40-55.

neurosis, iatrogenic (ī-a-trō-jen'ik) See *iatrogeny.*

neurosis, indemnity A neurotic craving for or lust of indemnity. Levy-Bruhl's term for compensation neurosis.

neurosis, infantile The neurosis that is to become manifest in the adult and is already present in the infant. Thus, whether the psychiatrist speaks of the adult neurosis or the infantile neurosis he speaks of the same neurosis. The infantile neurosis usually differs from the neurosis as it will appear later in adult life in not showing any symptoms at that (i.e. infantile) period, and if it does, the symptoms are so mild that they go unnoticed.

The basic structure of the neurosis is already present, however, and is hence termed infantile neurosis, although it will not *necessarily* manifest itself as a fullblown neurosis when adulthood is reached; but if the adult *does* exhibit neurosis it is *this* neurosis which will have overtaken him.

neurosis, infinity Neurotic preoccupation with the infinity of space and time, usually encountered in adolescents and/or a an expression of an autistic, dereistic lifeapproach.

neurosis insana (neu-rô'sēs ēn-sä'nà) (L. 'insane neurosis') *Obs.* Psychoneurosis.

neurosis, malignant A neurosis characterized by a progressive increase in the extent and severity of symptoms, which may ultimately prevent the performance of any activity. The patient may become a prisoner in his room or in his bed, or he may be paralyzed by indecisiveness and doubting. Many such cases are in actuality schizophrenics; see *schizophrenia, pseudoneurotic.*

Malignant neurosis is to be contrasted with *stationary neurosis*, in which the defenses operate successfully without further increase in anxiety or other symptoms.

neurosis, military War neurosis; *shellshock* (q.v.).

neurosis, mixed In Freud's earliest psychoanalytic communications this (now infrequent) term denoted a neurosis that contained phenomena of two or more subdivisions of the neuroses. It is now recognized that many of these more properly belong to the schizophrenic group, and particularly to the subtype described by Hoch and Polatin, the 'pseudoneurotic' schizophrenias.

neurosis, monosymptomatic See *monosymptomatic.*

neurosis, motor This term is sometimes applied to the neuroses that are characterized principally by disorders of movement, e.g. the various tics.

neurosis, obsessional See *obsessive-compulsive psychoneurosis.*

neurosis, occlusal (o-kloō'sal) This is 'a grinding, pounding, or setting of the teeth, when the mouth is empty; that is, entirely apart from the perfectly normal activity of mastication.' *Bruxism* is an occlusal neurosis occurring during the night. (Frohman, B.S. 'Occlusal Neurosis,' *Psychoanalytic Review 19*, 298, 1932)

neurosis, occupational (300.13) A psychogenic inhibition of actions that are essential to the performance of the patient's occupation, such as writer's cramp (a painful spasm of the muscles of the fingers used in writing), seamstress's cramp, musician's cramp, etc. Such inhibitions of working often represent oral conflicts over dependence and independence, or anal conflicts over rebellion and obedience.

neurosis, organ See *psychosomatic.*

neurosis, parent as carrier of 'The most common types of such parental carriers of neurosis to the children are: (a) The "cold" parents, who cannot give the warmth and love the children need; (b) the over-indulgent parents, who cannot expose their children to the disciplines and reality frustrations necessary to the child's development of adult survival traits; (c) the sexually frustrated parents, who displace their sexual needs onto the establishment of an over-intense emotional bond to their children as a substitute love-object; (d) the unconsciously hating parent, who visits repressed and denied aggression and hostility on his child, expressing repressed and denied jealousy and rivalry.' (Weiss, E. and O. English *Psychosomatic Medicine*, 2nd ed., Saunders, Philadelphia and London, 1949)

neurosis, pension A form of compensation neurosis.

neurosis, performance A mental disturbance which may take place in the course of any performance whose normal execution requires any degree of spontaneity. An illustration is an attack of trembling overcoming a violinist while playing. See *neurosis, occupational.*

neurosis, perhaps A type of obsessive neurosis, as exemplified in the formula: '*If* I had done this instead of that, *perhaps* my sister would still be alive.'

neurosis, population A collective or group-neurosis prevailing in the populace of a locality or region. 'The neuroses of a group are not simply the sum total of the neuroses among the individual members thereof. There is an interaction between individual members of a group so that there results a community type of response which has characteristics all of its own. The community, also, may show symptoms of tension and of symbolism as a mass reaction.' (Kraines, S.H. *The Therapy of Neuroses and Psychoses,* Lea & Febiger, Philadelphia, 1948)

neurosis, postconcussion (309.2) A form of traumatic neurosis following cerebral concussion; a postconcussion neurosis, according to Osnato, is symptomatic of traumatic encephalopathy. On the other hand, C.S. Mullin (*U.S. Armed Forces Medical Journal 4:* 1748-52, 1953) feels that 'blast concussion' bears a closer relationship to neurosis than to cerebral trauma. See *post-traumatic and post-encephalitic syndromes.*

neurosis, post-traumatic (post-traw-ma'-tik) Traumatic neurosis. See *post-traumatic and post-encephalitic syndromes.*

neurosis, prison See *chronophobia.*

neurosis, progredient (prō-grē'di-ent) A neurosis that takes a progressive course, with increasing severity of symptoms.

In progredient neurosis, the damming-up of instincts increases more and more. Because there is neither adequate discharge nor adequate defense, the neurosis becomes increasingly severe. For example, in a phobic patient conditions assume an ever-increasing scope. At first, the patient may not be able to walk across a particular square. Later on he cannot go out of doors, and finally, perhaps, not even out of his room. In the case of the compulsion-neurotic, 'ambivalences and doubts increase, until no decision whatsoever can be made.'

Another type of progression may occur when neuroses that have been stationary for a time suddenly become progredient again. A compulsive equilibrium may change into uncontrollable vegetative attacks, or a rigid character neurosis into a symptom neurosis with anxiety attacks, depressions, or other symptoms. (Fenichel, O. *The Psychoanalytic Theory of Neurosis,* Norton, New York, 1945)

neurosis, promotion Inability to function when given added responsibility or authority; seen most often in obsessional neurotics and described by others as 'failure through success.' See *success, failure through.*

neurosis, pseudo-schizophrenic Roth's term for the phobic anxiety-depersonalization neurosis. See *depersonalization.*

neurosis, regression According to Kempf's classification of neuroses, this subdivision is characterized by 'failure to compensate but regression to a preceding, more comfortable, irresponsible level, permitting wish-fulfilling fancies, postures and indulgences.' The symptoms are built around 'distressing visceral tensions, rare, but persistent maintenance of characteristic affective attitudes of the prenatal, infantile or preadolescent stage.' (Kempf, E.J. *Psychopathology,* Mosby, St. Louis, 1921)

neurosis, repression A neurosis in which there is 'vague consciousness to total unconsciousness of the nature and influence of the ungratifiable affective cravings.' The symptoms are the same as those in the suppression neurosis 'plus functional distortions of the projicient apparatus and changes in reactivity to the sense organs.' (Kempf, E.J. *Psychopathology,* Mosby, St. Louis, 1921)

neurosis, social Burrow's term for the common condition of disorder and conflict which exists throughout its structure though generally unrecognized by society. It is expressed symptomatically in nervous and mental disorder and also in man's so-called normal interrelations—in his peaceful social institutions, in economic conflict, crime, and war. (Burrow, T. *The Social Basis of Consciousness,* Harcourt, Brace, New York and London, 1927)

neurosis, space See *neurosis, infinity.*

neurosis, spinal *Obs.* Hysteria referable to the spinal region.

neurosis, substitution *Obs.* Obsessional neurosis.

neurosis, Sunday Ferenczi speaks of neuroses 'the oscillation of whose symptoms were dependent on the particular day of the week'—such as Sundays and holidays. (Ferenczi, S. *Further Contributions to the Theory and Technique of Psycho-Analysis,* tr. by Suttie, J.I., Leonard and Virginia Woolf and the Institute of Psychoanalysis, London, 1926.

neurosis, suppression From the standpoint of Kempf's psychopathology, in a *suppression-neurosis* there is 'clear to vague consciousness of the nature and effect of the ungratifiable affective cravings.' The symptoms are said to be due to 'distressing hypertensions or hypotensions of autonomic (visceral) segments (mild to severe).' (Kempf, E.J. *Psychopathology,* Mosby, St. Louis, 1921)

neurosis, transference A transference-neurosis, a 'new artificial neurosis,' occurs only during psychoanalytic treatment. It is the reappearance of the early infantile Oedipus situation. The analyst represents one or both parents as a love-object, as if he were really the original parent in the original infantile setting of the patient. The patient also lives out all his old ego attitudes and incest prohibitions. See *transference.*

Transference-neurosis represents 'a stage where the history of the patient's development, leading up to the infantile neurosis, is re-enacted in the analytic room—the patient plays the part of actor-manager, pressing into service (like the child in the nursery) all the stage property that the analytical room contains, first and foremost, the analyst himself.' (Glover, E.)

neurosis, traumatic (traw-ma'tik) 'A traumatic neurosis may be defined most simply as a psychogenic or nonstructural nervous disorder, shortly following a physical injury, and complicated or not by structural changes in the central nervous system or elsewhere.' (Huddleson, J.H. *Accidents,*

Neuroses and . Compensation, Williams and Wilkins, Baltimore, 1932.) The nature of the disorder often helps in the determination of the diagnosis. Many classifications have been suggested. Huddleson says that 'the symptomatology of traumatic is that of nontraumatic anxiety neuroses, neurasthenias, hypochondriases, and conversion hysterias, plus more or less of the wound-of-the-head syndrome. Ego-neuroses are more characteristic of the group as a whole than are psychosexual conflicts.

'Many symptom complexes are so superficial as scarcely to merit the designation of neuroses, particularly when monetary compensation is involved. Some exaggeration is the rule, and a preponderance of simulated over nonsimulated symptoms is not uncommon.' (ibid) Psychotic, neurotic, or behavioral reactions consequent upon trauma to the brain are classified as brain syndromes (organic reaction types); it is only those reactions to injury of the head or other parts of the body which are not dependent upon physical or structural alteration of brain functioning which are properly termed traumatic neuroses. Such neuroses are to be classified within the psychoneurotic type whose symptoms they present (such as phobic reaction or dissociative reaction) and are not given a separate listing as traumatic reaction.

While a traumatic experience can precipitate any of the well-known types of neurotic or psychotic disorders, the most common conditions seen in combat are hysteria, anxiety-states and exhaustion conditions. The essential features of traumatic neurosis are: (1) fixation on the trauma with amnesia for the traumatic situation which may be total or partial; (2) typical dream-life (dreams of annihilation, aggression dreams where the patient is the aggressor but is defeated, frustration or Sisyphus dreams, and occupational dreams in which it is the means of livelihood rather than the body-ego which is annihilated; (3) contraction of the general level of functioning, with constant fear of the environment, disorganized behavior, lowered efficiency, lack of co-ordinated goal activities, and profoundly altered functioning in the autonomic, motor, and sensory nervous system; (4) general irritability, and (5) a proclivity to explosive aggressive reactions. A malignant type of traumatic neurosis, *psychorrhexis* (q.v.), is seen in 2 to 3 per cent of war neuroses.

neurosis, vagabond See *dromomania.*

neurosis, vagus (vā'gus) An uncommonly used term for anxiety state.

neurosis, vascular (vas'kū-lēr) See *neurosis, cardiovascular.*

neurosis, vasomotor (vas-ō-mō'tēr) See *constitution, post-traumatic.*

neurosis, vegetative The expression of emotion, or unconscious emotional conflict, by disturbed functioning of the internal visceral organs. The term is usually employed in contradistinction to conversion hysteria: whereas conversion hysteria takes place in the voluntary neuromuscular, or sensory perceptive systems, the vegetative neurosis has its site in the internal visceral organs.

It is found that chronic repressed, suppressed, and denied resentment and anger are an invariable factor in the personality reactions of people with essential hypertension (high blood pressure). Similarly, those developing duodenal ulcer seem to suffer from long-standing, chronic conflict between independency-aggressive strivings and dependency-submissive trends. 'A vegetative neurosis is not an attempt to express an emotion, but is the physiological response of the vegetative organs to constant, or to periodically returning, emotional states.' (Alexander, F. *Psychosomatic Medicine,* Norton, New York, 1950)

The term vegetative neurosis is sometimes also used synonymously with *acrodynia* (q.v.).

neurosis, wish Bing thus denotes a traumatic neurosis in which the wish to be afflicted seems to constitute the essential etiology; traumatic hysteria.

neurosism (nū'rō-siz'm) *Obs.* Nervousness, neurasthenia, neuroticism; a condition of perverted or irritable nervous action.

neurosity (nū-ros'i-ti) *Obs.* Nerve-force.

neurosthenia (nū-rō-sthē'nē-à) *Obs.* Excessive quantity of so-called nervous energy.

neurosyphilis (-sif'i-lis) Neurosyphilis is a generic term for all forms of involvement of the nervous system by the spirochaeta pallida.

neurosyphilis, asymptomatic (à-simp-tō-mat'ik) Neurosyphilis without clinical symptoms but with physical signs and laboratory findings of syphilitic involvement of the nervous system.

neurosyphilis, congenital (292.x 309.0) Intrauterine infection of the nervous system by the spirochete; sometimes (mistakenly) called *inherited syphilis.* Approximately ten per cent of congenitally syphilitic children develop neurosyphilis, which, as in adult neurosyphilis, may be of the meningovascular or the parenchymatous type. Meningovascular syphilis is the more common form and resembles the adult form in pathology and clinical manifestations; these include mental retardation (31x.0), convulsions, pupillary abnormalities, optic atrophy, diplegia or hemiplegia, and slight hydrocephalus of the communicating type. Deafness, a common symptom of congenital syphilis, is more often due to a temporal bone lesion than to N. VIII involvement. See *syphilis, cerebral.*

Juvenile or *infantile general paresis* probably occurs in no more than one per cent of congenital syphilitics. Symptoms typically develop in early adolescence and mimic those of adult paretics except that the delusions are more puerile, the dementia is more complete and severe, and the course is more prolonged.

Congenital tabes often does not appear until early adult life; symptoms mimic those of adult tabetics.

neurosyphilis, ectodermogenic (ek-tō-dēr-mō-jen'ik) Cerebrospinal syphilis; see *syphilis, cerebral.*

neurosyphilis, interstitial (in-tēr-stish'àl) See *syphilis, cerebral.*

neurosyphilis, meningeal (men-in-jē'àl) Tertiary syphilis involving the leptomeninges (the pia mater and arachnoid membrane). See *syphilis, cerebral.*

neurosyphilis, parenchymatous (par-eng-kī'mà-tus) A general term that includes paresis, tabes, taboparesis, and juvenile general paresis. See *paresis, general.*

neurosyphilis, vascular (vas'kū-làr) See *syphilis, cerebral.*

neurotherapeutics, neurotherapy (-ther-à-pū'tiks, -ther'à-pē) *Obs.* The treatment of nervous disorders.

neurotic (nū-rot'ik) Relating to or affected by *neurosis* (q.v.).

neurotic process See *self, actual.*

neuroticism (nū-rot'i-siz'm) A neurotic condition; state of neurosis.

neurotigenic (nū-rot-i-jen'ik) Producing or favoring the induction of a neurosis.

neurotization (nū-rot-i-zā'shun) Direct implantation of nerve into a paralyzed muscle.

neurotrophasthenia (nū-rō-trof-as-thē'-nē-à) Defective nutrition of the nervous system.

neurypnology (nū-rip-nol'ō-jē) Braid's term for the science of hypnosis.

neuter, social A member of a group who has very little effect upon its structure and behavior because of his weakness, ineffectualness, or indifference. See *instigator; isolate; neutralizer.*

neutrality The role of therapist in activity group psychotherapy: here he is not only passive and permissive, but neither has nor applies criteria of right and wrong, proper and improper behavior on the part of the patient. According to Slavson, neutrality of therapist means 'that each patient can utilize him in accordance with his own particular needs. It is as though the therapist were a screen of neutral tone like that in a movie on which different colors are projected. Each member of the group projects on the therapist his unconscious attitudes toward adults. Neutrality on the part of the therapist makes this possible.' (Slavson, S.R. *An Introduction to Group Therapy,* The Commonwealth Fund, Oxford University Press, New York, 1943, p. 33)

neutralization In psychoanalysis, neutralization includes both *desexualization* (q.v.) and *desaggressivization* (q.v.). 'The term

neutralization implies that an activity of the individual which originally afforded drive satisfaction through discharge of cathexis ceases to do so and comes to be in the service of the ego, apparently nearly or quite independent of the need for gratification or discharge of cathexis in anything which even approaches its original instinctual form.' (Brenner, C. *An Elementary Textbook of Psychoanalysis.* International Universities Press, New York, 1955)

neutralizer A member of a therapy group who neutralizes, i.e. counteracts and controls, the aggressivity, impulsiveness, and destructiveness of other members of the group. See *instigator; isolate.*

névrospasmie (nā-vrô-spàs-mē') *Obs.* Neurasthenia.

nexus (nèk'sus) See *thought-nexus.*

nicotinic acid deficiency (294.1, 309.5) Pellagra; symptoms of this disorder, which occurs nowadays primarily in chronic alcoholics, include appearance of sucking and grasping reflexes, cogwheel rigidity of the extremities, progressive clouding of consciousness, and memory defects (which may persist despite otherwise successful treatment). Manic or melancholic states may also be seen, and there are usually accompanying diarrhea and skin lesions.

Niemann-Pick disease See *disease, Niemann-Pick.*

night-eating See *syndrome, night-eating.*

night hospital See *day hospital.*

night-phantasy See *phantasy, night.*

night-terror See *terror, night.*

nightmare A fright reaction during sleep. 'In the nightmare (ephialtes, incubus) the child awakens in terror from a dream usually characterized by a feeling of suffocation and helplessness. He can ordinarily relate his bad dream; he is well oriented, can recognize people about him, and can be calmed readily. Nightmares are often very vivid and the memory of them, accompanied by a sense of dread, sometimes recurs the following day when the child is awake. They are not uncommon and generally take place within an hour or two after going to bed.' (Bakwin and Bakwin. *Clinical Management of Behavior Disorders in Children,* Saunders, Philadelphia, 1953.) See *terror, night.*

nightshade poisoning See *poisoning, deadly nightshade.*

nihilism (nī'[h]il-iz'm) The delusion of non-existence. The delusion may be widespread in the sense that it includes everything—the patient himself and the entire world, or it may refer only to parts of the world or of himself.

Nirvana (nir-vä'nà) Death, extinction; oblivion to care, pain, or external reality.

In psychoanalysis the expression *nirvana-principle* (suggested by Barbara Low) is explained today by Freud as a manifestation of the action of the death instinct, 'the aim of which is to lead our throbbing existence into the stability of an inorganic state. Freud maintains that 'the *Nirvana*-principle expresses the tendency of the death-instinct, the *pleasure*-principle represents the claims of the libido, and that modification of it, the *reality*-principle, the influence of the outer world.' (Freud, S. *Collected Papers,* vol. 2, tr. by Riviere, J., Leonard and Virginia Woolf and The Institute of Psychoanalysis, London, 1924-25)

noasthenia (nō-as-thē'nē-à) *Obs.* Mental debility.

nocar (nō'kēr) *Obs.* Lethargy.

noctambulation (nok-tam-bū-lā'shun) Night-walking; sleep-walking.

noctiphobia (nok-ti-fō'bē-à) See *nyctophobia.*

nocturnal hemiplegia or paralysis See *paralysis, sleep.*

nodal behavior See *behavior, nodal.*

-noea (-nē'à) variant of *-noia.*

noematic (nō-ē-mat'ik) Relating to the mental processes.

Noguchi, Hideyo, (1876-1928) Japanese bacteriologist, worked in New York,

demonstrated spirochetes in brain of paretics (1911). Until this discovery, syphilis was not recognized as the etiologic agent in general paresis but was thought merely to predispose to its development.

-noia (-noi'à) Combining form meaning mind, mental state, from Gr. (para)*noia,* from *nóos, noûs,* mind.

nomadism A pathological tendency to roam from place to place, which is so strong that it gives rise to serious social maladjustment. 'Occasional and episodic nomadism apparently arises on the basis of a mental mechanism similar to that underlying resorting to alcohol or drugs. It is often associated with mental deficiency, epilepsy, and psychotic disease. It is not infrequently seen in children as residuals of epidemic encephalitis and may be part of the clinical picture of the residuals of cerebral birth trauma.' (Selling, L.S. *Synopsis of Neuropsychiatry,* Mosby, St. Louis, 1947.) See *wanderlust; dromomania.*

nomenclature, 1968 revision (DSM-II) This classification is based on the Section on Mental Disorders of the World Health Organization's Eighth Revision of the *International Classification of Diseases (ICD-8),* which was adopted in May, 1966, to become effective in 1968. The major deviations from ICD-8 are: (1) mental retardation is placed first in the listing, to emphasize that it is to be diagnosed whenever present and whatever its cause; (2) non-psychotic organic brain syndromes are also placed out of numerical order so as to keep all the organic brain syndromes together, as is customary in the United States; (3) multiple psychiatric diagnoses are encouraged when one will not suffice to account adequately for the clinical picture; and (4) a fifth coding digit was introduced to provide further specification of additional characteristics of mental disorders—in ICD-8, the first three digits designate the major disease category; the fourth digit (which follows the period) specifies additional detail (such as etiology); and in the U.S. nomenclature, an additional fifth digit allows still greater detailing. Thus, .x1 indicates acute, .x2 indicates chronic; .x5 indicates in remission.

The following table is adapted from *DSM-II, the Diagnostic and Statistical*

Manual of Mental Disorders, 2nd ed., American Psychiatric Association, Washington, D.C., 1968.

Mental Retardation

310. Borderline (I.Q. 68-83)
311. Mild (I.Q. 52-67)
312. Moderate (I.Q. 36-51)
313. Severe (I.Q. 20-35)
314. Profound (I.Q. under 20)
315. Unspecified

With each of the above: following or associated with
.0 Infection or intoxication
.1 Trauma or physical agent
.2 Disorders of metabolism, growth, or nutrition
.3 Gross brain disease (postnatal)
.4 Unknown prenatal influence
.5 Chromosomal abnormality
.6 Prematurity
.7 Major psychiatric disorder
.8 Psycho-social (environmental) deprivation
.9 Other condition

Organic Brain Syndromes (OBS)

A. Psychoses (290 - 294)
290. Senile and presenile dementia
.0 Senile dementia
.1 Presenile dementia
291. Alcoholic psychosis
.0 Delirium tremens
.1 Korsakov's psychosis
.2 Other alcoholic hallucinosis
.3 Alcohol paranoid state
.4 Acute alcohol intoxication
.5 Alcoholic deterioration
.6 Pathological intoxication
.9 Other alcoholic psychosis
292. Psychosis associated with intracranial infection
.0 General paralysis
.1 Other syphilis of central nervous system
.2 Epidemic encephalitis
.3 Other and unspecified encephalitis
.9 Other intracranial infection
293. Psychosis associated with other cerebral condition
.0 Cerebral arteriosclerosis
.1 Other cerebrovascular disturbance
.2 Epilepsy
.3 Intracranial neoplasm

.4 Degenerative disease of central nervous system
.5 Brain trauma
.9 Other cerebral condition
294. Psychosis associated with other physical condition
.0 Endocrine disorder
.1 Metabolic and nutritional disorder
.2 Systemic infection
.3 Drug or poison intoxication (other than alcohol)
.4 Childbirth
.8 Other and unspecified physical condition

B. Non-Psychotic OBS
309.0 Intracranial
309.13 Alcohol (simple drunkenness)
309.14 Other drug, poison, or systemic intoxication
309.2 Brain trauma
309.3 Circulatory disturbance
309.4 Epilepsy
309.5 Disturbance of metabolism, growth, or nutrition
309.6 Senile or pre-senile brain disease
309.7 Intracranial neoplasm
309.8 Degenerative disease of central nervous system
309.9 Other physical condition

Psychoses Not Attributed To Physical Conditions Listed Previously

295. Schizophrenia
.0 Simple
.1 Hebephrenic
.2 Catatonic
(.23 excited)
(.24 withdrawn)
.3 Paranoid
.4 Acute schizophrenic episode
.5 Latent
.6 Residual
.7 Schizo-affective
(.73 excited)
(.74 depressed)
.8 Childhood
.90 Chronic Undifferentiated
.99 Other schizophrenia
296. Major Affective Disorders
.0 Involutional melancholia
.1 Manic-depressive illness, manic
.2 Manic-depressive illness, depressed
.3 Manic depressive illness, circular
.8 Other major affective disorder
297. Paranoid States

.0 Paranoia
.1 Involutional paranoid state
.9 Other paranoid state
298. Other Psychoses
.0 Psychotic depressive reaction
299. Unspecified psychosis

Neuroses (300)

300.0 Anxiety neurosis
.1 Hysterical neurosis
(.13 conversion type)
(.14 dissociative type)
.2 Phobic neurosis
.3 Obsessive compulsive neurosis
.4 Depressive neurosis
.5 Neurasthenic neurosis
.6 Depersonalization neurosis
.7 Hypochondriacal neurosis
.8 Other neurosis

Personality Disorders
(301 - 304)

301. Personality disorders
.0 Paranoid personality
.1 Cyclothymic personality
.2 Schizoid personality
.3 Explosive personality
.4 Obsessive compulsive (anan-kastic) personality
.5 Hysterical personality
.6 Asthenic personality
.7 Antisocial personality
.81 Passive-aggressive personality
.82 Inadequate personality
.89 Other specified personality disorders
302. Sexual deviations
.0 Homosexuality
.1 Fetishism
.2 Pedophilia
.3 Transvestitism
.4 Exhibitionism
.5 Voyeurism
.6 Sadism
.7 Masochism
.8 Other sexual deviation
303. Alcoholism
.0 Episodic excessive drinking
.1 Habitual excessive drinking
.2 Alcohol addiction
.9 Other alcoholism
304. Drug dependence
.0 Opiates
.1 Synthetic analgesics with mor-phine-like effects
.2 Barbiturates
.3 Other hypnotics, sedatives, 'tranquilizers'

.4 Cocaine
.5 Cannabis sativa (marihuana)
.6 Other psycho-stimulants
.7 Hallucinogens
.8 Other drug dependence

Psychophysiologic Disorders (305)

305.0 Skin
.1 Musculoskeletal
.2 Respiratory
.3 Cardiovascular
.4 Hemic and lymphatic
.5 Gastrointestinal
.6 Genitourinary
.7 Endocrine
.8 Organ of special sense

Special Symptoms Not Elsewhere
Classified (306)

306.1 Specific learning disturbance
.2 Tic
.3 Other psychomotor disorder
.4 Disorders of sleep
.5 Feeding disturbance
.6 Enuresis
.7 Encopresis
.8 Cephalalgia
.9 Other

Transient Situational Disturbances
(Adjustment Reactions) (307)

307.0 Infancy
.1 Childhood
.2 Adolescence
.3 Adult life
.4 Late life

Behavior Disorders of Childhood and Adolescence (308)

308.0 Hyperkinetic reaction
.1 Withdrawing reaction
.2 Overanxious reaction
.3 Runaway reaction
.4 Unsocialized aggressive reaction
.5 Group deliquent reaction
.9 Other

Social Maladjustments Without Manifest Psychiatric
Disorder (316)

316.0 Marital maladjustment
.1 Social maladjustment
.2 Occupational maladjustment

.3   Dyssocial behavior
.9   Other social maladjustment

nomological *Nomothetic* (q.v.).

nomothetic Giving or generating laws; legislative; in psychiatry, used particularly to refer to the deriving of general laws through observation of many cases, as contrasted with the *ideographic* approach, which is concerned with the explanation and prediction of behavior in the single or unique case (usually on the basis of extensive knowledge of the history and biography of the person).

non compos mentis (nōn-kôm'pôs men'-tēs) (L. 'not of a sane mind, not in possession of his mind') Not of sound mind, mentally incapable of managing one's affairs.

nonaria (nō-nä'rē-à) (L. 'public prostitute') A prostitute: in ancient Rome a prostitute could not appear in the streets before the ninth hour (*nonus*, ninth).

non-directive therapy See *therapy, client-centered.*

non-reporting See *psychodynamics, adaptational.*

non-restraint Management of the psychotic patient without the use of the strait-jacket or other forms of restraint.

nonsense-syndrome *Ganser syndrome* (q.v.).

nonsense-witticism See *wit, nonsense in.*

noöklopia (nō-ō-klō'pē-à) N.D.C. Lewis defines the term as *thought theft obsessions*, i.e. the delusion that 'one's thoughts are being sucked out of his brain by some sinister personal magnetism.' (*Psychoanalytic Review XV*, 77, 1928) Also known as *castrophrenia.*

noölogy (nō-ol'ō-jē) The doctrine of the mind; the science of the understanding.

noöpsyche (nō-ō-sī'kē) Stransky coined this term with the idea that there are two separate psychic factors: (1) the *noöpsyche*, comprising all purely intellectual processes, and (2) the *thymopsy-*

che, made up of affective processes. In his opinion, intrapsychic ataxia, which results in marked incongruity between ideas and emotions, is a consequence of the more or less independent activities of the two psychic factors.

noösphales (nō-os'fal-ēz) *Obs.* Mentally deranged.

noösteresis (nō-ō-stē-rē'sis) *Obs.* Dementia.

noradrenalin (nor-ad-ren'à-lin) Norepinephrine, see *epinephrine.*

norepinephrine (nor-e-pin-e'frin) See *epinephrine.*

normosplanchnic (nor-mō-splangk'nik) In Viola's system of constitutional forms of body build, this term denotes the type which has a normal or average relationship between thoracic and abdominal size, owing to medium size of the abdominal and thoracic viscera. This type is further characterized by a proportionality between vertical and horizontal diameters, resulting in a harmonious physique.

Persons of this type correspond roughly to Kretschmer's *athletic* (q.v.) type.

normothymotic (nōr-mō-thī-mo'tik) Mood normalizer; specifically a pharmacologic agent that acts against a disorder of mood but does not affect normal mood.

normotonic (-ton'ik) In Tandler's system of constitutional types, a type characterized by normal or average tone of the voluntary muscles, in contrast to the *hypotonic* and *hypertonic* types.

normotype (nor'mō-tīp) In constitutional medicine a term for the structurally or morphologically average person. It is synonymous with eumorph.

normotypical (nor-mō-tip'i-kal) In constitutional medicine three types of body build are recognized: (1) dolichomorphic or longitypical; (2) brachymorphic or brachytypical; (3) eumorphic or normotypical or normosplanchnic.

norm, psychic (sī'kik) A psychically normal person is one who is in harmony with himself and with his environment. He conforms with the cultural requirements or injunctions of his community. He may possess organic deviation or disease, but as long as this does not impair his reasoning, judgment, intellectual capacity and ability to make harmonious personal and social adaptation he may be regarded as psychically sound or normal.

It appeared that normality developed as the result of repression of certain component-instincts and components of the infantile disposition, and of a subordination of the remainder under the primacy of the genital zone in the service of the reproductive function.' (Freud, S. *Collected Papers,* vol. 1, tr. by Riviere, J., Leonard and Virginia Woolf and The Institute of Psychoanalysis, London, 1924-25) This means harmonious relationship of the forces of the id, superego and ego. 'The original urges are not unhealthily inhibited, but rather are domesticated in the service of the individual and society.' (W. Healy, A.F. Bronner, and A.M. Bowers *The Structure and Meanings of Psychoanalysis,* Knopf, New York, 1930)

The 'normal' person is 'anyone who is free from symptoms, unhampered by mental conflict, and who shows satisfactory working and sexual capacity.' (Glover, E. *The Technique of Psycho-Analysis,* International Universities Press, New York, 1955) See *health, mental.*

nos(o)- (nos'[ō]-) Combining form meaning disease, from Gr. *nósos,* sickness, disease.

nosogenesis, nosogeny (nos-ō-jen'e-sis, nō-soj'ē-ni) Synonymous with *pathogenesis.*

nosography (nō-sog'rà-fē) The description of diseases.

nosology (nō-sol'ō-jē) The study of diseases and, particularly, of the classification of diseases.

nosomania (nos-ō-mā'nē-à) *Obs.* Hypochondriasis.

nosophobia Fear of disease; usually associated with no discoverable organic illness, or if the latter is present, the fear is grossly exaggerated and has been superimposed upon natural concern about the illness.

nostalgia Longing to return home or to one's native land; homesickness. This is explained by psychoanalysts as intense yearning for the members of one's family or for some particular member of the family. It is related to the dread of being alone, which is but another way of saying that the subject feels at ease when he is with someone to whom he is emotionally bound.

nostomania (nos-tō-mā'nē-à) An intense form of nostalgia; an irresistible impulse to return home.

nostras(is)ia (nos-tras'ē-à) *Obs.* Nostalgia.

not-me In Sullivan's system, symbolic representation of previous (usually infantile) interpersonal events that were associated with such overwhelming anxiety that they were dissociated from conscious awareness and memory; when the symbolic representations of such experiences threaten to invade consciousness (as in dreams, nightmares, fatigue states, intoxications, and schizophrenic reactions), the subject feels that the experience is foreign, unreal, and "not-me," and typically also is flooded with one or another of what Sullivan termed the "uncanny emotions"—awe, dread, horror, loathing. The feeling of unfamiliarity or foreignness is the opposite of *déjà vu* (q.v.), although in both phenomena the accompanying feelings are typically of the uncanny variety.

Nothnagel Carl Wilhelm Hermann (not'-nä-gel) (1841-1905) Austrian neurologist.

notogenesis (nō-tō-jen'e-sis) The later stages of *gastrulation* (q.v.), in which the *notochord,* or embryonic backbone, is formed. This period is associated with the appearance and development of the third germ layer, the *mesoderm* (q.v.), and thus implies a tridermic condition of the embryo.

Subsequently, at a stage overlapping the next salient step of development, *cephalogenesis,* the plates of the mesoderm become differentiated into a more robust *medial* portion, and a thinner *lateral* portion, the two connected by a constricted plate of the original mesoderm.

noumenal (noo'mē-nal) Intellectually,

not sensuously, intuitional; relating to the object of pure thought divorced from all concepts of time or space.

novelty In information theory, *incongruity* (q.v.).

noxa (nôk′sà) Any injurious agent, mental or physical.

noxious (nok′shus) Injurious; hurtful.

nuclear (nū′klē-ēr) Pertaining to, or having the character of, a nucleus.

nucleus (nū′klē-us) (L. 'a nut, kernel') In the minute structure of a typical cell, the *nucleus* is a denser body in the midst of its protoplasm, usually rounded in form and representing the directive center of most cellular activities. As it governs the mitotic process of cell division, it plays a decisive role in the chromosomal mechanism of hereditary transmission. See *chromosome*.

The actual seat of the genetic elements in the nucleus is a fine reticulum of various protein substances which stain very readily and are collectively called the *chromatin*. In addition to this chromatin network, the nucleus contains not only a liquid in which the chromatin floats, but frequently also one or more dense, rounded bodies, the *nucleoli*.

In a resting cell, the nucleus is surrounded by a thin membrane, the tension of which tends to keep the nucleus round. All cytoplasmic substances entering the nucleus must pass through this membrane.

nucleus, caudate (kaw′dāt) See *basal ganglia*.

nucleus, dentate (den′tāt) See *cerebellum*.

nucleus, Edinger-Westphal See *accommodation*.

nucleus, emboliform (em-bol′i-form) See *cerebellum*.

nucleus fastigius (noo-klā-oos fas-tig′ē-oos) See *cerebellum*.

nucleus globsus (glō-bō′soos) See *cerebellum*.

nucleus pulposus (pul-pō′soos) See *disk, herniated lumbar intervertebral*.

nucleus ruber (roo′ber) Red nucleus. See *midbrain*.

numbness, sleep See *paralysis, sleep*.

nyctalopia (nik-ta-lo′pē-à) Night-blindness; inability to see well at night or in dim light; sometimes due to vitamin A deficiency.

nyctiplanctus (nik-ti-plangk′tus) *Obs.* Somnambulistic agitation.

nyctobadia, nyctobatia (nik-tō-bad′ē-à, -bat′ē-à) *Obs.* Somnambulism.

nyctophobia Fear of night (or darkness).

nyctophonia (nik-tō-fō′nē-à) Night voice. The term denotes the ability to speak at night and implies the loss of the voice during daylight hours.

nympholepsy (nim′fō-lep-sē) *Obs.* Demoniac frenzy.

nymphomania (nim-fō-mā′nē-à) A morbid, insatiable impulse to heterosexuality in women. Compare with male pseudohypersexuality; see *Don Juan*.

nymphomania, active See *nymphomania, grave*.

nymphomania, grave Nymphomania severe in contrast to *slight or lesser nymphomania*.

Thoinot and Weyese further subdivide nymphomaniacs into an *active* and *platonic* type. 'The latter does not manifest her morbid desires outwardly; she is the equivalent of the *platonic* sadist and fetichist. Her desires are no less keen than those of the great [or grave] nymphomaniac, but she is mistress of them and knows how to content herself—apart from legitimate relations, which merely deceive her needs for a moment—by the enjoyment she experiences, with or without the aid of solitary masturbation at the sight or mental image of a man.' (Thoinot, L. and Weyese, A.W. *Medico-Legal Aspects of Moral Offenses*, Davis, Philadelphia, 1927)

nymphomania, platonic See *nymphomania, grave*.

nystagmus (nis-tag′mus) An involuntary

to-and-fro movement of the eyeballs induced when the patient looks upward or laterally. It is usually a pathological sign.

Nystagmus may be *horizontal,* the most common form, when the oscillations of the eyeballs are from side to side; or *vertical,* when the movements are up-and-down; or *rotatory,* when the oscillations are in a circular direction.

O

oaf *Obs.* Idiot; mental retardate.

obedience, automatic Many patients, particularly those with the catatonic form of schizophrenia, carry out the orders of others through blind obedience, that is, without critical or automatic judgment. 'The patients carry out any commands whatsoever, even if it is against their will, as for example, putting out their tongue when they know a pin will be stuck into it. . . .' (Bleuler, E. *Textbook of Psychiatry*, tr. by Brill, A.A., Macmillan, New York, 1930)

obedience, deferred According to Freud, a prohibition, command, or threat received early in life may be repressed and the effect deferred for many years until a neurotic illness occurs and the original prohibition or command is obeyed.

In spite of his father's opposition, a man became a painter. 'His incapacity to paint after the father's death would then . . . be an expression of the familiar "deferred obedience."' (Freud, S. *Collected Papers*, vol. 4, tr. by Riviere, J., Leonard and Virginia Woolf and The Institute of Psychoanalysis, London, 1924 -25)

obesity, psychogenic Corpulence or the state of being overweight as a result of emotional factors which lead to overeating. Overeating may be a nonspecific response to emotional tension, a substitute gratification in intolerable life situations, a specific symptom of emotional illness such as hysteria or depression, or a type of addiction. Bruch has claimed that there is a characteristic psychologic constellation in psychogenic obesity in children, consisting of maternal ambivalence, hostility, and compensatory overprotection. Most other investigators have failed to confirm these claims.

object From the instinctual point of view, 'the *object* of an instinct is that in or through which it can achieve its aim. It is the most variable thing about an instinct and is not originally connected with it, but becomes attached to it only in consequence of being fitted to provide satisfaction. The object is not necessarily an extraneous one; it may be part of the subject's own body.' (Freud, S. *Collected Papers*, vol. 4, tr. by Riviere, J., Leonard and Virginia Woolf and The Institute of Psychoanalysis, London, 1924 - 25)

Freud points out that the object of an instinct may, and usually does, change from time to time throughout life; moreover, 'the same object may serve for the satisfaction of several instincts simultaneously.'

object-addiction See *addict, object.*

object, bad A psychoanalytic concept that is part of the dichotomous formulation 'good object versus bad object.' 'Good' and 'bad' as used in this connotation refer essentially to moral, conscience (superego) evaluation: 'good' stands for nonsexual (clean), while 'bad' stands for sexual (dirty). In the unconscious the ultimate good object is equated with God, while the bad object means the Devil. See *position, paranoid-schizoid.*

object blindness Visual *agnosia* (q.v.).

object-cathexis See *cathexis.*

object-choice See *choice, object.*

object-finding See *finding, object.*

object, good See *position, paranoid-schizoid.*

object, homoerotic See *homosexuality, male.*

object-identification See *identification.*

object-ill A term applied by Stekel to the compulsive-neurotic who expresses his own mental conflict in the form of symbolization of objects pertaining to the outer world (i.e. outside his body) and also through symbolization of 'the function of his everyday life such as washing, dressing, eating, defecating . . . In compulsive diseases it is the patient's relationship to an object (usually a close member of the family) that is disturbed.'

In opposition to the object-ill patient, Stekel calls 'subject-ill' the person suffering from phobias, who uses his own body to symbolize his emotions. 'The patient shows an ambivalent emotional attitude toward this object, that is, the polar tension between the extremes of love and hate with regard to this object is also extreme . . .

'The "object-ill" is conscious of his abilities; he fails, because of his bipolar family fixations which create defiance, aggression and self-punishment; while the "subject-ill" feels that he has failed in his relations with the outer world and feels inferior to the demands of life . . . The "object-ill" is introverted and makes no attempts at extraversion; the "subject-ill," however, makes efforts to extravert himself in order to adjust himself to the world.' (Stekel, W. *Compulsion and Doubt*. Liveright, New York, 1949) See *subject-ill*.

object-libido (-li-bid'ō) See *ego-libido*.

object-love That portion of the libidinal energy of the psyche which is attached to some object outside the person himself (or to the intrapsychic representation of that object). At various times, Freud appears to have considered object-love to be the earliest type of relationship to the environment and thus to precede auto-erotism and narcissism; but at other times he considered autoerotism or narcissism to be primary. See *narcissism, primary*.

object-love, passive See *narcissism*.

objectivation A type of projection in which one's own unrecognized impulses or feelings are quickly detected and recognized in others. Objectivation may lead to overemphasis of the importance or significance of such impulses in others and, when present in the analyst, may produce troublesome counter-transference manifestations.

oblativity (ob-la-tiv'i-tē) Capacity for renunciation of the mother or mother-substitute; the ability to tolerate frustration in the process of achieving independence.

obliviscence The state or process of passing into oblivion; the tendency for a memory to fade with the passage of time.

obnubilation (ob-nū-bi-lā'shun) Clouding of consciousness, stupor.

OBS (1) Acronym for Organic Brain Syndrome—see *syndrome, organic*; (2) abbreviation for obstetrics.

obscenity Speech, gestures, writings, drawings or other actions that are offensive to taste or modesty, and/or that aim to incite the viewer to lewd and prurient thought or action. See *pornography*.

observation, delusion of Delusion of being watched.

observer, participant In psychoanalysis, the analyst as he is viewed by those who feel that he must be something more than an authoritarian sounding board or a mirror in which the patient's problems are reflected. Although the therapist must be objective, he also takes active part in the interpersonal process of therapy. The so-called cultural interpersonal school of psychoanalysis particularly emphasizes the participant role of the analyst. See *process, interpersonal*.

obsessed Beset with irresistible ideas or feelings, or with both—as is generally the case.

obsession An idea, emotion, or impulse that repetitively and insistently forces itself into consciousness even though it is unwelcome. An obsession may be regarded as essentially normal when it does not interfere substantially with thinking or other mental functions; such an obsession is short-lived and can usually be minimized or nullified by diverting attention onto other topics.

Morbid or pathological obsessions, in contrast, tend to be long-lived and may constitute a never-ending harrassment of mental functioning; they are but little subject to conscious control and force the sufferer into all sorts of maneuvers in his vain attempt to rid himself of the thoughts.

Most commonly, obsessions appear as *ideas*, or sensory images, which are strongly charged with emotions: (1) *intellectual obsessions*, often in the form of preoccupation with metaphysical questions concerning one's purpose in life, ultimate destiny, whereabouts after; death, etc.; see *brooding*; (2) *inhibiting obsessions* in the form of doubts or scruples about actions, or multiple phobias that may paralyze all activity; (3) *impulsive obsessions*, which are repetitively intruding ideas that lead to action (e.g. arithmomania, kleptomania, and other so-called *manias*).

Less commonly, obsessions appear as feelings, unaccompanied by clear-cut ideas, such as anxiety or panic, feelings of unreality or depersonalization. Some authorities, in addition, classify motor tics as impulsive obsessions. See *obsessive-compulsive psychoneurosis.*

obsession, masked An obsession which appears in the disguised (masked) form of other symptoms. One of the most interesting forms is the obsessive idea which disguises itself in the form of pain. 'The patients complain of pain, state that it drives them to suicide, yet they remain attached to the pain which—on closer scrutiny—may prove to represent pleasurable though tabooed memories . . . 'Such pain (for which usually no organic cause can be found) then appears as a mask of the obsessive idea. The real idea is hidden behind the pain, so that the patients, instead of complaining of obsessions, complain of pain. It is diagnostically important that the usual sedatives are always ineffective in these cases or, if forced upon the patient, may lead to narcotomania.' (Stekel, W. *Compulsion and Doubt,* Liveright, New York, 1949.)

obsession, somatic (sō-mat'ik) Morbid preoccupation with one's body or an individual organ. 'Usually these obsessions concerning the body or individual organs are connected with [the] patient's feeling of guilt and inferiority. The somatic obsessions are mostly monosymptomatic, though they are always parts of a more complicated neurotic system. A person not only is forced to think constantly of his nose, but also operates with a "nose-currency," so to speak, that is, in looking at people he sees only their noses and compares them with his own. No other human problem appears to be worthy of his attention.' (Stekel, W. *Compulsion and Doubt,* Liveright, New York, 1949)

obsession traumatic (traw-mat'ik) *Obs.* 'As regards classification of the subject, I propose to exclude a group of intense obsessions which are nothing but memories, unaltered images of important experiences. As an example, I will cite Pascal's obsession: he always thought he saw an abyss on his left hand "after he had nearly been thrown into the Seine in his coach." These obsessions and phobias, which might be called *traumatic,* are allied to the symptoms of hysteria.' (Freud, S. *Collected Papers,* vol. 1, tr. by Riviere, J., Leonard and Virginia Woolf and The Institute of Psychoanalysis, London, 1924 -25)

obsessive attack See *attack, obsessive.*

obsessive-compulsive (psycho)neurosis (300.3) Obsessive-compulsive reaction; a type of psychoneurosis characterized by disturbing, unwanted, anxiety-provoking, intruding thoughts or ideas, and repetitive impulses to perform acts (ceremonials, counting, hand-washing, etc.) which may be considered abnormal, undesirable, or distasteful to the patient. The 'psychasthenia' of earlier writers usually included obsessive-compulsive psychoneurosis.

Psychoanalytically, obsessive-compulsive psychoneurosis is interpreted as a defense against aggressive and/or sexual impulses, particularly in relation to the Oedipus complex. The initial defense is by regression to the anal-sadistic level, but the impulses at this level are also intolerable and must be warded off—by reaction-formation, isolation, and undoing. Because the use of these defenses renders superfluous the use of repression proper, the offensive impulses can exist in consciousness although when they do they are divorced from their affective significance and so remain meaningless to the patient. See *obsession; compulsion.*

obsessive-ruminative tension state. Adolf Meyer's term for *obsessive-compulsive psychoneurosis* (q.v.).

obstipatio paradoxa (ob-stē-pȧ'tē-ō pȧ-rȧ-dok'sȧ) Soiling associated with constipation. 'The child retains the stools, which become very hard and can be felt through the abdominal wall. Small pieces of firm stool are passed from time to time and are retained between the buttocks, macerating the perianal skin.' (Bakwin and Bakwin. *Clinical Management of Behavior Disorders in Children,* Saunders, Philadelphia, 1953) See *obstipation.*

obstipation (ob-sti-pa'shun) Extreme or intractable constipation; when of psychologic origin, it may appear either as a conversion symptom or as an organ-neurosis. Like all conversions, obstipation may be the somatic expression of a specific, repressed, unconscious sexual phantasy. Usually obstipation expresses retentive tendencies connected with pregnancy wishes or incorporation phantasies. This is 'in accordance with the equation child = penis = feces.'

As an organ-neurosis, obstipation is a physiological change in organic function, resulting from an unconscious attitude or affect. In the particular case of obstipation, the unconscious attitude is a chronically frustrated retentive pressure. The retentive pressure may exist for several reasons. It may represent an anal erotic fixation, a desire for anal retentive pleasure; or, the feces may represent introjected objects as in the case of the conversion. Again, in some other instances, the retentive pressure, with its resulting obstipation, might be associated with a continuous and repressed aggressiveness. (Fenichel, O. *The Psychoanalytic Theory of Neurosis*, Norton, New York, 1945)

obstruction *Blocking* (q.v.). 'Among the formal disturbances of the mental stream [of thought] the *obstructions* (deprivation of thought) are the most striking and when they occur too readily or too often or become too general and too persistent, they are positively pathognomonic of schizophrenia.' (Bleuler, E. *Textbook of Psychiatry*, tr. by Brill, A.A., Macmillan, New York, 1930)

Thought-deprivation or sudden cessation of thought may last for variable periods of time.

obstupescentia (ôbs-stoo-pes-ken′tē-à) *Obs.* Stupor.

occult Hidden from understanding or not susceptible to logical rational verification; includes magic, foretelling, telepathy, clairvoyance, etc. See *perception, extrasensory.*

occupation, sedative (sed′à-tiv) In occupational therapy a form of activity characterized by repetitious, uniform movements which, because of their monotonous recurrence, have a soothing and quieting effect. It is usually prescribed for overactive patients. An example of sedative occupation is simple weaving.

occupation, stimulating In occupational

therapy an occupation is regarded as stimulating when its processes are so varied that the lack of monotony and repetition tends to arouse and awaken to activity the slow, retarded, and depressed patient. For instance, the various activities associated with photography constitute a type of stimulating occupation.

occupational psychiatry See *psychiatry, industrial.*

occupational therapy See *therapy, occupational.*

oceanic feeling See *omnipotence; nautomania.*

ochlophobia (ok-lō-fō′bē-à) Fear of crowds.

ocnophile (àk′nō-fīl) Balint's term for the person with that type of primitive two-person relationship in which the subject is clingingly dependent on the overvalued object and is unable to make any move toward independence.

oculogyral crisis See *spasm, oculogyric.*

odaxesmus (ō-dak-sez′mus) Marshall Hall (English physician, 1790-1857), used this term to refer to the biting of tongue, cheek or lip during an epileptic seizure.

odontophobia (ō-don-tō-fō′bē-à) Fear of teeth.

-odynia (-ō-din′ē-à) Combining suffix meaning grief, pain from Gr. *odynē,* pain of body or mind, sorrow.

odynophobia Fear of pain.

oedipal (ed′i-pàl) Pertaining to Oedipus. This adjective is occasionally encountered, though as a rule the noun *Oedipus* is used unchanged as an adjective, as: Oedipus complex.

oedipism *Rare.* Self-inflicted injury to the eyes.

Oedipus, complete The simultaneous presence of both a positive and a negative (or inverted) Oedipus situation; the child displays mother object-love and father identification, and father object-love and mother identification. The quantity of cathexis (or emotional charge) given to each of these four conditions is a reflection in part of the strength of innate bisexuality, and in part of experiential factors.

Oedipus complex See *complex, Oedipus.*

Oedipus, inverted Same as *Oedipus, negative* (q.v.).

Oedipus, negative Also known as *inverted Oedipus* (complex), the negative Oedipus complex is a form of infantile psychosexual development in which the parental object is the opposite or reverse of the usual love object. The usual Oedipal love object for the male child is the mother; but should love for the father and hatred for the mother prevail, the boy would be said to demonstrate a negative Oedipus complex. In like fashion, should the girl's attachment remain fixed on the mother (instead of being transferred to the father, as is the usual course of events), she would be described as manifesting a negative Oedipus. See *complex, Oedipus.*

oenomania (ē-nō-mā′nē-à) *Oinomania* (q.v.).

oestromania, estromania (es-trō-mā′nē-à) Nymphomania.

oikiomania (oi-kē-ō-mā′nē-à) See *ecomania.*

oikiophobia (oi-kē-ō-fō′bē-à) See *oikophobia.*

oikofugic (oi-kō-fū′jik) Pertaining to or swayed by the impulse to wander or travel.

oikophobia (oi-kō-fō′bē-a) Fear of one's house or home.

oikotropic (-trop′ik) Homesick.

oinomania (oi-nō-mā′nē-à) Dipsomania; craving for alcoholic liquor; delirium tremens.

O.I.T. Organic integrity test. See *test, organic integrity.*

olfaction (ol-fak′shun) See *rhinencephalon.*

olfactophobia (ol-fak-tō-fō′bē-à) Fear of odors.

oligergasia (ol-i-gēr-gās′ē-à) Adolf Meyer's

term for intellectual deficiency or feeblemindedness.

olig(o)- (ol′i-gō-) Combining form meaning *little, few scanty,* from Gr. *oligos,* small, pl. *few.*

oligodactyly (à-li-gō-dak′ti-lē) See *syndrome, de Lange.*

oligodendroglia (ol-i-go-den-drog′lē-à) See *neuroglia.*

oligomania (ol-i-go-mā′nē-à) Insanity on a few subjects. Old term for monomania.

oligomania, affective *Obs. Mania mitis* (q.v.).

oligophrenia (ol-i-go-frē′nē-à) Mental deficiency.

oligophrenia, moral See *insanity, moral.*

oligophrenia, phenylpyruvic (fē-nil-pī-roō′vik) A constitutional type of mental deficiency characterized by the combination of mental deficiency and an inherited biochemical alteration in the body. (In DSM-II, 31x.2) 'A certain type of defective is found to excrete in the urine an aromatic compound, phenylpyruvic acid. The great majority of these patients are low grade defectives. Stature and general physical development are within normal limits, the blond type predominates, being more than 90% of the cases and coexisting generally with blue eyes and pale, delicate skin. In addition to constitutional traits, neurological signs are generally found, consisting of hypertonicity of muscles, increase of deep reflexes, hyperkinetic manifestations such as tremor, athetosis, tics. In a small percentage of cases marked psychotic trends may be observed. . . . The disease is characterized biochemically by an inhibition in the metabolism of phenylalanine in the stage of phenylpyruvic acid, the subject being unable to oxidize this keto acid at a normal rate.' (Jervis, G. *Archives of Neurology* 38, 944, 1937) Also known as *Folling's disease.*

oligopsychia (ol-i-go-sī′kē-à) *Obs.* Mental deficiency.

oligoria (ol-i-gor′ē-à) In certain forms of melancholia, an abnormal indifference toward or dislike of persons or things.

oligosthenic (ol-i-gō-sthen′ik) Kretschmer's variety of *asthenic* type characterized by moderate strength and intermediate between the *phthinoid* and the *eusthenic.*

oligothymia (-thī-mē-à) Poverty of affectivity; a term suggested by Davidson for the syndrome of psychopathy.

oliguresis, hysterical (ol-i-gū-rē′sis) Scanty or abnormally diminished urination, which usually appears as a conversion symptom. All conversion symptoms are the distorted physical expression of repressed instinctual impulses which have taken the form of sexual and/or aggressive phantasies. These phantasies usually relate to the Oedipus complex. The conversion symptom, which is a change in physical function, can be analyzed in the same way as dreams, and the repressed phantasies can thus be cleared up. The symptom of oliguresis lends itself to the expression of sexual phantasies because it is rooted in a period of infantile sexuality, when urination is 'still in the service of pleasure-seeking.' In particular, oliguresis may express 'retention tendencies connected with pregnancy wishes or incorporation phantasies.' According to Fenichel, the equation is 'child = penis = feces.' (Fenichel, O. *The Psychoanalytic Theory of Neurosis,* Norton, New York, 1945)

-oma (-ō′mà) Noun-forming suffix meaning affected or diseased state, from Gr. *-ōma.*

ombrophobia (om-brō-fō′bē-à) Fear of rain-(storm).

-ome (-ōm) Combining form from F. *-ome,* equivalent of *-oma.*

omega melancholium (ō′me-gà me-làn-kô′lē-oom) (L.L. 'melancholy omega') A wrinkle (between the eyebrows) in the shape of the last letter of the Greek alphabet, the omega (ω), assumed to indicate a state of melancholy.

ommatophobia (om-à-tō-fō′bē-à) Fear of eyes.

omnipotence (om-nip′ō-tens) Feelings of omnipotence and self-esteem undergo extensive development and change, concomitant with the development of the ego. There is a feeling of omnipotence from the very beginning, even before the conception of objects exists. The outside world is perceived by the organism as part of it (the organism), within itself, though there is as yet no non-ego. Similar phenomena are observed in mental patients when they lose contact with reality and relapse to a childlike level of emotional behavior: the person loses the distinction between his personality (ego) and the environment (reality). Such a person is in a state of primitive all-powerfulness, believes that he is omniscient and omnipotent, and has phantasies which know no bounds. To attain such a state of primitive all-powerfulness the patient usually passes through a phase of rebirth. He believes that he has gone back into his mother's womb: he acts the part, curls up in a fetal position, and behaves like a small infant. In such a state of omnipotence the patient can express ideas that he is able to move the universe, to create war and peace, to give birth to millions of children, etc. In delusional adults the symptom is more commonly called *megalomania.* (Hinsie, L.E. *Understandable Psychiatry,* Macmillan, New York, 1948)

This feeling of unlimited omnipotence, often termed the *'oceanic feeling,'* becomes limited as the ego and sense of reality develop: this occurs when the infant experiences tensions he cannot master, which in turn lead to unco-ordinated discharge movements. 'Something outside' becomes necessary to quiet the infant's tension and, through recognizing this 'something outside,' the infant makes his first distinction between ego and object. Also he develops a new concept of omnipotence. When his movements are understood by the environment to be a signal calling for a quieting of his tension, the child experiences this train of events as an 'omnipotence of movements.' However, he still longs for his original 'oceanic feeling.' His earliest reaction to objects is to swallow them; he tries to 'swallow' or incorporate all pleasurable sensations and, through introjection, to make parts of the external world flow, like tributaries, into his ego. Unpleasurable sensations are perceived as being non-ego and are 'spat out.' Thus, through introjection, anything pleasurable becomes part of the ego, and, through projection, anything unpleasant becomes non-ego.

These efforts to re-establish the 'oceanic feeling' of primary narcissism and also the 'omnipotence of movements' are doomed to failure, however, since, through his experiences, the child realizes he is not omnipotent. The adult is now considered omnipotent and, by reuniting with this omnipotent force in the external world, the child tries to share this omnipotence: either he incorporates parts of this world or has the phantasy of being incorporated by it. The latter type of omnipotence is at work in religious ecstasy and patriotism. Mass political movements may also attest the participation of the powerless followers in the omnipotence of their leaders. The feeling of having been reunited with the omnipotent force is known as secondary narcissism. The longing for the omnipotence of primary narcissism is the 'narcissistic need which all people experience. '"Self-esteem" is the awareness of how close the individual is to the original omnipotence.' Originally, the longing for omnipotence was a longing for the removal of instinctual tension, which would restore the objectless narcissistic state: self-esteem was restored by getting rid of an unpleasant stimulus. This was done through nourishment. Thus the first regulation of self-esteem and satisfaction of narcissistic need was through food. After the infant relinquishes its feeling of omnipotence, however, and tends to participate in the adult's omnipotence, his self-esteem is regulated by tokens of love from the adults. The child gains self-esteem when he gains affection and loses self-esteem when he loses affection: through the promise of these and the threats of withholding or withdrawing them, the child becomes ready to obey authority and forego other satisfactions. 'This is what makes children educable.'

In later development, needs for self-esteem, the narcissistic needs, are all-important: they develop in the relationship between ego and superego. Guilt-feeling lowers self-esteem and fulfillment of ideals raises it. But even in the relationship to objects in which the sexual needs develop, part of the relationship remains governed by the needs of self-esteem. In persons fixated at this level the dominant need from objects is narcissistic. These individuals may attempt to maintain their self-esteem either through aggressive or submissive behavior toward their objects or through both methods simultaneously. (Fenichel, O. *The Psychoanalytic Theory of Neurosis,* Norton, New York, 1945)

omnipotence, magic See *identification, cosmic.*

onanism (ō'nan-iz'm) Strictly speaking *onanism* is sexual intercourse interrupted before ejaculation.

Havelock Ellis says: 'Onan's device was not auto-erotic, but an early example of withdrawal before emission, or *coitus interruptus.*'

Some writers use the term *onanism* interchangeably with masturbation.

onanism, buccal Fellatio.

onanism, larval (lär'val) Masked or undercover masturbation.

onanism, primary Ferenczi thus denotes masturbation in an infant—'of a purely local genital excitement without the involvement of the rest of the psyche.' (Ferenczi, S. *Further Contributions to the Theory and Technique of Psycho-Analysis,* tr. by Suttie, J.E., Leonard and Virginia Woolf and The Institute of Psychoanalysis, London, 1926)

onanism, psychic (sī'kik) See *masturbation.*

oneirism (on'ī-riz'm) Dream-state while one is awake.

oneir(o)- (ō-nī-r[ō]-) Combining form meaning *dream,* from Gr. *oneiros,* dream.

oneiro-delirium (ō-nī-rō-dē-lir'ē-um) Literally, dream delirium. Certain French psychiatrists apply the term oneiro-deliria to that group of psychoses which is marked by delirium. Delirium tremens is the prototype of this group and is considered to be essentially a prolonged dream. Fever deliria are also part of this group, because they are so closely related to dreams. Although it is true that hallucinations can be interpreted in the same way as dreams, this does not mean that deliria, schizophrenic hallucinations, and dreams are etiologically the same, as this term would imply.

oneirodynia (-din'ē-à) One of the four great divisions of insanity recognized by Cullen. The four were amentia, melancholia, mania, and oneirodynia (somnambulism and nightmare).

oneirogonorrhea (-gon-ō-rē'à) Nocturnal emission of semen.

oneirogonos (ō-nī-rog'ō-nos) Oneironosus.

oneirology (ō-nī-rol'ō-jē) The science of dreams.

oneironosus (-nō'sus) Morbid dreaming.

oneirophrenia (-frē'nē-à) A term suggested by Meduna and McCulloch for a schizophrenoid psychosis which, like schizophrenia, shows disturbances in associations and in affectivity but, unlike schizophrenia, shows in addition clouding of the sensorium. Onset is usually acute, during the episode the patient is in a dream-like condition, and prognosis is usually good.

By others, oneirophrenia is considered to be an acute form of *schizophrenia* (q.v.).

oneiroscopy (ō-nī-ros'kō-pē) Dream-analysis, diagnosis of the mental state by a study of the person's dreams.

oniomania (ō-nē-ō-mā'nē-à) Irresistible impulse to buy, extending inordinately beyond the needs of the person. Women, in whom the symptom is said to predominate, carry out the act of purchasing without judgment of the consequences.

'They do not even feel the impulse, but they act out of their nature like a caterpillar devouring leaves.' (Bleuler, E. *Textbook of Psychiatry*, tr. by Brill, A.A., Macmillan, New York, 1930, p. 540)

onirism (on'ī-riz'm) A term suggested by Régis for a state of prolonged dreaming.

onology (ō-nol'ō-jē) *Rare.* Asinine talk.

onomatomania (on-ō-ma-tō-mā'nē-à) A type of obsessive thinking in which certain words of sentences obtrude themselves into the patient's thoughts. A patient with an obsessive-compulsive psychoneurosis was beset with anxiety, because a man's

name was incessantly forcing itself upon him. It was the surname of a man, with whose wife the patient had had intercourse; the anxiety was occasioned by the fear of being attacked by the husband, though the patient knew that he need have no fear of attack in the usual sense.

onomatophobia Fear of hearing a certain name.

onomatopoiesis, onomatopoesis (-poi-ē'sis, -pō-ē'sis) The formation of an echoic word, i.e. in imitation of the sound associated with the thing or action. The words, *hiss, swish, crash, hush, whizz, hum, buzz, thump, click, tick, tap, cackle, yap, (chug), boom, bing, hoepoe, whippoorwill, chickadee* closely resemble the sound. In psychiatry the phenomenon is often observed in morbid form among patients with schizophrenia, who create a number of neologisms on the basis of sound association.

ontoanalysis (on-tō-a-nal'i-sis) Existential analysis; see *existentialism*.

ontogenesis, ontogeny (on-tō-jen'e-sis, on-toj'ē-nē) In biology, the development of the individual organism as compared with the evolutionary or *phylogenetic* development of the species. This fundamental distinction was clarified by Haeckel, when in 1867 he formulated his famous 'biogenetic law' that 'ontogeny recapitulates phylogeny' (*Naturliche Schopfungsgeschichte.*) If the histories of the genealogical and of the individual development are distinguished in accordance with this law, it follows that 'the organism in its development is to a great extent an epitome of the form-modifications undergone by the successive ancestors of the species in the course of their historic evolution.'

In other fields of science one finds the term ontogenesis or *ontogeny* applied in a more limited and specialized sense. With bacteriologists it means the evolution of the individual germ. According to certain psychologists, ontogeny refers to factors in the life of human beings after their birth, as the psyche is believed to have its special form of development, its own embryology, physiology, structural evolution, and pathology (see *phylogenesis*).

ontogeny, psychic Development of the mind, and particularly the ways in which the organism relates its inborn needs to environmental demands. In psychoanalytic psychology, psychic ontogeny includes: (1) development of object relationships; (2) the vicissitudes of the drives in relation to reality; and (3) the development of mechanisms to achieve the foregoing. The development of object relationships is generally described according to the following schema:

a) autoerotic (or somatogenic) stage, from birth until about three years of age; see *autoeroticism.*
b) narcissistic stage, from three to six years of age; see *narcissism.*
c) homoerotic (or suigenderistic) stage, from six years until puberty; see *homoeroticism.*
d) heteroerotic (or altrigenderistic) stage during adolescence; see *heteroeroticism.*
e) alloerotic stage, the stage of maturity; see *alloeroticism.*

The vicissitudes of the drives are typically described in terms of libidinal phases, as follows:

1. pre-superego sexuality, from birth until about six years of age, including
   a) oral phase, from birth until two years; see *orality.*
   b) anal phase, from two until about four years; see *phase, anal.*
   c) phallic phase, from two until about six years; see *phallic.*
2. *latency* (q.v.), from 6 years to puberty.
3. *genitality* (q.v.)

The mechanisms developed to achieve the foregoing are those involved in the development of the ego and superego, and of the ego-defenses. See *ego; defense; superego.*

ontology (on-tol′ō-jē) Study of the nature, essential properties, and relations of being; *existentialism* (q.v.).

onychophagia (on-i-kō-fā′jē-à) Nail-biting. This is given by Kanner as one of the habitual manipulations of the body encountered in neurotic children and considered by him as one of the several forms of motor discharges of inner tension.

onychophagy (on-i-kà′fà-jē) Nail-biting.

oö- (ō′ō-) Combining form meaning *egg,* from Gr. *ō (i) on,* egg.

oöcyte (ō′ō-sīt) In sexual reproduction,

the female germ cells or *oögonia* divide into two unequal daughter cells, the larger of which is called the *primary* or *secondary oöcyte,* according to whether it is produced by the first or second meiotic division. See *egg.*

oögonia (-gō′nē-à) In sexual reproduction, the *oögonia* represent the first stage in the development of mature reproductive cells in the female. See *egg.*

oöphorectomy (-fō-rek′tō-mē) See *ovariotomy.*

oöphorepilepsy (-fō-rep′i-lep-sē) *Obs.* Epilepsy originating in the ovaries.

oöphoria (-fō′rē-à) Dr. Barnes's term for hysteria, which he thought to be caused by the condition of the ovaries.

oöphoromania (-fō-rō-mā′nē-à) *Obs.* Psychosis due to ovarian disease.

oöthecomania (-thē-kō-mā′nē-à) Mental disorder associated with ovarian disease.

open In group therapy, an open group is one to which members can be added, while a *closed* group is limited to those who started with the group. In questioning or interviewing, an open question is one that allows the person questioned maximal freedom in choosing the manner or content of his response.

open-door policy Approximately equivalent to *community, therapeutic* (q.v.). The term open-door emphasizes the growing trend in psychiatric hospitals to minimize or even eliminate completely any form of restraint or enforced confinement ('locked doors').

operant conditioning See *conditioning, operant.*

ophidiophilia (ō-fid′i-ō-fil′ē-à) A morbid fascination with snakes.

ophidiophobia (ō-fid′i-ō-fō′bē-à) Fear of snakes.

ophthalmoplegia (op-thal-mō-plē′jē-à) See *nerve, oculomotor.*

-opia, -opy (-ō′pē-à, -ō-pē) Combining form meaning defect of sight, from Gr. *ōps, ōpós,* eye.

opinion, public 'A composite opinion formed out of several opinions that are held in the public; or better, as the central tendency set by the striving among these separate opinions and consequently as being shaped by the relative strength and play of opposition among them.' (Blumer, H.E., in Park, R.E. *Principles of Sociology*, Barnes & Noble, New York, 1939)

opiomania (ō-pē-ō-mā'nē-à) Addiction to the use of opium or any of its derivatives.

opisthotonos (op-is-tot'ō-nos) See *arc de cercle*.

opium (ō'pē-um) A narcotic and analgesic obtained from the juice of unripe seeds of the poppy plant. The juice dries in the air to form a brown, gummy substance, which is further dried and powdered commercially to produce the opiates (i.e. morphine and its transformation products). All the opiates are potentially addicting drugs, as are the synthetic analgesics; morphine possesses perhaps the greatest potentiality in this direction, followed by heroin, Dilaudid, Metopon, Demerol, Methadone, and codeine, in that order. Because it is easier to traffic in illegally, heroin is the most commonly used of the group by opiate addicts, at least in the United States (304.0). All the opiates are characterized by the development of a high degree of tolerance in their users, and severe deprivation or abstinence syndromes are therefore the rule. See *addiction; dependency, drug.*

opotherapy (op-ō-ther'à-pē) See *endocrinotherapy.*

Oppenheim reflex See *reflex, Oppenheim.*

Oppenheimer treatment (Issac Oppenheimer, a New York physician.) A secret method of treatment of alcoholism and drug addiction.

Oppenheim's dystonia musculorum deformans (dis-tō-nē'à mus-koo-lō'room dā-for'mans) (Hermann Oppenheim, Berlin neurologist, 1858-1919) See *dystonia, torsion.*

opposite, reversal into the One of the major defensive processes of a psychological nature by which the ego handles, or defends itself from, the sexual instinct which impinges upon it while seeking direct gratification. The specific nature of this process consists of the transformation of the aim of an instinct into its opposite, and the substitution of the instinct itself for the external object. This process is called into play when the aim of a sexual instinct has been blocked from direct object gratification by internal intrapsychic or external environmental prohibition and restriction. In the process of reversal into the opposite, the active aim usually becomes a passive one.

-opsia (-op'sē-à) See *-opia.*

opsomania (op-sō-mā'nē-à) 'Either a craving for some particular aliment to the extent of insanity, or a morbid craving for dainties.' (Tuke, D.H. A *Dictionary of Psychological Medicine*, vols. 1-2, Blakiston, Philadelphia, 1892)

optimism, oral Optimism appearing as an oral character trait. Oral eroticism is extremely important for the formation of character. At the time when oral eroticism occurs in infantile development, children 'become acquainted with objects and learn to assume relationships with them.' Consequently, the way in which this happens 'remains basic in determining the whole subsequent relationship to reality.' Thus all positive or negative attitudes to taking and receiving have an oral origin. In particular, whenever there is unusually pronounced oral satisfaction in infancy, the results are a self-assurance and optimism which may persist throughout life. Fenichel remarks, however, that if frustration has followed this satisfaction, there may be created a state of 'vengefulness coupled with continuous demanding.' (Fenichel, O. *The Psychoanalytic Theory of Neurosis*, Norton, New York, 1945)

oral-aggressive See *defense, character.*

orality (ō-ral'i-tē) A general term referring to the oral components of sexuality, to manifestations of instinctual conflict centering about the oral stage of sexual development, to manifestations which indicate fixation at the oral stage of development, to manifestations of oral erogeneity. Orality is prominent in manic-depressive psychosis and addictions. A driving ambition in the field of oratory or speech-making is often based on oral conflicts. Excessive generosity in a person often has the following significance: 'As I shower you with love, in the same way do I want to be showered with love'; this mechanism is typical of the oral receptive person. The oral-sadistic person often shows extreme niggardliness: 'You must make up for the love denied me.' Volubility, restlessness, haste, and a tendency to obstinate silence are also indicative of extreme orality. Edmund Bergler (*Psychiatric Quarterly, 19,* 412, 657, 1945) believes that the mechanism of orality is as follows: (1) through his behavior the person provokes disappointment, thus identifying the outer world with the refusing, pre-oedipal mother; (2) he becomes aggressive, seemingly in self-defense; (3) he indulges in self-pity, a manifestation of his psychic masochism. See *character, oral.*

Probably for biological reasons, the main energies of the infant are concentrated first in the mouth area—feeding is his most important function and reality demands little else of him. Orality is, in essence, one of the steps in learning, and at this stage in ontogenetic development stress and distress stem primarily from the complex physiological processes that produce hunger. Gratification follows stimulation of the mouth area, and oral stimulation is what the infant seeks because of the pleasure it provides.

orchestromania (or-kes-trō-mā'nē-à) Chorea; St. Vitus's dance.

orderliness, organic A characteristic symptom of patients with organic brain disease, consisting of a stereotyped, meticulous, compulsive approach to the environment; the patient's possessions must always be arranged in the same order, any action must always be performed in the same sequence or in the same way, etc. See *syndrome, organic.*

-orexia (-ō-rek'sē-à) Combining form meaning appetite, desire, from Gr. *orexis,* appetite, desire, longing.

orexis That part of an act or response which is not the cognitive aspect; specifically, affect and conation are the orectic aspects of an action.

organ-erotic Relating to or characterized

by the attachment of the erotic instinctual component to an organ of the body.

'Bearing these facts in mind it will be easy to understand that the child's first sexual feelings have reference to its own body, more particularly to parts, segments, of its body; it is organ-erotic.' (Jelliffe, S.E. and White, W.A. *Diseases of the Nervous System,* 6th ed., Lea & Febiger, Philadelphia, 1935)

organ-erotism Libido or erotism situated in an organ.

organ, executive The organ that is used for the execution of responses to stimuli. 'In the infant the technique of mastery has two chief executive organs, the hand and the mouth, the eye being the leading auxiliary organ.' (Kardiner, A. and Spiegel, H.X. *War Stress and Neurotic Illness,* Hoeber, New York, 1947.) Thus when hunger is the stimulus, response to it is executed by way of the mouth; when the stimulus is the desire to grasp at an object, response to it is executed by means of the hand.

organic brain syndrome See *syndrome, organic.*

organic driveness See *driveness, organic.*

organic psychosis See *syndrome, organic.*

organic reaction See *syndrome, organic.*

organicism (or-gan'i-siz'm) 1. The theory which refers all disease to material lesions of organs. Disordered physiology may give rise to symptoms, yet there may be no demonstrable lesions.

2. The theory that all symptoms are organically determined.

3. In constitutional medicine—'the theory that the various organs of the body have each their own special constitution.' (Pende, N. *Constitutional Inadequacies,* tr. by Naccarati, S., Lea & Febiger, Philadelphia, 1928)

organicist As currently used in psychiatry, a pejorative designation for the psychiatrist who can admit of only material lesions in organs as etiologic agents in psychiatric disorders. The organicist is typically contrasted to the *psychodynamist* or *psychogeneticist,* but all three terms represent an unwelcome regression to the days of the nature-nurture conflict. They focus upon a dualism that exists only on a conceptual heuristic level, and ignore the reality of the functioning whole man whose mental and emotional processes are interwoven with and interdependent upon neurophysiologic substrata and sociocultural factors. See *ecology; psychosomatic.*

organization, libido (li-bēd'ō) See *zone, primacy.*

organization, pregenital (prē-jen'i-tal) The arrangement of the libido in the stages prior to that of infantile genitality.
'As a result of numerous impressions, and in particular of one specially cogent analytical experience, I came to the conclusion a few years later that in the development of the libido in man the phase of genital primacy must be preceded by a "pregenital organization" in which sadism and anal erotism play the leading parts.' (Freud, S. *Collected Papers,* vol. 2, tr. by Riviere, J., Leonard and Virginia Woolf and The Institute of Psychoanalysis, London, 1924-25)

organization, social 'Socially systematized schemes of behavior imposed as rules upon individuals.' (Thomas, W.I. and Znaniecki, F. *The Polish Peasant in Europe and America,* Knopf, New York, 1927)
'Every human group is organized; its individual components do not behave independently of one another, but are linked by bonds, the nature of which determines the types of social unit. Kinship, sex, age, co-residence, matrimonial status, community of religious or social interests, are among the unifying agencies; and in stratified societies members of the same level form a definite class.' (Lowie, R.H. *Social Organization; Encyclopaedia of the Social Sciences,* vol. 14, Macmillan, New York, 1934, p. 141)

organ-jargon See *jargon, organ.*

organ-libido (-li-bēd'ō) See *organ-erotism.*

organ-neurosis See *psychosomatic.*

organ-pleasure The excitement and satisfaction attained in the extragenital erogenous zones; used particularly to refer to the *partial instincts* in the pregenital period. Characteristic of infantile sexuality is the fact that the genitals themselves are but one of many erogenous zones, and that sexuality is undifferentiated and contains all the later part-instincts, which are not as yet subordinate to genital satisfaction. In the child, every kind of excitation can become a source of sexual excitement—oral, anal, urethral, mechanical and muscular stimuli, skin, temperature, and even pain. 'In time, however, the genitals begin to function as a special discharge apparatus, which concentrates all excitation upon itself and discharges it no matter in which erogenous zone it originated. It is called genital primacy when this function of the genitals has become dominant over the extragenital erogenous zones, and all sexual excitations become finally genitally oriented and climatically discharged.' (Fenichel, O. *The Psychoanalytic Theory of Neurosis,* Norton, 1945)

organ speech See *speech, organ.*

organ, target See *syndrome, general adaptation.*

organogenesis (-jen'ē-sis) *Somatogenesis* (q.v.).

organogenic, organogenetic (or-gan-ō-jen'ik, -ō-jē-net'ik) *Somatogenic.*

organotherapy (-ō-ther'à-pē) Treatment with preparations or substances as they are found naturally in the body. In general it is called 'replacement' therapy, because usually the object is to restore to the body in sufficient quantity to maintain health something that is lacking in the body. Endocrinotherapy is one form of organotherapy.

orgasm (or'gaz'm) The acme or peak of excitation in the genital zone; the sexual *climax.* Erotic arousal involves a series of physiologic and psychologic phenomena in response to tactile stimulation or phantasy or a combination of mechanical and psychologic stimuli. These changes include increased pulse rate and blood pressure, raised skin temperature, flow of blood into the erectile tissues of the eyes, lips, ear lobes, nipples, penis or clitoris, and the genital labia; usually also there is some degree of hyperextension of the trunk. All such changes build up to a maximum, at which point tension is suddenly released. The latter produces local spasms of the perineal musculature or more extensive convulsive-like contractions. Technically, the term orgasm refers to the moment of sudden release of tension; the perineal contractions immediately following produces, in the male, ejaculation of semen (i.e. the liquid secretions of the prostrate and seminal vesicles), following which there is a rapid return to a normal or even subnormal physiologic state and a feeling of contentment, peace, satiety, and—often—some degree of drowsiness.

Orgasm is somewhat more complex in the female, whose sexual act has been described as follows: 'In the beginning of arousal, the vagina becomes moist with the lubricating fluid secreted by the vulvovaginal glands of Bartholin. At the same time the clitoris becomes erect and pulsates, and to a lesser extent the erectile tissue of the labia minora also becomes engorged and firm. At this point the main desire of the woman is for clitoral massage and, equally important, a need for tenderness and love from the partner. After some two to five minutes of clitoral manipulation, and other preparatory activities, the desire shifts to a wish for insertion of the penis, and almost immediately thereafter to a wish for friction. Throughout, the physical pleasure increases gradually, reaching a peak finally after 30 to 50 frictional thrusts which last for about three minutes. Orgasm itself occurs typically just after the partner's orgasm and is identified by means of involuntary muscular contractions of the vagina, particularly the vaginal orifice, and perineum. Although sexual tension is released by orgasm, the woman continues to want the penis within her for some time after orgasm; then in her contentment and satiety, she usually desires to sleep.

'To be noted, then, is that the curve of arousal or sexual reactivity in the woman is slower in buildup, more prolonged in duration, and less abrupt in its cessation than is the man's; and also that the woman, anatomically and emotionally, has a bipartite sexual apparatus. In the beginning, her wish is for clitoral stimulation, and only after some minutes of this is there a transfer of feeling and desire to the vagina itself. The penis, by the way, does not come in contact with the clitoris once vaginal entrance has been made, a point of some practical significance in view of the varying needs of different women for prolongation of clitoral manipulation.' (Campbell, R.J. "Frigidity and Impotence," In Marriage: A Psychological and Moral Approach, edited by Bier, W., Fordham, New York, 1964)

orgasm, alimentary Rado's term for the feeling of bliss and rapid reduction in tension experienced by the infant at the height of breast feeding; he related the wish to re-experience alimentary orgasm to mania, melancholia, and drug dependency.

orgasm, pharmacogenic A term suggested for the drug addict's satisfaction (and accompanying reduction of sexual and aggressive drives) following drug administration.

orgasmus deficiens (ôr-gàz'moos dā-fē'kē-ens) (L. 'failing, deficient orgasm') Lack of sexual pleasure.

orgone (or'gōn) Wilhelm Reich's term for the life energy, which he believed to be specific and identifiable.

orientation 1. Awareness of one's physical relationship to reality as measured by the parameters of person, place, and time. A person with intact orientation knows his own identity and can correctly identify the people who are a part of his usual environment; he knows where he is; and he knows the year in which he lives, the month of the year, the day of the week, and whether it is morning, afternoon, or evening. A patient may be disoriented in any one or in any combination of these spheres; disorientation, or confusion, is usually indicative of organic brain disease, although some patients with functional disorders of reality testing may become confused secondary to withdrawal from and/or inattention to their environment.

2. One's direction or position in relation to a person, object, concept, or principle. Thus, when a psychiatrist is asked, 'What is your orientation?' the questioner is trying to determine the general theory of human behavior to which the psychiatrist subscribes, his theoretical frame of reference, the 'school of thought' within

psychology or psychiatry that guide his formulations and methods of treatment.

orientation, autopsychic Appreciation of oneself, of one's own personality, one's psychic self. When a person is aware that changes take place in his personality he is said to possess intact autopsychic orientation. For example, the patient with a manic-depressive disorder usually has full knowledge of the changes that have appeared in his personality. The patient with schizophrenia, however, ordinarily denies that he has changed in any way. He is autopsychically disoriented.

orientation, delusion of See *orientation, double.*

orientation, double Bleuler's term for the schizophrenic's ability to maintain some adequacy in day-to-day functioning and at the same time to believe sincerely in the most contradictory and phantastic delusions, such as the patient who works conscientiously as an elevator operator and at the same time feels that he is the President of the United States. Also known as *delusion of orientation.*

orientation, illusion of Misinterpretation or misidentification of something real in the environment because of an unclear sensorium, as in the toxic deliria. The patient hears the voice of his nurse, for example, and believes it to be that of his wife.

orientation, oral A method of approaching, evaluating, and relating oneself to the environment on the basis of the hunger drive, oral needs, etc. The infant, for example, is primarily orally oriented; the mouth is his most differentiated organ and he uses it as his chief perceptive apparatus. The primitive ego is an oral ego, for the infant first becomes aware of objects, identifies them, and recognizes the outside world by putting objects in his mouth. When the infant began to long for something already familiar to him, absent at the moment, but with the ability to gratify his needs, he became aware of an object for the first time. When the object appeared, the longing for it disappeared and sleep followed. Thus hunger compelled the awareness of objects, i.e. the recognition of the outside world.

Next, the experience of satiation which

first banished the hunger that had disturbed sleep became 'the model for the mastery of external stimuli in general.' That is, the taking of objects into his mouth was one of the first reactions to objects on the part of the infant. Thus the first recognition of reality on the part of the infant is for him to judge whether he should swallow an object or spit it out. In the way described above, the reaction to recognition of the outside world, that is, to the perception of objects on the part of the primitive ego, is taking-into-the-mouth: oral introjection. 'The incorporation which is the first reaction to objects in general and the precursor of the later sexual and destructive attitudes in a psychological sense destroys the existence of the object. The attitude that the object exists only for the ego's satisfaction and may disappear once satisfaction is achieved can still be observed in some childish types of love.' Fenichel emphasizes, however, that the aim to incorporate objects does not necessarily reflect subjective destructive tendencies toward those objects. The fact that in incorporation the object disappears, i.e. is destroyed, is an incidental consequence and shows merely that oral incorporation is an urge to get satisfaction without any further thought of the object. Rather, this primary oral attitude of incorporation is the attitude out of which love and destructive hate grow at a later stage of development. (Fenichel, O. *The Psychoanalytic Theory of Neurosis,* Norton, New York, 1945) See *character, oral; orality.*

orientation, reversed A state in which a person when walking in one direction feels that he is walking in the opposite direction. The condition is purely subjective; the person orients himself correctly by reasoning.

orientation sessions See *gatekeeper.*

original response See *popular response.*

ornithophobia (or-ni-thō-fō'bē-à) Fear of birds.

orthergasia (orth-ēr-gās'ē-à) See *euergasia.*

ortho- (or'thō-) Combining form meaning straight, right, correct, sound, from Gr. *orthós.*

orthopathic (or-thō-pa'thik) Burrow's term for feeling that is primary, direct, whole. Contrasted with autopathic.

orthophrenia (-frē'nē-à) Soundness of mind; also, the curing of a disordered mind.

orthopsychiatry (-sī-kī'à-trē) A subdivision of psychiatry which deals with the study and treatment of mental deviations that are known in general as borderland states; it also includes the study of methods of preventing mental disorders. The term is perhaps synonymous with *mental hygiene.*

orthostatic epileptoid See *epileptoid, orthostatic.*

orthovagotonia (-vā-gō-tō'nē-à) Exaggerated functioning of the vagotonic or parasympathetic nervous system, but only when this exaggerated functioning is in harmony with that of the sympathetic nervous system.

orthriogenesis (or-thrē-ō-jen'e-sis) Federn's term for the recapitulation by the ego of its whole development, which he felt occurs at the moment of awakening when the ego which has been without cathexis in deep sleep, suddenly has its cathexis restored.

-osis (-ō'sis) Noun-forming suffix meaning action, state, condition, process, from Gr. *-ōsis,* as in (metamórph)*ōsis.*

-osmia (-oz'mē-à) Combining form meaning smell, odor, from Gr. *osme,* smell, odor.

osmophobia (oz-mō-fō'bē-à) Fear of odors.

osphresia, osphresis (os-frē-zē-à, os-frē-sis) The sense of smell.

osphresiolagnia (os-frē-zē-ō-lag'nē-à) Morbid or fetishistic interest in odors, often associated with infantile sexuality. Some patients believe that their body sends out an odor that is disagreeable and harmful to others, that makes others sick or insane.

The schizophrenic patient, particularly the one with delusions of persecution, often projects the idea of bad odors upon others, coming to the delusion then that others force evil body odors upon him, the patient.

One who possesses a morbid idea regarding body odors is called an osphresiolagniac or a renifleur.

'It turned out that our patient, besides all his other characteristics, was a *renifleur* (or osphresiolagniac). By his own account, when he was a child he had recognized every one by·their smell, like a dog; and even when he was grown up he was more susceptible to sensations of smell than most people.' (Freud, S. *Collected Papers,* vol. 3, tr. by Strachey, A. and J., Leonard and Virginia Woolf and The Institute of Psychoanalysis, London, 1925)

Freud says that he has 'come to recognize that a tendency to osphresiolagnia, which has become extinct since childhood, may play a part in the genesis of neurosis.' (Freud, S. ibid) See *rhinencephalon.*

osphresiophilia Morbid attraction to or interest in odors and smells.

osphresiophobia Fear of odors. Some patients are morbidly afraid of odors, believing that they would be contaminated by them.

ossification (os-i-fi-ka'shun) Lewin's term for the relative rigidity of behavior patterns which have become second nature or autonomous because of frequent repetitions.

osteitis deformans (os-tē-ī'tis dē-for'mans) *Paget's disease* (q.v.).

O.T. Occupational therapy. See *therapy, occupational.*

otiumosis (ō-shē-um-ō'sis) An alternative term suggested by E. Bergler for *alysosis* (q.v.).

otohemineurasthenia (ō-tō-hem-ē-nū-ras-thē'nē-à) Functional deafness affecting one ear.

otoneurasthenia (-nū-ras-the'-nē-à) Functional deafness.

out-patient Ambulatory patient who is not listed on the hospital in-patient census.

output The amount of work performed

or completed within a specified period of time; in communications theory, any action or response that cues or signals another person or another communication system.

ovariomania (ō-vâr-i-ō-mā′nē-à)   *Obs.* Mania due to ovarian disorder.

ovariotomy (ō-vâr-i-ot′ō-mi) Surgical removal of one or both ovaries. Bilateral ovariotomy is required for the castration of a female and usually leads, if performed before puberty, to such marked disturbance in the sex balance as to produce a eunuchoid symptomatology with secondary male sex characteristics (see *castration*). Also called *oöphorectomy*.

over-activity, psycho-motor See *mania.*

overadequate-inadequate reciprocity See *psychotherapy, family.*

overcompensation The term has been made popular by Alfred Adler. When the feeling of inferiority is so great that the person fears he will never be able to compensate for his weakness, his striving for power and dominance is exaggerated and intensified to a pathological degree.

Such people endeavor to secure their position in life by extraordinary efforts, by greater haste and impatience, by more violent impulses, and without consideration for anyone else. Their attitudes are apt to have a certain grandiose quality.

Briefly then, according to Adler, overcompensation is the counterpose of an overwhelming feeling of inferiority which is profusely neutralized by steps toward a towering goal of dominance.

overconsciousness Exaggerated development of self-consciousness as the result of 'over-socialization with leveling of the object relations.' The term applies to parents who first identify themselves too strongly with their children as love-objects, and then perform acts ostensibly of 'self-sacrificing love,' which, in psychiatric terms, are mere expressions of an increased narcissism on the part of the parents. Overconsciousness, it may be said, is a narcissistic attitude developed as a result of object relations of a special intensity and character. (Schilder, P. *Mind, Perception and Thought,* Columbia University Press, New York, 1942)

overdependence, social See *psychodynamics, adaptational.*

overdetermination 'As a rule neuroses are *overdetermined;* that is to say, several factors in their etiology operate together.' (Freud, S. *Collected Papers,* vol. 1, tr. by Riviere, J., Leonard and Virginia Woolf and The Institute of Psychoanalysis, London, 1924-25) More properly, *multidetermination.*

overinclusiveness One of the many association disturbances that may be observed in schizophrenic speech; it is the inability to preserve conceptual boundaries, so that irrelevant or distantly associated elements become incorporated into concepts, making thought less precise and more abstract. See *associations, disturbances of.*

overprotection, maternal Overprotection of the growing infant by the mother can result in difficulties for the person in later life. Overindulged and overprotected at an early age, the infant has not learned to bear frustrations. As a result, at a later period of development, little frustrations that a less spoiled person could tolerate have the effect of a severe frustration. The infant will refuse to go further in development, and will demand the withheld gratification associated with the particular little frustrations. Thus there will be fixations at the level of development at which the frustrations occur. These fixations resulting from overprotection produce personality difficulties such as various neurotic defense symptoms, or character attitudes, and primitive types of love.

An overprotecting mother predisposes the child to passive, dependent types of mastery. As a result, he will be unable to adapt himself objectively, but his passive dependent needs will color all his activities and relationships, causing the inevitable illusions and disappointments.

over-reactive disorders See *psychodynamics, adaptational.*

over-repression Exaggerated and often unnecessary repression by the superego. 'Thus an over-severe Super-ego may exclude from consciousness "and therefore from access to the motor apparatus" many forms of outlet which would be by no means ego-dystonic, namely unacceptable to the Ego.' (Healy, W., Bronner, A.F., and Bowers, A.M. *The Structure and Meaning of Psychoanalysis*, Knopf, New York, 1930)

overtone, psychic (sī'kik) One of the many faintly perceived associated impressions grouped about a mental image.

ovum (ō'vum) (L. 'an egg') See *egg*.

oxycephaly (ok-sē-sef'a-lē) Tower-head; turrecephaly. A congenital anomaly in which there is premature closure (craniosynostosis) of the coronal and lambdoid sutures, resulting in an upward elongation of the head, which thus appears dome-shaped. The anomaly does not affect mentality or length of life, but in order to preserve vision the King corrective operation must be performed early in life.

P

P Rorschach scoring symbol for a *popular response* (q.v.).

P-element See *system.*

P-system See *system.*

pacemaker, cerebral A hypothesized central neurophysiologic mechansim which regulates and synchronizes the EEG rhythms of the two cerebral hemispheres. The cerebral pacemaker is believed to be located in the reticular substance of the upper brain stem or in the adjacent posterior hypothalamic region. (Aird, R. and Garoutte, B. *Neurology,* 8, 581, 1958)

pachymeningitis (pak-ē-men-in-jī'tis) See *meninges; meningitis.*

pachymeninx (pak-ē-men'ingks) See *meninges.*

pack In psychiatric nursing, the application of sheets to the patient's body. The pack may be wet or dry, hot or cold. In each case the patient is wrapped in several sheets. When a *cold pack* is used the sheets are immersed in water at a temperature of 60° F.; the temperature of the water in case of a *hot pack* is 130° to 145° F.
  Dry packs are sometimes used to induce increase of body temperature by lessening heat elimination.

paederastia (ped-ē-ras'tē-à) Pederasty.

paedicatio (pī-dē-kä'tē-ō) Pederasty.

paedicatio mulierum (pī-dē-kä'tē-ō mōō-lē'e-room) (L.'women's pederasty') The act of pederasty with girls as the passive agent.

paed(o)-, ped(o)- Combining form meaning childlike, or having to do with children.

paedophilia erotica (pī-dō-fē'lē-à e-rō'tē-kà) (Mod.L. 'erotic love of children') A term coined by Krafft-Ebing for *pederosis* (q.v.)

Paget's disease (Sir James Paget, English surgeon, 1814 - 1899) Osteitis deformans; bony overgrowth often produces neurological complications by exerting pressure on the cerebral nervous system or nerve roots.

paidicatio (pī-dē-kà-tē-ō) Pederasty; sodomy.

pain, ecstatic The *hunger for excitement* of some people comes about in this manner. There are people who must always be doing something; it matters little whether the situation is of a pleasurable or painful nature. Sometimes a decided preference is shown for the latter; they experience "ecstatic pain," martyrlike pleasure, and forever consider themselves unfairly treated.' (Bleuler, E. *Textbook of Psychiatry,* tr. by Brill, A.A., Macmillan, New York, 1930)

pain, psychic (sī'kik) Same as *psychalgia.*

pain, referred Irradiation of pain sensation, with or without hyperalgesia, into an area of skin when a viscus or muscle is the site of the lesion. Although the basis for referral of pain must be excitation of common pathways, it is uncertain whether the brain, the spinal cord, or the peripheral nerves are involved.

painting, finger Direct manipulation of the paint with the fingers and hands to achieve a graphic effect. In psychology, finger-painting is used as a projective technique, the assumption being that finger-painting is a form of expressive behavior, the analysis of which reveals significant characteristics of the subject. Finger-painting was developed by Miss Ruth F. Shaw (1934) as one of her educational techniques, and it has since been used as a diagnostic projective technique, as a means for stimulating free associations, as a part of psychotherapy and play therapy, and by occupational therapists in rehabilitation of spastic patients, the deaf, and the blind.

pal(a)eo- (pā'lē-ō-, pal'ē-ō-) Combining form meaning old, ancient, from Gr. *palaiós,* old ancient.

pal(a)eophrenia (pā-lē-ō-frē'nē-à, pal-ē-) This psychoanalytical term, meaning literally ancient or primitive mentality, was suggested by Oliver J. Osborne to be used instead of schizophrenia to emphasize the regression to a primitive type of thinking which is often seen in schizophrenics. (O'Connor, W.A. *Psychiatry: A Short Treatise*, Williams and Wilkins, Baltimore, 1948)

paleologic (-loj-ik) Archaic or ancient logic; with this term, Arieti refers to the same method of thinking which has been variously designated as pre-Aristotelian, prelogical (Levy-Bruhl) or paralogical (Von Domarus). Paleologic is seen most clearly in schizophrenic thinking disorders. See *pre-logical.*

paleomnesis (pā-lē-om-nē'sis) Memory for the remote past in the life of the subject.

paleopsychic (pā'lē'ō-sī'kik) Pertaining to or possessing primitive mentality.

paleopsychology (-sī-kol'ō-jē) The study of paleopsychic phenomena; it is believed by Freud, Jung, and many others that remote ancestral modes of mental activity reside in the unconscious of modern man.

paleosensation The term of the Dutch school of neurologists (Brouwer, Kappers) for *protopathic* sensations in contradistinction to the epicritic and deep, which they call *gnostic* or new sensations. See *gnostic; protopathic.*

paleosymbol A private symbol, which is highly individualistic, fleeting, flexible and mutable and which is evolved and maintained without regard for socialization or interpersonal relationships. Paleosymbols are seen as a form of *paleologic* (q.v.) and are characteristic of immediately prehuman races although they probably exist also in apes in rudimentary form.

pali- (pal'ē-) Combining form meaning morbid or obsessive repetition or reiteration, from Gr. *pálin*, backward, again.

paligraphia (graf'ē-à) The morbid or obsessive repetition of something (letters, words, phrases, etc.) in writing.

palilalia (-lā-lē-à) A rare speech disorder in which a phrase is repeated with increasing rapidity. The most common causes of palilalia are encephalitis or other conditions producing Parkinsonism and pseudo-bulbar palsy due to vascular lesions.

palilexia (-lek'sē-à) The morbid rereading of words or phrases.

palilogia (-lō'jē-à) Morbid or obsessive repetition of something spoken.

palingraphia (pā-lin-graf'ē-à) Mirror-writing.

palinlexia (pā-lin-leks'ē-à) Backward reading.

palinopia, palinopsia (pal-in-op'ē-à, -op'sē-à) A rare visual phenomenon consisting of visual perseveration in time, i.e. a prolonged after-image. Palinopia is suggestive of an occipital lobe lesion. See *polyopia.*

paliopsy (pal'ē-àp-sē) Visual perserveration; brief persistence in vision of objects no longer in the visual field, usually indicative of occipital lobe pathology.

paliphrasia (pā-li-frā-zē-à) The morbid repetition of phrases in speaking.

pallesthesia (pal-es-thē'zē-à) The vibratory sensation felt when the foot of a vibrating tuning-fork is placed over subcutaneous bony surfaces. Also known as *palmesthesia.*

pallidum (pà-lē-doom) See *basal ganglia.*

palmesthesia (pal-mes-thē'zē-à) *Pallesthesia* (q.v.).

palsy Paralysis.

palsy, cerebral *Little's disease* (q.v.).

palsy, progressive bulbar See *sclerosis, amyotrophic lateral.*

palsy, pseudobulbar (sū-dō-bul'bēr) See *sclerosis, amyotrophic lateral.*

palsy, shaking *Paralysis agitans* (q.v.); Parkinson's disease.

pamphobia (pam-fō'bē-à) *Obs.* Panophobia; fear of everything.

pamplegia, panplegia (pam, pan-plē'jē-à) *Obs.* Generalized paralysis (not the clinical entity, 'general paralysis').

pan-, pam (pan-, pam-) Combining form meaning all, total, from Gr. *păn*, neut. sing. of *pās, pantós*, all, whole.

pan-anxiety See *schizophrenia, pseudoneurotic.*

panchreston The state or quality of being adaptable to any and all uses; applied sometimes to the terminology of psychiatry and psychology, where words are used to explain everything, and in such a variety of ways as finally to become a meaningless jargon.

Pandy's reaction See *test, Pandy.*

panels, personality The concept of a four-panel Japanese screen, across which is painted a complete picture, moved Draper to introduce into the vocabulary of constitutional medicine the term panels of personality for the four main divisions of the human individuality representing themselves for systematic investigation.

These panels relate to the anatomical, physiological, psychological, and immunological elements of a person, each of which 'may be considered to occupy one panel of the great screen across which Man's personality is drawn.' (Draper, G. *Human Constitution*, Saunders, Philadelphia and London, 1924)

panglossia (pan-glos'ē-à) Garrulity, especially psychotic.

panic An attack of overwhelming anxiety. See *anxiety.* Some writers restrict the term to psychotic episodes characterized by unrealistically based and autistically determined anxiety of overwhelming proportions, such as is seen in homosexual panic (see *homosexual panic*) and in acute aggresion panic. The latter term refers to cases where homosexual content is lacking and, instead, a picture of undue malignant influence, physical violence, or impending death is seen.

panic, homosexual See *homosexual panic.*

panic, primordial Reactions of fright and anger combined with unfocused, disorganized motor responses akin to the infantile startle reaction; such reactions are seen in many schizophrenic children. Primordial panic is also termed *elemental anxiety* and is believed to be based on primary defects in the ego which result in an impairment in personal identity, self-awareness, and differentiation of the self from the non-self.

panmixia (pan-mik'sē-à) In genetic population studies this term indicates equal and unrestricted mating conditions of organisms with different racial characteristics in a mixed population group. See *homogamy.*

pan-neurosis (-nū-rō'sis) See *schizophrenia, pseudoneurotic.*

panphobia, panophobia, pantophobia (pan-fō'bē-à, pan-ō-, pan-tō-) Fear of everything.

pansexualism The doctrine that all human behavior stems from sex. There is no school of psychiatric medicine today whose leaders profess such a doctrine. Freud has frankly disavowed any connection between pansexualism and psychoanalysis.

pantophobia (pan-ta-fō'bē-à) *Obs.* Absolute fearlessness.

Papez's circle See *emotion, Papez's theory of.*

papilledema (pap-i-le-dē'mà) Papilledema or choked disk is a condition in which the optic nerve is literally choked at the optic foramen by increased intracranial, and especially intraventricular, pressure, leading to an increase in the intra-ocular tension. The condition is usually bilateral, although there may be differences in the degree of choking on the two sides. Ophthalmoscopically, the disk is raised, at times to five or six or more diopters; the margins of the disk are blurred; the veins are tortuous and full, the arteries thin; and hemorrhages may occur. Papilledema is most commonly caused by tumor of the brain. Other conditions producing choked disk include fracture of the skull, hydrocephalus, abscess of the brain, subarachnoid hemorrhage, sinus thrombosis, meningitis, encephalitis, and possibly multiple sclerosis and anemia.

para-, par- (par′ă) Prefix meaning beside, past, aside, beyond, i.e. perverted, amiss, wrong, faulty, irregular, disordered, abnormal, *mis-*, from Gr. *pará*, from (the side), beside, near, beyond, against.

parabulia (par-a-bū′lē-ă) Perversion of volition or will as when an impulse is partly or completely checked and is then replaced by another impulse. A patient had the impulse to strike his physician; he advanced toward the physician for that purpose, but suddenly stopped 'to regulate the universal voices.' Parabulia usually occurs as a manifestation of ambivalence of the will in schízophrenic disorders. See *will, disturbances of.*

paracenesthesia (-sen-es-thē′zē-ă) Any abnormality of the general sense of wellbeing.

parachromatopsia, parachromopsia (-kroma-top′sē-ă, -kro-mop′sē-ă) Partial color blindness, such as red-green color blindness.

paracope (par-ak′ō-pē) An obsolete term, by which Hippocrates denoted delirium accompanying fever; later synonymous with *insanity*.

paracousia, paracusia Any abnormality of hearing other than simple deafness; in psychiatric writings the term is often used to refer specifically to auditory illusions. *Paracousia loci* is impaired ability to determine the direction from which a sound proceeds. *Paracousia willisiana* is the ability, demonstrated by some partially deaf persons, to hear better in the presence of loud noise.

paracusis imaginaria (pà-rȧkōō′sēs ē-mȧgē-nä′rē-ă) Auditory hallucination.

paradementia (pa-ra-de-men′shē-ă) Brugias' term for dementia praecox (schizophrenia).

paradox, neurotic (nū-rot′ik) This term indicates that neurotic behavior often persists indefinitely despite the fact that it is

seriously self-defeating and even inimical to the individual. Freud attempted to explain this paradox by assuming that it was due to the retention of an over-severe superego, evolved from too zealous childhood training. This explanation, however, is contrary to all learning theory, which says that learning tends to undergo extinction unless periodically reinforced. It is more likely that the paradox results from infantile ego resistance to socializing forces, so that the basic values and attitudes of society are faultily assimilated into the personality. It may also be that the neurotic behavior represents a means to an end that is unconsciously determined, the desire for which overcomes the wish to conform.

paradoxia sexualis (pȧ-rȧ-dôk′sē-ȧ seksoo-ä′lēs) Sexual impulses contrary to the physiological age, whether in the old, or children. For example, masturbation in children, prior to the development of physiological sexuality, is a sexual paradox. This is what Krafft-Ebing meant in speaking of the 'sexual instinct manifesting itself independently of physiological processes.' (Krafft-Ebing, R.v. *Psychopathia Sexualis*, Login, New York, 1908)

paraerotism Perversion. See *metaerotism.*

paraflocculi (pȧ-rȧ-flō-kōō-lē) See *cerebellum.*

parageusia (par-ȧ-gū′sē-ȧ) Perverted sense of taste.

paragnomen (par-ag-nō′men) An unexpected action, not understandable for the subject's environment or by reason of his usual conduct or behavior, which at the moment it is performed is considered to be consciously performed and adequate to the situation but which later appears inexplicable even to the subject. Paragnomens are seen frequently in schizophrenic patients.

paragrammatism (pȧ-rȧ-gram′ȧ-tiz′m) Any speech disturbance characterized by faulty grammatical or syntactical relationships; the disturbance may be a part of the organic asphasias, or it may be found in schizophrenic speech. 'At times grammar fails them (*paragrammatism*). Many words are used incorrectly, thus, e.g. frequently the word "murder" that designates all the tortures that the patients suffer.' (Bleuler, E. *Textbook of Psychiatry*, Macmillan, New York, 1930)

paragraphia (-graf'ē-à) Perverted writing. Ordinarily, however, it does not refer to alterations in the handwriting itself, such as are manifested by tremors, rigid writing, flourishes and abnormalities in the size of the script; rather, it has to do with such errors as the omission and transposition of letters or words, or the substitution of a wrong letter or word. Errors of this kind are usually due to cerebral injury, although they may also occur in schizophrenic disorders. See *neologism*.

parahypnosis (-hip-nō'sis) Abnormal sleep as in hypnotism or somnambulism.

parakinesia (-ki-nē'sē-à) Bizarre and clumsily executed movement.

paralalia (-lā'lē-à) Any speech defect, especially the habitual substitution of one letter for another.

paralalia literalis (pà-rà-là'lē-à lē-te-rä'-lēs) Perversion in uttering certain sounds; usually combined with stammering.

paraleresis (par-à-lē-rē'sis) *Obs.* Mild delirium.

paralexia (-lek'sē-à) Misreading of printed or written words, other meaningless words being substituted for them. See *reading, disabilities of.*

paralipophobia (-lī-pō-fō'bē-à) Fear of neglecting duty.

paralogia (-lo'jē-à) Perverted logic or reasoning in speaking. 'Evasion or *paralogia* consists in this, that the idea which is next in the chain of thought is suppressed and replaced by another which is related to it.' (Kraepelin, E. *Dementia Praecox and Paraphrenia*, tr. by Barclay, R.M., Livingstone, Edinburgh, 1919)

paralogia, derailment or displacement See *acataphasia*.

paralogia, metaphoric (met-à-for'ik) See *by-idea*.

paralogia, thematic (thē-mat'ik) Perverted reasoning in relation chiefly to one theme or subject, upon which the mind dwells insistently. See *monomania*.

paralysis (pà-ral'i-sis) Loss of power of voluntary movement in a muscle due to injury or disease of its nerve supply.

paralysis, acute ascending *Landry's paralysis* (q.v.).

paralysis agitans (a'gi-tans) Parkinson's disease; a chronic, progressive disease of the central nervous system, occurring more frequently in males than in females, most often between the ages of 50 and 70 years. Onset is usually insidious, with gradual, slow progression; the characteristic symptoms are cogwheel rigidity and spontaneous tremor, with immobile and mask-like facies, loss of associated movements of the arms, dysarthritic speech, propulsive gait, etc. Tremors are often of the pill-rolling type, involving the thumb, index finger, or wrist, and are often accompanied by a to-and-fro tremor of the head.

Idiopathic or true Parkinson's disease is to be differentiated from parkinsonism (parkinsonian syndrome) which may be a side-effect of tranquilizers; carbon monoxide, manganese, nitrous oxide, or carbon disulphite poisoning; brain tumor; brain injury; neurosyphilis; and encephalitis. Idiopathic Parkinson's disease (including the arteriosclerotic cases) is characterized by degeneration of cells and tracts of the striate bodies and substantia nigra, perhaps secondary to disturbed metabolism of brain amines. In this disorder, both dopamine and serotonin (or their derivatives) are decreased in brain and in urine, and this decrease may be related to a relative deficiency in the enzyme dopa-decarboxylase.

Treatment is symptomatic, with belladonna derivatives, synthetic compounds with atropine-like action, and/or antihistamines; some patients benefit from stereotactic operations which destroy portions of the globus pallidus or the ventrolateral nucleus of the thalamus.

paralysis, catatonic cerebral A term applied to rare cases of catatonic excitement or delirium which terminate abruptly in death, often following the development of fever of unknown origin. The syndrome is also known as *Stauder's lethal catatonia*, and is generally regarded as a schizophrenic disorder; probably less than 1% of schizophrenic patients follow such a course.

paralysis, congenital spastic *Little's disease* (q.v.).

paralysis, divers Same as *disease, caisson* (q.v.).

paralysis, familial periodic A hereditary disorder consisting of abrupt, periodic attacks of flaccid paralysis which may last anywhere from hours to three or four days. The illness, which appears to be based on an abnormal demand for potassium, usually begins during adolescence. Prodromata such as hunger, thirst, or sweating are common, and the attacks themselves tend to occur in the early morning. The paralysis is at its height an hour after onset; the proximal limb is affected more than the distal portion and during the attack deep reflexes are abolished, but there is no loss of consciousness. Attacks may occur every few days, or only once every few years. They tend to be precipitated by exposure to the cold, excess sugar intake, fasting, or overexertion. Potassium chloride is used in the treatment of individual attacks and prophylactically when attacks occur frequently.

paralysis, hysterical A paralysis of psychogenic etiology, in contradistinction to a paralysis of organic origin. It is 'much more dissociated and systematized' than an organic paralysis. The aphasia will be total, the paralysis of a limb complete. Or one segment of a limb may be completely paralyzed, while other portions remain entirely normal. Or on the same side of the body, one limb may be paralyzed and not the other, or both limbs may be involved but not the remainder of that side. Further, the symptoms are produced 'in the severest degree.' The organic paralyses are never so complete as the hysterical paralyses. The hysterically paralyzed limb will be absolutely inert; the hysterical aphasic is completely mute. Thus, hysterical paralysis shows both 'an exact delimitation and an excessive intensity.' These two characteristics of hysterical paralysis indicate that the hysterical lesion is entirely independent of the anatomy of the nervous system. 'Hysteria behaves in its paralyses and other manifestations as if anatomy were nonexistent, or as if it had no knowledge of it.' (Freud, S. *Some Points in a Comparative Study of Organic and Hysterical Paralysis* in *Collected Papers*, vol. 2, The International Psycho-analytical Press, London, 1924)

paralysis, immobilization 'In wound-cases where there had been immobilization of a limb in splints for some time, the immobilization sometimes persisted long after the splints were removed—the so-called "immobilization-paralysis." The patient had "failed to realize when he had become well." The hysterical purpose was the same as in the unwounded cases of functional paralysis. The same phenomenon is encountered in the "traumatic," of peace time.' (Henderson, D.K. and Gillespie, R.D. *A Text-Book of Psychiatry*, 4th ed., Oxford University Press, London, 1936)

paralysis, infantile *Poliomyelitis* (q.v.).

paralysis, Landry's See *Landry's paralysis.*

paralysis, periodic See *paralysis, familial periodic.*

paralysis, progressive *Obsnt.* General paralysis.

paralysis, psychogenic (si-kō-jen'ik) Paralyses may occur as a result of unconscious conflicts without any discoverable organic pathology and represent conversion phenomena. They are often called *hysterical paralyses*. Neither the paralysis nor the anesthesia fits into a peripheral or segmental type of lesion. There is no loss of tone or of deep reflexes, little or no atrophy, few or no trophic disturbances, and no impairment of electrical reactions.

paralysis, saturnine pseudo-general Chronic encephalopathy due to *lead poisoning* (q.v.).

paralysis, sleep A benign neurological phenomenon, most probably due to some temporary dysfunction of the reticular activating system, consisting of brief episodes of inability to move and/or speak when awakening or, less commonly, when falling asleep. There is no accompanying disturbance of consciousness, and the subject has complete recall for the episode. The incidence of the phenomenon is highest in younger age groups (children and young adults), and much higher in males (80%) than in females. The terms by which the phenomenon has been known are: nocturnal hemiplegia, nocturnal paralysis, sleep numbness, delayed psychomotor awakening, cataplexy of awakening, and postdormital chalastic fits.

parameter (par-am'e-tēr) In psychoanalytic therapy, the operative factor in any technical device that departs from *classical technique* (i.e. one in which interpretation is the exclusive or prevailing tool). The term pseudoparameter is used to refer to technical devices which though not strictly interpretations, nonetheless have the same dynamic effect, such as telling the right joke at the right moment or repeating to the patient the words he has just said.

paramimia (par-à-mim'ē-à) Disturbance of sense for gestures or mimetic movements leading to incongruities between feeling and means of expression.

paramimism A movement or gesture that has a meaning for the patient different from the ordinarily accepted meaning.

paramnesia (par-am-nē'zē-à) Disturbance of memory in which real facts and phantasies are confused. Thus, a patient was unable to tell whether he had dreamed or actually experienced that of which he was giving an account. Paramnesia is a common phenomenon in dreams, and in the schizophrenias where it often appears as false recognition such as déjà fait, déjà vu, etc. Such paramnesiae may also occur in the normal person.

paramyotonia congenita A rare muscle disorder transmitted by a single autosomal dominant gene with nearly complete penetrance, characterized by two sets of symptoms: (1) myotonic cramps of the facial musculature and hands precipitated by cold and myotonia of the lingual muscles in response to percussion, and (2) attacks of weakness and flaccidity in the proximal muscles lasting for minutes or up to 24 hours.

paranee (par-à-nē') A term introduced by Dr. Richard M. Brickner to designate the 'victim' of a paranoid patient. (*American Journal of Orthopsychiatry*, *13*, 405, 1943)

paranoia, paranoea (par-à-noi'à, -nē'à) Although paranoia in the sense of mental derangement, delirium, occurs in Aeschylus (Theb. 756), Euripides, Orestes, 822, Plato, Laws 928E and elsewhere, i.e. the term is even pre-Hippocratic, credit is generally given to Vogel for having introduced or reintroduced the term in medicine in 1764.

Following this, the term was inconsistently applied to a great number of diverse conditions until 1883, when E.C. Spitzka, a New York psychiatrist, defined paranoia as it is known at the present time. Kahlbaum was among the first to use the term in the way in which it is generally used today, to refer to gradually developing, systematized delusional states, without hallucinations but with preservation of intelligence, and with emotional responses and behavior that remain congruous with and appropriate to the persecutory or grandiose delusions.

In DSM-II, *paranoid states* (297) include: 297.0—*Paranoia,* distinguished by an intricate, complex, slowly developing delusional system, frequently of a grandiose nature, and typically isolated from the rest of the personality and intellect; 297.1—*Involutional paranoid state* or *involutional paraphrenia,* formerly classified as the paranoid form of involutional melancholia and characterized by delusion formation with onset in the involutional period; and 297.9—*Other paranoid state.*

Even though the official nomenclature thus maintains the differentiation between paranoia and paranoid schizophrenia, there is—at least at the clinical level—an increasing tendency to include all or most such psychoses under the schizophrenic label. Paranoid developments occur also in association with other disorders, and particularly in the organic brain disorders, and are then classified under those disorders.

Several types of paranoia have been described on the basis of the type of delusion that predominates: litigious, depressed, persecutory, grandiose, erotic or erotomaniacal, and infidelity.

On the basis of his analysis of the Schreber case, Freud concluded that the core of the conflict in paranoia (at least in males) is a homosexual wish-phantasy of loving a man. The forms of paranoia represent the contradictions of the proposition: I, a man, love him, a man. This proposition is contradicted (a) in the subject, by delusions of jealousy: 'It is not I who love the man, it is she'; (b) in the predicate, by delusions of persecution: 'I do not love him, I hate him, and because of this he hates me and persecutes me'; (c) in the object, by erotomania: 'I do not love him, I love her, because she loves me'; and (d) by complete denial in megalomania: 'I do not love anyone else at all, but only myself.'

paranoia, abortive An inexact term that generally refers to mild or spontaneously remitting paranoid episodes, often with many affective components.

paranoia, acquired Krafft-Ebing described two principal forms of paranoia: (1) *original paranoia*, developing before or at puberty—always hereditary; (2) *acquired paranoia*, developing late in life, particularly at the involutional period.

paranoia, alcoholic (al-kō-hol'ik) An inexact term, used by some writers as equivalent to chronic alcoholic hallucinosis (see *hallucinosis, alcoholic*), by others to refer to infidelity delusions that develop in chronic alcoholics. Although alcoholics can develop any of the forms of *paranoia* (q.v.), they seem especially prone to jealousy delusions. See *alcoholic paranoid state.*

paranoia, ambitious *Obs.* Paranoia with delusions of omnipotence.

paranoia, amorous *Obs.* By some, used to refer to the jealous or infidelity form of paranoia; by others, used to refer to the erotomaniacal form. 'The condition of acute excitement with many hallucinations, general restlessness and abnormal motor activity constitutes, when coloured by religious ideas, what used to be called religious mania. The disorder where the patient shows an emotional excitement which is bound up with some sentiment, and is continually agitating for some wild

social scheme, is similar to the manic phase of manic-depressive psychosis. These two varieties constitute the so-called "eccentric paranoia," while the paranoid jealous reaction of the erotic patient is the so-called "amorous paranoia."' (Craig, M. and Beaton, T. *Psychological Medicine*, 4th ed., Churchill, London, 1926) The patient with amorous paranoia develops delusions of marital infidelity in relation to his spouse. According to Freud's analysis of the Schreber case, such delusions are based on a denial of unconscious homosexuality: 'It is not I who love the man, it is she.'

paranoia completa (pà-rà-noi'à kôm-plā'-tà) (Mod.L. 'complete, perfect, paranoia') A term coined by Magnan (*délire chronique à évolution systématique*) equivalent to present conceptions of the paranoid form of schizophrenia.

paranoia dissociativa (pà-rà-noi'à dēs-sô-kē-à-tē'và) (Mod.L. 'dissociative paranoia') An expression coined by Ziehen to designate states of acute confusion (amentia) with paranoid elements.

paranoia, eccentric (par-à-noi'à) See *paranoia, amorous.*

paranoia, idiopathic (par-à-noi'à id-i-ō-path'ik) *Obs.* Sandler thus denotes syndromes of paranoia that begin in early childhood.

paranoia, intermediate *Obs.* Paranoia in which there are no delusions, but a tendency to quibbling or quarreling. See *paranoia, querulous.*

paranoia, involutional By this term Kleist refers to a paranoid syndrome not uncommonly set free during the involutional period. See *psychosis, involutional.*

paranoia, latent See *paranoia, rudimentary.*

paranoia, litigious (li-ti'jus) Same as *paranoia querulans* (q.v.).

paranoia, mystic Pike's term for psychosis of association. See *association, psychosis of.*

paranoia, negative Paranoia in which the false beliefs of the person have to do with matters *favorable* to him rather than with those *unfavorable.* The delusionary material is characterized by praise, protection, and defense instead of persecution, accusation, destruction, and the like.

paranoia, original See *paranoia, acquired.*

paranoia originaria (på-rå-noi′å ô-rē-gē-nä′rē-å) (L. 'original paranoia') Sanders coined this rarely used expression to denote a paranoid state originating in childhood.

paranoia, periodic (par-å-noi′å) See *paranoia, abortive.*

paranoia persecutoria (på-rå-noi′å per-se-koo-tō′re-å) (L. 'persecutory paranoia') *Obs.* Paranoia in which the delusions of persecution are especially prominent.

paranoia querulans (kwe′roo-låns) A form of paranoia characterized by more or less incessant quarrelsomeness due to alleged persecution. Often starting from a factual injustice, the patient weaves a delusional trend about it and then seeks redress at the hands of the law.

paranoia, reformatory (par-å-noi′å) (that aims at reforms) 'That host of unbalanced dreamers who are frequently known as "cranks," and who may be further classified on the basis of the content of their delusional system into *inventive, reformatory, religious* and *erotic* varieties. These patients have made some wonderful invention, are destined to carry on great reforms, are the viceregent of God, or believe themselves beloved by some royal person.' (White, W.A. *Outlines of Psychiatry,* 12th ed., Nervous & Mental Disease Publishing Company, Washington, D.C., 1929)

paranoia religiosa (på-rå-moi′å re-lē-gē-ō′zå) (L. 'Religious paranoia') *Obs.* Paranoia characterized by religious delusions.

paranoia, rudimentary (par-å-noi′å) *Latent paranoia.* 'What distinguished the delusions of these patients from those of pronounced paranoia was their *vagueness* and the *absence of systematic working up.* Their fears and hopes were of a more indefinite kind, were brought forward as indications and conjectures, or they consisted in a strong personal valuation of actual events, which was not too far removed from the one-sidedness of normal individuals. As far as could be known, no internal connection of the individual component parts of the delusion with a paranoiac view of life had taken place. . . . At present the assumption appears to me to be well founded, that cases of undeveloped, "rudimentary" paranoia would not only fit in with our view of the character of the disease, but also come actually under observation.' (Kraepelin, E. *Manic-Depressive Insanity and Paranoia,* tr. by Barclay, R.M., Livingstone, Edinburgh, 1921). The expression was coined by Morselli.

paranoia, secondary An older expression, often synonymous with *dementia, secondary* (q.v.).

paranoia senilis (på-rå-noi′å se-nē′lēs) (L. 'senile paranoia') A paranoid syndrome appearing during the senile period; late *paraphrenia* (290.0). 'The forms showing a clear sensorium with delusional formation and eventually hallucinations are designated as *senile paranoia* (i.e. paranoid forms of dementia senilis); they are not frequent. Such people think they are spied on by neighbors, teased, robbed especially by those living in the same house; everywhere they find reference to themselves, and confirmation of their ideas in voices, etc.' (Bleuler, E. *Textbook of Psychiatry,* tr. by Brill, A.A., Macmillan, New York, 1930)

paranoia somatica Paranoia with pronounced hypochondriacal trends, often progressing to somatic delusions.

paranoia, true (par-å-noi′å) Same as *paranoia, idiopathic.*

paranoid, paranoidal (par′å-noid, -noi′dal) Relating to or resembling paranoia. Psychiatrists today speak of *paranoid states* (297.x), usually referring to clinical states that occupy a position between paranoia and the paranoid form of schizophrenia. In the eighth edition of his textbook Kraepelin uses the term *paraphrenia* to designate this group. He divided the group into four parts: (a) *paraphrenia systematica,* the equivalent perhaps of what today is known as paranoia; (b) *paraphrenia expansiva,* seen only in women and characterized by ideas of grandeur with exaltation; (c) *paraphrenia confabulans,* characterized by delusions of persecution and grandeur based upon falsification of memory; (d) *paraphrenia phantastica,* with auditory hallucinations, unsystematized delusions, and phantastic accounts of adventures.

paranoid dementia gravis (dē-men′shi-à grà′vis) See *dementia paranoides gravis.*

paranoid dementia mitis (mī′tis) See *dementia paranoides gravis.*

paranoid personality (301.0) In this type of personality disorder, the affected person is hypersensitive, rigid, and unwarrantedly suspicious, jealous and envious. He often has an exaggerated sense of self-importance, must always be right and/or prove others to be in the wrong, and has a tendency to blame others and to ascribe evil motives to them.

Often, the opposite-sex parent of such patients is domineering, overprotective, and ambivalent, while the same-sex parent is submissive, passive, and relatively unavailable as a suitable model or object for identification. In other cases, the same-sex parent has instilled feelings of inadequacy by intimidation, hostility, and the imposition of rigid controls. As a result of such rearing, the child fails to develop a stable self-image, gender role, or clear ego boundaries. He then may find it necessary to surrender to the omnipotent parent in a passive, more or less homosexual way; or he may resist and rebel defensively, but the necessary hypervigilance in his defensive operations may progress to ideas of reference.

paranoid-schizoid position See *position, paranoid-schizoid.*

paranoid schizophrenia See *schizophrenia, paranoid.*

paranoid state (297.9) Like *paranoia* (q.v.) the paranoid state is characterized by persistent persecutory or grandiose delusions, affect in harmony with the delusional ideas, and preservation of intellectual functions but, ordinarily, an absence of hallucinations. This condition is differentiated from paranoia by its lack of

extreme systematization, and from schizophrenia by its lack of fragmentation of associations and the absence of bizarre incongruities.

paranormal (par-à-nor′mal) Alongside or beyond the normal, as in paranormal cognition (telepathy). See *perception, extrasensory; telepathy.*

paranosic (-nō′sik) Relating to the primary advantage derived from an illness or paranosis.

parapathic proviso See *proviso, parapathic.*

parapathy (pà-rap′à-thē) Stekel's term for neurosis; he objects to the word neurosis because connotatively it indicates a functional nervous disorder. Parapathy, on the other hand, indicates that psychiatrists deal with emotions, not with nerves.

paraphasia (par-à-fā′zē-à) Perverted speech; jargon; most commonly used to refer to a form of expressive asphasia in which the patient, although he hears and comprehends words, is unable to speak correctly—one word is substituted for another—and sentences become so jumbled as to be unintelligible. Paraphasia occurs in many organic brain disorders, but most characteristically in bromide delirium, Pick's disease, and delirium tremens.

paraphemia (-fē′mē-à) *Rare.* Distorted speech such as neurotic lisping.

paraphia (par-af′ē-à) Perverted sense of touch. Impairment of tactile sensibility.

paraphilia Sexual *perversion* (q.v.).

paraphora (par-af′ō-rà) *Obs.* A mild state of mental disorder.

paraphrasia (par-à-frā′zē-à) Perverted sense or faculty of constructing a phrase; a speech disorder of a less severe nature than aphrasia from which it differs in degree, but not in kind. The difficulties of *aphrasia* (q.v.) and, consequently, of paraphrasia are of mental origin and are not due to cerebral injury as in aphasia. The phenomenon is especially common in the schizophrenias. Thus, a patient, wishing to refer to a certain person, says 'Saturday' instead; it was on a Saturday that a particularly intense emotional reaction took place between the patient and the person in question.

'We shall have to keep apart two chief forms of paraphrasic disorders; firstly, *derailments in finding words*, secondly, *disorders in connected speech.*' (Kraepelin, E. *Dementia Praecox and Paraphrenia*, tr. by Barclay, R.M., Livingstone, Edinburgh, 1919)

paraphrasia, thematic (thē-mat′ik) This expression was used by Arndt to denote incoherent speech 'wandering' from the theme or subject.

paraphrasia vesana (pȧ-rȧ-frȧ′zē-ȧ vä-sä′nȧ) (L. 'insane paraphrasia') '. . . if the formation of ideas and of thought is disturbed in its whole extent, so that it is only with difficulty that a single proper judgment can be expressed, and if new words are coined to express the imperfect and strange thoughts, such neologisms being but maimed fragments of regular words, veritably heaps of syllables, then we have *paraphrasia vesana,* an effect of profound psychic decadence.' (Bianchi, L. *A Text-Book of Psychiatry*, tr. by Mac-Donald, J.H., Bailliere, Tindall & Cox, London, 1906)

paraphrenesis (par-ȧ-fre-nē′sis) *Obs.* Delirium.

paraphrenia (par-ȧ-frē′nē-ȧ) Kraepelin uses the term in a special sense; see *paranoid.* Freud uses the expression to refer to dementia praecox or schizophrenia.

In the early part of the 19th century Guislain used this term synonymously with that of the clinical syndrome then known as *folly* (q.v.).

The most common usage of the term today is to denote a disorder characterized by phantastic, absurd, paralogical delusions without deterioration, dementia, or loss of contact with reality except in the area of the delusional system. In paranoid schizophrenia, on the other hand, there is deterioration and splitting off of many of the psychic functions, while in paranoia the delusions are so logical, at least on the surface, as to appear to be little more than an extension of the premorbid personality.

Late paraphrenia (290.0) is the term applied to that relatively distinct group of older (seventh and eighth decades) patients with predominantly paranoid symptoms of a highly systematized kind, typically revolving about the delusion that neighbors are trying to kill the patient to get his money, or about the erotic delusion that someone is in love with or is about to marry the patient. In such cases, dementia is rare, even after some years. Most late paraphrenics are of the female sex; premorbid personality is typically schizoid or paranoid, and many such patients have severe defects of hearing or, less commonly, of vision.

paraphrenia confabulans (pȧ-rȧ-fre′nē-ȧ kôn-fä′boo-lȧns) See *paranoid.*

paraphrenia expansiva (eks-pȧn-sē′vȧ) See *paranoid.*

paraphrenia, involutional (par-ȧ-frē′nē-ȧ) *Involutional paranoid state* (297.1). It is generally recognized that there are two principal psychiatric syndromes associated with the period of involution: one closely resembles manic-depressive psychosis; the other, schizophrenia. Lerko calls the latter *involutional paraphrenia.*

paraphrenia phantastica (pȧ-rȧ-frē′nē-ȧ fȧn-tȧs′tē-kȧ) See *paranoid.*

paraphrenia, pre-senile (par-ȧ-frē′nē-ȧ) Among the many psychiatric syndromes having their onset after the involutional and before the senile phase of life, there is a schizophrenic form which Albrecht calls pre-senile paraphrenia (in DSM-II, 209.1).

paraphrenia systematica (pȧ-rȧ-frē-nē-ȧ sēs-tȧ-mȧ′tē-kȧ) See *paranoid.*

paraphrenitis (par-ȧ-frē-nī′tis) *Obs.* Mental derangement in general.

paraphrosyne (pȧ-rȧ-fros′i-nē) *Obs.* 'It is a transitory insanity without a fever. A *delirium.* A symptomatic madness.' (Motherby, G. *A New Medical Dictionary*, 5th ed., for J. Johnson, St. Paul's Church-Yard, etc., London, 1801)

parapithymia (par-ep-i-thim′ē-ȧ, -thī′mē-ȧ) Perverted desire or craving.

paraplegia (par-à-plē'jē-à) Paralysis of the musculature of the lower extremities and of the torso, the latter to a lesser extent; when the upper extremities are paralyzed, the condition is called *superior paraplegia.*

paraplegia, ataxic (a-tak'sik) Unsteadiness of station and gait in association with paraplegia.

paraplegia, hereditary spastic (spas'tik) A familial disorder, usually affecting several siblings and occurring more frequently in males, which begins between the ages of 3 and 15 years with progressive destruction of the pyramidal tracts of the spinal cord, beginning in the lower limbs. To a lesser degree, there is also destruction of the posterior columns and of the cells of the precentral cortex. The disease is slowly progressive with a fatal termination after many years. Mentality is usually normal.

parapraxis (par-à-prak'sis) Misaction. Freud applies this term to symptomatic acts such as slips of the tongue, mislaying of objects, etc.

parapsychology (-sī-kol'-jē) The branch of psychology that deals with paranormal behavior and events such as telepathy, precognition, and clairvoyance, which are not explicable by present-day 'natural' laws. See *perception, extra-sensory.*

parapsychosis (-sī-kō'sis) See *apsychosis.*

para-reaction Reactions 'characterized by essentially formally correct, but short-circuited, reasoning, amounting to delusion formation. The tenacity of the false beliefs, and their growth and systematization are the earmarks of the insatiable need which is the affective investment of the complex material at work.' (Muncie, W. *psychobiology and Psychiatry,* Mosby, St. Louis, 1939) It includes such reactions as paranoia and paranoid states.

parasexuality Perverted sexuality, comprising such practices as pederasty, voyeurism, pedophilia, sodomy, sadism, masochism, etc.
'The various kinds of parasexuality are usually connected with a *premature appearance of the sex impulse* and hence

can become known very early, at the age of three or four.' (Bleuler, E. *Textbook of Psychiatry,* tr. by Brill, A.A., Macmillan, New York, 1930)

parasitophobia (par-à-sī-tō-fō'bē-à) Fear of parasites.

parasomnia (par-à-som'ni-à) Perverted or disordered sleep; sleep disturbance associated with lesion(s) of the nervous system. The term is used by some as a synonym for unconsciousness due to trauma, by others to refer to coma-vigil. See *mutism, akinetic.*

parastriate lobule (par-à-strī'at lob'ūl) See *lobe, occipital.*

parasympathetic nervous system (par-à-sim-pa-the'tik) See *autonomic nervous system.*

parasympathicotonia (par-à-sim-path-i-kō-tō'nē-à) Originally, in constitutional medicine this term denoted a particular hyperirritability of the whole parasympathetic system; now it has become identical with *vagotonia* since the latter's meaning is stretched to cover the entire parasympathetic system.

parasympatholytic See *mydriasis.*

parataxic See *distortion, parataxic.*

parateresiomania (-tē-rē-sē-ō-mā'nē-à) Morbid impulse to observe; peeping-mania; *scopophilia* (q.v.).

parathymia (-thim'ē-à, -thī'mē-à) Perversion of mood, as when a condition or occasion that should produce a certain mood evokes the opposite of the expected reaction. A patient, having asked for a new suit so that he might enjoy a coming party, was enraged when he received it.
'Parathymias are often indissolubly connected with *alteration of the impulses.*' (Bleuler, E. *Textbook of Psychiatry,* tr. by Brill, A.A., Macmillan, New York, 1930) Parathymia is one of the affect disturbances seen in the schizophrenias.

parathyroidism (-thī'roid-iz'm) Excessive functioning of the parathyroid gland.

paratonia progressiva (pà-rà-tō-nē-à prō-gre-sē-và) Bernstein's term for dementia praecox (schizophrenia).

paratype (par'à-tīp) The sum of all external, or *peristatic*, factors acting upon the phenotypical development of an organism or bringing about the individual manifestation of a genetic character. See *biotype*.

paravariation (par-à-vâr-ē-ā-shun) In genetics, synonym of *modification* (q.v.).

parenchyma, parenchyme (pà-reng'ki-mà, pàr'en-kīm) The specific or characteristic tissue of an organ or gland, as distinct from the connecting tissue or mesenchymal elements which support that gland. Paresis, for example, is also known as parenchymal syphilis because in this form of syphilis the spirochete invades and destroys nerve cells directly; cerebral syphilis, in contrast, is known as mesenchymal syphilis because it consists primarily of invasion of the arteries and arterioles within the meninges covering the brain and only secondarily does the process attack the cerebral tissue itself.

parent-surrogate See *surrogate*.

parental perplexity See *perplexity, parental*.

parents, problem Parents who, because of their own unresolved unconscious conflicts, manifest unhealthy attitudes toward their children, who, in turn, become problem children. The problems of children may in part be merely a reflection of the problems of the parent or parents. The morbid attitudes of parents, such as perfectionistic, overconscientious, overly critical, over-indulgent, over-ambitious, over-anxious, and rejecting attitudes, may play a major role in setting up sequences which later cause symptoms in their child.

parerethisis (par-ē-reth'i-sis) *Obs.* Perverted excitement.

parergasia (par-ēr-gas'ē-à) Perverted functioning; mismatched action. Kraepelin uses the term to refer to a form of parabulia in which the impulse to carry out an act is interrupted before the patient takes the first step toward performing the act. The interruption is occasioned by what he calls cross impulses, that is, by impulses which cross the path of the first impulse and thus check its further

course. The process is also known as *derailment of volition*. For example, a patient, who has the impulse to reach for a cup at the table, suddenly brushes his hair. 'The patient who is to show his tongue, opens his eyes widely instead; he flings the cup away instead of putting it to his mouth.' (Kraepelin, E. *Dementia Praecox and Paraphrenia*, tr. by Barclay, R.M., Livingstone, Edinburgh, 1919)

This is a psychiatric reaction-type characterized usually by deep regression, abandonment of reality, and reconstruction of the conception of the self, and by delusions and hallucinations; in other words, this term, coined by Adolf Meyer, refers to schizophrenia and to schizophrenoid syndromes.

pareosia (par-ē-rō'sē-à) *Rare.* Sexual perversion.

paresis (pà-rē'sis, par'ē-sis) Partial paralysis.

paresis, alcoholic See *pseudo-paresis, alcoholic*.

paresis, general (292.0; 309.0) Also known as *general paralysis of the insane (G.P.I.)*, *dementia paralytica, Bayle's disease;* the most malignant form of (tertiary) neurosyphilis consisting of direct invasion of the parenchyma of the brain producing a combination of both mental and neurologic symptoms. General paresis was first described by Haslan in 1798, and again by Bayle in 1822 and by Esquirol in 1826. The term general paralysis of the insane was first used by Delaye in 1824, and the relationship of the disorder to syphilis was first suggested in 1857 by Esmarch and Jessen. The identification of the spirochete as the cause, rather than merely a predisposing factor, was made possible in 1911, when Noguchi demonstrated the presence of organisms in the brains of paretic subjects.

Pathology includes shrinking and atrophy of brain substance and a thickening of the dura mater. Lymphocytes, plasma cells and giant cells infiltrate the meninges and the brain itself, where the ganglion cells show severe large areas of softening.

Mental symptoms may appear in various forms: as (1) simple dementia, the most common type, with deterioration of intellect, affect and social behavior;

(2) paranoid form, with persecutory delusions; (3) expansive or manic form, with delusions of grandiosity; or (4) depressive form, often with absurd nihilistic delusions. No matter what the form, intellectual functions show increasing impairment, with loss of more and more memory, confabulation, disorientation (especially in the area of time), carelessness in personal appearance and hygiene, irritability and restlessness, alcoholic excesses, and sexual aberrations.

Neurologic symptoms and signs that may appear are: (1) epileptiform attacks, which occur in 50% of cases; (2) Argyll Robertson pupil; (3) tremor, most on voluntary movement, that tends to effect the perioral musculature and also the muscles of the hands and fingers so that writing becomes tremulous, and words and letters are often left out or transposed; (4) vacant, mask-like facies, giving patient a wrinkle-free, youthful appearance; (5) impaired oculomotor activity; (6) optic atrophy; (7) impaired motor function, including ataxia, poor co-ordination, unsteady gait, weakness; (8) slurred speech (dysarthria); (9) hyperactive reflexes (but hyporeflexia if tabes dorsalis co-exists); (10) loss of bladder and bowel control. There are few or no sensory changes, unless tabes co-exists.

Cerebrospinal fluid pressure is elevated, as are cells (usually lymphocytes or monocytes) and globulin. The Lange colloidal gold curve is of the paretic type (first zone reaction), and the Wasserman is usually strongly positive in both blood and spinal fluid.

Penicillin is the cornerstone of treatment, whose degree of success is related to duration and severity of mental and neurological symptoms before treatment is initiated.

paresis, infantile See *neurosyphilis, congenital.*

paresis, juvenile See *neurosyphilis, congenital.*

paresis, Lissauer type (Heinrich Lissauer, German neurologist, 1861-91) An atypical form of general paresis characterized by (1) unusually well-retained intellectual functions and (2) severe focal symptoms, such as apoplectiform attacks, hemiplegia, aphasia, etc.

paresthesia (par-es-thē'zē-à) Perverted sense of touch. Unpleasant sensation, such as tingling, tickling, burning, etc. caused by a tactile stimulus.

paretic (pà-ret'ik, -rē'tik) Relating to or suffering from paresis.

paretic curve See *Lange's colloidal gold reaction.*

Parkinsonism (James Parkinson, English physician, 1775-1824) See *paralysis agitans.*

parole A system of supervision of a patient who is away from the hospital or any of its adjuncts—such as colonies—prior to his legal discharge. While on parole, a patient is considered as still on the books of the hospital, and may, if necessary, be returned to the hospital without the necessity for formal court action.

paroniria (par-ō-nī'rē-à) Morbid dreaming; sleep disturbance. See *ecphronia.*

paroniria ambulans (pà-rô-nē'rē-à àm'-boo-làns) *Obs.* Somnambulism

parorexia (par-ō-rek'si-à) Perverted appetite, dysorexia.

parosmia (par-oz'mē-à) Any disturbance of the sense of smell, whether organic or psychic in origin; the term includes osphresiolagnia, osphresiophilia, olfactory hallucinations, etc.

parosphresis (par-os-frē'sis) *Parosmia* (q.v.).

paroxysmal cerebral dysrhythmia (par-oks'mal ser'e-bral dis-rith'mē-à) *Epilepsy* (q.v.).

Parry-Romberg's syndrome See *hemiatrophy, facial.*

pars pro toto (pàrs' prō tō'tō) (L. 'part for the whole') In psychiatry a special form of psychic displacement. When a part of an object or a person stands for the whole object or person, the process is known as *pars pro toto.* A voice, a gesture, some physical trait, a bit of wearing apparel—each may be substituted for the total person.

part-brain See *third nervous system.*

part-instinct Partial instinct; see *organ-pleasure.*

parthenogenesis (pär-the-nō-jen′e-sis) Virgin reproduction. *Biol.* The uniparental mode of sexual reproduction, in which an egg develops into a new organism without having first been fertilized by a spermatozoon. Although organisms produced in this way have only one parent, they originate sexually, as they undergo a process similar to that of typical maturation. See *reproduction.*

The best known example of parthenogenetic origin is supplied by the honey bee, in which the haploid egg, if unfertilized, develops into a male bee (drone).

parthenophobia Fear of girls.

partial adjustments Sullivan's term for the schizophrenic person's defensive maneuvers that are aimed at reducing environmentally generated stress during the period immediately preceding an acute psychotic episode. These include *compensatory activities* (substitution of simpler activities for more complex ones), *sublimatory activities* (roundabout but socially acceptable ways of achieving some degree of satisfaction in an environment where direct pursuit of a goal generates intolerable anxiety), and defense reactions (complex activities and phantasies which no longer maintain conformity with social standards; e.g. evasions, rationalizations, projection, negativism, hypochondriasis).

partial hospitalization All forms of in-patient treatment other than full, 24-hour programs; includes day hospital, night hospital, weekend hospital. See *psychiatry, community.*

partialism (pär′shal-iz′m) A form of sexual-perversion in which the subject seeks gratification of the sexual impulse from a certain part of the partner's body, as the leg, thigh, buttock, and so on. Partialism must be differentiated from fetishism, in which the partner is eliminated and displaced by an object symbolic of the genitals.

partiality, sexual *Rare.* Fetishism; sexual idolatry.

partitive (pär′ti-tiv) In Burrow's usage behavior-processes whose interaction socially has become independent of and at variance with the primary motivation of man's organism as a whole. Partitive are the processes mediated by the organism's part-functions restricted to the cephalic segment and making contact only with the part-features (symbols) of outer objects. Partitive behavior is a function of the socio-cortical or symbolic segment with the development of language or of an inter-symbolic nexus of communication; this segment tends to supersede and dominate the behavior of man's organism in its phyloautonomic primacy. The term partitive applies to those feeling-reactions which have ceased to issue as a direct expression of the organism as a totality but which have been secondarily displaced into the symbolic segment and now issue in mere images of feeling, or in affects. In accordance with investigations in phylobiology the artificial supremacy of this partitive (affecto-symbolic) mode of behavior over the primary motivation of the organism as a whole constitutes the basis of both individual and social neurosis. Contrasted with total, organismic. Synonyms: affective, intercortical, symbolic. (Burrow, T. *The Biology of Human Conflict,* Macmillan, New York, 1937)

passio hypochondriaca (pà′sē-ō hē-pō-kon-drē-à′kà) *Obs.* Hypochondriasis.

passive-aggressive personality See *personality trait disturbance.*

passive-dependency One of the subtypes of passive-aggressive personality, characterized by helplessness, indecisiveness, and a tendency to cling to others in a parasitic way. See *dependence, oral; dependency; character, oral; character, receptive; personality trait disturbance.*

passive tremor See *tremor.*

passivism (pas′iv-iz′m) A form of sexual perversion in which the subject, usually male, is submissive to the will of the partner in the unnatural sexual practices.

passivity (pa-siv′i-tē) One of the several modalities of adaptation. For example, it is possible for the organism to adapt itself to its environment by going either forward to meet it or backward to escape it. The first procedure would be termed the modality of *activity* in adaptive maneuver, while the latter would be termed the modality of passivity.

In transference neurosis the consequences of inhibition of the modality of activity may find the organism simply abandoning this modality and falling back upon the modality of passivity. In traumatic neurosis, however, the modality of passivity cannot be resorted to when activity is inhibited, since it is impossible for the organism to remain completely passive to the outer world. One can retreat from an inhibiting *person*, but complete retreat from the inhibiting *forces* of the outer world is impossible—short of death.

past-pointing See *pointing.*

pastoral counseling See *counseling, pastoral.*

pathema (pà-thē'mà) *Obs.* Disease; often mental disease.

pathematology (pà-the-ma-tol'ō-jē) A general term for pathology, although it is ordinarily used to denote mental pathology. It has been replaced by the term psychopathology.

pathergasia (path-ēr-gas'ē-à) Adolf Meyer's term for personality maladjustment in association with organic, functional, or structural changes. It is approximately equivalent to Ferenczi's *pathoneurosis.*

pathetism (path'e-tiz'm) *Obs.* Synonym of mesmerism and hypnotism.

pathic¹ (path'ik) Pertaining to or affected by disease or disorder.

pathic² *Obs.* A male passive partner who submits to unnatural sexual practices. See *catomite; passivism.*

patho-, path- (path'o-) Combining form meaning suffering, passion, disease, from Gr. *páthos*, suffering, disease.

pathobiology (path-o-bī-ol'ō-jē) The study of diseased or disordered conditions arising from a biological source.

pathocratia, pathocratoria (-krat'ē-à, krat-ō'rē-à) *Obs.* Self-restraint.

pathoctonus (pà-thok'tō-nus) *Obs.* Killing of passion; self-restraint.

pathocure (path'ō-kūr) The disappearance of a neurosis upon the outbreak of an organic disease. Pathocure is seen in moral masochists whose neurosis is first of all, unconsciously, a suffering that pacifies the superego: the neurosis becomes superfluous as soon as it is replaced by another kind of suffering. Pathocure is the opposite of pathoneurosis, which is a neurosis developing as a result of somatic disease.

A pathocure was observed in a masochist who developed pulmonary tuberculosis. The patient had been a chronic failure in everything he undertook. Under analysis, he began to gain some insight into the masochistic nature of his character defenses. Analysis was interrupted by the tuberculous process, and after the patient's release from the hospital he went back to work. He functioned well on his job and previous symptomatology did not reappear. The disease in this instance was one especially suitable for the character type of the patient—it was chronic, it necessitated definite limitations of activity, and the likelihood of recurrence was ever present. Other pathocures of a more temporary nature had been observed when the organic disease was short-lived and required no permanent or long-term changes in the patient's way of living. In such cases, neurotic symptoms tend to reappear with the disappearance of the organic condition.

pathoformic (path-ō-for'mik) This term refers to the beginning of pathological states; to the symptoms occurring in the transitional stage between health and disease or disorder proper.

pathogenesis, pathogenesy, pathogeny (path-ō-jen'e-sis, -gen'e-sē, pà-thoj'e-nē) The way in which a disease or disorder originated or developed; also called nosogenesis.

pathognomonic, pathognomic (pà-thog-nō-mon'ik, path-og-nom'ik) Typical or thoroughly characteristic of a disease; diagnostic.

pathognomy (pà-thog′nō-mē) The science of recognizing or diagnosing a disease or pathological condition.

pathognostic (pà-thog-nos′tik) Pathognom(on)ic.

pathography (pà-thog′rà-fē) Description of a disease.

pathography, psychoanalytic The use of biography (and especially the biography of a predominantly pathological subject) to expand psychoanalytic knowledge or to demonstrate already existing psychoanalytic knowledge. See *biography in depth.*

patho-hysteria See *hysteria, fixation.*

patholesia (path-ō-le′zē-à) *Rare.* Any impairment or abnormality of the will. See *will, disturbances of.*

pathology (pà-thol′ō-jē) The science of the nature of diseases.

pathomania *Obs.* Mania without delirium; *moral insanity.*

pathomimesis, pathomimicry (path-o-mi-mē′sis, -mim′ik-rē) The mimicry of a disease or disorder; not uncommon in hysteria and hysteroid conditions; *malingering* (q.v.).

pathomorphism (-mor′fiz′m) Abnormal morphology such as extremes of bodily build.

pathoneurosis See *hysteria, fixation.*

pathopatridalgia (-pat-ri-dal′jē-à) *Obs.* Homesickness or nostalgia.

pathophobia *Obs.* Fear of disease; *hypochondriasis.*

pathophrenesis (-fren′e-sis) A nonspecific term for disturbance in the intelligence, regardless of its basis.

pathoplasty (path′ō-plas-tē) Birnbaum thus refers to the *form* of a disease, in contradistinction to the term pathogenesis, which relates to the *cause.*

pathopoeesia, pathopoiesis (path-ō-pē-ē′-à, -poi-ē′sis) *Obs.* Synonymous with pathogenesis.

pathopsychology (-sī-kol′ō-jē) Wilhelm Specht suggested this term for the study of abnormal psychic data from the point of view of general psychology. He proposed to restrict the expression *psychopathology* to the study of the same data from the standpoint of medical psychology.

pathopsychosis (-sī-kō′sis) When an organic process, such as brain tumor, general paresis, etc. gives rise to a psychotic condition, the syndrome is known as a pathopsychosis. See *hysteria, fixation; syndrome, organic.*

pathosis, attitudinal (pa-thō′sis) Thorne's term for a type of personality disorder, seen frequently in compensation and post-accident cases, in which the patient's attitude and self-righteous belief that because he was injured he cannot work or deserves special consideration forms a central core in all his thinking about the effects of his injury. Kamman distinguishes this reaction from traumatic neurosis (which term he would reserve for latent psychoneurosis precipitated by accident) and from compensation neurosis (where, although it is usually unconscious, the basic motive is the desire for cash compensation), mainly because of the conscious volitional element in attitudinal pathosis. This disorder is presumed to fall somewhere between psychopathic personality and traumatic neurosis. See *neurosis, compensation.*

patient-government Patient participation in the ward administration of a psychiatric hospital; one of the ways of implementing the concept of the psychiatric hospital as a therapeutic community.

patient-oriented consultation See *consultant.*

patient, person in the A term expressing the basic key-concept of the psychosomatic medical approach to the patient and emphasizing the patient's personality or character as a factor in the production of physical symptoms and complaints. Whereas the organic, or physical, approach tends to exclude awareness and interest in emotional, personality, and character factors as causative agents to be investigated and treated, the psychosomatic approach, conversely, tends to include these factors and give them central importance. It must be borne in mind, however, that the psychosomatic approach does not in any way exclude the usual physical and organic avenues of investigation.

The investigation into the personality of the patient requires a more inclusive time-consuming history of his psychosexual emotional development, as well as an understanding of his habits and habitual attitudes. A comprehensive grasp of the patient's character development, from infancy through childhood into adult life, is a basic necessity in this approach.

Paton, Stewart American psychiatrist and neurologist; wrote first modern textbook of psychiatry in America (1905); founded first university mental health clinic in America at Princeton University (1910).

patroiophobia (pat-roi-ō-fō′bē-à) Fear of heredity, and especially of hereditary disease.

pattern, expressive See *psychodynamics, adaptational.*

pattern, specific dynamic Franz Alexander's term for the specific nuclear conflict or dynamic configuration which is unique to a particular psychosomatic disorder or organ-neurosis. See *psychosomatic.*

Pavlov's theory of schizophrenia (Ivan Petrovich Pavlov, Russian physiologist, 1849-1936.) A theory propounded by Pavlov, who held that the symptoms of schizophrenia are the result of a state of inhibition of the cerebral cortex.

Pavlovian conditioning See *conditioning.*

pavor diurnus (pà′vôr dē-oor′noos) (L. 'daytime terror') Fear reactions which occur in the young child during the afternoon nap, similar to night terrors but not so frequent as the latter.

pavor nocturnus (nok-toor′noos) A rare type of sleep disturbance which differs from the nightmare '. . . in that the child does not waken fully and has no recollection of the incident. He is usually found sitting up in bed or standing or running

about, greatly agitated and screaming. Often there are hallucinations of strange people or animals in the room. The child is disoriented and does not recognize persons about him. The attacks subside after several minutes, the child dropping off to sleep without remembering the episode. It may be necessary to waken the youngster in order to terminate the attack.' (Bakwin, H., and Bakwin, R.M. *Clinical Management of Behavior Disorders in Children,* Saunders, Philadelphia, 1953) In contrast to this definition, which is generally accepted by American workers, Ernest Jones considers pavor nocturnus to be a wider term than nightmare, which he believes to be a very rare and special condition.

pavor sceleris (ske′lēr-is) Fear of 'bad men'—burglars, kidnappers, etc.

pcpt Abbreviation of *perception.*

Pcs Abbreviation of *pre-conscious.*

PEAQ *Personal Experience and Attitude Questionnaire* (q.v.).

peccatiphobia (pe-kā-ti-fō′bē-à) Fear of sinning. See *scrupulosity.*

pedantry, stool 'Exaggerated promptitude and punctuality' which are overcompensations 'for the infantile anal-erotic tendency to hold back the stool as long as possible.' (Ferenczi, S. *Further Contributions to the Theory and Technique of Psycho-Analysis,* tr. by Suttie, J.I., Leonard and Virginia Woolf and The Institute of Psychanalysis, London, 1926)

pederasty (ped′er-as-tē) The meaning of pederasty varies among different authors, though it is most commonly defined as *coitus per anum* practiced on boys. It is not considered synonymous with *sodomy* (q.v.), though at times confused with it.

pederosis (ped-ē-rō′sis) Pedophilia (302.2). Auguste Forel coined this term in 1905 and defined it as 'sexual passion for children.'

pedication (ped-i-ka′shun) *Pederasty; sodomy.*

pedigree See *method, pedigree.*

pediophobia (ped-ē-ō-fō′bē-à) Fear of dolls.

pedologia (bē-dō-lō′jēa) Infantile or childish speech, which omits all but the principal words and substitutes easily pronounced sounds for more difficult ones; baby talk.

pedomorphism Describing adult behavior in terms more appropriate to behavior of a child. See *adultomorphism; anthropomorph.*

pedophilia (302.2) Love of children. This term implies the love of children by an adult for sexual purposes.
Forel called it *pederosis;* Krafft-Ebing termed it *paedophilia erotica.*
A patient impotent with women was capable of sexual excitation only with young boys, with whom he frequently engaged in the acts of anal intercourse and fellatio.

peduncle, cerebral (ped′un-k′l) See *midbrain.*

peeping See *voyeurism.*

peeping Tom (From the name of the Coventry tailor who peeped at naked lady Godiva riding through the city's streets by order of her husband, lord of Coventry) Voyeur.

Pelizaeus-Merzbacher's disease (Friedrich Pelizaeus, German neurologist, b. 1850, and Ludwig Merzbacher, in Argentina, b. 1875) See *sclerosis, diffuse.*

pellagra (pel-làg′rà) (1294.1, 309.5) Nicotinic acid deficiency, characterized by gastrointestinal disturbances (especially diarrhea), erythema followed by desquamation of the affected area, and mental disturbances. Symptoms vary widely in incidence and intensity but tend to be worse in the spring. The most frequent early picture consists of fatigue and lassitude combined with depression. Mania, convulsions, dementia, stupor and unconsciousness may also occur, and if untreated the condition advances into delirious or subacute delirious states. Sucking and grasping reflexes may appear along with cogwheel rigidity of the extremities and progressive clouding of consciousness. Treatment with high doses of nicotonic acid or nicotinamide (and usually moderately high doses of the other B vitamins) usually results in amelioration of all symptoms, except that in some cases memory defects persist. Pellagra continues to be endemic in Mediterranean countries, the Far East, Africa, Mexico, and the southern United States; and it can be seen as a complication of chronic alcoholism in any part of the world.

penetrance See *chromosome; dominance; variation.*

penetration response See *barrier.*

penial (pē′ne-al) Penile.

peniaphobia (pē-nē-à-fō′bē-à) Fear of poverty.

penile (pē′nil) Relating to the penis.

penilingus Fellatio.

penis (pē′nis) The male organ of copulation. In psychoanalysis it refers to the organ after the boy has reached the stage of genital love. See *phallus.*

penis captivus (kap′tē-voos) *Vaginismus* (q.v.) occurring during sexual intercourse so that withdrawal of the erect penis is impossible. The condition is the subject of many anecdotes, but the paucity of clinical reports indicates that such anecdotes are based more on male castration fears and female active castration tendencies than on real occurrences.

penis-envy See *envy, penis.*

penis, female See *penis, women with.*

penis, women with A childhood theory (that every woman has a penis) or idea, stemming from a universal, albeit usually forgotten, experience in the psycho-sexual development of all boys and girls. It generally appears between the ages of two and five as a consequence of the child's discovering the crucial anatomical difference between males and females, i.e. the absence of the penis in females. On finding the supposed organic deficiency or inferiority, most little girls react to their discovery with varying degrees of shock. In boys the same discovery tends to make their dread of castration more real for them, since it confronts them with the actuality of 'the missing organ.'

The idea that a woman once possessed or possesses a penis functions as a protective defensive denial of the 'horrible' psychic reality, by which the child has theoretically explained to itself the observed absence of the penis in females.

pentothal interview (pen′tō-thal) See *narcotherapy.*

peotillomania (pē-ō-til-ō-mā′nē-à) False masturbation, pseudomasturbation; a nervous tic consisting in constant pulling at the penis.

percentile See *rank, percentile.*

percept The subject's meaningful interpretation of a sensory stimulus; a percept is a combination of subjective and objective elements and affords a link between the subject and his environment.

percept, body See *image, body.*

percept-image 'These are certain concrete images of hallucinatory clearness which may appear as phantasy or memory images . . . This class of experiences, namely, the percept-images, which in general have been lost to adults, represents, according to the researches of Jaensch, a primitive level of intellectual life.' (Storch, A. *The Primitive Archaic Forms in Schizophrenia,* tr. by Willard, C., Nervous and Mental Disease Publishing Company, New York and Washington, 1924) The phenomenon is common among schizophrenic patients.

perceptanalysis (pēr-sept-an-al′i-sis) Piotrowski's term for inferring personality traits from a subject's responses to the Rorschach ink blots. "The broadest and main assumption on which the logical structure of perceptanalysis rests states that the individual's sensory, intellectual, and motor handling, active

and/or passive, of the blot stimuli corresponds closely to the habitual manner in which he handles, actively and/or passively, his interhuman relationships." (Piotrowski, Z. *Percept analysis,* Macmillan, New York, 1957)

perception (pēr-sep′shun) The mental process by which the nature of an object is recognized through the association of a memory of its other qualities with the special sense, sight, taste, etc., bringing it at the time to consciousness.

perception, extrasensory Cognition which is paranormal, or a response to an external event which has not presented itself to any of the five known senses. *Telepathy* and *clairvoyance* are two modalities of this single surmised basic function—extra-sensory perception—and they differ only in the targets, thoughts, or objects upon which they operate: clairoyance is the extra-sensory perception of objective events; telepathy is the extra-sensory perception of the mental activities of another person. Abbreviated as E.S.P.

perception-hallucination See *hallucination of perception.*

perception, subconscious Perceptions of the environment which never even entered the fringe of the personal consciousness, i.e. of which the person was never even dimly aware. (Prince, J. *The Unconscious,* Macmillan, New York, 1916)

perceptions, abstract See *hallucination, blank.*

perceptivity (per-sep-tiv′i-tē) The power of perception; the character of being perceptive.

perceptorium (tō′rēum) Sensorium.

perceptualization (per-sep-choo-al-i-zā′-shun) The act or process of representing reality as it appears to the senses rather than to the intellect, as is seen in dreams and hallucinations. The term is also used to refer to regressive loss of higher conceptualization processes such as is seen in many schizophrenics whose ideas become more and more related to specific instances and less and less related to classes, groups, or categories. This is one of the expressions of *paleologic* (q.v.)· and leads, among other things, to *concretism* (q.v.)

percipient (per-sip'ē-ent) In parapsychology, the receiver of telepathically transmitted messages.

peregrinating problem patients A term for patients with Munchausen's syndrome.

periblepsis (per-i-blep'sis) The wild stare of a delirious person, with elements of bewilderment, consternation, and terror.

perichareia (-kà-rī'à) Delirious rejoicing.

perikaryon See *neuron.*

period, Oedipus The period beginning at about the age of three during the phallic stage of development and reaching its height at four to five years. Psychoanalysts believe that the *Oedipus complex* is characteristic of all individuals, the boy, normally, becoming sexually attached to his mother, the girl to her father. In the phallic period, sexual interest at first is autoerotic: (1) the boy identifies himself with the penis but soon merges his sexual interest into the sexuality of the mother; (2) the girl's clitoris sexuality leads to penis-envy and the belief that the mother has been the castrator, and the girl turns to the father as a sexual object. In the *male,* the Oedipus period *ends because of castration anxiety,* for the Oedipal object can be achieved only at the risk of losing the penis. In the *female,* on the other hand, the Oedipus situation *is brought about by castration anxiety.* Thus the Oedipus period is likely to be prolonged in the female; it has been suggested that its disappearance is due to the fact that the child is not mature enough to understand the full significance of the sexual organs. The fate of the Oedipus complex in the female is still unclear to psychiatry. See *complex, Oedipus.*

period, refractory See *refractory.*

peristasis (pe-ris'tà-sis) The external environment. Some geneticists prefer this term to environment, to indicate that the environment of any genetic factor includes all the biophysiological process-

es which take place in the organism itself and are essential to the pheno-typical development of the given genotype. According to modern physiological genetics, every inherited character necessarily becomes subject to the organism's *peristatic* conditions. See *ecology.*

permissiveness See *environment, permissive.*

pernoctation (pēr-nok-tā'shun) *Obs.* Insomnia.

peroneal muscular atrophy See *atrophy, peroneal muscular.*

perplexity, parental A type of relationship of parents to their children that has been found relatively frequently in schizophrenic families (although it is as yet unclear whether the parental behavior and attitudes are productive of the child's disabilities, or whether it is the primary deviancy of the child that has generated the parental reaction). 'This parental atmosphere is characterized by extreme parental indecisiveness, a lack of parental spontaneity and empathy with the child, the parents' inability to sense what the child's needs are and thus an inability to satisfy them at the proper moment, and an unusual absence of control and authority. In this type of unpatterned climate, positive re-inforcement of desirable traits and negative re-inforcement of undesirable traits are not administered. Instead, the child is left with feelings of confusion and an inclination to respond in a randomized, impoverished, and unpredictable fashion, when more focused, directed behaviors are lacking. (Goldfarb, W. *International Psychiatry Clinics 1,* 821-845, 1964)

perplexity, vague A symptom seen most commonly in the organic psychoses, especially in the acute brain syndromes associated with systemic infection as part of the beginning of a toxic delirium. The patient feels 'mixed-up in the head,' shows a deficient grasp of the total situation, drowsiness, torpor, and disturbances of the association, memory, attention, and will.

persécuteurs persécutés (pâr-sā-kü-tēr' pâr-sā-kü-tē')(F. 'persecuted persecutors') Some paranoid persecuted patients also become persecutors, in an effort, as they believe, to defend themselves against their persecutors. They are referred to as *persécuteurs persécutés.*

perseveration Involuntary continuation or recurrence of an experience or activity, most typically verbal, which is more appropriate to a preceding stimulus than to the succeeding stimuli which provoke the activity. It occurs most often in association with brain damage (e.g. after head injury, in presenile and arteriosclerotic brain syndromes, hepatic encephalopathy, etc.), and it may also appear with forced grasping, groping, and associated lesions of the premotor area (6a) of the brain. Perseveration may also appear in the schizophrenias as an association disturbance. See *verbigeration.*

Perseveration is often defined in a more operational way, particularly by experimental psychologists, as the inability to shift from one task to another or to break through an established set in order to perform a new task. It is generally agreed that factors of perseveration are of little value in differentiating between normals, neurotics, and psychotics.

person, composite A figure in a dream who is not an actual person at all but a composition or 'composite' of two or more actual persons. The dreamer is not able to identify the composite person as any person known to him but, upon psychoanalytic interpretation of his dream, he is able to see that two or more persons who *are* known to him have been fused into one.

The composite person is produced by the mechanism of *condensation* in dreammaking. 'The condensation is effected in several ways. A figure in a dream may be constituted by the fusion of traits belonging to more than one actual person, with some belonging to another, or by making prominent the traits common to the two and neglecting those not common to them. . . . The same process frequently occurs with names. . . . The neologism thus produced closely resembles those met with in the psychoses. . . .' (Jones, E.J. *Papers on Psycho-Analysis,* Williams and Wilkins, Baltimore, 1949)

person, disturbances in the One of the fundamental symptoms of the schizophrenias, according to Bleuler. Such disturbances arise by reason of the tendency to splitting of the psyche and domination of the personality by one or another of the patient's complexes. The ego is never fully intact, amd there results a lack of homogeneity and wholeness and stability of the personality organization.

persona (pēr-sō′nȧ) With this term Jung denotes the disguised or masked attitude assumed by a person, in contrast to the more deeply rooted personality components. 'Through his more or less complete identification with the attitude of the moment, he at least deceives others, and also often himself, as to his real character. He puts on a *mask,* which he knows corresponds with his conscious intentions, while it also meets with the requirements and opinions of his environment, so that first one motive then the other is in the ascendant. This mask, viz. the *ad hoc* adopted attitude, I have called the *persona,* which was the designation given to the mask worn by the actors of antiquity. A man who is identified with this mask I would call "personal" (as opposed to "individual").' (Jung, C.G. *Psychological Types,* tr. by Baynes, H.G., Harcourt, Brace, New York and London, 1923)

persona, organic Burrow's term for the constellation of reactions embodied in the organism's total principle of motivation. The subjective correlate of the organism's primarily integrated or total behavior-pattern. Contrasted with 'I'-persona, symbolic persona. Synonym: organic identity. (Burrow, T. *The Biology of Human Conflict,* Macmillan, New York, 1937, pp. 387-8)

personal See *persona.*

personal equation See *equation, personal.*

Personal Experience and Attitude Questionnaire A screening questionnaire which is said to be a highly significant discriminator of psychopathic behavior. The test contains 150 items covering criminalism, emotional instability, inadequate personality, sexual psychopathy, nomadism, and other psychopathic traits.

personalities, inmate The classification of the personalities of inmates of penal institutions has had many radical modifications under the influence of modern psychiatry. It differs from institution to institution, and is also affected by the particular laws of each state. In any case, there are two main groups: the administrative and the psychiatric.

ADMINISTRATIVE CLASSIFICATION
1. Colony Group
    (a) Extensive privilege
    (b) Limited privilege
2. Restricted Group
    (a) Temporary restricted
    (b) Prolonged tractable
    (c) Prolonged intractable
3. Psychiatric Group
    (a) Ambulatory
    (b) Observation
4. Hospital Group
5. Defective Delinquent
6. Insane

PSYCHIATRIC CLASSIFICATION
1. Normal
    (a) Without significant deviation
    (b) With moderate personality deviation
    (c) With pronounced personality deviation
    (d) With intellectual inferiorities
2. Feebleminded
3. Neuropathic
    (a) Psychopathic
    (b) Psychoneurotic
    (c) Epileptic
    (d) Drug Addict
    (e) Alcoholic
    (f) Post-encephalitic
    (g) Other brain abnormalities with psychoses
4. Psychotic
5. Potentially Psychotic

(Seliger, R.V. *et al. Contemporary Criminal Hygiene,* Oakridge Press, Baltimore, 1946)

personality *Character* (q.v.); the characteristic, and to some extent predictable, behavior-response patterns that each person evolves, both consciously and unconsciously, as his style of life. The personality represents a compromise between inner drives and needs, and the controls that limit or regulate their expression. Such controls are both internal (e.g. 'conscience,' 'superego') and external (reality demands). The personality functions to maintain a stable, reciprocal relationship between the person and his environ-

ment; it is thus a composite of the ego defenses, the autoplastic and the alloplastic maneuvers, that are automatically and customarily employed to maintain intrapsychic stability.

The personality, in other words, is a set of habits that characterize the person in his way of managing day-to-day living; under ordinary conditions it is relatively stable and predictable, and for the most part it is ego-syntonic. Because the various defensive operations ('ego mechanisms') that make up the personality are the very ones that appear in exaggerated form in recognized clinical entities, their identification will sometimes allow for prediction of what specific form of clinical disturbance the person is most likely to have, should he develop any kind of illness at all. Their identification does not, however, predict that any such illness will ever develop.

Because the personality is ego-syntonic, it is rare that the person will recognize his own personality as being deviant or abnormal (even if, in fact, it is). Any such evaluation is ordinarily a social diagnosis, and an outgrowth of the effects of that personality on the people about him—who may view his behavior as destructive, frightening, nonconforming, or otherwise unacceptable. The subject, in other words, is unlikely to seek out ways to alter his personality, which for him is the best way of avoiding tension and fulfilling his potential that he has been able to develop; rather, he may consent to counseling or psychotherapy if this is urged by others or because of social repercussions of his usual behavior.

It is difficult to draw a clear distinction between normal personality and the variations of personality and character that extend beyond the normal range. To some extent, the stability of even the normal personality is achieved at the expense of an ideal mobility—perhaps unattainable —to deal effectively with new or unusual interpersonal problems and conflicts. Yet there is no doubt that in many persons the stability of their ways of being and living is a rigidly fixed, immutable pattern that severely limits their potentialities for effective functioning and satisfying interpersonal relationships. Such conditions are variously termed *personality disorders, character disorders,* or *character neuroses.* These are deeply ingrained, chronic, and habitual patterns of reaction that are maladaptive in that they are relatively inflexible; they limit the optimal use of potentialities and often provoke the very counterreactions from the environment that the subject seeks to avoid. In DSM-I (1952 revision of psychiatric nomenclature), these were grouped under three headings: *personality pattern disturbance, personality trait disturbance,* and *sociopathic personality disturbance* (qq.v.). In DSM-II (1968 revision of psychiatric nomenclature), the classification is as follows:

301   Personality Disorders
301.0   *Paranoid personality* (q.v.)
301.1   Clyclothymic personality (Affective personality)— with recurring variations of mood that are not readily attributable to external circumstances; elated periods are characterized by ambition, energy, warmth, enthusiasm, and optimism; periods of dejection include pessimism, worry, low energy, and feelings of futility.
301.2   Schizoid   personality—with shyness hypersensitivity, seclusiveness,   frequent   daydreaming, avoidance of close or competitive relationships, detachment, inability to express hostility and ordinary aggressive feelings, and often eccentric behavior.
301.2   Explosive personality (Epileptoid   personality   disorder)— see *personality, epileptic.*
301.3   Obsessive compulsive personality (Anankastic personality)—order, parsimony, and obstinancy are key character traits in this type of person, who is overconcerned with conformity and adherence to standards of conscience; often he is rigid, overinhibited, overconscientious,   overdutiful, indecisive, perfectionistic, and unable to relax easily; there is an obligatory quality to life, such as a need for closure and task completion that may be inappropriate;   although   he hides his resentment behind an attitude of smiling submissiveness it creeps out in stubbornness, avarice, pos-

sessiveness,   arrogance,   and pretentiousness; others view him as obstructionistic, petty, irascible,   and   inordinately scrupulous (see also *anal-erotism*).
301.5   Hysterical   personality   (Histrionic personality disorder) —see *hysteria; hysterical personality; defense, character.*
301.6   Asthenic   personality—with easy fatigability, low energy level,   lack   of   enthusiasm, marked incapacity for enjoyment, oversensitivity to physical and emotional stress.
301.7   Antisocial   personality—see *psychopathic personality.*
301.81 Passive-aggressive personality — aggression,   which   often arises   from   resentment   at failing to find gratification in a relationship upon which the person is overdependent, is manifested   in   such   passive ways as obstructionism, pouting, procrastination, intentional inefficiency, and stubbornness.
301.82 Inadequate   personality— while he is neither physically nor   mentally   deficient,   the person is nonetheless inept, unadaptable, and ineffectual in his responses to emotional, social, intellectual, and physical demands; judgment is poor, and there is a lack of physical and emotional stamina; in some cases, emotional or   experiential   deprivation appears   to   be   the   major etiologic factor.
301.89 Other personality disorders of specified   types   (including immature personality)

In DSM-II, various disturbances that were formerly included among personality disorders are labelled 'other nonpsychotic mental disorders' and are coded separately:
302   Sexual deviations
303   Alcoholism
304   Drug dependence.
See *nomenclature, 1968 revision.*

personality, alternating Many consider this expression as synonymous with *per-*

sonality, split (q.v.), for the splitting of consciousness implies that the individual lives alternatingly now as one person and then as another (as in the familiar case of Dr. Jekyl and Mr. Hyde), but never as two persons simultaneously. 'A special type of disturbance of personality is the *alternating personality*, also known as *dual consciousness.*' (Bleuler, E. *Textbook of Psychiatry*, tr. by Brill, A.A., Macmillan, New York, 1930)

personality, anal See *character, anal.*

personality, antisocial See *psychopathic personality.*

personality, 'as if' A pre-psychotic condition indicative of loss of object cathexis in which the subject's whole relation to life has something about it that is lacking in genuineness. The phenomenon is closely related to depersonalization, but, unlike the latter, the 'as if' personality is not perceived as a disturbance by the patient himself. The expressions of emotion in such patients are formal, and interpersonal relationships are devoid of any traces of warmth. The person gives the impression of a good adjustment to reality, but this is based on mimicry and identification with the environment and leads to a completely passive attitude toward the environment and a readiness to adopt whatever attitudes or reactions seem to be expected. Thus there is no single, integrated personality; instead, the person seems to shift with the tide of his surroundings. Deutsch believes that the schizophrenic goes through an 'as if' stage before there is any delusional formation. ('Some Forms of Emotional Disturbance and Their Relationship to Schizophrenia,' *Psychiatric Quarterly II*, 301, 1942). She believes that the 'as if' personality represents a deep disturbance of the process of sublimation which results in a failure to synthesize various infantile identifications into an integrated personality; this leads to an imperfect, one-sided, and purely intellectual sublimation of the instinctual strivings.

M. Katan (*International Journal of Psycho-Analysis 39*, 265-270, 1958), on the other hand, noting that this personality occurs almost exclusively in women, has suggested that the 'as-if' personality arises as follows: while still in a stage

of strong oral dependence, the little girl is deprived of the mother figure and this, combined with another 'loss' (the absence of a phallus), forces the ego to remain dependent and to '. . . rely for its reactions completely upon the examples which it receives from the chance object to which it is attached at the moment. But this attachment never developed beyond a primary identification as it existed at the time the patient lost her mother.' (ibid., p. 268). The nature of this primary identification is clearly revealed in the patient's reaction to dissolution of an object relationship; '. . . a relinquished relationship is never followed up by an identification, but, contrary to such sequence, the identification disappears with the relationship.' (ibid., p. 266).

Katan differentiates between the 'as-if' personality and *'pseudo as-if'* (q.v.).

personality, compulsive See *personality trait disturbance; defense, character.*

personality, crowbar An example of post-traumatic mental deterioration that occured in a patient who had a segment of a crowbar imbedded in his left forebrain as a result of a premature dynamite explosion. Before the accident he had been a stable person of good character and exemplary conduct. After his head injury, he became a vulgar, short-tempered, irritable, disagreeable person who drank to excess, abused his wife and children, and finally abandoned them.

personality, cyclothymic (sī-klō-thī'mik) See *personality pattern disturbance.*

personality disorders Approximately equivalent to character disorders or character neuroses or behavioral reaction. For a discussion of the term as used currently, in the 1968 revision of psychiatric nomenclature (DSM-II), see *personality.*

In DSM-I (1952 nomenclature), this term referred to those cases in which the personality, in its struggle for adjustment to internal and external stresses, utilized primarily a pattern of action or behavior rather than symptoms in the mental, somatic, or emotional spheres. There is minimal subjective anxiety and little or no sense of distress. As thus defined, there are three main groups of personality disorder: personality pattern disturbance (including inadequate personality, schizoid personality, cyclothymic personality, and paranoid personality), personality trait disturbance (including emotionally unstable personality, passive-aggressive personality, and compulsive personality), and sociopathic personality disturbance (including antisocial reaction, dyssocial reaction, sexual deviation, and addiction).

personality disorder, post-traumatic (309.2) The changes occurring in the disposition or personality as a result of head- or brain-injury due to force directly or indirectly applied to the head. The manifest symptoms may include headache, explosive emotional reactions, low resistance to alcohol, fatigability, vasomotor instability, and occasionally convulsive seizures.

personality, emotionally unstable See *personality trait disturbance.*

personality, epileptic It is not clear whether what is called epileptic personality is a true epileptic character or merely a reaction to the chronic invalidism of epilepsy. As usually described, in any event, it probably does not occur in more than 20 per cent of known epileptics. Since its characteristics may appear in the form of a personality disorder in persons without evidence of epilepsy, it is better termed *epileptoid* or *explosive personality* (in DSM-II, 301.3, with *aggressive personality* as a subtype). The characteristics of this personality type include: rigidity, egocentricity, selfishness, religiosity, seculsiveness, explosive outbursts of emotion, and extreme rage reactions when frustrated (children especially become frenzied when refused their wishes). Enuresis is also said to be common. Probably the most frequently observed abnormality is a tendency to a certain morose egotism; and only one psychodynamic feature occurs in epilepsy which would in any way support the belief in a specific epileptic psychic constitution—phantasies of death and rebirth, which are more common here than in any other illness. See *dementia, epileptic.*

personality, hysterical See *hysterical personality.*

personality, ideal See *ego* (Jung's definition of).

personality, inadequate See *personality pattern disturbance.*

personality, intraconscious (in-tra-kon'-shus) A co-conscious personality that knows another personality's thoughts. In one type of multiple personality, one personality fumctions subconsciously, and when it is aware not only of the outer world but of the thoughts of the conscious personality in the same person, it is termed intraconscious personality.

personality, multiple A form of dissociative hysteria (300.14); the presence of two or more relatively distinct and separate sub-personalities in a single person, as in Dr. Jekyl and Mr. Hyde, or in Morton Prince's case of Miss Beauchamp, or in Cleckley and Thigpen's case of Eve. Multiple personality is popularly known as split personality, and this has led to the logical but incorrect inference that schizophrenia ('split personality') is identical with multiple personality. The latter is actually a dissociative reaction, and thus a form of hysteria. Splitting is seen in both hysteria and schizophrenia, but the splitting is quite different in each. In hysteria, the splitting is massive or molecular and consists of division into complicated and relatively complete sub-personalities. In the schizophrenias, on the other hand, individual psychic functions are split off from the personality as a whole and attain an autonomy of their own which is unrelated to and often contradictory to the major personality trends; thus the splitting in schizophrenia is often termed discrete, nuclear, or atomic.

In multiple personality, the original personality is termed the primary personality, and the dissociated or split-off personality is termed the secondary (and tertiary, etc.) personality.

personality, multiplication of Schizophrenic patients in particular often express the delusion that they are many other people, that others actually reside in them, often displacing the patient entirely. One patient changed her identity many times within a short period.

'Most remarkable, however, is the division and multiplication of the personality unit into various separate persons which appear to her as strange, though, as she also distinctly feels, they represent her own thought complexes and aspirations.' (Storch, A. *The Primitive Archaic Forms in Schizophrenia,* tr. by Willard C., Nervous and Mental Disease Publishing Company, New York and Washington, 1924)

personality, panels of See *panels, personality.*

personality, paranoid (par'à-noid) See *personality pattern disturbance.*

personality pattern disturbance In the 1952 revision of psychiatric nomenclature, this term was used to refer to personality types or character structures which are more or less fixed and only minimally liable to any basic alteration. 'The depth of the psychopathology here allows these individuals little room to maneuver under conditions of stress, except into actual psychosis.' (*Diagnostic and Statistical Manual of Mental Disorders,* American Psychiatric Association of Mental Hospital Service, Washington, D.C., 1952). Included in this group are:
(1) Inadequate personality—inadaptability, ineptness, poor judgment, lack of physical and emotional stamina, social incompatibility, etc.
(2) Schizoid Personality—avoidance of close interpersonal relationships, inability to express hostility, autistic thinking, etc.
(3) Cyclothymic Personality—extraverted type of relationships with reality, competitive, frequently alternating moods, etc.
(4) Paranoid Personality—hypersensitivity in interpersonal relationships, suspiciousness, envy, jealousy, stubbornness, and similar projection mechanisms.

personality, prepsychotic (prē-sī-kot'ik) The patient's personality make-up or the character structure considered usual for him before the development of a psychotic disorder.

personality, pretraumatic (prē-trawmat'ik) In the case of a person who has developed an emotional or mental illness in consequence of an injury, this psychiatric term denotes the personality as it was before the injury and illness. Knowledge of the details of the patient's pre-traumatic personality is essential for proper therapeutic understanding and management in any of the traumatic neuroses and psychoses, i.e. psychiatric disorders attributable to injury.
'The traumatic neurosis is the record of the lasting consequences of an abrupt change in the external environment to which the resources of the individual are unequal. This situation we designated as a trauma. The neurosis is, therefore, the record of the disturbance created by the trauma on the previously established adaptations [i.e. pretraumatic personality].'
It is necessary to understand 'the relation of the traumatic neurosis to the personality as a whole, and the relation of the trauma to the pretraumatic personality, or the predisposition to the neurosis.' (Kardiner, A. *War Stress and Neurotic Illness,* Hoeber, New York and London, 1947)

personality, primary See *personality, multiple.*

personality, psychopathic See *psychopathic personality.*

personality, schizoid (skiz'oid) See *personality.*

personality, secondary See *personality, multiple.*

personality, split See *personality, multiple.*

personality, stormy Arieti's term for a personality type, found often in preschizophrenic patients, consisting of repeated changes in the person's attitude to life which may be slow or abrupt and commonly are sudden, violent, and drastic. Such people have no stable sense of self-identity and are forever searching for their role in life, without success. Life often seems to be little more than a series of crises for them.

personality, subconscious 'A subconscious personality is a condition where complexes of subconscious processes have been constellated into a personal system, manifesting a secondary system of self-consciousness endowed with volition, intelligence, etc. Such a subconscious personality is capable of communicating with the experimenter and describing its own mental processes. It can, after repression of the primary personality, become the sole personality for the time being, and then remember its previous subconscious life, as we all remember our past conscious life, and can give full and explicit information regarding the nature of the subconscious process.' (Prince, J. *The Unconscious,* Macmillan, New York, 1916)

personality trait disturbance In the 1952 revision of psychiatric nomenclature, this term was used to refer to '. . . individuals who are unable to maintain their emotional equilibrium and independence under minor or major stress because of disturbances in emotional development. Some individuals fall into this group because their personality pattern disturbance is related to fixation and exaggeration of certain character and behavior patterns; others, because their behavior is a regressive reaction due to environmental or endopsychic stress.' *(Diagnostic and Statistical Manual of Mental Disorders.* American Psychiatric Association of Mental Hospital Service, Washington, D.C., 1952). Included in this group are:

(1) Emotionally unstable personality— excitability, ineffectiveness and poor judgment when under even minor stress; poorly controlled hostility, guilt, and anxiety; formerly called 'psychopathic personality with emotional instability.'

(2) Passive-aggressive personality— passive-dependent type, passive-aggressive type, and aggressive type.

(3) Compulsive personality—overinhibited, overconscientious, rigid adherence to standards of conscience or conformity. See *defense, character.*

personality types For a psychoanalytic description of personality types, see *defense, character.* Jung recognizes two 'general attitude' types, described from the standpoint of the direction of the flow of libido. When the general direction of the flow of libido is away from the subject, the expression *extraversion* is used and the person is called an *extravert.* When the libido is mainly turned inwardly upon the person himself, the condition is known as *introversion* and the person as an *introvert.* These two are known as *temperamental* types.

Jung describes four basic *functional* types known as thinking, feeling, sensation, and intuition. Any one of these four functions may be(come) preponderant over the other three and, in that case,

it is called the *superior function.* On the other hand, an *inferior function* is one less powerful than the other three. The remaining two functions are then said to öccupy an intermediate position.

Kretschmer speaks of two general biotypes, the *schizothymic* and the *cyclothymic,* each of which is subdivided into several other types, such as 'gushing jolly people,' 'quiet humorists,' etc. (Kretschmer, E. *Physique and Character,* tr. by Sprott, W.J.H., Kegan Paul, Trench, Trubner, London, 1925)

personification (pēr-son-i-fi-cā'shun) Endowing another with pleasant or unpleasant attributes as a result of frustration of one's desires or wishes. For example, one schizophrenic patient whose letter was not answered accused his doctor of intercepting the mail. Personification is a form of projection wherein the desirable or undesirable properties of reality are attributed to some person, even though the latter is unrelated to the happening itself. Thus schizophrenic persecutory delusions develop only after an obstacle to gratification is felt by the patient; a persecutor is chosen to take on the qualities necessary to explain the frustration. Delusions of persecution convert obstacles into machinations of certain people, the persecutors.

personification, eidetic See *eidetic personification.*

personology (pēr-son-ol'ō-jē) The science or study of the personality as a whole, of man's functioning in society, his perceptions, his actions, and especially his thoughts and feelings and their reasons for being. The scope of personology includes the totality of mental life, the dynamics and economics of the entire personality; and its task is to trace the laws and phases of personality development in the individual life. In contrast, metapsychology is the pure-science aspect of the study of personality and yields information regarding the general laws of mental life. Personology supplies the understanding of how to use this knowledge in relation to the specific individual as an organic-psychic whole whose every action can be understood only in terms of the whole. See *holism.*

persuasion A type of supportive *psychotherapy* (q.v.). It is perhaps a part of all types of psychotherapy, achieving merit as an adjunct. Dubois was particularly instrumental in fostering persuasion, yet it never became known as a method, in the sense that the psychoanalysis of Freud, or the analytical psychology of Jung, are methods.

'In this method, the physician tries to clarify the development of the symptoms, their relation to situational and personality difficulties; and he explains to the patient the interrelations of these factors and how the difficulties and symptoms can be overcome.' (Diethelm, O. *Treatment in Psychiatry,* Macmillan, New York, 1936)

Persuasion is a method of carrying conviction that aims to prompt the acceptance of a point of view.

perverse, polymorphous (po-li-mor'fus) Pertaining to one whose sexual behavior includes many different forms, expressing both adult and infantile tendencies, both normal and abnormal trends. Though it often appears during mental disorders, polymorphous perversion is said to be normal in early childhood, embracing activities observed in the period of infancy and also in adulthood in the form of perversions. As Freud says, 'sexual excitation of the child flows from diverse sources.' There are the excitations associated with the erotogenic zones; furthermore, there is 'gratification which is experienced with other organic processes': excitation of erotogenic zones by peripheral stimulation; sexual excitation through looking, showing, cruelty, etc.; excitation through rhythmic activities, such as swinging, dancing, rocking, etc.; sexual exciting influence of some painful affects, such as fear, shuddering, and horror, is felt by a great many people. . . .'; and 'mental application or the concentration of attention on an intellectual accomplishment will result, especially often in youthful persons, but in older persons as well, in a simultaneous sexual excitement.' (Freud, S. *Three Contributions to the Theory of Sex,* 4th ed., tr. by Brill, A.A., Nervous and Mental Disease Publishing Company, New York and Washington, 1930)

Abraham says that 'we learn from his [Freud's] investigations that the first traces of sexual activity appear very early and that for some time they are of an autoerotic character. A stage follows in which the child turns to "object-love"; but its

sexual object need not be of the opposite sex. In addition to heterosexual and homosexual impulses certain other impulses, that of a sadistic and masochistic character, find expression. Hence Freud speaks of a polymorphous-perverse stage.' (Abraham, K. *Selected Papers,* tr. by Bryan, D. and Strachey, A., Leonard and Virginia Woolf and The Institute of Psychoanalysis, London, 1927)

perversion Abnormality, aberration, distortion, dysfunction; any deviation from the correct, proper, expected, or normal range. In psychiatry, most commonly used to refer to *sexual deviation* (q.v.), i.e. any sexual practice that deviates from the normal, or any abnormal means of achieving genital orgasm. Among the perversions are homosexuality, fetishism, pedophilia, transvestitism, exhibitionism, voyeurism, sadism, masochism, necrophilia, coprophilia, and urolagnia. Normal sexual behavior often includes elements of the perversions, typically as a part of *forepleasure* (q.v.). For the sexual pervert, in contrast, the activity is not merely an elective prelude to intercourse, but rather it has become an end in itself, usually sought after with an insistent, compelling, demanding quality that is reminiscent of compulsions. But unlike compulsions, the perverse activity brings positive pleasure and orgasm and does not merely serve to relieve the subject of psychic pain. The pervert is forced to like something, and even though this be undesired it nonetheless is ego-syntonic; the compulsive, in contrast, is forced to perform an ego-alien action.

Early in the development of psychoanalytic psychology, the neuroses were considered to be 'the negative of the perversions,' in that neurotic symptoms seemed often to be a disguised expression of the very tendencies that were expressed overtly in the perversions. It is now believed that such an interpretation is tenable in few cases, for perverts are not notably free of neurotic conflicts. Most demonstrate instead a hypertrophy of one component of infantile sexuality with a secondary repression of all else; often the pervert is found to have regressed to an infantile fixation point in order to reassure himself against castration fears.

pervert (pĕr'vĕrt). One who practices perversions or forms of genital activity not in accordance with the general culture or mores of his community or state.

pervigilium (pĕr-vi-jil'ē-um) (L. 'an all-night watching') Coma vigil.

petit mal (p'tē' màl') (F. 'little disease') See *epilepsy.*

petrification (pet-ri-fi-kā'shun) The process of turning, or being turned, into stony-like substance or stone; often in myths, fairy tales, phantasies, etc. it is a punishment for scopophilic or voyeuristic impulses. The sensations associated with looking are a source of erotic pleasure. This pleasure may become the object of specific repressions. As a result inhibitions of looking arise. The inhibitions are a defense against either temptations for the scopophilia or a feared punishment associated with it.

There are several factors involved in the inhibition of scopophilic impulses. First, through episodes in his life, the child may have learned to fear voyeuristic impulses. For example, he may have been threatened with severe punishment (which the child might interpret as castration) because of efforts to observe his parents in the 'primal scene.' Secondly, pleasurable looking has in the infant the archaic quality of incorporation through the eyes and frequently destruction of the perceived object. Thus, with the erotic pleasure of looking will be associated the animistic dread of retaliation from the 'evil eye,' this retaliation turns the person into stone and destroys him.

The punishment appears to be specific for scopophilic interests. Petrification signifies a paralyzing fright associated with castration or death. (Fenichel, O. *The Psychoanalytic Theory of Neurosis,* Norton, New York, 1945)

petrification Fixity, rigidity; used to describe the attitude and behavior of chronic schizophrenics whose symptoms in time tend to become colorless, repetitive, and robot-like.

pettifog (pet'i-fog) A popular term denoting mental confusion.

peyotism (pā-yot'iz'm) (304.7) Intoxication with peyote, the dried blossoms of the mescal cactus. Peyote was used by the Southwest American Indians to produce ectasies as part of a religious ritual. Results included beautiful visual and sometimes auditory hallucinations, a sense of timelessness, and a complete withdrawal from reality. Mescaline, the active principle of the cactus, has been used more recently in experimental psychiatry to produce a model psychosis. See *mescaline.*

Pfaundler-Hurler syndrome *Gargoylism* (q.v.).

PGR Psychogalvanic reflex. See *reflex, psychogalvanic.*

phacomatosis (fa-kō-mà-to'sis) Van der Hoeve's term for ectodermal disorders, the most common of which are: von Recklinghausen's disease or *neurofibromatosis* (q.v.), Pringle-Bourneville disease or tuberous sclerosis, *Lindau's disease* (q.v.), Sturge-Weber's disease (intracranial hemangioma), and naevus epitheliomatodes multiplex.

phaged(a)ena (faj-ē-dē'nà) Bulimia; insatiable hunger.

-phagia, -phagy (-fā'jē-à -fa-jē) Combining form meaning eating, food, from Gr. *phageîn,* to have eaten, devoured.

phagomania (fag-ō-mā'nē-à) Uncontrollable or insatiable desire to eat.

phagophobia Fear of eating.

phallic (fal'ik) In psychoanalysis the term relates to the penis during the phase of infantile sexuality.

phallic love See *love, phallic.*

phallic pride See *pride, penis.*

phallicism (fal'i-siz'm) Phallic worship.

phallism Phallic worship.

phallus (fal'us) In psychoanalysis, the penis during the period of infantile sexuality when it is intensely charged or cathected with narcissitic love. When the narcissistic qualities, associated with one's own genital organ, are directed outwardly upon a love-object, it is said that the stage of *genital love* has been reached. Thus, genital love in the male may be called penile love, in contrast to phallic love.

phallus girl See *girl, phallus.*

phaneromania (fan-ēr-ō-mā-nē-à) An irresistible impulse to touch some part of one's own body especially an exterior growth on it. It is a form of repetition-compulsion, related to tic-like movements. A patient had the compulsion to rub his nose; to him the nose, a centrally placed, unpaired organ, was equated with the penis. A homosexual woman, infuriated by all manifestations of effeminacy, constantly stroked her breasts, as if trying to rub something off them.

phantasia *Phantasy* (q.v.).

phantasm (fan'taz'm) A sense perception, appearing in the form of illusion or hallucination.
'The most important psychopathic manifestations in the centripetal fields are the sensory deceptions (Phantasms).' (Bleuler, E. *Textbook of Psychiatry,* tr. by Brill, A.A., Macmillan, New York, 1930)
Phantasms are classed as pseudo-hallucinations in that they are usually recognized as being illusory or imaginary; often the illusion is of an absent person seen in the form of a spirit or ghost.

phantasmagoria (fan-taz-mà-gō'rē-à) The raising or recalling of spirits of the dead.

phantasmatomoria (-ma-tō-mo'rē-à) *Obs.* Dementia with delusions.

phantasmophrenosis (-mō-fren-ō'sis) Daydreaming (coined by Schultz).

phantasmoscopia (-mo-skō'pē-à) Hallucinations involving spectres, ghosts, or spirits.

phantastica (fan-tas'tē-kà) See *psychotomimetic.*

phantasy, fantasy A product of *imagination* (q.v.) consisting of a group of symbols synthesized into a unified story by the secondary process. The phantasy may originate from conflicts secondary to unsatisfied instinctual wishes or secondary to frustration in external reality; it may be a substitute for action, or it may prepare the way for later action; it may afford gratification for id impulses, it may serve the ego as a defense, or it may subserve

superego functions by providing the imagery on which moral concepts, for example, are based. 'Fantasies may be conscious or unconscious. In either case they are manifestations of ego functions. It is, I believe, a theoretical error to speak of "id fantasies" or the "repression of fantasies into the id." The more accurate formulation is that unconscious fantasies indicate an unconscious ego function. They are, of course, derivatives of id impulses, and the motivating power or the unconscious fantasy takes its energy from the id drives.' (Beres, D. *International Journal of Psycho-Analysis, XLI,* 327, 1960)

phantasy, anal rape The idea or fear of being raped per anum. Mouth, anus, and vagina are often equated unconsciously by both sexes, and such phantasies may occur in either male or female. See *anal-erotism; anality; cloaca.*

phantasy-cathexis See *cathexis.*

phantasy, creative Symbol-forming activity. 'Besides the will . . . we have also creative phantasy, an irrational, instinctive function, which alone has the power of yielding the will a content of such a character as can unite the opposites. It is this function which Schiller intuitively apprehended as the source of symbols.' (Jung, C.G. *Psychological Types,* tr. by Baynes, H.G., Harcourt, Brace, New York and London, 1923)

phantasy, forced A technique devised by Ferenczi, based upon his finding that there is a type of person who 'both in analysis and life is particularly poor in phantasies, if not actually without them, on whom the most impressive experiences leave no apparent trace.' The people may reproduce experiences, but these are devoid of adequate or significant affects. Ferenczi advocated forcing affect into the memories, as by asking the patient to fabricate or guess about the memories, or even by telling him what he should have felt and phantasied.
Ferenczi believed that phantasies should be forced only at the end of a psychoanalysis. Moreover, he believed that there are mainly three topics that lend themselves to forced phantasies. They are (1) positive and negative phantasies

of the transference, (2) phantasies relating to infancy, and (3) onanistic phantasies. (Ferenczi, S. *Further Contributions to the Theory and Technique of Psycho-Analysis,* tr. by Suttie, J.I., Leonard and Virginia Woolf and The Institute of Psychoanalysis, London, 1926)

phantasy-formation See *phantasy-life.*

phantasy, hetaeral (hē-tē'ral) Phantasy in women of being, and in men of possessing, a courtesan or female paramour.

phantasy, king-slave 'Another extraordinary type of phantasy which has received as yet too little attention at the hands of psychoanalysts is the king-slave phantasy, in which the individual phantasies himself perhaps as now king, now slave, bound to service even by invisible golden chains.' (Healy, W., Bronner, A.F., and Bowers, A.M. *The Structure and Meaning of Psychoanalysis,* Knopf, New York, 1930)

phantasy-life Day-dreaming in contradistinction to thinking that is logical and realistic. Varendonck says, that phantasy-life 'gives the illusion that wishes and aspirations have been fulfilled; it thinks obstacles away; it transforms impossibilities into possibilities and realities.' He adds that it is 'a search for pleasurable representations and an avoidance of everything likely to cause pain.' (Varendonck, J. *The Psychology of Day Dreams,* Macmillan, New York, 1921)

Freud holds that there are two principal groups of phantasies, egoistic and erotic. Varendonck likens phantasy to a safety valve for the abreaction of strong affects.

Often the real meaning of a phantasy is not clear. In this condition it is called screen-phantasy (see *phantasy, screen*), for it is believed to cover up a deeply repressed urge.

Phantasies may be conscious or unconscious. Unconscious phantasies are said to express the impulses of the infantile period of life. See *day-dream; phantasy, unconscious.*

phantasy, magic The phantasy based upon the idea of limitless power and authority attributed to the analyst by the patient, who consequently, expects the impossible from the analyst.

phantasy, masturbation See *masturbation.*

phantasy, night In distinguishing night-phantasies from dreams, in the psychoanalytic sense, Freud held that night-phantasies occur during the sleeping state, but unlike dreams, do not undergo additions or alterations of any kind and in all other ways are similar to day-dreams.

phantasy of being eaten See *eaten, phantasy of being.*

phantasy, Pompadour (Jeanne Antionette Poisson le Normant d'Etioles, Marquise de Pompadour [1721-64], mistress of Louis XV [1710-74], King of France [1715-74]) 'One could give this name to that type of hetaeral phantasy in which even the most chaste women indulge—in day-dreams. The exaltation of the partner to kingly rank makes thoughts and wishes possible which would otherwise be rejected as immoral.' (Ferenczi, S. *Further Contributions to the Theory and Technique of Psycho-analysis,* tr. by Suttie, J.I., Leonard and Virginia Woolf and The Institute of Psychoanalysis, London, 1926)

phantasy, primal See *phantasy, unconscious.*

phantasy, rescue See *romance, family.*

phantasy, screen A memory or phantasy that conceals or stands for another phantasy. See *memory, screen; phantasy-life.*

phantasy, secondary See *phantasy, unconscious.*

phantasy-thinking Autism.

phantasy, unconscious Unconscious phantasies 'have either always been unconscious and formed in the unconscious, or more often, they were once conscious phantasies, day-dreaming' which were repressed into the unconscious. (Freud, S. *Collected Papers,* vol. 2, tr. by Riviere, J., Leonard and Virginia Woolf and The Institute of Psychoanalysis, London, 1924-25)

Such phantasies are revealed through mental analyses of adults and children, and dream-analyses. The unconscious phantasies of young children, the 'primal phantasies' of Freud, are derived from several sources, such as the Oedipus situation, ideas of procreation, the phenomena of birth, the castration complex, etc.

Secondary unconscious phantasies are as a rule some modification of the foregoing primal phantasies. For instance, the revival of the Oedipus complex at puberty gives rise to a new set of phantasies with certain adult sexual issues added.

phantasy, womb The phantasy of remaining within or returning to the womb, a frequent phantasy in psychiatric patients although almost always symbolically expressed. When it appears in consciousness it is highly disguised. It is commonly depicted as living alone on an island void of all things or as living in a cave of mother-earth, or as being alone in a room or church. The possible representations are legion.

Freud draws a distinction between womb-phantasy and rebirth. For instance, while speaking of the homosexual fixation of a boy for his father, Freud says: 'This instance, I think, throws light upon the meaning and origin of the womb-phantasy as well as that of re-birth. The former, the womb-phantasy, is frequently derived (as it was in the present case) from an attachment to the father. There is a wish to be inside the mother's womb in order to replace her during coitus—in order to take her place in regard to the father. The phantasy of re-birth, on the other hand, is in all probability regularly a softened substitute (a euphemism, one might say) for the phantasy of incestuous intercourse with the mother.' (Freud, S. *Collected Papers*, vol. 3, tr. by Strachey, A. and J., Leonard and Virginia Woolf, Hogarth Press, London, 1925)

phantom-limb See *limb, phantom.*

pharmacomania (fär-må-kō-mā′ne-a) Morbid impulse to take medicines.

pharmacophobia Fear of medicines.

pharmaco-psychoanalysis Narcoanalysis; see *narcotherapy.*

pharmacopsychosis (-sī-kō′sis) A term suggested by Southard for psychoses associated with alcohol, drugs, and other similar poisons.

pharmacothymia (-thim′ē-à -thī′mē-à) A neurotic or temperamental avidity for drugs.

phase, anal A psychoanalytical term designating (chronologically) the second libidinal or psychosexual development, immediately following the primary or oral stage. The anal phase (or stage) is subdivided into the early or *first anal phase,* commonly occurring in the third and fourth year of life, and the late or *second anal phase,* occurring between the ages of four and six. See *ontogeny, psychic.*

(1) The first anal phase is characterized by pleasure in the passage of the fecal mass (or 'fecal stick') over the anal mucous membrane at the sensitive muco-cutaneous junction area. At this period children will hold back their stools for the purpose of increasing the sensory stimulus through increased size of the mass with secondary increased expulsive pressure. In addition to direct anal sensory pleasure, there may occur 'hostility intent' pleasure, as the expelled stool mass may represent to the child an object which is destroyed in the expulsion.

(2) The second anal phase occurs usually in the period between four and six years of age, in the libidinal (emotional) development of a child. It is marked by a predominant interest and pleasure in the *retention,* or holding back, of stool. This is in direct contrast to the first anal phase, which is characterized by *expulsive* excretory *anal pleasure.* In this second anal phase, stool is treated as a possession with an inordinately high value.

Many adult traits of stinginess, hoarding, and interest in hobby collections find here their original prototype. All folklore is replete with observations equating the identity of excrement with money and gold. As examples of this unconscious identity, we have such phrases as 'filthy rich,' 'filthy with money,' 'money stinks' (Latin—*pecunia olet*), 'he likes to be around the smell of money,' etc.

Often a mother's or nurse's oversolicitude toward the child's stool 'regularity' serves to intensify this tendency to overvalue the stool; thus, when withheld, it becomes a powerful tool for getting inordinate attention and solicitude focused upon the child. When the stool is finally 'passed,' it is bestowed as a gift, reward, or largess on the anxious mother or nurse. (Sterba, R. *Introduction to the Psychoanalytic Theory of the Libido,* Nervous and Mental Disease Monographs No. 68, New York, 1942)

phase, magic A phase in the evolution of thinking in which the mere imagining of an object seems to the thinker the equivalent of his having created it. In other words, this is the magic-phase stage of thinking in which the world is seemingly created by the thinker. Freud referred to it as 'omnipotence of thought.' The various phases in the evolution of thinking can be studied in the development of thought in primitive man, in the child, in the schizophrenic, and in the normal adult. Thinking receives its direction toward reality, its respect for facts, only in the last phases of its evolution. Before this maturity takes place, there is the magic-phase stage in which the child operates directly (without any intervening medium) in his thoughts in such a way that every effect will seem to him to be the result of his wish, or, in other words, that there can be action by wish only. (Schilder, P. *Mind, Perception and Thought,* Columbia University Press, New York, 1942)

phase, oral incorporative The period (in early infantile development) marked by the appearance of possessiveness and its derivatives: voracity, greed, and envy, in association with 'cannibalistic' urges toward incorporation of bodily parts, such as mother's nipple, breast, finger, etc. In this way the danger of loss or separation from the 'loved' or 'security' object is obviated. Oral incorporation thus represents the ultimate of closeness.

When thwarted, the urge to possess becomes the drive for aggression, i.e. taking by force that which has been withheld. Later, these possessive, aggressive drives become the source of primary guilt-feelings, or early conscience. (Alexander, F. *Psychosomatic Medicine,* Norton, New York, 1950)

phase, phallic That stage of libidinal development in which libidinal and aggressive energies are concentrated mainly in the genital area (penis and clitoris); the phallic phase follows the anal phase and is generally in evidence during the period of four to six years of age. Concentration of drive energies in the genital area is due in part to increasing physical maturation, and in part to the child's increasing awareness of and natural curiosity about the differences between the sexes. Manipulation of the genitalia can certainly be observed before this phase, but masturbation now is characteristically accompanied by phantasies which relate to the use of the penis as an executive of libido and/or aggression. Object love in the phallic period is very close to what it will be in adolescence and adulthood, but there are two factors that decisively limit sexuality to a still infantile level. One is physiologic immaturity, and maturation here will have to wait until adolescence; the other is the danger attendant upon the choice of the love object. The child is restricted in his social contacts, and the mother who has been more or less the only other actor on his stage retains her leading role. She will be the object of his psychic energies here, just as she was in earlier days; this is the relationship termed *Oedipal.* The dangers of this relationship—rejection by the mother, retaliation by the father, etc.—necessitate a strong blockade against libidinal impulses. The ego achieves this by mobilizing aggressive energies against the id. Libidinal energies are repressed, and the child passes into the period of *latency* (q.v.). See *ontogeny, psychic.*

phase, preambivalent (prē-am-biv′à-lent) The earlier phase of the oral stage, when no conception of objects as yet exists. As infantile sexuality develops, it passes through several stages associated with the various erogenous zones. The libido is organized successively around these various erogenous zones. The earliest stage in infantile sexuality is the oral stage, in which the libido is organized around the mouth, for the earliest tensions and satisfactions which the infant experiences are those of hunger and its satiation.

The development of object-love is interwoven with the development of sexuality. As infantile sexuality develops, the type of relationship to objects changes, for associated with each stage and related to the particular erogenous zone around which the libido is being organized is a different type of relationship to objects. The stages of object-love before real love is reached are denoted as ambivalent: in these stages, the process of achieving satisfaction destroys the object. This is based chiefly on the physiological nature of oral and anal erogeneities which are the usual models for these object relationships. For example, in the oral stage, the libidinous aim is to incorporate the object, that is, to put it into the mouth. 'However, incorporation destroys the object objectively.'

Oral incorporation is the first object relationship, for the first awareness of an object was the longing for something already familiar to the infant which could gratify his needs but which was not present at the moment. And the gratification of hunger was the earliest need.

Before this concept of object arose, the infant was not yet aware of the outside world: he was aware only of his own tension and relaxation. Thus, since in the earlier phase of the oral stage oral eroticism had no object, there could not be an ambivalent attitude toward the object. As a result this early objectless period of the oral stage in the development of infantile sexuality is known as the preambivalent phase. It has been noted that in the preambivalent phase oral erotic pleasure is gained not only from the gratification of hunger but also from stimulation of the erogenous oral mucous membrane. This is easily seen in thumb-sucking. Accordingly, this preambivalent phase is also characterized as the 'early oral sucking stage of libidinal organization' or as the 'autoerotic stage' in the development of object-love. (Fenichel, O. *The Psychoanalytic Theory of Neurosis*, Norton, New York, 1945)

phase, pre-superego The early years of life before the superego has been formed. It is generally believed that the superego comes into being when it replaces the Oedipus complex. The pre-superego stage lasts until the child is five or six years of age, and includes the oral, anal, and phallic phases, as well as the development of the Oedipus complex in the phallic stage. A clear distinction is made between the pre-superego stage and the superego stage because of the different type of anxiety that is typical of each. In the pre-superego stage, anxiety is objective and more closely related to reality situations than in the adult superego stage, where anxiety is typically determined by the pre-

cepts of the fully developed superego, of whose role the individual is not consciously aware.

-phasia (-fā'zhē-à) Combining form meaning faculty or power of speech, from Gr. *phásis*, saying, word, from *phánai*, to speak.

phasmophobia (faz-mō-fō'bē-à) Fear of ghosts.

phasophrenias A group of benign degenerative psychoses with atypical symptoms that usually begin with cyclical phases or episodes from which the patient recovers spontaneously; called by Kleist 'degeneration psychoses.'

phengophobia (feng-gō-fō'bē-à) Fear of daylight (comfort being felt only at night).

phenocopy (fē'no-ko-pē) Imitation of the phenotype of a well-known mutant by a nonhereditary, externally produced variation which is virtually indistinguishable from an inherited variation.

phenomena, release Hughlings Jackson (1834-1911) conceived the term and mechanism of what he called the 'release phenomena.' By this he meant the unhampered activity of a lower center when a higher inhibiting center acting as a control is removed or destroyed, so that the 'released' structure can spontaneously discharge motor impulses.

phenomenology The study of events and happenings in their own right, rather than from the point of view of inferred causes; specifically, the theory that behavior is determined by the way in which the subject perceives reality at any moment, and not by reality as it can be described in physical, objective terms. See *existentialism*.

phenomenon, Aschner ocular (Bernhardt Aschner, Austrian gynecologist, b. 1883) Pressure exerted over eyeball produces a slowing of the pulse; also known as the oculocardiac reflex.

phenomenon, autokinetic Perception of varying degrees of apparent movement by a stationary light; when exposed to a pinpoint of light at a distance of 12 feet in a totally dark room for 10 minutes, some subjects experience no apparent movement while others report varying amounts of movement.

phenomenon, Napalkov (A.V. Napalkov, contemporary Russian neurophysiologist) An exception to the usual conditioned reflex experiment occurring in some phobic patients, in which the conditioning stimulus (e.g. a traumatic event) does not immediately produce a fear reaction; instead, the fear increases in time, rather than being extinguished as it ordinarily would during exposure to the unreinforced conditioning stimulus.

phenothiazine Class name for a group of psychotropic drugs. The phenothiazines are 'major tranquilizers' and are sometimes subdivided on the basis of chemical structure into:
alipathic group—including chlorpromazine, promazine, triflupromazine; piperazine group—including perphenazine, prochlorperazine, trifluoperazine, fluphenazine;
piperidine group—including mepazine, thioridazine.

phenotype (fē'nō-tīp) The changeable picture of an organism's appearance as produced and modified by its external life situation. In contrast to the *genotypical* structure, the *phenotype* of an organism is the sum of all its manifested attributes.

phenylketonuria (fē-nil-ke-tō-nur'ē-à) A hereditary disorder of phenylalanine metabolism, inherited as a Mendelian recessive, which appears in infancy and whose most striking manifestation is severe mental deficiency (most patients are idiots, with intelligence quotients below 20). Normally, phenylalanine is almost completely converted into tyrosine; in phenylketonuria, this metabolic pathway is blocked and phenylalanine is instead converted into phenylpyruvic acid (which is excreted as phenylketones in the urine). The associated mental defect is believed to be due to intoxication by the accumulated phenylalanine and/or its breakdown products in the brain.

phenylpyruvic oligophrenia (fē-nil-pī-roo'vik ol-i-gō-frē'nē-à) See *phenylketonuria.*

philo-, phil- (fil'ō-, fil-) Combining form meaning loving, from Gr. *phílos,* loving, friend(ly).

philobat (fī'lō-bat) Balint's term for the person with that type of primitive relationship to the environment characterized by an indifference to objects, which are typically considered as untrustworthy hazards, and a preference for objectless expanses such as mountains, deserts, sea, and air.

philoenia (fi-lē'nē-à) *Obs.* Love of wine.

philogenitive (fil-ō-jen'i-tiv) *Rare.* Erotic.

philomimesia (-mi-mē'sē-à) Morbid impulse to imitate or mimic.

philoneism (fi-lon'ē-is'm) Intense passion for novelty (Lombroso).

philopatridomania (fil-ō-pà-tri-dō-mā'-nē-à) Nostalgia.

philoprogeneity (-prō-jē-nē'i-tē) *Rare.* Love of offspring.

philoprogenitive (-prō-jen'i-tiv) Erotic; manifesting abnormal love for children.

phlebotomomania (flē-bot-ō-mō-mā'nē-à) *Obs.* A mania for bloodletting as a curative measure.

phlegmatic (fleg-ma'tik) See *type, phlegmatic.*

phobanthropy (fō-ban'thrō-pē) Fear of people; anthropophobia.

phobia (fō'bē-à) A phobia is a morbid fear associated with morbid anxiety. After excluding *traumatic* obsessions and phobias, because they are 'nothing but memories, unaltered images of important experiences,' Freud says: 'We must distinguish: (a) obsessions proper; (b) phobias. The essential difference between them is the following:
'Two components are found in every obsession: (1) an idea that forces itself upon the patient; (2) an associated emotional state. Now in the group of phobias this emotional state is always one of "morbid anxiety," while in true obsessions other emotional states, such as doubt, remorse, anger, may occur in the same

capacity as fear does in the phobias.' (Freud, S. *Collected Papers,* vol. 1, tr. by Riviere, J., Leonard and Virginia Woolf and The Institute of Psychoanalysis, London, 1924-25)

According to Freud phobias may be divided into two groups, 'according to the nature of the object feared: (1) common phobias, an exaggerated fear of all those things that everyone detests or fears to some extent; such as night, solitude, death, illness, dangers in general, snakes, etc.; (2) specific phobias, the fear of special circumstances that inspire no fear in the normal man; for example, agoraphobia and the other phobias of locomotion.' (Freud, S. ibid) See *anxiety-hysteria;* see also listings under *fear of.*

phobia, bathroom A fear of the toilet or bathroom, seen often in children and obsessive-compulsive neurotics. The phobia is frequently expressed as a fear of falling into the toilet, of being attacked by some monster coming from it, or as a fear of being infected. As a rule, such phobias represent a condensation of ideas of dirt (representing anal-erotic temptations) with ideas of castration.

phobia, bug Fear of small animals such as insects, spiders, flies, etc. Although animal phobias are usually distorted representations of the passionate, sexual, aggressive, 'animal-like' father, fears of small animals may be a direct projection of one's own drives. Creatures of this sort commonly represent genitals, feces, or little children (brothers and sisters).

phobia, cancer A fear of being eaten away or eaten up by neoplastic cells. The fear of being eaten up, whatever rationalized form it takes, is common in neurotics and is based upon fears of retaliation for having sadistically introjected an object. The dangerous introject may have different meanings on different psychic levels; thus it may represent a child, a penis, the breast, milk, etc. In like manner, the fear may be expressed in various ways—as a phantasy of impregnation, as a delusion or fear of being poisoned, as a fear of infection, as a fear of cancer, etc.

phobia, death A morbid fear of dying, most commonly an outgrowth of the idea of death as a punishment for death wishes against other persons, or of the idea of

death as the ultimate in relaxation consequent upon orgastic relief of one's own excitement, or of the idea of death as a reunion with a dead person.

phobia, doorknob A phobia in which the situation to be avoided (because it produces anxiety) is the touching of a doorknob. On first examination it would appear that this anxiety is related to touching an object which is believed to be dirty, as a doorknob must be. Thus the patient is protected against 'anal-erotic wishes to be dirty or to soil,' for in magical thinking the characteristics of an object are communicated by touching it.

As Fenichel points out, however, occasionally what appears to be only a protection against anal-erotic wishes may in reality be a protection against other impulses altered by regression, so that they seem to be anal-erotic impulses. He explains that the goal of all impulses involves touching an object, whether it be another person or one's own body. In this way, for example, the patient can achieve security against a wish to masturbate. 'Not infrequently a wish to masturbate that has been warded off has been altered by regression, so that the phobia appears to be a protection against anal-erotic wishes to be dirty or to soil.' (Fenichel, O. *The Psychoanalytic Theory of Neurosis,* Norton, New York, 1945)

phobia, hypochondriacal (hī-pō-kon-drī'-a-kal) Morbid fear of organic disease in the absence of known pathology.

phobia, impregnation See *phobia, cancer.*

phobia, infection See *phobia, cancer.*

phobia, insect See *phobia, bug.*

phobia, landscape Morbid fear which arises when the patient finds himself in some particular locale: e.g. mountains, plains, the sea, gently rolling woodlands, etc. This fear may reach the intensity of a landscape phobia, that is, morbid avoidance of the particular type of landscape causing the fear. Animism is at work in such a phobia. The patient has projected certain of his painful emotions or feelings onto a particular type of landscape. Whenever he finds himself in such an environment, these painful feelings are aroused in him by a sort of introjection. Probably there are certain landscapes which can more readily than others communicate a particular type of feeling, even to different sorts of people—that is, they can more easily give rise to certain emotions. Thus, endless prairies bring on melancholy, mountains engender activity and energy, etc.

Fenichel states that the painful emotions aroused by particular landscapes are associated with unmastered infantile excitation. Finding himself in the particular landscape toward which he is phobic, the patient feels threatened with a loss of the forces protecting him against dangerous infantile excitement. (Fenichel, O. *The Psychoanalytic Theory of Neurosis*, Norton, New York, 1945)

phobia, light-and-shadow A phobia or a morbid fear concerning light-and-shadow effects which works in a way similar to the mechanisms described in the *landscape phobia* (q.v.). 'Probably many phobias of darkness or twilight contain memories of primal scenes.' (Fenichel, O. *The Psychoanalytic Theory of Neurosis*, Norton, New York, 1945)

phobia, live burial A fear of being buried alive is a special 'mother's womb' type of claustrophobia which represents the mother's womb, one's own body sensations, and/or the interior of one's own body. The patient attempts to rid himself of his aggressive or sexual sensations by projection and, as with other claustrophobias, the need for sudden escape is a need for escape from one's own feared excitement as soon as it has reached a certain intensity.

phobia, poisoning See *phobia, cancer*.

phobia, school (307.1) School refusal syndrome; inability to attend school on a regular, five-day basis because of pervasive anxiety and somatic complaints (e.g. nausea, abdominal pain, headache). Usually, the condition is not a true phobia, but rather anxiety about separation from mother and home, often with obsessional concern about the safety of the mother. The central focus in management is prompt return to school.

phobia, street A common, morbid fear of being in a street; agoraphobia.

As with all phobias, the feared street may represent a temptation (especially a situation which would ordinarily call forth an aggressive or a sexual response), or it may represent punishment for the forbidden impulse directly or indirectly through symbolism, or it may be a fear that the anxiety will return because the initial anxiety attack occurred in the street. Any phobia may represent castration and punishment directly, or it may represent a loss of love.

phobia, toilet See *phobia, bathroom*.

phobia, traumatic (traw-mat'ik) See *obsession, traumatic*.

phobia, vehicle A fear of trains, boats, airplanes, automobiles, and/or other forms of transportation. Often these represent a struggle against sexual excitation as perceived in the pleasurable sensations of equilibrium, or a fear that one will be unable to escape from a confined area, this latter representing a need for escape from one's feared excitement as soon as it has reached a certain intensity.

phobic anxiety-depersonalization neurosis See *depersonalization*.

phobic neurosis *Anxiety-hysteria* (q.v.).

phobo-, phob- (fō'bō-, fōb-) Combining form meaning fearing, from Gr. *phóbos*, flight, (panic) fear.

phobodipsia, phobodipson (fō-bō-dip'sē-à, -dip'sun) *Obs.* Hydrophobia.

phobophobia Fear of fearing.

phocomelia A deformity of the limbs, seen in some types of mental retardation, in which the hands are attached directly to the shoulders without interposed arms.

phoneme (fō'nēm) In linguistics, a speech-sound that serves to distinguish words of different meanings; a word- (or meaning-) distinguishing sound: the vowels in: t*a*n, t*e*n, t*i*n, t*o*n, t*u*n; the consonants in *p*an, *b*an, *t*en, *d*en, *s*eal, *z*eal, *s*ink, *z*inc. There is a rigid sequence in the process of acquisition of new phonemes by a child learning to speak, and, accordingly, this process is reversed in various species of aphasic speech disorders: the patient loses those phonemes first which he has acquired most recently. In other words, the successive stages of speech disintegration are exactly contrary to the chronological process of their having been learned or acquired.

phonism (fō'niz'm) See *sensation, secondary.*

phonomania (fō-nō-mā'nē-à) Homicidal mania.

phonophobia (fō-nō-fō'bē-à) Fear of sounds; fear of one's own voice.

photic driving (fō'tik) See *electroencephalogram.*

photism See *sensation, secondary.*

photomania (fō-tō-mā'nē-à) Morbid craving for light; sun-worship.

photophobia Literally, fear of light, but rarely used to indicate a phobic avoidance reaction. More commonly the term is used to refer to an organically determined hypersensitivity to light (as in many acute infectious diseases with conjunctivitis) which results in severe pain and marked tearing when the patient is exposed to light.

-phrasia (-frā'zē-à) Combining form meaning phrase, phraseology, from Gr. *phrásis,* speech, way of speaking, phraseology.

phren (fren) The mind.

phrenalgia (fre-nal'jē-à) Guislain classified mental disorders as follows: phrenalgia or melancholy; phrenoplexia or ecstasy; hyperphrenia or mania; paraphrenia or folly; ideophrenia or delirium; aphrenia or dementia.

phrenasthenia *Obs.* Mental retardation; feeblemindedness.

phrenatrophia (fre-nà-trō'fē-à) *Obs.* Atrophy of the brain.

phrenesia (fre-nē'zē-à) *Obs.* Encephalitis.

phrenesis (fre-nē'sis) *Obs.* Phrenitis.

phrenetiasis (-net-ī'à-sis) *Obs.* Phrenitis.

phrenetic (fre-net'ik) Relating to or affected by phrenesis, phrenitis.

phrenhypnotic (fren-hip-not'ik) *Obs.* Pertaining to phrenology and hypnosis.

-phrenia (-frē'nē-à) Combining form meaning mind, mentality, from Gr. *phren,* mind.

phreniatry (fre-nī'à-trē) *Obs.* Cure of mental disorders.

phrenic (fren'ik) Pertaining to the mind or the diaphragm.

phrenicula (fre-nik'ū-là) *Obs.* Brain fever.

phrenismus (fre-niz'mus) *Obs.* Encephalitis.

phrenitic (fre-nit'ik) Phrenic.

phrenitis (fre-nī'tis) This term was used by Hippocrates (Aphorisms, 1248 ff.) for inflammation of the brain.
Celsus distinguished three forms: mental disorders accompanied by fever; a second form, characterized by melancholy and caused by black bile, was without fever; and a third class, with two subdivisions, 'for some err in having false images, and not in their whole mind, as Ajax and Orestes are represented in poetic fables; in others, the whole mind or judgment is affected.'

phrenitis aphrodisiaca (fre-nē'tēs à-frō-dē-zē'à-kà) *Obs.* Erotomania.

phrenitis apyreta (a-pē-rā'tà) *Obs.* Mania.

phrenitis potatorum (pô-tä-tō'room) *Obs.* Delirium tremens.

phreno- (fren'ō-) combining form meaning brain, mind; diaphragm, from Gr. *phren, phrenós,* mind, brain.

phrenoblabia (fren-ō-blā'bē-à) *Obs.* Dementia.

phrenocardia (-kär'dē-à) Herz uses this term for cardiac neurosis.

phrenolepsia (-lep'sē-à) *Obs.* Insanity.

phrenology (fre-nol′ō-jē) 'The doctrine that the different mental faculties have their seats respectively in particular tracts of brain-surface, and that the relative predominance of the faculties can be diagnosticated from the conformation of the parts of the skull overlying those traits.' (Foster, F.P. *Medical Dictionary*, Appleton, New York, 1892-94)

phrenomania (fren-ō-mā′nē-à) Collapse delirium; delirious mania; Bell's mania; typhomania. See *mania*.

phrenomesmerism (-mez′mēr-iz′m) Theory of animal magnetism.

phrenonarcosis (-när-kō′sis) Stupefaction; dulling of mental faculties.

phrenoparalysis (-pà-ral′i-sis) *Rare.* Psychogenic paralysis.

phrenopath (fren′ō-path) *Obs.* An alienist.

phrenopathia, phrenopathy (-path′ē-à, frē-nop′à-thē) *Obs.* Disorder or disease of the mind.

phrenophagia (-fā′jē-à) A term suggested by Radzinski to refer to the suppression and/or liquidation of those whose personalities and convictions are incompatible with or non-conforming to existing authoritarian standards, such as is practiced by the Communist party in Russia today.

phrenoplegia, phrenoplegy (-plē′jē-à, fren′ō-plē-jē) A sudden attack of mental derangement.

phrenoplexia (-plek′sē-à) Guislain's term for the clinical syndrome then (early part of 19th century) known as *ecstasy* (q.v.).

phrenopraxic (prak′sik) One of the many terms used to describe the drugs which have an action on the mind or psyche; viz. the tranquilizers, ataractics, psychotropics, etc.

phrenorthosis (frēn-or-thō′sis) *Obs.* Sound-mindedness.

phrenotherapy (fren-ō-ther′à-pē) *Obs.* Psychiatry.

phrenotropic (-trō′pik) Having an action on the mind. The term is usually used to describe certain pharmacologic agents, such as psychotomimetics, tranquilizers, and energizers, which have an effect on mental processes. See *psychotropics*.

phrenzy *Phrenitis* (q.v.); inflammation of the brain.

phricasmus (fri-kaz′mus) *Obs.* Shivering of psychic origin.

phrictopathia (frik-tō-path′ē-à) Sensation of touch, as unpleasantly tingling.

phronemophobia (fro-nē-mō-fō′bē-à) Fear of thinking.

phthinoid ([f]tin′oid) In Kretschmer's system of constitutional types this term refers to the variety of the *asthenic* type which is so underdeveloped as to represent a morbid condition in itself. This category of the asthenic type is contrasted with the *oligosthenic* and *eusthenic* varieties of moderately or considerably greater vigor, respectively.

In a more general sense, the term refers particularly to the flat, narrow chest characteristic of the tuberculous patient. Sometimes it is applied to any characteristic of the asthenic physique.

phthisical insanity ([f]tiz′i-kal) *Obs.* A psychotic state associated with pulmonary tuberculosis.

phthisiophobia ([f]thiz′ē-ō-fō-bē-à) Fear of tuberculosis.

phylo- (fī′lō-) Combining form meaning tribe, race, from Gr. *phylon*, race, tribe, clan, people, nation.

phyloanalysis (fī-lō-à-nal′i-sis) A method developed by Burrow which induces in the patient an awareness of his partitive or dissipative behavior, personally and socially, by contrasting the internal tensions concomitant to this type of behavior-reaction with an internal pattern of reaction that is concomitant to the organism's total motivation individually and as a phylum. Phyloanalysis regards the symptoms of the individual and of society as but outer aspects of impaired tensional processes which affect the balance of the organism's internal reaction as a whole. (Burrow, T. *The Biology of Human Conflict*, Macmillan, New York, 1937)

phylobiology (-bī-ol'ō-ji) The science of behavior that studies the organism's reactions in their phyletic motivation as these reactions mediate man's basic rapport with the external environment. Phylobiology posits a biological unity as a central governing principle motivating the behavior of the organism as an individual and as a species. (Burrow, T. *The Biology of Human Conflict*, Macmillan, New York, 1937)

phylogenesis, phylogeny (fī-lō-jen'ē-sis, fī-loj'ē-ni) Originally a biological term denoting the genealogical history and evolutionary development of a species or group as distinguished from the *ontogenetic* development of the individual. According to Haeckel's 'biogenetic law,' phylogeny is always recapitulated by *ontogeny* (q.v.).

The biological concept of phylogenesis has been used in different ways for analytical analogies in the psychological sphere, in order to emphasize the role of racial elements in the manifestations of the psyche. In accordance with the theory of analytical psychology that the mind or psyche, as an organ of the person, has archaic history, it is believed that patterns of the psyche are derived from racial activities.

As Dewey expressed it: 'We need to know about the social conditions which have educated original activities into definite and significant dispositions before we can discuss the psychological element in society. . . . Native human nature supplies the raw materials, but custom furnishes the machinery and the designs.' (Dewey, J. *Democracy and Education*, Macmillan, New York, 1916)

Jung speaks of psychic elements called *archetypes*, which he considers to be 'the fundamental elements of the unconscious mind, hidden in the depths of the psyche, or to use another comparison, they are the roots of the mind, sunk not only in the earth in the narrower sense, but in the world in general. Archetypes are symptoms of preparedness that are at the same time images and emotions. They are inherited with the structure of the brain of which they represent the psychic aspect.' (Jung, C.G. *Contributions to Analytical Psychology*, tr. by Baynes, H.G. and C.F., Kegan Paul, Trench, Trubner, London, 1928)

If applied in such a special metaphorical sense, the term phylogeny becomes synonymous with *archaic inheritance*, thus losing all connection with its original biological meaning. It is obvious that the psychoanalytical interpretation of the continuation of social and cultural conditions through 'inheritance' has been derived without reference to the biological conception of inheritance as expressed in the laws of human genetics.

Nietsche said that 'the dream carries us back to a condition of human culture far removed from the present and furnishes us with the means of a better understanding of that former condition.'

'The extension of the field of individual psychology into that of racial psychology, the psychological analysis of the myths, fairy tales, and magic practices of primitive peoples and early societies, opened up to the clinician a surprising perspective and gave rise to a multitude of new and stimulating problems.' (Storch, A. *The Primitive Archaic Forms in Schizophrefia*, tr. by Willard, C., Nervous and Mental Disease Publishing Company, New York and Washington, 1924)

'Primitive man is known to us by the stages of development through which he has passed: that is, through the inanimate monuments and implements which he has left behind for us, through our knowledge of his art, his religion and his attitude towards life, which we have received either directly or through the medium of legends, myths and fairy tales; and through the remnants of his ways of thinking that survive in our own manners and customs.' (Freud, S. *Totem and Taboo*, tr. by Brill, A.A., New Republic, New York, 1931)

phylogenetic symptoms See *schizophrenia, hebephrenic.*

phyloörganism (fī-lō-or'gan-iz'm) Burrow's term to denote the species man regarded as an organismic whole in which the element or individual is a phylically integrated unit.

phylopathology (-pà-thol'ō-jē) The scientific investigation of the underlying causal factors in behavior-disorders as envisaged from the background of phylobiology.

physiatrist (fiz'i-a-trist) See *physical medicine*.

physical Pertaining to the *physique*, or body build, or soma.

physical medicine The diagnosis and treatment of disease by physical means, which are a form of applied medical biophysics. The term includes physical therapy and rehabilitation. In 1947, a specialty board was established for this branch of medicine in the United States; a physician certified by this board is known as a physiatrist.

physical therapy See *therapy, physical*.

physiogenesis (fiz-ē-ō-jen'e-sis) Origin in the functioning of an organ of the body. Thus, intellectual deficiencies due to impairment of organic (cerebral) functioning are described as physiogenic manifestations.

physiognomy (fiz-ē-og'nō-mē) The physical appearance of the face; also, judging personality from facial appearance.

physioneurosis See *neurosis, actual*.

physiopathology (-pà-thol'ō-jē) The study of disturbances of physiology, whether functional or organic in nature. The capacity for growth and adjustment inheres in physical structure and function. 'The general psychological factors of an individual's personality are inherent in, and depend upon: (1) the nature of his physical state, (2) the degree of its effect upon his personal goals, (3) the cumulative effect of a physical deficiency affected by any other dysgenic element in the personality, (4) the local effect of the physical condition, but more especially in terms of the total personality, (5) the secondary effects of the physical condition in the light of social response to it as it conditions his education, occupation, recreation, social responsiveness and adaptability.' (Wile, I.S. *Physiopathology in Child Guidance* in *Handbook of Child Guidance*, ed. by Harms, E., Child Care Publications, New York, 1947)

physioplastic See *stage, physioplastic*.

physiotherapy See *therapy, physical*.

physique (fi-zēk') The *physical* structure of a human organism, the general build of the body as it is to be classified according to the various systems of *constitutional types* (q.v.).

pia mater (pē'à mä'ter) (L. 'tender mother') A delicate fibrous membrane closely enveloping the brain and spinal cord.

piblokot A type of disturbance reported in Eskimos, similar to *latah* (q.v.), imu, and mirachit.

pica (pī'kà) *Rare*. Perverted appetite. The young infant brings to his mouth everything his hand or mouth can reach. Gradually in the course of development, as well as a result of training, the child learns to discriminate between articles fit for oral consumption and those that are not. Pica is the recurrence of this early developmental characteristic at a later age and is found in children suffering from neurosis, or as a psychotic manifestation. It is also found in some children without any of these characteristics. 'Some children will constantly pluck out hairs and eat them, or will devour particles of fluff from the blankets. Others will seize every opportunity to eat unpleasant things, such as earth, sand, mud, or dirt of any sort.' (Cameron, H.C. *The Nervous Child*, Oxford University Press, Oxford, 1929)

Pica is rarely seen in normal people, except for pregnant women; it is found occasionally in the neurotic, but clinically it most frequently appears in schizophrenics, and in neglected and retarded children who are inadequately nourished.

picatio (pē-kà'tē-ō) *Obs.* Pica.

Pick's disease (Arnold Pick, Prague psychiatrist, 1851-1924) (290.1, 309.6) A pre-senile psychosis; also known as *circumscribed cortical atrophy*, lobar sclerosis. It consists of progressive dementia with severe emotional impairment and social and ethical aberrations. Like *Alzheimer's disease* (q.v.), Pick's disease occurs more in women than in men and average age of onset is 55 years. Pathologically, there is focal atrophy of the cortical cells in the temporal and frontal regions. There is more often a family history of heredodegenerative traits in

Pick's disease than in Alzheimer's, and while the dementia is less pronounced the emotions are more severely impaired.

picture, concrete 'Perhaps the most prominent feature of primitive thinking is the tendency to employ "full concrete pictures" instead of abstract ideas. The thought of primitive man works with total percepts of phenomena without analytic discrimination of their essential constituent parts; he thinks in full concrete pictures just as they are encountered in real experience. . . . In this connection it should be remembered that our own ideas of number have grown out of concrete sensory perceptions. The word *five* is derived from the Sanskrit *pancha*, meaning hand; the Roman number V represents the hand.' (Storch, A. *The Primitive Archaic Forms in Schizophrenia*, tr. by Willard, C., Nervous and Mental Disease Publishing Company, New York and Washington, 1924) Many psychiatric patients, particularly those with schizophrenia, abandon the use of abstract ideas, concrete ideas taking their place.

picture, inward An internally apprehended image or picture, as commonly presented in dreams, phantasies, and visions: the pictorialized expression of material from the deeper levels of the unconscious part of the psyche. It is an 'inward picture' not only because it *occurs* 'inwardly' but also because (according to Jung, whose expression it is) it is a picture of our most 'inward,' innermost self—the *true* SELF.

Jacobi says: 'In Jungian dream-analysis . . . the psychic images [i.e. inward pictures] in the dream as in all their other manifestations are at once reflection and essence of the dynamics of the psyche. They are at once reflection and essence of the dynamics of the mind, just as in the case of a waterfall the waterfall is at once reflection and essence of force itself. For without force, i.e. physical energy (which in itself is only a working hypothesis), there could be no waterfall, whose essence it therefore is; but simultaneously it reflects too in its form of being this energy, which without the waterfall, in which it becomes visible as it were, would be wholly inaccessible to observation and verification. They are the real energy-transformers in psychic events. They have at the same time expressive and impressive character, expressing on the one hand internal psychic happenings pictorially, and on the other hand influencing—after having been transformed into images—through their meaningful content these same happenings, thus furthering the flow of the psychological processes. For example, the symbol of the withered Tree of Life, which was meant to convey the idea of an overintellectualized existence that had lost its natural instinctive basis, would on the one hand express this meaning pictorially before the very eyes of the dreamer, and on the other hand, by thus presenting itself to him, would impress him and thereby influence his psychic dynamism in a certain direction. One can continually observe in the course of an analysis how the various pictorial motives determine and lead into one another. In the beginning they still appear in the guise of personal experiences; they bear the characteristics of childhood or other remembrances. As the analysis penetrates to deeper levels, however, they exhibit the outlines of the archetypes ever more clearly, the field becomes dominated ever more definitely by the symbol alone.' (Jacobi, J. *The Psychology of C.G. Jung*, Kegan Paul, Trench, Trubner, London, 1942)

pigmentary retinal lipoid neuronal heredo-degeneration (pig'men-tēr-ē ret'in-al lip'oid nū-ron'al he-red-ō-de-gen-er-ā'shun) Spielmeyer-Vogt's disease, a type of *amaurotic family idiocy* (q.v.).

pineal substance See *therapy, pineal*.

Pinel's system Named after Philippe Pinel, a Parisian psychiatrist, 1745 - 1826, through whose efforts forcible restraint in the management of the mentally ill was abolished.

pink disease *Acrodynia* (q.v.).

pinocytosis (pē-nō-sī-tō'sis) Entrapment of fluid by the folds of undulating cellular membranes, with the formation of vacuoles that migrate through the cytoplasm; this is perhaps the major method by which the glia contribute to metabolic transport within the central nervous system.

pithiatism (pith'ē-à-tiz'm) A forced suggestion; a method of removing hysterical symptoms by way of persuasion. The word was coined by Babinski, who held that everything that is hysterical may be caused by suggestion.

'In no case, however, can I accept Babinski's "explanation," according to which stigmata (like hysterical symptoms in general) are only pithiatisms suggested by the doctor.' (Ferenczi, S. *Further Contributions to the Theory of Psycho-Analysis,* tr. by Suttie, J. I., Leonard and Virginia Woolf and The Institute of Psychoanalysis, London, 1926)

pithiatric (pith-ē-at'rik) Curable by persuasion or suggestion, referring to the class of hysterical symptoms which can be made to disappear or be reproduced by means of suggestion.

Pitres' rule A statement of the usual course of recovery of language functions in polyglots: a polyglot who becomes aphasic as the result of vascular ictus or craniocerebral trauma usually begins to understand and then to speak the language most familiar to him and in which he was most fluent at the onset of aphasia; only later are other previously known languages reestablished, more slowly and less completely.

pituitarism (pi-tū'i-tēr-iz'm) Overactivity of the pituitary gland.

pituitary cachexia See *cachexia, hypophysial.*

pity Compassion or sympathy for another's misfortune or sufferings. The term generally implies that the object of pity is regarded as inferior to the subject. Pity may appear as a character trait in persons with conflicts about unconscious passive-feminine wishes in which case it may signify "I shower you with love as I wish I had been loved." It may also represent a passive-feminine masochistic identification with the sufferer.

PKU *Phenylketonuria* (q.v.).

placebo (plà-se'bō, plà-kā'bō) (L. 'I am to placate') Any medication used to relieve symptoms, not by reason of specific pharmacologic action but solely by reinforcing the patient's favorable expectancies from treatment. Also known as *dummy,* particularly in Britain. Although a placebo may be an inert substance, as used in present-day research placebos more commonly contain active substances that at least in part mimic the side-effects of the specific therapeutic agent with which the placebo is being compared. Placebo effects include all those psychologic and psychophysiologic benefits and undesirable reactions which reflect the patient's expectations; they depend upon the diminution or augmentation of apprehension produced by the symbolism of medication or by the symbolic implications of the physician's behavior and attitudes.

The term may be defined even more broadly to include *any* therapeutic procedure that has an effect on a symptom or disease, although objectively it has no specific action on the condition being treated.

plan, life With this term Adler indicates the entire system of behavior by means of which the person prevents his 'superiority' from being subjected to the test of reality.

plane, subjective 'By interpretation upon the subjective plane, I understand that conception of a dream or phantasy in which the persons or conditions appearing therein are related to subjective factors entirely belonging to the subject's own psyche. It is common knowledge that the image of an object existing in our psyche is never exactly like the object, but at most only similar.'

'In the analytical treatment of unconscious products, therefore, it is essential that the image shall not immediately be assumed to be identical with the object; it is wiser to regard it as an image of the subjective relation to the object. That is what is meant by the consideration of a product upon the subjective plane.' (Jung, C.G. *Psychological Types,* tr. by Baynes, H.G., Harcourt, Brace, New York and London, 1923)

planning, social See *social policy planning.*

planomania (plan-ō-mā'nē-à) Morbid impulse 'to wander from home and throw off the restraints of society.' 'I think it is the instinct of mental self-preservation that makes young men sometimes fly from the influences of civilization and to take to the backwoods, the "planomania" of some authors.' (Clouston, T.S. *Clinical*

Lectures on Mental Diseases, 6th ed., Churchill, London, 1904)

planophrasia (plan-ō-frā′zē-à) Wandering speech; usually used to refer to flight of ideas in manic syndromes.

plaques, senile See *senile psychoses.*

plasm, germ The theory developed by Weismann conceives the *germ plasm* (the reproductive tissue which produces the germ cells) as separate and distinct from the other body tissues representing the *somatoplasm.* It is the basis of the important genetic concept that attributes acquired by the organism during the life time of its phenotype are never inheritable.

According to this concept (true only in higher animals and therefore of limited value) the germ plasm is the sole seat of hereditary characters and thus represents the potentially immortal part of an organism, through the continuing succession of its reproductive cells. The environment may cause many variations in the somatoplasm, but it has been shown by Weismann and other geneticists that these changes are not transferred to the germ plasm and, therefore, cannot be hereditarily transmitted to the offspring.

plasmon (plaz′mon) This biological term was introduced by von Wettstein to characterize the independent gene-like elements in the cytoplasm, in contradistinction to the nuclear system of Mendelian gene-units, for which he proposed the term *genome.*

plate, neural (nū′ral) See *cephalogenesis.*

platonic nymphomania See *nymphomania, grave.*

platonization (From *platonize,* to make platonic in character, idealize, as in platonic love, which in Plato's view passed from physical passion on to higher contemplation of the ideal, i.e. to love free from sexual desire.) A mental mechanism consisting of considering the desired act without actually performing it. Platonization is thus a mechanism of defense against impulses and would be considered by some as evidence of prelogical, primitive thinking wherein thought has become

an equivalent of action by reason of infantile belief in the magical omnipotence of thought. Platonization is typical of paranoia, where thought rather than action reigns supreme. But, like any other mechanism of defense, such as repression, sublimation, or projection, platonization need not imply gross psychiatric abnormality in the person who uses the mechanism.

platybasia (pla-ti-bā′zē-à) Basilar impression; an abnormality of the base of the skull, often congenital, in which the angle between the basisphenoid and the basilar portion of the occipital bone is widened. The neck is abnormally short and the head is sometimes mushroom-shaped.

platycephaly (pla-ti-sef′à-lē) Flattening of the crown of the head.

play See *activity, ludic.*

pleasure-ego See *ego, pleasure.*

pleasure, function Enjoyment of functioning or doing or exercising one's own capacities. Function pleasure is obtained when an act can be accomplished without anxiety; such pleasure is the basis for subsequent repetitions of situations which originally induced excitation and anxiety, as is seen frequently in children who enjoy endless repetitions of the same game or of the same story, which has to be retold in exactly the same words.

pleasure, muscle Pleasure connected with body movements.

pleasure-pain-principle See *principle, pleasure.*

pleasure-principle See *principle, pleasure.*

-plegia, -plegy (-plē′jē-à, -plē′jē) Combining form meaning (paralytic) stroke, attack, from Gr. *plēge,* blow, stroke.

pleniloquence (plē-nil′ō-kwens) Excessive talking.

pleocytosis (plē-ō-sī-tō′sis) Excess of cells; pleocytosis of the cerebrospinal fluid indicates meningeal irritation.

pleonasm (plē′ō-naz′m) Redundancy or

the use of more than enough words to express an idea, as is seen in *circumstantiality* (q.v.).

pleonexia (plē-ō-nek′sē-à) Excessive greediness; a psychosis characterized by an uncontrollable desire for acquisition or gain.

pleurothotonos, pleurotetanus (ploo-rō-thot′ō-nos, -tet′à-nus) Lateral bending or arching of the body; sometimes observed in hysteria.

plot, melody See *speech, plateau*.

plumbism *Lead poisoning* (q.v.).

pluralism The concept that behavior is causally determined by a multiplicity of complexly interrelated factors. 'Freud and Meyer were among the first to appreciate the importance of the setting, the *theme*, the emergence of a behavior item or action tendency from a complexly-integrated set of experiences and their meaning to the experiencing individual. Freud could show how the early "family drama" was a theme which had a profound significance throughout a person's life, influencing his ambitions, identifications, choice of a mate, and even the contents of his dreams. Meyer's pluralistic orientation could not be satisfied with the study of behavior as a self-contained phenomenon: he was too much aware of the multiplicity of factors at play in any situation. His relativistic mode of thinking caused him to look for the cohesion and interdependence of these factors. . . .

'Behavior, thus considered, is an integral function which derives its existence, its form and its meaning from the totality of its setting. Hence it can be understood only in terms of its setting. The setting is the resultant of relationships and experiences which have begun to exert themselves from the beginning of life and toward which a person has formed his own accepting or rejecting, defensive, aggressive or submissive reaction tendencies. Behavior of the moment thus appears as the temporarily last scene of an uninterrupted plot or theme, during which a person has developed a certain readiness to perform in the particular manner in which he does perform.' (Kanner, L. *Child Psychiatry*, Thomas, Springfield, Ill., 1948)

plus complementarity See *complementarity*.

plutomania (plōō-tō-mā′nē-à) Wealth-greediness.

pneuma (nū′mà) The principle of life, according to Hippocrates.

pneumatopathy (n⁻u-mà-top′à-thē) *Obs.* Healing by psychic cure; mind cure.

pneumoencephalogram (nū-mō-en-sef′a-lō-gram) An X-ray of the skull following replacement of measured quantities of cerebrospinal fluid with air or some other gas by means of lumbar or cisternal puncture.

pnigerophobia (nī-jē-rō-fō′bē-à) Fear of smothering.

pnigophobia (nig-ō-fō′bē-à) Fear of choking.

Po Rorschach scoring symbol for a position response, i.e. a response determined or suggested by the location of the particular stimulus area on the card.

poena talionis (poi′nà tà-lē-ō′nēs) (L. 'punishment by retaliation') That law of ancient Rome according to which the culprit was subjected to the identical injury or material loss as he had caused to the plaintiff.

poikilothymia (poi-ki-lō-thī′mē-à, -thim′-ē-à) By this term E. Kahn designates a mental constitution closely akin to cyclothymia, differing from the latter in that in poikilothymia the mood variations are more intense.

poinephobia (poi-nē-fō′bē-à) Fear of punishment.

point, critical The event, occurrence, or situation in which the patient's problem comes to a head and he mobilizes his resources for dealing with the problem. Slavson, who suggested the term, believes that in nearly all therapy an ultimum point is reached in the specific intrapsychic or environmental situation which is the culminating point of therapy. See *problem, nuclear*.

point, flicker-fusion Critical flicker frequency. See *flicker.*

pointing A test for vestibular rather than pure cerebellar function; patient is requested to extend his arm and perform the movements at the shoulder; examiner stands in front of him, and patient touches with his extended index finger the examiner's two index fingers which are held together in a fixed position; with eyes open, there is no deviation normally; on closing the eyes, and knowing the position of the examiner's fingers, the patient should be able to touch the same spot every time; if he deviates to the left or right there is said to be past-pointing.

poisoning, deadly nightshade (294.3) Strychnomania. Deadly nightshade is a plant of the genus Solanum. Poisoning may follow ingestion of the black berries of the plant. The mouth and tongue become dry and vision is impaired; any or all of the following symptoms may then appear: visual hallucinations, mutism, restlessness, unresponsiveness, widely dilated pupils, disorientation and confusion, with increasing agitation. The patient then falls into a deep sleep and awakes asymptomatic but with amnesia for the agitated period. During the disturbed period, a misdiagnosis of acute schizophrenic reaction is commonly made.

polar body See *body, polar.*

polarity (pō-lar'i-tē) Possession of opposite properties, as if opposite pole.
From the psychoanalytic point of view, 'mental life as a whole is governed by *three polarities,* namely, the following antitheses: Subject (ego)—Object (external world); Pleasure-Pain; Active-Passive.
(Freud, S. *Collected Papers,* vol. 4, tr. by Riviere, J., Leonard and Virginia Woolf and The Institute of Psychoanalysis, London, 1924-25)

policy, open-door See *open-door policy; community, therapeutic.*

polioclastic (pō-lē-ō-klas'tik) Destructive to gray matter of the central nervous system; ordinarily used to refer to neurotropic viruses.

poliodystrophy, progressive infantile cerebral (pō-lē-ō-dis'trō-fē) (31x.x) Also known as *Alpers' disease;* a nonlipid neuronal destruction of cerebral tissue with preservation of myelinated structures, probably most commonly due to cerebral anoxia, less commonly to maternal toxemia or genetic factors. Seizures and mental retardation are the usual symptoms.

polio-encephalitis hemorrhagica superior (pō-lē-ō-en-sef-à-lī'tis hem-or-à'ji-ka soo-per'i-or) See *Wernicke's encephalopathy.*

poliomyelitis (pō'lē-o-mī-e-lī'tis) Infantile paralysis; Heine-Medin's disease. An acute infectious disease due to a virus which attacks the anterior horn cells of the spinal cord and brain-stem. The usual route of infection is the alimentary tract via personal contact with healthy carriers and abortive cases, and via the fecal contamination of food. It has been suggested that the virus travels from the alimentary tract to the central nervous system by way of the autonomic nerves. The peak incidence is in the late summer and early fall; the young are most susceptible, and the disease is rare after the age of 25, although in both the United States and Great Britain the age incidence has been rising. Reports to date indicate that 'Salk vaccine' affords highly efficacious prophylaxis at least against the paralytic symptoms.
Symptoms may appear in several ways: there may be development of immunity without any symptoms of illness; the symptoms may never be more than those of a mild general infection; symptoms of general illness may be combined with pleocytosis of the cerebrospinal fluid, without further progression (this is the most usual form during epidemics); and in a minority, the infection runs its full course and causes paralysis.
Symptoms are divided into two stages, the pre-paralytic and the paralytic. In the pre-paralytic stage, there is an early phase with symptoms of general infection and a late phase with more severe headache, pain in the back and limbs, and hyperesthesia of both superficial and deep tissues. Symptoms of the paralytic stage depend upon the area of central nervous system attacked, i.e. spinal or brain-stem symptoms. Paralysis may be widespread or localized, and usually maximal damage is done within the first 24 hours. Thus only a portion of the muscles initially

affected will remain permanently paralyzed. In the brain-stem form, there is danger of involvement of the cardiac and respiratory centers.

poliomyelitis, chronic See *sclerosis, amyotrophic lateral.*

pollakiuria (pol-à-kē-ū'rē-à) Abnormally frequent urination.

pollution The discharge of semen and seminal fluid in the absence of sexual intercourse; the term is often used synonymously with *nocturnal emission.*

polyandry (pol'i-an-drē) Having more than one husband.

polychromate, abnormal (pol-i-krō'māt) One who distinguishes most colors, but fails to perceive one or two, or confuses two colors.

polyclonia epileptoides continua (pô-lē-klō'nē-à e-pē-lãp-tô-ē'dãs kôn-tē'noo-à) See *epilepsy, continuous.*

polycratism (pō-lik'rà-tiz'm) (From Polyerates, tyrant of Samos [535-512 B.C.] who wished to allay the envy of the gods, because all his enterprises were invariably highly successful. In a galley fitted out with regal splendor Polycrates sailed out on a pleasure trip. As if inadvertently his favorite signet-ring fell overboard and with ostentatious grief Polycrates returned home, inwardly happy that he had appeased the gods. Two or three days later a fisherman brought to the palace a huge fish he thought fit only for the ruler's table. When Polycrates carved the fish at the repast, he found his ring, which the fish had swallowed. The gods were not to be appeased—Polycrates met death by crucifixion.) 'By analogy with Schiller's poem "The Ring of Polycrates" one could give this name to the superstition that dreads lest things should "go too well" with one, because then a proportionately heavier punishment is to be expected from God. In an analysis it could be traced to a bad conscience due to personal phantasies that were reprehensible.' (Ferenczi, S. *Further Contributions to the Theory and Technique of Psycho-Analysis,* tr. by Suttie, J.I., Leonard and Virginia Woolf and The Institute of Psychoanalysis, London, 1926)

polydipsia (pol-ē-dip'sē-à) Excessive thirst.

polydipsia ebriosa (pô-lē-dēp'sē-à à-brē-ō'zà) A craving for intoxicants.

polygamy (po-lig'à-mē) Having more than one mate. This term is thus more general than *polyandry* and *polygyny* (qq.v.), both of which it includes.

polyglot (pol'ē-glot) See *reaction, polyglot.*

polyglot neophasia See *neophasia, polyglot.*

polygraph, Keeler Lie detector.

polygyny (pol'ig-i-nē) Having more than one wife.

polyhybrid (pol-ē-hī'brid) In genetics this characterizes *hybrids* which differ in more than three hereditary characters. See *hybrid.*

polylogia (-lō'jē-à) See *tachylogia.*

polymorph, polymorphous perverse See *perverse, polymorphous.*

polyneuritis (-nū-rī'tis) A disease in which there usually is simultaneous inflammation of a large number of peripheral nerves. The signs and symptoms are usually bilateral and frequently symmetrical, although not all the nerves are affected with equal severity. The condition is due either to an infectious agent or an endogenous or exogenous poison, probably operating through the circulatory system. Prominent symptoms include severe pain, wasting of the muscles and paralysis. Clinical examples are alcoholic polyneuritis, arsenic polyneuritis, diabetic polyneuritis, polyneuritis of pregnancy, etc.

polyneuritis, acute infective *Guillain-Barré's syndrome* (q.v.).

polyneuritis, acute toxic *Guillain-Barré's syndrome* (q.v.).

polyneuritis, erythroedema (e-rith-rō-ē-dē'mà) *Acrodynia* (q.v.).

polyneuritis, rheumatic (rū-ma'tik) *Guillain-Barré's syndrome* (q.v.).

polyopia, polyopsia (pol-ē-op'ē-à, -op'sē-à) A rare visual phenomenon consisting of multiple vision, or visual perseveration in space; apperception of one object appears to the subject as two or more objects. Polyopia may be of organic origin (associated with pathology in the ocular apparatus, with nystagmus, or with occipital lobe dysfunction), and it may also appear as a conversion symptom in hysteria. See *palinopia.*

polyparesis (-par'ē-sis) General paralysis of the insane; see *paresis, general.*

polyphagia (-fā'jē-à) Excessive eating; gluttony.

polyphobia (-fō'bē-à) Fear of many things.

polypnoea (pol-ip'nē-à) Deep, labored, and rapid respiration. It may be physically or psychically determined.

polyposia (pol-ē-pō'sē-à) Craving for intoxicating drinks.

polypsychism (-sī'kiz'm) The concept (sometimes found in psychotic patients) that each person possesses several souls.

polyradiculoneuritis (-ra-dik-ū-lō-nū-rī'-tis) *Gullain-Barré's syndrome* (q.v.).

polyuria (-ū'rē-à) Excessive excretion of urine; profuse micturition.

Pompadour phantasy See *phantasy, Pompadour.*

ponopathy (pō-nop'à-thē) Synonymous with *nervous exhaustion.* See *neurasthenia.*

ponophobia (pon-ō-fō'bē-à) Fear of overwork.

pons That portion of the metencephalon which forms the floor of the fourth ventricle; the pons is continuous with the midbrain anteriorly, and with the medulla oblongata posteriorly. The pons contains the pontine nuclei which connect the cerebellum with the cerebrum, and the nuclei of cranial nerves 4, 5 (in part), 6, and 7. Transverse fibers of the pons form the brachium pontis, or middle cerebellar peduncle; the longitudinal fibers of the pons contain the pyramidal tracts and the corticopontile fibers.

pontocerebellar angle tumor (pon-tō-ser-e-bel'ēr) See *syndrome, pontocerebellar angle.*

popular response In Rorschach scoring, any response which is among those responses given more frequently by healthy subjects than any other responses. Various writers, on the basis of statistical analysis of their case protocols, have constructed itemized lists of the responses to be classified as popular.

A response is classified as *original* if it occurs not more than once in 100 records, and as *individual* if it is given by only one subject.

population genetics See *genetics.*

porencephaly (pō-ren-sef'à-lē) A developmental anomaly in which there occur small or large unilateral or bilateral cavities in the brain substance.

poriomania (pō-rē-ō-mā'nē-à) An irresistible impulse to journey. The latter may be carried out with the full and complete knowledge of the person or there may be complete amnesia for all activities associated with the trip. States of poriomania may be associated with criminal acts.

poriomaniac One affected by poriomania. 'There are people who, under the influence of a strong inner affect, feel themselves compelled to run around for hours; they seek, so-to-say, the land of their longing, of their desire.' 'Those gruesome sexual crimes reported again and again by newspapers are usually commited in similar twilight states by pathological poriomaniacs.' (Stekel, W. *Encyclopaedia Sexualis,* edited by Robinson, V., Dingwall-Rock, New York, 1936)

pornerastic (por-nēr-as'tik) Fond of prostitutes.

pornographomania (por-nō-graf-ō-mā'nē-à) Morbid impulse to write obscene letters.

pornography (por-nog'rà-fē) Obscene, lewd, lascivious, prurient drawing or writing, and especially that which aims to arouse the viewer or reader sexually. Obscenity is an intrinsic tendency of the work itself and not the reaction of a particular person to it, be he genius, moron, or pervert.

pornolagnia (por-nō-lag'nē-à) A perverted lustful attraction for prostitutes.

porphyria, acute intermittent (por-fē'-ri-à) A familial metabolic disorder of the pyrroles, resulting in the production of abnormal types of porphyrins, which appear in the urine; first described by Gunther and Waldenstrom. Females are four times as frequently affected as males, usually between the ages of 20 and 35. The first symptom is usually abdominal pain, often with nausea, vomiting, low-grade fever, leukocytosis, and tachycardia. These symptoms continue and to them are added psychic changes (irritability, tension, and often progression to a schizophreniform psychosis) and, later, neurologic symptoms (muscular weakness and other signs of peripheral neuritis). There is no known treatment. The disease is fatal in about half of the cases; mortality is higher (60-90%) in those with cranial nerve involvement.

porphyrinuria (por-ē-rif-nūr'ē-à) See *porphyria, acute intermittent.*

porphyrismus The mental changes associated with porphyria; see *porphyria, acute intermittent.*

porropsia (po-rop'sē-à) Inability to gauge the real distance of objects, which appear more distant than they really are, without any alteration in their size.

port-wine stain See *angiomatosis, trigeminal cerebral.*

posiomania (pō-sē-ō-mā'nē-à) Dipsomania.

position, depressive One of the stages in mental development hypothesized by Melanie Klein. This position succeeds the paranoid-schizoid position (see *position, paranoid-schizoid*) and is believed to be at its peak at the sixth month of life. Following the development of the paranoid-schizoid position, the ego continues to gain strength and shows a growing capacity for integration and synthesis. In the depressive position, the child's fear is of destroying and then losing the beloved and indispensable object. In contrast to the eariler position, the injured object in the depressive position appears not so much a persecutor as a love object toward whom the child feels guilty and wants to make reparation.

position, paranoid-schizoid One of the stages in mental development hypothesized by Melanie Klein. This position is believed to be at its peak during the third or fourth month of life and is an outcome of the method used by the infant to protect himself from destruction by his death instinct. Aggression is deflected (projected) onto the external object; this makes the object into a persecutor. But some aggression is retained by the ego, and this leads to aggression being turned actively against the persecutory object. The infant is thus compelled to destroy the object to escape persecution. At the same time, the primal process of introjection is used to defend the ego against the death instinct, and the breast is internalized and split into a helpful, loved object on the one hand, and into a frightening, hated object on the other. The internalized *good object* supports the ego in its binding of the death instinct by libido. Part of the death instinct is projected into a part of the ego itself and contributes to the formation of the superego. But some internalized *bad objects* are so terrifying that they are not handled in this way; instead, they are split off and relegated to the deeper layers of the unconscious.

The paranoid-schizoid position is normally succeeded by the depressive position. See *position, depressive.*

P.O.S.M. Acronym for patient-operated selected mechanisms, i.e. electromechanical devices that can be controlled by patients with high cord lesions or extreme disability from other causes.

possum Same as *P.O.S.M.* (q.v.).

postambivalence See *stage, postambivalent.*

postcentral gyrus (gī'rus) See *lobe, parietal.*

post coitum triste (pôst' kô'ē-toom tris'-te) (L. 'gloom after sexual intercourse') See *impotence, psychic.*

postconcussion neurosis See *neurosis, post-concussion.*

postdormital chalastic fits See *paralysis, sleep.*

post-encephalitic syndromes See *post-traumatic and post-encephalitic syndromes, classification of.*

posterolateral sclerosis See *sclerosis, posterolateral.*

postpartum psychosis See *psychosis, puerperal.*

post-traumatic and post-encephalitic syndromes, classification of (pōst-traw-ma'-tik, pōst-en-sef-à-li'tik) Blau (*Research Publications, Association for Nervous and Mental Diseases 34:* 404-423, 1954) has suggested the following classification:
I. Etiologic Classification
   A. Cerebral birth injury
      1. Direct injury—prolonged molding, disturbed labor, breech extraction, instrumental delivery, etc.
      2. Anoxemia—prolonged labor, abnormalities of pregnancy, placenta previa, strangulated cord, etc.
   B. Cerebral trauma—accidental head injury with or without skull fracture, concussion, contusion, subdural hematoma, etc.
   C. Cerebral inflammatory and degenerative diseases
      1. Encephalitis—epidemic, variola, vaccinia, rubella, measles, mumps, meningitis, etc.
      2. Encephalopathy — pertussis, burns, lead, epilepsy, etc.
II. Psychiatric Classification (see *syndrome, organic*)
   A. Intellectual defect conditions
      1. Focal defects (309.2)—memory disturbances, paraphasias, attention defects, concentration, etc.
      2. Generalized intellectual defect (31x.1)—general mental retardation, secondary dementia, learning difficulties, etc.

B. Personality disorders (293.5; 309.2)—conduct and behavior disorders, delinquency, psychoneurosis, psychosis, character disorders, etc.

potamophobia (pot-à-mō-fō'bē-à) Fear of rivers.

potence, potency The ability (of the male) to consummate the act of sexual intercourse.

potential, action See *action current.*

potential, specific action See *instinct.*

potestas coeundi (pô-tes'tàs kô-e-oon'dē) (L. 'ability to copulate') Sexual potency.

potomania (pō-tō-mā'nē-à) *Obs.* Morbid impulse for intoxicating drinks; *dipsomania; delirium tremens* (qq.v.).

pototromania (pō-tot-rō-mā'nē-à) *Obs.* Delirium tremens.

pototromoparanoia (pō-tō-trom-ō-par-à-noi'à) *Obs.* Delirium tremens.

Potzl's syndrome See *syndrome, Potzl's.*

POW See *syndrome, prisoner of war.*

praecox, heboid (prē'koks, hē'boid) 'Not infrequently the principal changes [in dementia praecox] are shown in an emotional dulling, indifference and stupidity without the occurrence of hallucinations or developed delusions. These cases in which the dementia seems to be the principal symptom, and in which the accessory symptoms play a small part, have also been spoken of as simple or heboid precox.' (Barnes, F.M. *An Introduction to the Study of Mental Disorders,* 2nd ed., Mosby, St. Louis, 1923)

praecox, predementia (prē-dē-men'shē-à prē'koks) The personality constitution of the schizophrenic prior to the appearance of overt symptoms of the disorder.
   'Dementia praecox is thus the culmination of a long-continued series of faulty mental habits. The predementia praecox character is one in which the individual habitually ceases to apply himself vigorously to the real facts of life. His thoughts are devoted to day-dreams

and fantasies, and by constantly seeking refuge in evasions he loses the capacity for grappling with difficulties. Thus, in the presence of some added stress, which the ordinary individual would be prepared to meet, "the sensitive and weakened individual will react with manifestations constituting the deterioration process" of dementia praecox.' (Kraepelin, E. *Lectures on Clinical Psychiatry*, 3rd ed., revised and edited by Johnstone, T.H., Bailliére, Tindall & Cox, London, 1913) Kraepelin credits Adolf Meyer with having first delineated the character syndrome observed in predementia praecox.

Pragung (prà'gooNg) *Imprinting* (q.v.).

-praxia (-prak'sē-à) Combining form meaning acting, doing, act(-ion), from Gr. *práxis*, a doing, acting, action, from *prássein*, to achieve, accomplish, practice, do.

praxiology (prak-sē-ol'ō-jē) Dunlap's term for the science of behavior which excludes the study of consciousness and similar non-objective, metaphysical concepts.

praxi-therapeutics (-ther-à-pū'tiks) An old term for occupational treatment; ergotherapy.

pre- (prē-') Prefix meaning earlier, before, ahead, from L. *prae-*, before.

preadaptive attitude See *attitude, preadaptive.*

preambivalence See *phase, preambivalent.*

precentral area, convolution, gyrus See *lobe, frontal; motor cortex.*

precocity (prē-kos'i-tē) In a child, the premature or exceptionally early development of certain mental or physical capacities and endowments normally and characteristically exhibited only by children of a more advanced age group.

precognition Prescience; knowledge of future events, presumably by means of extra-sensory perception.

preconscious Foreconscious; in psychoanalysis, one of the three topographical divisions of the psyche, and often abbreviated Pcs. The preconscious division includes those thoughts, memories, and similar mental elements which, although not conscious at the moment, can readily be brought into consciousness (Cs.) by an effort of attention. This is in contrast to the unconscious (Ucs.) division, whose elements are barred from access to consciousness by some intrapsychic force such as repression.

preconscious Burrow uses this term to denote the primary phase or mode of consciousness described by him; it represents the infant's original identification with the mother organism. This mode relates to a non-libidinal, pre-objective phase in the organism's development. It finds symbolic expression in poetry and in literature, in dreams, in the phantasies both of the psychoneurotic and of the normal individual. Not to be confused with the psychoanalytic term 'preconscious' or 'foreconscious.' Synonyms: primary identification, the nest instinct. (Burrow, T. *The Biology of Human Conflict*, Macmillan, New York, 1937). See *co-conscious.*

predementia praecox See *praecox, predementia.*

predisposition The inherited ability of an organism to develop a certain attribute or morbid trait when the necessary peristatic conditions for the given character are present. According to genetic principles, there is no inheritance of fully developed hereditary characters, but only a transmission of *predisposing* genetic factors depending for their phenotypical manifestation on various constitutional and dispositional influences. See *heredity.*

prefrontal lobotomy See *psychosurgery.*

pregenital Antedating the phase of genital primacy. See *organization, pregenital; ontogeny, psychic.*

pregenital organization See *organization, pregenital.*

pregnancy phantasy See *concept, feces-child-penis.*

prehension (prē-hen'shun) 'An intelligible alteration of the personality by an impinging event.' (Sullivan, H.S. in *Psychiatry*, vol. 1, p. 124, 1938)

pre-industrial Pre-vocational.

prejudice, race See *race-prejudice*.

pre-logical The mode of thinking may regress, as it often does in schizophrenic subjects, from the logical to the pre-logical. It has frequently been pointed out that thought and language in their development change from *feeling, concreteness* and *perception* in the direction of *reasoning, differentiation and abstraction*. See *paleologic*.

premaniacal (prē-mà-nī'à-kal) Preceding a maniacal outbreak.

premium, incitement *Fore-pleasure* (q.v.).

premotor area See *lobe, frontal*.

prenatal Relating to the phase of development before birth.

prenubile Referring to the period of life from birth to puberty.

preoccipital area (prē-ok-sip'i-tal) See *lobe, occipital*.

preoccupation The state of being self-absorbed or engrossed in one's own thoughts, typically to a degree that hinders effective contact with or relationship to external reality. Preoccupation may sometimes be no more than absent-mindedness; in other instances, it is part of an autistic schizophrenic's withdrawal from reality and turning inward upon the self; in other cases, it represents a mild degree of interference with consciousness and the level of attention and thus betokens an underlying disturbance in brain cell functioning. See *stupor*.

pre-oedipal (prē-ed'i-pal) Relating to the stages of infantile development antedating the Oedipus complex (psychoanalysis).
   'The pre-oedipal phase . . . is for both sexes that earliest period of attachment to the first love object, the mother, before the advent of the father as a rival. It is the period during which an exclusive relation exists between mother and child.'

(Brunswick, R.M., *The Psychoanalytic Quarterly IX*, 295, 1940)

prephallic (-fal'ik) Referring to the period of psychosexual development preceding the phallic phase; i.e. the oral and anal phases or stages. While the term pregenital is often used interchangeably with the term prephallic, this is not technically correct since the phallic and genital phases are quite distinct and separate.

prepotent Ascendant; dominant. In neurophysiology, that reflex is prepotent which, when two stimuli that would evoke dissimilar reflexes are applied simultaneously, displaces the second reflex. 'The outcome of the rivalry depends upon a number of circumstances: (i) the nature of the reflexes, (ii) the intensity of the several stimuli and (iii) the duration of action of the reflex.' (Fulton, J.F. *Physiology of the Nervous System*, 3rd ed., Oxford University Press, New York, 1949) In general, nociceptive reflexes, such as the flexion reflex, are prepotent to all other types of reflex competing for the final common pathway; other things being equal, the more intense stimulus results in prepotency of its reflex; and the longer a reflex has been in operation, the easier will its prepotency be lost.

pre-psychotic Pertaining to the period before psychosis became evident. Some authors (e.g. Katan) use this term in a more restricted sense to refer to that phase of psychosis in which the patient, although he deviates from normality, has not yet proceeded to develop such grossly psychotic symptoms as delusions and hallucinations.

prepubertal (-pū'bēr-tal) Relating to the phase of life antedating puberty.

presbyophrenia (pres-bē-ō-frē'nē-à) Kahlbaum-Wernicke syndrome; one form of the *senile psychoses* (q.v.) (290.0, 309.6). Its principal characteristics are marked confusional disorientation, confabulation, mistakes in identity, and agitation without accomplishment of any objective. Presbyophrenic confabulations typically show a poverty, monotony, puerility, and naïveté of content. Because ethical conduct is preserved for a relatively long time, the patient is able to fit into limited social contacts, and particularly so since his affect tends toward the euphoric and the amiable.

presence, psychic (sī'kik) This term, introduced by Edoardo Weiss, refers to images 'with almost hallucinatory vividness'. . . 'which pursue the guilty person.' Weiss cites the case of a young man who 'thought that he would be able to commit the crime [stealing] without a sense of guilt. . . . While he was arranging the details of the theft, the reproachful image of his father appeared in his mind with almost hallucinatory vividness.' (*Bulletin of the Menninger Clinic, 3,* 179, 1939)

presenile (prē-sē'nīl) Relating to the period of life antedating senility or old age. See *Alzheimer's disease; Pick's disease.*

presentation Freud uses this term to mean the mode by which an instinct expresses itself. He says that it is not possible to identify an instinct existing as an entity by itself; it is recognizable only when it is conveyed or presented by some vehicle of expression. For example, a patient had a dread of sharp instruments; the instruments comprised the *presentation* by which the dread was expressed.

'It follows that the fate of the charge of affect belonging to the presentation is far more important than that of the ideational content of it. . . .' (Freud, S. *Collected Papers,* vol. 4, tr. by Riviere, J., Leonard and Virginia Woolf and The Institute of Psychoanalysis, London, 1924-25)

This is a term used in a special sense by Jung (analytical psychology). 'To my mind, a simple stringing together of representations, such as is described by certain psychologists as *associative thinking* is not thinking at all, but mere *presentation*. The term "thinking" should, in my view, be confined to the linking up of representations by means of a concept, where, in other words, an act of judgment prevails, whether such act be the product of one's intention or not.' (Jung, C.G. *Psychological Types,* tr. by Baynes, H.G., Harcourt, Brace, New York and London, 1923)

pressure of ideas See *thought pressure.*

pressures, social 'Socially created sanct-

ions which emanate from less sanctioned or less responsible sources [than the] direct authoritarian controls, effected through officials or other accredited social agents and expressive of established codes.' (McIver, R.M. *Pressures, Social; Encyclopaedia of the Social Sciences,* vol. 11, Macmillan, New York, 1933, p. 344)

prestige-suggestion See *suggestion; suggestion, prestige.*

prevalence (pre'va-lens) In epidemiology, prevalence is the number of cases presently existing and active in a given population at any particular time.

$$\text{Prevalence rate (or ratio) of illness} = \frac{\text{Number of cases of illness existing on a specific date}}{\text{Number of persons in population on same date}} \times 100,000$$

See *epidemiology; incidence; rate.*

prevention See *psychiatry, community.*

priapism (prī'ap-iz'm) A term used by many in its psychiatric meaning as the equivalent of satyriasis. It is also used to denote persistent erection of the penis, particularly when the erection is due to organic disease and not to sexual desire.

Priapus (prī-ā'pus) (Priapus, the son of Venus and Mercury (or Bacchus) is the god of procreation and hence of gardens and vineyards, as the embodiment of the generative force in nature. The Priapic cult was associated with the worship of the membrum virile, and Priapus became equivalent with a satyr and the phallus, and *priapism* became a synonym of lewdness.) Priapus has become a common noun and means the penis, though rarely so in psychiatry.

pride, brute Real pride, i.e. pride based on self-assertive rage. See *pride, domesticated.*

pride, domesticated Rado's term for the type of pride and overevaluation of self seen in the obsessive patient, whose pride is based on guilty fear and its resultant humiliation, which have been repressed. Such a patient has no awareness of the guilty fear which is the foundation on which his pride rests; this is in contradistinction to the individual with *real pride* in his self-assertive rage. Domesticated pride is also known as *moral pride.*

pride, moral See *pride, domesticated.*

pride, penis A term employed to designate the feeling of superiority and power attendant to the possession of the male genital organ. The concept has been emphasized by Melanie Klein in her analysis of the child's instinctual life. 'In describing the development of the boy, I have drawn attention to certain factors which tend, as I think, to increase yet more the central importance which the penis possesses for him. They may be summed up as follows: (1) The anxiety arising from his earliest danger situations, his fears of being attacked in all parts of his body and inside it, which include all his fears belonging to the feminine position, are displaced onto the penis or an external organ, where they can be more successfully mastered. The increased pride the boy takes in his penis and all that this involves may also be said to be a method of mastering those fears and disappointments which his feminine position lays him open to more particularly. (2) The fact that the penis is a vehicle first of the boy's destructive and then of his creative omnipotence, enhances its importance as a means of mastering anxiety. In this ministering to his sense of omnipotence, assisting him in the task of testing by reality and promoting his object — relationships . . . in fact, in subserving the all-important function of mastering anxiety — the penis is brought into specially close relation with the ego and is made into a representative of the ego and the conscious; while the interior of the body, the imagos and the faeces — what is invisible and unknown, that is — are compared to the unconscious.' (Klein, M. *The Psycho-Analysis of Children,* tr. by Strachey, A., Norton, New York, 1932)

pride, real See *pride, domesticated.*

primacy, complete genital From the psychoanalytic point of view, genitality is divided into two principal sub-stages. The first is the phallic phase. The second is reached only at puberty; it is the stage of late genital, or complete genital primacy. See *ontogeny, psychic.*

primacy, early genital See *primacy, phallic.*

primacy, oral This term refers to the infant's contacting and first comprehending the world primarily in terms of the mouth. According to Freud, this is determined by the erotic satisfaction derived from mouth contact. Other analysts believe that Freud over-emphasized the erotization of a situation that may be purely developmental, and that the infant first contacts the world by mouth because it is his most efficient and adequate organ. Thus oral primacy is a generally recognized organic fact, but to many psychoanalysts the important aspect of the oral phase is not so much the biological background as the differences in experience which occur during this biologically determined period. 'Moreover, the kind of world contacted through the mouth is not universally the same, and the differences in experience make a more significant impression on personality development than does the organic fact of a period of oral primacy.' (Thompson, C. *Psychoanalysis, Evolution and Development,* Hermitage House, New York, 1950)

primacy, phallic (fal'ik) When libido becomes preponderantly associated with the penis, during the stage of infantile sexuality, the expression *phallic primacy* is used to designate such concentration. See *ontogeny, psychic.*

primal scene See *scene, primal.*

primary behavior disorders See *behavior disorders.*

primary ictal automatism (ik'tal aw-tō'-ma-tiz'm) A type of psychomotor epilepsy. See *epilepsy.*

primary micro-orchidism See *syndrome, Klinefelter's.*

primary physician See *caregiver.*

primary psychic process See *process, primary psychic.*

primary thought-disorder See *thought-disorder, primary.*

primitivation (prim-i-ti-vā'shun) Regression of the ego to the primitive stage in its development. Apparently this term is used only in reference to those states of regression which involve the loss of all the higher ego functions. Thus objective thinking will have been replaced by magical thinking or wish-fulfilling hallucinations; object relationships and love will be of the helpless, passive dependent type, or there may even be a lack of objects; sexuality will be colored with oral eroticism; all perceptions, even those associated with incorporation, may be completely blocked; unco-ordinated discharge movements will replace purposeful actions. According to Fenichel, primitivation occurs in both the traumatic neuroses and schizophrenia. In the former, the patients often exhibit an attitude of utter helplessness and passive dependence in which the behavior is that of an infant. But in traumatic neuroses the regression of the ego comes out most dramatically when perceptions and actions are temporarily blocked. The patient may show constant weakness and fatigue, be unable to undertake any active tasks, encounter difficulty in concentration and memory, show various levels of disturbance of consciousness. Of course, fainting is the most primitive response to a trauma. Fenichel explains that this primitivation appears in the traumatic neuroses as an emergency phenomenon. All mental energies are required to master the intruding overwhelming excitation. Thus the ego functions are blocked and have to relinquish their energies in favor of the emergency task. Moreover, in this way further excitations are excluded.

In schizophrenia, too, many of the symptoms are 'direct expressions of a regressive breakdown of the ego and an undoing of differentiations acquired through mental development.' There is a 'return to the time when the ego was not yet established or had just begun to be established.' For example, world-destruction phantasies are caused by the inner perception of the loss of object relationships; feelings of grandeur express the increase in narcissism that occurs as the psychic energy withdrawn from objects is invested in the ego; schizophrenic thinking is the archaic magical thinking that precedes the development of reality-testing in the small child; hebephrenia is a vegetative existence expressing the old passive receptive or even intra-uterine adaptations. (Fenichel, O. *The Psychoanalytic Theory of Neurosis,* Norton, New York, 1945)

primitivization *Primitivation* (q.v.).

Prince, Morton (1854 - 1929) American psychiatrist and neurologist; hysteria, multiple personality, *Dissociation of a Personality* (1908).

principle, echo Imitative patterning, such as is seen in children who exhibit certain behavior or behaviorisms similar to those seen in their parents but not necessarily indicative of inheritance. For example, a child learns to speak English or French not because of specific genetic predisposition, but because English or French is spoken in his home.

principle, homeopathic (hō-mē-ō-path'ik) See *principle, isopathic.*

principle, isopathic (ī-sō-path'ik) An expression coined by Jones, which he had earlier called the *homeopathic principle,* 'according to which the cause cures the effect.' (Jones, E. *Papers on Psycho-Analysis,* 4th ed., Wood, Baltimore, 1938) 'It is curious, and seemingly a paradox, that guilt can be relieved by an exhibition of the very thing—namely, hate—which was the generating occasion of the guilt itself. We are familiar with the talion principle in psychology and with the exactness with which the punishment is made to fit the crime. We have here an example of a very similar principle, which might be termed the *isopathic principle,* according to which the cause cures the effect.' (Jones, E. ibid)

principle of anticipatory maturation See *maturation, anticipatory, principle of.*

principle of inertia (in-ēr'shē-à) The *principle of inertia,* a term introduced in psychoanalysis by Alexander, is the same as the principle of *repetition-compulsion* (q.v.). Alexander lays stress upon the consideration that the tendency to automatic action is greater than that involving constantly changing and active mental efforts.

principle, pleasure A hypothesized regulatory mechanism of mental life whose function is to reduce psychic tension that has arisen as a result of drives pressing for discharge. The pleasure-pain principle tries to undo the effects of disturbing stimuli (pain) in a way that will most easily provide satisfaction (pleasure). It comes into operation later than the repetition-compulsion principle and is concerned mainly with the stimuli afforded by the action of the drives or instincts, while the earlier principle is concerned with damping external stimuli and merely tries to restore the organism to as near its original state as possible. The pleasure-pain principle operates earlier than the reality principle. See *repetition-compulsion*.

'The *Nirvana*-principle expresses the tendency of the death instincts, the *pleasure*-principle represents the claims of the libido, and that modification of it, the *reality*-principle, the influence of the outer world.' (Freud, S. *Collected Papers*, vol. 2, tr. by Riviere, J., Leonard and Virginia Woolf and The Institute of Psychoanalysis, London, 1924-25)

principle, reality The reality-principle, while entering into the service of the pleasure-principle, causes the latter to be appreciably modified. As Freud maintains, 'the *Nirvana*-principle expresses the tendency of the death-instincts, the *pleasure*-principle represents the claims of the libido and that modification of it, the *reality*-principle, the influence of the outer world.' (Freud, S. *Collected Papers*, vol. 2, tr. by Riviere, J., Leonard and Virginia Woolf and The Institute of Psychoanalysis, London, 1924-25)

principle, treble safeguard The variable regulation of all growth functions by means of integration of endocrine and individual organ activities with the molecular dynamics of the nervous system.

prison neurosis *Chronophobia* (q.v.).

prison psychosis See *psychosis, prison*.

privacy 'Withdrawal from the group with, at the same time, ready access to it.' (Park, R.E. and Burgess, E.W. *Introduction to the Science of Sociology*, University of Chicago Press, Chicago, 1921)

privilege See *communication, privileged*.

proband (prō'band) In genetic studies of tainted families, the original cases constituting the starting point of a family study. These cases are called *probands*, or *probati*, because they must be proved

representative of the type of trait-carrier whose blood-relations are to be investigated as to the recurrence of the trait under observation. Although the probands are not the main object of such a family study, their examination comes first and is of pre-eminent importance, since it must determine the hereditary trait so positively that a group of their blood-relations must have likewise inherited that trait.

The practicable statistical method of probands in the study of selective population groups was devised by Weinberg and is called the *proband method*.

probatus (prô-bä'toos) See *proband*.

problem, behavior See *behavior disorders*.

problem child See *child, problem*.

problem drinker See *alcoholism, chronic*.

problem, feeding See *feeding-problem*.

problem, nuclear The patient's central conflict on which therapy should be focused. It is believed that the manifestations of a number of maladjustments and defenses in a patient usually emanate from one central conflict. Examples of these are inadequate resolution of the Oedipal conflict, feelings of inadequacy, unwholesome sexual identifications, sibling rivalry, and so forth. The critical event has a dynamic relation to the nuclear problem. (Slavson, S.R. *An Introduction to Group Therapy*, The Commonwealth Fund, Oxford University Press, New York, 1943, p. 124.) See *conflict, actual; conflict, root*.

process, cultural The process by which the folkways, mores, and social values are transmitted from generation to generation and are modified in adjustment to social change.

process, elementary D. Nachmansohn's theory of neural excitation and transmission: excitation of the neural membrane results in a dissociation of bound acetylcholine into an active form (the ester); free acetylcholine acts on a protein receptor and thereby increases the permeability of nerve membrane to ions. Thus the bioelectric potential is generated and acts as a stimulus to adjoining nerve segments or to the synapse, resulting in propagation and transmission of the impulse. Meanwhile, the free ester of acetylcholine undergoes hydrolysis by the enzyme cholinesterase, and the protein receptor returns to its resting condition. The barrier to ionic movement is thus re-established.

process, interpersonal In psychoanalysis, this term refers to the fact that in the therapeutic situation the analyst is more than a mirror reflecting the patient's problems. Just as there is transference on the patient's part, so is there counter-transference on the analyst's part. Still, not every attitude toward the analyst is a transference attitude. The patient can like or dislike the analyst for what he really is, and the analyst cannot completely conceal what kind of person he is. The analyst sometimes transfers elements from his past or present problems to the analytic situation.

'I think it is clear that Freud's conception of countertransference is to be distinguished from the present-day conception of analysis as an interpersonal process. In the interpersonal situation, the analyst is seen as relating to his patient not only with his distorted affects but with his healthy personality also. That is, the analytic situation is essentially a human relationship in which, while one person is more immediately detached than the other and has less at stake, he is nevertheless an active participant.' (Thompson, C. *Psychoanalysis, Evolution and Development*, Hermitage House, New York, 1950)

process, neurotic See *self, actual.*

process, primary (psychic) Freud's term for the laws that govern unconscious processes. The term 'primary process' is used to refer to a type of thinking, characteristic of childhood (and dreams), and/or to the way in which libidinal or aggressive energy is mobilized and discharged. The basic characteristics of the primary process are a tendency to immediate discharge of drive energy (i.e. immediate gratification) and an extreme mobility of cathexis so that substitute methods of discharge can be achieved with relative ease. Primary process thinking is characterized by the absence of any negatives, conditionals, or other qualifying conjunctions;

by the lack of any sense of time; and by the use of allusion, analogy, displacement, condensation, and symbolic representation. Drive energy characteristically remains unneutralized during the period of operation of the primary process.

In essence, the primary process is identical with Freud's formulation of the pleasure principle. The difference between them is that while the pleasure principle is described in subjective terms, the primary process is described in objective terms.

process psychosis See *psychosis, process.*

process, secondary (psychic) A name given by Freud to the laws 'which regulate events in the preconscious or ego.' The *ego* (q.v.) is that part of the individual's mental apparatus which regulates the discharge of excitations arising either from external stimuli or from internal stimuli (instinctual demands). In executing this function, the ego is concerned with self-preservation, i.e. avoiding danger. In the case of external stimuli, the ego determines when they should be avoided, when it should adapt itself, and when the external world can be modified. In the case of internal stimuli (those arising from instinctual demands) the ego decides when the demands can be satisfied, when the satisfaction should be postponed, and when the demands or excitations should be completely suppressed. (The dangers of instinctual demands are, first, that their satisfaction might involve dangers in the external world, and, second, that an excessive strength of instinct can damage the organization of the ego.)

By means of its faculties of judgment and intelligence, by the application of logic and reality-testing, the ego blocks the tendency of the instincts toward immediate discharge. Instead, the ego decides under what conditions it would be safe to satisfy the instincts, if at all. The process by which the ego regulates the discharge of instinctual demands, that is, through the above-mentioned logical thinking, is the mode of operation of the conscious and preconscious mind and is called the secondary process. (Freud, S. *An Outline of Psychoanalysis*, Norton, New York, 1949)

processes, unconscious The processes going on in the unconscious part of the psyche. In Freud's conception of the total personality the psyche is divided into: (1) the conscious, or consciousness, which exists within the level of awareness; (2) the preconscious, which exists outside awareness, but can be readily called into awareness when needed; and (3) the unconscious, which exists outside the level of awareness and is not subject to recall into consciousness under ordinary circumstances. Freud also divided the psyche into ego, id, and superego, and these three areas are not to be confused with the three described above, for they are not synonymous. 'Freud saw the newborn infant as chiefly Id, that is, masses of impulse without an organizing or directing consciousness. Contact with the world gradually modifies a portion of this Id, and the Ego, a small area of consciousness, slowly emerges from it. It is developed out of the necessity for reality testing. However, the Ego is not synonymous with consciousness. Only a small part even of the Ego is conscious at any one time. A great part of the Ego as now defined exists outside of awareness, but can readily be recalled when needed. This part was called the preconscious. Still another part of the Ego is unconscious and cannot readily be made conscious. This consists of the experiences and feelings which have been repressed. By the repression these experiences are somehow brought into more intimate contact with the forces of the Id.

'The Id is a mass of seething excitement which cannot become conscious directly. Many of its forces never reach awareness, but from time to time portions of its energy can find some expression in the Ego by becoming connected with the memory-traces of repressed experience and thus participating in the formation of symptoms; becoming distorted as in dream symbols; or by undergoing modification chiefly as a result of the influence of the Super-ego as in sublimation. The Id Freud conceived of as of tremendous size in comparison with the Ego. He thought of it as the generator of energy, the dynamo of the personality. It is somehow closely associated with the organic processes of the body.

'In the course of time, the Ego takes over certain standards from the culture, chiefly through the training by parents in early childhood. These standards become incorporated as parent images within the Ego as a part of itself and this part is called the Super-ego. It exercises a criticizing and censoring power. The functions of dream censor and resistance described in Freud's earlier writings are now seen as part of the Super-ego. The Super-ego, in brief, represents the incorporated standards of society. It includes the parental attitudes, especially as these attitudes were understood and interpreted by the child in his early years. It includes also the person's own ideals for himself, and Freud even indicates that certain phylogenetic experiences such as those described by Jung under the concept of the collective unconscious may also be part of the Super-ego. Much of the Super-ego is unconscious, because it was incorporated by the child very early and without his awareness. This means that like all unconscious material this portion is not available for reality testing.' (Thompson, C. *Psychoanalysis, Evolution and Development*, Hermitage House, New York, 1950)

Unconscious processes, then, refer to methods of handling the environment and the instinctual needs on a level outside that of conscious awareness. These include repression, regression, reaction-formation, isolation, undoing, introjection, turning against the self, reversal, sublimation, and the development of character structure. These terms are defined elsewhere individually.

processomania (pros-es-ō-mā′nē-à) Bianchi's term for mania for litigation.

proctalgia fugax Fleeting rectal pain, more often than not of psychologic origin and seen typically in anxious, tense perfectionists.

prodigy See *child, bright.*

prodigy, idiotic *Idiot-savant* (q.v.).

prodromata (prō-drōm′à-tà) The aggregate of prodromes.

prodrome (prō′drōm) Precursor. An early or premonitory symptom of a disease or disorder.

progeria (prō-jē′rē-à) Gilford introduced this term for a special form of dwarfism characterized by a combination of infantilistic traits and premature senility. The dwarfs of this type show infantile proportions of the skeleton, complete absence of hair, a senile face with a long, aquiline nose, deficient secondary sexual characteristics in spite of a fairly normal development of the sex organs, thickened ends of the long bones, average intelligence, and a tendency to vascular sclerosis; they are practically identical with the subgroup of dwarfism called *senile nanism* by Variot and Pironneau.

prognosis (prog-nō'sis) Forecast or estimation of the course, outcome, and duration of an illness—the opinion being formed during the course of the illness.

prognosis, direction This is a term used by Bleuler to designate the type of reaction that a disorder may be expected to develop. Thus, 'within the realm of schizophrenia there are again different directions such as the paranoid, catatonic dementia, etc., that have to be considered in the prognosis.' (Bleuler, E. *Textbook of Psychiatry*, tr. by Brill, A.A., Macmillan, New York, 1930)
Direction prognosis is distinguished from *extent prognosis*, which has to do with the prediction relating to the progress of the disorder in a given period of time.

prognosis, extent See *prognosis, direction.*

progredient See *neurosis, progredient.*

progressive degenerative subcortical encephalopathy (de-jen'er-à-tiv sub-kor'tikal en-sef-al-op'à-thi) See *sclerosis, diffuse.*

projection In psychiatry, the process of throwing out upon another the ideas or impulses that belong to oneself. It is the act of giving objective or seeming reality to what is subjective. The expression implies that what is cast upon another is considered undesirable to the one who projects. The person who blames another for his own mistakes or seeks a scapegoat is using the projection mechanism.
It is to be recognized that the person orients himself by means of both inner and outer perceptions. The latter can be managed by motor activity, which is another way of saying that if reality is uncomfortable one may alter or avoid it. Inner perceptions, such as the instincts and

their representations, cannot be handled with the same facility; one cannot flee from the 'merciless claims of his instincts.' Whatever is painful or dangerous from within may be projected onto another person or upon some part of reality. When the conflicting issue has been externalized, the person may handle it as if it had always been an external situation. For example, the paranoid schizophrenic, beset with unconscious homosexual urges, projects the urges upon some man or men in the environment and then struggles against the urges as they seem to arise from outside sources.
In its morbid manifestations, the projection mechanism is clearly an unconscious process, at least, in the sense that the conscious ego is not at all aware of the process.
According to Ferenczi, projection is one of the first defensive or protective measures employed by the child in defense of its narcissism. When the child realizes that he is not omnipotent, he begins to ascribe omnipotence to those about him and comes to realize that others control him. He does not, however, abandon the feeling of his own importance and of his magical powers.
'Projection is a return to or persistence of the infantile system whereby an inner pleasure-ego is kept free from inner pain-elements by projecting the latter into an outer "painful" world. So the patient, whenever possible, projects his "painful" ideas, e.g. it is not he who is inferior or who deserves punishment for entertaining guilty ideas: it is the analyst who is a fool or who deserves to be exposed.' (Glover, E. *The Technique of Psycho-analysis*, International Universities Press, New York, 1955)
Alexander says that the projection mechanism serves to create harmony between reality (which the child reshapes) and the id. See *reference, ideas of; reality-testing; externalization.*

projection fibers See *commissure.*

projection, impersonal Projection alone means attributing one's own ideas or impulses to another. By implication, this is done because one finds his own ideas or impulses objectionable. Impersonal projection refers to the same mechanism applied not to objectionable material but to impersonal or neutral material. One example of impersonal projection is found in the echo of reading aloud, when the subject feels that someone else is saying the words which he himself is reading. Approximately 47 per cent of patients who admit to auditory hallucinations also hear the echo of reading. These patients do not feel that the echo occurs more with one type of reading material than with another, and it is therefore difficult to think of apparently innocuous reading material selected at random as having assumed some objectionable significance to such a large percentage of patients. Marjorie C. Meehan feels that impersonal projection may indicate the extreme feeling of passivity and domination by an external agent so characteristic of certain schizophrenics; the symptom may also suggest that there is some mechanism, possibly physiological, which transforms internal speech so that it seems to the patient to be heard from without. (*Psychiatric Quarterly 16,* 156, 1942)

projective test See *test, projective.*

prolonged sleep therapy See *treatment, continuous sleep.*

promiscuity Indiscriminate, casual sexual encounters; high frequency of sexual relationships with a large number of partners, such as found in nymphomania, satyriasis, Don Juans, and many homosexuals.

promotion neurosis Inability to function when given added responsibility or authority; seen most often in obsessional neurotics and described by others as 'failure through success.' See *success, failure through.*

proneness, accident Liability or tendency toward involvement in mishaps that cause some pain or injury to the subject. It has long been recognized in industrial psychiatry that the majority of accidents occur within a comparatively small percentage of the total work force, and that that same percentage tends to be involved in multiple accidents. It was also noted in wartime that some soldiers appeared to be wounded largely because of their emotional state, and that the stress of battle often affected judgment and muscular control adversely. In some instances, accident proneness can be traced

to a specific emotional state existing prior to the injury. In many others, however, a tendency to repeated accidents appears to be an expression of deep-seated personality traits and unconscious conflicts.

The typical accident-prone person is a young male who is decisive or even impulsive; he concentrates upon immediate pleasures and satisfactions and acts on the spur of the moment. He likes excitement and adventure, eschewing planning and preparation. Often he will be found to have been reared strictly and harbors an unusual amount of resentment against authority; he is a rebel who cannot tolerate even self-discipline. At the same time he feels guilty about his rebellion, but in the unconsciously provoked accident he is able to express his resentment and to atone for his rebellion through the injury.

propaganda (prop-à-gan′dà) 'A deliberately worked and guided campaign to induce people to accept a given view, sentiment, or value.' (Blumer, H.E., in Park, R.E., *Principles of Sociology,* Barnes & Noble, New York, 1939)

propfschizophrenia (propf-skiz-ō-frē′nē-à) A schizophrenic syndrome superimposed, engrafted, so to speak, upon an intellectual deficiency (oligophrenia). However, schizophrenia may be engrafted upon any organic disease. It is generally considered that the disease facilitates the development of the schizophrenic syndrome in a predisposed subject.

prophase (prō′fāz) The initial stage of a cell division by mitosis. See *division, cell.*

prophylaxis (prof-i-lak′sis) The branch of medical science which has to do with protection against the onset of a disease or disorder. For example, the treatment of a person showing marked schizoidism in an effort to prevent the development of schizophrenia is termed prophylaxis.

propinquity (prō-pin′kwi-tē) Proximity; in genetics, nearness of blood relationship.

proprioception (prō-prē-ō-sep′shun) The ability to appreciate sensations of muscle, joint, tendon, and vibration.

proprium See *Allport, Gordon Willard.*

propulsion Rapid, forward running with short steps, in paralysis agitans.

prosencephalon (pros-en-sef′ă-lon) *Forebrain* (q.v.).

prosopagnosia (prō-so-pag-nō′sē-à) Inability to recognize faces, and particularly a failure to react to the combination of those specific properties or features of an object that endow it with uniqueness. This may be congenital or acquired, but it rarely occurs as an isolated defect.

prosopalgia (prō-sō-pal′jē-à) See *tic douloureux*.

prosoplegia (prō-sō-plē′jē-à) Bell's palsy. See *nerve, facial*.

prosopoplegia (prō-sō-pō-plē′jē-à) Peripheral facial paralysis or Bell's palsy.

protanopia (prō-tan-op′ē-à) A form of color-blindness, usually referred to as red-blindness, in which red and blue-green are confused.

protest, body A term coined by Esther L. Richards to indicate that physical dysfunctions may serve as outlets for worries, disappointments, frustrations, etc.

protest, masculine This is a technical term applied by Adler both to men and women, to describe a desire to escape from the feminine role. This concept he regards as the main motive force in neurotic disease. It represents the distorted apprehension of sex-differences caused by the striving for superiority. If it takes an active form in women, they attempt from an early age to usurp the male position. They become aggressive in manner, adopt definitely masculine habits or 'tricks' of behavior, and endeavor to domineer everyone about them.

The masculine protest in a male indicates that he has never fully recovered from an infantile doubt as to whether he really is male. He strives for an ideal masculinity invariably conceived as the possession by himself of freedom, love, and power, 'which in this egoistic conception amounts simply to irresponsibility, the *conquest* of women or friends, and the surpassing or overthrowing of others.' (Mairet, P. *ABC of Adler's Psychology*, Kegan Paul, Trench Trubner, London, 1928)

prothymia (prō-thī′mē-à, -thim′ē-à) Mental alertness.

proto- (prō′tō-) Combining form meaning first, original, primitive, from Gr. *prōtos*, first, foremost.

protocol The individual case record; the 'raw material' of a study or experiment before it has been included into the conclusions or overall results of the study. In clinical psychiatry, the protocol commonly refers to the complete case history and workup, in contrast to the case summary or final conclusions about the individual case.

protomasochism (prō-tō-maz′ok-iz'm) The primary, ancestral tendency of the death instinct to lead all human beings into annihilation; a drive into nothingness. Reik uses the term to describe 'a pleasure of destruction directed against the ego, a kind of sadism which has chosen the ego for its victim.' In Freud's opinion, the death-instinct that is not neutralized by the erotic urges or channeled into the outer world remains effective within the organism, directing its forces against the ego proper, as it did in primitive man. (Reik, T. *Masochism in Modern Man*, Farrar and Rinehart, New York, 1941)

protopathic (-path′ik) Of primary sensitiveness, i.e. pertaining to sensory nerves in the skin with a primary, grosser, or more limited sensibility to stimuli. Opposed to *epicritic*. The ability to appreciate deep pain sensation and marked variations in temperature such as hot and cold; distinguished from epicritic sensibility.

proto-phallic (-fal′ik) Jones says that there are two stages to what Freud calls the phallic phase: 'The first of the two — let us call it the *proto-phallic* phase — would be marked by innocence or ignorance — at least in consciousness — where there is no conflict over the matter in question, it being confidently assumed by the child that the rest of the world is built like itself and has a satisfactory male organ — penis or clitoris, as the case may be. In the second, or *deutero-phallic* phase, there is a dawning suspicion that the world is divided into two classes; not male and female in the proper sense, but penis-possessing and castrated (though actually the two classifications overlap pretty closely).' (Jones, E. *Papers on Psycho-Analysis*, 4th ed., Wood, Baltimore, 1938)

protoplasm (prō'tō-plaz'm) In biology, the cellular substance with which the life of living beings is associated. All vital activities of an organism, such as growth, repair, and reproduction, are ultimately referred to the properties of this transparent and jelly-like cell material which usually shows a fibrillar structure with a honeycombed reticulum and consists of a mixture of proteins, carbohydrates, fats, lipoids, salts, and water.

The protoplasmic matter of each cell is endowed with the structural and functional peculiarities characteristic of the species of animals or plants to which the cell belongs. It is subject to the complex biochemical processes which are the fundamental basis of all cell functions.

Of particular importance in the biological mechanism of inheritance are the proteins, which are built up of one or more of the amino acids. They are very specific in their chemical relations and do certain things with such great precision that the enormous number of different kinds of organisms can be maintained with a high degree of persistence.

protopsyche (sī'kē) In discussing *The Phenomena of Hysterical Materialization*, Ferenczi says: 'If, therefore, the reflex process is considered not only as a prototype but as a preliminary stage of the psychic process, a stage to which indeed the highest psychic elaboration always remains inclined to regress, then the puzzling leap from mental to bodily in the conversion symptom and the reflex wish-fulfilling phenomenon of materialization become less amazing. It is simply regression to the "protopsyche."' (Ferenczi, S. *Further Contributions to the Theory and Technique of Psycho-Analysis*, tr. by Suttie, J.I., Leonard and Virginia Woolf and The Institute of Psychoanalysis, London, 1926)

prototaxic Of, or relating to, the earliest period in time or development; Sullivan applied the term to the early period of infancy, when the child has no awareness of himself as distinct from others and no concept of time or space.

proviso, parapathic (pro-vī'zō, par-à-path'ik) Stekel's term for a compromise or bargain which the neurotic makes with his illness—e.g. the patient who thinks that as long as he remains ill, his father will not die: it is a 'clause,' or stipulation with the neurosis in order to justify its existence. In other words, 'if the patient accepts his neurosis, some disaster which he dreads will not happen.' Adler referred to this mental mechanism as *junctim*; another name for it is *neurotic proviso*. (Stekel, W. *The Interpretation of Dreams*, Liveright, New York, 1943)

proxemics (prok-sē'miks) The study of how microspace is structured (usually unconsciously) in such areas as the distance between people in daily transactions, the organization of space in homes and buildings, and the layout of the towns in which people live.

prudery Exaggerated concern about minor points of the moral or ethical code. This is almost always a reaction-formation, the prude decrying in others the very impulses and behavior he must deny in himself.

pruritus, psychogenic (prōō-rī'tus, sī-kō-jen'ik) An itching dermatitis of a functional nature (305.0). The diagnosis of psychogenic pruritus is made only after organic factors have been ruled out by complete allergy studies, search for foci of infection, physical examination, blood count, serology, chest x-ray, etc. Psychogenic pruritus is produced or aggravated by environmental stress, and for this reason it has been felt that men with a predisposition to the disease should be excluded from the armed forces. Patients with functional pruritus are usually of the obsessive-compulsive character type, are rigid, defensive, and not readily susceptible to suggestion or reassurance. The disease is difficult to cure.

Sullivan and Bereston distinguish four psychosomatic dermatological syndromes: psychogenic pruritus, neurodermatitis, psychogenic urticaria, and hyperhidrosis. (Sullivan, D.J., and Bereston, E.S. 'Psychosomatic Dermatological Syndromes in Military Service,' *American Journal of Psychiatry 103*, 42, 1946)

psammoma-body (sam-ō'mà-) A collection of fibroglia, collagen fibers, and small calcified concretions seen often in meningiomas.

psellism ([p] sel′iz′m) Stammering; indistinct or faulty pronunciation.

psellismus haesitans (sel-ēs-moos hes′i-tans) *Obs.* Stammering; ischnophonia.

pseudacusis (sū-dȧ-kū′sis) *Obs.* Auditory hallucinations and illusions.

pseudamnesia (sū-dam-nē′zē-ȧ) *Obs.* A transitory amnesia, usually associated with an organic brain disease.

pseudesthesia (sū-des-thē′zē-ȧ) Sensation or perception without a corresponding stimulus. An imaginary or illusory sensation, such as phantom limb.

pseudo- (sū′dō-) Combining form meaning false, spurious, from Gr. *pseúdos,* falsehood, lie, *pseudes,* lying, false.

pseudoaggression A false aggressiveness developed in neurotics as a result of denial of their basic psychic masochism. In other words, the basic desire is to be mistreated. This desire gains only reproach from the superego, and a defense of pseudoaggression is constructed. 'No, I do not want to be mistreated by this person. The situation is just the opposite —I want to kill this person or mistreat him.' This pseudoaggression also receives reproach from the superego and is itself denied, but the neurotic is more willing to accept the guilt for his pseudoaggression than that for his underlying masochism. Bergler believes that neurotics have no true ego aggression, for almost all of their aggression is in the superego. He explains stage fright in actors in this way. Superficially, the symptom refers to a fear of one's aggressive exhibitionism. In reality, however, this aggressiveness is a false front with which the patient deludes himself and others to deny the basic fear, that his masochism will be uncovered. Under successful psychoanalytic treatment, a more equitable distribution of aggression between superego and ego can be achieved and the patient can become truly aggressive as the need for aggression arises in reality situations. (E. Bergler, *Psychoanalytic Quarterly Supplement 23,* 317, 1949)

'pseudo as-if' Katan's term for a type of reaction, seen often within the framework of a hysterical disturbance, that simulates the 'as if' personality but differs from the latter in that the disturbance arises not from early loss of the mother but rather as a result of the mother keeping the child too dependent orally. In consequence, the ego is weakened and in response to stress it falls back on dependence on the mother or her substitutes. Pseudo 'as-if' reactions are seen also in adolescents and in prepsychotic patients as temporary attempts at mastering conflicts during a process of disintegration. See *personality, 'as-if.'*

pseudoasthma A functional disorder of respiration characterized by breathing difficulties very similar to those observed in true asthma, but differing from those present in the latter disease by reason of emotional origin (305.2). Instances of pseudoasthma are often traceable to a severe anxiety arising out of some conflict going on in the unconscious. The following case, excerpted and condensed from Kanner (*Child Psychiatry,* 2nd ed., Thomas, Springfield, Ill., 1948) is illustrative. George H., age nine and a half, was the son of parents who were oversolicitous and overprotective to a damaging degree. At the age of one year, George had an upper respiratory infection which lasted one month. A physician diagnosed the condition as asthma. He warned the parents that the asthma might return in the future and advised that the child be watched closely and brought back whenever the slightest sign of breathing disorder was noticed. But George had no trouble with breathing until he was nine years old. In the interim, however, his parents had kept waiting for the anticipated return of asthma and had frequently reminded George of such a contingency. They had him sleep in their bedroom so that nocturnal panting would not escape their attention, and suggested that he open the window and loosen his belt as soon as he had trouble breathing. Thus, poor George had been conditioned to expect asthma. Through the years he learned that the slightest hint of this condition instantly brought him the loving solicitude and care of his parents. A major environmental change made by the family resulted in a change of schools for George, then nine years old. The boy was very reluctant, extremely fearful, and filled with anxiety about this change. On his very first day at the new school, George at lunch time hurried home, rushed into the house struggling for breath, opened the window, and loosened his belt. The doctor's prediction, made eight years before, seemed to have come true. George had 'asthma.' Of course, he could not continue at school. This time, the condition was properly diagnosed as pseudoasthma. Over a period of time it gradually yielded to diligent psychiatric treatment of the underlying anxiety situation from which it had developed.

pseudo-athetosis (sū-dō-ath-ē-tō'sis) Athetoid movement which is not spontaneous, but elicited when the patient closes his eyes and extends his hands; it occurs in those whose sense of position is impaired such as in tabes or combined sclerosis.

pseudoblepsis (-blep'sis) *Obs.* Visual hallucinations or illusions.

pseudocatatonia, traumatic (-kat-ȧ-tō'nē-ȧ, traw-ma'tik) A catatonic-like state following an injury.

pseudocommunity Norman Cameron's term for the progressive desocialization seen in the schizophrenias in which social language habits are replaced with personal, highly individual habits. The pseudocommunity is a behavioral organization which the patient constructs from his distorted observations, inferences, and phantasies; most commonly, the patient sees himself as the victim of some concerted action.

pseudoconvulsion An attack which simulates a convulsion, with falling and muscular contractions, but with no loss of consciousness, no pupillary changes, amnesia, or postconvulsive confusion. Such an attack usually occurs in hysteria. It may be consciously or unconsciously exaggerated for the sake of gaining sympathy or attention.

pseudocyesis (sū-dō-sī-ē'sis) Spurious pregnancy.

pseudodebility (-de-bil'i-tē) *Pseudoimbecility* (q.v.).

pseudodementia (-dē-men'shē-ȧ) A condition of exaggerated indifference to one's surroundings without actual mental impairment.

pseudodementia, hysterical Wernicke thus denotes a syndrome of hysteria in which the patient appears unable to answer the simplest questions, or to give any information about himself. The patient gives the appearance of being feebleminded.

As a rule the patient, exhibiting this syndrome, regresses to the behavior of early childhood, showing the condition known as *hysterical puerilism.* See *feeblemindedness, affective; Ganser syndrome.*

pseudo-feeblemindedness Feeblemindedness sometimes indicated by a low I.Q. but actually non-existent. Untoward psychological and emotional factors operative at the time of testing can result in a low score misrepresenting the actual mental endowment: this blunder is especially likely to come about when children are tested. The label feeblemindedness resulting from a score of this nature is a misnomer, and the proper term is pseudo-feeblemindedness.

pseudo-flexibilitas (psew-dô-flek-sē-bē'le-tȧs) When a person, whose movements are more or less normal, maintains for a relatively long period a posture imposed upon him, the condition is known as *pseudo-flexibilitas.*

pseudogeusia (sū-dō-gū'sē-ȧ) False perception of taste.

pseudo-giftedness Apparent unusual talents in a child, resulting not from specific or permanent trends but rather from the ability of the bright child to imitate, adopt, and assimilate the behavior patterns of others. Pseudo-giftedness is usually inspired by momentary influence from without rather than by any inborn ability or urge from within. 'The current educational fad for child art has, at the moment, America's parents gasping for breath. As simple art technics are very easy to adopt, and as children in the pre-intellectual period have a natural urge for self-expression of a formalistic type, art is a natural and vital sort of juvenile language just as it has always been to primitive man.' (Harms, E., ed. *The Guidance of the Superior Child and the Prodigy* in *Handbook of Child Guidance,* Child Care Publications, New York, 1947) Such juvenile abilities commonly disappear after adolescence, with the advance of intellectual and scientific forms of expression.

pseudographia (sū-dō-graf′ē-à) 'Katatoniacs perform all sorts of tricks with their writing, just as they do in other departments of voluntary action. Their style is apt to be stilted and circumlocutory. They form their letters with unnecessary care or perhaps have some fantastic alphabet of their own *(pseudographia).*' (Stoddart, W.H.B. *Mind and Its Disorders,* 5th ed., Lewis, London, 1926)

pseudo-hallucination A hallucination, which the patient knows to be such. 'Hallucinations, the morbidness of which is recognized in spite of the vividness of the deceptive perception (pseudo-hallucinations), occur most readily in the visual sense.' (Bleuler, E. *Textbook of Psychiatry,* tr. by Brill, A.A., Macmillan, New York, 1930)
'In pseudo-hallucinations the patient has the vivid sensory experience, but realizes that it has no external foundations.' (Henderson, D.K. and Gillespie, R.D. *A Text-Book of Psychiatry,* 4th ed., Oxford University Press, London, 1936)

pseudo-homosexual Used in adaptational psychodynamic formulations to refer to the non-sexual motivations in homosexual behavior: specifically, dependency motivations and power motivations. 'It should be emphasized that even in the overt homosexual, when the ultimate goal is orgastic pleasure, the sexual component does not operate in isolation, but always in association with the dependency and power components.' (Ovesey, L., et al. *Archives of General Psychiatry* 9, 19-31, 1963)

pseudo-hydrophobia (-hī-drō-fō′bē-à) Cynophobia.

pseudohypersexuality (hī-pēr-sek-shoo-al′i-tē) A term used by Fenichel interchangeably with the term *hypersexuality.* (Fenichel, O. *The Psychoanalytic Theory of Neurosis,* Norton, New York, 1945)

pseudo-hypnosis (-hip-nō′sis) See *captivation.*

pseudo-identification A method of dealing with people in the environment by apparently identifying oneself with, or assimilating oneself to, the person with whom one chances to be in contact at any given moment. Pseudo-identification is illustrated by the case of the man who asserted that he had found the ideal way of adapting himself to reality: he assimilated himself to the person with whom he chanced to be talking and so had no external conflicts. But in reality, such a method of adaptation led to many conflicts; the man found that he had assimilated himself to A at one time, to B at another, and that A and B were in disagreement. Since pseudo-identification is not insincerity, but rather the conviction that the subject has in fact become one with the other person, such conflicting identifications lead to many reality problems. Pseudo-identification appears somewhat akin to paranoid projection in that the patient's ideas are prevented from entering consciousness and are ascribed to the object, with whom the patient then identifies himself. Unlike the ideas of paranoia, however, those of pseudo-identification are apparently innocent. The dynamics of the process are still poorly understood.

pseudo-imbecility Pathological limitation and restriction of intellectual functions of the ego. This intellectual restriction or inhibition may mean (1) that intellectual functions have been erotized and so are given up to escape-conflicts; (2) that the restriction disguises aggression in order to escape retaliation; (3) that it is a display of castration to escape the fear of literal castration and the loss of a love-object; or (4) that it represents an attempt to restore or maintain a secret libidinous rapport within the family. A mask of stupidity enables the child or infantile adult to participate in the sexual life of the parents and other adults to an amazingly unlimited extent which if overtly expressed, would be strictly and definitely forbidden. Such utilization of stupidity is widespread, because it affords an opportunity for the mutual sexual desires of parent and child to be gratified on a preverbal affective level without becoming conscious through word pictures. Thus, repression or other defense measures are unnecessary, and the child and his parents can maintain a distorted but gratifying affective communion that would otherwise be limited to mother and infant. The analysis of an 18-year-old pseudo-imbecile, who had manifested his pathological behavior since early childhood, revealed that in the phallic stage of psychic development he had had to give up competition with his aggressive twin brother. He was unable to pass the phallic stage successfully and so regressed to the immediately preceding anal stage. Acting as a counterpart to anal exhibitionism was an intense sexual curiosity against which he had to maintain strong defenses, because of the threats of his father. With pseudo-imbecility, however, he was able unconsciously to satisfy his curiosity, for his parents and siblings permitted his presence even during intercourse. He was regarded as a pet animal that does no harm by it presence and neither understands nor participates in what it sees.

pseudo-insanity *Obs.* Simulation.

pseudo-intoxication *Obs.* A trance-like state in which there is a tendency to staggering and stammering with excitement and irritability.

pseudolalia (sū-dō-lā′lē-à) Suggested by Stoddart to denote 'meaningless sounds' produced by patients.
'Patients presenting this symptom apparently pretend to speak; but in reality they utter a series of meaningless sounds, such as "camalaba, dink-a-di-dink-goosey-goosey-wadlum." The reduplicative tendency of this mode of speech suggests that it is of instinctive origin.' (Stoddart, W.H.B. *Mind and Its Disorders,* 5th ed., Lewis, London, 1926)

pseudologia fantastica (psew-dō-lō′gē-à fan-tas′ti-kà) A clinical syndrome characterized by phantasy construction, usually extensive, consisting of a superstructure of some actualities erected upon a foundation of phantasy. Pseudologia fantastica is seen mainly in the so-called psychopathic group and in other acting-out types of disturbance, and appears often to arise in an attempt to produce an ego lift; the phantasy is believed only momentarily and is quickly dropped when the patient is confronted with contradictory evidence. Pseudologia fantastica is to be differentiated from *confabulation* (q.v.).

pseudologue (sū′dō-log) Pathological liar. Kraepelin used the term as a subgroup of 'psychopathic personality.' His distinction between the criminal liar and the pseudologue was not very clear.

pseudomania A symptom in which the patient accuses himself of having committed crimes of which he is really innocent; shame psychosis.

pseudo-melancholia (-mel-an-kō′lē-à) *Obs.* Juliusburger's term for the clinical syndrome characterized by subjective inhibition and depersonalization.

pseudomnesia (sū-dom-nē′zē-à) *Obs.* The patient's belief in having a clear recollection of events that had never taken place or things that had never existed.

pseudomotivations Bleuler uses this term to refer to those after-the-fact justifications of behavior which are common in schizophrenia. One hebephrenic patient stated that he got into debt only to show that he could obtain money without his wife's assistance. Another patient flew into a rage and stated that he did so because his doctor was wearing a gray suit. 'According to my experience the patient really becomes furious for quite different reasons which have some relationship to his complexes. He then, purely at random, mentions the grey suit as the reason for his fury.' (Bleuler, E. *Dementia Praecox or the Group of Schizophrenias,* International Universities Press, New York, 1950.) Although the patient himself believes in his ex post facto pseudomotivations, he may subsequently become aware that he has made up the motivations. Ordinarily, however, the patient is unaware of, and indifferent to, even the grossest contradictions.

pseudonarcotism (sū-dō-när′kō-tiz′m) Stupor of hysterical nature, not induced by drugs.

pseudonecrophilia Masturbation with phantasies of corpses as the sexual object.

pseudoneurotic (-nū-ro′tik) See *schizophrenia, pseudoneurotic.*

pseudonomania (-nō-mā′nē-à) Morbid impulse to falsify, to lie.

pseudoparameter See *parameter.*

pseudoparanoia (-par-à-noi'à) An uncommon term for unsystematized paranoid trends that are not strictly associated with schizophrenia. For example, paranoid delusions may occasionally be observed in deaf people, sometimes in the feebleminded; the delusions are generally scattered and transitory or at least they do not constitute the preponderant part of the disorder.

pseudo-paresis, alcoholic (-par'ē-sis) When a clinical syndrome resembling general paresis appeared as a result of alcoholic encephalopathy it was customary to speak of alcoholic pseudo-paresis, or, as Kraepelin called it, alcoholic paresis. Usually the diagnosis was suggested because of the Argyll Robertson pupils and the slurring speech.
  'Alcoholic paresis is a mental deterioration with ideas of grandeur, emotional dulness, hallucinations, delusions of jealousy, sometimes pupils stiff to light, speech defect, tremors and polyneuritis. Epileptiform attacks are frequent.' (Strecker, E.A. and Ebaugh, F.G. *Practical Clinical Psychiatry,* 4th ed., Blakiston, Philadelphia, 1935)

pseudopersonality A constellation of habits and reaction patterns consciously recognized as false by the subject. The development of a pseudopersonality is characteristic of many prostitutes, who strive to maintain an incognito quality in their sexual contacts and fortify this with fictitious tales about themselves and their families. Their pseudopersonality usually includes a false toughness, meanness, and indifference. It is obvious that, with time, the recognition of the falseness of the pseudopersonality may gradually dwindle so that it finally becomes a true *character defense,* and in therapy must be handled as such. See *defense, character.* (T. Agoston. *International Journal of Psychoanalysis 26,* 321, 1945)

pseudopsia (sū-dop'sē-à) *Obs.* Visual hallucination or illusion.

pseudopsychopathic schizophrenia (sū-dō-sī-kō-path'ik skiz-ō-frē'nē-à) See *schizophrenia.*

pseudo-querulant 'The *pseudo-querulants* are usually described as a separate type. . . . They are very irritable. Hence they readily come into collision with other people, and regard trifling differences as grave injustices. They are also arrogant, and this combination of irritability and arrogance leads them not only into quarrels, but into actual lawsuits.' They are to be distinguished from the litigous paranoid type 'by the fact that in the pseudo-querulants the tendency exists from youth up.' (Henderson, D.K. and Gillespie, R.D. *A Text-Book of Psychiatry,* 4th ed., Oxford University Press, London, 1936)

pseudo-reminiscence Pseudologia fantastica.

pseudoschizophrenia (-skiz-ō-frē'nē-à) See *psychosis, process.*

pseudosclerosis of Westphal-Strümpell (-skle-rō'sis) (Adolf von Strumpell, German physician, 1853-1925; Alexander Karl Otto Westphal, German neurologist, 1863-1941) See *degeneration, hepato-lenticular.*

pseudosclerosis, spastic See *degeneration, cortico-striato-spinal.*

pseudoseizure (300.13) Pseudoepilepsy; *hystero-epilepsy* (q.v.); "a clinical event which superficially resembles an epileptic attack, but under closer scrutiny is found lacking in an essential epileptic component such as a concomitant electro-encephalographic dysrhythmia or possessing a feature not compatible with epilepsy such as the characteristic of being precipitated, modified or stopped by a simple command, a hypnotic suggestion or withdrawal of the attention of observers." (Liske, E. and Forster, F.M. *Neurology 14,* 41, 1964)

pseudo-sexuality See *masturbation, compulsive.*

pseudosmia (sū-doz'mē-à) False sense of smell.

pseudosphresia (sū-dos-frē'zē-à) Pseudosmia.

pseudotransference A result of inexact interpretations in psychoanalytic treatment in which the patient, responding to the suggestions of the analyst, builds up a relationship that is expressive of the analyst's hunches rather than related to problems of the patient that are of dynamic significance.

pseudotumor cerebri (psew-dō-tōō'môr kā-rā-brē) A condition of uncertain etiology consisting of increased pressure of cerebrospinal fluid and formation of small cysts in the arachnoid. Symptoms include headaches, vomiting, diplopia, papilledema, somnolence, and few if any focal signs. Also known as serous meningitis; arachnoiditis; toxic hydrocephalus.

psi (sī) In parapsychology, this term refers to whatever it is that enables a person to perceive extra-sensorially. See *perception, extra-sensory.*

psi- (or ψ) **system** See *system.*

psittacism (sit'à-siz'm) A type of neologism which is totally devoid of any content. See *glossolalia.*

psopholalia (sō-fō-lā'lē-à) Lallation; babbling, infantile, slovenly, incomprehensible speech.

PST Abbreviation for prefrontal sonic treatment; see *irradiation, ultrasonic.*

psychagogy (sī'kà-gō-jē) Educational and re-educational psychotherapeutic procedures, with special emphasis upon the relationship of the patient to his environment. The general principles behind psychagogy are essentially in agreement with those behind objective psychobiology; both stress socialization.

psychal (sī'kal) *Rare.* Psychical.

psychalgalia (sī-kal-gā'lē-à) See *psychalgia.*

psychalgia (sī-kal'je-à) Discomfort or pain, usually in the head, which accompanies mental activity (including obsessions, hallucinations, etc.), and is recognized by the patient as being emotional in origin. Probably it is due to the pressure of intolerable anxiety. Depressed patients complain of peculiar head pains due to their horrible ideas. The schizophrenic patient complains, often with laughter, of the unbearable pains in his 'head,' induced by electric currents that come from a distant machine operated by a persecutor.

psychalia (sī-kā'lē-à) *Rare.* A mental syndrome characterized by auditory and visual hallucinations; also known as *mentalia.*

psychanopsia (sī-kan-op'sē-à) Psychic blindness.

psychasthenia (sī-kas-thē'nē-à) *Obs.* The nosologic syndrome characterized by fears or phobias. Strecker and Ebaugh say that 'in the anxiety states belongs much of the material that was formerly described as psychasthenia, with a prominent display of the so-called phobias or fears.' (Strecker, E.A. and Ebaugh, F.G. *Practical Clinical Psychiatry,* 4th ed., Blakiston, Philadelphia, 1935)

Pierre Janet recognizes two subgroups of psychoneuroses, namely, hysteria and psychasthenia. In general he includes under psychasthenia all psychoneurotic syndromes which are not classified under hysteria.

'Psychasthenia resembles hysteria in that both of these psychoneurotic disorders may be traced to a conflict over a forbidden pleasure. The essential difference lies in the fact that the conscience of the hysterical person is intolerant of even the thought of such pleasure while the psychasthenic has an ambivalent attitude.' (Henry, G.W. *Essentials of Psychiatry,* 3rd ed., Williams and Wilkins, Baltimore, 1938)

psychataxia (sī-kà-tak'sē-à) Mental confusion, inability to fix the attention or to make any continued mental effort.

psychauditory (sī-kaw'di-tō-rē) Relating to the mental perception and interpretation of sounds.

psyche (sī'kē) The mind. In modern psychiatry the psyche is regarded in its own way as an 'organ' of the person. The psyche, like other organs, possesses its own form and function, its embryology, gross and microscopic anatomy, physiology, and pathology.

The most comprehensive schematization of the psyche is that drawn by Freud, consisting in general of the conscious and unconscious divisions, each of which is made up of a great number of components. The mind, like all other organs of the body has its own local functions and those functions that are intimately associated with adjacent and distant organs. It is like the cardiovascular system in that it reaches all parts of the body; it also serves to adjust the total organism to the needs or demands of the environment.

psycheclampsia (sī-kek-lamp'sē-à) *Obs.* T.S. Clouston's synonym for *mania.*

psyche, contrasexual component of Jacobi's term for the 'repressed side' in Jung's theory of analytical psychology. Jung maintains that there is a male and a female side to everyone, the side which is not dominant being repressed; i.e. in the male the female side is repressed and vice versa. "The second stage of the individuation process (self-realization through Jungian analysis) is characterized by the meeting with the figure of the "soul-image," named by Jung the ANIMA in the man, the ANIMUS in the woman. The archetypal figure of the soul-image stands for the respective contrasexual portion of the psyche, showing partly how our personal relation thereto is constituted, partly the precipitate of all human experience pertaining to the opposite sex. In other words, it is the image of the other sex that we carry in us, both as individuals and as representatives of a species. "Jeder Mann trägt seine Eva in sich" (Every man carries his Eve in himself) affirms a popular saying. According to psychic law . . . everything latent, unexperienced, undifferentiated in the psyche, everything that lies in the unconscious and therefore the man's "Eve" and the woman's "Adam" as well, is always projected. In consequence one experiences the elements of the opposite sex that are present in one's psyche no otherwise than, for example, one experiences his shadow—in the other person. One chooses another, one binds one's self to another, who represents the qualities of one's own soul.

'The soul-image is a "more or less firmly constituted functional complex, and the inability to distinguish one's self from it leads to such phenomena as those of the moody`man, dominated by feminine drives, ruled by his emotions, or of the rationalizing, animus-obsessed woman who always knows better and reacts in a

masculine way, not instinctively." (Wolff, T. *Einfuhrung in die Grundlagen der Komplexen Psychologie,* p. 112.) 'One has then the impression that another, a strange person, has "taken possession" of the individual, "a different spirit has got into him," etc., as proverbial speech so profoundly expresses it. Or we see the man who blindly falls victim to a certain type of woman—how often one sees precisely highly cultivated intellectuals abandon themselves helplessly to hussies because their feminine, emotional side is wholly undifferentiated—or the woman who, apparently incomprehensibly, falls for an adventurer or swindler and cannot get loose from him. The character of our soul-image, the anima or animus of our dreams, is the natural measure of our internal psychological situation. It deserves very special consideration in the way of self-knowledge.' (Jacobi, J. *The Psychology of C.G. Jung.* Kegan Paul, Trench, Trubner, London, 1942)

psychedelic (sī-ke-del'ik) Mind-manifesting; sometimes used to describe certain pharmacologic agents which have an effect on mental processes. See *psychotropics.*

psychehormic (sī-ke-hor'mik) Mind-rousing; sometimes used to describe certain pharmacologic agents which have an effect on mental processes.

psycheism Mesmerism; animal magnetism.

psychelytic (sī-ke-li'tik) Mind-releasing; sometimes used to describe certain pharmacologic agents which have an effect on mental processes.

psychentonia (sī-ken-tō'nē-à) Mental (usually high) tension.

psychephoric (sī-ke-for'ik) Mind-moving; sometimes used to describe certain pharmacologic agents which have an effect on mental processes.

psycheplastic (sī-ke-plas'tik) Mind-molding; sometimes used to describe certain pharmacologic agents which have an effect on mental processes.

psycherhexic (sī-ker-ek'sik) Mind-bursting forth; sometimes used to describe certain pharmacologic agents which have an effect on mental processes.

psychezymic (sī-ke-zī'mik) Mind-fermenting; sometimes used to describe certain pharmacologic agents which have an effect on mental processes.

psychiasis (sī-kī'à-sis) Spiritual healing.

psychiater (sī-kī'à-tēr) Psychiatrist.

psychiatria (sī-kē-at'rē-à) Psychiatry.

psychiatric disorders, classification of See *nomenclature, 1968 revision.*

psychiatric social work See *social work, psychiatric.*

psychiatrics The theory or practice of psychiatry.

psychiatrism (sī-kī'àtriz'm) The injudicious and fallacious application of psychiatric principles in an unwarrantedly mechanistic way, without careful investigation of the dynamics of the individual case to which the principle is applied. Psychiatrism is perhaps best illustrated by the novice student of psychology who reads Freud's work on dream-interpretation and begins blandly to interpret all his friends' dreams on the basis of the symbols mentioned by Freud. Thus psychiatrism tends to standardize and over-simplify complex problems of relationship and causality, and ignores the enormous importance of the individual variation. It is based on the fallacy of hypothetical concepts of unconscious personality forces being accepted in an unscientific, matter-of-fact fashion.

psychiatrist One versed in that branch of medicine which deals with the prevention, diagnosis, and treatment of mental and emotional disorders. A psychiatrist is a physician who has had advanced training in the diagnosis and treatment of mental disorders. This advanced training ordinarily includes the study of *psychotherapy* (q.v.), and since the methods of psychotherapy are often based on a particular theory or system of psychology, the individual psychiatrist will often characterize his orientation as 'psychoanalytic,' 'Freudian,' 'Jungian,' 'Adlerian,' etc. Such appellations are to be considered as indica-

tive of the philosophy or psychological system to which the psychiatrist adheres; they are, as it were, subgroupings within the more general field of psychiatry. A certain amount of confusion has arisen in regard to differentiation between the terms psychiatrist and psychoanalyst. In the United States, the term psychoanalyst generally refers to a physician who has had advanced training in the specialty of psychiatry and whose theoretical background is psychoanalytic. There are, however, certain people (particularly in Europe) who are psychoanalysts but not psychiatrists; these 'lay analysts' are not physicians but have had intensive training in the psychoanalytic method of psychotherapy and their theoretical orientation is psychoanalytic. Certain such persons in the United States have been trained in academic psychology and may thus be termed clinical psychologists.

psychiatrize (sī-kī'à-trīz) To exert psychiatric influence.

psychiatry (sī-kī'à-trē) The science of curing or healing disorders of the psyche. The medical specialty concerned with the study, diagnosis, treatment, and prevention of behavior disorders.

psychiatry, asylum A term used by Ernest Jones to describe the field of psychiatry which deals with major mental disorders under treatment in institutions.

psychiatry, child The science of healing or curing disorders of the psyche in children.

psychiatry, community That branch of psychiatry concerned with the provision and delivery of a co-ordinated program of mental health care to a specified population. While following the medical model in general, with the methods and techniques of clinical psychiatry as its cornerstone, community psychiatry in addition uses public health methods to assess the psychiatric needs of any specified population, to identify the various environmental factors that contribute to or otherwise modify psychosocial disorder, and to evaluate the effects of therapeutic intervention on the identified patient and the social units of which he is a part.

The techniques of community psychiatry are not new, but their fusion into a co-ordinated, comprehensive program designed to ensure equal care of high quality and ready accessibility for all is a departure from the usual clinical emphasis on the individual patient or patient-therapist dyad. It carries with it the acceptance of continuing responsibility for the mental health needs of a community. Although the importance of intrapsychic conflict in the production of some kinds of emotional disorder is not ignored, the emphasis in community psychiatry is on extrapsychic, interpersonal, environmental, and cultural forces that engender, precipitate, intensify, prolong, or otherwise complicate maladaptive patterns and their response to treatment. The earlier psychoanalytic theory, that mental health is threatened by over-control or excessive restriction of drive, has been modified to include the finding that optimal control of drive depends upon a combination of ego mastery and social organization.

Despite the fact that much psychosocial pathology reflects chronic illness rather than acute, self-limited disorder, experience has suggested that intensive, definitive, short-term care can often restore the patient who might otherwise languish indefinitely in a custodial-care institution to some degree of contented functioning in his usual environment. Currently, the *Community Mental Health Center* is the executive locus for the application of community psychiatry's concepts. Such centers include in-patient (24-hour) facilities, partial hospitalization (such as day, night, and weekend hospitals), out-patient departments, emergency services, and consultation and education units.

The foregoing are considered essential elements by the various Federal, State, and local agencies that provide economic support for Community Mental Health Centers; the following auxiliary elements are usually incorporated organizationally within those essential elements and/or are structured as equally essential divisions: diagnostic services, rehabilitation services, pre-care and after-care services, training sections (with educational programs for each discipline involved in the delivery of mental health services), and research and evaluation units.

The core concept of the Community Mental Health Center is that it will function as the nucleus for mental health services of the community it serves—usually defined geographically and termed the *catchment area.* Depending upon the number, quality, and effectiveness of pre-existing health (general as well as mental), education, and welfare agencies in the catchment area, the Center may house, staff, or directly implement *all* the services necessary to meet the mental health needs of the community. More typically, however, a major function of the Center is to achieve integration of already existing agencies, to supplement rather than supplant services, and to maintain liaison with each of them, with adjoining Centers, and with comprehensive medical or general health centers that service the community (hence the aphorism, the Community Mental Health Center is a concept, not a building).

An essential element in the delivery of such services is *continuity of care*— often misinterpreted to mean that the patient has the same therapist throughout every phase of his treatment and rehabilitation program, although more properly it refers to the provision of an organizational structure that will guarantee that the patient receive whatever kind of care he needs at the time he needs it. The therapy program is thus flexible, and tailored to the shifting needs of the patient, his pathology, and his community, rather than limited to the one or two techniques that may comprise the total armamentarium of a particular therapist.

Quite clearly, the mere existence of mental health services does not ensure their optimal utilization, for those who do come to the attention of established psychiatric agencies may not even constitute a majority of those who need psychiatric help. Furthermore, psychiatry as traditionally practiced may not be the best approach for many patients. As Lindeman and others have pointed out, it is a fiction that schizophrenia, to take one example, resides only in the patient. And it has long been known that the mentally ill who are placed in such settings as the Gheel colony or the Scottish boarding out system do not show the *social breakdown syndrome* so common in institutionalized patients. The conclusion to be drawn is obvious—that providing health services, particularly for that non-participant, voiceless segment of the population currently labeled *the disadvantaged,* is not enough. Truly comprehensive health centers must in addition function as agents in effecting social change that will promote mental health and prevent mental disease. Certainly they will continue to focus on early treatment and quick return to functioning, by providing the broadest possible range of therapies, somatic and psychologic, that have been developed to date. But they will be equally committed to *prevention*, in all its forms: *tertiary prevention* (rehabilitation) —the return of the identified patient to his peak potential of functioning, by concentrating on his assets and recoverable functions rather than on the liabilities of his psychopathology, by focusing on complications of disuse (such as the social breakdown syndrome) that have often been mistaken as part of the basic disease process; *secondary prevention*—early case-finding; and *primary prevention*— promotion of mental health, and prevention of psychosocial disorder.

But how this is to be done, and where, and when, and by whom, remain unsettled issues in *social psychiatry* (the body of knowledge and theory on which the methods and techniques of community psychiatry are based). Is community psychiatry a medical science or a social movement? Does it address itself to the mentally ill, or to the whole population, or to the entire social system within which it exists? Many in the field believe that evaluation of psychosocial disorder should include not only analysis, but ultimately also manipulation of existing social structures and systems. Others term such direct social or community action *social engineering* and include it as a part of social psychiatry. Still others view this as an unwarranted and potentially dangerous assumption of political power that is beyond the realm of medicine.

Community action may always be necessary if the causes of psychosocial disorder are to be influenced. Most would agree that utilization and mobilization of local resources are mandatory steps in such action, but there is less agreement on what kind and what extent of participation by the population involved are optimal—even though 'maximal feasible participation' is a stated requirement for funding of many community action programs. And there is still less agreement on whether the community psychiatrist's primary role should be as a provider of direct services, a social catalyst, or both.

In view of the continuing controversy over the orientation, ideology, and philosophy basic to community psychiatry, it is little wonder that currently operating Community Mental Health Centers are organized along very different lines, or with different models. In the *medical model*, the focus is on treatment of the identified patient. In the *crisis-intervention model*, the focus is on transitional-developmental and accidental-situational demands for novel adaptational responses. Because minimal intervention at such times tends to achieve maximal and optimal effects, such a model is more readily applicable to population groups than the medical model. In the *metabolic-nutritional model*, the focus is on long-term studies to assess the presence of deprivations, toxins, etc. in population groups, and on attempts to modify, reduce, or abolish those threats to health. A subtype of this model is the *social integration-disintegration model*, whose basic premise is that, other things being equal, a better organized society promotes better adaptation. The *educational-socialization model* views a population as a social system containing people who have certain roles. This is a sociologic approach that asks how well are people fulfilling their roles, and whose focus is often on newcomers to the group (children, immigrants, etc.) and on refitting to appropriate roles those who have deviated (rehabilitation and tertiary prevention of residual defects). In the *public health model*, the focus is on epidemiology and the population at risk, not only to assess the incidence and prevalence of disease but also to discover the conditions that produce it. Finally, there is the *ecological systems model*, which views disorder not only as a deviance of the person himself but as a reflection of deviance or disequilibrium in that series of systems with which he articulates.

Ecology is the study of the mutual relationships of living things and their environments. One of its basic tenets is that no form of life can continue to multiply indefinitely without eventually coming to terms with the limitations imposed by its environment. Ecology includes such studies as the differential incidence of mental disorder in various populations and the distribution of crime and delinquency within a specified geographical area. The ecologist (or social psychiatrist) is particularly interested in why one person falls ill while his neighbor (or sibling, or parent) maintains good health. The ecological model provides a network approach to psychosocial disorder that may try to manipulate the expectations that impose specific roles on subsystems, and this is the model that involves itself most directly in social engineering and community action. In such a model, the primary role of the psychiatrist is as a *change agent* in social action and community organization, who uses his knowledge of group process to mediate and reconcile opposing forces that produce social disequilibrium and to stimulate new approaches through interpersonal transactions. See *social policy planning.*

psychiatry, comparative Cultural psychiatry; that branch of psychiatry concerned with the influence of the culture on the mental health of members of that culture. Comparative psychiatry has also been termed social psychiatry, ethnopsychology, and clinical sociology. When the focus is on different cultures, rather than differences within a single culture, the term *transcultural psychiatry* is used. See *ecology; psychiatry, community.*

psychiatry, consultation See *consultant.*

psychiatry, cultural See *psychiatry, comparative.*

psychiatry, descriptive See *descriptive.*

psychiatry, dynamic See *descriptive.*

psychiatry, experimental As used today, this term generally refers to the use of chemical agents in the development of a science of human behavior, and particularly to research on the properties and pathways of action of the *psychotomimetics* (q.v.) In experimental psychiatry, drugs which alter behavior are used as devices for the detection and manipulation of significant variables in naturally occurring mental disorders.

psychiatry, forensic (fŏ-ren'sik) Psychiatry in its legal aspects, including criminology, penology, commitment of the mentally ill, the psychiatric role in compensation cases, the problems of releasing information to the court, of expert testimony, etc.

psychiatry, industrial The branch of psychiatry that deals with the worker's adjustment to his job and with the effects of the business organization on its members; specifically, it includes such areas and functions as: (1) personality factors in the worker that affect his work fitness; (2) early detection of psychiatric illness within the unit; (3) rehabilitation of the worker who has had a major mental illness; (4) placement, promotions, transfers, etc.; (5) assessment of psychiatric factors in compensation cases, accidents, and absenteeism; (6) training of management for appropriate handling of their subordinates' behavior.

psychiatry, liaison See *consultant.*

psychiatry, pastoral The branch of psychiatry that is related to religion, and particularly to the integration of psychiatry and religion for the purpose of alleviating emotional ailments—the psychotherapeutic role which the clergyman must often play in his relationship to his parishioners. The term includes such things as vocational and marriage counseling.

Organized religion as a whole represents centuries of interpersonal experiences which have given pragmatic validation to certain tenets and doctrines. Therefore, when based on these doctrines, advice and other therapeutic measures are often psychologically valid, even though the dynamics as such may not be recognized or understood. And, at least with certain types of patients, the results may be excellent. The many 'cures' at the shrine of Lourdes, France, afford an example of this.

Pastoral psychiatry at the present time is confined largely to reassurance and relief of guilt-feelings, affording opportunity for catharsis, and alleviation of anxiety in general by directive and non-interpretive methods. In addition religion offers the possibility of identification with the omnipotent Father, and engenders reaction formations and sublimation. In certain aspects, organized religion may be likened to group psychotherapy of an educative type. Unlike the latter, however, religion is generally devoid of an understanding of the psychodynamics involved.

psychiatry, political The application of psychiatric knowledge to politics.

psychiatry, psychoanalytic (sī-kō-an-à-lit'-ik) See *psychoanalysis.*

psychiatry, social In psychiatry, the stress laid on the environmental influences and the impact of the social group on the individual. This emphasis is made not only with regard to etiology, but also for purposes of treatment and, more important, in preventive work. See *ecology; psychiatry, community; psychiatry, comparative.*

psychic (sī'kik) Relating to or affected in the mind or psyche.

psychic equivalent Psychomotor epilepsy. See *epilepsy.*

psychic suicide See *suicide, psychic.*

psychical (sī'ki-kal) Psychic.

psychical reality See *reality, psychical.*

psychicism (sī'ki-siz'm) Psychical research.

psychics (sī'kiks) Psychology.

psychinosis (sī-ki-nō'sis) *Rare.* Psychosis.

psychlampsia (sī-klamp'sē-à) *Obs.* Mania.

psychnosia (sik-nō'sē-à) A term used by Moshcowitz for syndromes of physical symptoms on the basis of emotional conflicts (e.g. essential hypertension, Grave's syndrome, cardiospasm, irritable colon, mucous colitis). (Moshcowitz, E. 'The Psychogenic Origin of Organic Disease,' *New England Journal of Medicine* 212, 603 - 11, 1935)

psychnosis (sīk-nō'sis) *Rare.* Psychopathy.

psychoactive When used in reference to psychopharmacologic agents, the term usually means psychic energizer (antidepressant), although it is sometimes used less specifically to refer to any drug (stimulant, depressant, or tranquilizer) with an effect on mental processes.

psychoanalyeptic See *analeptic.*

psychoanaleptica (sī-kō-an-a-lep'ti-kà) See *psycholeptica.*

psychoanalysis (-an-al'i-sis) The separation or resolution of the psyche into its constituent elements. The term has three separate meanings: (1) a procedure, devised by Sigmund Freud, for investigating mental processes by means of free-association, dream-interpretation, and interpretation of resistance and transference manifestations; (2) a theory of psychology developed by Freud out of his clinical experience with hysterical patients, and (3) a form of psychiatric treatment developed by Freud which utilizes the psychoanalytic procedure (definition 1 above) and which is based on psychoanalytic psychology (definition 2 above). Freud considered the cornerstones of psychoanalytic theory to be: the assumption of unconscious mental processes, recognition of resistance and repression, appreciation of the importance of sexuality (and aggressivity), and the Oedipus complex. Ernest Jones has delineated seven major principles of Freud's psychology: (1) determinism–psychical processes are not a chance occurrence; (2) affective processes have a certain autonomy and can be detached and displaced; (3) mental processes are dynamic and tend constantly to discharge the energy associated with them; (4) repression; (5) intrapsychic conflict; (6) infantile mental processes—the wishes of later life are important only as they ally themselves with those of childhood; (7) psychosexual trends are present in childhood. For a short summary of Freud's instinct theories, see *neurosis.*

Other schools of thought within psychology and psychiatry are sometimes referred to (loosely, and not wholly correctly) as 'psychoanalytic.' Chief among these are:

(A) Jung's 'analytical psychology,' which emphasizes the collective unconscious, a concept bearing on ethnological psychology. Jung considers that libido arises not from the sexual instinct but from a universal force or life urge; mind is not only a Has Been but also a Becoming, that is, it has aims and strives to realize certain goals within itself. Reminiscences of experience are relegated to the personal unconscious and then link up with and are used to express fundamental ideas and trends, the 'archetypes,' which represent not only the past stages but also the future potentials of race development.

(B) Adler's 'individual psychology,' which is based on the egoistic side of man's nature, on the striving for power as a compensation for inferiority (psychic and organic). Neurosis is an attempt to free oneself from the feeling of inferiority.

(C) Sullivan's dynamic-cultural school (see *Sullivan, Harry Stack*).

(D) Horney's dynamic-cultural school (see *Horney, Karen*).

(E) Rado's adaptational school (see *psychodynamics, adaptational*).

psychoanalysis, applied The use of established psychoanalytic knowledge to contribute to the understanding of psychic phenomena that occur outside the realm of psychoanalytic therapy, as in *biography in depth* (q.v.), art, history, anthropology, education, sociology, etc.

psychoanalysis, wild A term used to describe psychotherapeutic techniques which use a limited amount of interpretation or which attack the patient directly with deep interpretations.

psychoanalyst One who adheres to the doctrine and/or uses the methods of psychoanalysis. See *psychoanalysis; psychiatrist.*

psychoataxia (sī-kō-à-tak'sē-à) Intrapsychic ataxia. *Rare.* See *ataxia.*

psychobacillosis (-bas-i-lō'sis) Treatment of schizophrenia by bacterial preparations.

psychobioanalysis See *bioanalysis.*

psychobiogram (-bī'ō-gram) E. Kretschmer devised the psychobiogram for purposes of practical investigation of the personality. It is made up of several parts. The first two parts consist of the data concerning the patient's heredity and past history. The other parts consist of a detailed description of the person's temperament, his sociological attitude, intelligence, physical findings, etc., and the classification from the point of view of the somatotype. (*Textbook of Medical Psychology,* tr. by Strauss, E.B., Oxford Medical Publications, London, 1934)

psychobiology The study of the biology of the psyche. It includes such subdi-

visions as the organization ('anatomy'), physiology, and pathology of the mind.

The term was used with a variety of meanings in the early part of the 20th century. Adolf Meyer first used the term in 1915, and in the United States, it is generally associated with his name. Meyer generally calls his point of view *objective psychobiology,* with particular stress upon the relationship of the individual to his environment.

The term is also known as *biopsychology.*

Meyer's school of objective psychobiology concerns itself with the overt and implicit behavior of the individual, which is a function of the total organism. The mind is the integration of the whole-functions of the total personality. Ideal mental health is the maximal ability of, plus the best opportunity for, getting along with people, without the interference of inner conflicts or external frictions, in a manner that would make for full mutual satisfaction on a constant give-and-take basis. Psychobiology is a genetic-dynamic science which studies personality development in the light of environmental setting and longitudinal growth. Meyer's central theme is 'the mind in action' and he stresses the relationship between the conscious drives and the environment. The aim of objective psychobiology as it is applied to patients (*distributive analysis and synthesis*) is to adapt the patient to his surroundings, both directly by working with him and indirectly via environmental manipulation and work with other social agencies. The therapist attempts to correct the patient's faulty mental habits. Psychobiology is particularly useful in the psychoses, where the conflict to a large extent is between the ego and the environment; but in the neuroses, the conflict is between the ego and the id.

psychobiology, objective See *psychobiology.*

psychocatharsis *Catharsis* (q.v.).

psychochemist A chemist 'grounded in biochemistry as well as in psychiatry' and equipped to 'investigate the problems of normal and abnormal behavior from the standpoint of altered chemical reactions in . . . the central nervous system.' (Freeman, W. *Journal of the American Medical Association* 97, 293, 1931)

psychochemistry Freeman's term for biochemistry as applied to psychiatric problems.

psychocinesia (sī-kō-si-nē'zē-à) See *psychokinesia.*

psychocoma (-kō'mà) *Obs.* T.S. Clouston's term for *stupor.*

psychocortical (-kor'ti-kal) Relating to the cortex of the brain as the seat of the mind.

psychodiagnostics (dī-ag-nos'tiks) A term used by German writers to designate the Rorschach test.

psychodietetics (-dī-e-tet'iks) 'The science of the feeding of an individual in sickness and in health with particular reference to the mental aspect. . . . This definition clearly designates the field which concerns the relationship between diet and mental life. Broadly speaking, the term psychodietetics may be used to cover not only those cases where diet is a factor in the direct causation of mental phenomena but also where behavior has a dietary expression as, for example, in the case of food fads due to peculiar notion on the part of the individual.' (Fritz, M.F. 'The Field of Psychodietetics,' *The Psychological Clinic XXII,* 3, 181-6, Sept.-Nov. 1933.)

psychodometer (-dom'ē-tēr) An instrument for measuring the rapidity of psychic processes.

psychodometry The measurement of psychic processes.

psychodrama 'The psychodrama deals with the private personality of the patient and his catharsis, with the persons within his milieu and with the roles in which he and they have interacted in the past, in the present, and in which they may interact in the future. Techniques have been devised to bring the underlying spontaneous processes to expression. Psychodramatic work is usually best organized in a therapeutic theatre, but it may be carried out wherever the patient lives, if his problem requires it.

'One of the techniques is that of self-presentation. The psychiatrist asks the patient to live through and portray or duplicate situations which are a part of his daily life, especially crucial conflicts in which he is involved. He must also enact and represent as concretely and as thoroughly as possible every person near to his problem. This may be done in collaboration with a partner or partners, either real or a person or persons functioning as substitutes—auxiliary egos.

'Another technique of the psychodrama is that of soliloquy. Here a deeper level of the inter-personal world is brought to expression. It is used by the patient to duplicate hidden feelings and thoughts which he actually has or had in a situation with a partner in real life, but which he did not or does not express. Expression of these hidden feelings, in the psychodrama, has a cathartic value for the patient.

'In the technique of spontaneous improvisation the patient acts in fictitious or symbolic roles which are carefully selected by the psychiatrist on the basis of the patient's problem. During the acts the patient reveals many elements of his private personality which offer an open target for analysis without the patient's awareness.

'In the psychodrama on a non-semantic level, feeling complexes—the pantomime, the dance, music, and the (apparently) nonsensical—are trained with therapeutic effect. An example is the technique of nonsensical expression where the patient is told to resist the emergence of verbal utterance and to produce sounds and words at random. The vowels and consonants are to be brought together into any possible combinations as they come to him spontaneously. This exercise has been useful in the training of patients with vocal defects.

'In the case of patients with whom any sort of communication is reduced to a minimum, the psychodrama attempts to create an auxiliary world, or a world within which the patient functions. This may require the use of a staff of auxiliary egos who are to embody the psychotic world of the patient. In this manner, the psychiatrist (through the auxiliary egos making up the auxiliary world) is able to "act with" the patient on the patient's spontaneous level.

'*Psychodramatic catharsis* is a process which takes place between the actual partners in a problem or mental disturbance. Analysis before or after psychodramatic action may prepare a cathartic development, but the genuine phase of catharsis takes place in the course of the psychodrama itself.' (Moreno, J.L. *Das Stegreif Theater*, Potsdam, Germany)

psychodrama, forms of (1) *Psychodrama.* Focuses on the individual, being a synthesis of psychological analysis with drama (action). Psychodrama aims at the *active* building up of private worlds and individual ideologies.

(2) *Sociodrama.* Focuses on the group, being a synthesis of the *socius* with psychodrama. It aims at the active structuring of *social* worlds and collective ideologies.

(3) *Physiodrama.* Focuses on the soma, being a synthesis of physical culture (sports) and psychodrama. The physical condition of the participants before, during, and after the production is *measured*. It gives diagnostic (possibly also prognostic) clues for training requirements, provides the set-up for retraining.

(4) *Axiodrama* (Gr. *axios*, worth, worthy of value, goodly.) Focuses on ethics and general values, and aims to dramatize eternal verities (truth, justice, beauty, grace, piety, eternity, peace, etc.).

(5) *Hypnodrama.* The synthesis of *hypnosis* (q.v.) and (psycho)drama.

(6) *Psychomusic.* A synthesis of *spontaneous* music with (psycho)drama.

(7) *Psychodance.* A synthesis of *spontaneous* dancing with (psycho)drama. 'The synthesis of all other forms of art as: sculpture, painting, creative writing etc. with psychodrama opens the way for action—as well as group methods.'

(8) *Therapeutic motion picture.* A synthesis of motion picture with psychodrama. (Moreno, J.L. 'Forms of Psychodrama; Terms and Definitions,' *Sociatry 1*, 4, 447-8, and bibliography, 1947)

psychodynamic (-dī-nam′ik) Relating to the forces of the mind. Ideas and impulses are charged with emotions, to which the general expression *psychic energy* is given. For example, delusions of persecution or obsessions or compulsions are described as psychodynamic phenomena, in that they are said to represent the results of activity of psychic forces. See *psychodynamics.*

psychodynamic cerebral system See *psychodynamics, adaptational.*

psychodynamics The science of mental forces in action. Essentially, psychodynamics are a formulation or description of how the mind develops, and of how the hypothesized energies of the mind are distributed in the course of its various adaptational maneuvers. See *ego; id; ontogeny, psychic; superego.*

psychodynamics, adaptational Rado's system of psychoanalytic psychiatry. 'This science is based on the psychoanalytic method of investigation. As we have just seen, it studies the part played by motivation and control in the organism's interaction with its cultural environment. It deals with pleasure and pain, emotion and thought, desire and executive action, interpreting them in terms of organismic utility, that is, in an adaptational framework. In the theory of evolution, the pivotal concept is adaptation; since the organism's life cycle is but a phase of evolution, it is consistent to make the same concept basic to the study of behavior.

'We define ontogenetic adaptations as improvements in the organism's pattern of interaction with its environment that increase its chances for survival, cultural self-realization, and perpetuation of its type. Autoplastic adaptations result from changes undergone by the organism itself; alloplastic adaptations from changes wrought by the organism on its environment. In ontogenetic adaptations, the master mechanisms are learning, creative imagination, and goal-directed activity.' (Rado, S. *Psychoanalysis of Behavior.* Grune & Stratton, New York, 1956)

'The organism's systemic requirements are known as its needs. Like its other traits, they are an outcome of the interaction between inherited predisposition (genotype) and environment. We speak of aboriginal needs that show predominantly the forming influence of the culture in which the organism lives.' (ibid.)

In Rado's terminology, the psychodynamic central system refers to mind and unconscious mind and includes (1) that range of the brain's neurophysiologic activity which comes to the awareness of the organism, the self-reporting range, and (2) that range of non-reporting activity which is accessible to extrapolative investigation by psychodynamic methods and/or to investigation by physiologic methods. The aim of adaptational psychodynamics is to discover the mechanisms by which the psychodynamic cerebral system accomplishes its integrative task. The integrative apparatus of the system is composed of four units, which are hierarchically ordered levels reflecting the course of evolutionary history—hedonic, brute emotions, emotional thought, and unemotional thought. At the hedonic level, the organism moves toward pleasure and away from pain. In the next two levels, the emotions are the controlling means of integration (divided into the emotions based on present pain or the expectation of pain, such as fear, rage, retroflexed rage, guilty fear, and guilty rage; and the welfare emotions based on present pleasure or the expectation of pleasure, such as pleasurable desire, affection, love, joy, self-respect and pride). At the level of unemotional thought, reason, common sense and science prepare the ground for intelligent action and self-restraint.

Behavior disorders are disturbances of psychodynamic integration which interfere with the organism's adaptive life performance, its attainment of utility and pleasure. The simplest forms of behavior disorder occur when the organism responds to danger with an overproduction of the emergency emotions; such emergency dyscontrol is in itself a threat to the organism from within and leads to processes of miscarried prevention and miscarried repair.

More complex behavior disorders arise when emergency dyscontrol acts in combination with additional pathogenic agents. With emergency dyscontrol as a point of departure, Rado classifies behavior disorders according to the increasing complexity of their patterns and mechanisms as follows:

'Class I. Overreactive Disorders.
'(1) Emergency Dyscontrol: The emotional outflow, the riddance through dreams, the phobic, the inhibitory, the repressive, and the hypochondriac patterns; the gainful exploitation of illness. (2) Descending Dyscontrol. (3) Sexual Disorders: The impairments and failures of standard performance. Dependence on reparative patterns: Organ replacement and organ avoidance; the criminal, dramatic and hidden forms of sexual paindependence; the formation of homogeneous pairs. Firesetting and shoplifting as sexual equivalents. (4) Social Overdependence: The continuous search for an ersatzparent; the mechanisms of forced competition, avoidance of competition, and of self-harming defiance. (5) Common Maladaptation: A combination of sexual disorder with social overdependence. (6) The Expressive Pattern (Expressive elaboration of common maladaptation): Ostentatious self-presentation; dreamlike interludes; rudimentary pantomimes; disease-copies and the expressive complication of incidental disease. (7) The Obsessive Pattern (obsessive elaboration of common maladaptations): Broodings, rituals, and overt temptations. Tic and stammering as obsessive equivalents; bed wetting, nailbiting, grinding of teeth in sleep, as precursors of the obsessive pattern. (8) The Paranoid Pattern (nondisintegrative elaboration of common maladaptation): The hypochondriac, self-referential, persecutory and grandiose stages of the Magnan sequence.

'Class II. Moodcyclic Disorders.
'Cycles of depression; cycles of reparative elation; the pattern of alternate cycles, cycles of minor elation; cycles of depression marked by elation; cycles of preventive elation.

'Class III. Schizotypal Disorders.
'(1) Compensated schizo-adaptation. (2) Decompensated schizo-adaptation. (3) Schizotypal disintegration marked by adaptive incompetence.

'Class IV. Extractive Disorders.
'The ingratiating ("smile and suck") and extortive ("hit and grab") patterns of transgressive conduct.

'Class V. Lesional Disorders.
'Class VI. Narcotic Disorders.
'Class VII. Disorders of War Adaptation. (Rado, S. ibid.)

Rado divides the methods of psychotherapy into two classes—reconstructive (adaptational technique of psychoanalytic therapy) and reparative (less ambitious treatment methods with limited goals but in general also of shorter duration).

psychodynamy (-dī'nam-ē) Animal magnetism.

psychodysleptica (-dis-lep'ti-ka) See *psychotropics*.

psycho-embryological schedule of ego See *dedifferentiation*.

psychoepilepsy (-ep′i-lep-sē) By some, this term is used synonymously with idopatic or genuine epilepsy; an unfortunate term in that it implies a psychogenic basis for epilepsy, evidence for which is minimal. See *epilepsy*.

psychoexploration A generic term used to refer to the various procedures known as abreaction, psychocatharsis, narcoanalysis, narcosynthesis, etc.

psychogender The psychological or emotional sex of a person; the term is ordinarily confined to intersexed patients to differentiate psychological sexual identification from somatic sex.

psychogenesis (-jen′e-sis) Origination within the mind or psyche.

psychogenia (-jē′nē-à) *Rare*. Mental disorder due to impaired mentality.

psychogenic, psychogenetic (-jen′ik, -jē-net′ik) Relating to or characterized by psychogenesis; due to psychic, mental, or emotional factors and not to detectable organic or somatic factors.

psychogeny (sī-koj′e-nē) Psychogenesis.

psychogerontology Geriatric psychiatry; the study of the psychosocial aspects of old age.

psychogeusic (sī-kō-gū′sik) Pertaining to taste perception.

psychognosis (sī-kog′nō-sis) *Rare*. Diagnosis of psychic disorders or psychiatric states.

psychogonical (sī-kō-gon′i-kal) Psychogenic.

psychogony (sī-kog′ō-nē) The doctrine of the development of the mind.

psychogram (sīkō-gram) A chart depicting personality traits. The term is often synonymous with psychograph.

psychograph More frequently used in psychology than in psychiatry. It has two special meanings. It refers to a chart depicting personality traits or it may relate to the history of a person from the point of view of personality.

psychography (sī-kog′rà-fē) The natural history of the mind. It includes description of the phenomena of the mind. The psychoanalysis of Freud, analytical psychology of Jung, the individual psychology of Adler and the psychobiology of Meyer represent divisions of psychography.

psycho-hygiene (sī-kō-hī′jēn, -hī′ji-ēn) *Obs*. Mental hygiene.

psycho-infantilism (-in-fan′ti-liz′m) 'Persistence, in the adult, of mental qualities characteristic of the child. Psycho-infantile behavior is referable to the hopelessness, uncertainty and desire for guidance and authority distinctive of childhood. It is manifested in tractability and dependence, which often takes the form of a strong emotional fixation frequently to the mother or the father, but sometimes to other persons, even chance acquaintances. The psycho-infantile person gives the normal adult the same feeling of detachment and the same urge to protect as the child. It is the latter attribute which lies back of the terms "naive," "childish" and "artless" so often used to describe his personality.' (Lindberg, B.J. *Psycho-Infantilism*. Ejnar Munksgaard, Copenhagen, 1950)
   '*Psycho-infantilism* is not a disease, nor is it the common denominator for psychoneurotic or psychosomatic disorders. It is a form of mental weakness, inasmuch as the psycho-infantile person is particularly vulnerable to mental insufficiency when confronted with decisive events in his life. He is specially apt to break down when he himself has to make an important decision, the more so if circumstances have deprived him of the person he has been used to leaning ·upon.
   'A psycho-infantile attitude is often met with outside the hospital walls and may be adopted by almost anyone in the face of crisis. Although psycho-infantilism as defined here is easy to recognize and to define as an independent syndrome, it is not a sufficient diagnosis in itself for a psychiatric case. The word "psycho-infantilism" must always be complemented with information regarding the other personality traits and naturally regarding the mental insufficiency in question.' (ibid.)

psychokinesia, psychokinesis (-kī-nē′-zē-à, -nē′sis) T.S. Clouston's term for defective inhibition; formerly it also referred to the clinical syndrome known as *impulse insanity*.

psychokym(e) (-kīm) 'Psychic processes conceived physiologically, namely, that which is conceived analogous to a form of energy, that something which flows through the central nervous system and which is at the basis of psychic processes. "Neurokym" is used to designate the nervous processes in general.' (Bleuler, E. *Textbook of Psychiatry*, tr. by Brill, A.A., Macmillan, New York, 1930)

psycholagny (sī'kō-lag-nē) Sexual excitation that begins, continues, and ends with mental imagery; mental masturbation, that is, the occurrence of masturbatory phenomena stimulated by mental forces alone.

psycholepsy, psycholepsis (sī'ko-lep-sē, -lep'sis) Sudden, intense lowering of psychic tension, associated with morbid ideas and actions.
'Individuals in whom psychological tension is unstable, suffer from sudden relaxations of this tension, succumb to psycholeptic crises which have been brought on by their relationships with certain persons in their immediate circle.' (Janet, P. *Psychological Healing*, vols. 1-2, tr. by Paul, E. and C., Macmillan, New York, 1925) When psychic tension mounts to great heights, 'in which feelings of ecstacy and indescribable happiness' appear, there may be a sudden fall in tension 'culminating in a psycholeptic crisis and even in an epileptic fit.' (ibid) Some people who have triumphed in a given work may terminate the triumph with a morbid clinical syndrome.

psycholeptica (-lep'ti-kà) Delay's term for phrenotropic drugs, whose principal effect is on the psyche, in contrast to neuroleptica, whose principal effect is on psychomotor activity. The psycholeptica include: (1) the 'minor' tranquilizers or ataractics, i.e. diphenylmethane derivatives and substituted propanediols (see *tranquilizers*); (2) psychoanaleptica (psychic 'tonics,' euphoriants, and antidepressives) and (3) psychodysleptica, which produce disintegration of psychic functions (lysergic acid, mescaline, etc.). See *psychotropics*.

psycholinguistic abilities See *Illinois Test of Psycholinguistic Abilities*.

psycholinguistics The study of the factors that affect the communication and comprehension of verbal information.

psychological Relating to psychology.

psychologist One versed in psychology.

psychologist, clinical One versed in psychology who deals with clinical cases and who uses his training in the theory and techniques of psychology to aid in the diagnosis and (under medical supervision) in the treatment of mental and emotional disorders. See *psychiatrist*.

psychology The science which deals with the mind and mental processes—consciousness, sensation, ideation, memory, etc.

psychology, applied Utilization of all knowledge available in the areas of psychology, sociology, etc., in order to achieve optimal effectiveness in any operation. Applied psychology is ordinarily subdivided according to the field in which the operation occurs; e.g. business psychology, educational psychology, industrial psychology.

psychology, atomistic Any psychology based on the doctrine that perceptions, thoughts, and all mental processes are built up through the combination of simple elements or atoms. According to the doctrine of atomism, the physical universe (or, as is sometimes taught, the whole universe both physical and mental) is composed of simple, indivisible, and minute particles or atoms. Many thinkers have endeavored to interpret atomism from a psychical point of view, treating the atoms either as *mind stuff* or as composed of sense elements. Mind stuff, a term first used by W.K. Clifford, is 'the elemental material, internally of the nature of mind, externally, or as it appears to us, in the form of matter, which is assumed to be the ground of reality.' (*Webster's New International Dictionary*, 2nd ed., Merriam, Springfield, Mass., 1948) 'The distinguishing feature of Freud's instinct theory is that it is based on a conative-appetitive-striving, rather than a structural principle like sensation or reflex. But, as with the classical psychologies and behaviorism, psychoanalysis is an *atomistic psychology* which attempts to derive complex entities from the action of a synthetic principle (association, conditioning, integration) on or about a basic unit. A conative principle is used as an atomic unit to reconstruct the molecules of experience.' (Kardiner, A., and Spiegel, H. *War Stress and Neurotic Illness*, Hoeber, New York, 1947)

psychology, 'blame' The tendency of persons with serious inhibitions in social competitive relationships to find expression for these inhibitions in hatred and persecution of some blameless scapegoat. 'This blame psychology also permits the individual to harbor a secret grandiose conception of himself.' (Kardiner, A., *et al. The Psychological Frontiers of Society*, Columbia University Press, New York, 1945)

psychology, centralist That subdivision of psychology which emphasizes the role of higher brain centers in determining behavior. In contrast to this is *peripheralist psychology* (including behaviorism), which attributes the major role in behavior to the receptor and effector organs.

psychology, educational That branch of psychology concerned with the derivation of psychological principles and methods that can be applied directly to problems of education.

psychology, gestalt (ge-stalt') A school of psychology that is concerned primarily with perceptual processes. Its development is associated particularly with the names of Max Wertheimer, Wolfgang Koehler, and Kurt Koffka, and represents an outgrowth of opposition to the traditional association psychology.

'Gestalt psychology holds that the whole or total quality of the image is perceived. This is in contrast to association psychology, which states that stimuli are perceived as parts and built into images. According to gestalt psychology, the organization of the stimuli into the image is based upon laws of perception which include proximity, similarity, direction, and inclusiveness of parts of the stimuli. The perceptual experience is a gestalt or configuration or pattern in which the whole is more than the sum of its parts. Organized units or structuralized configurations are the primary form of biological reactions. In the sensory field, these gestalten correspond to the configuration of the stimulating world.

'The organism has a "gestalt function" which is defined as that function of the integrative organism whereby it responds to a given constellation of stimuli as a whole, the response being a constellation or pattern or gestalt which differs from the original stimulus pattern by the process of the integrative mechanism of the individual who experiences the perception. The whole setting of the stimulus and the whole integrative state of the organism determine the pattern or response.

'There is a tendency not only to perceive gestalten but to complete gestalten and to reorganize them according to principles biologically determined by the sensory motor pattern of action which may be expected to vary in different maturation or growth levels and in pathological states organically or functionally determined.' (Bender, L. *Child Psychiatric Techniques*, Thomas, Springfield, Ill., 1952)

psychology, individual Adlerian psychology, a discipline elaborated by the Viennese psychiatrist Alfred Adler. The complete name of his system is 'comparative individual-psychology.' 'By starting with the assumption of the *unity of the individual*, an attempt is made to obtain a picture of this unified personality regarded as a variant of individual life-manifestations and forms of expression. The individual traits are then compared with one another, brought into a common plane, and finally fused together to form a composite portrait that is, in turn, individualized.' (Adler, A. *The Practice and Theory of Individual Psychology*, tr. by Radin, P., Kegan Paul, Trench, Trubner, London, 1924)

'Individual psychology is not psychoanalysis. It is a method initiated by Dr. Adler of Vienna, of gaining knowledge of individuals, including knowledge of their inner life, but it is a method founded upon a view of the individual as whole in himself, an indivisible unit of human society. It relates everything that the individual does in such a way as to obtain a picture of a single, coherent and intelligible tendency, expressed in most various ways, direct and indirect. Thus it is a method of unifying the psyche much more than of dissecting it.' (Mairet, P. *ABC of Adler's Psychology*, Kegan Paul, Trench, Trubner, London, 1928)

psychology, mob The psychology of mob behavior is considered by Fenichel to have much in common with a certain type of character defense against guilt-feelings. In this type of defense, the guilt-laden character feels admiration and relief when someone else does something which he has been striving to do, but has been inhibited from doing through guilt-feelings. The meaning of the admiration and relief is 'Since others do it, it cannot be so bad, after all.'

The attainment of relief from guilt-feelings in this way is a powerful force for group formation. Others have dared to do what the individual has felt guilt about doing. And 'If my whole group acts this way, I may, too.' In this way, the relief from guilt-feelings is described as 'one of the cornerstones of "mob psychology."' Indeed Fenichel points out that 'individuals acting as a group are capable of instinctual outbreaks that would be entirely impossible for them as individuals.' (Fenichel, O. *The Psychoanalytic Theory of Neurosis*, Norton, New York, 1945)

psychology, peripheralist See *psychology, centralist.*

psychology, rational Any system of psychology in which *a priori* assumptions (usually of a philosophical or theological nature) form the background into which any observed facts must be fit.

psychology, topographical See *topography, mental.*

psychology, uprooted The changed mentality exhibited by one who has been uprooted by force of circumstance, i.e. has had to leave his native place with its physical, social, and cultural background that had surrounded him all his life.

When removed from their customary environment and dislocated from their protective moral background, uprooted people deviate markedly from their inculcated reverence for original values and show symptoms parallel to those found in migrating hordes: recklessness, unregulated and indiscriminate sexuality, a marked lowered responsibility toward human life and property. (Baynes, H.G. *Mythology of the Soul*, Williams and Wilkins, Baltimore, 1940)

psychometrics Mental testing. See *examinations, psychometric.*

psychometry (sī-kom′e-trē) Measurement of the duration and force of mental processes.

psychomotility (sī-kō-mō-til′i-tē) Any motor action, attitude, or habit pattern that is influenced by mental processes and thus reflects the individual's personality make-up. Certain psychomotor phenomena such as tics, sterotypies, catatonia, dysarthria, stammering, and tremor have long been used in diagnosis as signs of psychomotor disturbance. Recently, postural attitudes and gait have been under investigation by clinicians as objective signs of psychomotor disturbance. Handwriting, also, has long been known as a valuable aid in investigating psychomotility, for it gives some indication of the individual's motivation. Certain features of handwriting have been regarded as suggestive of certain personality traits. Preliminary investigations of a nature more scientific than mere palmistry indicate that correlations do exist between handwritings of different types and symptoms, syndromes, and character traits noted in the patient's records.

psychomotor Relating to movement that is psychically determined in contradistinction to that which is definitely recognized as extra-psychic or organic in cause.

psychoneuroid (sī-ko-nū′roid) Resembling or like psychoneurosis or psychoneurotic.

psychoneurosis See *neurosis.*

psychoneurosis, battle War neurosis. See *neurosis, traumatic.*

psychoneurosis, defense Freud's term for hysteria and various neuroses and psychoses caused by some idea or sensation, so painful that the sufferer endeavors to dismiss it from the mind; at times, instead of being absolutely forgotten, the thought sinks down into the unconscious and acts as the hidden cause of the psychoneurotic disturbances.

psychoneurosis maïdica (mà-id′i-kà) Pellagra.

psychonoetism (-nō′e-tiz'm) A term introduced by L.E. Hinsie to designate the tranference of personal conflicts to the intellect. Often patients are seen 'who shift their doubts, fears, obsessions and delusions from their original source in the unconscious to the sphere of the intellect. Thus a patient who was a great objector and had to contradict everything and everyone was really denying a strong Oedipus complex and unconscious instinctual demands directed toward his mother. However, he had transferred his denial of his unconscious instincts to the intellectual sphere, where it became an obsessive doubting of all ideas and statements. This is the process termed psychonoetism.' (Hinsie, L.E. *Understandable Psychiatry,* Macmillan, New York, 1948)

psychonomics (-nom'iks) The science of the laws of mind: psychology.

psychonomy (sī-kon'ō-mē) The branch of psychology treating of the laws of mental action.

psychonosema (sī-kō-nō-sē'mà) *Obs.* Mental disease.

psychonosology (-nō-sol'ō-jē) The classification of mental disorders.

psychoparesis (-par'ē-sis) *Rare.* Mental enfeeblement.

psychopath, sexual See *psychopathia sexualis.*

psychopathia (-path'ē-à) Psychopathy.

psychopathia martialis (psē-kô-pà'thē-à màr-tē-à'lēs) Shell-shock.

psychopathia sexualis (sek-soo-ä'lēs) The expression, referring to sexual perversions, was introduced by the German sexologist Richard Krafft-Ebing (1840-1903), whose classical book on sexology bears that title.

psychopathic personality Antisocial personality (301.7). Although the 1968 revision of psychiatric nomenclature does not recognize psychopathic personality as a discrete entity, the attempts to define more clearly the nature of the various behavior patterns which make up this poorly understood group have not been wholly successful, and the term continues to appear in the psychiatric literature.

It was J.C. Prichard who first offered a systematic description of the so-called 'moral disorders'; in 1835 he described a series of cases (which he termed 'moral insanity' and 'moral imbecility') which were the prototypes of the psychopathic state as it is generally understood today. In 1888 Koch introduced the term 'psychopathic inferiority,' and Kraepelin later included in this group a variety of syndromes described in terms of the most obvious presenting symptom, e.g. excitability, impulsivity, lying, criminality. The term 'constitutional psychopathic inferior' was used by Adolf Meyer in 1905; it should be noted, however, that Meyer did not use the term constitutional in the sense of congenital, but rather to indicate that the traits in question were acquired early and were thoroughly ingrained in the personality. In general, at least according to current usage, psychopathic personality (or psychopathic disorder) is any behavioral dysfunction that is primary ('idiopathic' or non-organic) and manifests itself in abnormally aggressive or seriously irresponsible conduct.

Cleckley (1941), who considers psychopathic personality a psychosis because of the lack of integration of the affective components into the personality, lists the following characteristics: '(1) Superficial charm and good "intelligence." (2) Absence of delusions and other signs of irrational "thinking." (3) Absence of "nervousness" or psychoneurotic manifestations. (4) Unreliability. (5) Untruthfulness and insincerity. (6) Lack of remorse or shame. (7) Inadequately motivated antisocial behavior. (8) Poor judgment and failure to learn by experience. (9) Pathologic egocentricity and incapacity for love. (10) General poverty in major affective reactions. (11) Specific loss of insight. (12) Unresponsiveness in general interpersonal relations. (13) Fantastic and uninviting behavior with drink and sometimes without. (14) Suicide rarely carried out. (15) Sex life impersonal, trivial and poorly integrated. (16) Failure to follow any life plan.' (Cleckley, H. *The Mask of Sanity,* Mosby, St. Louis, 1941) The maladjustment is a chronic one, and the psychopath tends to project the blame for his actions onto others. He tends to act out his conflicts so that the environment suffers, rather than the patient. He is a rebellious individualist and a non-conformist.

E. Glover classifies psychopathy into three main sub-groups: (1) sexual psychopathy, with predominantly sexual symptoms combined with some degree of ego disorder; (2) 'benign' psychopathy, manifested in the main as social incapacity, but usually with accompanying psycho-sexual disorder; and (3) antisocial psychopathy characterized by an unstable ego, delinquent outbursts, and some degree of sexual maladjustment. (*The Technique of Psycho-Analysis*, International Universities Press, New York, 1955)

The etiology is unknown; some claim an exclusively organic etiology, others maintain that it is due to psychogenic factors. Many writers have emphasized difficulties in identification leading to a formless or confused ego-ideal. An unstable, inconsistent maternal figure or rejection and emotional deprivation early in life are believed to produce such difficulties in identification. According to M.S. Guttmacher (in Hoch, P. and Zubin, J. *Current Problems in Psychiatric Diagnosis*, Grune and Stratton, N.Y., 1953), psychopathic behavior is '. . . generally the result of affect starvation during the first years of life. The most malignant anti-social psychopaths are probably the products of affect starvation plus sadistic treatment in early childhood.'

Karpman suggests that those cases of psychogenic etiology be termed secondary or symptomatic psychopathy; the others he calls primary psychopathy or *anethopathy* (q.v.). See also *psychopathy, passive parasitic*.

Various workers have noted a high incidence of cerebral dysrhythmia in patients diagnosed psychopathic personality; a high alpha index and theta activity are among the most commonly observed abnormalities.

psychopathist (sī-kop'ā-thist) *Obs.* Psychiatrist; alienist.

psychopathologist (sī-kō-pā-thol'ō-jist) A person who specializes in psychopathology.

psychopathology The branch of science that deals with morbidity or pathology of the psyche or mind.

psychopathosis (sī-kō-pa-thō'sis) Southard's term for what is more commonly termed *psychopathic personality* (q.v.)

psychopathy (sī-kop'ā-thē) General term for mental disease or disorders.

psychopathy, benign See *psychopathic personality*.

psychopathy, passive parasitic (par-ā-sit'ik) A term which defines a clinical subdivision of anethopathy *(psychopathic personality)*. Karpman suggests the term *anethopathy* (q.v.) to replace idiopathic, constitutional, or primary psychopathy. Anethopathy is subdivided into two distinct clinical types: the aggressive predatory type and the passive parasitic type. In regard to the latter, Karpman says: 'Instead of being actively aggressive, this type of an individual has much less of energy output and feeds himself by "sponging" on his environment for all his needs in a passive and entirely parasitic way. Its victims are willing, yet unwilling hosts. Such aggression as there may be, is very minimal and no more than is absolutely necessary to satisfy immediate needs.' (*Psychoanalytic Review 34*, 102, 1947.) Typical of such patients is the lack of any positive or generous human emotions, of sympathetic or tender affect, of gratitude or appreciation. These patients show no guilt, remorse, or regret. Their total picture is one of self-gratification. There are almost no unconscious mechanisms, because there is no repression of instinctual demands and no deferment of pleasure. Further, the patients are completely lacking in insight into the nature of their disturbances.

psychopedagogy (-ped'ā-gō-jē) A combination of conventional pedagogy and Adlerian psychology which aims to stimulate, cultivate, and amplify the natural qualities of the child and do away with unnecessary authority.

psychopetal (sī-kop'e-tal) The term *psychopetal* literally refers to objects that seek the psyche. Ordinarily, however, psychiatrists prefer the term *centripetal*. Bleuler says: 'I do not speak of "psychopetal" functions, because although there is a given "direction" yet both incoming and outgoing functions, as far as psychology is concerned, take place within the psyche.' (Bleuler, E. *Textbook of Psychiatry*, tr. by Brill, A.A., Macmillan, New York, 1930)

psychopharmacology The study of drugs that affect mental and behavioral activity, and in particular those drugs classified as *psychotropics* (q.v.).

psychophysical (-fiz′i-kal) Psychosomatic.

psychophysics (-fiz′iks) The science of the relation between mental action and physical phenomena.

psychophysiologic disorders (sī-kō-fiz-i-ō-loj′ik) Psychosomatic disorders,' 'somatization reactions,' 'organ neuroses,' etc. (305.x) These disorders are disturbances of visceral function secondary to chronic attitudes or long-continued insufficiency of affective discharge and may present themselves as dysfunction involving any of the organ systems: skin, musculoskeletal, respiratory, cardiovascular, hemic and lymphatic, gastro-intestinal, genito-urinary, endocrine, nervous system or organs of special sense. In this system of classification, ulcerative colitis, for example, would be labeled 'psychophysiologic gastro-intestinal reaction.'

psychophysiology (-fiz-i-ol′ō-jē) Physiology in relation to the mind and its processes.

psychoplegia (-plē′jē-à) *Rare.* A rapidly developing form of dementia.

psychopneumatology (-nū-mà-tol′ō-jē) Study of the interactions of mind and body; psychosomatology.

psycho-reaction Much and Holzmann used this expression for psychophysical interrelationship. They asserted that when they injected cobra poison into patients with schizophrenia, they observed lysis of the red blood corpuscles in a way that was characgeristic of schizophrenia. Their claims were short-lived.

psychorhythm (-riTH'm) T.S. Clouston's term, synonymous with *alternating insanity.*

psychorhythmia (-riTH′mē-à) Involuntary repetition, by the mind, of its formerly volitional action.

psychorrhagia, psychorraghy (sī-kō-rā′-jē-a, sī-kor′à-jē) The death-struggle.

psychorrhea (-rē′à) A form of hebephrenic schizophrenia characterized by vague and often bizarre theories of philosophy; usually the stream of thought is incoherent.

psychorrhexis (-rek′sis) A malignant type of anxiety reaction seen in 2 to 3 per cent of war neuroses, according to Emilio Mira. Anguish and perplexity, rather than fear or excitement, are the cardinal features. Pulse remains above 120, respiration about 40. Temperature rises rapidly after seven days, the tongue becomes ulcerated, and jaundice and tympanitic abdomen may appear. Patients become restless, develop automatic movements and facial spasms. In fatal cases, death ensues after three or four days. Psychorrhexis occurs in patients with pre-existing lability of the sympathetic system, with sudden severe mental trauma in conditions of physical exhaustion, and when there is long delay before sedative treatment is instituted.

psychosensory (sī-kō-sen′sō-rē) Pertaining to: 1. The mental perception and interpretation of sensory stimuli, or 2. A hallucination which, by an effort, the mind is able to distinguish from an actuality (pseudohallucination).

psychoses, alcoholic (sī-kō′sēs) See *alcoholism.*

psychosexual Relating to sexuality as it manifests itself in the mind, in contradistinction to its physical or somatic manifestations.

psychosexuality Psychosexual condition or state. *Psychosexuality* is distinguished from sexuality expressed somatically (somatosexual). For example, ideas of a sexual character are manifestations of psychosexuality. See *ontogeny, psychic.*

psychosis Loosely, any mental disorder (including whatever is meant by the obsolete terms 'insanity,' 'lunacy,' and 'madness'); more specifically, the term is used to refer to a particular class or group of mental disorders, and particularly to differentiate this group from neurosis, sociopathy (or psychopathy), character disorder, psychosomatic disorder, and mental retardation. Traditionally, the psychoses or *psychotic disorders* are subdivided into:
A. Organic Brain Syndromes
B. 'Functional' Psychoses

1. Schizophrenias
2. Affective Psychoses (Involutional Melancholia, Manic-Depressive Psychosis)
3. Paranoid States
4. Psychotic Depressive Reaction

While there might be general agreement that the term 'psychosis' should be used as indicated above in a qualifying sense to refer to a particular group of psychiatric disorders, use of the term in fact has not been so precise or definite. Instead, 'psychosis' (and its adjectival form, 'psychotic') has often been used in a quantifying sense to indicate severity of disorder; thus a person with the psychosis, schizophrenia, may be labelled psychotic only at certain times when the symptoms of his disorder reach a certain intensity and/or adversely affect his mental competence.

As a result of conflicting usage, there is no single acceptable definition of what psychosis is. In general, however, the disorders labelled psychoses differ from the other groups of psychiatric disorders in one or more of the following:

1. severity—the psychoses are 'major' disorders that are more severe, intense, and disruptive; they tend to affect all areas of the patient's life (in Adolph Meyer's terms, a psychosis is a 'whole-reaction' rather than a 'part-reaction').

2. degree of withdrawal—the psychotic patient is less able to maintain effective object relationships; external, objective reality has less meaning for the patient or is perceived in a distorted way.

3. affectivity—the emotions are often qualitatively different from the normal, at other times are so exaggerated quantitatively that they constitute the whole existence of the patient.

4. intellect—intellectual functions may be directly involved by the psychotic process so that language and thinking are disturbed; judgment often fails; hallucinations and delusions may appear.

5. regression—there may be generalized failure of functioning and a falling back to very early behavioral levels; such regression is more than a temporary lapse in maturity and may include a return to early and even primitive patterns.

psychosis, accidental *Rare.* Organic psychosis.

psychosis, acute shock An acute psychiatric disturbance occurring during war.

Its most prominent symptoms are a completely unconscious state (with flaccid limbs and closed eyes), lasting from minutes to hours; insensitivity to pain with no reaction to external stimuli; the eyelids flutter, the eyeballs are mobile and are rolled outward and upward. The condition occurs most commonly during active warfare, especially on forced marches and in active campaigns.

psychosis, affective A general term used to refer to any of those psychoses whose prominent feature is a disturbance in mood or emotion, viz. manic-depressive psychosis and involutional melancholia.

psychosis, akinetic (ak-i-net′ik) Wernicke used the term akinetic motor psychosis to refer to that extreme of catatonia which is marked by stupor, 'attonita,' and cerea flexibilitas. Flexor action of the musculature predominates, and movement may be reduced almost to zero. At the other extreme of catatonia is the hyperkinetic motor psychosis, which corresponds to what in present-day use is termed catatonic excitement.

psychosis, alcoholic Korsakov When associated with alcoholism, the *Korsakov psychosis* is also known as *chronic alcoholic delirium* (291.1). Some authors also refer to it as *chronic delirium tremens*, because the syndrome frequently follows (acute) delirium tremens. Bleuler says that 'the Korsakov psychosis in the majority of cases begins with a delirium tremens that recedes somewhat slowly and leaves behind the organic syndrome.' The basic symptomatology comprises memory defects, confabulations, impairment of apperception and attention, disorientation, ideational and affective disorders, in addition to such physical symptoms as are associated with general neuritis (pains, paralyses, atrophies, etc.). (Bleuler, E. *Textbook of Psychiatry*, tr. by Brill, A. A., Macmillan, New York, 1930) See *psychosis, Korsakov.*

psychosis, alternating The circular form of manic-depressive psychosis in which manic episodes alternate with depressive episodes in the same patient. This form was originally described by Falret, Jr. as folie circulaire.' It is not as common as either the recurrent depressive or the recurrent manic types of manic-depressive psychosis.

psychosis, arteriosclerotic (ar-tēr-ī-ō-sklerot'ik)'Organic brain syndrome associated with cerebral arteriosclerosis (293.0). See *arteriosclerosis, cerebral.* The term cerebral arteriosclerosis refers to degenerative changes in the arteries of the brain, the most important causes of which are: (1) primary degeneration of the intima; (2) degeneration secondary to high blood pressure; (3) endarteritis (usually syphilis); (4) thromboangiitis obliterans; (5) polyarteritis nodosa or periarteritis nodosa, and (6) temporal arteritis. The effect of progressive occlusion of the cerebral blood vessels is an impairment of circulation in the regions they supply. As a result of this, impairment of cerebral function occurs before any vessel is completely blocked.

Pathologically, the primary and most important changes are in the elastic tissues, especially in the internal elastic membrane of the cerebral arterioles. Two main types of elastic alterations are seen, hyperplastic and hypoplastic degeneration. Focal parenchymatous changes in the brain tend to be associated with hyperplastic degeneration, while gross hemorrhagic softenings are more prevalent in the hypoplastic type. The hyperplastic type tends to be associated with focal neurologic symptoms; the hypoplastic type shows predominantly mental symptoms.

The onset of the disease is often insidious, and its course is slowly progressive. Mental symptoms consist of a general reduction in intellectual capacity with memory impairment and emotional instability. The patient becomes self-centered and hostile to change in all forms. In more severe cases, loosely constructed delusions occur, often with a paranoid coloring. Depression is not uncommon and there may be attacks of confusion. Still greater deterioration leads to a profound dementia.

Neurologic symptoms include epileptiform attacks, various forms of aphasia, agnosia, and apraxia, signs of pyramidal tract lesions, senile tremor, athetosis, Parkinsonism, and often some degree of visual impairment.

psychosis, autistic (aw-tis'tik) See *psychosis, symbiotic infantile.*

psychosis, barbed wire A psychosis developing in prisoners of war, characterized by irritability and loss of memory for prewar occurrences.

psychosis, biogenic (bī-ō-jen'ik) Craig and Beaton write that 'the group of disorders called the biogenic psychoses are abnormal reactions to experience which should normally build up the personality; they have no other cause than the patient's failure to master life. The conception originated with Kraepelin, who differentiated by the term dementia praecox a class of reactions which he supposed to run a dementing course.' The psychoses known as biogenic are dementia praecox, (schizophrenia), dementia paranoides, paraphrenia, paranoia, manic-depressive psychosis, and the involutional states.

psychosis, borderline See *borderline psychosis.*

psychosis, buffoonery A form of hyperkinetic catatonia (catatonic excitement) in which the patient constantly makes disconnected caricatured grimaces and gestures. This psychosis probably represents a flight into disease as an escape from reality. 'One has the impression that these patients want to play the buffoon, though they do this in a most awkward and inept fashion. They contrive any number of stupidities and sillinesses, such as beating their own knees, interchanging pillows for blankets when they go to bed, pouring water out on the floor instead of into a cup, lifting doors off their hinges. The patients will do all this while they are seemingly well oriented. As a rule they speak very little or not at all and what they have to say is, in the main, completely illogical cursing or other nonsense. Undoubtedly the "faxen-psychosis" has an origin similar to that of the Ganserian twilight state. It usually involves individuals who for some unconscious reason pretend to be mentally deranged.' (Bleuler, E. *Dementia Praecox or the Group of Schizophrenias,* International Universities Press, New York, 1950) Also called *faxen-psychosis.*

psychosis, cardiac Confused mental state associated with heart failure.

psychosis, Cheyne-Stokes (John Cheyne, Scottish physician, 1777 - 1836, and William Stokes, Irish physician, 1804 - 1878) An abnormal mental state, characterized by anxiety and restlessness, associated with Cheyne-Stokes breathing.

psychosis, circular See *mania.*

psychosis, circulatory Confused mental state associated with cardiovascular failure.

psychosis, climacteric (klī-mak-ter′ik) Any psychotic reaction associated with the climacterium or 'change of life.' See *psychosis, involutional.*

psychosis, collective The term for psychic defense mechanisms that are utilized by an entire group in adapting to other cultures and societies. Freud's instinctual theories recognized two basic drives, sex and aggression. Freud felt that the aggressive trends of man lead him and his culture to fatal conflicts. Man's aggressiveness within a culture is diverted to people outside his own 'psychic mass.' This diversion of hostile trends implies a process of projection of the superego's aggressive component, so that the individual's hostility can be ascribed to other groups. Flescher thinks that this paranoid projection is inherent in the formation of the mass and constitutes the collective psychosis. Present-day Russia affords an example of collective psychosis, with the Russians accusing the United States, for one, of capitalistic war-mongering and aggression. According to the theory above, these accusations represent a projection of the Russians' own aggression, which cannot be openly expressed against their government.

psychosis, defect *Obs.* Mental retardation; feeblemindedness.

psychosis, defense Now obsolete, this was a general term used by Freud to emphasize the defensive value of a psychosis. He then employed the phrase *defense-neurosis* to express a similar concept in the neuroses.

psychosis, degeneration A term suggested for a group of atypical affective psychoses which show, in addition to the more typical manic-depressive symptoms, periodic hallucinosis, stupor, excitement, and paranoid phases. The term 'degeneration' was used because of the marked hereditary taint found in families in which such variants occur.

psychosis, degenerative *Obs.* Any psychosis with regressive tendencies or manifestations; by some, used in a more spe-

cific way to refer to organic psychoses with irreversible dementia.

psychosis, exhaustive *Collapse delirium.* Binswanger subdivides exhaustive psychosis as follows: *exhaustion stupor; exhaustive amentia; delirium acutum exhaustivum.* See *delirium, collapse.*

psychosis, febrile (fē′brĭl, feb′ril) *Obs.* Infective-exhaustive psychosis.

psychosis, functional See *functional.*

psychosis, 'furlough' An episode of the acute schizophrenic type secondary to the sudden emotional readjustments required by a military furlough or leave. Dynamically, the outbreak of the psychotic behavior seems to be related to the sudden release of the soldier from military authority, on which he has become dependent. Symptoms appear suddenly a few days after the apparently well-adjusted person has returned home. Affect becomes inappropriate, delusional trends and ideas of reference are prominent, and suicidal tendencies are frequent. In the ensuing week or two, severe confusion with blocking of thought processes becomes marked. Gradual improvement occurs within two months, irrespective of any particular form of therapy. The patient cannot return to duty, because flattening of affect and unpredictable behavior usually remain. (*American Journal of Psychiatry 102,* 670, 1945 - 6)

psychosis, gestational (jes-tā′shun-al) *Obs.* Psychosis developing during pregnancy.

psychosis, governess 'For decades, the idea has been preserved that governesses were especially prone to develop schizophrenia. Some authors even spoke of a "governess-psychosis"; and it has even been maintained that governesses suffer a particularly severe (and unpleasant) form of the disease. There may be something in this, inasmuch as young women become governesses who have ambitions of raising their social standing ·beyond their capacities and among whom there must be many with schizophrenic predisposition.' (Bleuler, E. *Dementia Praecox or the Group of Schizophrenias,* International Universities Press, New York, 1950) Statistics do not, in fact, indicate that the incidence ·of schizophrenia is higher in governesses than in other vocations.

psychosis, housewife's See *neurosis, housewife's.*

psychosis, hysterical See *hysterical psychosis; hysteria.*

psychosis, iatrogenic (ī-at-rō-jen'ik) See *iatrogeny.*

psychosis, idiophrenic (id-i-ō-fren'ik) Obs. Organic psychosis.

psychosis, infective-exhaustive An older term for acute brain syndrome associated with systemic infection;· also known as acute toxic encephalopathy, acute toxic encephalitis, or acute serous encephalitis.

psychosis, influenced Gordon's term for psychosis of association. See *association, psychosis of.*

psychosis, invocational A rare psychotic reaction to incantations, prayers, etc. such as is sometimes seen in revivalist meetings.

psychosis, involutional Climacteric psychosis; involutional melancholia; involutional psychotic reaction; agitated depression of middle life—all these terms are used more or less interchangeably ·to refer to depressive psychoses appearing during the involutional period (40 to 55 years for women, 50 to 65 years for men) in people who have no history of previous mental illness. (296.0) Characteristically, such depressions manifest a triad of symptoms, consisting of delusions of sin and guilt and/or of poverty, an obsession with death, and a delusional fixation on the gastro-intestinal tract, all in a setting of agitation and dejection. In some (involutional paranoid state, 297.1), a fourth major symptom is present in self-referential or persecutory delusions, .and this second group with a vivid admixture of paranoid symptoms has a poorer prognosis than the more purely depressive variety. Concern over finances, physical illness, bereavement, enforced retirement, and 'loss' of children to marriage or other forms of independence are frequent precipitants. Involutional psychoses account for 5 - 10% of first admissions

to mental hospitals; their actual incidence is difficult to estimate because many respond favorably to anti-depressant drugs or to electroconvulsive therapy administered on an out-patient basis.

psychosis, juvenile A psychosis occurring between the ages of 15 and 25, approximately. This term is sometimes used, incorrectly, as synonymous with schizophrenia. All psychoses occur in this age group, and, because schizophrenia is the most common of the psychoses, it is also the most common in this age group. But there is no characteristic juvenile psychosis or psychosis typical for the age of puberty.

psychosis, Korsakov (Syergey Syergeyvich Korsakov, Russian neurologist, 1854 - 1900) A chronic brain· disorder that may arise as a toxic complication of any chronic brain disease, but it is probably associated more often with brain damage due to chronic alcholism than with any other single entity. (291.1) In approximately half of those affected there is an associated polyneuritis,· but the characteristic mental symptom is *confabulation* (q.v.). The patient develops a marked memory retention defect and is unable to integrate new material into his memory; he fills the memory gaps with his confabulations. Often, in addition, grandiose delusions and emotional incontinence appear, and although the former may subside some degree of emotional lability generally persists. See *psychosis, alcoholic Korsakov.*

psychosis, lactation *Rare.* This expression refers to any type of psychiatric condition that occurs during the period of lactation.

psychosis, malignant By this term Fenichel designates that type of schizophrenia which is progressive (slowly or rapidly) and terminates in permanent dementia. He contrasts these malignant psychoses with schizophrenic episodes which are temporary attacks in persons who are apparently well both before and after their psychotic episode.

The question arises whether these two general types of schizophrenia can have anything in common. Fenichel · believes that both the malignant 'schizophrenic process' and the shorter-termed 'schizophrenic episode' have certain common features. These are 'the bizarrity of the symptoms, the absurdity and unpredictability of the affects and intellectual ideas and the obviously inadequate connection between these two.' Moreover, the symptoms in both types can be explained by the concept of regression of the ego to a much deeper level than in the neurosis, i.e. to the time of 'primary narcissism' when 'the ego was not yet established or had just begun to be established.' Apparently no factors, of either an organic or a psychogenic nature, have yet been discerned which might explain the different courses taken by these different types of schizophrenic illness. (Fenichel, O. *The Psychoanalytic Theory of Neurosis*, Norton, New York, 1945)

The term malignant psychosis is approximately equivalent to the terms process psychosis and nuclear schizophrenia, and to 'dementia praecox' as used by contemporary European psychiatrists.

psychosis, manic-depressive (296.x) A term introduced by Kraepelin in 1896 to differentiate between those psychoses which typically progress to profound dementia (dementia praecox, or the group of schizophrenias) and those which do not lead to a true deterioration (manic-depressive psychosis). The term thus came to include periodic and circular insanity, simple mania, melancholia, and many types of confusion or delirium. Although involutional melancholia was later included in the manic-depressive group, the tendency in both the United States and Great Britain has been to keep the involutional group separate; and in many classificatory schemes, involutional melancholia and manic-depressive psychosis are considered the two major subdivisions of the broader category, affective psychoses.

Manic-depressive psychosis accounts for 5 to 15 per cent of the total first admissions to mental hospitals in the United States; it occurs more frequently in women, who account for approximately 70 per cent of cases, and is more common among Jews than is any other mental illness. Kallmann estimates that the general average frequency of manic-depressive psychosis does not exceed 0.4 per cent; but the expectancy in half-siblings is approximately 17 per cent, in siblings and in parents approximately 23 per cent, in di-zygotic co-twins approximately 26 per cent, and in one-egg twin partners approximately 100 per cent. These numbers are based upon fairly strict diagnostic criteria; Kallmann used as manic-depressive subjects only those whose illness is cyclic, with periodicity of acute, self-limited mood swings, onset before the fifth decade and with no progressive or residual personality disintegration before or after psychotic episodes of elation or depression. Reactive and situational depressions, hallucinatory episodes, and agitated anxiety states associated with hypertension are excluded. Primary menopausal and presenile depressions, and other non-periodic forms of depressive behavior in the involutional period are placed in the category of involutional psychosis. Kallmann concludes: 'The recurring ability to exceed the normal range of emotional responses with extreme but self-limited mood alterations seems to be associated with a specific neurohormonal disturbance, which depends on the mutative effect of a single dominant gene with incomplete penetrance. The dynamics identified with this specific ability cannot be considered to be part of a person's normal biological equipment nor are they out of line with current concepts of psychodynamic phenomena as observed in potentially vulnerable persons.' (Kallmann, Franz J. *Genetic Principles in Manic-Depressive Psychosis*, in Hoch, P.H., and Zubin, J. *Depression*, Grune & Stratton, New York, 1954)

Clinically, manic-depressive psychosis may appear in any of several forms: as a depressive episode (296.2) in varying degrees of severity (simple depression or simple retardation, acute depression and, according to some, depressive stupor, although many feel that this latter form is always a manifestation of catatonic schizophrenia); or as an elated or manic episode (296.1) in varying degrees of severity (simple mania or hypomania, acute mania, and delirious mania, the latter being also known as Bell's mania, typhomania, delirium grave and collapse delirium). A fourth type of mania, chronic mania, has also been described; the symptoms here are of the same degree as acute mania, but they continue uninterruptedly for an indefinite number of years.

Some manic-depressive patients have only manic attacks throughout their lives (recurrent mania); others have only depressive episodes (recurrent depressions), and in a few the circular or alternating form (296.3) is seen: a continuous alter-

nation for years between states of depression and states of elation. In addition to these types, Kraepelin described a number of mixed states (e.g. maniacal stupor, unproductive mania), but closer scrutiny usually reveals these to be types of schizophrenic episodes.
See *melancholia; suicide.*

psychosis, masturbatic This is an older diagnostic term, formulated when masturbation was viewed as a causative agent in the production of a psychosis. Modern authorities consider the concept erroneous.

psychosis, menstrual Psychiatric state associated with the menses. Bleuler says that 'menstrual moodiness which is not uncommon in "normal women" might be heightened to a degree that may be designated as melancholic depression; at all events suicides among women occur noticeably often at this time.' He adds that a 'menstrual insanity' 'in any definite sense has not been demonstrated in spite of different attempts.' (Bleuler, E. *Textbook of Psychiatry,* tr. by Brill, A.A., Macmillan, New York, 1930)

psychosis, model Experiemental psychosis and, particularly, such as is produced by mescaline or lysergic acid or similar psychotomimetic drugs.

psychosis, motility A type of manic-depressive psychosis described by Ewald; symptoms are mainly hyperkinetic in character, and the episode often occurs only once in a lifetime, with complete remission.

psychosis, motor See *psychosis, sensory.*

psychosis of association See *association, psychosis of.*

psychosis of degeneracy *Obs.* That class of psychoses intimately associated with the environment, in contradistinction to the so-called real psychoses in which the environment plays no essential role.

psychosis, organic See *syndrome, organic.*

psychosis, perplexity A subdivision of manic-depressive psychosis, characterized by 'peculiar distress that goes with subjective perplexity.' Hoch and Kirby first described this type in 1919.

psychosis, polyneuritic Korsakov's psychosis.

psychosis, post-infectious (294.2) Mental disturbances may follow such acute diseases as influenza, pneumonia, typhoid fever, acute rheumatic fever, etc. in their post-febrile period or may occur during the period of convalescence. These mental disturbances may be observed as mild forms of confusion, or suspicious, irritable, depressive reactions. Occasionally states of mental enfeeblement occur following such acute infectious diseases.

psychosis, prison A mental disorder precipitated by anticipated or actual incarceration; the form of psychiatric syndrome depends upon the type of person affected; thus, a prison psychosis may resemble or be a schizophrenic, manic-depressive, or psychoneurotic disorder. See *Ganser syndrome.*

psychosis, private Used by Ferenczi as a synonym of *neurotic character,* because, as he says, it is tolerated by the ego.

psychosis, process The malignant type of schizophrenic psychosis which terminates in permanent dementia. It has always been recognized that schizophrenic phenomena have many diverse manifestations: there are the passing schizophrenic episodes in persons who apparently are well both before and after these periods; then, there are the severe psychoses which sooner or later end in permanent dementia. All the schizophrenic manifestations, however, have the common features of queer and bizarre symptoms, absurd and unpredictable affects and intellectual ideas, and the obviously inadequate connection between these two.
The question arises whether there is any etiological basis for differentiating schizophrenic episodes and schizophrenic processes. Some authors have felt that schizophrenic episodes result from traumata and impediments in early infantile life, whereas the process psychosis is due to unknown organic factors. Fenichel feels, however, that there is no basis for such a differentiation and that both psychogenic influences and organic disposition are contributory causes in the majority of cases. Certainly the prognosis in the 'process' type of cases (in which there

has been slow chronic development of the disease) is very poor. The prognosis is better in the acute cases, because some of them recover quickly and entirely. This is especially true of the cases in which the episode is the retroaction to an acute and severe frustration or narcissistic hurt. (Fenichel, O. *The Psychoanalytic Theory of Neurosis,* Norton and Company, New York, 1945) See *psychosis, malignant.*

'The European tendency is to use the term nuclear or process schizophrenia, or dementia praecox, to refer to unquestionable cases with a high tendency to deterioration and little tendency to remission or recovery. The others are called by Ruemke the pseudoschizophrenias, by Lunn (Denmark) the schizophreniform psychoses. The nuclear types may or may not show the accessory symptoms of Bleuler (delusions, hallucinations, etc.), but the fundamental symptoms are prominent. In the other types, the accessory symptoms are in the foreground and the fundamental symptoms may not be readily apparent. As Bleuler pointed out, the accessory symptoms are not diagnostic of schizophrenia for they occur also in many other disorders, especially in the organic group.' (Campbell, R.J. *Psychiatric Quarterly 32:* 318-34, 1958)

psychosis, progressive Same as *psychosis, process.*

psychosis, puberty As Bleuler says, 'A "puberty psychosis" peculiar to the period of development is not yet known.' Many psychiatric conditions may appear at the period of puberty, such as schizophrenia, hysteria, etc. (Bleuler, E. *Textbook of Psychiatry,* tr. by Brill, A.A., Macmillan, New York, 1930)

psychosis, puerperal Post-partum psychosis; any psychosis associated with the puerperium (the period from the termination of labor to the complete involution of the uterus). There is no single psychiatric condition that occurs during this period, and except for those states that are definitely connected with organic disorders, there is nothing in the puerperium as such, save psychic factors, which gives rise to a psychosis. The expression puerperal psychosis has about the same weight as that given to *pregnancy psychosis, lactation psychosis,* etc.

psychosis, purpose While all psychiatric states serve a purpose, usually an unconscious one, there are some (such as the Ganser syndrome) whose motives are quite clear-cut. 'The maximum of wish fulfillment is achieved by the ecstasies. These syndromes are also called *purpose psychoses.*' (Bleuler, E. *Textbook of Psychiatry,* tr. by Brill, A.A., Macmillan, New York, 1930)

psychosis, reactive When a psychosis is believed to be instigated principally by an environmental condition, it is designated as a *reactive* or *situational* psychosis.

'One class of the psychoses shows itself as a morbid reaction to an affect experience, as a prison psychosis to a confinement, and an hysterical twilight state to a jilting on the part of the beloved *(reactive psychoses, situation psychoses).*' (Bleuler, E. *Textbook of Psychiatry,* tr. by Brill, A.A., Macmillan, New York, 1930)

psychosis, schizoaffective (skiz-ō-a-fec'tiv) A subtype of schizophrenia in which manic (295.73) or melancholic (295.74) symptoms are prominent. The affective symptoms are often so pronounced in the early stages as to mask the underlying schizophrenic process, and such cases account for the majority of diagnoses of manic-depressive psychosis in children and adolescents. Later in the course of the disease, however, the affective symptoms tend to abate as the schizophrenic elements become more obvious. Such cases usually end in hebephrenic or simple deterioration. (Campbell, R.J. *Psychiatric Quaterly 32:* 318-34, 1958)

psychosis, schizophreniform (skiz-ō-fren'iform) See *psychosis, process.*

psychosis, senile See *senile psychosis.*

psychosis, sensory Bucknill and Tuke suggested that mental disorders be divided into two large classes, called sensory psychoses and motor psychoses. The former were to include all forms of psychiatric syndromes in which feeling, emotion, sensory perception, and ideation predominated. The latter would comprise those reactions characterized by disorders in the intellectual and motor spheres. The classification (suggested in the latter half of the 19th century) was not adopted.

psychosis, septicemia (sep-ti-sē'mē-à) An acute organic psychosis due to severe infection and characterized mainly by a delirium. Nosologically, this condition belongs to the toxic psychoses (deliria) associated with toxic-infectious diseases, and would today be classified as organic brain syndrome associated with systemic infection, with psychosis (294.2).

psychosis, shock A particular type of mental reaction observed in soldiers overcome by shock or fright in combat. Many of the soldiers who were picked up immediately after the shock and sent to a hospital had initial anxious deliriums, during which they regarded everything in the environment as hostile, and anybody who approached them excited violent fear reactions. Wild motor activity with mutism, depression, and disturbances of sleep sometimes followed.

'The most common form of this psychosis was perhaps the acute, passive, negativistic stupor, with mutism, complete immobility, total anesthesia, inability to take food, incontinence, total unconsciousness at first and cloudy states later, and inability to stand or walk. These patients had gradually to relearn sphincter control and the enunciation of words; at first they said only "yes" and "no" and then answered to their names. Very gradually they were taught how to grasp objects and how to feed themselves. Familiarity with the environment was also regained slowly; some time elapsed before these patients began to take an interest in their destiny. Of interest is the fact that most of them were able to recall the traumatic event; they remembered some details of their behavior such as making certain efforts to save themselves just before they lost consciousness. Gaupp reported a patient with no recollection of the accompaniments of the exploding shell which caused him to lose consciousness. This observation is important, because the psychic experience—the feelings and ideas excited by the explosion—called forth the powerful action of the entire organism, that is, unconsciousness and other symptoms of fright, as a defense against it. Gaupp believes that, between the moment of the explosion and the following psychic disturbance, an interval exists during which the perception of the effects of the explosion, the sight of multilated comrades, and the excitation of

fright aggravate the reaction to the trauma.

'Patients in fright stupor were not always passive and without feeling. Very frequently they shouted in their stupor: "The enemy is coming!" "They are coming!" "Get em!" "Fight em!"' (Kardiner, A., and Spiegel, H. *War Stress and Neurotic Illness*, Hoeber, New York, 1947)

psychosis, situational See *psychosis, reactive.*

psychosis, somatic (sō-mat'ik) Dunbar used this term for the somatic expression of tension, aggression, and resentment in diabetic patients. 'Much of the aggression and resentment in these patients seems to have been driven inward in a manner which suggests patients with rheumatic heart disease, but they have not given in so much to the passive masochistic role. In addition to being expressed in tension of striated and smooth musculature, it gnaws at their vitals, and, probably because of their infantile regression and extreme ambivalence, brings about what might be called a *somatic psychosis.*' (Dunbar, F. *Psychosomatic Diagnosis*, Hoeber, New York, 1943)

psychosis symbiotic infantile (sim-bi-ot'-ik) (295.8) Mahler's term for a disturbance seen in certain children at the time when separation from the mother would ordinarily be effected. Under the threat of separation, the symbiotic child's rage and panic are projected into the world, which is perceived as hostile and destructive. The child defends himself by maintaining or restoring the infantile delusion of omnipotence and oneness with the mother, by means of omnipotence phantasies, introjection, projection, delusions, and hallucinations.

Mahler differentiates between the symbiotic psychosis and the autistic psychosis. The latter arises in a child with a constitutionally defective ego anlage and thus the symbiotic mother-infant relationship is interfered with from the beginning. Autism is used as a major defense against external stimuli and inner excitations. See *depression, anaclitic; anxiety, separation.*

psychosis, symptomatic (sim-tō-ma'tik) Brain dysfunction as a result of some general physical disease, the most common feature of which is a delirious state. This may occur in the course of an acute infectious disease such as penumonia, influenza, typhoid fever, meningitis, etc., or in the course of acute chorea, pellagra, or pelvic infections following childbirth.

psychosis, toxic Organic brain syndromes due to intoxication (294.3).

psychosis, toxic-infectious Mental condition accompanying or following an infective illness or poisoning by some exogenous toxin (294.2 and 294.3). The symptoms include delirium, dazed and stuporous conditions, epileptiform attacks, hallucinoses, incoherence, and confusion. Examples of diseases which may produce this reaction-type include influenza, malaria, acute rheumatic fever, pneumonia, typhoid and typhus fever, smallpox, and scarlet fever.

psychosis, transitory A syndrome 'characterized by emotional turmoil, various kinetic phenomena, and dissociation with confusion and hallucinations, followed by complete recovery and amnesia' for the episode. (Kasanin, J. 'The Syndrome of Episodic Confusions,' *American Journal of Psychiatry* 93, 637, 1936-37)

psychosis, traumatic (traw-ma'tik) Mental disorder caused by or associated with an injury (if psychotic, 293.5; if nonpsychotic, 309.2). Fenton found traumatic psychoses in 28 of 830 patients, who had earlier in their illness been diagnosed as traumatic neuroses. See *neurosis, traumatic.*

In 1904 Adolf Meyer classified the traumatic psychoses as follows:
1. Direct post-traumatic deliria.
2. Post-traumatic constitution.
3. Traumatic defect states.
4. Post-traumatic psychoses.
5. Post-traumatic psychoses not directly involving the head.

See *constitution, traumatic; contusion, brain; post-traumatic and post-encephalitic syndromes, classification of.*

psychosis with cardio-renal disease. See *cardio-renal disease, psychosis with.*

psychosis with mental deficiency. See *retardation, mental, psychosis with.*

psychosis, zoöphil (zō'ō-fil) *Obs.* A psychosis marked by morbid affection for or interest in animals.

psychosoma (sī-kō-so'ma) The union of physical and psychical components is often designated by the term *psychosoma.* For example, conversion hysteria comprises psychosomatic phenomena, in that a mental conflict gains outlet through somatic agencies.

Infrequently the term *psychosoma* is condensed into *psysoma* (Draper, G.).

psychosomatiatria (-sō-mat-ī-at'rē-à) *Obs.* Medical treatment of mind and body.

psychosomatic (-so-ma'tik) This term may be used in a methodological sense only, to refer to a type of approach in the study and treatment of certain disturbances of body function. More commonly, however, the term is used in a nosological or classificatory sense to refer to a group of disorders whose etiology at least in part is believed to be related to emotional factors; in the 1968 revision of psychiatric nomenclature such 'psychosomatic disorders' are called 'psychophysiologic disorders.' (305.x)

As used in the second sense, the term psychosomatic is unfortunate, for it implies a dualism which does not exist. No somatic disease is entirely free from psychic influence, just as even in the purest psychic disturbances there are organic-constitutionai factors, somatic compliance, etc. While it is generally recognized that many symptoms and diseases occur in the setting of difficult life situations, there is no accepted answer as to why some people get one disease, some get another. Various hypotheses have been put forward: some have tried to show that there is a personality pattern common to all patients with the same disease; others have tried to demonstrate a single personality trait associated with a particular disease; others have maintained that a specific nuclear conflict or dynamic configuration is unique to a particular disease; others have emphasized what has happened to the patient previously, especially in childhood, as in a search for toilet-training problems in patients with intestinal disorders; and, finally, some have tried to correlate the occurrence of particular symptoms with particular life situations. None of the attempts has been wholly satisfactory. Not all patients fit into the pattern they should;

many patients show more than one of the illnesses in question, and this is difficult to reconcile with the idea of fixed personality patterns; many patients show the specific dynamic configuration without developing the expected disease; and often there is little similarity between the various situations which provoke recurrences in the same patient.

Many psychoanalysts (e.g. O. Fenichel, *The Psychoanalytic Theory of Neurosis,* Norton, New York, 1945) prefer the term 'organ neurosis' to 'psychosomatic disorder.' An organ neurosis is defined as a type of functional disorder which is physical in nature and which consists of physiologic changes caused by the inappropriate use of the function in question. Thus organ neuroses and conversion neuroses are quite different—in conversion neuroses, the symptom has a specific unconscious meaning and is an expression of a phantasy in 'body language'; in organ neuroses, the change in function *per se* has no unconscious meaning, but instead the chronic, unconscious attitudes of the patient have secondarily produced a change in function. In other words, in the organ neuroses a persistent emotional disturbance has secondarily altered the physiology of an organ system; but in the conversion neuroses, a persistent emotional disturbance is directly symbolized by a disturbance in bodily function, and the physiology of the organ system in question need not be altered.

F. Alexander (*Psychosomatic Medicine, Its Principles and Applications,* Norton, New York, 1950) maintains the theory of specificity in organ neuroses: physiological responses to emotional stimuli, both normal and morbid, vary according to the nature of the precipitating emotional states. He differentiates two types of organ neuroses, the sympathetic and the parasympathetic. 'Whenever the expression of competitive, aggressive, and hostile attitudes is inhibited in voluntary behavior, the sympathetic adrenal system is in sustained excitation. The vegetative symptoms result from the sustained sympathetic excitation, which persists because no consummation of the fight or flight reaction takes place in the field of co-ordinated voluntary behavior, as exemplified by the patient suffering from essential hypertension who in his overt behavior appears inhibited and under

excessive control.' Besides essential hypertension, the sympathetic group includes migraine and hyperthyroidism. 'In those cases in which the gratification of help-seeking, regressive tendencies is absent from overt behavior either because of internal denial of these tendencies or because of external circumstances, the vegetative responses are apt to manifest themselves in dysfunctions which are the results of an increased parasympathetic activity. Examples are the overtly hyperactive, energetic peptic ulcer patient who does not allow gratification of his dependent needs, and the patient who develops chronic incapacitating fatigue whenever he tries to engage in some activity requiring concentrated effort.' Bronchial asthma and ulcerative colitis are also in this parasympathetic group.

psychosomatic disorders See *psychophysiologic disorders.*

psychosomimetic (-sō-mi-met'ik) *Psychotomimetic* (q.v.).

psychostimulant See *psychotropics.*

psychosurgery 'Psychosurgery is a general term now used to describe any form of brain operation done to relieve mental illness or intractable pain. The usual operation in psychosurgery has been lateral transcranial lobotomy. In addition to this transorbital lobotomy, topectomy, gyrectomy, thalamotomy, and so on, have been performed. Such operations have been found to lead to an amelioration of mental illness in a fair proportion of cases.' (Landes, C. and Erlick, D. *American Journal of Psychology LXIII,* 557, 1950)

psychosynthesis (-sin'the-sis) The act of combining individual components of the mind into a whole; it is the opposite of *psychoanalysis.*

'I employ "constructive" and "synthetic," in describing a method that is opposed to the reductive. The constructive method is concerned with the elaboration of unconscious products (dreams, phantasies, etc.). It takes the unconscious product as a basis or starting point, as a *symbolical* expression, which, stretching on ahead as it were, represents a coming

phase of psychological development.' (Jung, C.G. *Psychological Types*, tr. by Baynes, H.G., Harcourt, Brace, New York and London, 1923)
'They [Freudians] state that the Jungian transference and the active role played in the attempts at psychosynthesis create a permanent state of dependence upon the analyst.' (Henry, G.W. *Essentials of Psychiatry*, 3rd ed., Williams and Wilkins, Baltimore, 1938)
'In the final synthesis one must try to harmonize the various strivings and tendencies and consider whether they may co-exist in a personality or whether they disturb or exclude each other, and with what result.' (Diethelm, O. *Treatment in Psychiatry*, Macmillan, New York, 1936)
'I cannot imagine, however, that any new task for us is to be found in this psycho-synthesis. If I were to permit myself to be honest and uncivil I should say it was nothing but a meaningless phrase.' (Freud, S. *Collected Papers*, vol. 2, tr. by Riviere, J., Leonard and Virginia Woolf and The Institute of Psychoanalysis, London, 1924-25)

psychotaxis (-tak′sis) A term suggested by T.V. Moore 'to signify the mental adjustments of individuals to pleasant and unpleasant situations. . . . We wish a root to designate the tendency of the mind to adjust itself to pleasant and unpleasant situations. Though taxis suggests a passive arrangement rather than an active adjustment, those of us who have become familiar with its use to designate the movements of the protozoa will feel that no great violence is done if it is used to signify the mental adjustments of individuals to pleasant and unpleasant situations, especially since such reactions often consist in a rearrangement of one's ideas in which some drop below consciousness and others appear on the surface. . . . The tendency to enjoy pleasant states of mind or to make use of pleasant emotions and feelings . . . by analogy with the tropism or taxis could be termed a positive psychotaxis. The opposite tendency to avoid unpleasant situations is a negative psychotaxis.' (Moore, T.V. 'The Parataxes,' *Psychoanalytic Review 8*, 258, 1921)

psychotechnics (-tek′niks) The practical application of psychological methods in the study of economics, sociology and other problems.

psychotherapeusis (-ther-à-pū′sis) *Psychotherapy* (q.v.).

psychotherapeutics Psychotherapy.

psychotherapy Any form of treatment for mental illnesses, behavioral maladaptations, and/or other problems that are assumed to be of an emotional nature, in which a trained person deliberately establishes a professional relationship with a patient for the purpose of removing, modifying, or retarding existing symptoms, of attenuating or reversing disturbed patterns of behavior, and of promoting positive personality growth and development.
There are numerous forms of psychotherapy—ranging from guidance, counseling, persuasion, and hypnosis to re-education and psychoanalytic reconstructive therapy—and many possible applications of each form—including disabling psychosomatic symptoms, interpersonal conflicts and pathologic attitudes secondary to recognizable (organic) disturbance of central nervous system functions, the so-called functional psychoses, character and behavior disorders, psychoneuroses, and marital conflict, to name a few; but in general it may be said that all forms of psychotherapy in all their applications employ the relationship established between patient and therapist to influence the patient to unlearn old and/or maladaptive response patterns and to learn better ones.
Psychotherapy has also been characterized as "an undefined technique applied to unspecified problems with unpredictable outcome; for this technique we recommend rigorous training.' (Conference on Graduate Education in Clinical Psychology, 1949) While such a definition may seem so pessimistic as to approach nihilism, it emphasizes what would seem to be an irrefragable fact; viz. that despite centuries of its use, and despite decades of study of its various forms, psychotherapy and the means by which it achieves its results are but poorly understood.

'The patient's experience in the therapeutic relationship is assumed to be a sample in microcosm of the significant factors that brought on or related to his problems. Observing the patient's behavior (both verbal and non-verbal), and using his empathic understanding of the patient's behavior in relation to himself, the therapist comments on what he observes. The patient, witnessing the same behavior, and viewing it in the light of the therapist's comments as well as in the light of his own reactions, is now in a position to re-evaluate his own past behavior and to prepare for or begin to change. While all the factors involved in the change are not clear, it is assumed to involve the general principles of learning.' (Stein, M.I. *Contemporary Psychotherapies*, Glencoe, 1961)

Because the term 'psychotherapy' has been applied to a variety of dissimilar operations, the phrase *definitive forms of psychotherapy* has been suggested to exclude such procedures as environmental manipulation, general medical treatment as psychotherapy, physical examination as psychotherapy, and all procedures in which more than two people participate. In this sense, psychotherapy is a procedure undertaken in order to foster the acquisition of self-knowledge. 'The patient seeks self-knowledge for the purpose of changing his feelings and/or his behavior. The therapist, as participant-observer, fosters learning by decoding and interpreting the patient's unconscious messages. As in all sustained and important relationships, some learning or change also occurs as the result of imitation, identification and various subthe influences. The situation is not (and cannot be) value-free, but the highest premium is placed on the patient's self-determination.' (Hollender, M.H. *Archives of General Psychiatry 10,* 361, 1964)

L.R. Wolberg (*The Technique of Psychotherapy*, Grune & Stratton, New York, 1954) distinguishes three types of psychotherapy: supportive, re-educative, and reconstructive.

(1) *Supportive therapy* consists of encouraging or promoting the development of maximal, optimal use of the patient's assets; its objectives are to strengthen existing defenses, elaborate better mechanisms to maintain control, and restore to an adaptive equilibrium. Included in supportive therapy are guidance, environmental manipulation, externalization of interests, reassurance, pressure and coercion, persuasion, catharsis, desensitization, and inspirational group therapy. (It might be noted that in psychoanalysis the term 'reassurance' has a slightly different meaning: any method of reducing or removing anxiety other than interpretation.)

(2) *Re-educative therapy,* which aims at giving the patient insight into the more conscious conflicts, with deliberate efforts at goal modification and maximal utilization of existing potentialities. Included in re-educative therapy are relationship therapy, attitude therapy, psychobiology, counseling, reconditioning, and re-educative group therapy.

(3) *Reconstructive therapy,* which aims at giving the patient insight into his unconscious conflicts and extensive alteration of his character structure. Included in reconstructive therapy are psychoanalysis (Freudian), Adlerian and Jungian therapy, the treatment techniques of the 'cultural-interpersonal' school (Sullivan, Horney), and psychoanalytically oriented psychotherapy.

psychotherapy, active analytical See *analysis, active.*

psychotherapy, analytic group See *psychotherapy, group.*

psychotherapy, brief Any form of *psychotherapy* (q.v.) designed to produce therapeutic change within a minimal amount of time (generally, not more than 20 sessions). Brief psychotherapy is usually active and directive; it is most clearly indicated with clearly defined symptoms and/or with specific, limited goals.

psychotherapy by reciprocal inhibition See *behavior theory.*

psychotherapy, co-operative See *psychotherapy, multiple.*

psychotherapy, didactic group A strictly tutorial practice in which definite outlines, texts, and visual aids are used for teaching patients in special subjects.

psychotherapy, family A form of treatment (for the most part confined to therapy of schizophrenics) in which all members of the family attend all psychotherapy sessions together. Family psychotherapy is based on the hypothesis that the patient's psychosis is a symptom manifestation of a problem involving all members of the family. (Bowen, M. 'Family Relationships in Schizophrenia,' Chap.7 edited by Auerback, A. in *Schizophrenia —An Integrated Approach*, Ronald, New York, 1959) Bowen and his co-workers find that the father, the mother, and the patient (the *interdependent triad*) are the primary members involved. These investigators have further noted that in all their schizophrenic families there is a striking emotional distance between the parents (*emotional divorce*) which is maintained by a combination of controlled positiveness and physical distance. In such families, both parents are immature and true family teamwork is never possible. Instead, one parent will seize authority and make decisions for himself and his spouse, forcing the latter into a submissive, helpless role. This pattern has been termed the *overadequate-inadequate reciprocity*.

psychotherapy, group A method of treating emotional disturbances, social maladjustments, and psychotic states in which two or more patients participate simultaneously in the presence of one psychotherapist or more.

The techniques in group psychotherapy vary to a great extent in accordance with the different schools of psychiatric thought and the preferences of individual psychiatrists and other psychotherapists. S.R. Slavson separates group psychotherapy under three major categories: I activity; II analytic; III directive.

I. *Activity group therapy*, which he originated, is suitable for children in latency. Children selected by criteria which he had described are given the opportunity to act out their aggressions or withdrawal in the presence of a neutral, permissive, and understanding adult. The patients draw upon one another for support. The accessibility of the patients to each other and to the environment, and their interaction, generate certain inhibitive controls which improve the superego formation and strengthen the ego of each participant. Slavson believes that this type of therapy is predominantly ego therapy and is an experience in which character changes occur. He, therefore, recommends selecting patients on the basis of these two factors. No interpretation is given to the children and a minimal restraint of their behavior is exercised by the therapist and, at that, only when the group cannot bring itself under control.

II. *Analytic group psychotherapy* is a technique in which interpretation is given to the patients, activity and verbalization are encouraged and interpreted, and insight is evoked. In this technique the therapist is more active than he is in activity group psychotherapy, where he is predominantly a passive agent. Slavson divides analytic group psychotherapy into three subdivisions: (1) play group psychotherapy; (2) activity-interview group psychotherapy; (3) interview psychotherapy. (1) *Play group psychotherapy* is suitable for young children in the prelatency period, where the catharsis occurs through play with specially selected materials through which the children in the group can act out their preoccupations, phantasies, and anxieties. (2) *Activity-interview group psychotherapy* has been designed by him for children in latency who suffer from severe psychoneuroses, who are given the opportunity to act out against each other and against their environment as in activity group psychotherapy, but interpretation of the latent meaning of the behavior is given by the children to each other and by the therapist. Spontaneous and planned discussions are held with individual children or with a number of the children in the group or the group as a whole. These are intended to stimulate understanding by the children of the meaning of their behavior and to evoke insight into the unconscious motivations and phantasies. (3) *Interview group psychotherapy* is intended for adolescents and adults who are selected by definite criteria and are grouped together so that the patients would have a therapeutic effect upon one another. The basic criterion suggested by Slavson is syndrome (not symptom or diagnosis) homogeneity. Other group psychotherapists do not use this criterion but group the patients without any special considerations, provided the patients can accept and gain from a group experience. In analytic group psychotherapy the procedure is the same as in individual psychotherapy. Since the patients are adolescents and adults, the catharsis occurs through verbalization and free association. The psychotherapist here, as in individual treatment, interprets, explores, and helps patients to uncover their repressed, guilt-producing, and anxiety-evoking feelings, attitudes, values, and behavior.

III. Under *directive group treatment* Slavson includes such activities as didactic or therapeutically educational group work, particularly with psychotics, group guidance, group counseling, therapeutic recreation, and many other group efforts to help patients, particularly psychotic patients, adjust to their environment.

Group psychotherapy is also referred to as *group therapy.* The two terms are synonymous. (Slavson, S.R. *An Introduction to Group Therapy,* The Commonwealth Fund, Oxford University Press, New York, 1950)

psychotherapy, multiple Role-divided, three-cornered therapy; co-therapy; cooperative psychotherapy; dual leadership all refer to the use of more than one therapist at one time in individual or group psychotherapy.

psychotherapy, reconstructive See *psychodynamics, adaptational; psychotherapy.*

psychotherapy, short-contact Treatment of mental disorders, similar to brief psychotherapy, but used in child-guidance clinics when the therapy is of short duration.

psychotic Showing signs of or having the characteristics of severe mental disorder; afflicted with *psychosis* (q.v.). This term has various meanings, and the reader will ordinarily have to depend on context to determine the specific meaning intended by the author. Sometimes the term is used in a quasi-legal sense, in which case it is approximately equivalent to the term insane; or it may refer to a patient in an acute episode of psychosis, without reference to competence or other legal issues; or, less commonly, it may refer to a patient with chronic mental disorder, such as schizophrenia, even though he may not be in an acute phase of psychosis and even though he may not be insane in the legal sense.

psychotic disorder See *psychosis.*

psychotica (sī-kot′i-ka) See *psychotomimetic.*

psychotogen (sī-kot′ō-gen) See *psychotomimetic.*

psychotogenic *Psychotomimetic* (q.v.).

psychotoid (sī-kot′oid) According to Selling, psychotoid personalities are 'individuals who might be classed as very mild cases of some psychosis, by virtue of their symptoms. However, they are not psychotic persons and their symptoms are of long standing without change and do not respond to the same treatment as the true psychoses which have similar but more exaggerated symptoms. They have more insight than psychotics.' (Selling, L.S. *Synopsis of Neuropsychiatry,* Mosby, St. Louis, 1947)

psychotomimetic (sī-kot-ō-mi-met′ik) Resembling or mimicking naturally occurring psychosis, especially schizophrenia; also known as psychosomimetic, schizomimetic, hallucinogenic. While any number of drugs can produce a psychosis, the term psychotomimetic agent is confined to those substances which produce psychological changes in a high proportion of subjects exposed to the drug without producing the gross impairment of memory and orientation characteristic of the organic reaction type. Among the known psychotomimetics are lysergic acid diethylamide (LSD), mescaline, adrenochrome, harmine, tetrahydrocannabinol, diisopropyl flourophosphates (DFP), tetraethylpyrophosphate (TEPP), N-allylnormorphine and bufotenin. Such drugs are also known as *phantastica.* See *ergotropic; psychotropics.*

psycho-toxicomania (sī-kō-tok-si-kō-mā'-nē-à) Toxicomania; drug dependency or addiction.

psychralgie (psē-kral'zhē) 'A morbid state characterized by painful subjective sensations of cold.' (Foster, F.P. *Medical Dictionary*, Appleton, New York, 1892-94)

psychotropics Drugs with an effect on psychic function, behavior, or experience; also known as *phrenotropics*. The term can include a wide variety of pharmacologic agents, but in psychiatry five groups of phrenotropic or psychotropic agents can be differentiated on the basis of clinical efficacy:

(1) *Neuroleptics* — also known as *antipsychotics, ataractics, major tranquilizers;* they have antipsychotic and sedative effects; many of them also have neurologic effects, particularly on the extra-pyramidal system; included in the group are phenothiazines, butyrophenones, thioxanthenes, reserpine derivatives, and benzoquinolizines.

(2) *Anxiolytic sedatives* — also known as *minor tranquilizers, psycholeptics;* they reduce pathologic anxiety, tension, and agitation without therapeutic effects on disturbed cognitive or perceptual processes; they usually do not produce autonomic or extrapyramidal effects, but they may lower the convulsive threshold and have a high potential for drug dependency; included in the group are meprobamate and derivatives, diazepoxides, and barbiturates.

(3) *Anti-depressants* — also known as *psychic energizers, thymoleptics;* they reduce pathologic depression; included in the group are monoamine oxidase inhibitors and imipramine and other tricyclic compounds.

(4) *Psychostimulants* — these increase the level of alertness and/or motivation; included are amphetamine, methylphenidate, pipradol, and caffeine.

(5) *Psychodysleptics* — also known as *hallucinogens, psychedelics, psychotomimetics;* they produce abnormal mental phenomena, particularly in the cognitive and perceptual spheres; included in the group are d-lysergic acid diethylamide, mescaline, psilo-

cybin, dimethyltryptophan, and cannabis. See *dependency, drug; ergotropic.*

psychrophobia (sī-krō-fō'bē-à) Fear of cold.

psychrotherapy (-ther'à-pē) Treatment by the application of cold in any form. It was at one time extensively employed in the form of hydrotherapy as a stimulating agent for inactive or retarded patients, e.g. those with the depressive type of manic-depressive psychosis.

psyoma (sī-sō'mà) Rare. Contracted form of *psychosoma.*

PTA 1. Abbreviation for Parent-Teachers Association. 2. Abbreviation for post-traumatic amnesia, generally considered to be one of the most sensitive and reliable indices of severity of head trauma.

pteronophobia ([p]ter-ō-nō-fō'bē-à) Fear of feathers.

ptosis (tō'sis) Lid-drop. See *nerve, oculomotor.*

ptosis, walking A functional paralysis of the upper eyelid, occurring temporarily in the anemic or neurotic person on awaking.

puberal, pubertal (pū'bēr-al, -tal) Relating to the age of puberty, extending from the termination of the period of puerilism to the beginning of the adolescent period.

puberism, persistent Condition characterized by hypogenesis and prolongation, or even lifelong persistence, of puberal characteristics. The individual seems an eternal adolescent with incompletely developed secondary sexual characteristics in contrast with the types distinguished by *infantilism* or *juvenilism.*

pubertas praecox (pōō-ber'gàs prī'kôks) (L. 'premature puberty') Premature puberty. See *macrogenitosomia.*

puberty, puberism (pū'bēr-ti, -iz'm) The stage of growth extending from the termination of the puerile to the beginning of the adolescent period. It begins with the acquisition of secondary sexual characteristics and continues for approximately two or three years thereafter.

puberty, precocious Macrogenitosomia.

pubescence, pubescency (pū-bes'ens, pū-bes'en-si) Puberty.

pubescent (pū-bes'ent) Pubertal.

public health model See *psychiatry, community.*

pudendal (pū-den'dal) Pertaining to or subserving the genitals.

pudendum pl. **pudenda** (pū-den'dum, pū-den'da) Genitals; the private parts.

pudibilia (pū-di-bil'ē-à) Pudenda, the privy parts.

pudibund (pū'di-bund) *Obs.* Bashful.

pudic (pū'dik), rarely **pudical** (pū'di-kal) *Obs.* Modest; *Anat.* Pudendal.

pudicity (pū-dis'i-ti) Modesty, chastity.

puella publica (poo-el'là pōō'blē-kà) (L. 'public girl') Hirschfeld's term for a prostitute.

puer aeternus (poo'er ī-ter'noos) (L. 'eternal lad, youth') A term denoting a specific archetype of Jung, viz. the eternal youth, *puer aeternus.* See *archetype (in Jung's psychology); archetype, mother.*

puerilism (pū'ēr-il-iz'm) From the standpoint of psychiatry *puerilism* is childishness; it is the stage following infantilism or infantility and is followed by the stage of puberism or puberty.

puerilism, hysterical See *pseudodementia, hysterical.*

puerperium (poo-ēr-per'i-um) The period of time and/or the state of the mother following childbirth. See *psychosis, puerperal.*

pulling, ear Pulling of the ears is believed by Kanner to be a substitute for thumbsucking; in psychoanalysis it is believed to be a masturbatory equivalent.

pulvinar (pul'vi-nēr) See *thalamus.*

punch-drunk Martland uses this term to denote a concussion syndrome observed among pugilists; the symptoms are a reflection of an encephalopathy following repeated concussions (in DSM-II, 293.5 if psychotic, 309.2 if non-psychotic).

'The early symptoms of punch-drunk usually appear in the extremities. There may be only an occasional and very slight flopping of one foot or leg in walking, noticeable only at intervals; or a slight unsteadiness in gait or uncertainty in equilibrium. . . . In some cases periods of slight mental confusion may occur as well as distinct slowing of muscular action. . . . Many cases remain mild. . . . In others a very distinct dragging of the leg may develop and with this there is a general slowing down in muscular movements, a peculiar mental attitude characterized by hesitancy in speech, tremors of the hand and nodding movements of the head.' (*Journal of the American Medical Association 91,* 1103, 1928)

punch-drunkenness A chronic traumatic encephalopathy, occurring frequently in boxers, characterized by deterioration of the personality, impairment of memory, dysarthria, tremor, and ataxia.

puncture, cistern (sis'tērn) A technique for gaining access to the subarachnoid space by means of introduction of a needle into the cisterna magna. Cistern puncture is performed when lumbar puncture is for some reason impossible; it is also used for the injection of air or opaque media for diagnostic purposes and for the introduction of therapeutic substances. It is contraindicated in cases of tumor or abscess in the posterior fossa, in cases of increased intracranial pressure, and when the cisterna magna is likely to be obliterated by inflammatory adhesions. See *puncture, suboccipital.*

puncture, lumbar (lum'bēr) A technique for gaining access to the subarachnoid space by means of introduction of a needle into the lumbar cul-de-sac of the subarachnoid space below the termination of the spinal cord at the first lumbar vertebra. Lumbar puncture (L.P.) is used to obtain cerebrospinal fluid for diagnostic purposes, to relieve increased intracranial pressure, to introduce therapeutic substances or local anesthetics, to introduce air preparatory to encephalography and myelography, and to introduce opaque media for radiography.

puncture, suboccipital (sub-ok-sip'i-tal) Suboccipital or *cisternal puncture* is a procedure, introduced by Ayer and his co-workers, for determining spinal subarachnoid block and for therapeutic purposes.
'The method consists in withdrawing fluid from the cisterna magna at the base of the brain behind the medulla. With the patient on the side, the head bent forward, the needle is introduced in the midline at a point midway between the external occipital protuberance and the spine of the axis or second cervical vertebra. The needle is directed forward and upward in the direction of the eyes or glabella. One should never penetrate to a depth beyond 4½ to 5 cm., generally 3½ to 4 are sufficient . . . The same click is felt when the dura is pierced as in spinal puncture.' (Wechsler, I.S. *Textbook of Clinical Neurology*, 4th ed., Saunders, Philadelphia, 1939) See *puncture, cistern.*

puncture, ventricle (ven'tri-k'l) A surgical technique for gaining access to the intraventricular space of the lateral ventricles. The principle indications for ventricle puncture are: (1) to relieve increased intracranial pressure before operation for intracranial tumor; (2) to inject air for ventriculography; (3) to inject therapeutic substances such as penicillin or streptomycin; (4) to obtain cerebrospinal fluid for diagnostic examination when lumbar or cisternal puncture cannot be performed.

punishment, Midas See *masturbation, compulsive.*

punishment, unconscious need for See *criminal from sense of guilt.*

pupil, Adie's See *pupil, tonic.*

pupil, Argyll Robertson (Argyll Robertson, Scottish physician, 1837-1909) 'A

usually but not invariably myotic pupil with sound vision that does not respond to light, even in a darkroom, but does to accommodation, and reacts slowly to mydriatics is known as an Argyll Robertson pupil.' (Jelliffe, S.E. and White, W.A. *Diseases of the Nervous System*, 6th ed., Lea & Febiger, Philadelphia, 1935)
It is usually found in patients with neurosyphilis, although it may appear in other conditions (traumatic brain injury, brain tumor, infectious disorders of the brain, multiple sclerosis, etc.).

pupil, fixed A pupil which does not react to light, to accommodation, or to convergence.

pupillary reflex The alterations in size of the pupil in response to light, convergence, and accomodation. Certain abnormalities of reaction are associated with lesions affecting portions of the pupil reflex arc.

pupillotonia Adie's syndrome; see *pupil, tonic.*

pupil, tonic (of Adie) (William John Adie, British neurologist, 1886-1935) A unilateral condition in which the pupil responds poorly to light and very slowly to convergence.

puppy-love A state of love in the late adolescent or young adult period, highly romantic in nature, with little stability in the relationship formed, so that the courtship swiftly disintegrates. This is in the nature of a developmental activity, occurring in the course of emotional maturation; another designation for this emotional phenomenon is *calf-love.*

pure line See *line, pure.*

Purkinje cell See *cell, Purkinje; cerebellum.*

purposeful In occupational therapy this common term indicates that an activity has been planned with a definite result or effect in view. It may apply to the practical use of a project.

purposive Characterized by or serving a purpose.

putamen (poo-tà'men) See *basal ganglia.*

Putnam, James Jackson (1846 - 1918) American psychiatrist.

pycnic (pik′nik) See *type, pyknic.*

pycnoepilepsy (pik-nō-ep′i-lep-sē) Repeated slight epileptic seizures.

pycnolepsy (pik′nō-lep-sē) Same as *pyknolepsy.*

pygmalionism (pig-mā′li-on-iz′m) The condition of falling in love with a creation of one's own. A patient with paranoia, strongly homosexual, devised what he called a 'perpetual-motion' machine, to which he ascribed all masculine attributes; the machine was given a masculine name. The patient avowed his 'unqualified love for Albert' and acted toward Albert as if Albert were a human being.

The term is sometimes loosely applied to a tendency of a psychotherapist to assume that his patient knows little or nothing and must be treated as a child, whose parent (the therapist) always knows best.

pygmeism (pig′mē-iz′m) The constitutional anomaly characterized by a *dwarfed,* but well-proportioned stature as compared with the average type of the given racial group. It corresponds to the other special forms of *microsomia,* called *nanosomia primordialis* by Hansemann and *heredo-familial essential microsomia* by E. Levi and occurs in certain peoples as a more or less physiological condition (African Negrillos and Negritos, Bushmen, etc.). Nevertheless, as has been stressed by Pende, 'this extreme variant must not be regarded as without detriment to health, but must rather be looked upon as a constitutional inferiority.' (Pende, N. *Constitutional Inadequacies,* tr. by Naccarati, S., Lea & Febiger, Philadelphia, 1928)

pyknic (pik′nik) Compact, thick-set, round-bodied. See *type, pyknic.*

pyknoepilepsy (pik-nō-ep′i-lep-sē) See *pyknolepsy.*

pyknolepsy, pycnolepsy (pik′nō-lep-sē) A disorder characterized by frequent, brief interruptions in consciousness, and usually discussed in conjunction with epilepsy, although Furstner, Heilbronner,

and others have classified it as a hysterical disorder. In children who are otherwise healthy, it occurs, as a rule before the age of seven, as frequent, short, and incomplete cloudings of consciousness. The onset is usually abrupt, the disease runs a monotonous course without intellectual deterioration and shows little response to therapy, but the prognosis is generally favorable. During attacks, which may be as frequent as 150 times a day, the eyes turn upward, arms and trunk become somewhat tonic; but pulse and respiration are unaffected, there are no convulsive movements, and spontaneous recovery is common. Owen and Berlinrood ('Clinical Electroencephalographic Studies in Pyknolepsy,' *American Journal of Psychiatry 98,* 757 - 66, 1941 - 42) believe that '. . . pyknolepsy is a form of petit mal epilepsy because of: 1. the similarity in the clinical picture; 2. the electroencephalographic pattern in the active phase showing a wave and spike formation found in petit mal epilepsy; 3. the lack of evidence of definite psychogenic factors; 4. the high incidence of epilepsy in families of patients with pyknolepsy as revealed by a study of the literature.' Lennox used *pyknoepilepsy* (which is by many considered synonymous with pyknolepsy, or dart and dome dysrhythmia) for the ordinary *petit mal* form of epilepsy (q.v.).

pyknophrasia (pik-nō-frā′zhē-à) Thickness of utterance.

pyramid The prominence on the anterior surface of the medulla oblongata where the pyramidal tract decussates. See *tract, pyramidal.*

pyramis See *cerebellum.*

pyrexiophobia (pī-rek-sē-ō-fō′bē-à) Fear of fever.

pyrolagnia (pī-rō-lag′nē-à) Sexual excitement aroused by the sight of conflagrations; erotic pyromania.

pyromania Morbid impulse to set fire to things; the term, however, generally means the actual setting on fire.

'The analysis of many neurotics and the observation of the doings of children show us that "setting on fire," the delight in conflagrations, indeed, too, the tendency to incendiarism, is an urethra-erotic character trait. Many incendiarists were excessive bed-wetters. . . . In a collection of criminal cases of incendiarism there were quite a number in which incendiaries set fire to their *beds*, as though to indicate the still active enuristic primitive source of their pyromanic character trait.' (Ferenczi, S. *Further Contributions to the Theory and Technique of*

Psycho-Analysis, tr. by Suttie, J.I., Leonard and Virginia Woolf and The Institute of Psychoanalysis, London, 1926)

pyromania, erotic *Pyrolagnia* (q.v.).

pyrophobia Fear of fire. See *pyromania*.

pyrosis (pī-rō'sis) Heartburn.

Q

Q-sort A personality rating technique, developed by William Stephenson (1953), in which statements or phrases about those aspects of personality or performance that are relevant to the needs of the person or organization requesting the rating, are written on separate cards. The rater (who may be the subject himself) sorts the cards into eleven piles, with those most descriptive of the subject in the first pile, those least descriptive in the last pile. Q-sorts are of particular value for obtaining complex, comprehensive descriptions of a single subject, especially since they permit evaluations by multiple raters whose results can be compared.

quadrantanopia, quadrantanopsia (kwad-ran-tan-ō′pē-à, -op′sē-à) See *field defect.*

quadrantic hemianopia (kwad-ran′tik hē-mi-an-op′ē-à) See *field defect.*

quadriplegia (kwad-ri-plē′jē-à) Tetraplegia; paralysis affecting the four extremities.

quadruplet In human genetics one of four children born at the same birth (see *birth, multiple*).

quality, determining A term used by Freud in connection with the etiology of hysteria. He states, 'That tracing an hysterical symptom back to a traumatic scene assists our understanding only if the scene in question fultills two conditions—if it possesses the required *determining quality* and if we can credit it with the necessary *traumatic power.*' (Freud, S. *Collected Papers,* vol. 1, tr. by Riviere, J., Leonard and Virginia Woolf and The Institute of Psychoanalysis, London, 1924-25)

By this he means that a traumatic scene must be sufficient, alone, or more usually through another association, to explain the hysterical symptom. For example, a hysterical symptom of vomiting was attributed to the shock of a railway accident. This derivation of the symptom lacks *determining quality,* although it may be said to possess traumatic power. However, on further analysis this accident woke the memory of another event which had happened previously, during which the patient saw a decomposing corpse, a sight which aroused in her horror and disgust. This connection now supplies the *determining quality* for the hysterical symptom of vomiting. The antecedent experience justifiably gave rise to a high degree of disgust.

quasi-action See *activity, ludic.*

quaternity (kwà-tēr′ni-ti) Any unit composed by the union of four factors; a group of four. In psychiatry, the term quaternity refers to the fact that Jung's system of psychology 'is based on an archetype that finds its special expression as "tetrasomy," four-foldness—cf. the theory of the four functions, the pictorial arrangement of the four, the orientation according to the four points of the compass, etc. The number four can often be observed in the arrangement of dream contents as well. Probably the universal distribution and magical significance of the cross or the circle divided into four can be explained through the archetypal quality of the quaternity.' (Jung, C.G. *The Integration of the Personality,* Farrar and Rhinehart, New York, 1939, p. 154) Jung says: 'It is a peculiar *lusu naturae* [play of nature] that the principal chemical constituent of the bodily organism is carbon, characterized by four valences; the "diamond" too is, as is well known, a carbon crystal. Carbon is black; the diamond is "brightest water.". . . Such an analogy would be a regrettable lack of intellectual taste if the phenomenon of the four were a mere creation of consciousness and not a spontaneous product of the objective-psychic, of the unconscious.' (ibid., p. 198) 'It might even be considered more than a mere coincidence that in an epoch which, particularly in consequence of revolutionary discoveries in the domain of the exact natural sciences, stands on the verge of transition from "three-dimensional" to "four-dimensional" thinking, the most modern system of depth psychology, the complex-psychology of Jung, taking its start from an altogether different point, has elevated the archetype of the four to the central structural concept of its doctrine.' (Jacobi, J. *The Psychology of C.G. Jung*, Kegan Paul, Trench, Trubner, London, 1942)

querulent Ever suspicious, always opposing any suggestion, complaining of illtreatment and of being slighted or misunderstood, easily enraged, and dissatisfied with conditions as they exist.

question, key In the Adlerian approach, a question designed to uncover the purpose of the patient's psychiatric symptoms (e.g. What would you do if you were well?). The answer should indicate the patient's purpose in being sick and the personal things to which his symptoms are directed.

question, Pigem's A projective question asked of the patient such as, 'What three things would you like most to change (or to do, or to be) in your life?' or, 'If you could be changed into something else by a fairy, what would it be?'

Quételet-Gauss, binomial law of Quetelet was the first to show that the distribution of human characters, such as height, may be adequately described by the normal curve. Thus law was first described in mathematical language by A. De Moivre, a French Huguenot who lived in exile in London, and was later rediscovered independently by Laplace and Gauss. According to this law, frequencies which may be adequately described by it are distributed symmetrically about a mean value, which is also the maximum or mode. The frequencies decrease regularly on either side of the mean. For any deviation above the mean there will be a frequency equal to that between the mean and a corresponding deviation below the mean. Frequencies taper off very rapidly from the mean to the end of the curve in either direction, approaching the base line as an asymptote.

Quincke disease (Heinrich Irenaeus Quincke, physician in Kiel, 1842-1922) See *edema, angioneurotic*

quintuplet In human genetics one of five children born at the same birth (see *birth, multiple*).

quotient, intelligence The ratio of a subject's intelligence (determined by mental measures) to so-called average or normal intelligence for his age. The most common method for determining the intelligence quotient is to divide the assigned mental age by the chronological age.

R

R In Rorschach test scoring, the total number of responses to the cards.

rabies (rā'bēz) *Hydrophobia* (q.v.); a virus infection of the central nervous system, transmitted by the bite of a rabid animal (dog, jackal, cat, wolf; rarely, horse or cow).

race 'Applied to human beings, the term race implies a blood related group with characteristic and common hereditary traits. . . . Primary races or sub-species —the Caucasian, the Mongoloid, and the Negroid—are generalized racial types, hypothetical stocks, rather than living races. . . . Aside from all questions of a biological nature, it [race] is made the symbol of cultural status and thus serves to justify the exploitation of the weaker group with the inevitable political and cultural consequences.' (Reuter, E.B. *The American Race Problem*, Crowell, New York, 1938)

race, disease Group of individuals susceptible to the same disease. Draper uses the term *race* in a special way. In his efforts to establish correlations between constitutional characteristics of an individual and disease entities, he uses such expressions as gastric ulcer race, gallbladder race, etc. Thus, he says, 'by the same token, any other series of constant similarities, whether physiologic, psychologic or immunologic, might as justifiably be used as proper criteria of racial entity. One might conceive, therefore, as well of a gastric ulcer race, a manic-depressive race, a meningococcus susceptible race, or gall-bladder race, as of the present customarily accepted black, yellow, or white divisions of mankind.' (Draper, G. *Disease and the Man*, Macmillan, New York, 1930)

rachischisis (rā-kis'ki-sis) See *spina bifida*.

racial saturation point See *saturation point, racial*.

radiation In neurophysiology, the spreading of excitation to adjacent neurons.

radiculitis (rȧ-dik-ū-lī'tis) Inflammation of the intradural portion of a spinal nerve root prior to its entrance into the intervertebral foramen or of the portion between that foramen and the nerve plexus.

radio-isotope See *encephalography, radio-isotopic.*

radix (ra'diks) Nerve root.

rage Fury; violent, intense anger; often used in psychoanalytic writings to emphasize the overpowering and unbridled aspect of infantile anger. See *aggression*.

rage, defiant In Rado's terminology, the angry resistance or opposition to demands and orders, as in the child whose temper tantrum more or less obviously expresses the idea "I won't." Defiant rage is a typical reaction, at least in the American culture, to bowel training; opposed to this reaction is guilty fear and fearful obedience, which arise in response to the mother's punishments, threats, and demands for expiation. The resulting conflict between the opposing tensions of defiant rage and guilty fear is of particular significance in the genesis of obsessive behavior. See *attack, obsessive*.

rage, retroflexed See *psychodynamics, adaptational*.

rage, sham The term first used to denote the spontaneous outbursts of motor activity resembling fear and rage which occur in decorticate or diencephalic animals. (Cannon, W.B. and Britton, S.W. 'Studies on the Conditions of Activity in Endocrine Glands,' *American Journal of Physiology* 72, 283, April 1925) Such outbursts are accompanied by changes in the internal organs and in the composition of the blood which are similar to those characteristic of human emotional behavior. It has been shown that sham rage depends on the functional integrity of the caudal hypothalamus. The question naturally is: 'How real or sham is such behavior? Does uninhibited action of the hypothalamus give rise to the experience of fear and rage, or does it affect merely the sympathetic and motor concomitants of the emotions?' Sham rage differs from normal rage in animals as follows: (1) the animal rarely attempts to avoid the stimulus that called forth the reaction; and (2) the response of sham rage rarely outlasts the duration of the stimulus, i.e. after-discharge is minimal. These differences are also seen in cases of sham rage in humans, which is never purposeful. In humans sham rage has been observed as a result of extensive cortical damage secondary to prolonged hypoglycemia and carbon monoxide poisoning: the response pattern was uniform to all strong stimuli, it lasted from 30 seconds to one minute, and the strength of stimulus had no apparent effect on the duration of the sham rage. In these cases, loud noises and painful stimuli produce dilation of the pupil, widening of the palpebral fissures, exophthalmos, and marked increase in pulse rate and systolic pressure. A patient with carbon monoxide poisoning clenched and ground her teeth and emitted hissing sounds.

All in all, both animal and human data would seem to imply that the hypothalamus is not the emotional center. 'It would, therefore, seem that while subcortical centers (the hypothalamus) may integrate and possibly reinforce the effector neural responses controlling some of the sympathetic and motor manifestations of fear and rage, there is little or no basis for the thesis that the hypothalamus governs or even mediates the emotional experiences themselves.' (Wortis, H. and Mauer, U.S. *American Journal of Psychiatry* 98, 637-44, 1941-42) See *Cannon hypothalamic theory of emotion; emotion, Papez' theory of; ergotropic.*

rami communicantes (rȧ-mē kō-moo-nē-kan'tēs) Branches of the spinal nerves which pass to the sympathetic trunk. The white ramus is present only in thoracic and upper lumbar nerves; the gray ramus is present in all spinal nerves.

random Uncontrolled, spontaneous, unplanned, occurring by chance. The term is used most commonly in statistics to refer to the choosing of experimental subjects on the basis of chance rather than on the basis of particular selective factors.

rank Position in a series when the components of the series are arranged in order of magnitude; thus a rank of 20 indicates that the component-part is 20th from the top (or bottom) when all components have been arranged in order of size. Because the meaningfulness of any given rank will depend upon the number of component-parts in the series, rank is more meaningful if expressed in relative terms as a percentile rank. See *rank, percentile.*

Rank, Otto (1884-1939) Viennese psychoanalyst; birth trauma, will therapy.

rank, percentile Position in a series expressed as a number which represents the per cent of cases in the total group lying below the given score value. Example: if a subject makes a score of 82 in an examination, and it is found that this score is higher than that made by 93 per cent of the total number of those taking that examination, we would say that he is at the 93rd percentile on this particular examination. Percentile ranks are used to facilitate the interpretation of a single measure in a distribution of such measures, as a means of describing the variability and form of a frequency distribution, and as a means of comparing measures which were originally expressed in different units. Thus a student may make a score of 82 on one test and a score of 127 on a second; as raw scores these would be relatively meaningless, but when it is known that the score of 82 represents the 93rd percentile on the first test, and that the score of 127 represents the 92nd percentile on the second, the subject's performance on the two tests is seen in more meaningful perspective.

Rapaport, David (1911-1960) Hungarian-born U.S. psychologist; systematizer of psychoanalytic theory; *Emotions and Memory* (1942); *Diagnostic Psychological Testing* (1945-46, with Roy Schafer and Merton Gill); *Organization and Pathology of Thought* (1951).

rape-phantasy, anal See *phantasy, anal rape.*

rapport (rà-pawr′) (F. 'relation, ratio, proportion') Harmonious relation, accord. In the group: 'the existence of a mutual responsiveness such that every member reacts immediately, spontaneously, and sympathetically to the sentiments and attitudes of every other member.' (Park, R.E. and Burgess, E.W. *Introduction to the Science of Sociology,* University of Chicago Press, Chicago, 1921)

'In his treatment of her case, Breuer could make use of a very intense suggestible *rapport* on the part of the patient, which may serve us as a prototype of what we call "transference" today.' (Freud, S. *Collected Papers,* vol. 1, tr. by Riviere, J., Leonard and Virginia Woolf and The Institute of Psychoanalysis, London, 1924-25)

rapport, psychological In Jung's terminology, *transference* (q.v.).

raptus (rap′tus) A type of action seen in some catatonic schizophrenics consisting of unco-ordinated discharge movements which tend to relieve extreme tension. Cataleptic general muscular rigidity is a common form of raptus action.

raptus impulsive Rare. A sudden, unprovoked attack of extreme agitation that occurs sometimes in cases of catatonic schizophrenia.

raptus melancholicus (ràp′toos me-làng-kô′lē-koos) (L. 'melancholic seizure') An attack of extreme agitation or frenzy occurring in the course of melancholia.

R.A.S. Reticular activating system. See *formation, reticular.*

rate In epidemiology, the rate is the level of occurrence of a disease or reaction in relation to a given population, such as 10 cases per 1,000 population, or per 10,000, or per 100,000. See *incidence; prevalence.*

rate, death The ratio of the number of persons dying within a specified period, usually a year, to the number who were in the original group. In institutional statistics the true death rate is usually approximated by finding the ratio of deaths to the average number under treatment during the period. The number of admissions and the total number under care have been used incorrectly as the base for the death rate.

rate, discharge The ratio of the number discharged within a given period (usually a year) to the total number in the original group. In institutional statistics this rate is usually approximated by relating the number discharged in a given period to the number who were admitted during the same period. See *readmission.*

Example: If there are 620 admissions to a mental hospital during the calendar year, and if there are 527 discharges from that hospital during the same period, the discharge rate is

$$\frac{527}{620} = 85 \text{ per cent.}$$

rate, improvement The improvement rate is the ratio of the number discharged as improved within a given period (usually a year) to the total number in the original group. In institutional statistics this rate is usually approximated by relating the number discharged as improved in a given period to the number who were admitted during the same period.

Example: In one psychiatric hospital in New York City, 616 patients were admitted during the calendar year 1958. During the same period, 542 patients were discharged as improved. The improvement rate is

$$\frac{542}{616} = 88 \text{ per cent.}$$

See *rate, discharge.*

rate of first admissions The rate of first admissions (i.e. to hospitals for mental disease) is the ratio of all first admissions within a year to the average general population during that year.

Between 1922 and 1950, there has been a definite increase in mental disease in the United States as a whole, and in New York State. But as shown in the following table (adapted from Malzberg, B. 'Important Statistical Data About Mental Illness,' Chapter 7 in *American*

Handbook of Psychiatry, edited by Arieti, S., volume 1, Basic Books, New York, 1959), that increase is due not to any great increase in the incidence of 'functional' psychoses, but rather to a great increase in the number of first admissions diagnosed cerebral arteriosclerosis or senile brain disorders.

New York State-First Admissions
per 100,000 Population

	Male	Female	Total	% of Total
Total:				
1922	69.3	61.0	65.1	100
1950	109.9	102.4	106.0	100
Cerebral Arteriosclerosis:				
1922	6.6	4.3	5.4	8.3
1950	24.6	20.4	22.4	21.1
Senile Brain Disorders:				
1922	4.9	8.0	6.4	9.8
1950	12.9	19.4	16.3	15.2
Paresis:				
1922	12.6	2.9	7.7	11.8
1950	3.8	1.4	2.6	2.0
Alcoholic Psychoses:				
1922	3.6	0.7	2.2	3.4
1950	11.0	3.2	7.0	6.7
Manic-Depressive Psychosis:				
1922	6.8	12.1	9.4	14.4
1950	1.9	3.1	2.5	2.3
Schizophrenias:				
1922	19.2	16.3	17.8	27.4
1950	31.5	31.0	31.2	29.1

In general, both in the United States and Europe, males exceed females in the incidence of schizophrenia, organic brain disorders (except for the senile and presenile psychoses), and alcoholism, while females lead in manic-depressive disorders, neuroses, psychopathy, and senile and presenile psychoses.

rate, recovery The ratio of the number discharged as recovered within a given period (usually a year) to the total number in the original group. In institutional statistics this rate is usually approximated by relating the number discharged as recovered in a given period to the number who were admitted during the same period.

rate, residence In institutional statistics, the residence rate is based upon the population actually in institutions of a given type on any specified date. For example, it is the ratio of the resident population to the total population of the State. See *readmission*.

rate, specific A rate is specific when it is based upon a population and a class of that population both of which are homogeneous, or nearly so, with respect to a specific character: e.g. the number of male patients dying at ages 20-24 per 1,000 male patients aged 20-24.

rate, standardized A hypothetical rate which would prevail if a given population had the same relative distribution (i.e. with respect to age) as another population called the standard.

ratio, affective The ratio of the total number of responses to the colored Rorschach cards (cards VIII, IX, and X) to the total number of responses to the achromatic cards (I through VII). This ratio is an expression of the degree to which color increases responsiveness and is interpreted as an index of affectivity.

ratio, critical See *CR*.

ration, sex The proportional distribution of males and females at birth. The usual sex ratio 106:100 has been cited as evidence that boys are stronger and better able to survive the ordeal of being born.

Recent genetic studies have shown, however, that more boys are born, because more boys are *conceived*, and that the excess of males over females conceived is still greater than the ratio at birth. Investigation of embryos aborted when about three months old has shown that males outnumber females almost four to one. It must be assumed, therefore, that male embryos are not stronger, but just on the contrary, *weaker* than female ones, and therefore more likely to perish under adverse intrauterine conditions.

ration, type token An index of the balance between repetition and variety of words, used as a quantitative measurement of certain aspects of verbal communication during psychiatric sessions. Repetition gives a low index, variety of words gives a high index.

rational Reasoning, sensible. From the standpoint of Jung 'the rational is the reasonable, that which accords with reason. I conceive reason as an attitude whose principle is to shape thought, feeling, and action in accordance with objective values.' (Jung, C.G. *Psychological Types*, tr. by Baynes, H.G., Harcourt, Brace, New York and London, 1923) 'Thinking and feeling are rational functions in so far as they are decisively influenced by the motive of reflection. They attain their fullest significance when in fullest possible accord with the laws of reason. The irrational functions, on the contrary, are such as aim at pure perception, e.g., intuition and sensation; because, as far as possible, they are forced to dispense with the rational (which presupposes the exclusion of everything that 'is outside reason) in order to be able to reach the most complete perception of the whole course of events.' (ibid)

rational type See *type, rational.*

rationalization This term was introduced into psychoanalysis by Ernest Jones. It means justification, or making a thing appear reasonable, when otherwise its irrationality would be evident. It is said that a person 'covers up,' justifies, rationalizes an act or an idea that is unreasonable and illogical. For example, when a dehypnotized subject obeys a command received while under hypnosis and of which he is not consciously aware, and then proceeds to give a specious explanation for his act, he resorts to rationalization. Let us assume that he had been commanded to remove his shoes, when there was no reason for the removal. When the hypnotic stage is ended and he begins to take off his shoes, he explains that the shoes are too tight, or there are pebbles in them, or he gives some explanation that has the appearance of rationality. In other words, 'rationalization is a *screening* process, intended to cover a flaw in repression, e.g. to cover ideas or actions which are intended to gratify an unconscious need.' (Glover, E. *The Technique of Psycho-Analysis,* International Universities Press, New York, 1955) 'Rationalization is the work of the unconscious Ego by which it evades the recognition of irrational and inconsistent behavior which really arises on the basis of unconscious urges. It can be seen that the Ego's narcism is always largely involved in the process of rationalization.' (Healy, W., Bronner, A.F., and Bowers, A.M. *The Structure and Meaning of Psychoanalysis,* Knopf, New York, 1930)

rationalize To invent a reason 'for an attitude or action, the motive of which is not recognized.' (Jones, E. *Papers on Psycho-Analysis,* 4th ed., Wood, Baltimore, 1938)

Rat-Man The patient reported on by Freud in his 1909 paper, 'Notes upon a Case of Obsessional Neurosis,' so called because of the experience which was the direct occasion of his consulting a psychiatrist: on military maneuvers he had heard a story of a type of punishment used in the Far East, the punishment consisting of overturning a pot of rats onto the buttocks of the prisoner so that the rats would bore their way into his anus.

Ray, Isaac (1807 - 81) American psychiatrist; mental hygiene; forensic psychiatry; one of the founders of the American Psychiatric Association.

reaction Counter-action; response to a stimulus.

reaction, alarm The first stage of the general adaptation syndrome. The alarm reaction is a response to stress and as observed in experimental animals consists of: adrenocortical enlargement with histologic signs of hyperactivity, thymicolymphatic involution, gastrointestinal ulcers, and often other manifestations of damage or shock. See *syndrome, general adaptation.*

reaction, alcohol-Antabuse See *Antabuse.*

reaction, all-or-none In psychiatry this expression means that instinctive processes, when stimulated, respond with full force or not at all.

In neurophysiology, the all-or-none (or all-or-nothing) principle refers to the fact that individual neurons either transmit their messages maximally or not at all. Differences in intensity are conveyed by means of spatial and temporal summation of impulses.

reaction, antisocial See *antisocial reaction.*

reaction, anxiety According to the 1952 revision of psychiatric nomenclature, this is the acceptable term for conditions formerly diagnosed anxiety state, or anxiety-neurosis. See *anxiety-neurosis.*

reaction, arousal See *arousal.*

reaction, aversion A response of avoidance or turning away from disturbing or frightening stimuli.

reaction, behavioral See *personality disorder.*

reaction, defensive *Defense* (q.v.).

reaction, delirious See *syndrome, organic.*

reaction, dissociate-dysmnesic substitution Adolf Meyer's term for conversion hysteria, which emphasizes the fundamental role of memory dissociation in the development of symptoms. See *hysteria.*

reaction, duplicative A perceptual disturbance described most commonly in schizophrenic children; because he does not conceptualize objects as continuing and unitary when they are out of direct sensory contact, the schizophrenic child 'seeing the same person in different settings or at different times thinks he is seeing more than one person.' (Goldfarb, W. *International Psychiatry Clinics 1,* 821-845, 1964)

reaction-formation Reversal-formation; 'the development in the ego of conscious, socialized attitudes and interests which are the antithesis of certain infantile unsocialized trends which continue to persist in the unconscious.' (Healy, W., Bronner, A.F., and Bowers, A.M. *The Structure and Meaning of Psychoanalysis,* Knopf, New York, 1930) When, for instance, oversolicitude is the conscious response to unconscious hate, the condition (oversolicitude) is known as a reaction-formation.

Reaction-formation is a form of de-

fense against urges which are unacceptable to the ego. It is one of the earliest of the defense-mechanisms and one of the most fragile. As Freud says it is 'insecure and constantly threatened by the impulse which lurks in the unconscious.' There is always the danger in reaction-formation of a return of the repressed impulse to consciousness.

'Repression, as it invariably does, has brought about a withdrawal of libido, but for this purpose it has made use of a *reaction-formation,* by intensifying an antithesis. So here the substitute-formation has the same mechanism as the repression and at bottom coincides with it, while yet chronologically, as well as in its content, it is distinct from symptom-formation.' (Freud, S. *Collected Papers,* vol. 4, tr. by Riviere, J., Leonard and Virginia Woolf and The Institute of Psychoanalysis, London, 1924-25)

Reaction-formation, then, is a type of repression, but it is distinguished from the latter by two features: (1) in reaction-formation, the counter-cathexis is manifest in the form of the denying attitude, and thus the necessity for often repeated secondary repressions is avoided; and (2) the counter-cathexis is constantly manifested as a definitive change of personality rather than a momentary arousal of defensive maneuvers in response to an immediate danger.

'In a sense the superego can be considered a reaction formation of the ego, a complicated reaction to the oedipus complex. The fully developed superego in turn stimulates the ego to further reaction formations. The ego has to change its structure according to internal and external needs. It has the difficult task of maintaining itself in the face of three kinds of influences—the superego, the external world, and the id. Although its core is stable, the structure of the ego as a whole changes according to the influences to which it is subjected. Instead of reacting to these influences, that is, perceiving and discharging or abreacting them, the ego assimilates them and creates something new.' (Nunberg, H. *Principles of Psychoanalysis,* International Universities Press, New York, 1955) Such reaction-formations contribute extensively to the final structure of the character.

Two commonly observed reaction-formations are disgust (a reaction-formation of the ego to an oral sexual impulse) and shame (a reaction-formation to exhibitionistic impulses).

It is to be emphasized that reaction-formation is an unconscious defense mechanism of the ego; conscious dissimulation or hypocrisy is not reaction-formation. Further, reaction-formation is not to be confused with sublimation; in the former, the unconscious impulse is repressed, and the constant counter-cathexis required to maintain such constant repression drains off energy which would otherwise be available to the ego. In the case of sublimation, on the other hand, the original impulse is superseded and its energy remains available to the ego for the fulfillment of its various tasks.

'To clarify the relation between reaction formation and sublimation let us compare (a) a child who learns to write well and enjoys it very much, (b) a child who has an inhibition for writing, (c) a child who writes very constrainedly and meticulously, and (d) a child who smears. All of them have displaced anal-erotic instinctual quantities to the function of writing. In the first child a sublimation has taken place; he no longer wishes to smear but to write. The other children have not succeeded in channelizing this impulse. They are forced to inhibit it through a countercathexis, or to "robot" through reaction-formations, or even to retain the original impulse in an unchanged way.' (Fenichel, O. *The Psychoanalytic Theory of Neurosis,* Norton, New York, 1945)

While reaction-formation can be seen as an element of any neurosis or psychosis, it is a typical mechanism of the obsessive-compulsive psychoneurosis.

reaction, hand-to-mouth Observed in young infants, bringing to the mouth, for the purpose of sucking, all objects within reach of the infant's hand. These may be parts of the infant's body (hand, foot) or any outside object. According to Gesell, this reaction disappears at about twelve months of age.

reaction, Herxheimer See *Jarisch-Herxheimer reaction.*

reaction, manic-depressive See *psychosis, manic-depressive.*

reaction, Much-Holzmann (Hans Much, W. Holzmann, German physicians.) The alleged property of the serum from a person affected with schizophrenia or manic-depressive psychosis, to inhibit hemolysis by cobra venom.

reaction, polyglot In aphasia, any exception to the general rule that in persons who are multilingual, the mother tongue is the first to return.

reaction, psychotic See *psychosis; psychotic disorder.*

reaction, spoiled child Behavior reaction of children due to parental oversolicitude, overindulgence and overprotection. Such children do not learn the value or even the meaning of regularity, self-care, responsibility, or independence.

reaction, thymonoic (thī-mō-nō'ik) 'Thymonoic reactions are closely related to catathymic reactions. They are distinguished by the presence of strong affective factors and equally strong tendency to systematization of thought (in the direction of depressive delusion), each factor springing from the same experiential and personality sources, and each feeding on and becoming more strongly fixed because of the other. These are the strongly "intellectualized" and "rationalized" depressions, with marked systematized content, at times entirely autopsychic, but also at times with allopsychic manifestations.' (Muncie, W. *Psychobiology and Psychiatry,* Mosby, St. Louis, 1939)

reaction-time Length of delay between application of stimulus and appearance of response. In word association tests, a long reaction-time signalizes a 'complex.'

reaction-type A syndrome described in terms of the preponderating or essential symptoms. Adolf Meyer, for example, described six reation-types: organic, delirious, affective, paranoic, substitutive, and deteriorated.

reaction-type, affective A syndrome whose preponderant symptoms are of an affective or emotional nature, such as manic-depressive disorder.

reaction-type, delirious Adolf Meyer's expression for a type of psychiatric response due to toxic, infective, or exhaustive influences. The syndrome is characterized by dream-like imaginations, hallucinations, and impairment of the sensorium. See *syndrome, organic.*

reaction-type deterioration When regression, accompanied as a rule by delusional and hallucinatory phenomena, is a principal characteristic of a psychiatric syndrome, as it is in schizophrenia, Adolph Meyer classifies the syndrome as a deterioration reaction-type.

reaction-type, organic See *syndrome, organic.*

reaction-type, substitutive When mental conflicts are repressed into the unconscious and appear in the field of consciousness in disguised or substituted form, Adolf Meyer classifies the syndrome as *substitutive.* The psychoneuroses in general are substitutive reaction-types.

reactive Secondary to, resulting from, or precipitated by an identifiable happening; thus, a depressive episode following the death of a loved one could be termed reactive depression. In general, reactive episodes—be they depressive, manic, or schizophrenic in nature—carry a more favorable prognosis than those which arise endogenously and without apparent relationship to adversity or trauma in the patient's life. This fact has favored a regrettable equating of 'reactive' with 'non-psychotic' or 'neurotic,' even though it is well-known that the same patient can have both reactive and endogenous episodes in the course of a recurrent or relapsing psychosis.

read-out See *memory.*

readiness, complex The tendency of unconscious feelings or impulses to find substitute expression in the behavior or routine of everyday life, as in lapses in speaking, reading, and writing.

readiness, explosion Readiness to explode, or burst forth violently. See *diathesis, explosive.*

reading, disabilities of The term 'reading disability' includes a variety of clinical entities of apparently different etiology and treatment need.

'In our total caseload, which now numbers some 250 children and adolescents, we have been impressed with the emergence of three major groups:

'1. Those in whom the reading retardation is due to frank brain damage manifested by gross neurologic deficits. In these cases there are clearly demonstrable major aphasic difficulties, and they are similar to adult dyslexic syndromes. An example is that of a 9-year-old boy who sustained a severe head injury with prolonged coma, followed by a right hemiparesis and expressive aphasia.

'2. Those with no history or gross clinical findings to suggest neurologic disease but in whom the reading retardation is viewed as primary. The defect appears to be in basic capacity to integrate written material and to associate concepts with symbols. On the basis of findings to be presented later in this paper a neurologic deficit is suspected and, because the defect is basic or biologic in its origin, we have called these cases *primary reading retardation.'* (306.1)

'3. Those cases demonstrating reading retardation on standard tests but in whom there appears to be no defect in basic reading learning capacity. These children have a normal potential for learning to read but this has not been utilized because of *exogenous* factors, common among which are anxiety, negativism, emotional blocking and limited schooling opportunities. We diagnose these cases as *secondary reading retardation.'* (Rabinovitch, R.D., Drew, A.L., De Jong, R.N., Ingram, W., and Withey, L. 'A Research Approach to Reading Retardation,' *Research Publications, Association for Nervous and Mental Diseases 34:* 363-96, 1954, p. 366)

Failure to distinguish between these major types of reading disability has led to confusion among workers in the field, and innumerable terms have been coined to describe various types of reading defects, many terms frequently referring to the same concept. Among such terms currently in use are: word-blindness, congenital symbolamblyopia, congenital typholexia, congenital alexia, amnesia visualis verbalis, congenital dyslexia, developmental alexia, analfabetia partialis, bradylexia, strephosymbolia, constitutional dyslexia, specific dyslexia.

In the primary group described above, '. . . the defect appears to be part of a larger disturbance in integration. Our findings suggest that we are dealing with a developmental discrepancy rather than an acquired brain injury. The specific areas of difficulty manifested in the clinical examinations are those commonly associated with parietal and parietal-occipital dysfunction.' (ibid; p. 387)

readmission A person admitted or entered on the rolls more than once to any institution of a given class (e.g. mental hospitals). Until recently, the number of hospitalized mental patients increased each year in most states. In New York State, for example, the resident population of state hospitals doubled between 1929 and 1955, at which time a peak of 93,300 patients was reached. That upward trend was abruptly halted and inverted into a decline coincident with the use of tranquilizing drugs, which more than any other single factor were responsible for an increasing discharge rate. To some extent this has been balanced by an increasing readmission rate, since patients enabled to be discharged earlier than previously may require more frequent periods of rehospitalization. For some groups of patients, a pattern of early admission—speedy discharge—readmission(s) seems to have been established; such a pattern is often referred to as the *revolving door* phenomenon.

reality The whole of the objective world, embracing all that may be perceived by the five senses.

reality-ego See *ego, reality.*

reality-principle See *principle, reality.*

reality-system See *ego, stability of.*

reality-testing A fundamental ego function which consists of the objective evaluation and judgment of the world outside the ego or self. Reality-testing depends upon the simpler ego-functions of perception and memory and upon differentiation between ego and non-ego. Reality-testing

provides the ego with a mechanism for handling both the external world and its own excitation, for it makes it possible for the ego to anticipate the future in the imagination. External objects represent a threat to the ego and/or potential gratification, and the ego can best protect itself against threats and can secure maximal gratification by using reality-testing to judge reality objectively and direct its actions accordingly.

A stage of primary hallucinatory wish-fulfillment precedes the development of reality-testing, and a counterpart of the former is the ability to deny unpleasant parts of reality. As reality-testing develops along with the acquisition of speech and thinking proper, such wholesale falsification of reality becomes impossible. Serious and important denials, then, are seen only in very early childhood and in pathological conditions such as psychosis, where the ego has been weakened by narcissistic regression. Projection, too, can be used extensively only when reality-testing is seriously impaired, as in psychosis, or when adequate demarcation between ego and non-ego has not yet been achieved, as in childhood. Only when the boundaries between ego and non-ego are blurred can the ego ward off the unpleasant by 'spitting it out' and feeling it as being outside the ego.

Neurotics do, however, show some impairment of reality-testing at least to the extent that warded-off impulses and their derivatives interfere with differentiated thinking and block the ego's capacity to organize its experiences, and insofar as present-day objects become mere 'transference' representations of past objects and are reacted to with inappropriate and anachronistic feelings.

reassociation A process of renewed or refreshed association occurring in hypno-analysis of the war neurosis, during which the patient relives the traumatic event with emotional vividness. Such forgotten experiences will then become a part of his normal personality and consciousness.

reassurance A type of supportive psychotherapy.

rebound phenomenon of Gordon Holmes (British physician, b. 1876) A test for ataxia, specifically illustrating the loss of cerebellar 'check' on co-ordinated movement; if an attempt is made to extend the flexed forearm against resistance and suddenly let go, the hand or fist flies unchecked against the mouth or shoulder.

recall See *memory.*

recapitulation, pubertal sexual The concept that the successive stages in the development of adult sexuality recapitulate those of infantile sexuality. The development of adult sexuality begins with puberty and is normally completed somewhere between the ages of sixteen and twenty-one. The developmental stages of adult sexuality 'repeat' those of infantile sexuality and rarely are conflicts found which have not had their forerunners in the earlier development. 'At puberty a regression takes place in the direction of infancy, of the first period of all, and the person lives over again, though on another plain, the development he passed through in the first five years of life. This correlation between adolescence and infancy is of considerable importance as affording the key to many of the problems of adolescence.' (Jones, E.J. *Papers on Psycho-Analysis,* Williams and Wilkins, Baltimore, 1949)

While it is true that conflicts in adolescent sexual development which have not had their forerunners in infantile sexual development are rarely encountered, nevertheless 'experiences in puberty may solve conflicts or shift conflicts into a final direction; moreover, they may give older and oscillating constellations a final and definitive form. Many neurotics give an impression of adolescence. They have not succeeded in getting on good terms with their sexuality. Therefore, they continue the behavior patterns of adolescent children, that is, of an age at which it is usually considered normal not to have achieved these good terms and to feel life as a provisional state, with "full reality" still waiting in an indefinite future.' (Fenichel, O. *The Psychoanalytic Theory of Neurosis,* Norton, New York, 1945)

receiving type See *assimilation.*

receptive Passive, accepting, dependent. See *character, receptive.*

receptors, distance The visual and auditory apparatus, as contrasted with *proximal receptors* (touch, taste, smell). Schizophrenic children typically avoid distance receptors and prefer the use of proximal receptors, the reverse of the normal situation. As a result of avoidance of distance receptors, such children often have a glassy, non-seeing stare; they seem to look through others rather than at them, and often cannot meet the direct gaze of the examiner.

receptors, proximal See *receptors, distance.*

recessiveness The meaning of this genetic term is best understood as the mirror image of *dominance* (q.v.); a recessive factor remains *hidden* as an independent genetic entity, as long, and as far, as it is covered by the dominant member of a given allelic pair of hereditary factors.

According to modern genetic theories, a recessive character does not really 'disappear' as was suggested by the old presence-absence theory of Bateson, but it can be phenotypically manifested only in a *homozygous* condition when it is inherited by a hybrid from both parents. In the case of a single-recessive cross, this is true in 25 per cent of the entire hybrid generation.

In the recessive or *indirect* mode of inheritance we observe as a rule that the heterozygotes are germinally affected, but phenotypically healthy. Since a recessive trait can appear only in the phenotype of a homozygote, all trait-carriers must be homozygous. The occurrence of such a trait among the offspring is not possible, unless both parents are, at least, heterozygotes.

The probability of a union between two recessive taint-carriers (heterozygotes) is clearly the greater the more frequent this recessive trait is in the general population. The probability is the greatest in the cases of *intermarriage* between blood-relations, unless the trait in question is very common in the normal average population. Apart from this particular instance of *cousin marriages,* the direct transmission of a recessive trait is the exception and the indirect inheritance through the collateral lines is the rule.

recidivism (rē-sid'i-viz'm) Repetition of delinquent or criminal acts by the same offender who is called, accordingly, a recidivist.

'A large proportion of the inmates of penal institutions in most countries are "repeaters"; persons who have been committed to a penal institution after having served one or more terms.' (Cantor, N. *Encyclopaedia of the Social Sciences*, vol. 13, Macmillan, New York, 1934, p. 157)

Less commonly, recidivism is used to refer to relapse or recurrence of a psychiatric disorder. See *schizophrenia, recidives in.*

reciprocal inhibition psychotherapy See *behavior theory.*

reciprocity, overadequate-inadequate See *psychotherapy, family.*

recollections, early See *constancy.*

recombination The genetic process by which linked factors break up their original combinations, so that originally separate genes become united in one gamete, or originally united genes become separated. These recombining phenomena are also known as *crossovers.*

'Under independent assortment the parental combinations and the recombinations are approximately equal in number. Under linkage the parental combinations are always more numerous than the recombinations. Linkage may vary greatly with different genes, producing all the way from very few to nearly 50 per cent of recombinations.' (Sinnott, E.W. and Dunn, L.C. *Principles of Genetics*, 3rd ed., McGraw-Hill, New York and London, 1939)

When crossovers occur and lead to a separation of linked genes, the genes which have crossed over are bound to enter different gametes and to appear in different individuals among the progeny. See *linkage.*

recommencement, mania of Janet's term for the behavior of some obsessive-compulsive patients who must do things many times before they can feel some assurance that they have been done correctly — opening and shutting doors, locking and

unlocking doors, dressing and undressing, constant repetition of prayers and penances, etc.

reconditioning A type of psychotherapy based on the belief that neurosis is a result of faulty conditioning. In Salter's method, the patient is authoritatively directed to abandon destructive patterns of behavior and to practice new habits which will be of value to him. The patient is considered to be in a state of pathologic inhibition which is itself a conditioned response that blocks free emotional expression ('excitation'). Treatment is directed to unlearning conditioned inhibitory reflexes and replacing them with conditioned excitatory reflexes by means of deliberate practicing of excitatory emotional reactions until they are established as conditioned reflexes.

reconstruction See *psychotherapy.*

recreation Leisure activity engaged in for its own sake. The term is also used to refer to a type of ancillary treatment and is then called recreation(al) therapy or R.T. John E. Davis (*Clinical Applications of Recreational Therapy*, Thomas, Springfield, Ill., 1952) defines recreation therapy as '. . . any free, voluntary and expressive activity; motor, sensory or mental, vitalized by the expansive play spirit, sustained by deep-rooted pleasurable attitudes and evoked by wholesome emotional release; prescribed by medical authority as an adjuvant in treatment.' Recreation therapy includes such activities as dressmaking, drama, puppetry, lectures, films, music appreciation, dancing, discussion groups, clubs, painting, singing, excursions, bowling, and athletic games of all sorts.

recreation, active In occupational therapy any form of diversional endeavor or pastime in which the patient actually engages and in the participation of which it is necessary for him to make some physical exertion. For example, dancing is a form of active recreation.

recreation, passive Entertainment or amusement which is planned and presented by others for the patient and in which he does not participate, but plays the passive part of onlooker. For example, moving pictures or a concert are forms of passive recreation.

recruiting system See *system, intralaminar.*

recruitment In neurophysiology, spread of response if stimulation is prolonged.

red nucleus See *midbrain.*

redintegration (red-in-te-grā'shun) Hollingworth's term for the process in which part of a complex antecedent provokes the complete consequent that was previously made to the antecedent as a whole. The conditioned response is an example of redintegration. Redintegration is the basis of the value of souvenirs and keepsakes, which tend to arouse the same attitudes as were originally connected with the experiences to which they pertain.

Redintegration is also sometimes used synonymously with reintegration. See *integration.*

reductionism The philosophy, theory, or belief that everything is to be, and can be, explained in terms of simple, elemental components. Many theories of human behavior are based on the *drive-reduction theory:* the aim or function of every instinct, defense, action, habit, or phantasy is to reduce or eliminate either stimulation or excitation within the nervous system. That theory implies that in the absence of such motivation, the organism will become quiescent; in fact, however, the organism does not, and in their attempts to overcome such a basic contradiction between hypothesis and observed data many theorists have taken refuge in naming instincts, postulating drives in terms of their telic significance, and/or speculating on the existence of spontaneous activity.

reductive 'I employ this expression to denote that method of psychological interpretation which regards the unconscious product not from the symbolic point of view, but merely as a *semiotic* expression, a sort of sign or symptom of an underlying process. Accordingly the reductive method treats the unconscious

product in the sense of a leading-back to the elements and basic processes, irrespective of whether such products are reminiscences of actual events, or whether they arise from elementary processes affecting the psyche. Hence, the reductive method is orientated backwards (in contrast to the constructive method), whether in the historical sense or in the merely figurative sense of a tracing back of complex and differentiated factors to the general and elementary.' (Jung, C.G. *Psychological Types,* tr. by Baynes, H.G., Harcourt, Brace, New York and London, 1923)

re-education See *psychotherapy.*

reefers Slang expression for marihuana cigarettes. Possibly the weed was first brought by sailors from the 'reefs' of Mariguana Island in the Bahamas.

re-enactment, emotional See *abreaction.*

reference, delusion of See *reference, ideas of.*

reference, ideas of When a person projects his own, usually unconscious, ideas upon another or other persons and then proceeds to act toward those ideas as if they originated from an outside source, he is said to show *ideas of reference.* For instance, a patient with an unconscious impulse to steal, was preoccupied with the idea, delusional, that others asserted he intended to steal. The psychic process involves criticism of the projected urges, so that the patient may not know that he is really criticizing some undesirable impulse within himself.

The term also includes the tendency to read a personal meaning into everything that goes on about one, to feel that every action or happening in the outside world is specifically and purposely related to the patient.

The paranoid patient almost always exhibits ideas of reference. He misinterprets the activities of others, believing that they have personal reference of a derogatory character to him. See *projection.*

referred pain See *pain, referred.*

reflection In psychiatry and psychology,

this may refer (1) to a type of thinking characterized by introspection, deliberation, or contemplation, or (2) to a psychotherapeutic technique in which a patient's statements are restated or rephrased to the patient so as to emphasize their emotional significance.

reflex A sensorimotor reaction, the simplest form of involuntary response to a stimulus. Stimulation of the receptor organ or cell excites the afferent neuron, from which the impulse travels to one or more intercalated neurons in the central nervous system and thence, via the efferent neuron, to the effector organ or cell.

reflex, abdominal The upper (or epigastric) and lower abdominal reflexes are superficial skin reflexes tested by stroking the skin of the abdomen. This results in contraction of the abdominal muscles beneath the skin area stroked and usually also movement of the umbilicus in the direction of the area stroked. The upper abdominals depend on thoracic nerves 7 to 10; the lower abdominals depend on thoracic nerves 10 to 12.

reflex, accommodation See *accommodation.*

reflex, acute affective Kretschmer's term for the earliest indications of emotional discharge (usually, tremors) in response to great stress.

reflex, bar A pathologic postural reaction consisting of involuntary following by one leg when the other leg of the recumbent patient is moved laterally or vertically. The bar phenomenon is seen mainly in cases with lesions of the prefrontal areas (especially in cases of brain tumor).

reflex, biceps A deep reflex; patient's forearm is placed half-way between flexion and extension and slightly pronated; examiner's finger is on the tendon, and a blow on this digit results in flexion of the forearm. This reflex depends upon the musculocutaneous nerve for its afferents and efferents; its center is C_{5-6}.

reflex, Chaddock (Charles Gilbert Chaddock, American neurologist) Dorsal ex-

tension of the great toe, induced by stroking the skin over the external malleolus. This is one of several pathologic reflexes which may be seen when the lower motor neuron is released from the normal suppressor effect of higher centers, as in pyramidal tract lesions.

reflex, consensual When light enters the pupil of one eye only, the iris of the other eye contracts; the phenomenon is known as the consensual light reflex.

reflex, corneal Bilateral blinking induced by touching the cornea with a wisp of cotton. The afferent nerve of the corneal reflex is the 5th cranial nerve; its efferent is the 7th cranial nerve, and its center is in the pons.

reflex, corneal-pterygoideal Touching the cornea is followed by contraction of the external pterygoid, which produces deviation of the lower jaw of the opposite side.

reflex, cremasteric (krē-mas-ter'ik) A superficial reflex; stroking the inner and upper side of the thigh causes contraction of the cremaster and elevation of the testicle on the same side. The afferents of this reflex depend upon the femoral nerve, the efferents on the genitofemoral nerve; the center is L_1.

reflex, cuboidodigital (kū-boi-dō-dij'i-tal) See *Bechtereff-Mendel reflex.*

reflex, deep Any one of the tendon and periosteal reflexes, which include the jaw-jerk, pectoral, triceps, biceps, radial, ulnar, knee-jerk, suprapatellar, tibio-adductor, flexion of the leg, ankle-jerk, and Bechtereff-Mendel reflexes.

reflex, dorsocuboidal (dawr-sō-kū-boid'al) See *Bechtereff-Mendel reflex.*

reflex, emptying See *reflex, gastrocolic.*

reflex, epigastric See *reflex, abdominal.*

reflexes, grasping and groping These reflexes are elicited when the palms and the fingers are stroked, causing a closure of the hand on the stimulating object. Normally this occurs in infants below one year of age. Otherwise it is indicative of frontal lobe lesions.

reflex, flexion, of the leg A deep reflex; patient's leg is semiflexed at the knee; the examiner's finger grasps the tendons of the semimembranosus and semitendinosus muscles; this finger is tapped, and that results in contraction of these muscles and flexion of the leg.

reflex, gastrocolic (gas-trō-kol′ik) Contraction of the colon following stretching of the muscle wall of the stomach (as by filling of the stomach); also known as emptying reflex.

reflex, gluteal (glōō-tē′al) A superficial reflex; stroking the buttocks causes contraction of the glutei.

reflex, Gordon (Alfred Gordon, American neurologist, b. 1869) Dorsal extension of the great toe, induced by compression of the calf muscle.

reflex, grasp Same as forced grasping, forced groping, or instinctive grasp reaction. See *lobe, frontal.*

reflex, Landau A reaction normally present from the age of 3 months to about one year of age, consisting of raising the head and arching the back with the concavity upwards when the infant is supported horizontally in the prone position. Absence of the reflex is seen with motor weakness, such as occurs in cerebral palsy, motor neurone disease, and mental retardation.

reflex, mass In very severe injury to or complete interruption of the spinal cord, stimulation below the level of the lesion produces the following reflexes: 1) flexion reflex, 2) contraction of the abdominal wall, 3) automatic evacuation of the bladder, 4) sweating of the skin below the level of the lesion. This *mass-reflex* was described by Riddoch.

reflex, Moro A type of mass reflex seen in the neonate in response to the examiner's slapping the surface on which the infant is lying; it consists of immediate flexion of the limbs and contraction of the abdominal wall with later interruptions of the spasm that produce clonic-like jerkings.

reflex, myxedema (miks-e-dē′mà) Also known as *Woltman's sign;* the myxedema reflex is the symptom of pathologically slow relaxation of reflexes in myxedema.

reflex, oculocardiac (ok-ū-lō-kar′dē-ak) Slowing of the pulse in response to pressure exerted on the eyeball; also known as the Aschner ocular phenomenon.

reflex, Oppenheim (H. Oppenheim, 1858-1919, German neurologist) Dorsal extension of the great toe, induced by stroking distally along the median side of the tibia. This is one of several pathologic reflexes that may be seen when the lower motor neuron is released from the normal suppressor effect of higher centers, as in pyramidal tract lesions.

reflex, palmar A superficial reflex; scratching or irritation of the palm results in flexion of the fingers.

reflex, palmomental Contraction of the mentalis muscle following mechanical stimulation of the thenar and hypothenar eminences. This reflex is rare in normal persons and is considered to be indicative of diffuse, toxic brain damage. Also known as the *palm-chin* or *pollico-mental* reflex.

reflex, patellar (pa-tel′ēr) See *reflex, suprapatellar.*

reflex, periosteal (per-ē-os′tē-al) The response to tapping certain bones which lie just beneath the skin; for example, the radial and ulnar periosteal, and the tibial adductor reflexes.

reflex, plantar A superficial reflex; stroking the sole of the foot causes flexion of the toes. This reflex depends upon the tibial nerve for its afferents and efferents; its center is at S_{1-2}.

reflex, pollicomental See *reflex, palmomental.*

reflex, psychogalvanic (sī-kō-gal-van′ik) Changes in skin resistance to the passage of a weak electric current which occur as part of the physicochemical response to emotional stimuli. Also known as PGR, galvanic skin response (GSR), electrodermal response (EDR), Féré phenomenon.

reflex, quadrupedal extensor (kwad-roope'dal ek-sten'sor) Russel Brain described this reflex in organic hemiplegia. It consists in the extension of the hemiplegic flexed arm on the assumption of the quadrupedal position. An additional feature may be the further flexion of the arm if the head is bent forward and extension of the arm if the head is bent back.

reflex, radial A deep reflex; also known as the extension reflex of the wrist. When the styloid process of the radius is tapped, the wrist extends. This reflex depends upon the radial nerve for its afferents and efferents; its center is C_{7-8}.

reflex, Ros(s)olimo's (Grigoriy Ivanovich Rosolimo, Russian neurologist, born in Odessa in 1860 of Greek parents) Plantar flexion of the toes, induced by tapping the balls of the toes. this is one of several pathologic reflexes which may be seen when the lower motor neuron is released from the normal suppressor effect of higher centers, as in pyramidal tract lesions.

reflex, Schaeffer (Max Schaeffer, German neurologist, 1852-1923) Dorsal reflexion of the great toe, induced by pinching the tendo Achillis. this is one of several pathologic reflexes which may be seen when the lower motor neuron is released from the normal suppressor effect of higher centers, as in pyramidal tract lesions.

reflex, scrotal (skrō'tal) By stroking the perineum or applying a cold object to it, a slow, vermicular contraction of the dartos muscle occurs. This is a purely automatic reflex with the cremasteric reflex.

reflex, superficial The response to stroking or pressing upon certain portions of the skin; for example, the plantar, cremasteric, and abdominal reflexes.

reflex, suprapatellar (soo-pra-pa-tel'ĕr) A deep reflex; patient's leg is extended with

patella movable; examiner places index finger above patella, pushing down slightly, then striking this finger; the result is a kick-back of the patella.

This reflex is also known as the patellar reflex. It depends upon the femoral nerve for its afferents and efferents; its center is L_{2-4}.

reflex, tendon The contraction of a muscle in response to tapping its tendon; for example the triceps, quadriceps femoris (patellar), and gastrocnemius (Achilles or ankle) reflexes.

reflex, thumb-chin See *reflex, palmomental.*

reflex time, central See *facilitation.*

reflex, triceps (trī'seps) A deep reflex; the patient's forearm, partly flexed at the elbow, is held by the examiner; the striking of the tendon just above the olecranon process results in extension of the forearm. This reflex depends upon the radial nerve for its afferents and efferents; its center is C_{6-7}.

reflex, ulnar (ul'nĕr) A deep reflex; also known as the flexion reflex of the wrist; when the styloid process of the ulna is tapped, the wrist flexes (pronation and adduction of the hand). This reflex depends on the median nerve for its afferents and efferents; its center is C_{6-8}.

reflex, wrist See. *reflex, radial; reflex, ulnar.*

refractory Resistant, unresponsive, unmanageable, obstinate, stubborn. In neurophysiology, the refractory period is the time following stimulation during which a nerve or muscle remains unresponsive to a second stimulus. The absolute refractory period is that during which there is no response to any stimulus; the relative refractory period is that during which response can be elicited only if the stimulus is very strong.

refusal, school See *phobia, school.*

regimen The specific details of a treatment plan, including the scheduling and regulation of diet, medication, and other therapeutic measures designed to operate over a period of time. The term regime is often used incorrectly in this sense.

registration In learning psychology, registration refers to impressibility or notation ability and implies either the ability to notice, or the ability to make a record, or both. Impaired registration of recent impressions is the most striking symptom of Korsakov's psychosis. See *memory*.

regression From the psychiatric point of view *regression* refers to the act of returning to some earlier level of adaptation. The mentally healthy individual progresses through many so-called levels. Following the designations of Freud, they are (1) intrauterine; (2) infancy (early and late; extending from birth to approximately the fifth year; this period includes, among other things, the phases of oral, anal, and genital organization); (3) latency (extending from about the age of five to puberty; one of its chief characteristics is sublimation); (4) puberty (beginning at the onset of manhood or womanhood and continuing for two or three years; one of its main attributes is adult sexuality); (5) adolescence (beginning at the termination of puberty and ending in the early or middle twenties; its principal characteristics revolve around the reality-principle, heterosexuality, and sublimated interest); (6) adulthood (extending from the termination of the adolescent period to senescence; the characteristics of adolescence are amplified during this stage); (7) climacterium; (8) senescence (the phase of decadence).

When a person, say, at the age of forty, begins to show symptoms of schizophrenia and subsequently undergoes deep regression, he sometimes passes through the various levels of adaptation formerly lived through by him. Thus, with the abandonment of the qualities of adulthood, he regressively becomes, so to speak, adolescent, pubertal, puerile, and finally infantile; he may also regress to a stage resembling that of the intrauterine period of existence. As a rule, regression in schizophrenia or in any of the psychogenic psychiatric disorders is accomplished by means of symbolic manifestations. From the psychoanalytic standpoint, regression and *fixation* (q.v.) are commonly associated with each other. When fixation is intense, frustrations on the part of reality may easily lead to regression. But internal frustrations are even more important, according to Freud.

'According to the concept of finality, causes are understood as means to an end. A simple example is the process of regression. Regarded causally, regression is determined, for example, by "mother fixation." But from the final standpoint, the libido returns to the mother-imago in order to find there the memory associations by means of which further development can take place, as, for instance, from an emotional system into an intellectual system.' (Jung, C.G. *Contributions to Analytical Psychology*, tr. by baynes, H.G. and C.F., Kegan Paul, trench, trubner, London, 1928)

regressive EST See *therapy, regressive electro-shock*.

rehabilitation The use of all forms of physical medicine in conjunction with psychosocial adjustment and vocational retraining in an attempt to achieve maximal function and adjustment, and to prepare the patient physically, mentally, socially, and vocationally for the fullest possible life compatible with his abilities and disabilities. Rehabilitation is a dynamic, purposeful program in which, ideally, activities are scheduled for each patient for the entire day; such schedules are built around activities prescribed by the physician, with guidance, psychological services, adult education, prevocational shop training, and directed socialization supplementing the prescribed therapy and retraining.

Rehabilitation aims to restore a handicapped person to a situation in which he can make best use of his residual capacities within as normal as possible a social context. The handicaps themselves are of two varieties: *primary*—the chronic symptoms that are an inherent part of illness plus the accumulated losses of skills through illness; and *secondary*—unhealthy personal reactions to illness plus unfavorable, inappropriate attitudes toward the handicapped person that develop in his relatives, employers, hospital staff, etc. (see *syndrome, social break-down.*) In general, rehabilitation techniques are more applicable to decreasing or preventing secondary handicaps, and to increasing social acceptability of patients, than they are to modifying or removing chronic symptoms of psychosis.

The chief areas to which rehabilitative efforts are directed are: (1) the highest degree of physical improvement; (2) vocational placement that enables the patient to work at maximal capacity; and (3) satisfactory adjustment in personal and social relationships so the patient can again function as a useful member of society.

Rehabilitation is some times called the fourth leg of medical practice, the others being prevention, diagnosis, and treatment.

rehearsal, obsessional A preliminary 'try-out' often used by obsessional patients, who must carry out their compulsions but at the same time try to make their behavior conform to the requirements of the social milieu. In the obsessional rehearsal the patient performs his compulsion, but surveys the scene to determine how he can best work his compulsive activity into the pattern of behavior expected of him at some later date. Reik cites the case of the man whose compulsion was a stamping of the foot to ward off danger as he crossed the border of a country. The patient had arranged to go driving with a woman friend, and their tour was to include crossing a border. On the day before their meeting, the patient drove out to the border and surveyed the scene.

On the following day, when he was in his car with the woman friend, he was able to introduce a discussion of waltz music at just the right moment, so that when the car did cross the border he could beat time with his foot. In this way his compulsion could be performed without alerting anyone to its pathological features. The obsessional rehearsal was necessary so that the patient would know when he was approaching the border, and so know when to introduce his discussion of waltz music. (Reik, T. *American Imago 2*, 86, 1941)

The obsessional neurotic also often shows peculiar deliberations and anticipations in thought. These are test phantasies, which Reik calls thought-rehearsals.

reification (rē-if-i-kā'shun) Treating the abstract as though it were concrete; a type of thinking seen often in schizophrenia but observable also is essentially normal subjects.

reinforcement In neurophysiology, facilitation; i.e. the enhancement of response to a stimulus by simultaneous excitation of response(s) in other neural circuits, as when the knee jerk is facilitated by having the subject clasp his hands tightly at the same time that his patellar tendon is tapped. In conditioning theory, reinforcement refers to re-introduction of the original, unconditioned stimulus along with the conditioned stimulus, thus strengthening the conditioned response; reinforcement in this sense is sometimes loosely referred to as reward.

reinforcement, Jendrassik (Ernst Jendrassik, Slovakian physician, 1858-1922) A weak response of the knee-jerk may often be reinforced, that is, strengthened, by having the patient grasp his own hands and pull vigorously on them.

reinforcement, reactive 'For repression is often achieved by means of an excessive reinforcement of the thought contrary to the one which is to be repressed. This process I call *reactive reinforcement,* and the thought which asserts itself exaggeratedly in consciousness and (in the same way as a prejudice) cannot be removed I call a *reactive thought.'* (Freud, S. *Collected Papers*, vol. 3, tr. by Strachey, A. and J., Leonard and Virginia Woolf, Hogarth Press, London, 1925)

reinstinctualization (rē-in-stinkt-choo-al-ī-zā'shun) Deneutralization of drive energy which would normally be available to the ego for the execution of its various functions. As a result, the functions may be affected adversely by the wishes or conflicts arising from the drives. Reinstinctualization is one aspect of the phenomenon of regression.

In hysterical blindness, for example,

the neutralized drive energy which made seeing possible regardless of inner conflict has been lost to the ego; the energy is deneutralized or reinstinctualized so that the function of seeing must be suspended just as the drive itself (aggression or sexuality) must be denied.

reintegration See *integration*.

rejuvenation (rē-joō-ve-nā'shun) A special *vasectomy* operation introduced by Steinach to mitigate in men certain pathological symptoms of old age, sexual impotence, hypertrophy of the prostate, or eunuchoidism.

While the ordinary vasectomy technique resulting in sterilization is bilateral and leaves the proximal end of the seminal ducts open, the 'rejuvenating' operation is performed unilaterally and provides for ligatures at both ends of the given vas deferens. The effect of rejuvenation is said to be achieved by a renewed activity of the proliferating and regenerating interstitial secretory tissue of the testicles, which is considered to be the hormone-bearing apparatus mainly responsible in men for sexual libido and potency, as well as by an equally favorable response of the other endocrine glands.

No similar surgical technique has as yet been developed for the rejuvenation of women.

relapse A patient who has recovered or improved and who subsequently suffers a recurrence of symptoms is said to have experienced a relapse.

relatedness The interrelation between two or more people who reciprocally influence each other, as patient-therapist, mother-child, etc. Normal relatedness is based on security in interpersonal relations and in large part is a result of early childhood experiences. S. Arieti (*Archives of General Psychiatry 6*, 112-122, 1962) emphasizes that *basic trust* is essential for the development of normal or satisfactory relatedness. 'Basic trust is an "atmospheric feeling" which predisposes one to expect "good things" and is a prerequisite to a normal development of self-esteem. . . . The mother expects the child

to become a healthy and mature person. The child later perceives this faith of the mother and accepts it. . . . He finally introjects this trust of the significant adults, and he trusts himself.'

relatedness, functional The arrangement of objects that are organically and dynamically related to each other: for example, placing woodworking tools near the woodworking bench and nails and other objects involved in woodworking near by; placing drawing paper near crayons and paints in the proximity of an easel.

relationship, inversion of 'A transposition of natural roles, as a young girl taking the mother's responsibilities or place in the home, or an adult playing the child's role in the family group.' (Hamilton, G. *A Medical Social Terminology*, Presbyterian Hospital, New York, 1930)

relationship, mother-child See *mother-child relationship*.

release In neurology, the removal of the inhibitory effect of higher centers on the activity of lower nervous centers. In psychiatry, a form of psychotherapy in which the patient is allowed to express wishes, thoughts and impulses which he is unable to discharge adequately under usual environmental conditions; in this sense, release is approximately equivalent to catharsis. In child psychiatry, release therapy refers to the use of play methods as an avenue for the expression of the child's anxieties.

release phenomena See *phenomena, release*.

releaser, social Any object or situation which serves as an adequate stimulus to instinctive behavior; e.g. the shadow of a toy airplane moving overhead under certain conditions will make new-born chicks run for cover, as if they had sighted a flying hawk. Permanent modification of behavior by a social releaser is termed *imprinting* (q.v.).

releasing mechanism, inherited See *instinct*.

reliability The degree to which a test measures consistently; the dependability of a measure; the standard deviation is used as a measure of variability and when so used is known as the standard error. See *deviation, mean.* Reliability is inversely proportional to the standard error.

REM Rapid eye movement. See *dream.*

reminiscence Recalling or recollection of past experiences, particularly when the recall has a 'now you see it, now you don't' quality. In contrast to memory, reminiscence consists of a peculiarly irregular alternation between remembering and forgetting so that a memory apparently lost suddenly appears, while one that was just there disappears.

remission Abatement of the symptoms and signs of a disorder or disease. The abatement may be partial or complete.

remorse Feelings of regret or guilt about something that has been done; Freud differentiated between remorse and guilt, in that the latter refers to aggressive wishes that have not yet been satisfied.

renifleur (rē-nē-flēr′) See *osphresiolagniac.*

renunciation, instinctual Disavowal of and refusal, on the part of the ego, to' satisfy an instinctual (id) demand, for any number of reasons. In the first place, instinctual renunciation takes place in obedience to the reality principle when the satisfying action would bring serious danger to the ego from the outside world. In this case, the unsatisfied instincts would engender a lasting painful tension unless the strength of the instinctual urge were diminished through a displacement of its energies. Second, instinctual renunciation takes place in obedience to the demands of the superego. That is, the ego will not satisfy the instincts if such a satisfying would run counter to the individual's conscience, the prohibitions of his superego. In this case, too, painful tension will spring from the unsatisfied instinct. When, however, the instinctual renunciation takes place because of the superego's objections, it brings about, besides the pain, 'a gain in

pleasure to the ego—as it were, or substituted satisfaction.' This gain in pleasure through obedience to the superego is a direct outgrowth of the child's relationship to its parents. The child is concerned with retaining his parents' love. He achieved this by renouncing his instincts and, instead, obeying his parents' precepts and thus avoiding a threatened loss of love. This gives him security and satisfaction. In later life, 'the super-ego is the successor and representative of the parents (and educators)' and 'perpetuates their functions almost without a change.' Thus the ego is concerned with retaining the love and appreciation of the superego, which it feels as relief and satisfaction, a pleasurable feeling. This will occur when an instinctual renunciation, a sacrifice to the superego, has taken place. (Freud, S. *Moses and Monotheism,* Hogarth Press, London, 1939)

repersonalization (rē-pēr-sun-al-i-zā′-shun) Morton Prince suggested this term in place of *hypnotism.*

repetition-compulsion 'The blind impulse to repeat earlier experiences and situations quite irrespective of any advantage that doing so might bring from a pleasure-pain point of view.' (Jones, E. *Papers on Psycho-Analysis,* 4th ed., Wood, Baltimore, 1938)
  The impulse to redramatize or to re-enact some earlier emotional experience. The principle is more fundamental, according to Freud, than the pleasure-principle and generally differs widely from it, in that the experience repeated is usually a painful one, that contains 'no potentiality of pleasure and which could at no time have been' satisfactory.
  'It must be explained that we are able to postulate the principle of a *repetition-compulsion* in the unconscious mind, based upon instinctual activity and probably inherent in the very nature of the instincts—a principle powerful enough to overrule the pleasure-principle, lending to certain aspects of the mind their daemonic character, and still very clearly expressed in the tendencies of small children.' (Freud, S. *Collected Papers,* vol. 4, tr. by Riviere, J., Leonard and Virginia Woolf and The Institute of Psychoanalysis, London, 1924-25)

repetition-reaction See *repetition-compulsion.*

replacement In psychiatric occupational therapy the substitution of normal and healthy thoughts and actions for unhealthy, abnormal ones. The means used to achieve this result include the employment of various activities such as the handicrafts, recreation, and other interests of a constructive nature.

replacement-formation See *formation, replacement.*

replacement-memory See *memory, replacement.*

representation, coitus (kō'i-tus) The representation of sexual intercourse in terms of symptom formations or by other symbolizations. 'In this analysis the girl's stammering proved to be determined by the libidinal cathexis of speaking as well as of singing. The rise and fall of the voice and the movements of the tongue represented coitus.' (Klein, M. *Contributions to Psycho-analysis* 1921-1945, Hogarth Press, London, 1948)

representations, collective 'The concepts which embody the objectives of group activity.' (Park, R.E. and Burgess, E.W. *Introduction to the Science of Sociology,* University of Chicago Press, Chicago, 1921)

representatives, instinct The psychic manifestations, such as strivings and emotions which ally themselves with ideas and give rise to wishes, of an instinct or drive. The instincts are not observable directly but are expressed by means of such representatives.

repress To force material from the realm of consciousness into the unconscious; to prevent material which was never conscious from gaining the level of consciousness.

repressed, return of the The return to consciousness of an idea or set of ideas that had been repressed into the sphere of the unconscious.

'So far as we know at present, it seems probable that the two [i.e. substitute-formation and symptom-formation] are widely divergent, that it is not the repression itself which produces substitute-formations and symptoms but that these later constitute indications of a *return of the repressed* and owe their existence to quite other processes.' (Freud, S. *Collected Papers,* vol. 4, tr. by Riviere, J., Leonard and Virginia Woolf and The Institute of Psychoanalysis, London, 1924-25)

repression The active process of keeping out and ejecting, banishing from consciousness, ideas or impulses that are unacceptable to it.

When an instinct-presentation (i.e. an idea or group of ideas charged with affect) is painful to the contents of consciousness, an effort is made to thrust it into the sphere of the unconscious. It is possible to reduce to a minimum the influence of such an instinct-presentation by first breaking it up into its two basic components: the idea and the affective charge. This means that there are three things that are subject to repression: (1) the instinct-presentation; (2) the idea; (3) the affect. In many instances, when the entire instinct cannot be successfully repressed, either the ideational or the affective part may be. If the idea is repressed, the affect with which it was associated may be transferred to another idea (in consciousness) that has no apparent connection with the original idea. Or, if the affect is repressed, the idea, remaining, so to speak, alone in consciousness may be linked with a pleasant affect. Finally, if the whole instinct-presentation is repressed, it may at some later time return to consciousness in the form of a symbol.

For example, a son may consciously hate his father. The idea and the affect are repellent to him. He may repress both, but if the idea is strongly charged with affect, it strives to re-enter consciousness. It may return to consciousness in disguised form, for example, as hatred for some superior, unconnected with the father. If the idea alone of the father is repressed, the hate may be transferred to someone else, who is not recognized as standing for the father. If the hate alone is repressed, the idea (father) may be cathected with love; in this last instance the hate may return to consciousness to be connected with someone not known to be a father-substitute.

All the foregoing observations refer to *repression proper,* which Freud at times calls *after-expulsion,* because the material repressed is that which was once in the conscious realm.

There is another subdivision called *primal repression.* The ego has also the task of keeping repressed in the unconscious the material that has never been in consciousness. 'Now we have reason for assuming *a primal repression,* a first phase of repression, which consists in a denial of entry into consciousness to the mental (ideational) presentation of the instinct. This is accompanied by a *fixation;* the ideational presentation in question persists unaltered from then onwards and the instinct remains attached to it.' (Freud, S. *Collected Papers,* vol. 4, tr. by Riviere, J., Leonard and Virginia Woolf and The Institute of Psychoanalysis, London, 1924-25)

Primal repression is maintained by means of anti-cathexis, which Freud says 'is the sole mechanism of primal repression.'

Anna 'Freud pointed out that 'repression occupies a unique place among the defences. It accomplishes more than others, acting once only through the anti-cathexis. It is also the most ego-limiting, because whole tracts of mental life are withdrawn from the ego in repression. In distinguishing repression from the other mechanisms of defence, she says "it may be that these other methods (other defences) have only to complete what repression has left undone, or to deal with such prohibited ideas as return to consciousness when repression fails."' (Leveton, A.F. *International Journal of Psychoanalysis XLII,* 506, 1961)

According to Jung, repression plays an important role. For example, when the *superior function* is *thinking* (e.g. the extraverted thinking type), the *feeling* function is subordinated. When the individual tries to meet all the requirements of living by the *thinking function,* 'sooner or later—in accordance with outer circumstances and inner gifts—the forms of

life repressed [i.e. feeling, intuition and sensation] by the intellectual attitude become indirectly perceptible, through a gradual disturbance of the conscious conduct of life. Whenever disturbances of this kind reach a definite intensity, one speaks of a neurosis.' (Jung, C.G. *Psychological Types,* tr. by Baynes, H.G., Harcourt, Brace, New York and London, 1923)

repression, organic A special type of amnesia that occurs in cases of head injuries independently of any personal problems that the patient wishes to forget. It is a retroactive amnesia: as in (the so-called) psychogenic amnesia, the subject turns away from a part of his experiences. In organic repression, however, no specific personal motives are discernible. The person forgets, more or less extensively, the events of his life prior to the accident, as if he were trying to get rid of knowledge of his experiences, although such a desire is not present even in the subconscious.

repression, primal See *repression.*

repression proper See *repression.*

repression-resistance See *resistance, ego.*

repression, secondary Synonymous with *repression;* the word 'secondary' is seldom used.

repressive personality *Hysterical personality* (q.v.).

reproduction The creative process by which organic life is transmitted from one organism to a succession of new ones. Although the origin of new organisms takes place in very different ways, the ultimate aim and sense of the reproductive process is always to maintain the preservation of a species and to guarantee the continuity between successive generations.

Plants and the simplest types of animals originate by *asexual* or *vegetative* reproduction, which simply divides the parental body into two or more parts, each of which grows into a new organism. The division into two *equal* new cells usually occurs in unicellular organisms like amoebae and is called *fission.* However, even in the case of an *unequal* division, or *budding*, it holds true that the offspring can be expected to be practically identical with the parent. If differences between offspring and parents arise in asexual reproduction, they may primarily be attributed to *mutations* which do not depend on the type of reproduction and constitute the basis of most evolutionary developments. See *mutation*.

The typical form of *sexual* reproduction is biparental and presupposes the differentiation of a species into two sexes capable of producing individual germ cells. Among higher animals, the two types of specialized *sexual cells* or *gametes* are known as *spermatozoa* and *ova*, according to whether they are produced in the testis of a male or in the ovary of a female. At fertilization a male and a female gamete unite, the nucleus of one fusing completely with that of the other, and they form one *single* cell, the fertilized egg or *zygote*, from which a new organism develops by cell division.

Wherever sexual reproduction occurs, it is bound to lead to variations among the offspring as well as to differences between offspring and parents. Mature germ cells have only half of the chromosomes of the individual producing the germ cells, and homologous chromosomes are similar, but not usually identical. The nature of a germ cell depends on which of the two chromosomes it has received from each pair. See *miosis*.

In certain groups of animals, for instance in the honey-bee, an egg may develop into a new organism without having been fertilized by a spermatozoon. Such uniparental mode of reproduction is called *parthenogenesis* and is regarded as sexual, although offspring produced parthenogenetically have only one parent.

repulsion A modifying process in the recombination of genetic factors, which was discovered by Bateson and Punnett both as an exception to the Mendelian principle of independent assortment and as the antithesis of the phenomenon of *coupling* (q.v.). Its mechanism consists of an 'aversion' of the genes introduced by different parents to entering the same gametes, and its effect is similar to that of coupling, leading to the formation of an

excess of the parental combinations of genes and a deficiency of the new type of combinations.

According to Morgan's chromosome theory repulsion and coupling are manifestations of a single important phenomenon now usually called *linkage*.

rescue phantasy   See *romance, family*.

research, action Scientific study of ongoing process, such research being aimed toward achieving some improvement in the methods of the operating program.

residua, brain (re-zid'ū-à) See *neurogram*.

residual schizophrenia See *schizophrenia*.

residue, archaic Remnants of primitive mentality; see *function-engram*.

residue, night Persistence of any psychic material from sleeping and dreaming during the waking day; the manifest dream (i.e. the dream as remembered by the subject) is the most common example of night residue. The night residue persists because of failure of repression at the time the sleeper wakes, at least according to some theories of dream-function. See *dream*.

resignation, neurotic In Horney's terminology, avoidance of any part of reality that brings inner conflicts into awareness, whether by means of withdrawal into inactivity, pressured hyperactivity in all other parts of reality, or neurotic rebelliousness against all rules and regulations.

resistance 'The instinctive opposition displayed towards any attempt to lay bare the unconscious; a manifestation of the repressing forces.' (Jones, E. *Papers on Psycho-Analysis*, 4th ed., Wood, Baltimore, 1938) See *resistance, ego*.

resistance, character See *defense, character*.

resistance, conscious Freud's term for the intentional withholding of information by the patient because of distrust of the analyst, shame, fear of rejection, or the like. In his early work, Freud discovered that patients cannot maintain free association uninterruptedly, and sooner or later fail to mention something that occurs to them. They show other signs of difficulty with the treatment process—tardiness or failure to keep appointments, loss of interest in their own problems, and turning all their attention to trying to win the analyst's love or to engaging in a battle of wits with him, etc. Exhortation can usually induce the patient to overcome these conscious difficulties.

Unconscious resistance, on the other hand, is more significant and more difficult to overcome, arising as it does from the ego as a defense against uncovering the repressed material, which the ego constantly strives to avoid, since it produces anxiety. Unconscious resistance is more than a phenomenon appearing early in treatment and later overcome once and for all. It is a conservative force seeking to maintain the *status quo* and appearing throughout the analysis whenever significant data are under discussion. See *silence, selective.*

resistance, ego Much of the resistance to be overcome in analysis is produced by the ego, 'which clings tenaciously to its anti-cathexes.' In other words, the ego 'finds it difficult to turn its attention to perceptions and ideas the avoidance of which it had until then made a rule, or to acknowledge as belonging to it impulses which constitute the most complete antithesis to those familiar to it as its own.' This resistance of the ego is known more specifically as repression resistance. It is often unconscious. When the resistance has been made conscious, logical arguments are used to induce the ego to give it up, and the gains that will result therefrom are pointed out.

Freud describes two more categories of ego-resistance. One, which is of the same character as repression-resistance but exists specifically with reference to the analytical situation, is the transference-resistance: the repression constantly exerted by the ego is in this case related specifically to the person of the analyst and thus appears in the analysis in different and more definite ways than simple repression-resistance. The other (third) category of ego-resistance is related to the

gain of the illness. Symptoms in warding off dangerous instinctual impulses both relieve anxiety and serve as a means of gratifying these instinctual impulses. The ego opposes the renunciation of both the gratification and relief which are 'based upon the inclusion of the symptom in the ego.'

It should be added that in analysis there are also resistances which derive from sources other than the ego. These are (1) the 'resistance of the unconscious' or of the id, which derives from the 'repetition-compulsion,' and (2) the 'resistance of the super-ego,' which derives from 'the sense of guilt or need of punishment.' (Freud, S. *The Problem of Anxiety,* Norton, New York, 1936)

resistance, id A type of resistance, seen most clearly in patients in psychoanalytic treatment, that derives from the repetition compulsion and is manifested typically as situations of mistrust, grievance, depreciation, and the like—that dominate the analytic situation during periods of seeming stalemate. No matter how many interpretations are given by the analyst, and no matter how valid each interpretation seems to be, the same material continues to recur. 'In short, having exhausted the possibilities of resistance arising from the ego or the super-ego, we are faced with the bare fact that a set of presentations is being repeated before us again and again. That is, at the same time, a clue to the understanding of the situation, because the nearer we get to seemingly blind repetition, the nearer we are to a characteristic of instinctual excitation.' What has happened is that '. . . the id has made use of weakened ego defenses to exercise an increased attraction on preconscious presentations. . . . For this reason Freud described the manifestation as being the *resistance of mind.*' (Glover, E. The *Technique of Psycho-Analysis,* New York, International Universities Press, 1955) The only method with which to counter id-resistance is *working-through* (q.v.).

resistance, stage of See *syndrome, general adaptation.*

resistance, superego Also called the *nega-*

tive therapeutic reaction; a type of resistance encountered in patients in psychoanalytic treatment in which the need for punishment, as manifested in guilt feelings and 'masochistic' behavior, continues to produce symptoms and is the only barrier to their resolution. Superego resistance is most frequently manifested by obsessionals whose anxiety is a fear of the loss of the superego's love.

resistance, transference See *transference-resistance.*

response, barrier See *barrier.*

response, conditioned See *conditioning.*

response, galvanic skin See *reflex, psychogalvanic.*

response (in marriage) Understanding, co-operative, sympathetic, or affectionate interreaction between two persons married to each other. 'The human being appears to have a basic need to live with some one of the other sex to the fullest possible meaning of the words "live with." This need has been termed the need for "response." Mowrer says: "The desire for response is universal among human beings. In the marriage relation it involves the demonstration of affection, the sharing of interests, aspirations, and ideals by husband and wife."' (Lemkau, P.V. *Mental Hygiene in Public Health,* McGraw-Hill, New York, 1949)

response, negativistic (neg-à-tiv-is'tik) A tendency to do the exact opposite of what is requested or ordered. When asked to open his eyes, the patient shuts them tightly; when asked to come forward, he backs away. This condition is most common in the catatonic type of schizophrenia. See *negativism.*

responsibility, limited See *insanity, partial.*

response, penetration See *barrier.*

responsibility, criminal The culpability of a person, as determined by due process of law, for any of his actions that are defined as criminal. Determination of such responsibility is a legal function, not a psychiatric one, although a psychiatrist may be called upon to present evidence to the court in order to aid the judge or jury in reaching a decision as to responsibility. Determination of responsibility varies with the laws of the state in which the accused is being tried, but in general all states base their laws on three famous judicial decisions concerning criminal responsibility:

1. *the M'Naghten* (or McNaughton) *rule,* also known as the *right and wrong test* or the *knowledge test*—In 1843, Daniel M'Naghten shot and killed Drummond, private secretary to Sir Robert Peel. He had mistaken Drummond for the latter. For some years, M'Naghten had suffered from delusions of persecution and had finally woven Sir Robert Peel into his delusional system. He was determined to right his imaginary wrongs by killing Peel. When he was brought to trial the court recognized that the killing was an outcome of his delusions of persecution; he was declared of unsound mind and committed to an institution for the criminally insane. Following this trial, the Judges of England enunciated two rules to determine the responsibility of an accused who pleads insanity as a defense: (a) to establish such a defense the accused, at the time the act was committed, must be shown to have been laboring under such defect of reason as not to know the nature and quality of the act he was doing, or (b) if he did know it, he did not know that what he was doing was wrong.

2. *the irresistible impulse test,* recommended as an addition to the M'Naghten rule in 1922—'a person charged criminally with an offense is irresponsible for his act when the act is committed under an impulse which the prisoner was by mental disease in substance deprived of any power to resist.'

3. *the Durham decision*—a 1954 ruling by the United States Court of Appeals that 'an accused is not criminally responsible if his unlawful act was the product of mental disease or mental defect.' Prior to this decision, psychiatric testimony relating to the mental status of the accused was confined to a determination of whether the accused could distinguish right and wrong, or acted under an irre-

sistible impulse at the time of the offense. Under the Durham test, however, the psychiatrist may give any relevant testimony concerning the mental illness at issue.

R.E.S.T. Regressive electric shock therapy. See *therapy, regressive electroshock.*

rest-cure The term is usually associated with the psychiatrist Silas Weir Mitchell (1829-1914), who stressed the value of rest, environmental change, fattening diet, massage, and mild exercise. It has not achieved much distinction as an isolated method of treatment, though the individual procedures (rest, environmental change, etc.) are known to be highly valuable.

rest tremor See *tremor.*

restitution See *schizophrenia, restitutional symptoms.*

restless legs syndrome *Tachyathetosis* (q.v.).

restraint In the treatment of the violently psychotic patient, a measure whereby he is prevented (by the camisole or restraint-sheet) from doing injury to himself or others.

restraint, situational Employed especially in activity group psychotherapy, this type of restraint is differentiated from direct or authoritative restraint in that it is practiced by creating a situation which by its very nature will prevent the individual from committing dangerous or destructive acts. In activity group psychotherapy, windows are screened so that they will not be broken and furniture is placed in such a way that the children will not need to or cannot move it about. Placing materials according to their *functional relatedness* is also a form of situational restraint.

resymbolization A new symbolization adopted in the life of a patient on regaining a healthy mentality. 'A recovered patient, as he makes a new adaptation to life, must redefine all his conceptions, particularly those related to his own con-

flict. This is essentially a resymbolization of his life concepts and in itself denotes a healthy attitude and a good prognosis. ... Resymbolization is a universal phenomenon in our daily life and of which the resymbolization as used by psychotics is only one of the pathological forms.' (Karpman, B. *Psychoanalytic Review* 9, 348, 1922)

retardation Slowness or backwardness of intellectual development; when used in this sense, *mental retardation* is the usual phrase. Slowness of response, a slowing down of thinking and/or a decrease in psychomotor activity; in this later sense, the term *psychomotor retardation* is the appropriate phrase. Psychomotor retardation is characteristic of clinical depressions.

retardation, Amsterdam type See *syndrome, de Lange.*

retardation, developmental See *acceleration, developmental*

retardation, mental Mental deficiency, intellectual inadequacy, feeblemindedness, hypophrenia, oligophrenia, oligergasia. In the 1968 revision of psychiatric nomenclature (DSM-II), mental retardation refers to subnormal general intellectual functioning that originates during the developmental period and is associated with impairment of learning and social adjustment, or maturation, or both. It is subdivided on the basis of degree of defect, and on the basis of etiology, as follows:
310 Borderline mental retardation (I.Q. 68-83)
311 Mild mental retardation (I.Q. 52-67)
312 Moderate mental retardation (I.Q. 36-51)
313 Severe mental retardation (I.Q. 20-35)
314 Profound mental retardation (I.Q. under 20)
315 Unspecified mental retardation (when level of functioning cannot be evaluated precisely)
Etiology is coded as a fourth digit of the above categories:

.0 Following infection and intoxication (thus 313.0 is severe mental retardation due to infectious or toxic agent)
.1 Following trauma or physical agent
.2 With disorders of metabolism, growth, or nutrition
.3 Associated with gross brain disease (postnatal)
.4 Associated with diseases and conditions due to unknown prenatal influence
.5 With chromosomal abnormality
.6 Associated with prematurity
.7 Following major psychiatric disorder
.8 With psychosocial (environmental) deprivation
.9 With other (and unspecified) condition

Intellectual deficit, or mental subnormality, denotes a lack of equipment, motivation, or opportunity to acquire knowledge at the usual pace. By some, mental deficiency is used specifically to refer to cases with demonstrable cerebral impairment. Others, however, do not make such a distinction or even use the terms in exactly the opposite way. Thus, W.F. Windle (*Science 140;* 1186, 1963) defines mental retardation as "An organic condition of arrested or limited neural development that blocks successful evolution of the capacity of the brain to function; as a result of this block, behavior and (at least in man) intellectual ability are impaired. Forms of behavioral and intellectual impairment that are related solely to socio-environmental factors are excluded, since in these cases there is no detectable pathology.' See also *amentia; dementia.*

Fashions in labeling this group change almost from year to year; in the 1960's, mental retardation was the favorite appellation, and justifiably so in that it does not imply that inheritance or constitutional defects are always the cause of mental retardation. In 1941, Gregg demonstrated the association of rubella in the first trimester of pregnancy with mental retardation and thereby showed that the condition could result not from an inferior constitution but from what had happened to the child. Since then, there has been increasing recognition of the importance of psychosocial factors in exaggerating or even, in some cases, producing mental retardation, and two major approaches to such factors have developed.

The *stimulation theory* supposes that mental retardation may be a consequence of lack of stimulation, lack of opportunities, or deprivation. The *disorder theory* regards mental retardation as a disorder of mental processes due to failure of the family to give sufficient protection from stress or overstimulation during critical periods of learning in early childhood. As with some habits in animals (see *imprinting; releaser, social*), there are believed to be optimal periods in the human during which learning proceeds rapidly, although at other times those habits will be learned only slowly or not at all. Thus a child may not learn because family conditions or other elements in his environment are not favorable to acquiring the habit when he is in a critical or sensitive period; or if he is exposed to adverse circumstances soon after acquiring a habit, it may regress and his skill may disintegrate; and even if later moved into more favorable circumstances he may fail to learn because the sensitive period has passed.

retardation, mental, psychosis with Occasionally, mental defectives or those suffering from feeblemindedness may show psychotic reactions which are usually of an acute transitory nature. These psychotic manifestations include episodes of excitement with depression, hallucinatory attacks, or paranoid trends.

retardation, psychopathology of Primary psychopathology of the mental retardation syndrome includes the intellectual impairment plus the characteristics of emotional development that are more closely related to the degree of retardation than to any other factors such as deprivation. The primary psychopathology consists of the intellectual impairment or specific learning difficulty, the slow rate of development, and disturbances in the quality of emotional development such as impairment in differentiation of ego functions producing infantile or immature character structure, nonpsychotic autism, repetitiveness, inflexibility, passivity, etc. (Webster, T.G. *American Journal of Psychiatry 120,* 37, 1963)

retardation, reading A term suggested by Rabinovitch *et al.* (1954) to describe all subjects in whom the level of reading achievement is two years or more below the mental age obtained in performance tests. See *reading, disabilities of.*

retardation, simple See *melancholia; psychosis, manic-depressive.*

retention Non-evacuation of the bladder or bowels. In psychological testing, retention refers to the ability to learn, remember, or recall (see *memory*). In psychoanalytic psychology, retention refers to any number of traits or symptoms believed to develop on the basis of the need or desire to withhold the feces during the anal stage of development; collecting mania, stubbornness, secretiveness, niggardliness, etc. are generally considered to be instances of anal retention or retentiveness.

retention, anal In psychoanalysis, the holding back of the fecal mass as part of toilet training and the characterologic or symptomatic carry-overs of this in later life. Frugality, for example, is considered to be a continuation of the anal habit of retention; stubbornness and obstinacy are more complicated developments of this same habit which are related to the child's ability to spite parental efforts by tightening his sphincters. Psychodynamically, anal retention is seen to contain two components, fear of loss of body contents or of control over instinctual impulses, and enjoyment of erogenous pleasure; and later anal character traits represent an outgrowth of one or the other or both of these components. See *anal-erotism; character, anal.*

reticular activating system See *formation, reticular.*

reticular formation See *formation, reticular.*

reticulum (re-tik'ū-lum) (L., a little net) *Biol.* A finely meshed network in a cell or in some delicate tissue system.

rétifism (rā'ti-fiz'm) (Rétif de la Bretonne (1734-1806), a famous French educator, known for this sexual perversion.) Ivan Bloch coined this term for fetishism of the foot and shoe; in this form of sexual perversion the foot or shoe or both possess the value of the genital organs for the rétifist. A patient 'loved,' as he put it, the female shoe to the same degree that 'others are attracted to the female genitals.' He looked upon the shoe as if it were a real person—gaining full and complete sexual satisfaction, including 'intercourse,' with the object; he used it as an agency of masturbation.

retinodiencephalic degeneration See *syndrome, Lawrence-Moon-Biedl.*

retreat, vegetative The tendency of some neurotic persons to meet an inimical or dangerous reality situation not by appropriate self-assertive behavior and actions, but by recourse to infantile or childish function of the visceral apparatus, which, to them, anachronistically stands for praise or succor from strong or omnipotent parents. It thus represents a return to the pseudo-power of the 'helpless' and dependent child and warrants the descriptive term 'regressive,' because it is a resort to the old infantile ways of handling frustration and stress. See also *hypoglycemia.*

A common example of this phenomenon is the man who develops diarrhea when in danger, instead of carrying out an appropriate action directed against the dangerous enemy or situation. As a harbinger of protection and approval, this vegetative reaction, or achievement, is inappropriate for adult life, but logical for infancy, where it brought mother's care. There is on record the case of a married woman who found herself sucking her thumbs whenever thwarted or rejected by her husband. (Alexander, F. *Psychosomatic Medicine,* Norton, New York, 1950)

retrieval See *memory.*

retroflexion A turning backwards, especially upon the self. In psychoanalysis, the term is used particularly by Rado, who speaks of retroflexed rage, i.e. one's own rage turned back upon the self. See *psychodynamics, adaptational.*

retrogenesis (ret-rō-jen'e-sis) The regression to earlier or lower stages that are often essential before further development can be achieved; Staercke termed it the *Law of Retrogenesis*. 'It is remarkable to know in the matter of conscience the universal rule once more applies: that that which is newly formed does not develop from the highest (in the sense of the most recent) existing formation but out of a lower part which has remained hitherto undeveloped. Every line of development is a blind-alley: the new sprouts from a bud which is further, sometimes much further, down. The path of development is not that of *evolution* but of *revolution*. Only out of temporary chaos does renewal proceed.' (A. Staercke, *International Journal of Psychoanalysis X*, 186, 1929)

retrograde See *amnesia, retrograde.*

retrogression A return to earlier behavior or techniques when more recently developed techniques prove unsatisfactory. The term is synonymous with *regression* but avoids the psychoanalytic connotations of the latter.

retropulsion Rapid running backward with short steps, in paralysis agitans; as if drawn by an uncontrollable force.

return of the repressed See *repressed, return of the.*

revenge Retaliation; vindication; the wish of the injured person to retaliate against the aggressor, which often leads in the neurotic to a fear of retaliation and a consequent need to repress or deny his own aggression.

reverie, revery A type of phantasy in which the subject is lost in thought or abstract musing which is not purposively directed.

reverie, hypnagogic (hip-nà-goj'ik) The phantasies occurring between sleep and waking. Kubie has shown that the institution of a state of hypnagogic reverie can bring about easier access to unconscious material. When employing hypnosis, the analyst can take advantage of it by

permitting his patients to associate freely in the waking state, until a resistance is manifested. Hypnosis is then induced and the last few statements uttered by the patient before the onset of resistance are repeated to him. Usually free association will continue during hypnosis from this point on.' (Wolberg, L.R. *Hypnoanalysis*, Grune and Stratton, New York, 1945)

reversal In psychoanalysis the reversal of an instinct into its opposite means a change of it from an active to a passive instinct or vice versa. The *aim* of the instinct does not change; its object does. For example, the destructive instinct may be directed outwardly, as sadism, or it may be turned against oneself, as masochism. 'The reversal here concerns only the aims of the instincts. The passive aim (to be tortured . . .) has been substituted for the active aim (to torture . . .).' (Freud, S. *Collected Papers*, vol. 4, tr. by Riviere, J., Leonard and Virginia Woolf and The Institute of Psychoanalysis, London, 1924-25)

Freud says also that there may be *reversal* of content. 'Reversal of content is found in the single instance of the change of love into hate.' (ibid) See *opposite, reversal into the.*

reversal-formation See *reaction-formation.*

reversal, of affect See *affect, inversion of.*

reversal, sex The phenomenon in which chromosomal sex, as determined by any of the various sex chromatin tests, differs from anatomical sex. Etiology is unknown; chromosomal abnormalities, early deficiency of primordial germ-cells, and/or hormonal imbalance have been suggested as playing an important role.

It has been produced in many animals 'to the extent of changing the histological character of the gonads and to some extent the ducts, but the change has seldom gone far enough in an adult animal, to permit the individual to function as of the new sex.' (Shull, A.F. *Heredity*, 3rd ed., McGraw-Hill, New York and London, 1938)

The most remarkable instance of complete sex reversal was observed by Crew, in an adult hen that had laid normal eggs producing normal chicks, before she changed into a cock that became the father of two normal chicks. An autopsy showed that the original ovary had been destroyed by a tumor, and a testis had been produced in its place by regeneration.

reversion A genetic phenomenon which occurs in crosses between true-breeding varieties and produces offspring resembling a remote ancestor more than either parent. These 'throwbacks' had been observed for many years by plant and animal breeders, but for lack of satisfactory explanation had been regarded as due to some mysterious force which caused the retention and subsequent reappearance of a remote ancestral trait.

According to E.W. Sinnott and L.C. Dunn (*Principles of Genetics*, 3rd ed., McGraw-Hill, New York and London, 1939) every kind of reversion is now readily explained in terms of ordinary Mendelian inheritance. 'The reappearance of an old trait is usually due to the reunion of the two or more factors, necessary for its production, which had become separated in the history of the plant or animal.'

Reversion is also used synonymously with regression or retrogression; less commonly, it is used synonymously with reversal-formation or reaction-formation.

revindication, delirium of, insanity of (rē-vin-di-kā'shun, dē-lir'i-um) See *interpretation, delirium of.*

revolution 'A sudden and far reaching change, a major break in the continuity of development.' (Mensel, A. *Revolution and Counter-Revolution; Encyclopaedia of the Social Sciences*, vol. 13, Macmillan, New York, 1934, p. 367)

'A mass movement which seeks to change the mores by destroying the existing social order.' (Park, R.E. and Burgess, E.W. *Introduction to the Science of Sociology*, University of Chicago Press, Chicago, 1921)

Three major types of revolution are: *cultural,* where profound changes take place in the mores; *industrial,* where sud-

den changes result from technological discoveries and inventions; and *political,* where violent change takes place in the political order.

revolving door See *readmission.*

rhabdophobia (rab-dō-fō'bē-à) Fear of the rod, instrument of punishment.

rhathymia (ra-thī'mē-à) Outgoing, carefree, happy-go-lucky behavior such as is seen in so-called oral optimists.

rhembasmus (rem-baz'mus) Indecision, mental uncertainty.

rhinencephalon (rī-en-sef'a-lon) A phylogenetically old portion of the cerebral hemispheres that includes: olfactory bulb and tract, anterior perforated substance, subcallosal gyrus, hippocampus, uncus, amygdala, fornix, and anterior commissure. Rhinencephalon is sometimes used synonymously with olfactory brain. In man, the olfactory brain is overshadowed by the neocortex (isocortex), but olfaction appears to be important in the psychic apparatus of the human. The physiology of the rhinencephalon is poorly understood and is largely based on inferences drawn from its anatomical relations. Animal experiments indicate that the olfactory tract terminates in the prepyriform area, the amygdala, the periamygdaloid cortex, and the opposite olfactory bulb. Although the hippocampus is generally regarded as part of the olfactory system, it is to be noted that no anatomical connections of the hippocampus with the olfactory tract have been demonstrated. Instead, the hippocampus appears to be primarily an efferent system projecting to the medial and lateral mammillary nuclei of the hypothalamus, and as such it is probably concerned with control of autonomic functions. Rhinencephalic structures may exert an inhibitory effect on brain-stem mechanisms concerned with emotional expression. Lesions of these structures result in restlessness and hyperactivity. The limbic system is sometimes referred to as the 'visceral brain'; it includes the limbic lobe (Brodmann's area 24) and infolded hippocampus, and also certain subcortical structures: amygdala, septal nuclei, hypothalamus, anterior thalamic nuclei, parts of the basal ganglia, and the epithalamus.

rhinolalia (rin-ō-lā'lē-à) Nasality of speech. Rhinolalia is of two types: rhinolalia aperta, in which the passages at the back of the nose and mouth fail to close during speech; and rhinolalia clausa, in which obstructions in the nasopharynx interfere with nasal resonance.

rhombencephalon (rom-ben-sef'à-lon) Hindbrain (q.v.).

rhypophagy (rī-pof'à-jē) The eating of filth or excrement; scatophagy.

rhypophobia (rī-pō-fō'bē-à) Fear of dirt or filth.

ribonucleic acid See *chromosome*.

ribosomal RNA See *chromosome*.

riddance This term, coined by S. Rado, refers to 'many reflexes designed to eliminate pain-causing agents from the surface or inside of the body. The scratch reflex, the shedding of tears, sneezing, coughing, spitting, vomiting, colic bowel movement are but a few well-known instances of this principle of pain control in our bodily organization. This principle I have called the *riddance principle*, and its physiological embodiments the *riddance reflexes.*' ('Developments in the Psychoanalytic Conception and Treatment of the Neuroses,' *The Psychoanalytic Quarterly*, VIII, 434-35, 1939)

right and left When the concepts *right* and *left* appear in dreams they are understood in an ethical sense. 'The right-hand path always signifies the way to righteousness, the left-hand path the path to crime. Thus the left may signify homosexuality, incest, and perversion, while the right signifies marriage, relations with a prostitute, etc. The meaning is always determined by the particular moral standpoint of the dreamer.' (Stekel, W. *Bi-Sexual Love*, tr. by van Teslaar, J.S., Badger, Boston, 1922)

right and wrong test See *responsibility, criminal.*

right-handedness See *dextrality-sinistrality.*

right-left disorientation One of the symptoms of the *Gerstmann syndrome* (q.v.).

rigidity, affective When the emotions or affects remain constant in the face of topics that normally call for changes in affect, the condition is known as affective rigidity. Many patients with schizophrenia show no mood changes in spite of discussions covering a wide variety of experiences.

Rigidity of the affect, or affect-block, is common also in obsessive-compulsive neurosis. See *block, affect.*

rigidity, decerebrate (de-ser'e-brāt) A syndrome of exaggerated posture in continuous spasm of muscles produced by transection of the brain at a pre-pontine level. The extensor muscles are particularly affected and exhibit lengthening and shortening (clasp-knife) reactions.

rigidity, lead pipe *Rare.* (humorously, as lead possesses practically no rigidity) Waxy flexibility. See *catalepsy.*

ring, Kayser-Fleischer (Bernhard Kayser, German ophthalmologist, b. 1869, and Richard Fleischer, German physician, 1848-1909) See *degeneration, hepatolenticular.*

risk level *Confidence level* (q.v.).

rites, puberty In many primitive cultures it is customary for boys at puberty to undergo certain initiatory rites as a part of the religious pattern of that culture. One of the commonest rituals is a pretense of killing the boy and bringing him to life again. In another primitive group, part of the proceedings consists of knocking out a tooth and giving a new name to the boy being initiated, indicating thereby the change from youth to manhood. In still another tribe, the puberty rites comprise operations of circumcision and subincision. All of these ceremonies are conducted in absolute secrecy and only those already initiated may attend them. No female is ever permitted to witness these events.

ritual 'Formal behavior for occasions not given over to technological routine [which occur] both as the spontaneous invention of the individual, especially of the compulsion neurotic, and as a cultural trait.' (Benedict, R. *Ritual; Encyclopaedia of the Social Sciences,* vol. 13, Macmillan, New York, 1934, p. 397)

ritual-making One of Rado's subdivisions of obsessive attacks is called *bouts of ritual making:* repetitive sequences which must be continued until the patient is exhausted. Typically, these rituals are ceremonial, distortive, and stereotyped elaborations of some routine of daily life, such as bathing, dressing, and sexual activity.

rivalry 'A sublimated form of conflict where the struggle of individuals is subordinated to the welfare of the group.' (Park, R.E. and Burgess, E.W. *Introduction to the Science of Sociology,* University of Chicago Press, Chicago, 1921)

rivalry, sibling The usual family situation wherein brothers and sisters engage in an intense and highly emotional competition, one against the other, for the love, attention, affection, and approval of one or the other or both of the parents. This intense competition between rival sibs (brothers or sisters) can be an important determinant of later specific character or personality traits.

Sibling rivalry, however, is usually evaluated in relation to other important experiences in the child's early life, such as the oedipal relationship to the parents; the discovery of and reaction to sexual differences; that specific reaction which is called 'the castration complex'; self-comforting trends, such as thumb-sucking and masturbation, and conflicts concerning their prohibition and gratification.

RLS person A person who finds difficulty in pronouncing the sounds of *r, l, s;* by hardly justified extension—a *stammerer* (q.v.). See *stammering.*

RNA Abbreviation for ribonucleic acid. See *chromosome.*

role 'The pattern or type of behavior which the child—and the adult—builds up in terms of what others expect or demand of him.' (Young, K. *An Introductory Sociology,* American Book, New York, 1934)

An automatic, learned, goal directed pattern or sequence of acts developed under the influence of the significant people in the growing child's environment; such patterns provide the child with a repertoire of expected or appropriate responses to the behavior of those with whom he interacts. When the person's behavior does in fact conform with what is expected in a given situation or relationship, his role is termed *complementary* to the roles of the other people in the situation; such complementarity is desirable and comfortable. Non-complementarity or disequilibrium of roles, as occurs when people's expectations from others are disappointed, leads to disruption of interpersonal relationships and breakdowns in group living. See *complementarity; complementary.* Roles are labelled *explicit* when they are consciously motivated and exposed to observation and awareness of the interacting participants; roles are *implicit* when they are more remote from consciousness and awareness and often are not recognized as such by actor or participant. Typically, implicit roles express personality attributes originating in early internalizations or identifications; they are an outgrowth of early transactions between mother and child, child and teacher, etc.

romance, family A type of phantasy in which the subject maintains that he is not the child of his real parents, but is instead the offspring of other parents (usually of higher station). The rescue phantasy, of saving the life of the father (or king, or emperor, etc.) or of the mother, is a common variant of the family romance. Another variant, the *Mignon delusion,* is the fixed belief that one is the child of a distinguished family. Usually, the family romance arises on the basis of disillusionment with the real parents (who have failed to demonstrate the omnipotence with which the child has endowed them) and/or as a defense against the aggressive sexual elements of the oedipal period.

romance, memory In psychoanalysis, the phantasy standing between infantile impressions and later symptoms. Thus, in speaking of hysteria Freud says that the symptoms now no longer appeared as direct derivations of repressed memories of sexual experiences in childhood; but, on the contrary, it appeared that between the symptoms and the infantile impressions were interpolated the patient's phantasies (memory-romances), created mostly during the years of adolescence and relating on the one side to the infantile memories on which they were founded, and on the other side to the symptoms into which they were directly transformed.' (Freud, S. Collected Papers, vol. 2, tr. by Riviere, J., Leonard and Virginia Woolf and The Institute of Psychoanalysis, London, 1924-25)

Romberg sign See sign, Romberg.

rooming-in The modern concept in pediatrics which recognizes the essential unity of mother and child after the birth of the child in a hospital. The mother and child are housed in the same room, the infant's crib standing alongside or near the mother's bed. It is essentially a rooming-in of the baby with the mother. The usual hospital nursery plays no role in this practice. The rooming-in process permits the mother to touch, fondle, and caress her child, to feed it when it is hungry, and to diaper it when it soils. This is said to make her immediately familiar with her baby and to allay considerable anxiety in the mother as well as in the child.

root-pain Pain in the segmental area innervated by the affected nerve root, usually excited or intensified by coughing, sneezing, or changes of posture.

Rorschach test See test, Rorschach.

Rosenbach's sign See sign, Rosenbach.

Rosolimo's reflex See reflex, Rosolimo.

Ross-Jones test See test, Ross-Jones.

rotation See system, rotation.

RSBT Rhythmic sensory bombardment therapy. See therapy, rhythmic sensory bombardment.

R.T. Reaction time, also, recreation(al) therapy. See recreation.

rubella, congenital See retardation,

Rüdin, Ernst (b. 1874) (rü'din) German psychiatrist and geneticist.

rule, basic The fundamental precept governing the activity of the patient in psychoanalytic therapy: to think aloud, and by means of free association to overcome censorship and resistance to unconscious content. See association, free.

rule, M'Naghten (or McNaughton) See responsibility, criminal.

ruler, negative, of the soul See ego, negation of.

rum-fits See delirium tremens.

ruminate To regurgitate, remasticate and reswallow; to ponder; to meditate. See merycism.

ruminative tension state Obsessive ruminative tension state (q.v.).

Rumpf's sign See sign, Rumpf.

rupophobia (roo-pō-fō'bē-à) Same as rhypophobia.

Rush, Benjamin (1745-1813) Father of American psychiatry; first American to propose an original systematization of psychiatry.

rypophobia (rī-pō-fō'bē-à) Same as rhypophobia.

S

S An abbreviation for experimental subject or for stimulus; also used as a Rorschach scoring symbol to indicate a response to the white space on the card. Rorschach believed the S indicated habitual oppositional tendencies.

sabotage, masochistic The self-defeating attitude or behavior of some patients that aims unconsciously to provoke insult, punishment, scorn, etc. from the environment. It appears in many forms during analytic treatment, ranging from obstinate silence to insolent remarks and behavior directed against the analyst or the analytic setting. (Reik, T. *Masochism in Modern Man,* Farrar and Rinehart, New York, 1941)

sadism (sad'iz'm; often, although incorrectly, sād'iz'm) (After Donatien Alphonse Francois Sade, usually called Marquis de Sade (1740-1814), a French writer who described persons whose sexual pleasure depended upon inflicting cruelty upon others) A sexual perversion (302.6) in which orgasm is dependent upon torturing others or inflicting pain, ill-treatment and humiliation on others. Krafft-Ebing defined sadism as sexual emotions associated with the wish to inflict pain and use violence. Moll defined it as a state in which the sexual impulse is manifested as a tendency to strike, misuse, or humiliate the love object.

Viewed as a perversion, sadism is a defense against castration fears and fears of one's own sexual excitement. What might happen to the subject passively is done actively to others—'identification with the aggressor.' Further, the castration performed in the sadistic act is a symbolic one, not a real one, and such pseudo-castration assures the sadist that his fears are ungrounded. The sadist tries to force his victim to love him; this love is conceived of as a forgiveness, which removes the guilt feelings that interfere with sexual satisfaction.

While sadism is sometimes considered to be a deflection outside the self of the destructive or death instinct, it will be seen that the perversion of sadism depends upon fusion of destructive energy with libidinal energy. The discharge of aggression in itself may be pleasurable, but sadism further implies pleasure in the destruction of others. But at the same time, the manifestations of the aggressive drive progress through the same developmental stages as the sexual (oral, anal, phallic), and in this context such manifestations are generally called sadistic—thus, oral-sadistic, anal-sadistic and phallic-sadistic.

sadism, anal The aggression, destructiveness, negativism, and externally directed rage that are typical components of the anal stage of development; manifestations of the death instinct during the anal phase; the second portion of the anal stage of development, and its holdovers in later life. See *anal erotism; instinct, death; phase, anal; sadism, oral.*

sadism, id The primary primitive instinctual destructive urges, which are seen in their unmodified form in the early years of infancy. They are closely tied up with drives toward omnipotent gratification and security, and seem to be brought out by frustration in early infancy. Much of this primary sadism suffers repression under the aegis of the striving for goodness and approval, and the fear of the reality consequences to the subject of external retaliation and its internal equivalent, conscience pangs.

sadism, larval (lär'val) (L. *larva,* 'ghost, specter, mask') Hirschfeld uses the term larva in one of its original meanings, a mask; hence, larval sadism is masked or concealed sadism.

sadism, manual A type of sadism in which the torture of the object is achieved through muscular eroticism. Any sadistic activity in which the sexual pleasure achieved by the sadist is intimately associated with the use of his musculature (as, for example, in beating or kicking his partner).

sadism, omnipotent infantile See *sadism, id.*

sadism, oral The expression of infantile, primordial, aggressive, instinctive urges toward omnipotent mastery, through phantasy function of the mouth, lips, and teeth. These phantasy functions represent distortions of the reality functions of the mouth, lips, teeth, tongue, cheeks, and pharynx.

Oral sadistic wishes, strivings, and phantasies appear normally in the earliest stages of infantile development, immediately after birth. As the child matures and develops, these wishes and strivings undergo various vicissitudes, to appear and persist later in adult life in modified and disguised form as components of neurotic symptoms; as perversions and foreplay desires and gratifications; as character traits; and as socially approvable and desirable sublimation activities. See *phase, oral incorporative; sadism, unconscious.*

sadism, phallic (fal'ik) Aggression associated with the phallic stage of development. The child ordinarily comprehends sexual intercourse as an aggressive and sadistic act on the part of the male, and specifically on the part of the penis. Evidence that the penis is phantasied as a weapon of violence and destruction comes from unconscious productions of normal adults. Limericks, for instance, often refer to the penis as square, or too large, etc., so that intercourse is dangerous and painful for the partner. This may well be a projection of the male's own fear of coitus.

Scop(t)ophilia may result at the phallic stage, secondary to such sadism. The looking gives reassurance that the sadistically perceived object is not yet dead.

sadism, primal A certain portion of the death-instinct always remains within the person; it is called *primal sadism* and according to Freud is identical with masochism. 'After the chief part of it [i.e. the death instinct] has been directed outwards towards objects, there remains as a residuum within the organism the true erotogenic masochism, which on the one hand becomes a component of the

libido and on the other still has the subject itself for an object.' (Freud, S. *Collected Papers*, vol. 2, tr. by Riviere, J., Leonard and Virginia Woolf and The Institute of Psychoanalysis, London, 1924-25)

sadism, superego The intense cruelty, rigidity, and pain-giving punitive aspects of conscience (superego). In the developing child, the infantile sadism (primordial aggressivity) is eventually mastered by the erection and development within the child of equally powerful controlling and countervailing forces. These forces of character, warning the child of the reality consequences of its unbridled aggressive trends, become organized into what is called *the conscience,* 'that still small voice' that silently warns us when we are about to succumb to our urges and do something wrong. The warnings emanate from the internalized (introjected) pictures or images that the child has, not necessarily of his real parents, but rather of what he conceives the parents would be if they discovered the attempt to carry out his own violently aggressive wishes against them.

The internal image of the violently angry, discovering parent is formed in the old talionic formula of an 'eye for an eye.' The child feels that the discovering parent must become the punishing parent, seeking vengeance in proportion to the strength and enormity of the child's own phantasies and aggressive wishes. Thus, in the last analysis, the intensity of the sadism of the superego, or conscience, stems from the enormity and violence of the child's own infantile, primordial, sadistic phantasies and strivings, which have succumbed to the control of an equal and opposite repressive power. (Sharpe, E.F. *Collected Papers on Psycho-analysis,* Hogarth Press and The Institute of Psychoanalysis, London, 1950)

sadomasochism (sad'ō-maz'ok-iz'm) A condition of combined sadism and masochism: co-existence of submissive and aggressive attitudes in social and sexual relations to other persons, with a considerable degree of destructiveness present; a condition assumed to be charged with libidinal energy. The subject is affected

by an interplay between the two instinctual components of love and hate, in which
the destructive impulses momentarily
have the upper hand. In a general way,
in human relations a person may have
three different kinds of attitude toward
other persons: first, he is interested in
having the other exist as his equal; second,
he considers himself either superior or
inferior to the other person, though still
remaining interested in the óther person's
existence; and third, he is swayed by aggression and submission simultaneously in
such a way that he wishes the other person's destruction and preservation at the
same time. In normal social relations the
existence of the other person not only is
necessary but fulfills the inner psychic
demands, although a certain amount of
destructive impulse is always present.
Only when a high degree of destructiveness is present in the relationship between
two persons may one speak of sadomasochism.

safeguard, treble See *principle, treble
safeguard.*

Saint Dymphna's disease See *disease,
Saint Dymphna's.*

Saint John's evil Epilepsy.

Saint Martin's evil Dipsomania.

Saint Vitus' dance (St. Vitus, a Christian
child [martyred under Diocletian, 245-
313 A.D.] whose chapels, especially the
one at Ulm, were filled with sufferers from
epilepsy, invoking the saint for cure.)
Chorea; see *chorea, Sydenham's.*

Sakel, Manfred (1900-1957) Polish psychiatrist trained in Vienna; in 1933 reported his discovery of the hypoglycemic
insulin treatment of schizophrenia and
soon after came to the U.S.A., where he
remained until his death.

salaam spasm See *spasm, salaam.*

salad, word See *word-salad.*

Salk vaccine See *poliomyelitis.*

Salmon, Thomas W. (1876-1927) American psychiatrist; mental hygiene, military
psychiatry.

salpingectomy (sal-pin-jek'tō-mē) This is
a general medical term for the operation
which aims at, or results in, the *sterilization* of the woman. It is performed, for
surgical or eugenic reasons, by cutting
and tying off the Fallopian tubes. *Tubectomy* or *fallectomy* are other expressions
for this sterilizing operation on the female,
while *vasectomy* is the corresponding
operation on the male. The operation
removing the ovaries and resulting in the
castration of the woman is usually called
ovariotomy or *oophorectomy*. See *sterilization; castration.*

saltatory Pertaining to leaping or dancing; proceeding by leaps and bounds
rather than in measured, even progression. See *spasm, saltatory.*

sanable (san'ab'l) Curable.

sanatorium An institution for the treatment of chronic diseases, such as tuberculosis, nervous and mental disorders,
chronic rheumatism, etc., and as a place
for recuperation under medical supervision; often improperly called sanitarium.

sanction The defensive measure that
the obsessional neurotic is obliged to
adopt in order to prevent a phantasy
from being fulfilled. This may take the
form of a formula, as in the case of the
rat man, in which he employed the following formula: 'but,' accompanied by a
gesture of repudiation, and the phrase
'whatever are you thinking of?' (Freud,
S. *Collected Papers*, vol. 3, tr. by Strachey, A. and J., Leonard and Virginia
Woolf, Hogarth Press, London, 1925)

Sandler's triad A symptom group consisting of low self-esteem with confusion
of identity, sadomasochistic behavior
toward military authorities, and impotence, seen frequently as an essential
part of *camptocormia* (q.v.).

sane Sound of mind.

Sanger, Margaret Higgins (1884-1966)
American nurse; pioneered in family
planning and coined the phrase 'birth
control.'

sanguine See *type, sanguine.*

sanguinem menstruationis amicae lambit et devorat A form of sexual perversion, namely, to drink and swallow menstrual blood. Quoted from Stekel.

sanity Soundness of mind. See *responsibility, criminal.*

sa(p)phism (saf'iz'm) (Greek poetess *Sappho,* or in her native Aeolian dialect *Psappho,* a Lesbian by birth [born 600 B.C. in the island Lesbos], who was a female homosexual) The sensual and sexual desire of woman for members of her own sex; Lesbianism; female homosexuality. See *homosexuality, female.*

satanophobia (sā-tan-ō-fō'bē-à) Fear of the devil.

satisfaction 'A better term for a stimulus of instinctual origin is a "need"; that which does away with this need is "satisfaction." This can be attained only by a suitable (adequate) alteration of the inner sources of stimulations.' (Freud, S. *Collected Papers,* vol. 4, tr. by Riviere, J., Leonard and Virginia Woolf and The Institute of Psychoanalysis, London, 1924-25)
    In occupational therapy this term means a feeling of gratification, of accomplishment; often used in relation to the progress of an activity or interest.

saturation point, racial 'A given population may be saturated with a certain minority group at a given time. If an excess of members of the minority group move into the community from the outside in numbers exceeding this point—the racial saturation point—frictions and various disturbances break out.' (Moreno, J.L. *Who Shall Survive?* Nervous & Mental Disease Publishing Company, Washington, D.C., 1934)

satyriasis (sat-i-rī'à-sis) Pathological, excessive heterosexuality in the male. See *Don Juan. Obs.* Leprosy.

satyrismus (-riz'mus) *Obs.* Satyriasis.

satyromania (-rō-mā'nē-à) *Rare.* Satyriasis.

Saunders-Sutton syndrome *Delirium tremens* (q.v.).

savants, idiot (sà-vänt, ēd-yot') 'Amentia is often characterized by an irregular as well as a defective mental development, and in a small number of patients this is so marked as to result in special aptitudes which are quite phenomenal, not merely in comparison with aments, but often with the acquirements of ordinary persons. These persons are conveniently described as "idiot savants."' Usually such 'idiots' are not of the lowest grade of mental deficiency. (Tredgold, A.F. *A Text-Book of Mental Deficiency,* 6th ed., Wood, Baltimore, 1937)

scabiophobia (skā-bē-ō-fō'bē-à) Fear of scabies.

scale, Columbia Mental Maturity See *CMMS.*

scale, Lorr See *MSRPP.*

scanning Skimming; a method of rapid reading in which the reader searches for specific content or tries quickly to grasp the general sense of the passage but does not attempt to read the complete text. *Scanning speech* is a slurred, ataxic, drawling monotone or sing-song; it occurs, for example, in some cases of multiple sclerosis.
    Scanning is also use to denote a method of diagnosis employing radio-isotopes; see *encephalography, radio-isotopic.*

scapegoat The person or object who is blamed for the actions of others; the object of *projection* (q.v.).

scar, psychic (sī'kik) 'Cure with a defect is also spoken of by formulating the conception, suitable only to few cases, that the acute disease has left a defect just as a healed wound leaves a scar. A "psychic scar" may be formed by definite "residual symptoms," as in the case of a delusion which in spite of returned clearness following a delirium is no longer corrected.' (Bleuler, E. *Text-book of Psychiatry,* tr. by Brill, A.A., Macmillan, New York, 1930)

Scarpa's ganglion (Antonio Scarpa, Italian anatomist and surgeon, 1748-1832) See *nerve, acoustic.*

scatology The study of excrement and/or preoccupation with excrement and filth. 'The whole significance of the anal zone is mirrored in the fact that there are but few neurotics who have not had their special scatologic customs, ceremonies, etc., which they retain with cautious secrecy.' (Freud, S. *The Basic Writings of Sigmund Freud*, tr. by Brill, A.A., Random House, New York, 1938) See *analerotism* and the several words beginning with *copro-*.

scatophagy (skȧ-tof'ȧ-jē) Eating of excrement; see *rhypophagy*.

scatophobia (skat-ō-fō'bē-ȧ) A morbid dread of contamination by excrement.

scattering One of the schizophrenic thinking disorders in which associations are sometimes irrelevant or tangential, with the result that speech productions are occasionally incomprehensible. The term is also used in clinical psychology to refer to widely divergent test scores, as when a schizophrenic patient passes all the year X items in an intelligence test but shows many failures at the year VI level, or as when there is marked inconsistency on subtest scores.

scelerophobia (ske-lêr-ō-fō'bē-ȧ) *Pavor sceleris* (q.v.).

scene, primal A child's first observation of sexual intercourse between the parents. In his description of the 'wolf-man' case, Freud claims that the primal scene was influential in determining later morbid personality reactions.

scene, traumatic Any psychic experience that the subject wishes to forget or repress because it is disagreeable, painful, threatening, or unbearable. Freud speaks of traumatic situations and emphasizes that neurotic symptoms are 'complete reproductions of such situations.' It is as if the patient cannot get rid of the original painful experience and remains attached to it, an attachment which Freud called 'fixation to traumas.' Such is the case of the girl who had developed an abnormal erotic attachment to her father (traumatic situation, or scene) and was constantly ill after his death, so that she would be in no condition to marry and could thus remain with her father, her original love-object.

In the opinion of Breuer and Freud, the psychic energies that cannot be lived out in the normal way, when the patient tries to forget or repress the traumatic scene, are diverted into other pathways and there provoke symptoms in the somatic sphere. Later, Freud referred to it as a 'psychosexual trauma,' the term used especially by Schilder. (Schilder, P. *Psychotherapy*, Norton, New York, 1938)

Schaeffer reflex See *reflex, Schaeffer.*

schedule A form on which may be given many summarized items of information concerning a patient; it is arranged so that each item may be easily abstracted and made available for tabulation.

schedule, self-demand See *feeding, demand.*

Scheid, cyanotic syndrome of Scheid attempted to explain sudden death in excited manic patients and in catatonic states as a somatic condition somehow related to a somatic febrile or toxic etiology of the psychosis itself. This view is not widely held at the present time, it being more generally believed that such deaths are due to physiologic exhaustion secondary to pathologic overactivity; but some authors continue to speak of a catatonic cerebral paralysis as a primary somatic change which explains the occasional (probably not more than 1 per cent) occurrence of unexpected death in this group.

schema, body Same as body percept, which is one part of the body image. See *image, body.*

Schicksal analysis See *analysis, Schicksal.*

Schilder's disease (Paul Ferdinand Schilder, Vienna and New York neurologist and psychiatrist, 1886-1940) Encephalitis periaxialis diffusa. See *sclerosis, diffuse.*

schizo- (skiz'ō-) Combining form meaning split(ting), cleavage, rift, division, from Gr. *schizein*, to split, cleave, rive.

schizo-affective schizophrenia See *schizophrenia.*

schizocaria (skiz-ō-kā'rē-ȧ) An acute and highly malignant form of schizophrenia which leads to rapid deterioration of the personality. Mauz uses the term 'catastrophic schizophrenia' synonymously with schizocaria.

schizogen (skiz'ō-gen) See *psychotomimetic.*

schizoid (skiz'oid) Resembling the division, separation or split of the personality that is characteristic of schizophrenia.

schizoid personality See *personality.*

schizoid position See *position, paranoid-schizoid.*

schizoidia (skiz-oi'di-à) Schizoidism.

schizoidism (skiz'oid-iz'm) The aggregate of personality traits known as introversion, namely, quietness, seclusiveness, 'shut-in-ness.' The schizoid person splits or separates from his surroundings to a greater or lesser degree, confining his psychic interests more or less to himself. The intensely schizoid person may become schizophrenic; it is estimated that not less than sixty per cent of schizophrenic patients show exaggerated schizoid tendencies prior to the development of schizophrenia.

Many contemporary European writers use the term schizoidism to refer to the hereditary or 'nuclear' factor in schizophrenia. These same authors tend to use the term 'dementia praecox' to refer to a type of schizophrenia showing a high tendency to deterioration and little tendency to remission or recovery. (Campbell, R.J. *Psychiatric Quarterly 32; 318-34, 1958*)

schizomania (skiz-ō-mā'nē-à) A psychotic state presenting a mixture of schizophrenic and manic symptoms.

schizomimetic (-mi-mē'tik) *Psychotomimetic* (q.v.).

schizophasia (-fā'zē-à) Word-salad.

schizophrene (skiz'ō-frēn) One affected by schizophrenia.

schizophrenese The associational defects of the schizophrenic patient as manifested in his speech; it is to be recognized that there is no specific schizophrenic language, and schizophrenics' thinking disorders vary from patient to patient. 'What is uniform is merely an absence of normal expectancy. It is also noteworthy that in the absence of such culturally standard cues for meta-communicative expression, the listener feels disengaged and the schizophrenic child is further isolated from human rapport.' (Goldfarb, W. *International Psychiatry Clinics 1, 821-845, 1964*)

schizophrenia (skiz-ō-frē'nē-à) (295.x) A term which Bleuler suggested as a replacement for the now generally obsolete term *dementia praecox* (q.v.). By the term, Bleuler meant to designate what he considered to be one of the fundamental characteristics of patients so diagnosed, namely, the splitting off of portions of the psyche, which portions may then dominate the psychic life of the subject for a time and lead an independent existence even though these may be contrary and contradictory to the personality as a whole. Bleuler rejected the term dementia praecox because in his experience profound deterioration (dementia) was not the inevitable end-result of the disease process, and because it did not always appear by the time of adolescence.

'In 1911, Eugen Bleuler described the schizophrenias as a slowly progressive deterioration of the entire personality, which involves mainly the affective life, and expresses itself in disorders of feeling, thought and conduct, and a tendency to withdraw from reality. Bleuler noted that the schizophrenias were at times progressive, at times intermittent, and could stop or retrogress at any stage; but that they showed a tendency toward deterioration and, having once appeared, did not permit of a full *restitutio ad integrum*. Bleuler established the multidimensional nature of the schizophrenias and believed them to be organic; but at the same time, he stressed the interaction of psychogenic and physiogenic features in their psychopathology and development.' (Campbell, R.J. *Psychiatric Quarterly 32: 318-34, 1958*).

Bleuler subdivided the symptoms of the schizophrenias into two groups: (1) the fundamental, primary, or basic symptoms, which are characteristic and pathognomonic of the disease process; and (2) the accessory or secondary symptoms, which are often seen in the schizophrenias and which may even occupy the forefront of the symptom-picture, but which are seen in other nosologic groups as well and particularly in the organic reaction types (acute and chronic brain syndromes). In this second group are included such symptoms as hallucinations, delusions, ideas of reference, memory disturbances (e.g. déjà fait, déjà vu), etc. The fundamental symptoms of the schizophrenias include: (1) disturbances in associations, (2) disturbances of affect, (3) ambivalence of the affect, intellect, and/or will, (4) autism, (5) attention defects, (6) disturbances of the will, (7) changes in 'the person,' (8) schizophrenic dementia, and (9) disturbances of activity and behavior.

While the specific etiology remains unknown, mounting evidence favors the conception of the schizophrenias as a heredogenetic disease involving particularly certain enzyme systems of the body. The average expectance of schizophrenia in the general population probably does not exceed 1 per cent; it is not, therefore, a universal potentiality and not everyone could become a schizophrenic under certain conditions. It occurs in every segment of the population, without regard for race, culture, or social class. It occurs, too, in all the forms generally recognized, although the content of the symptoms appears to be determined in large part by the culture. To state this in a different way: the fundamental symptoms are the same, no matter where schizophrenia appears. 'Kallmann reports the following findings: (a) the majority of schizophrenic hospital patients (90 per cent) come from non-schizophrenic parents; (b) one schizophrenic parent is not enough to produce the disease in his off-spring, although one schizophrenic parent will raise the expectancy of schizophrenia in his off-spring to 16 per cent; (c) at the same time, a non-schizophrenic, adequate home is not able to prevent the development of schizophrenia in vulnerable off-spring; (d) both one-egg twins are six times more likely to develop schizophrenia than both two-egg twins, regardless of whether they are reared alone or apart.' (ibid.) Kallmann feels that schizophrenia is a gene-specific, metabolic deficiency transmitted as a receptive unit-factor and manifested as a lack of ability to respond to certain environmental stimuli. The basic integrative deficiency is not yet identified; it may be an overproduction or underproduction of central synap-

tic neurohumors such as norepinephrine or serotonin; it may be a production of abnormal metabolites such as adrenochrome or adrenolutin; it may be production of abnormal forms of copper-containing enzymes, such as Heath's 'taraxein'; it may be inadequate production of enzymes normally responsible for the breakdown of various potentially toxic amines.

Forms of the disease. Bleuler subdivided the schizophrenias into acute and chronic forms, depending upon the predominant symptoms of any particular episode. As already indicated, the predominant symptoms are often the accessory symptoms, and before subtyping of an episode is made the diagnosis of schizophrenia is first established by reason of the presence of the fundamental symptoms.

The acute syndromes are:

(1) melancholia—in contrast to non-schizophrenic depressions, the affect here tends to be superficial, inappropriate, and/or unconvincing, and hypochondriacal delusions are frequent.

(2) mania—the prevailing mood is capriciousness rather than euphoria or triumph, and withdrawal can usually be seen.

(3) catatonia—stupor, cerea flexibilitas, *faxenpsychosis* (q.v.) or other hyperkinetic syndromes.

(4) delusional states with hallucinations, which are often visual and less stereotyped than the hallucinations seen in the chronic syndromes.

(5) twilight states—including religious ecstasies and other dream-like conditions in which desires, impulses, or fears are represented in a direct or symbolic way as being already fulfilled.

(6) Benommenheit (psychic 'benumbing')—in which there is a slowing up of all psychic processes, usually in conjunction with an incapacity for dealing with any relatively complicated or unusual situation.

(7) confusion, incoherence—as a result of fragmentation of associations, speech is disconnected, sentences are half broken, and activity is excessive, purposeless, and random.

(8) anger states—with cursing, vilification, uncontrolled rage outbursts, often in relation to seemingly insignificant external events.

(9) anniversary excitements—episodes of agitation appearing only on definite

calendar days, usually related to a specific event in the patient's past.

(10) stupor

(11) deliria—acute hallucinatory episodes often resembling the fever deliria. These states are sometimes termed oneirophrenia and include those patients who become dazed and bewildered with narrowing of consciousness, often following specific traumata such as childbirth, postoperative exhaustion, and battlefield experiences. While such cases are often said to be benign, there is a percentage of cases that recur with decreasing recovery after each episode.

(12) fugue states—running away in intercurrent episodes of agitation and excitement, sometimes in response to a hallucinatory command.

(13) dipsomania—tense, anxious moods drive some patients to drink heavily until they become exhausted.

The chronic forms are:

(1) paranoid—see *schizophrenia, paranoid.*

(2) catatonic—see *schizophrenia, catatonic.*

(3) hebephrenic—see *schizophrenia, hebephrenic.*

(4) simple—see *schizophrenia, simple.*

Various other forms have been described since Bleuler's subdivision, among which are:

(1) *schizophrenia, childhood* (q.v.)

(2) *schizophrenia, pseudoneurotic* (q.v.)

(3) *schizophrenia, ambulatory* (q.v.)

(4) schizophrenia, acute episode (295.4) —those acute forms in which clearcut crystallization into one of the generally recognized chronic forms has not yet occurred.

(5) schizophrenia, chronic undifferentiated (295.90)—mixed forms and also those termed 'latent,' 'incipient,' 'borderline,' 'prepsychotic,' etc.

(6) schizophrenia, schizo-affective (295.7)—including the acute melancholic and manic forms of Bleuler; this type often has its onset during adolescence and with recurrences the affective picture tends to abate and to be replaced by hebephrenic or simple or paranoid symptoms.

(7) schizophrenia, pseudopsychopathic (295.5)—with predominant asocial, dyssocial or antisocial trends.

(8) schizophrenia, residual (295.6)—cases in a state of relative remission or

improvement between acute psychotic episodes.

(9) other forms (295.99).

schizophrenia, ambulatory (295.5) The term ambulatory schizophrenia (non-hospitalized) has been applied to the disease of the group of schizophrenics who, on the surface, appear normal, but can suddenly commit acts which reveal their abnormality. (Zilboorg, G. *Psychiatry, 4,* 154, 1941) The puzzling aggressive, asocial acts committed by apparently sane persons have very often turned out to be acts of ambulatory schizophrenics. (Abrahamsen, D. *Crime and the Human Mind,* Columbia University Press, New York, 1944)

schizophrenia, arrest of The subsidence of acute schizophrenic symptoms. This may occur at any time in the process of the disease, and if the disease itself is not too far advanced, there may be little of a pathological nature to appear. In other words, schizophrenia does not necessarily imply progressive deterioration.

schizophrenia, catastrophic See *schizocaria.*

schizophrenia, catatonic (ka-ta-ton′ik) (295.2) One of the subgroups of schizophrenia (in the older literature, dementia praecox) which may appear as a chronic form or as an acute episode in the course of a schizophrenic pattern. As with any type of schizophrenia, the fundamental symptoms afford the basis for the diagnosis, although the subgrouping into the catatonic type is largely dependent upon certain secondary or accessory symptoms—catalepsy, stupor, hyperkinesiae, stereotypies, mannerisms, negativism, automatisms, and impulsivity.

Onset is acute in 41 per cent of cases; in 31 per cent of cases chronic paranoid symptoms precede the development of catatonic symptoms, and in the remaining cases the onset is subacute. In general, symptoms may be seen to fall into one of two categories: (1) catatonic stupor, including catalepsy, stupor, and negativism; and (2) catatonic excitement, including hyperkinesiae, stereotypies, mannerisms, automatisms, and impulsivity.

Catalepsy may appear as immobile or mask-like facies, as posturing, resistance to movements, decreased spontaneity in movement, or less commonly, as cerea flexibilitas (waxy flexibility). The hyperkinesiae include arbitrary, automatic, pseudospontaneous movements while the stereotypies include movements, actions, posturings, speech, writings, or drawings which are monotonously repetitive and which bear little obvious relationship to external reality. *Schnauzkrampf* (q.v.) is a particular type of stereotypy. Mannerisms are not necessarily stereotyped but they are nonetheless inappropriate, inadequately modifiable, and caricature-like. Negativism may appear in several forms: (a) external negativism, or negation of commands; (b) inner negativism, or oppositional thoughts (actually a type of intellectual ambivalence, but often misinterpreted as 'obsessive thinking'); (c) active negativism, the active opposition of commands; (d) passive negativism, which often appears as stubbornness or unco-operativeness; (e) command-negativism, or doing exactly the opposite of what is ordered. Automatisms may also be expressed in various ways, such as echopraxia or echolalia (forms of command-automatism), or as fugues, self-injuries, or coprolalia. Impulsivity is commonly seen in catatonic schizophrenia and on occasion can lead to suicidal attempts or homicidal outbursts.

schizophrenia, childhood (295.8) A clinical entity occurring in childhood, usually after the age of one and before the age of 11, characterized chiefly by disturbance in the ability to make affective contact with the environment and by autistic thinking. It has long been believed by many clinicians that such pictures represented early-appearing schizophrenia rather than any different or unique syndrome, and Kallmann's genetic studies support this view. The criteria for establishing such a diagnosis, however, are not as well defined as in adult schizophrenia, so that various definitions of the disorder (or group of disorders) are given by various authors. Thus Bender says: 'We now define childhood schizophrenia as a maturational lag at the embryonic level in all the areas which integrate biological and psychological behavior; an embryonic primitivity or plasticity characterizes the pattern of the behavior disturbance in all areas of personality functioning. It is determined before birth and hereditary fac-

tors appear to be important. It may be precipitated by a physiological crisis, which may be birth itself, especially a traumatic birth.' (in Caplan, G. *Emotional Problems of Early Childhood*, Basic Books, New York, 1955) Mahler distinguishes between symbiotic infantile psychosis, which she described in 1952, and early infantile autism (Kanner's term), and considers both of them types of childhood schizophrenia. Others would limit the term childhood schizophrenia more narrowly and consider it as a separate entity from early infantile autism and from psychoses associated with mental deficiency. See *psychosis, symbiotic infantile.*

Bender describes the following symptoms:
(1) vasovegetative—undifferentiated homeostatic functions; unpredictable temperature responses in illness; flushing, sweating, color changes, cold extremities; disturbed rhythm of sleeping and fluctuation in and out of torporous states of consciousness; disturbances in eating, elimination, and respiration; growth discrepancies; soft visceral tone leading to many 'psychosomatic disturbances';
(2) motility—undifferentiated reactions and hypersensitivity to external stimuli; lack of suppression of early reflex patterns (e.g. startle response); soft muscular tone, plasticity, awkwardness, infantile posture; insecurity with new motor patterns; residual primitive reflex patterned activities; oral mannerisms; head-turning and *whirling* (whose persistence after the age of 6 years she considers almost pathognomonic);
(3) dependence on contact with others—motor compliance; woodenlike mechanical voice;
(4) disturbances in the perceptual, thought and language spheres, with incongruous early and late patterns; and
(5) deep concern with problems of identity, body image, body functions, and orientation in time and space.

schizophrenia, co-enaesthetic A term suggested by G. Huber (1957) for a chronic form of schizophrenia characterized by abnormal phenomena in the sphere of bodily sensation and by associated vegetative, motor, and sensory symptoms. According to Huber, this form is steadily progressive, and is organically determined by disturbances in the diencephalic and thalamic areas.

schizophrenia, compensation Term coined by N.D.C. Lewis for the type of schizophrenia characterized by overcompensation of the feelings of inferiority. Delusions of grandeur form the core of this psychosis.

schizophrenia deliriosa (skē-zô-fre′nē-à dä-lē-rē-ō′zà) Menninger's term for a form of schizophrenia which starts as a delirium and is frequently associated with or directly follows a physical illness such as influenza. *(American Journal of Psychiatry 1, 573-88, 1921-22)*

schizophrenia, engrafted See *propfschizophrenia.*

schizophrenia, hebephrenic (hē-be-frē′nik) (295.1) A chronic form of schizophrenia characterized by marked disorders in thinking, incoherence, severe emotional disturbance, wild excitement alternating with tearfulness and depression, vivid hallucinations, and absurd, bizarre delusions which are prolific, fleeting, and frequently concerned with ideas of omnipotence, sex change, cosmic identity, and rebirth (the so-called phylogenetic symptoms). The hebephrenic forms tend to have an early onset, usually before the age of 20. Bleuler classified as hebephrenic all those schizophrenias with an acute onset that were not characterized by catatonic symptoms (e.g. the manic, melancholic, amented, and twilight states) and also all those chronic forms where the accessory symptoms are not dominant. Others have depended upon the presence of the silly, inappropriate 'teenager' symptoms to establish the diagnosis.

Hebephrenic schizophrenia in almost all reported series has been associated with a poor prognosis; i.e. with a relatively rapid deterioration and schizophrenic dementia. It is this form which contributes most heavily to the group termed nuclear or process schizophrenia by other workers.

schizophrenia, induced Delusions or other schizophrenic symptoms imposed by one member of the family on other members. (See *association, psychosis of*). In one such case, a schizophrenic mother trans-

mitted her ideas of grandeur to her two daughters, one of whom was clearly schizophrenic, while the other could be convinced of the falsity of her beliefs and then showed no further evidence of the disease. This case, incidentally, is an example of *folie à trois*. 'Therefore, we must assume that an energetic patient can suggest his delusions to other members of the family if and when they articulate with the complexes (wishes and desires) of these same members. However, schizophrenia will only develop if the disease is already latent in those individuals. In induced insanity, not the disease as such is determined by induction but only its delusional content, and perhaps also the manifest outbreak.' (Bleuler, E. *Dementia Praecox or the Group of Schizophrenias*, International Universities Press, New York, 1950) See *folie à deux.*

schizophrenia, latent (295.5) That form of schizophrenia in which, despite the existence of fundamental symptoms, no clear-cut psychotic episode or gross break with reality has occurred. Pseudoneurotic, pseudopsychopathic, borderline, ambulatory, and similar forms are included here so long as there has been no acute psychotic episode (a requirement that differentiates latent schizophrenia from the *residual* type).

The latent type of schizophrenia includes what some authors variously term incipient, pre-psychotic, pseudoneurotic, pseudopsychopathic, or borderline schizophrenia, and these latter are more appropriately included under the latent group (295.5), than with the chronic undifferentiated forms (295.90) or under 'other' types (295.99).

The group named *schizophrenia, residual type* (295.6) includes only those patients who, having had a psychotic episode, improve to the degree that they are not considered psychotic, even though signs of the schizophrenic disorder remain.

schizophrenia, mixed An instance of schizophrenia that shows symptoms of more than one of the disease's four generally accepted and clearly distinguished categories: simple, paranoid, catatonic, hebephrenic. Such cases are often called chronic undifferentiated schizophrenia.

schizophrenia,   paranoid   (par′à-noid)

(295.3) One of the chronic forms of schizophrenia. In addition to the fundamental schizophrenic symptoms, the paranoid type shows the following features: a feeling that external reality has changed and somehow become different; suspiciousness and ideas of dedication; ideas of reference; hallucinations, especially of body sensations; delusions of persecution or of grandiosity. Some paranoid schizophrenics may act in accord with their delusions and turn on their tormentors, while others may become suicidal in an attempt to escape their persecutors.

Several types of paranoid schizophrenia are recognized: litigious, depressed, persecutory, grandiose, erotomaniacal, etc. In general, paranoid forms of schizophrenia develop later than do the other forms, the highest incidence being between the ages of 30 and 35. In contrast to paranoia (q.v.), in paranoid schizophrenia the delusions are multiple, less highly systematized, changeable, illogical, and bizarre.

schizophrenia, postemotive (pōst-ē-mō'-tiv) This term indicates that in a person constitutionally predisposed, schizophrenia may be precipitated by an emotional trauma, especially in the face of situations which threaten self-preservation, the social self, or the sexual life.

A 21-year-old schizoid man, who had made a happy work adjustment for the preceding six years in a candy factory, developed postemotive schizophrenia. His right arm was caught in a machine pulley belt and he suffered severe muscular contusions. He was hospitalized for two weeks, but was unable to return to work after discharge from the hospital, because of his 'nervous state caused by the accident.' After two months, he finally went back to work, but did poorly and seemed terrified by machine work. He worked for several days but had to leave his job, because he began to tremble all over, could not sleep, developed numerous hypochondriacal complaints and crying spells, became generally apprehensive, with acute fear reactions. Shortly thereafter he began to neglect his personal appearance, and a widespread retraction of interest was noted. He became absorbed in himself, talked and laughed senselessly in a childish voice, and at times demonstrated verbigeration. He was institutionalized, and a diagnosis of schizophrenia, hebephrenic type, was made. After seven years, there was no improvement in his condition.

Most postemotive reactions eventually and spontaneously disappear and are self-limited syndromes. But when emotional stress precipitates a psychosis in a predisposed person, prognosis is made on the basis of the psychosis itself rather than on the nature of the precipitating factor. Many authorities feel that schizophrenia is nearly always postemotive, that detailed anamnestic investigation would reveal specific emotional traumata as precipitating factors in the majority of cases. (*Psychiatric Quarterly 13*, 278, 1939)

schizophrenia, pseudoneurotic (sū-dō-nū-rot'ik) (295.5) Hoch and Polatin (*Psychiatric Quarterly 23*, 248, 1949) apply this term to those patients whose defense mechanisims are, at least superficially, neurotic in type, but who, on close investigation, show the basic schizophrenic mechanisms. The most important diagnostic features are *pan-anxiety* and *pan-neurosis*. The all-pervading anxiety structure leaves no life-approach of the person free from tension. Usually not only one or two different neurotic mechanisms are seen, but all symptoms known in neurotic illness tend to be present at the same time — anxiety, conversion symptoms, gross hysterical or vegetative manifestations, phobias, and obsessive-compulsive mechanisms. These neurotic mechanisms dominate the patient; they constantly shift but are never completely absent.

The life-approach of these patients is always autistic and dereistic, although this may be very subtly expressed. Withdrawal from reality is more general than is the case even in the neurotic with schizoid features. Some inappropriate emotional connections are usually manifest, and there is a lack of modulation and flexibility in emotion display. Often, these patients appear cold and controlled in responding to major frustrations, but over-react to trivial ones. Hate reactions, particularly toward the family, are more open and less discriminating than in the neurotic. Commonly there is depression or an *anhedonic* state wherein the patient derives pleasure from nothing. Thinking disorders may also be too subtle to be on the surface: condensations and concept displacements, catathymic thinking, expression of omnipotence emanating from the patient, or the feeling of an omnipotential attitude of the environment toward the patient. Unlike neurotics, such patients do not try to rationalize their symptoms in a logical and coherent fashion. Instead, the component elements of their story always remain vaguely conflicting; they are unable to give details of the development of the symptoms, and repeat and reiterate their complaints in a stereotyped and sterile way. There is usually an inability to associate freely in spite of their ordinarily good intelligence and signal ability to verbalize. Psychosexually, such patients show a chaotic organization and a mixture of all levels of libidinal development. Marked sadistic or sadomasochistic behavior is often linked with this sexual material. The Rorschach test in such patients often shows thinking disorders such as concrete thinking, an unpredictable attitude toward various situations, lack of constructive planfulness, passive opportunism, and marked anxiety. In the Rorschach results there is often noticed that marked variability of performance which is so characteristic of schizophrenia. Amytal interviews frequently release some of the more overtly psychotic material.

Many of these patients develop psychotic episodes which are often of short duration with complete reintegration. These short-lived attacks are called 'micropsychoses' and are characterized by the simultaneous development of three very significant features: hypochondriacal ideas, ideas of reference, and feelings of depersonalization. The patients zig-zag, repeatedly trespassing beyond the reality line.

The following case illustrates pseudoneurotic schizophrenia. The patient was a single white female, 38 years old. Though an unwanted child, she had a normal early development, was very affectionate and obedient, and mixed well with her contemporaries. With advancing age the patient appeared to grow progressively more schizoid in personality, but never enough to interfere with her functioning. After completing high school, she obtained a position with a dentist, and several years later was discharged, because her employer felt that she had lost interest in her work, had become listless. Her arms hung down at her sides and she slouched along as she walked. After that, the patient found employment in a hospital and began to complain of ab-

dominal pain. Appendectomy was performed, but her complaints continued, including new ones about marked weakness and lack of strength, but there was no real depression. Later, constipation and a 'foggy feeling' began to trouble her. She was much irritated by her mother and sister, because they did not understand her and regarded her complaints as caused by laziness. She also complained that her heart hurt her. On admission to the hospital, the patient appeared cooperative but somewhat self-absorbed. Whenever she had to talk with people in the course of social contacts, she showed fear and shame, and marked feelings of inferiority. Later the patient complained that her subconscious mind played tricks on her, that she had a feeling as if a voice were telling her to go to sleep. Finally, this last complaint crystallized into frank ideas of reference and persecution and auditory hallucinations.

schizophrenia, recidives in (res'i-divz) Recurring, intermittent, acute episodes of schizophrenia, or other evidences of deterioration which begin after prolonged remission. The recurring attacks often duplicate the previous ones, but new features may appear. There is no definite correlation between initial disease symptoms and recidives.

schizophrenia, regressive symptoms Those schizophrenic symptoms which represent an undoing or primitivization of differentiations acquired through mental development; included here are such symptoms as phantasies of world destruction, physical sensations and delusions, depersonalization, delusions of grandeur, archaic speech and thought, most hebephrenic symptoms, and certain catatonic symptoms (negativism, echolalia, echopraxia, automatic obedience, posturing, stereotypy). See *schizophrenia, restitutional symptoms.*

schizophrenia, residual (295.6) Interepisodic schizophrenia; the condition of being without gross psychotic symptoms following a psychotic scizophrenic episode. To be contrasted with *schizophrenia, latent* (q.v.).

schizophrenia, restitutional symptoms Those schizophrenic symptoms which represent an attempt at regaining reality, which has been lost by regression; included are such symptoms as hallucinations, delusions, most of the social and speech peculiarities of schizophrenia, and certain catatonic symptoms (stereotypy, mannerisms, automatic obedience, rigidity).

schizophrenia, reversible Menninger's term for a schizophrenic state with a potentiality for recovery. See *psychosis, process.*

schizophrenia, simple (295.1) One of the chronic forms of schizophrenia; also called dementia praecox, simple type; dementia simplex; schizophrenia simplex; primary dementia.

In the simple form of schizophrenia, there is an insidious psychic impoverishment which affects the emotions, the intellect, and the will. Chronic dissatisfaction or complete indifference to reality are characteristic, and the simple schizophrenic is isolated, estranged, and asocial. Affect is markedly blunted and dulled, there is little phantasy life, and there may be few or no accessory symptoms. Dementia, in Bleuler's sense, is marked — patients make many foolish mistakes, are highly suggestible and gullible, and speech is filled with senseless generalizations. Thought is vacuous and banal, ideas are insipid and unintegrated. Such patients tend to sink to low and relatively simple social levels that make little or no demands on them and may come to lead almost a vegetative existence. They often become day laborers, peddlers, or vagabonds, and they contribute heavily to the group of eccentric recluses.

schizophrenia, toxic *Toxiphrenia* (q.v.).

schizophreniform (skiz-o-fren'i-form) Resembling schizophrenia. See *psychosis, process.*

schizophrenosis (-frē-nō'sis) Southard's term for schizophrenic reactions in general.

schizothyme (skiz'ō-thīm) One who has a schizoid personality.

schizothymia (-thī'mē-à, -thim'ē-à) Introversion; schizoidism.

schizotypal disorders (skiz'ō-tī-pal) See *psychodynamics, adaptational.*

Schmidt's syndrome (Johann Friedrich Moritz Schmidt, German laryngologist, 1838-1907) A bulbar syndrome due to involvement of the vagus and spinal accessory nerves. Symptoms are: homolateral paralysis of the soft palate, pharynx, and larynx, and homolateral sternocleidomastoid paralysis.

schnauzkrampf (shnouts'krämpf) A term, coined by Karl Ludwig Kahlbaum (1828-99), for protrusion of the lips so that they resemble a snout. The condition is found almost exclusively in the catatonic form of schizophrenia.

Scholz's disease (Willibald Scholz, German neurologist, b. 1889) See *sclerosis, diffuse.*

school-marmitis A personality type seen in some teachers, characterized by 'magnified self-awareness of herself in the role of dispenser of knowledge and wisdom to children and, on occasion, to their parents; a tendency to "lord it over" and a patronizing attitude toward others.' (Kanner, L. *Child Psychiatry,* Thomas, Springfield, Ill., 1948) Emotional attitudes of a schoolteacher can be powerful determinants of the child's own attitude, for good or ill, as the case may be. This is especially true if the child is already emotionally insecure in his home life. Happily, there also exist teacher-attitudes that reflect a healthy degree of emotional integration at a high level of personal maturity.

school phobia See *phobia, school.*

school refusal syndrome See *phobia, school.*

schoolsickness J.V. Treynor classifies schoolsickness as an occupational neurosis in children maladjusted to their school situation. It is characterized by anxiety, restlessness, and irritability. (*Iowa State Medical Society Journal 19,* 451, 1929)

Schreber, Schreber-case In 1911, Freud published *Psycho-Analytic Notes Upon an Autobiographical Account of a Case of Paranoia (Dementia Paranoides).* This consisted of an analysis of *Memoirs of a Neurotic,* a previously published (1903) autobiographical account by Dr. jur. Daniel Paul Schreber. Freud's analysis of these memoirs formed the basis for the psychoanalytic view of paranoid delusions which, at least in the male, are interpreted as attempts to contradict the underlying homosexual wish-phantasy of loving a man.

Schrenck-Notzing, Albert (1862 - 1929) German psychiatrist.

Schuele's sign *Omega melancholium* (q.v.).

Schüller-Christian-Hand's syndrome *Xanthomatosis* (q.v.).

sciatica (sī-a′ti-ka) See *disk, herniated lumbar intervertebral.*

scierneuropsia See *scieropia.*

scieropia (sī-êr-ō′pē-à) Visual defect in which objects appear to be in a shadow; when of emotional or psychologic origin, such defect is termed *scierneuropsia.*

sclerosis, amyotrophic lateral (skle-rō′sis, am-ī-ō-trō′fik) Progressive muscular atrophy; progressive bulbar palsy; chronic poliomyelitis. Some authorities believe that amyotrophic lateral sclerosis is a hereditary disorder; but most feel that it is due to a toxin with a predilection for the anterior horn cells. It begins between the ages of 50 and 70, is twice as frequent in males as in females, and usually has an insidious onset. Pathological changes include progressive degeneration of the anterior horn cells of the spinal cord, the medullary motor nuclei, and the pyramidal tracts. Wasting begins in the upper limbs, first in the hands and later in the forearm and shoulder. Then it spreads to the tongue, palate, larynx, and pharynx, resulting in slurred speech. Degeneration of both pyramidal tracts above the medulla produces pseudobulbar palsy: dysarthria, dysphagia, and spasticity of the muscles; when severe, pseudobulbar palsy results in impaired voluntary control over emotional reactions which may be exaggerated, explosive, and quite inappropriate. The disease is fatal within 3 to 10 years.

sclerosis, atrophic lobar (a-trō′fik lō′bēr) *Little's disease* (q.v.).

sclerosis, diffuse 'A group of progressive diseases usually occurring early in life and characterized pathologically by wide-

spread demyelination of the white matter of the cerebral hemispheres, and clinically in typical cases by visual failure, mental deterioration, and spastic paralysis. Both sporadic and familial cases are encountered. The aetiology of these disorders is unknown and there is no general agreement as to their classification. At present their resemblances to one another appear to outweigh their differences and they are therefore included under a common title.' (Brain, W.R. *Diseases of the Nervous System,* 4th ed., Oxford University Press, London, 1951) The various entities which Brain includes are: encephalitis periaxialis diffusa (Schilder's disease), centrolobar sclerosis, encephaloleukopathia scleroticans, progressive degenerative subcortical encephalopathy, leukodystrophy, leuko-encephalopathia myeloclastica primitiva, encephalomyelomalacia chronica diffusa, concentric demyelination (Baló's disease), Krabbe's disease, Scholz's disease, and Pelizaeus-Merzbacher's disease. It has been suggested that some of this group are caused by specific biochemical defects affecting different stages in the metabolism of myelin.

The demyelination typically begins symmetrically in both occipital lobes and spreads forward. Onset is usually before the age of 14; males are more frequently affected than females. Symptoms may begin acutely or insidiously and include: headache, giddiness, visual impairment progressing to blindness; diplopia, nystagmus; spastic diplegia, aphasia and/or spastic dysarthria, epileptiform attacks, and progressive dementia. Survival period ir rarely longer than three years after the onset of symptoms. There is no known treatment.

sclerosis, disseminated Multiple sclerosis.

sclerosis en plaque (sklē-rō′sis äN plàk′) (F. 'in patches') Multiple sclerosis.

sclerosis, multiple Insular sclerosis; disseminated sclerosis. One of the demyelinating diseases of the nervous system and, at least in temperate zones, one of the most common neurological disorders. It is characterized pathologically by swelling and then demyelination of the medullary sheath, which is followed by glial proliferation. The result is an irregular scattering of well-demarcated sclerotic plaques throughout the white and gray matter of the brain and spinal cord. The lesions show a predilection for the pyramidal tracts and posterior columns of the spinal cord, the posterior longitudinal bundle and cerebellar connections of the brain-stem, the white matter of the frontal lobes, and the optic tracts. The disease was first described by Cruveilhier in 1835 and Carswell in 1838. Charcot described a triad of symptoms—nystagmus, intention tremor, and scanning speech—but this is found only in about 10 per cent of cases and even then usually only when lesions are far advanced.

The etiology of multiple sclerosis is unknown; some would implicate a spirochetal or viral agent, or various constitutional factors. The highest incidence of the disorder is in Northern Europe and Switzerland; the incidence in Great Britain is about half that in Switzerland, and the incidence in the United States is about one-quarter that in Great Britain. In the United States, incidence is considerably greater in the North than in the South. While heredity may be a contributing factor in the genesis of the disorder, evidence does not substantiate its designation as a major factor.

The disease usually begins between the ages of 20 and 40; the average age at onset is 30 years for females and 34 years for males. The age at onset tends to be lowest in those areas with the highest incidence. In 50 per cent of cases, the initial symptom is weakness or loss of control over one or more limbs; in 29 per cent the initial symptom involves the visual apparatus (blindness, dimness of vision, double vision, field defects, etc.); in 11 per cent the initial symptom is numbness or similar painless paresthesia. The earliest symptoms tend to be fleeting and fluctuating, so that a misdiagnosis of hysteria is often made. The disappearance or alleviation of symptoms may last for months or years until the patient suffers another exacerbation. In general, three main types can be distinguished: an acute form, with a survival period of one to two years; a chronic, progressive form with a slowly downhill course that may last for 20 or 30 years; and a remittent form in which there is almost complete relief from symptoms during the period between acute exacerbations. The average life expectancy after the onset of the illness has been estimated to be 20 to 25 years.

'The end is distressing. An account of it is given by a sufferer who was also a graphic writer, W.N.P. Barbellion, in *The Diary of a Disappointed Man* and *Enjoying Life*. Ataxia, weakness, and spasticity confine the patient to bed and prevent him from carrying out the simplest actions for himself. Swallowing becomes difficult and speech almost unintelligible. Urinary or cutaneous infection or pneumonia finally releases the sufferer. In rare cases the last event is an acute exacerbation of the disease itself, taking the form of an acute myelitis or encephalomyelitis.' (Brain, W.R. *Diseases of the Nervous System*, 4th ed., Oxford University Press, London, 1951)

In the mental sphere, euphoria with a sense of mental and physical well-being despite obvious handicaps is characteristic, although dejection, irritability, and emotional lability are seen in some patients. Usually there is some reduction in intellectual capacity, and a few patients develop a delusional state or a terminal dementia.

There is no known treatment for the disorder.

sclerosis, posterolateral (post-ĕr-o-lat'ĕr-al) Subacute combined degeneration of the spinal cord; a deficiency disease due to lack of intrinsic factor (which combines with extrinsic factor to form the cobalt-containing complex, or vitamin B_{12}), seen in pernicious anemia, sprue, cachexia, and post-gastrectomy cases. Pathological changes include irregular demyelination of the posterolateral columns and peripheral nerves. Symptoms are: paresthesiae; early loss of position and vibratory sensation; later loss of touch and pain sensation, often with a glove and stocking type of anesthesia; sphincter disturbances; moderate muscular wasting; and ataxia. Symptoms usually begin in the lower limbs. Various mental changes may be seen: mild dementia, confusional psychosis, Korsakov psychosis, or affective reactions. Associated with the neuropsychiatric changes are gastric achlorhydria, glossitis, and anemia. Duration of life in untreated cases is approximately two years. Present-day treatment with vitamin B_{12} can restore the patient to good health indefinitely.

sclerosis, tuberous (tū'bĕr-us) Epiloia. A chronic disease from unknown cause, beginning in early childhood. It is characterized by mental deterioration (31x.3) often resulting in idiocy, epileptic convulsions, and special tumors (adenoma sebaceum) of the skin and viscera. Pathologically, there are various malformations and numerous glial tumors within the brain. The disease was originally described by Bourneville.

-scopia, -scopo, -scopy (-skō'pē-à, -skō'pō, -skō'pē) Combining form meaning looking at, examination, scrutiny, from Gr. *skopeīn*, to look at, examine, inquire.

scopolagnia (skō-pō-lag'nē-à) Voyeurism; scop(t)ophilia.

scopophilia Sexual pleasure derived from contemplation or looking (302.5). It is a component-instinct and stands in the same relation to exhibitionism as sadism does to masochism. Freud calls them paired instincts. See *voyeur; voyeurism.*

Autoscopophilia refers to the pleasure of looking at one's own body. Active scopophilia is the pleasure derived from looking at the sexual organs of another. Passive scopophilia is the desire to be looked at by others and is thus seen to be equivalent to active exhibitionism.

'The pleasure which a person takes in his own sexual organ may become associated with scoptophilia (or sexual pleasure in looking) in its active and passive forms. . . .' (Freud, S. *Collected Papers,* vol. 3, tr. by Strachey, A. and J., Leonard and Virginia Woolf, Hogarth Press, London, 1925)

In Freudian literature the German *Schaulust* has been translated as scoptophilia, but scopophilia is the more correct form.

scopophobia Fear of being looked at; morbid shyness.

scoptophilia See *scopophilia.*

scotoma (skō-tō'ma) An abnormal blind spot in the visual field.

scotoma, mental Lack of insight; a 'blind spot' for the problem before one's eyes.

scotomization (skot-ō-mi-zā'shun) 'In an earlier work I have defined scotomization (or the forming of mental "blind spots") as a process of psychic depreciation, by means of which the individual attempts to deny everything which conflicts with his ego.' (R. Laforgue. *Inter-*

national Journal of Psychoanalysis VIII, 473, 1927)

scotophobia (skō-tō-fō'bēà) Fear of darkness.

screen A form of concealment. When, for instance, in a dream one person stands for another or others, in virtue of some common feature, the person so standing is called a screen.

'Identification consists in giving representation in the dream-content to only one of two or more persons who are related by some common feature, while the second person or other persons appear to be suppressed as far as the dream is concerned. In the dream this one "screening" person enters into all the relations and situations which derive from the persons whom he screens.' (Freud, S. *The Interpretation of Dreams,* 3rd ed., tr. by Brill, A.A., Macmillan, New York, 1933)

screen, dream See *hallucination, blank.*

screen-memory See *memory, screen.*

screen-phantasy See *phantasy, screen.*

scruple, defloration Hirschfeld's term for a compulsion neurosis in young men about to marry; it implies a dread of being the first one to 'injure' a woman and carries with it also the fear of castration on the part of the male.

scruple, virginity Doubt on the part of the man regarding his wife's virginity; delusion of infidelity.

scrupulosity (skrōō-pū-là'si-tē) Excessive meticulousness or punctiliousness, most often displayed in relation to questions of right or wrong and hence often couched in religious or moral terms. The scrupulous patient sees evil where there is no evil, serious sin where there is no serious sin, and obligation where there is no obligation. Scrupulosity may appear as part of an obsessive-compulsive pattern but if long maintained it is suggestive of an underlying schizophrenic process.

sebastomania (sē-bas-tō-mā'nē-à) *Obs.* Religious psychosis.

secondary defense symptom See *symptom, secondary defense.*

secondary gain See *gain, epinosic.*

security operations H.S. Sullivan's term for feelings—such as anger, boredom, contempt, depression, or irritation—that, no matter how rational or explicable at first glance, are really defenses against the recognition or experiencing of anxiety; the term is approximately equivalent to *defense* (q.v.).

sedation　　threshold　　See　　*threshold, sedation.*

seed psychosurgery See *tractotomy, stereotactic.*

Séglas type See *type, Séglas.*

segmentation Synonymous with *cleavage.*

segregation Segregation is a 'form of isolation in which social distance is based upon physical separation.' (Wirth, L., *Segregation; Encyclopaedia of the Social Sciences,* Vol. 13, Macmillan, New York, 1934, p. 643)
'Segregation is the sifting of like social and population types, as well as industrial and commercial facilities, into specific districts where each unit tends to have the same economic function and competitive strength.' (Hollingshead, A.B., in Park, R.E. *Principles of Sociology,* Barnes & Noble, New York, 1939)
In genetics this term refers to that most essential principle in the Mendelian mechanism of inheritance, which implies that the gene units derived from the two parents segregate out in the hybrid, as if independent of each other. This phenomenon allows the gene units to enter into new combinations, especially in those involving more than one pair (see *Mendelism*).
As a eugenic term, segregation means placing in mental hospitals or special institutions (colonies) the insane, mentally defective or criminal individuals until the end of their capacity for reproduction, in order to prevent their having offspring.

Seitelberger's disease See *degeneration, neuro-axonal.*

seizure An attack, or sudden onset of a disease or of certain symptoms, such as convulsions.

seizure, audiogenic (aw-dē-ō-gen'ik) Convulsion or fit induced by prolonged exposure to intense sounds of high frequency.

seizure, erotic See *epilepsy, erotic.*

seizure, gustatory A form of epilepsy in which the sensation of a definite and usually peculiar taste is a part of the seizure pattern. The seizures are often also associated with sensations of peculiar odors.

seizure, psychic (sī'kik) A type of psychomotor epilepsy. See *epilepsy; psycholepsis.*

seizure, subjective A type of psychomotor epilepsy. See *epilepsy.*

seizure, temporal lobe Psychomotor epilepsy. See *epilepsy.*

seizures, automatic A type of psychomotor epilepsy. See *epilepsy.*

sejunction (sē-jungk'shun) Wernicke's term for blocking and other forms of dissociation. The concept is seldom used today, because it includes forms of dissociation which are widely removed both psychologically and nosographically.

selaphobia (sē-là-fō'bē-à) Fear of a flash.

selection In a specific biological sense, this term applies in a mixed population to the intentional or unintentional choice of those individuals who possess a particular genetic character or a certain combination of characters. This choice may be exercised by the failure to reproduce or by the lack of an adequate partner for marriage, if preference is given to other types or the given type is biologically incapable of reproduction.
According to the doctrine of survival of the fittest, *natural selection* takes place in evolution through a variety of processes which enable types (adapted to their environment) to reproduce their kind in marked degree, so that an improvement is gradually carried on from one stage of development to the other.
In human genetics, one usually distinguishes between *positive* and *negative* factors of selection, according to (1) whether a given factor is favorable to the reproduction of healthy or tainted family

stocks, or (2) whether the general life conditions of a population facilitate or hinder the reproduction of the average type.

seleniasmus (sē-lē-nē-az'mus) *Obs.* Lunacy.

selenogamia (-nō-gam'ē-à) ('state of being wedded to the moon') *Obs.* Somnambulism.

self The psychophysical total of the person at any given moment, including both conscious and unconscious attributes. Horney's term for self as thus defined is *actual self*, or *empirical self*. See Jung's definition of *ego*.

self-abuse *Obs.* A moralistic term for *masturbation* (q.v.).

self, actual In Horney's terms, the whole person—somatic as well as psychic, conscious and unconscious—as he really exists at any point in time. The *real self* is the person's potential for further growth and development. The person the neurotic believes himself to be (the result of identification with an idealized image of what he feels he should be) is the *idealized self*.

The *neurotic process* includes all the behavior and mechanisms by which the person maintains his identification with the idealized image even though this alienates him from his real self and requires him to deny and reject his actual self.

self-awareness See *image, body*.

self, bad A psychoanalytic concept referring to the tendency on the part of both analyst and patient to project on each other their guilty images of their instinct-ridden selves. Behind the shield of unconscious counter-transference, an analyst may make the patient a whipping boy for his own unconscious image of his infantile instinctual self. Conversely, the analyst must frequently tolerate (and analyze) the patient's tendency to project his own instinctual urges onto the analyst and to castigate him (the analyst) for them.

Much 'holier than thou' missionary zeal in the psychopathology of everyday life finds its source in this process of projection of the 'bad self' upon others. E.F. Sharpe (*Collected Papers on Psychoanalysis*, Hogarth Press, and The Institute of Psychoanalysis, London, 1950) says: 'The analyst must be sufficiently analysed to enable him to detect, and so consciously control, any tendency to regard the patient as the "Bad Self" who needs reforming.'

self-dynamism The fabric of the motivational forces and processes which lead to the development of the *self-system*, in Sullivan's theory of interpersonal relations. The human personality is founded on a biological substrate and is the product of the interpersonal and social forces acting on the person from the time of birth. The human being is concerned with two goals: (1) the pursuit of satisfaction, which deals chiefly with biological needs; and (2) the pursuit of security, which deals primarily with cultural pressures. To maintain security and avoid anxiety, the child develops and strengthens those sides of his nature which are pleasing or acceptable to the significant adults. The resulting configuration of traits is the *self-system* (q.v.).

self-effacement Horney's term for the behavior of the type of neurotic character that idealizes compliance, dependence, and love as a result of identification with the despised self.

self-esteem A state in which narcissistic supplies emanating from the superego are maintained so that the person does not fear punishment or abandonment by the superego. In other words, self-esteem is a state of being on good terms with one's superego. Pathologic loss of self-esteem is characteristic of clinical depression.

self, ethical See *superego*.

self-extension In social work, the 'effort to assert one's ego generally as a compensation for inferiorities and inadequacies; drive for ascendency; showing off; aggressiveness.' (Hamilton, G. *A Medical Social Terminology*, Presbyterian Hospital, New York, 1930)

self-extinction Horney's term for that form of neurotic behavior in which the person lives vicariously, through the actions of others, and has no personality that he experiences or identifies as his own. See *personality, as-if.*

self-fellator See *auto-fellatio.*

self, hidden See *personality, multiple.*

self-hypnosis (-hip-nō'sis) See *auto-hypnosis.*

self, idealized See *self, actual.*

self-identification A process in which the subject projects his own personality upon another and then proceeds to admire himself as he appears in the other person. While this is the usual process of self-identification, it is possible to include under the term the process of projecting one's undesirable traits upon another and then hating his own traits, as if they belonged to another. The latter happens in paranoid states.

Self-identification is based upon narcissism and homosexuality.

self-irrumation (-ir-ōō-mā'shun) Auto-fellatio.

self-maximation The drive (involving a part of the ego) associated with the numerous competitive situations a person encounters in the course of living, such as competitions for affection, attention, and status, at home, at school, in groups of peers, and elsewhere. There are competitions in the vocational, intellectual, and social fields, as well as for love-objects. This drive is to maintain feelings of personal adequacy.

self-observation Scrutiny of one's physical and/or mental state or functioning, one of the perceptive tasks of the *ego* (q.v.).

self-peeping, narcissistic (när-si-sis'tik) Self-voyeurism on the basis of primary *narcissism* (q.v.). Ordinarily, the original self-voyeurism is transformed into voyeurism directed against the parents. Bergler considers this voyeurism to be the true basis for choosing acting as a profession. In the beginning, the child says: 'I want to be a voyeur of mother and father, later of intimacies between them.' But the superego reproaches the child

for this wish, and the child denies having this wish by asserting the opposite: 'No, I am not a voyeur, I am just the opposite — an exhibitionist.' This, too, receives reproaches from the superego, and the desire is sublimated: 'I am neither a voyeur nor an exhibitionist; I merely want to give other people pleasure, so I am an actor.' (Bergler, E. *Psychoanalytic Quarterly Supplement 23,* 313, 1949)

self-punishment See *ego-suffering; masochism; resistance, superego.*

self-punishment, expiatory See *expiation.*

self, real See *self, actual.*

self-reporting See *psychodynamics, adaptational.*

self, secondary See *personality, multiple.*

self-sentience Awareness of self; in Sullivan's terminology, recognition of the bodily self as 'me,' and differentiated from the rest of the world or the 'not me.' See *ego, body.*

self, subconscious See *personality, multiple.*

self, subliminal (sub-lim'i-nal) See *personality, multiple.*

self-system A term used by Sullivan, in his theory of personality development, to denote final formation of self from a limited number sifted out of a greater number of potentialities, through parental influence on the developing personality of the child. Security rests on the feeling of belonging and being accepted. The child's actions or attributes that meet with disapproval tend to be blocked out of awareness and dissociated. As the child realizes that certain earlier devices for obtaining satisfaction, such as crying when hungry, bring on disapproval in the environment, the earlier pattern of behavior is inhibited: the child tends to develop and emphasize those aspects of his nature which are pleasing or acceptable to the significant adults, and the configuration of the traits which have met with approval constitutes the self-system.

After the self-system has been established, secondary anxiety appears whenever there is a possibility that the dissociated thoughts or feelings will become conscious: the dissociated impulses are not necessarily destructive, but because there is an emotional stake in maintaining the self-system, anything threatening it will nonetheless produce anxiety. It is obvious that the self-system tends to lead to a rigidity in personality and that even many positive potentialities of the person may never be realized or put into operation.

'The self-system of Sullivan has this in common with Freud's concept of character: it is formed as a result of the influence of the parents on the developing personality of the child. Freud presents this idea more mechanistically when he says character is the result of the sublimation of instincts under the influence of the Superego, the Superego being mainly the incorporated attitude of the parents and society. The self-system is different from the concept of character in that it includes more than sublimation, whereas Freud seems to conceive of character as nothing but sublimation. No ·true comparison of the two can be made, because the frames of reference are entirely different. Freud's system emphasizes what happens to instincts. Sullivan's system stresses what goes on between people. For Sullivan personality does not develop mechanically. Always the emphasis is on a dynamic interaction between people. Freud's orientation is mechanistic-biological; Sullivan's dynamic-cultural (inter-personal).' (Thompson, C. *Psychoanalysis, Evolution and Development*, Hermitage House, New York, 1950)

self, true The sum total of a person's potentialities which might be developed under the most favorable social and cultural conditions. Fromm considers neurosis in terms of cultural pressures (which often thwart potentialities) and the interaction of people. Since some of the patient's best potentialities are repressed, therapy aims at helping the patient to become himself and discover his 'true self.' Neurosis stems from the new needs a person's culture creates in him and, as a secondary concomitant to cultural pressures, from the person's deprivations and the frustrations of his potentialities.

'Fromm points out that in the course of therapy one often needs to stress the es-

sential healthiness of some of the patient's tendencies which had met with the disapproval of his environment. The goal of therapy is not primarily to make the person adjusted to his culture but to develop a sense of integrity and a respect for his true self. All adjustments to the culture which violate a person's integrity produce the feeling of guilt and shame and a loss of self-esteem. Fromm sees a real respect for oneself as essential to genuine love and respect for others.' (Thompson, C. *Psychoanalysis, Evolution and Development*, Hermitage House, New York, 1950)

semantic dissociation See *dissociation, semantic.*

semeiology, semiology (sē-mī-o′lō-jē) The study of signs, signals, symbols, or symptoms; symptomatology.

semiconscious Imperfectly conscious.

semi-obsession ˋa deux (à-dē′) 'The name "semi-obsession *à deux*" follows the expression *folie à deux*, by which is understood an identical and simultaneous psychosis in two members of a family group. However, while in *folie à deux* the psychosis in one individual is induced and/or influenced by the partner, we wish to call a symptom a phenomenon *à deux* when it occurs in two members of a group independently from each other.' (Wilder, J. 'A Semi-Obsession A Deux,' *American Journal of Psychotherapy 1*, 193, 1947)

semiopathic (sē-mē-ō-path′ik) Relating to the organism's affective or emotionally distorted use of the symbol. The result of the impingement of the symbolic or semiotic (partitive) reaction-pattern upon the organism's total pattern of behavior and the concomitant substitution of projected affects for intrinsic feeling. (Burrow, T. *The Biology of Human Conflict.* Macmillan, New York, 1937)

semiotic (sē-mī-ot′ik) Relating to symptoms. (See *semeiology*) 'Every view which interprets the symbolic expression as an analogous or abbreviated expression of a known thing is semiotic. A conception which interprets the symbolic expression as the best possible formulation of a relatively unknown thing which cannot conceivably, therefore, be more clearly or characteristically represented is symbolic.' . . . 'the explanation of the Cross as a symbol of Divine Love is *semiotic*, since Divine Love describes the fact to be expressed better and more aptly than a cross, which can have many other meanings.' (Jung, C.G. *Psychological Types*, tr. by Baynes, H.G., Harcourt, Brace, New York and London, 1923)

senile (sē'nīl) Relating to, characterized by, or manifesting old age.

senile psychosis (290.0, 309.6) *Senile dementia*, characterized by shrinkage and atrophy of the brain secondary to loss of nerve cells and shrinkage of cells. Senile plaques are always present; these are roundish areas of tissue degeneration with granular or filament-like detritus. Sometimes Alzheimer neurofibrillary whorls are seen within the cytoplasm. But there is no direct correlation between amount of pathological change and the appearance of symptoms, indicating that tissue damage alone is not responsible for the various syndromes included in the phrase, senile psychoses.

Ordinarily, diagnosis of senile brain disorder is not made unless the patient is 65 or 70 years of age. General symptoms and signs are: (1) defective orientation for time and space, this often leading to confusional states or sudden amnesic crises; (2) impaired memory, with earliest loss in the recall of recent concrete events; (3) gradual disorganization of speech; (4) mild affective displacements early, although later the affect changes may become the outstanding feature; (5) ethical obtuseness; (6) misoneism, obsessiveness, and stereotypy; (7) fleeting, unsystematized, drab, and colorless delusions, and visual or auditory hallucinations; (8) physical changes include early impairment of vibratory sense, dysesthesiae, impaired auditory and visual acuity, poverty of movement, sluggish reflexes, and focal neurologic signs if arteriosclerosis is a complicating factor; (9) EEG is usually normal, or there may be focal abnormalities especially in the fronto-temporal region.

In addition to depressive, paranoid, and agitated states, which are much the same here as elsewhere except for an absurd or phantastic quality because of senile failure of judgment, certain types of senile psychosis are generally recognized: (a) simple senile deterioration (see *deterioration, simple senile*); (b) senile delirium (see *delirium, senile*); and (c) *presbyophrenia* (q.v.).

senility (sē-nil'i-tē) Old age, but almost invariably it is intended to convey the idea that the person or some part of him has undergone involution or degeneration attendant upon advanced age. The onset of senility varies considerably, though in general it begins clinically at about the age of seventy.

senium (sē-nē-um) Feebleness of old age; also, the period of old age. In general, psychoses, psychoneuroses, or behavioral reactions appearing in old age are not considered due to senility and senile brain deterioration unless the patient is seventy years or older.

W. Mayer-Gross et al. (*Clinical Psychiatry*, 2nd ed. Baltimore, Williams and Wilkins, 1960) classify the mental diseases of old age as follows: (1) affective psychosis; (2) *senile psychosis* (q.v.); (3) arteriosclerotic psychosis (see *arteriosclerosis, cerebral*); (4) delirious states (see *delirium; delirium, senile*); (5) late *paraphrenia* (q.v.); and (6) miscellaneous disorders such as paresis, epilepsy, head injury, organic brain syndrome associated with cardiovascular disorder, and the like.

senium praecox (prē'koks) (L. 'premature old age') Premature senility. As average senility begins, at least clinically, at about the age of 70, senile manifestations under the age of fifty-five may be regarded as definitely premature. In psychiatry senium praecox is associated, for example, with Pick's disease or Alzheimer's disease.

sensation, feelings See *feeling-sensation*.

sensation, kinesthetic (kin-es-thet'ik) The sensation derived from muscles, joints, and inner ear, giving the perception of body weight, position, location, and movement. Schilder points out that primitive perception shows in motion in the majority of the senses, and emphasizes his belief that this inner motion is an important factor for the recognition and understanding of the space in which the body moves. Kinesthetic sensation is an important element 'for the final evaluation of space in our minds.' Without such a knowledge, achieved through kinesthetic sensation, the individual would not have a complete perception of his own body, nor would he be able to evaluate his relationship to all other objects. (Schilder, P. *Mind, Perception and Thought*, Columbia University Press, New York, 1942)

sensation, proprioceptive (prō-prē-ō-sep'-tiv) See *proprioception*.

sensation, secondary Stoddart uses this expression as synonymous with the *synesthesias*. They are those sensations 'which accompany sensations of another modality; for example, some people experience with every auditory sensation an accompanying visual sensation: the tone G is perhaps associated with the colour red or the tone D with blue. Similar sensations of color may accompany perceptions of taste, touch, pain, heat or cold: they are called "photisms." With some people certain words are accompanied by a sense of color, varying with different words (verbochromia). Again, there are secondary auditory sensations called "phonisms," secondary taste sensations called "gustatisms," secondary smell sensations called "olfactisms," and so on.' (Stoddart, W.H.B. *Mind and Its Disorders*, 5th ed., Lewis, London, 1926)

sensorium (sen-sō-rē-um) (L. 'the seat of organ of sensation') The hypothetical 'seat of sensation' or 'sense center,' located in the brain, is usually contrasted with the *motorium*, the two constituting the so-called 'animal organ-system,' while the *nutritive* and *reproductive* apparatus make up the 'vegetative organ-system.' Occasionally this term is applied to the entire sensory apparatus of the body.

When a person is clearly aware of the nature of his surroundings, his sensorium is said to be 'clear' or 'intact.' For example, correct orientation is a manifestation of a clear sensorium. When a person is unclear, from a sensory (not a delusional) standpoint, his sensorium is described as impaired or 'cloudy'.

Psychiatrists interchange the term *sensorium* with (organic) *consciousness*.

The sensorium may appear to be disordered, when the psyche is intensely active, as it is in severe manic states, or when the patient is completely out of the environment, as he may be while in a phase of depressive stupor.

sensory deprivation See *deprivation, sensory*.

sentience Mere sensation, apprehension, or cognition, without accompanying associations or affect.

sentiment 'Inasmuch as a sentiment . . . involves an affective element, it is obvious that *a sentiment is an idea of an object with which one or more emotions are organized.*' (Prince, M. *The Unconscious*, Macmillan, New York, 1916)

According to McDougall, a sentiment is an organized system of emotional tendencies concerning an object or a class of objects. It is a learned form of behavior, built upon experiences and acting in the form of emotional tension. Sentiments are not pure emotions or motives because they cannot exist apart from a relationship to some person or object. The object may call forth different emotional behavior at different times, but this behavior is still consistent with the sentiment.

sentinel-activity *Vigilance* (q.v.).

separation See *depression, anaclitic; anxiety, separation*.

separation anxiety Fear, anxiety, etc. occasioned by the threat or actuality of separation from mother and home. *School phobia* is a type of separation anxiety.

sequela (sē-kwel'à) The after-effect of an illness and, particularly, permanent or persistent dysfunction. Mental defect, epilepsy, and spastic palsies, for example, are possible *sequelae* of viral encephalitis.

sequence, genetic Growth sequence; the genically determined order of development of structures or functions.

sequestration *Isolation* (q.v.) or *denial* (q.v.) of those parts of one's psyche that are unacceptable or cannot be controlled.

Séquin, O. Edouard (1812-1880) (sē-qwin', sā-gâN') French-American psychiatrist.

seriatim functions See *functions, seriatim*.

serotonin (ser-ō-tō'nin) A potent cerebral synaptic inhibitor, also known as 5-

hydroxytryptamine, and identical with enteramine (which is found in the enterochromaffin system of the mammalian gastro-intestinal tract). Various functions have been attributed to serotonin, but its chief interest for psychiatry lies in the evidence that serotonin is normally involved as a synaptic agent in the regulation of centers in the brain concerned with wakefulness, temperature regulation, blood-pressure regulation, and various other autonomic functions. The nature of the effects produced makes it likely that serotonin, rather than acetylcholine, is the synaptic transmitter in the central parasympathetic system (the 'trophotropic' system, in Hess' terminology); and norepinephrine might well be the chemical transmitter in the central sympathetic ('ergotropic') nervous system. *Monoamine oxidase* (q.v.) is believed to be one of the agents in the metabolic breakdown of serotonin. See *ergotropic*.

servomechanism A governing or regulating device for maintaining output of a system at the desired rate or strength or in the desired direction.

set A group or series, such as a *set* of rules; a readiness to respond in a certain way or to respond selectively to certain stimuli.

setting, social Milieu.

sex The fundamental biological mechanism which differentiates higher animals as males, females, or intermediate sex forms.

As *maleness* is the state associated with the production of spermatozoa, a male is an individual that is efficiently equipped for the elaboration of functional sperms and for the conveyance of these to the site of fertilization. *Femaleness* is always associated with the elaboration of ova and in mammals, in addition to possessing the property of producing eggs, the female has an equipment for the prenatal care of the embryo and foetus and for the nurture of the offspring. If both maleness and femaleness are exhibited in one and the same individual he is called a *hermaphrodite*.

Where the sexes are distinct, male is to be distinguished from female by differences in (1) the form and structure of the gonads or reproductive organs, the

male's being testes, the female's, ovaries; (2) the accessory sexual apparatus of ducts and associated glands concerned with the transit of the products of the gonads; (3) the external organs of reproduction; and (4) certain skeletal, cutaneous, and other less definite physiological, biochemical, and psychological characters.

The organs that carry on the reproductive functions are known as *primary* sex organs. Those that distinguish the sexes from each other but play no direct part in reproduction are called *secondary* sexual characters.

sex-chromosome (-krō'mō-sōm) The pair of heterosomal chromosomes which differ in the male and female members of a species, in contrast to the other pairs of autosomal chromosomes which are alike in both sexes. See *chromosome*.

sex-determination In biology the term *sex-determination* relates to the genetic mechanism, by which in bisexual organisms the primary difference between the sexes originates in accordance with the laws of heredity. It is a difference in the heterosomal chromosome constitution between male and female individuals which explains the generally sharp segregation of the two sexes. See *sex-chromosome*.

In the female homogametic animals sex is determined by whether an X-bearing or Y-bearing sperm fertilizes the ovum, resulting in a female and a male offspring respectively. In male homogametic animals sex depends on whether a sperm fertilizes an X-bearing or Y-bearing egg, resulting in male and female offspring respectively.

Before the era of physiological genetics it was dogmatically held that the fully developed sex characters in the phenotype are dependent on this simple mechanism of sex-determination. Since Goldschmidt's studies of sex-differentiation it has been realized, however, that it is only the *predisposition* to sex that is transmitted by heredity, and that the expression in the phenotype is furthered or inhibited by physiological and environmental conditions as well as by age factors. See *sex-differentiation*.

sex-differentiation Although this term sometimes embraces both sex-determination and also sex-differentiation, it actually relates only to the developmental processes operating in the manifestation of sex differences in higher animals as expressed by Goldschmidt's 'balance theory.' The term thus indicates what happens during development after two sexually different types of zygotes have been formed by the chromosomal mechanism of *sex-determination* (q.v.).

The conception of sex-differentiation in terms of a ratio between male-determining and female-determining elements is based upon the observation that in a number of species of animals there have appeared, in addition to normal males and females, peculiar individuals which are neither typical males nor typical females. These *intersexes* (q.v.) have some male and some female characters which 'may be so intimately mixed as to give their possessors the appearance of being true intermediates between maleness and femaleness.' (Sinnott, E.W. and Dunn, L.C. *Principles of Genetics*, 3rd ed., McGraw-Hill, New York and London, 1939) They suggest that sex-differentiation is 'a competition between opposed tendencies in which the race is eventually won by that type of process (either male or female) which proceeds most rapidly at the critical period of determination.'

In normal sexual growth, the 23rd pair of chromosomes contains an XX complex in females, and the normal female pattern of cell nuclei is chromatin-positive. In males, on the other hand, the 23rd pair of chromosomes contains an XY complex, and the normal male pattern of cell nuclei is chromatin-negative. In true hermaphrodites (who have both ovarian and testicular functioning tissues) and in pseudohermaphrodites (where the external genitalia are of the sex opposite to the genetic sex) there is often difficulty in deciding on the sex of the infant. In general, infants with anomalous sex development should be reared in accordance with their genetic sex and given appropriate hormonal treatment.

sex-limitation The principle of a trait occurring in one sex only, namely, one characterized by the phenotypical development of those physiological sex characters that are the necessary anatomical basis of the trait in question.

In contrast to *sex-linked* characters produced by genes which are bound to the X

or Y chromosomes, the phenomenon of *sex-limitation* is *not* due directly to differences in the manifestation of the effects of genes located in one sex-chromosome. See *sex-linkage*.

sex-linkage The genetic phenomenon of the coupling of a hereditary factor with an individual's sex-chromosome structure responsible for the development of the respective sex. It rests upon the fact that in bisexual organisms the sex distinction is transmitted by heredity in accordance with the Mendelian law of segregation, and is not to be confused with the more common mechanism of *sex-limitation*. If one of the sex-chromosomes carries a gene for a certain character, the transmission of the character and the distribution of the sexes must run together. See *sex-determination*.

The particular distribution of the sex-chromosomes in man, having heterogametic XY males, explains why sex-linkage gives different sex proportions of linked characters with respect to dominance or recessiveness. *Dominant* sex-linked characters are able to appear when only one predisposition is present. Their manifestation is therefore twice as frequent in females as in males, since the number of X chromosomes is double in females.

Recessive sex-linked anomalies can be manifested by a female only when she is a homozygote for the factor in question. As the female has two X chromosomes, one from each parent, the heterozygotic manifestation of a recessive trait, transmitted on a mother's X chromosome to her daughter, is antagonized by the effect of the X chromosome which she has from her father. In males, however, the anomaly is manifested in the heterozygotic condition, since in the case of a son who receives his single X chromosome from his mother, there is no paternal X chromosome with a dominant gene to overcome the recessive gene on the X chromosome of the mother.

Consequently, these recessive traits, of which hemophilia and color blindness are the classic examples, are usually transmitted by the female and suffered for by the male. They do not appear in both father and son unless the mother also possesses the gene. It is the rule that, through their daughters, who do not exhibit it, men transmit the trait to half of the daughters' sons.

sexology (seks-ol'ō-jē) The science of the sexes and their interrelationship.

sexopathy (seks-op'ȧ-thē) Sexual abnormality; sexual perversion. Roland Dalbiez uses this term in preference to perversion, because of the undesirable moralistic connotation of the latter. Sexopathy includes both anomalies of sexual aim and anomalies of sexual object, no matter what their etiology. 'Like Havelock Ellis he [Dalbiez] is disinclined to preserve the word perversion in sexology, being of the opinion that it carries with it the moralist's veto; he suggests the word sexopathy instead.' (O'Connor, W.A. *Psychiatry, A Short Treatise*, Williams and Wilkins, Baltimore, 1948)

sex reversal See *reversal, sex.*

sex role inversion Adoption of the sex role of, and introjection of the psychologic identity of, the opposite sex.

sex, third Bisexuality; homosexuality. Freud speaks of three series of sexual characteristics; (1) 'physical sexual characteristics (physical hermaphroditism); (2) mental sexual characteristics (masculine, or feminine attitude); (3) and kind of object-choice.'
'Moreover, the tendencious publications block the way leading to a deeper insight into all that is uniformly designated homosexuality by rejecting two fundamental facts which have been revealed by psychoanalytic investigation. The first of these is that homosexual men have experienced a specially strong fixation in regard to the mother; the second, that, in addition to their manifest heterosexuality, a very considerable measure of latent or unconscious homosexuality can be detected in all normal people. If these findings are taken into account, then, to be sure, the supposition that nature in a freakish mood created a "third sex" falls to the ground.' (Freud, S. *Collected Papers*, vol. 2, tr. by Riviere, J., Leonard and Virginia Woolf and The Institute of Psychoanalysis, London, 1924-25)

sexual (sek'shoo-al) Pertaining to, characterized by, springing from or endowed with sex. In biology the term *sexual*, pertaining to the property of being male or female, is used not only to characterize what is peculiar to sex or the sexes, but also to denote the method of reproduction by sexes, as distinguished from *asexual* reproduction.

sexual, contrary Synonymous with *homosexual* and *(sexual) invert.*

sexual deviation See *deviation, sexual.*

sexualism Sexuality (q.v.); rarely used in psychiatry.

sexualitas senilis (sek-soo-ä'lē-tȧs se-nē'-lēs) Krafft-Ebing's expression for sexual potency exhibited in the senile period of life.

sexuality Freud's concept of sexuality is to be understood in a broad sense. Psychic energy connected with sensual and somatic satisfactions is said to be sexual energy; the latter is expressed also in the multiple forms of sublimation. 'We suppose that there are two fundamentally different kinds of instincts, the sexual instincts in the widest sense of the word (*Eros*, if you prefer that name) and the aggressive instincts, whose aim is destruction.' (Freud, S. *New Introductory Lectures on Psychoanalysis*, tr. by Sprott, W.J.H., Norton, New York, 1933)
'An attempt to formulate the general characteristics of the sexual instincts would run as follows: they are numerous, emanate from manifold organic sources, act in the first instance independently of one another and only at a later stage achieve a more or less complete synthesis. The aim which each strives to attain is "organ-pleasure"; only when the synthesis is complete do they enter the service of the function of reproduction, becoming thereby generally recognizable as sexual instincts.' (Freud, S. *Collected Papers*, vol. 4, tr. by Riviere, J., Leonard and Virginia Woolf and The Institute of Psychoanalysis, London, 1924-25)
The meaning of *sexuality* to Freud apparently is two-fold; rather, one should say that the sexual instincts serve two major functions—those associated with self-preservation and those with race-preservation.
The race-preservative component is really not put into actual service of reproduction until some time after puberty. There seems to be no objection, indeed, there is universal agreement, to referring to the instincts, devoted to the reproductive act, as sexual.

It has been difficult, however, to accept the idea that the sexual instincts are present and operative during the so-called latency period (from the age of five to puberty). It is not reasonable to believe that, without any conditioning whatever, the sexual instinct is dormant somewhere for 12 or 14 years, only to put in a sudden appearance at puberty in an individual wholly unprepared for adult sexuality.

Freud holds that the preparations for adult sexuality are intensive and cover a long period. The sexual instincts, so universally acknowledged after puberty, are given definite assignments already during the latency period, for purposes of preparing the person for the severest test of all, the harmonious union of the sexes, culminating in reproduction. During the latency period, however, the sexual energies do not possess specific sexual coloring; they are sublimated or hidden under the cloak of non-reproductive forms of activities. But, their purpose is race-preservation. It might have been more expedient to have given the sexual instincts of the latency period other names, which should more aptly describe the immediate nature of their service. Wheat is not bread until it has passed through many processes. It will eventually be a part of bread. The sexual instincts of the latency period are the 'wheat' of adult sexuality. See *altrigenderism; suigenderism.*

Freud uses the term *sexual* to refer to many activities of the infantile period (extending from birth until approximately the fifth year). There is sexuality, for instance, associated with infantile oral, anal, and genital organization. It seems true that part of the energies of the erogenous zones is destined for final adult sexual participation; moreover, that the zones themselves, particularly the oral and genital, are prepared from early life for the participation.

Jung is not as comprehensive as Freud in the meaning of sexuality. What he includes under the term more closely approximates the general opinion of scientists. 'We ought to be able to recognize and to admit that much in the psyche really depends on sex, at times even everything, but that at other times little depends on sex, and nearly everything comes under the factor of self-preservation, or the power-instinct, as Adler calls it. . . .

At times sex is dominant, at other times self-assertion or some other instinct. . . . When sex prevails, everything becomes sexualized, as everything then either expresses or serves the sexual purpose.' (Jung, C.G. *Contributions to Analytical Psychology,* tr. by Baynes, H.G. and C.F., Kegan Paul, Trench, Trubner, London, 1928)

Adler's general concept of sex is not greatly unlike Jung's. 'The desire for knowledge of sex differences, the uncertainty concerning his own sexual role, may be looked upon as causes of the arousing of the feeling of inferiority. Likewise the realization and grouping of traits believed to be feminine, the vacillating, doubting, hermaphroditic apperception and hermaphroditic predisposition. Predisposition to the psychic gestures of the feminine role always entail greater passivity, anxious anticipation, etc., but call forth the masculine protest, stronger emotivity. (Adler, A. *The Neurotic Constitution,* tr. by Glueck, B. and Lind, J.E., Moffat, Yard, New York, 1917) The foregoing is said by Adler to be a 'typical cause of the onset of a neurosis.' Other typical causes, described by him, are: onset of menstruation, epoch of menstrual activity, epoch of sexual activity, the stage of fitness for marriage, pregnancy, puerperium, climacteric, reduction of potency, etc.

In biology the term *sexuality* relates to the state of being distinguished by sex. See *sex-determination.*

sexuality-index See *index of sexuality.*

sexuality, infantile See *sexuality.*

sexualization (sek-shoo-al-i-zā'shun) The act of sexualizing. See *sexuality.*

sexualize (sek'shoo-al-īz) To endow with sexual energy or instinct. The genitals become sexualized at an early age. Other parts of the body (breasts, oral region, hands, etc.) may possess sexual qualities. Thoughts may be sexualized, as for example, when they appear in the form of sexual jokes.

shadow In Jung's analytical psychology, the unconscious.

'For the sake of understanding, it is, I think, a good thing to detach the man from his shadow, the unconscious. . . . One sees much in another man which does not belong to his conscious psychology, but which gleams out from his unconscious, and one is rather tempted to regard the observed quality as belonging to the conscious ego.' (Jung, C.G. *Psychological Types*, tr. by Baynes, H.G., Harcourt, Brace, New York and London, 1923)

shame Psychodynamically, shame is considered to be the specific force directed against urethral-eroticism, just as the fear of being eaten is the specific oral fear, and the fear of being robbed of body contents is the specific anal fear. Ambition is the fight against this shame.

Shame is also used as a defense against exhibitionism and voyeurism; 'I feel ashamed'means 'I do not want to be seen.'

shell-shock A general term, particularly wide in its application to psychic disorders occurring during active warfare. Many of the illnesses called shell-shock, or *combat neurosis*, are encountered in civil life and are then usually regarded as traumatic neuroses. See *neurosis, traumatic*.

shock 1. A sudden physical or mental disturbance.

2. A state of profound mental and physical depression consequent upon severe physical injury or an emotional disturbance.

3. In Rorschach scoring, any delay or failure in responding to the blot; shock indicates ambivalence regarding the advisability of acting out the traits revealed by the blot component causing the shock. Thus *color shock* (as on plate II and/or VIII) is interpreted as ambivalence in relation to gratifying emotional needs, and human movement shock (M shock or Plate III shock) reflects ambivalence over acting in accordance with one's prototypal life role. M shock in addition indicates conflict over insufficiently strong heterosexual tendencies.

shock, psychodramatic 'A procedure which throws a patient, barely escaped from a psychosis, back into a re-experience of the psychotic attack is a psychodramatic shock treatment. The patient is asked to throw himself back into the hallucinatory experience when it is still most vivid in his mind. He is not asked to describe it; he must act. He puts his

body into the position as it was then and acts as he acted then. He may select any members of the staff to recreate the hallucinatory situations. This makes the procedure a "psychodrama." The patient usually shows a violent resistance against being thrown back into the painful experience from which he has just escaped. Doing this, despite a violent fear, produces a "shock."

'Acting upon a psychotic level at a time when he is extremely sensitive to the vanished mental syndrome, the patient learns to check himself. It is a training in mastering of psychotic invasions, not through analysis but through a reconstruction of the psychotic experiences from act to act, from role to role, and from delusion to delusion, until the whole sphere of the psychosis is projected upon the therapeutic stage. It is a preventative therapy. The patient is trained to develop spontaneous controls with which to ward off the sudden onset of a psychotic invasion. The procedure produces a cathartic effect. Psychodramatic procedure, as differentiated from other shock procedures which leave a patient helpless and inarticulate, insists that the patient reproduce with his own body that fantastic world in which he has been lost.' (Moreno, J.L. *Sociometry 2*, 6, 1939)

shock-therapy See *therapy, shock; treatment, shock*.

shock-treatment See *treatment, shock*.

short stare epilepsy A type of petit mal epilepsy. See *epilepsy*.

short-term Brief; see *psychotherapy, brief*.

shortening reaction See *rigidity, decerebrate*.

show, half See *half-show*.

ShR In Rorschach scoring, shading response. Piotrowski (*Perceptanalysis*, MacMillan, New York, 1957) differentiates four categories: c, Fc, c', Fc' (qq.v.). The ShR indicate the self-regulating mechanisms of control over outward manifestations of emotion; c responses indicate that action tendencies are inhibited or delayed, while c' responses indicate a readiness to do something overt and definite to alleviate anxiety. Reaction-formation is characteristic of c types, while acting out is characteristic of c' types. The greater the number of c' responses, and the more the number of c responses exceeds the number of C responses, the greater is the amount of anxiety and/or pathological fears.

shut-in August Hoch's term for the pre-morbid personality which is seen in approximately 60 per cent of schizophrenics: quiet, reserved, asocial, withdrawn, seclusive, 'lone-wolf' types, those who live among but not with, etc. Bleuler's term, schizoid, is approximately equivalent to 'shut-in.'

sialorrh(o)ea (sī-à-lo-rē'à) Excessive salivation.

sibling (sib'ling) In human genetics, one of two or more children not simultaneously born of the same two parents. It thus excludes twins or other multiples as well as half-brothers and half-sisters, and step-brothers and step-sisters. However, the definition in all leading dictionaries makes it a far less restricted term.

sibship A genetic term pertaining to one series of siblings, that is, to all the biological children of a union of two parents, excluding multiples. See *birth, multiple.*

sibship method See *method, sibship.*

sicchasia (si-kā'zē-à) Disgust for food.

side-impulse See *impulse, side.*

siderodromophobia (sid-ĕr-ō-drom-ō-fō'-bē-à, -drō-mō-fō'bē-à) Fear of railroads or trains.

siderophobia (sid-ĕr-ō-fō'bē-à) Fear of the heavens and what comes from them — the elements, etc. Bianchi writes that 'the subject turns pale, suffers from tremors, dryness of the mouth, visceral movements, diarrhoeic discharges, sometimes nausea, palpitation, oppression, or even a fit of real anguish *(siderophobia).*' (Bianchi, L. *A Text-Book of Psychiatry,* tr. by Mac-Donald, J.H., Ballière, Tindall & Cox, London, 1906)

Sidis, Boris (1876-1923) American psychiatrist.

Siemerling, Ernst (1857-1931) (zē'mēr-ling) German psychiatrist and neurologist.

sigmatism (sig'mà-tiz'm). Difficulty in pronouncing the *S* (and *Z*) sound.

sign, Brudzinski (broo-jēñ'ski) (J. Brudzinski, Polish physician, 1874-1917) The Brudzinski sign is essentially significant of meningitis. By passively flexing the head on the chest, a flexion of the lower limbs is produced.

sign, echo *Rare.* A speech-disorder observed in epileptic patients characterized by the repetition of a word in some part of a sentence.

sign, eyelash In a case of unconsciousness due to functional disease, such as hysteria, stroking the eyelashes will make the lids move, but no such reflex will occur in case of organic brain lesion such as apoplexy, fracture of the skull, or other severe traumatism.

sign, Hoffmann (Johann Hoffmann, German neurologist, 1857-1919) In hemiplegia due to organic brain disease, snapping of the index or ring finger produces flexion to the thumb.

sign, Kernig's Waldemar Kernig, Russian physician, 1840-1917) The Kernig sign is observed in meningitis. Flexing the thigh at the hip, and extending the leg at the knee, produces pain and resistance.

sign, Litten's (Moritz Litten, German physician, 1845-1907) In paralysis of the diaphragm, non-projection of shadow by the diaphragm x-rayed during respiration.

sign, Marcus Gunn (Marcus Gunn, contemporary British surgeon) The raising of a ptosed lid on opening the mouth and moving the jaw to the opposite side.

sign, mirror A symptom seen frequently in schizophrenic patients, who tend to stand in front of a mirror or other shining surface for an unduly long time. The mirror sign is generally regarded as an expression of the patient's autistic withdrawal.

The same sign can also occur in advanced organic dementia (e.g. Alzheimer's disease): the patient sits for hours in front of a mirror, talking to his own reflection; because of complete loss of personal identify, the patient does not realize that the reflection is his own.

sign, Romberg (Moritz Heinrich Romberg, German physician, 1795-1873) Swaying of the body when the patient stands with the feet together and the eyes closed, suggestive of ataxia.

sign, Rosenbach's (Ottomar Rosenbach, German physician, 1851-1907) Inability of neurasthenics to close the eyes immediately and completely on command.

sign, Rumpf (Theodor Rumpf, German physician, 1862-1923) In cases of neurasthenia pressure over a painful point will accelerate the pulse from ten to twenty beats per minute.

sign, Schuele's (Heinrich Schuele, German psychiatrist, 1839-1916) See *omega melancholicum.*

sign, Stiller's (Berthold Stiller, Budapest physician, 1837-1922) The presence of a floating tenth rib as indicative of a neurasthenic tendency; called also costal stigma.

sign, Strümpell (Adolf von Strümpell, German neurologist, 1853-1925) In organic hemiplegia, dorsiflexion of the hand occurs on making a fist.

sign, tibialis In organic hemiplegia, dorsal flexion of the foot occurs on flexion at the knee and hip.

sign, Westphal's (vest'fălz) (Carl Friedrich Otto Westphal, German neurologist, 1833-1890) Loss of the knee jerk.

sign, wobbly knee See *knee, wobbly.*

sign, Woltman's See *reflex, myxedema.*

signal anxiety See *anxiety.*

signe de Magnan (sēn'yu dû man-yan') *Formication* (q.v.).

signe du miroir (sēn'yu dê mēr-wàr') Mirror sign; see *sign, mirror.*

significance Meaning; value; importance. Statistical significance is the likelihood or probability that the value or score obtained is not due to chance but is instead meaningfully related to some specific factor or variable.

signs, soft A phrase applied to subtle signs of disability or dysfunction; used particularly to refer to the results of neurologic examination of children who are schizophrenic and/or who have suffered minimal brain damage. In both categories, it is difficult to pinpoint specific damage, but tests of patterned motor and perceptual behavior are often suggestive of subtle, slight deviations from the normal. See *impulse-disorder, hyperkinetic.*

silence, insane An older expression used by T.S. Clouston to denote insanity with mutism.

silence, selective Deliberate withholding of response, information, or free-association which a patient resorts to at a point of anxiety or negative transference toward the therapist or the group in order to resist the therapeutic situation.

silver cord syndrome See *syndrome, silver cord.*

Simmonds' disease (Morris Simmonds, German physician, 1855-1925) See *cachexia, hypophysial.*

Simon-Binet tests See *tests, Binet-Simon.*

simple schizophrenia See *schizophrenia, simple.*

simulant Simulator, malingerer.

simulate Malinger, deceive.

simultagnosia Ability to describe the action represented in a picture; often lacking in children with generalized brain dysfunction, who may merely name the objects represented rather than being able to discuss the action of the picture.

Simultanagnosia is the lack of, or any disability in, such simultaneous form perception, and is suggestive of a lesion in the anterior part of the left occipital lobe.

simultaneous tactile sensation See *tactile sensation, double simultaneous.*

singultus (sing-gul′tus, L. sēng-gool′toos) Hiccough.

sinistrad Toward the left; sinistrad writing is mirror-writing. See *strephosymbolia.*

sinistrality See *dextrality-sinistrality.*

sinistrosis (sin-is-trō′sis) Shell-shock.

sitiophobia (sit-i-ō-fō′bē-à) Sitophobia.

sitomania (sī-tō-mā′nē-à) Bulimia; a morbid, voracious appetite.

sitophobia Fear of (eating) food.

situation, danger See *anxiety.*

situation, either-or The term for a situation of doubt and vacillation in which the neurotic places himself, especially in dreams. In such situations the patient desires two different things at the same time and does not know which to choose. An example of this is the neurotic patient with a strong mother attachment who is also deeply in love with his fiancée: in his dreams he symbolizes either his mother or his fiancée, but always with a profound doubt about which of them he should love more. The patient vacillates between two principles and this vacillation may refer to persons, objects, or ideas.

situational reaction See *transient situational personality disorders.*

sixty-nine A slang expression referring to fellatio and/or cunnilinction practiced simultaneously by two persons, the head of each being near the feet of the other.

Sjobring, Henrik (1879-1956) Swedish psychiatrist; described certain personality types and reactions to stress as based on constitutional psychological variables and cerebral lesions.

skelic See *index, skelic.*

sketch, biographic This expression is often used in the field of objective psychobiology (Adolf Meyer) to refer to the life history of the patient as the latter records it. To facilitate the recording Meyer devised what he calls *The Life Chart,* consisting of topical guides for the person who is writing his biographic sketch.

skew-deviation See *deviation, skew.*

skoptsy (skop-tsē′) A Russian religious sect (a subdivision of the *raskol′nike,* the schismatics or dissenters) whose adherents practice castration, in conformity with the passage: 'And there be eunuchs, which have made themselves eunuchs for the kingdom of heaven's sake. He that is able to receive it, let him receive it.' (St. Math. XIX, 12; cf. also V, 29-30; XVIII, 8-9; St. Mark IX, 43-7; Rom. VIII, 13; Col. III, 5)

Castration among the skoptsy is of two degrees: (1) *the small seal (first purity; mounting a piebald horse),* involving removal of scrotum only, with the testicles. (2) *the grand seal (second purity; mounting a white horse),* total castration, with the excision of both the scrotum and reproductive organ. Women, too, undergo castration and even remove their breasts.

The skoptsy seek salvation through mortifying the flesh by castration. They await the Second Advent when the Savior will 'roll in on a fiery chariot, will ring the bell of St. John's Church in Moscow and assemble for his Kingdom his faithful little children.'

The sect of skoptsy is an outgrowth of the *Kristovshchina* (Christist faith), who elect a Christ, Theotokos (Mother of God, Virgin Mary), the Apostles, and an Old Maid from among their numbers.

In economic life, the skoptsy have plied the trade of money-changers almost exclusively and 'all their passions have turned into profit and acquisitiveness.' In appearance they usually look bloated, with a flabby, livid skin, light-colored sparse hair (none on the upper lip or chin), piping effeminate voice, and phlegmatic movements.

slavering *Obs.* Drooling.

sleep, activated See *dream.*

sleep, continous See *treatment, continuous sleep.*

sleep-drunkenness Somnolentia; a half-waking condition in which the faculty of orientation is in abeyance, and, under the influence of nightmare-like ideas, the person becomes actively excited and violent, sometimes to the extent of inflicting injury upon others.

sleep paralysis or numbness See *paralysis, sleep.*

sleep, paroxysmal Sleep epilepsy, narcolepsy; a sudden uncontrollable disposition to sleep occurring at irregular intervals, with or without obvious predisposing or exciting cause.

sleep, thrombencephalic See *dream.*

sleep, telencephalic See *dream.*

sleep-walking See *somnambulism.*

sleep, yen (Chinese *yen,* smoke, opium) A slang expression used by morphine or heroin addicts for the somnolence that affects them when the drug is withdrawn.

slip of tongue *Lapsus linguae;* see *act, symptomatic.*

Sluder's syndrome Sphenopalatine neuralgia; vidian neuralgia. See *headaches, cluster.*

slum An urban area characterized by physical deterioration and social disorganization so marked as to result in the personal disorganization of its residents in the form of juvenile delinquency, adult crime, vice, alcoholism, gambling, mental disorders, etc. Children of the slums are both materially and emotionally disadvantaged and underprivileged.

smother-love See *love, smother.*

snake, symbol of Symbols of snakes are based on symbolization of the male genital. Before he knew the principles of biology, primitive man could think of only one thing: that because the genitals produce life they were, therefore, the symbols of life; hence snakes or symbols of them were carried in processions and worshipped. Though there is no obvious resemblance between the snake and the male genital, to the conscious eye there is nevertheless suggested a hidden simi-

larity for the unconscious to draw the analogy. The story of Adam and Eve has a truly allegorical significance. Adam and Eve represent humanity in its infancy, when it was untroubled, naked, and free, when life was a paradise. But then comes the snake, the symbol of sex, and the situation takes on an altogether different aspect. Dreams about snakes are very common, but we must guard against the conclusion that the snake always signifies the male genital. (Brill, A.A., *Basic Principles of Psychoanalysis,* Doubleday, New York, 1949)

snow (From the cocaine powder's resemblance to snow both in whiteness and powder consistence) Slang expression for cocaine.

snow-bird Slang expression for a cocaine addict.

social breakdown syndrome See *syndrome, social breakdown.*

social impulse, fundamental See *impulse, fundamental social.*

social integration-disintegration model See *psychiatry, community.*

social interest See *interest, social.*

social policy planning Known variously as *community organization, community action, social action,* and *social engineering,* social policy planning is a deliberate, organized, and collaborative approach to the analysis and manipulation of social structures and systems. It aims to improve the quality of life in a community, which is viewed as an organism, a total biotype, an ecological entity. Emphasis is upon superordinate goals (viz. the welfare of people), rather than on institutionally defined goals (e.g. the pathology and condition of specific people who appear at the door of a mental health center). Its methods may even include such an approach as founding a new town with a sociopetal arrangement to promote participation by such means as organization, architectural structure, and other environmental factors that program behavior. The goal is to develop a process within the community—not to devise a specific prescription, but to initiate interaction and expand the spectrum of possible action in overcoming poverty, minority problems, and other urban crises, which currently are ordinarily defined in terms of jobs, housing, education, crime on the streets, drug and alcohol abuse, and suicide. See *psychiatry, community.*

social psychiatry See *ecology; psychiatry, comparative; psychiatry, community.*

social therapy Rehabilitation therapy; any form of treatment whose primary focus is on the patient's level of social functioning and whose aim is to improve the patient's ability to function in a socially approved manner. The social therapies include any number of socio-environmental approaches that concern themselves with the patient's behavior, rather than his intrapsychic state—the therapeutic community, patient government, remotivation, attitude therapy, compensated work, etc.

social type See *type, social.*

social work, family 'Family social work is a field of organized practice having to do with human relationships. Its main purpose is to help individuals deal effectively with difficulties experienced in relating themselves to others in their families and in their communities. This practice is based on a growing body of knowledge about human beings as functioning members of society and it employs the technique and art termed social case work.' (Lund, H.H. *Social Work Year Book 1939*, ed. by Kurtz, R.H., Russell Sage Foundation, New York)

social work, psychiatric The adaptation and application of social psychiatry and mental hygiene to case-work practice. 'Psychiatric social workers are usually concerned with the social case study and treatment of children or adults whose personal and social maladjustments are primarily due to mental health problems, including nervous and mental diseases and defects, and emotional behavior, and habit disorders.' (C. Bassett. *Social Work Year Book 1939*, ed. by R.H. Kurtz. Russell Sage Foundation, New York)

The term has also been defined as 'the branch of social case work that deals with cases of social maladjustment in which a mental factor or a behavior problem is of primary importance.' ('Vocational Aspects

of Psychiatric Social Work,' *Mental Hygiene*, 1925)

socialization 'The development of a social nature or character—a social state of mind—in the individuals who associate.' (Giddings, F.H. *Theory of Socialization*, Macmillan, New York, 1897)

'The interactional process by which the individual is taught his place in the social order.' (Young, K. *An Introductory Sociology*, American Book, New York, 1934)

'From the standpoint of the group, [socialization] is the psychic articulation of the individual into the collective activities. From the standpoint of the person, socialization is the participation of the individual in the spirit and purpose, knowledge and methods, decision and action of the group.' (Burgess, E.W. *The Function of Socialization in Social Evolution*, University of Chicago Press, 1910)

In occupational therapy this term is applied to the development (in a patient) of those tendencies which induce him to be companionable and inclined to seek and mingle easily with a group.

In psychiatry the term means the condition in which inner impulses (i.e. instincts and their derivatives) are expressed or lived out in conformity with the cultural demands of the environment. It is synonymous with *sublimation* (q.v.).

socialize 1. To *sublimate* (q.v.) 2. To mix in a group.

society Society may be regarded 'as the most general term referring to the whole complex of the relations of man to his fellows.' (Parsons, T. *Society: Encyclopaedia of the Social Sciences*, vol. 14, Macmillan, New York, 1934, p. 225)

It is 'the system of social relationships in and through which we live' (McIver, R.M. *Society, A Textbook of Sociology*, Farrar & Rinehart, New York, 1937), and 'the sum total of social institutions.' (Park, R.E. and Burgess, E.W. *Introduction to the Science of Sociology*, University of Chicago Press, Chicago, 1921)

Society is 'a highly intricate network of partial or complete understandings between the members of organizational units of every degree of size and complexity, ranging from a pair of lovers or a family to a league of nations.' (Sapir, E. *Communication; Encyclopaedia of the Social Sciences*, vol. 4, Macmillan, New York, 1931, p. 78)

sociogram (sō'sē-ō-gram) 'The sociogram projects the results of sociometric, spontaneity and population tests into a pattern and makes visible the relationship of every individual to every other individual of the group tested. Thus, the position of every individual is defined as well as the configuration of the total structure.

The sociogram is primarily a method for exploring the invisible structure of society. As a guide it has led to discoveries of social structures which could not have been revealed through other means. It showed, for example, the positions of emotional isolates in a group, of pair attractions and pair rejections, of triangles, of chains of interpersonal relations, the positions of leader structures and the cliques of individuals who are separated from the group as a whole.' (Moreno, J.L. *Sociometry, 1*, 212, 1937)

sociology, clinical See *psychiatry, comparative.*

sociometry (sō-sē-om'e-trē). 'Sociometry is the study of the actual psychological structure of human society. This structure, rarely visible on the surface of social processes, consists of complex interpersonal patterns which are studied by quantitative and qualitative procedures.

'Sociometry proceeds upon the premise that there is some sort of order in the phenomena with which it deals. The psychological situation of a community viewed as a whole has a discernible ordered pattern. It presents itself in laws and tendencies which are discoverable by means of experiment and analysis.

'From the point of view of a "medical" sociology, it is essential to know the actual structure of human society at a given moment. The sociometric procedure obtains this knowledge by considering every individual in his concreteness and not as a symbol. Every relationship an individual may have with another person or persons is also considered in its concreteness. The actual structure is best obtained when the individuals are placed in a situation where they spontaneously uncover their relationships. A fundamental part of the sociometric procedure is to apply to a community an actual social situation which is confronting its people at the moment. The social situation applied is of such a nature as to make repetition possible at any time in the future without loss of spontaneous participation. In this manner, the procedure reveals the organization and evolution of groups and the position of individuals within them.' (Moreno, J.L. 'Inter-Personal Therapy,' *Sociometry 1,* 19, 1937)

sociopath (sō'sē-ō-path) A term that was proposed to designate the *psychopathic personality,* since the symptoms of psychopathy are manifested in the field of social behavior.

sociopathic personality disturbance In the 1952 revision of psychiatric nomenclature, this term was used to refer to those who are ill primarily in terms of society and of conformity with social, cultural, and ethical demands. This group does *not* include those whose conduct and behavior is symptomatic of more primary personality disturbance. Included in this group were:

(1) *Antisocial reaction* (q.v.)—approximately equivalent to the older terms 'constitutional psychopathy' and 'psychopathic personality.'

(2) Dyssocial reaction—disregard for and conflict with the social code as the result of having lived their lives in an abnormal moral environment.

(3) Sexual deviation—such as homosexuality, transvestism, pedophilia, fetishism, sexual sadism.

(4) *Addiction* (q.v.).

   (a) *Alcoholism* (q.v.).

   (b) Drug Addiction.

sociopathology (sō-sē-ō-pà-thol'ō-jē) The pathology of society. Society at large, or any segment of society, is composed of or comprises an aggregate of individuals, and the psychopathology of the patient as an individual or of a few or many of the group is quantitatively and qualitatively reflected ultimately as the psychopathology of the society that contains the individuals. Individual psychopathology is thus closely intermeshed with communal sociopathology.

sociopathy (sō-sē-op'à-thē) 1. This term has generally been used to designate an abnormal or pathological mental attitude toward the environment. Thus criminality and vagabondage are regarded by some authorities as manifestations of sociopathy.

In this sense the term refers to mental states that are commonly subsumed under psychopathy.
2. Abnormality or pathology of society or social units.

sociotherapy Any type of treatment whose primary emphasis is on socioenvironmental and interpersonal factors in adjustment; the term is sometimes used to refer specifically to the establishment of a therapeutic community. See *community, therapeutic.*

sodomist (sod'um-ist) One who practices sodomy; a sodomite.

sodomite One who practices sodomy; a sodomist.

sodomy (sod'um-ē) 'Sodomy, in the widest use, is carnal copulation by human beings with each other against nature or with a beast. In the narrower sense, "sodomy is carnal copulation between two human beings per anum, or by a human being in any manner with a beast." Present sodomy laws may cover homosexual acts, certain acts between heterosexual partners, acts with animals, fowls, or corpses, and, in one or two states, mutual masturbation or incitement to masturbation. In the act per anum, the term mankind includes females.' (Bowman, K.M., and Enger, B. *American Journal of Psychiatry 112:* 577-83, 1956)

soft signs See *signs, soft.*

soiling See *encopresis.*

soliloquy, sexual Hirschfeld says that many sexually timid individuals, who find difficulty in suppressing or repressing their sexual impulses, engage in long soliloquies as a means of relieving their sexual tensions.

solipsism (sol'ip-siz'm) The doctrine that *my self, alone,* is the essence of existence and that nothing counts except my ego, in which all else is reflected.

soluble RNA See *chromosome.*

solution, auxiliary In Horney's terminology, any partial or temporary solution of intrapsychic conflict, such as automatic control of feelings, compartmentalization, externalization, intellectualization, or self-alienation.

solution, comprehensive In Horney's terminology, an unrealistic avoidance of conflict by believing oneself to be the *idealized self* (q.v.), i.e. by actualizing the idealized image of oneself.

solution, expansive See *expansiveness.*

solution, major In Horney's terminology, a type of neurotic solution consisting of repression and denial of trends that conflict with the idealized self, or withdrawal into resignation.

soma (sō'mȧ) The organic tissues of the body. Whether correctly or not, the terms *soma* and *psyche* are often employed as if they were opposites. The psyche, however, is currently considered as an organ of the total person; it is not looked upon as an antithesis of the soma, but rather as a harmonious constituent of the entire organism. See *psyche; psychosomatic.*

somatalgia (sō-mȧ-tal'jē-ȧ) Pain due to organic causes, as distinguished from psychalgia or pain due to psychical causes.
To a patient, pain may have all the appearances of being organically determined, yet the organ from which the pain seems to come may serve merely as the vehicle for expressing psychical pain. This is a common phenomenon in conversion hysteria, in which condition complaints of a severe character about an organ have no connection with known organic anatomy, physiology, or pathology, but are identified closely with matters in the psyche. See *hypochondriasis; psychalgia.*

somatic (sō-mat'ik) Relating to or involving the soma.

somatist (sō'mȧ-tist) Psychiatrist or scientist who regards any particular neurosis or psychosis as of organic or physical origin.

somatization (sō-mȧ-ti-zā'shun) Stekel's term for a type of bodily disorder arising from a deep-seated neurotic cause. It is as if the organs of the body were translating into a physiopathological language the mental troubles of the individual. The term somatization is identical with the phenomena Freud calls 'conversion.' Stekel refers to it also in terms of 'organ-speech of the mind,' meaning the organic expression of mental processes. Such physical expressions are also encountered in dreams, and when they occur, the oneiric phenomena or process is known as 'functional dream.' See *dream, functional.*

It seems that in somatization there are 'certain areas of predilection' for the organic expression of the psychic conflicts. (Stekel, W. *The Interpretation of Dreams,* Liveright, New York, 1943)

somato- (sō'mȧ-tō-) Combining form meaning body, from Gr. *soma, -atos,* body.

somatobiology The study of the biology of the body, as contrasted with psychobiology, which is the study of the biology of the mind. (Hinsie, L.E. *Understandable Psychiatry,* Macmillan, New York, 1948)

somatogenesis (so-mȧ-tō-jen'e-sis) Origination in organic tissue (the soma).

somatognosia (sō-mȧ-tog-nō'sē-ȧ) The awareness of one's own body as a functioning object in space. *Macrosomatognosia* is a disturbance of the body scheme in which the body or parts of the body are experienced as abnormally large; *microsomatognosia* is a disturbance of the body scheme in which the body or parts of the body are experienced as abnormally small. Such disturbances have been reported in organic neurological lesions, epilepsy, migraine, schizophrenia, and experimental psychosis. See *ego, body; image, body.*

somatoplasm (sō'mȧ-tō-plaz'm) In biology, the somatic tissues of an animal body, to distinguish them, according to the *germ plasm* theory, from the reproductive tissue which produces the germ cells.

Hence, from the genetic standpoint, the somatoplasm represents the temporary, perishable envelope of an organism, the body, which the *gametes* can produce anew in each generation. While the germ plasm gives rise to both new germ cells and body cells, the soma never gives rise to germ plasm.

somatopsychic (sō-mȧ-tō-sī'kik) Relating to or originating in both body and mind.

somatopsychonoologia (-sī-kō-nō-ō-loj'-ē-ȧ) *Obs.* Psychosomatism. The term was introduced in 1823 by Thomas Forster.

somatopsychosis (-sī-kō'sis) Southard's term for a psychosis associated with visceral disease.

somatosexual (-sek'shoo-al) Pertaining to or characterized by organic manifestations of sexuality.

somatosexuality (-sek-shoo-al'i-tē) Somatosexual condition or state, or sexuality as it exists in the tissues or soma or organs. For example, sexuality, expressing itself through the genitals, is a form of somatosexuality.

somatotonia (-tō'nē-ȧ) A personality type described by Sheldon which is correlated with the mesomorph body type and which shows a predominance of vigorous assertiveness and muscular activity.

somatotopagnosia (top-ag-nō'zē-ȧ) *Autotopagnosia* (q.v.).

somatotype (sō'mȧ-tō-tīp) In some systems of constitutional medicine, the physical structure and build of a person as assessed by particular photographic techniques of *anthropometry.* Its 'scientific meaning thus applies only to one aspect of an *anthrotype* which has physiological, immunological and psychological aspects as well. See *anthrotype.*

-some (-sōm) Combining form meaning body, from Gr. *sŏma,* body.

somesthetic area (som-es-thet'ik) See *lobe, parietal.*

somite (sō'mīt) In the development of an embryo, a mesodermic segment formed by the medial portions of the third germ layer or *mesoderm.*

Sommer, Robert (1864 - 1937) (zôm'mēr) German psychiatrist.

somnambulism Sleep-walking. 'Somnambulisms are dissociated states identical with the above [i.e. fugue] except that they begin during sleep. They are common in childhood, when their motivation often appears on the surface. For example, a patient who in late life developed a depressive illness had been in his childhood much attached to his mother, and antagonistic to his father, who treated him badly. In his somnambulism he would make for his parents' bedroom and endeavor to get in at the side of the bed on which his mother slept.' (Henderson, D.K. and Gillespie, R.D. *A Text-Book of Psychiatry*, 4th ed., Oxford University Press, London, 1936)

Somnambulism is primarily a male disorder, is rare in homosexuals of either sex, and in one series reported 35% of sleepwalkers were overtly schizophrenic, and another 28% were markedly schizoid in character. Dynamic characteristics of this series were inadequate male identification, passive-dependent strivings, and conflicting feelings over aggression. (Sours, J.A. *Archives of General Psychiatry* 9, 400, 1963)

somnambulism, cataleptic (kat-à-lep'tik) A cataleptic state occurring during somnambulism.

somnambulism, monoideic (mon-ō-ī-dē'-ik) When the ideational content associated with the state of somnambulism revolves about a single idea, Janet speaks of monoideic somnambulism. When the content contains many ideas he calls it polyideic somnambulism.

somnambulism, polydeic (pol-ē-ī-dē'ik) See *somnambulism, monoideic.*

somnial (som'nē-al) *Rare.* Pertaining to dreams.

somnifacient (som-ni-fā'shent) Hypnotic; sleep-inducing.

somniferous (som-nif'ēr-us) Hypnotic; somnific.

somnific Somniferous; hypnotic.

somnifugous (som-nif'ū-gus) Driving sleep away; agrypnotic.

somniloquism (som-nil'ō-kwiz'm) Talking in sleep. Somniloquism is not pathognomonic of any specific disorder and is only rarely presented as a symptom or chief complaint.

somniloquy Talking in sleep.

somnipathist (som-nip'à-thist) One affected by or under the influence of somnipathy.

somnipathy 1. Any sleep disorder; 2. hypnotism.

somnocyclism (som-nō-sīk'liz'm) *Obs.* Bicycle-riding in a state of somnambulism.

somnolence (som-nō'lens) Unnatural sleepiness, drowsiness.

somnolent detachment See *detachment, somnolent.*

somnolentia (sôm-nō-len'tē-à) 1. Sleep-drunkenness. 2. Somnolence.

somnolism (som'nō-liz'm) Hypnotism.

somnovigil (som-no-vij'il) *Obs.* Somnambulism.

sonoencephalogram Echo-encephalogram; often abbreviated to SEG. See *echoencephalography.*

sophomania (sof-ō-mā'nē-à) A form of megalomania in which the patient stresses the excellence of his wisdom.

sopient (sō'pē-ent) Soporific.

sopite (sō-pīt') *Rare.* Drowsy.

sopor (sō'por) (L. 'deep sleep') Torpor.

soporiferous (sō-pō-rif'ēr-us) Soporific, making drowsy.

soporific, soporifical Any sleep-inducing agent.

soporose (sop'ō-rōs) Characterized or affected by morbid sleepiness.

soteria (sō-ter'ē-à) Possessions and objects that bring security and protection, as the objects that a collector admits to his collection. Collecting and soteric objects are to be distinguished from accumulation and the objects accumulated; *accumulation* is '. . . the continued possession of unclassified, useless, meaningless, annoying objects . . .' and, unlike true collecting, '. . . cannot be understood in terms of its symbolic meaning, but is a byproduct of the accumulator's indecision, an unwillingness to commit himself to a clear and realistic self-definition.' (Phillips, R.H. *Archives of General Psychiatry* 6, 474, 1962)

soul See *anima.*

soul, folk A kind of mystical group-mind, the presence of which is deduced from the way each individual displays properties and modes of reaction not present when he remains outside the group. The folk soul is considered a sort of supermind which is transcendental and possesses more good than the individual minds that contribute to it. The following terms are nearly synonymous with folk soul: group-mind (McDougall); general will (Rousseau); collective consciousness (Renan); social consciousness (Espinas, Durkheim, Wundt); group consciousness (Heard). Many do not accept the presence of a folk soul or group-mind and, instead, would explain collective reactions like communism and anarchism as racial neurosis (see *psychosis, collective*). Freud explains group psychology on the basis of individual identification with one another, secondary to the sharing of a common emotional situation.

source In psychoanalysis the term *source* (of an instinct) refers to 'that somatic process in an organ or part of the body from which there results a stimulus represented in mental life by an instinct.' (Freud, S. *Collected Papers*, vol. 4, tr. by Riviere, J., Leonard and Virginia Woolf and The Institute of Psychoanalysis, London, 1924-25) Freud claims that 'the study of the sources of instincts is outside the scope of psychology,' because it probably involves physiochemical processes. He then adds that 'although its source in the body is what gives the instinct its distinct and essential character, yet in mental life we know it merely by its aims.' (ibid)

Southard, Elmer Ernest (1876-1920) American psychiatrist; social psychiatry, industrial hygiene.

space, subarachnoid (sub-ar-ak′noid) See *meninges.*

span, auditory The number of digits (or letters, or words) that can be repeated after one hearing; determination of audi-tory span is a common test of immediate memory.

span of attention See *attention; memory.*

spasm A slow, at times prolonged, pattern movement of a muscle or groups of muscles occurring anywhere in the body.

spasm, masticatory Tonic closure of the jaw; it may be part of a syndrome of hysteria, meningitis, tetanus, epilepsy; it occasionally occurs in tumors or other diseases of the pons.

spasm, nodding A disorder that occurs in infants, characterized by head-shaking and nystagmus. Kanner describes the spasm as 'continuous or intermittent, mostly arrhythmic, involuntary, horizontal, vertical or rotary movements of the head.' The head-shaking is usually accompanied by unilateral or bilateral nystagmus and by vertical, horizontal, or rotary eye movements. 'The condition is confined to the first two or three years of life. It is an involuntary reaction and does not seem to be (specifically) associated with emotional disturbances.' (Kanner, L. *Child Psychiatry,* Thomas, Springfield, Ill., 1948)

spasm, oculogyric An involuntary tonic contraction of the extraocular muscles characterized by fixed upward gaze (or forced conjugate movements in other directions) that lasts from several minutes to several hours. Oculogyric crises or spasms are often a sequel of encephalitis, or they may appear as an acute dystonic side-effect of medication with phenothiazines.

spasm, salaam (or **salutation**) A variety of spasm seen in young children, consisting of 'periodic and rhythmic move-ments of the head and upper part of the body of about two seconds duration with intervals of approximately ten seconds. They resemble the oriental form of greeting. The condition is mostly associated with neuro-pathologic findings.' (Kanner, L. *Child Psychiatry,* Thomas, Springfield, Ill., 1948)

spasm, saltatory (sal′tà-tō-ri) Spasm of the muscles of the lower extremities producing jumping or skipping movements, usually of hysterical origin.

spasmophemia (spaz-mō-fē'mē-à) *Obs.* Speaking in spasms; stammering or stuttering.

spasmophilia 1. A neuropsychiatric syndrome, described by Joyeux in 1958, consisting of moderate anxiety, irritability, hypermotivity, insomnia, dysfunction in various organ systems (gastro-intestinal, cardiovascular, genital, skin), and positive Chvostek sign. All the symptoms may be precipitated or aggravated by hyperventilation.
2. In general and constitutional medicine a syndrome characterized by undersecretion of the parathyroids and frequently associated with a generalized hypoparathyroid constitution. See *constitution, hypoparathyroid.*

spasmus nutans (spàz'moos nōō'tàns) (L. 'nutant, nodding spasm') A rhythmic nodding or rotatory tremor of the head occurring in infants between the ages of six and twelve months; frequently accompanied by nystagmus. See *spasm, nodding.*

spatial summation See *summation.*

species In natural science, a group of animals or plants which rank below the genus and divisible into varieties or *subspecies.* The individuals forming a species are assumed to resemble one another in the essential features of their organization and to produce fertile offspring that vary from the general type of the group to a limited extent only.

specific *Biol.* Pertaining to a *species.*

specific dynamic pattern Franz Alexander's term for the specific nuclear conflict or dynamic configuration which is unique to a particular psychosomatic disorder or organ-neurosis. See *psychosomatic.*

specificity, symptom The phenomenon of heightened reactivity to stress in that organ system in which a psychosomatic patient's symptoms are localized; e.g. greater heart rate and heart rate variability in patients with cardiovascular complaints, than in subjects without such complaints.

spectrophobia (spek-trō-fō'bē-à) 'The hysterical phobia for mirrors and the dread of catching sight on one's own face in a mirror had in one case a "functional" and a "material" origin. The functional one was dread of *self-knowledge;* the material, the flight from the *pleasure of looking and exhibitionism.* In the unconscious phantasies the parts of the face represented, as in so many instances, parts of the genitals.' (Ferenczi, S. *Further Contributions to the Theory and Technique of Psycho-Analysis,* tr. by Suttie, J.I. Leonard and Virginia Woolf and The Institute of Psychoanalysis, London, 1926)

spectrum, psychotherapeutic (sī-kō-ther-à-pū'tik) A psychiatric term based on the concept (in optics) of the nature of the light spectrum as containing the entire range of colors from red to violet. Similarly, the term psychotherapeutic spectrum embraces all the branches and varieties of psychotherapeutics or psychotherapy.

speech, cerebellar (ser-e-bel'ēr) In diseases of the cerebellum, the speech may be jerky, explosive, irregular, and scanning. This condition is also called *asynergic* or *ataxic speech.*

speech disorders Disorganization of speech (306.0). The term is here synonymous with *language. Language* may be expressed as gesture, voice, and picture. Accordingly speech disorders fall into three groups:
1. *Amimia* (absence of or disordered gestures).
2. *Aphonia* (absence of or disordered sound or voice).
3. *Agraphia* (absence of or distorted pictorial symbols).
Since all communication involves at least two persons—the communicator and the communiquee—speech disorder may be found at either end of the line of communication.
These two aspects of speech (motor and sensory) really move the source a step further back; inability to produce speech goes back to *apraxia,* 'the loss of previously acquired skilled acts (without paralysis), or failure to develop normal skills'; and the inability to grasp speech goes back to *agnosia,* the inability to recognize the import of sensations.
In this way *motor* disabilities in the three groups of communication are of like nature when compared one with the other, namely:

1. Inability to utter (speak) a sound, syllable, word, or phrase— *aphasia*.
2. Inability to write a certain letter, syllable, word, or phrase— *agraphia*.
3. Inability to gesticulate— *amimia*.

The foregoing are paralleled by *sensory* or *perceptive* disabilities in the same three groups:

1. Inability to perceive or understand certain sounds, syllables, words, or phrases— *sensory aphasia*.
2. Inability to read certain letters, syllables, words, or phrases— *alexia*.
3. Inability to understand gestures— *sensory amimia*.

Disorders of speaking in the strict sense of the word are denoted by the same term on both the *-praxia* side and the *-gnosia* side.

Certain sounds are habitually mispronounced. For example:

r's may become burrs or guttural grunts or *w*'s or *l*'s *(rhotacism)*;

l's may become *w*'s or *oo*'s or *y* *(lambdacism)*;

s's may become *sh*'s or *h*'s, *th*'s, *f*'s *(sigmatism)*;

g's and *k*'s become *d*'s and *t*'s *(gammacism)*.

A person may form letters satisfactorily or range or align them badly, or interchange them within the words or reverse them 'mirror-fashion' *(strephyosymbolia)* or he may substitute other letters, syllables, or words for the appropriate ones, or write meaningless combinations.

Some people retain their ability to read or write and yet are afflicted with the specific disorder *asymbolia (asemia, asemasia)*— the inability to grasp or write various signs and symbols, such as are used in mathematics or chemistry; a switchman or a trainman may lose all understanding or ability to distinguish the railroad signals; or a musician past middle age may suddenly find himself staring blankly at a sheet of music that no longer conveys any meaning to him. Naturally in all these cases of aphasia, alexia, and agraphia, the symptoms may be milder and fall under the categories denoted by the prefixes *brady-, dys-, mogi-, moli,-* and *para-,* instead of the total *a-*.

Similarly the disorder may occur in the field of gestures or mimicry, with analogous results, which would be fatal to an actor, or to a pantomimist.

Although various authorities have introduced their own terms, there are certain combining forms which have gained universal acceptance. Almost without exception these terms have been treated under respective title-entries.

1. *a-* or *an-* means absence of a faculty or (total) loss of one acquired: *a*phasia, *a*phemia, *a*lalia, *a*phonia, *a*lexia, *a*graphia, *a*gnosia, *a*praxia, *a*semasia, *a*semia, *a*symbolia, *a*musia, *a*narthria, *a*phthongia, *a*syllabia, *a*phrasia, *a*grammatism, *a*kataphasia, *a*catamathesia. A modifying word or phrase may narrow the scope of the disorder and make it more specific: *sensory aphasia, functional aphasia, syntactic aphasia*.

2. *dys-* denotes a partial disorder or a specific disability; inability to produce certain elements; faulty or distorted performance or function: *dys*arthria, *dys*lexia, *dys*mimia, *dys*lalia, *dys*logia, all imply that only particular sounds, letters, words, or gestures are outside one's powers or are produced or perceived faultily or imperfectly.

3. *mogi-, moli-* refer to the difficulty in or a labored, effortful functioning: *mogi*lalia, *mogi*mimia, *mogi*phrasia, etc.

4. Excess or insufficiency of functioning, though the mechanics of speech are otherwise unimpaired:

(a) *swift* or above normal is denoted by *tachy-*: *tachy*lalia, *tachy*glossia.

(b) *slow* or subnormal is denoted by *brady-*: *brady*lalia, *brady*arthria, *brady*glossia, *brady*lexia, *brady*logia, *brady*phasia, *brady*phrasia.

(c) *above normal: hyper*logia; *hyper*mimia; *macro*mimia.

(d) *subnormal: hypo-*.

5. *para-* means qualitative perversion of the faculty, the substitution of a wrong element (something inappropriate) for the correct or proper one: *para*lalia, or the habitual production of wrong sounds, substitution of one sound for another (proper) one; *para*phasia (or less commonly and properly, *para*phemia) is the improper use of a word; *para*phrasia is the use of a wrong phrase in the sentence; *para*grammatism is the employment of a wrong grammatical construction; *thematic paraphrasia* (wandering, incoherent speech) denotes a still larger unit in the scale of speech-elements— the theme or subject of a speech.

. . *Para*graphia is the transposition of letters or words, or the use of wrong ones in writing; *para*lexia is misreading, substitution of wrong letters or meaningless words; *paramimia* is inappropriate gesture or facial expression; *parapraxia* is symptomatic misaction like a slip of the tongue.

As for the means to denote more specific aspects of speech disorders (that is, smaller or larger *elements* of speech), the terms range through:

Alalia—inability to produce sounds.

Anarthria—inability to produce articulate speech.

Asyllabia—inability to form syllables from individual sounds.

Aphrasia—inability to mold separate words into phrases.

Agrammatism—inability to subject seperate words to the rules of grammar.

Asyntacticism or *syntactic aphasia*—inability to arrange words into sentences.

Other sundry prefixes denoting various specific aspects of speech disorders are:

agito-, to denote a state of agitation, e.g. *agito*lalia.

embolo-, interlarding of speech, writing, or gestures at intervals with meaningless words, phrases, or mimicry.

echo-, repetition of words or gestures coming from others: *echo*lalia, *echo*phrasia, *echo*mimia, *echo*pathy, *echo*praxia.

Instead of the more generally accepted prefix *para-* for 'perversion' in the sense of *substitution* of another or inappropriate element, some authorities use *hetero-*; for example, *hetero*phasia, *hetero*lalia, *hetero*phonia, *hetero*phemy.

Likewise excess or insufficiency or lack of speech are denoted by such terms as: *pheniloquence, hyperlogia, logodiarrhea, logorrhea, logomania, logomonomania*— each of these denoting excessive talking; *tachylogia, tachyphemia, tachyphrasia, tachyglossia, lerema, leresis, leschenoma* —all meaning rapid speech.

speech, labyrinthine See *labyrinthine.*

speech, organ Communication or self-expression by means of an organ or organs of the body. 'Schizophrenic speech displays a hypochondriac trait: it has become "organ-speech."' (Freud, S.) He quotes from Tausk, whose patient said that her eyes were not right, they were twisted. This type of 'speech' is very common in schizophrenia. Freud 'would call attention to the manner in which the whole train of thought is dominated by that element which has for its content a bodily innervation (or, rather, the sensa-

tion of it). An hysteric would . . . have convulsively rolled her eyes,' without knowing why she did so; but, schizophrenic patients draw a direct connection between the organ-speech and the alleged cause for it.' (Freud, S. *Collected Papers,* vol. 4, tr. by Riviere, J., Leonard and Virginia Woolf and The Institute of Psychoanalysis, London, 1924-25)

speech, plateau Each vowel has its (average) specific pitch, which, in pronunciation, constantly rises and then steadily falls to the end, thus forming (if graphically represented) a bulging curve, termed its 'melody plot' by Drs. L. Pierce Clark and E.W. Scripture. It is the result of plotting and joining on graph paper the points representing the consecutive pitches in the vowel. These are obtained by measuring the successive waves registered on a smoked drum of the kymograph, or wave-register, by the inscribing point set in vibration by 'air puffs' from the lungs of the patient speaking into the 'tambour' or mouthpiece covered with thin rubber material. The typical epileptic voice has been proven 'monotonous' (i.e. the individual pitches of the various vowels are reduced to an average pitch or 'tone' in contrast to a normal person's speech) and, accordingly, it keeps to a certain more or less uniform level or 'plateau,' i.e. the epileptic's 'melody proceeds by even steps.'

speech, scattered A type of speech commonly found in hebephrenic schizophrenia and marked especially by the lack of relevancy and coherence. This lack is due primarily to the patient's tendencies to condensation and the formation of neologisms. The patient condenses 'a whole series of allied events into a single word or phrase.' Thus many ideas are expressed in one or two words. He will also string together several words, 'one each from separate series of events,' the result sounding 'like a hodgepodge to which the technical term neologism is given.' (Hinsie, L.E. *Understandable Psychiatry,* Macmillan, New York, 1948) See *scattering.*

spell, vacant Absence.

spells of doubting and brooding See *brooding-spells.*

sperm, spermatozoön (spērm, spēr-mȧ-tō-zō'on) In contradistinction to the large and passive reproductive cells in the female, which are called *eggs* (or ova), the *spermatozoa* (or sperms) are the very small male germ cells. They are of peculiar form, unlike any other kind of cell, and like the eggs, are subject to *meiosis* (q.v.). When mature they have only half the number of chromosomes characteristic of the individual that produces the germ cells.

Before undergoing meiosis, the spermatozoa multiply by repeated cell divisions of the ordinary duplicating type and are call *spermatogonia*. When these cells cease to divide by ordinary division, they become *primary spermatocytes*, but grow considerably less than the oöcytes. See *egg*.

The first meiotic division produces in the male two *equal* cells, both functional, which are known as *secondary spermatocytes*. Each cell produced by this first *maturation division* immediately proceeds to divide again *(equation division)*. The two identical new cells are called *spermatids* and, by changing shape, produce the *mature spermatozoa*.

In the process of fertilization, a spermatozoön enters an egg either after the maturation is completed or at some earlier time during the maturation process. When an egg is fertilized, a new individual is started.

spermatid (spēr'mȧ-tid) In genetics a stage in the development of a mature *spermatozoön* (q.v.).

spermatocyte (spēr-ma'-tō-sīt) In sexual reproduction, the *spermatogonium* divide into *primary* and *secondary* spermatocytes, before maturing into a *spermatozoön* (q.v.).

spermatogonium (spēr-ma-tō-gō'nē-um) In sexual reproduction, the *spermatogonium* represents the first stage in the development of a male's mature reproductive cell. See *spermatozoön*.

spermatophobia Fear of semen.

spes phthisica (spās' ftē'zē-kȧ) (L. 'tubercular hopefulness') The feeling of hopefulness and confidence of recovery experienced by many sufferers from tuberculosis even in the later stages of the disease.

sphacelismus (sfas-ē-liz'mus) *Obs. Phrenitis* (q.v.).

spheresthesia (sfer-es-thē'zē-ȧ) *Globus hystericus* (q.v.).

sphincter morality See *morality, sphincter.*

Spielmeyer-Vogt's disease (Walter Spielmeyer, German neurologist, 1879-1935, and Oskar Vogt, contemporary German neurologist) A type of *amaurotic family idiocy* (q.v.); pigmentary retinal lipoid neuronal heredodegeneration.

spike-and-wave The dart-and-dome type of electroencephalographic tracing seen in petit mal epilepsy. See *epilepsy.*

spina bifida (spē'nȧ bē'fē-dȧ) (L. 'cleft spine') Rachischisis; a developmental defect in the spinal column due to failure of fusion of the dorsal walls of the primitive ectodermal neural canal. Although this defect may exist anywhere along the spine, it is usually situated posteriorly in the median line in the lumbar region.

spina bifida occulta (ôk-kool'tȧ) (L. 'hidden cleft spine') That type of spina bifida in which the bony defect is covered by skin.

spine, railway A general term for injuries, real or feigned, to the back or spine, sustained during a railway accident.

'Some railway spines must be cases of pure malingering, but exaggeration added to traumatic neurosis will account for the majority of them.' (Huddleson, J.H. *Accidents, Neuroses and Compensation,* Williams and Wilkins, Baltimore, 1932)

splanchnic (splangh'nik) Referring to the viscera. In psychiatry, the term ordinarily has reference to Viola's system of typology. See *type, normosplanchnic; type, megalosplanchnic; type, microsplanchnic.*

split double-bind See *bind, double.*

splitting According to Melanie Klein, splitting is an ego mechanism that precedes, and to some extent determines the type of, repression. See *position, paranoid-schizoid; personality, multiple.*

splurge, stealing A form of behavior disorder in children: the child strives to attain status in the group either by proving itself daring and competent in acts of stealing or by using the articles or money stolen as gifts to purchase the favor of the other members of the group.

spoiled-child reaction See *reaction, spoiled-child.*

spondylitis (spon-di-lī′tis) Inflammation of one or more of the vertebrae.

spontaneity See *state, spontaneity.*

spontaneous imagery See *imagery, spontaneous.*

spoon feeding Feeding of another person (e.g. an infant) by putting a spoon filled with food to his lips; by extension, the expression has come to refer to any manifestation of oversolicitude that prevents or obstructs the development of independence on the part of the one being 'fed.' Psychiatric residents, for example, who receive so much individual case supervision that they are never in the position of handling a patient completely by themselves are spoken of as being spoon-fed.

spoonerism See *cluttering.*

spot, hypnogenic (hip-nō-jen′ik) In susceptible patients the body sometimes presents a spot or point, pressure upon which will throw the person into a hypnotic state. See *zone, hysterogenic.*

stage, biting A subdivision of the oral phase of libido development. Abraham divided this phase into two parts. One is the sucking stage and the other, in consequence of the appearance of teeth, is the biting stage. Based on the nature of the fixation at the oral stage the distinguishing marks of the oral character will be: (1) submissive, if the fixation takes place in the sucking stage, or (2) aggressive, if in the biting stage. Thus, psychoanalysts speak of oral receptive and oral aggressive characters.

stage-fright A type of anxiety hysteria in which the patient, an actor, fears to go onto the stage, or if he goes on, forgets his lines and/or begins to stutter. Stage-fright is often based upon a need to ward off heightened exhibitionism and scopo-

philia, which if indulged in might provoke castration, and at the same time to gain reassurance from the audience that the dreaded castration has not occurred.

stage, ideoplastic (id-ē-ō-plas′tik) Verworn's term, which refers to the fact that the young child draws what he knows rather than what he sees. In the ideoplastic stage the child tends to exaggerate items which seem important or interesting and to minimize or omit the other parts.

stage, physioplastic (fiz-ē-ō-plas′tik) Verworn's term which refers to the ability to draw what is seen, in contrast to the ideoplastic stage, in which the child draws what he knows. See *stage, idioplastic.*

stage, postambivalent The final stage in the development of object-love in which real love for an object is possible. As infantile sexuality develops, it passes through several stages associated with the various erogenous zones. The libido is organized successively around these various erogenous zones. The final stage in the development of sexuality is the genital stage and it occurs when all sexual excitations can be discharged through the use of the genital apparatus.

Development of object-love is interwoven with the development of sexuality. As infantile sexuality develops, the type of relationship to objects changes, for associated with each stage and related to the particular erogenous zone around which the libido is being organized is a different type of relationship to objects. In general, the development proceeds from an objectless state associated with the early oral (sucking) stage to the final stage of real love.

The stages of object-love before real love is reached are ambivalent: in these stages, the process of achieving satisfaction destroys the object. This is based chiefly on the physiological nature of oral and anal erogeneities—that is, biting, swallowing, defecating, etc.—which are the usual models for these object-relationships. The personality of the object itself does not matter, as the object is important only insofar as it can give satisfaction to the individual. When satisfaction has been achieved, the object itself may disappear—as far as the infant is concerned.

The final stage of object-relationship,

real love, is termed the postambivalent stage. No traces of hateful or destructive feelings toward the object remain. Instead, 'consideration of the object goes so far that one's own satisfaction is impossible without satisfying the object, too.' The prerequisite for real love is genital primacy, the ability to attain full satisfaction through genital orgasm. This emerges only in the final genital stage of libidinal organization. (Fenichel, O. *The Psychoanalytic Theory of Neurosis*, Norton, New York, 1945)

stalemate, analytic See *resistance, id.*

staleness See *neurasthenia, aviator's.*

stammering A speech disorder characterized by spasmodic, halting, or hesitating utterance. The term is used by many authorities interchangeably with *stuttering* (q.v.).

standard deviation See *deviation, standard.*

'standing mute' A defendant, who refuses to plead or say anything when arraigned, is said to be *standing mute.*

'Today, almost without exception, it is provided by statute in the American states that if a defendant refuses to plead, the court may order a plea of not guilty entered for him, and the mere fact that a defendant refuses to plead does not of itself require the question of his physical or mental capacity to be submitted to a jury.' (Weihofen, H. *Insanity as a Defense in Criminal Law*, Commonwealth Fund, Oxford University Press, New York, 1933)

Stanford-Binet Intelligence Scale See *tests, Binet-Simon.*

stasibasiphobia (stas-i-bā-si-fō′bē-à) 'A phobic phenomenon. Sometimes the patients are so convinced of their helplessness that they do not even make enough effort to enable them to stand up on their feet or to take a single step. They just let themselves go, and sink down helpless.' (Déjérine, J. and Gauckler, E. *The Psychoneuroses and their Treatment by Psychotherapy*, 2nd ed., tr. by Jelliffe, S.E., Lippincott, Philadelphia and London, 1915) See *astasia; abasia.*

stasiphobia (stas-i-fō′bē-à) Fear of standing (up), delusion of inability to stand. See *astasia.*

stasis, libido (stā′sis, stas′is, li-bēd′ō) Accumulation of libidinous excitations or tensions consequent upon blockage of their motor discharge. When the free flow of libido has been thus dammed, a stasis (libido stasis) results, giving rise to the feeling of anxiety.

According to Kardiner, 'Freud made an early attempt to describe the *Aktualneurosen,* and in this category were anxiety neurosis and neurasthenia. In connection with these neuroses Freud noted irritability, a diminished ability to tolerate accumulations of excitation, auditory hyperesthesia, anxious expectation, hypochondria, paresthesias, vasomotor disturbances, and so on. The essential pathology Freud considered an "accumulation of tensions which were prevented from motor discharge."'

The physiological accompaniments of anxiety are mediated by way of the autonomic nervous system. Kardiner points out that stasis phenomena resulting from overactivity of this system do not necessarily produce anxiety. He writes: 'The autonomic phenomena need to be explained as regards their role in the failure reaction which is traumatic neurosis. . . . These phenomena may be considered "discharge" manifestations. One may say that [the inhibitions of a traumatic neurosis] . . . produce stasis phenomena, on the principle that since the demands of the external world continue to be the same as those before the neurosis was established, and the executive apparatus cannot carry out the necessary adaptive manipulations, stasis of some kind will accumulate. In other words it is as if the internal environment were geared for action, and the executive apparatus not. Hence autonomic activity that is shunted from its proper function continues unaccompanied by the activity of which it was originally an integral part.

'In the traumatic neurosis the place of the autonomic system in the action system is quite clear. It stands in direct relation to activity that is inhibited and in this neurosis is a part of the disorganization phenomena. The relations of autonomic disturbances in other neuroses are more difficult to disentangle. . . .

'The disorders of this autonomic system

can be classified roughly by their correspondence to the normal physiologic accompaniments of anxiety. Such a picture is found in the usual autonomic imbalance of what is called by Lewis "the soldier's heart" or "effort-syndrome." This autonomic picture may or may not be accompanied by the affect of anxiety or terror in the chronic forms of the disturbance. The affect of anxiety may completely disappear and in proportion as it disappears the more obtrusive these autonomic disturbances may become. In place of the anxiety or terror there remains a residual irritability. In the chronic cases the affect is generally not present nor are there any displacement phobias. But there is one constant in the traumatic neurosis, the fact that the motility is blocked or guarded while the need tensions which can only be released by activity continue unabated. Hence one can regard these autonomic phenomena as evidence of stasis, since the autonomic system is not susceptible to inhibition—at least not by the same quantities of stimuli that are effective in inhibiting the skeletal system.' (Kardiner, A., and Spiegel, H. *War Stress and Neurotic Illness,* Hoeber, New York, 1947)

stasobasophobia   (stas-ō-bā-sō-fō'bē-à) Stasibasiphobia.

stasophobia (stas-ō-fō'bē-à) Stasiphobia.

stataesthesia (stat-es-thē'zha) Perception of constancy of pressure, as in maintaining pressure in a balloon by hand compression.

state, central excitatory See *summation.*

state, clouded See *sensorium.*

state, dreamy A state of arrested consciousness, akin to epileptiform seizures, but unaccompanied by convulsions. The patient suddenly passes off into a dream world, often with olfactory, auditory and/or visual hallucinations, and usually recovers within a few minutes. Such states are most commonly associated with temporal lobe lesions.

state, fatigue See *hypoglycemia.*

state, paraphonic (pàrà-fon'ik) See *action, automatic.*

state, spontaneity 'Spontaneity state is the condition which a subject has to attain in order to produce an emotion or role at will. The state is usually felt by the subject as a novel experience and frequently without a concrete precedent in his life history. Ordinarily, emotions like anger and jealousy are determined by the influence of common tensions and stresses. The emotions produced during the spontaneity state are voluntary. The subject must make an effort to reach the state or to warm up to it. Getting angry or jealous may be enforced upon the subject in life situations by determinants he cannot control, but getting angry or jealous in a spontaneity state is exactly the opposite. The subject voluntarily realizes a state which he usually experiences as something coming up against his will. In the spontaneity state he develops a relative distance from the states or roles which he ordinarily embodies. Spontaneity and spontaneity state are operational terms and cannot be fully understood by intellectual definition.' (Moreno, J.L. *Das Stegreif Theater,* Potsdam, Germany)

state, twilight In Bleuler's classification, one of the acute syndromes in *schizophrenia* (q.v.). The twilight-states appear as waking dreams which portray desires, wishes, or fears in a direct or symbolic way as being already fulfilled. They often persist for long periods; duration for six months is not uncommon.

statistical trend See *trend, statistical.*

statistics The branch of mathematics which deals with data that vary relatively as a result of the interaction of many causes. A body of data, numerical facts, or enumerations which must be analyzed in accordance with the statistical method.

status (stā'tus) (L. 'manner of standing, position in society, condition, state, rank') Status is the 'relative position, rank, or standing of a person in a group, or of a group in reference to some larger grouping.' (Young, K. *An Introductory Sociology,* American Book, New York, 1934)

In medicine this term implies the presence of some abnormal state or pathological condition and requires further qualification by an adjective for the particular type of condition.

status degenerativus (stå′toos dā-ge-ne-rā-tē′voos) Bauer describes this as an accumulation, in a given person, of extreme variants of certain constitutional characteristics which, taken alone, may have little, if any, pathological significance, such as a scaphoid shoulder-blade, a supernumerary breast, a deformed ear lobe or an anomalous distribution of hair. However, any combination of these anomalies in the same person may be taken to indicate a type of general constitution which deviates too much from the average type and, therefore, is to be regarded as 'biologically inferior.'

This definition shows that from the constitutional standpoint *degeneration* simply implies a marked deviation from the type of a species, without regard to the clinical value of the deviation itself. It is equally clear that the actual *status degenerativus* 'includes not only those variants that are extreme in deficit, but also those extreme in excess.' (Pende, N. *Constitution Inadequacies,* tr. by Naccarati, S., Lea & Febiger, Philadelphia, 1928)

status dysraphicus (dēs-rà′fē-koos) A variety of developmental anomalies resulting from faulty closure of the neural groove at an early embryological stage. It seems to be hereditary and is believed to be the basis of such neurological diseases as hereditary ataxia and spinal gliosis (syringomyelia).

status epilepticus (e-pē-lep′tē-koos) The recurrence without interruption of grand mal seizures in an epileptic.

Status epilepticus is the most common cause of death in epileptics. It occurs more frequently in symptomatic than in idiopathic epilepsy, and it often appears to be precipitated by withdrawal or change of anticonvulsant medication, or by intercurrent infection (where pyrexia may produce a state of internal withdrawal from medication).

status hypoplasticus (hē-pô-plàs′tē-koos) Bartel and Wiesel use this term for a constitutional type characterized by generalized hypoevolutism, fibrous diathesis, hyperplasia of the lymphatic tissue, and the ready aging of the differentiated elements. This general hypoplastic condition is bound to lead to a poor functional capacity of the natural defense mechanisms and to a tendency on the part of the connective tissue to replace the elements constituting the parenchyma, which easily undergoes atrophy.

status hystericus (his-te′rē-koos) 'In some instances one attack [of grand hysteria] follows another without appreciable interval, or some feature of the attack, as the stupor of the first period or the delirium of the fourth, may be prolonged for hours and days, constituting a *status hystericus.*' (Church, A. and Peterson, F. *Nervous and Mental Diseases,* 8th ed., Saunders, Philadelphia and London, 1916)

status lymphaticus (lēm-fä′tē-koos) A constitutional type characterized by hyperplasia of the lymphatic tissue system and poor development of the blood vessels. Slight injuries to a person in this state may prove fatal.

status marmoratus (mar-mō-rà′toos) See *dystonia, torsion.*

status, mental See *mental status*

status raptus (ràp′toos) *Ecstasy* (q.v.).

status thymico-lymphaticus (thē′mē-kō-lim-fä′tē-koos) Those cases of status lymphaticus in which an enlargement of the thymus is conspicuous. The condition may be *primary* and congenital or acquired *secondarily* in extra-uterine life, especially through changes in other endocrine glands, occurring before the period of physiological involution of the thymus.

The symptomatology of both forms chiefly consists of enlarged thymus, gener hyperplasia of the glands, dissemination of hyperplastic lymphatic tissue throughout the body, hyperthyroidism, sclerosis of ovaries and testes, and hypoplasia of the circulatory system. This condition attains its significance for constitutional medicine from the fact that the persons affected by it are under constant threat of infection and even of sudden death from minor psychical or physical traumata.

statuvolence (stach-ū-vō′lens) *Obs.* Statuvolent state; self-induced hypnotism.

Stauder's lethal catatonia See *paralysis, catatonic.*

steal, subclavian See *syndrome, subclavian steal.*

steatopygia, steatopygy (stē-à-tō-pī'jē-à, stē-à-top'i-jē) Excessive fatness of the buttocks, a biological peculiarity observed among Hottentot and Bushman women.

Stedman, Charles H. (1805-66) American psychiatrist; one of 'original thirteen' founders of Association of Medical Superintendents of America (forerunner of American Psychiatric Association).

Stekel, Wilhelm (1868-1940) German sexologist and psychoanalyst; advocated activity as a means to shorten the duration of treatment. Through sympathy and imaginative or intuitive insight the therapist alerts himself to the patient's repressed complexes and then is expected to intervene actively to make the patient aware of them.

stem, brain This refers to the *pons* (q.v.) and *medulla oblongata* (q.v.).

stema (stē'mà) *Obs.* Penis.

stereo-encephalotomy Production of cortical or subcortical lesions through the use of the stereotaxic apparatus which permits carefully controlled penetration of brain matter by the needle.

stereognosis (stē-rē-og-nō'sis) The ability to judge the shape and form of an object by means of touch.

stereopsyche (stē-rē-ō-sī'kē) The primitive part of the mind which has to do with primitive types of motility. Storch applied this term to certain motor manifestations seen in schizophrenia: the catatonic postures and movements which seem to be isolated from the personality and to have a meaning independent of the rest of the psychic structure. These archaic types of motility arise from the deeper layers of the motor apparatus after the ego has disintegrated. They indicate an indistinct apperception of objects, indistinct ego boundaries, and a deep ambivalence toward reality objects in general. An example is the fetal position assumed by catatonics: this position suggests that at least certain motor manifestations in the catatonic are carry-overs from the intra-uterine period of existence.

stereotactic tractotomy See *tractotomy, stereotactic.*

stereotype An individual motor pattern that was originally meaningful to the subject and/or carried some private, autistic meaning for him. Stereotypes are thus to be distinguished from *primitive motor patterns* which are meaningless, inborn, or acquired very early in life, and which consist of simple movements or groups of simple movements.

stereotype, dynamic A term used mainly by Russian neurophysiologists to refer to the end-result of cortical analysis and synthesis of all stimuli arising from both the external and the internal world. The dynamic stereotype represents a balanced, classified and homogeneous arrangement of all the conditioned and unconditioned processes reflected in the cortex.

stereotypy (stē-rē-ot'i-pi) The constant repetition of any action, such as incessantly rubbing some part of the body.
The foregoing is often called stereotypy of motion. There is also stereotypy of posture, the patients maintaining a given posture for inordinately long periods. And there is stereotypy of place; catatonic patients may occupy an identical place month in, month out, year in, year out.
In Rorschach testing, stereotypy of responses suggests a lack of imagination, one of whose indicators is a high a %.

sterile Incapable of producing offspring.

sterility Sterility is the state or quality of being unfertile or barren. This condition may be produced either by primary genetic disturbances in the sex chromosome constitution of an individual, or by secondary effects on the phenotype both of internal pathological processes and of surgical interference for medical or eugenic purposes. See *sterilization.*
The pathological processes disturbing the physiology of normal reproduction may affect (1) the sexual center in the hypothalamus, (2) the anterior pituitary gland with the follicle-stimulating and the luteinizing hormones, (3) the ovaries with the follicle and the corpus luteum hormones and (4) the uterus. About 50 per cent of sterile women are reported by Wiesbader to show evidence of endo-

crine disturbance, a form of sterility which is usually subdivided into the pituitary, ovarian, and hyperthyroid types. The Froehlich syndrome and Cushing's pituitary basophilism are the best-known instances of the pituitary type of sterility.

sterilization Any process (brought about spontaneously or by deliberate action) which causes a person to become sterile.

When performed for *eugenic* reasons, it aims at rendering conception impossible, without affecting the ovaries or testes, respectively. Accordingly it is not an 'unsexing' operation, and neither inhibits sex desires nor interferes with normal sex-functioning. In men it is the simple process of cutting and tying the vas deferens, while in women it requires an abdominal incision to tie the fallopian tubes. See *eugenics*.

Stewart-Morel syndrome See *syndrome, Stewart-Morel.*

STH Somatotrophic or growth hormone; one of the anterior pituitary hormones. See *syndrome, general adaptation.*

sthenia (sthē'-ne-à) In a general medical sense, strength and vigor.

sthenic (sthen'ik) In general medicine, strong and active. It is applied especially to morbid states with excessive action of the vital processes, as for instance, in sthenic fever or sthenic mental (delusional) reaction.

In constitutional medicine, the term is applicable in a general way to all types which correspond to Kretschmer's *athletic type* or its equivalents in other systems. It is even used by Mills for one of his three types. See *type, athletic.*

In general psychology, the term indicates strength and vigor in different fields of emotional reactivity and adaptability. In accordance with this concept, the psychopathological behavior of a sthenic type has been described by Kretschmer as inclined to delusional reactions of a predominantly aggressive nature (paranoia, querulous ideas of reference), in contrast to the introspective tendency of paranoid or hypochondriac reactions in sensitive types.

sthenoplastic (sthen-ō-plas'tik) In constitutional medicine, a type contrasted by

Bounack with the *euryplastic*, and corresponding to the *asthenic* in Kretschmer's system, the *microsplanchnic hypovegetative* constitution of Pende.

stick, fecal Fecal mass. See *phase, anal.*

stigmata (stig-mà'tà) Marks resembling the wounds on the crucified body of Christ. Most psychoanalytic writers consider these monosymptomatic conversions, the afflicated areas unconsciously symbolizing the genitals, the hyperemia and swelling representing erection, and abnormal sensations imitating genital sensations. The first person known to have experienced stigmata was St. Francis of Assisi; since that time, more than 300 cases have been reported, most of them in women.

stigmata, external See *insufficiency, segmental.*

Stiller's sign See *sign, Stiller's.*

stimulation See *activation.*

stimuli, accidental Among the four general types of dream-stimuli, which are (1) external sensory; (2) internal sensory (subjective); (3) internal physical (organic); (4) psychic, the group of accidental stimuli belongs to the first type—external sensory. Accidental stimuli denote those chance happenings which take place in the environment of the sleeper and seemingly precipitate dreams or become part of them. For example, the backfire of an automobile passing in the street may emerge in the dream as the firing of a gun or as the 'pop' of a champagne cork. The pain of muscles cramped by an awkward position during sleep may start a dream of being hurt in that area of the body. An alarm clock ringing may be heard by the sleeper simultaneously dreaming of that very thing.

stimulus, dream See *dream-stimulus.*

stimulus-tension The tension produced by a stimulus. 'But we have unquestioningly identified the pleasure-pain-principle with this Nirvana-principle. From this it would follow that every "pain" coincides with a heightening, every pleasure with a lowering, of the stimulus-tension existing in the mind.' (Freud, S. *Collected Papers*, vol. 2, tr. by Riviere, J., Leonard and

Virginia Woolf and The Institute of Psychoanalysis, London, 1924-25)

stimulus-word The word used in association tests to provoke a response. See *association.*

stir-fever See *psychosis, prison.*

stirps (pl. stirpes) Stem; stock; the person from whom a family is descended. In genetics, all the genes that are present in, and determine the development of, the fertilized egg.

STP An hallucinogenic drug that appears to be identical with DOM (2,5-dimethoxy-4-methylamphetamine); in low dosage (less than 3 mg.), DOM produces mild euphoria, but in higher dosage it produces hallucinogenic effects that last for about 8 hours. Blackmarket preparations of STP usually contain about 10 mg. of DOM. The name is derived from a commercial gasoline additive (although some maintain it is an abbreviation for serenity-tranquility-peace).

strabismus (stra-biz'mus) Squint; heterotropia; deviation of one or both eyes from the normal axis. See *nerve, oculomotor.*

strait-jacket See *camisole.*

strait-jacket, chemical An uncommonly used term to denote the arresting of psychomotor overactivity by chemical means, specifically by the hypodermic injection of morphine sulphate, $\frac{1}{4}$ grain and hyoscine hydrobromide, $\frac{1}{50}$ grain.

Stransky, Erwin (1877-1962) Viennese neuropsychiatrist, pupil of Wagner von Jauregg; first to publish textbook on mental health in Germany; concept of intrapsychic ataxia, the dissociation of the thymopsyche from the noöpsyche, as the essential characteristic of schizophrenia.

Strauss syndrome See *impulse-disorder, hyperkinetic.*

strength, ego See *ego-strength.*

strephosymbolia (stref-ō-sim-bō'lē-à) The perception of objects or graphic symbols reversed as if in a mirror. A term coined by Orton for the specific reading disability due, he believes, to poorly established

hemisphere dominance, so that visual impressions, coming to both hemispheres are not clearly differentiated, and symmetrical engrams oriented in opposite directions are confused, as *b* and *d*, *p* and *q*. 'At the outset it is characterized by confusion between similarly formed, but oppositely oriented letters and a tendency to a changing order of direction in reading.' (Orton, S.T. *Reading, Writing and Speech Problems in Children*, Norton, New York, 1937)

Strephosymbolia is frequently encountered in left-handed children converted to right-handedness. See *minimal brain dysfunction.*

stress 'Any interference which disturbs the functioning of the organism at any level, and which produces a situation which is natural for the organism to avoid.' (Howard, L. *British Journal of Medical Psychology 33*, 185-194, 1960). The total effect, obviously, is influenced greatly by the meaning of the stress-stimulus to the person. Reactions to stress are typically manifested as disturbed psychologic and/or physiologic functioning; in psychiatry, they are seen most commonly when strong, involuntary, often unconscious internal impulses press for action that conflicts with the subject's conscious, reality-oriented behavior.

stress, ego Broadly speaking, anything requiring adaptation maneuvers on the part of the ego, although usually the term implies that the strain is such as to require unusual defensive reactions. The stress itself may arise from the external world (the demands of reality), or from within (the pressure of the id for discharge and gratification of drives, or superego demands). As stress increases so will defenses increase until there may result distortion or even alteration of the ego. Responses may vary from normal emergency reactions (phantasy, reaction formation, etc.), to exaggerations of normal function (somatization), to partial withdrawal (depersonalization, dissociation), to transitory ego rupture (panic, oneiric episodes), to retreat with phantasies (psychoses), to complete disintegration (suicide). (Menninger, K. *Journal of the American Psychoanalytic Association 2*, 67, 1954)

stress interview A type of interview in

which the patient is intentionally pressured, and the usual ways of reducing anxiety during the session are deliberately avoided. Such interviews may be useful in diagnosis, but their repeated use is generally contraindicated in the course of psychotherapy.

Stribling, Francis T. (1810-74) American psychiatrist; advocated training of psychiatric attendants, occupational therapy.

stridor dentium (strē'dôr den'tē-oom) (L. grating of teeth') Grinding of teeth; see also *bruxism, bruxomania.*

striving, appetitive Striving in one particular direction, toward the particular goal appropriate for the gratification of the appetite involved. 'The distinguishing feature of Freud's instinct theory is that it is based on a conative-appetitive-striving, rather than on a structural principle like sensation or reflex. But, as with the classical psychologies and behaviorism, psychoanalysis is an atomistic psychology which attempts to derive complex entities from the action of a synthetic principle (association, conditioning, integration) on or about a basic unit.' (Kardiner, A., and Spiegel, H. *War Stress and Neurotic Illness,* Hoeber, New York, 1947)

structural hypothesis See *id.*

structure, character The term for a relatively permanent constellation of habitual ways of reacting to the world, connoting only habitual attitudes developed as reactions to life-situations. This is not to be confused with *temperament.*
'Character structure, as Freud saw it, is the result of sublimation or reaction formation. That is, it is formed unconsciously through the efforts of the Superego to bind the forces of the Id in such a way that the Ego accepts them, and its relation to the outside world is not jeopardized. It is, in effect, a defensive mechanism. Although the result, sublimation, seems to be a positive attitude of the Ego, it is formed primarily as a defense against instincts. Freud's philosophy of character makes it the result of the transformation of instinctual drives.' (Thompson, C. *Psychoanalysis, Evolution and Development,* Hermitage House, New York, 1950) See *defense, character.*

structure, mental The organization of the *psyche* (q.v.).

strychnomania (strik-nō-mā'nē-à) See *poisoning, deadly nightshade.*

stupemania (stū-pē-mā'nē-à) Manic stupor. See *mania.*

stupor (stū'pēr) A state in which the sensibilities are deadened or dazed and the subject has little or no appreciation of the nature of his surroundings. The term is commonly synonymous with *unconsciousness,* in an organic, not in a psychic sense.
Further, in a second meaning that has no relationship with the condition of the sensorium, stupor is synonymous with *mutism.* For example, a patient may possess all the characteristics of the manic or depressed phase of manic-depressive psychosis, save that of talking; he is said to exhibit a manic or a depressive stupor; there need not be any essential disorder in intellectual or sensorial clarity. In the condition known as catatonic stupor the patient is ordinarily well aware of the nature of his surroundings.

stupor, affective See *stupor, emotional.*

stupor, akinetic (a-ki-net'ik) *Cairns' stupor* (q.v.).

stupor, anergic (an-er'jik) Stupor with immobility. As a rule patients showing the psychogenic stuporous reaction are inactive, immobile, anergic.
According to older concepts *anergic stupor* was synonymous with *primary dementia* and *stuporous insanity.*

stupor, benign *Depressive stupor,* usually described as the most severe form of manic-depressive disorder, depressed type; termed benign in that it was believed to share the generally favorable prognosis of manic-depressive psychoses. Most such cases are in fact schizophrenic and in time show a more classical deteriorative course; they would thus more appropriately be termed *malignant stupors.*

stupor, Cairns' See *Cairns' stupor.*

stupor, catatonic See *schizophrenia, catatonic.*

stupor, depressive See *stupor, benign.*

stupor, diencephalic (dī-en-se-fal'ik) *Cairns' stupor* (q.v.).

stupor, emotional Emotional stupor (or affective stupor) is characterized by mutism and intense anxiety or depression. 'Emotional stupor is a syndrome seen in different conditions, especially in the different kinds of "nervosities," in the widest sense, and in the oligophrenias.' (Bleuler, E. *Textbook of Psychiatry,* tr. by Brill, A.A., Macmillan, New York, 1930)

stupor, examination When the affects are so strong as to 'bring to a standstill thoughts and actions,' Bleuler speaks of *examination* or *emotional stupor.* See *anxiety, examination.*

stupor, exhaustive Stupor or coma as a result of infection or intoxication. See *psychosis, infective-exhaustive.*

stupor, malignant See *stupor, benign.*

stupor, manic See *mania.*

stupor vigilans (stoo'pôr vē'gē-lâns) (L. 'vigilant, wakeful stupor') An old term for *catalepsy.*

stuporous Relating to or under the influence of stupor; comatose or semi-comatose.

Sturge-Weber-Dimitri's disease See *angiomatosis, trigeminal cerebral.*

stuttering A spasmodic utterance with involuntary halts, breaks, and repetitions, usually characterized (in severer cases) externally by sputtering due to violent expulsion of breath following a halt or stop. For the sake of convenience, stuttering will be assumed a visually more violent or explosive form of stammering without intention to settle the prevailing disagreement as to whether *stutter* or *stammer* is the more appropriate term and whether they denote two different disorders or not.

The long-standing controversy in medical literature as to whether the halts and reiterations involved only consonants, vowels, or parts of words, and likewise initially or medially, was an academic discussion with useless waste of energy, practically without foundation, as has been proven by closer studies and experimental phonetics, particularly by Dr. E.W. Scripture and Dr. S.T. Orton. Any sound, in any position, any part of a word and any word may be the obstacle in stuttering, varying with the individual stutter or the severity of the symptom.

Some authorities hold that stuttering is the result of an organic brain disease or physiological defect, but that is still a moot question. The first hesitations and halts in a child's speech are as normal as the missteps, stumbles, and falls in the child's earliest attempts in walking, due to lack of co-ordination and control of the walking-mechanism, which in comparison with the speech-mechanism is as simple as that of a wheelbarrow by the side of a delicate watch-movement. The staggering burden on the child's powers to reproduce the movements of speech organs (many of them concealed from his view within the other people's mouths) can be surmised from the exertions adults have to make in learning the sounds of a new language even from a teacher with the aid of diagrams, illustrations, and mirrors.

Whether originating in a physiological disorder or not, in its subsequent stages, the symptom is predominantly a psychic condition—shrinking from speaking through fear of not succeeding, and the remedy of *relaxation* (to reduce or entirely do away with the nervous and muscular tension) has worked nearly always in the various institutions for stutter-curing.

'Of the initial stage of speech development, the mental process is in advance of the powers of muscular control, and the resulting lack of muscular co-ordination often produces a *temporary stammer* [read *stutter*]. If the child is worried and nervous during this period of adjustment, he will become conscious of his speech and of the difficulties surrounding its acquisition, and at once the second stage is reached—that of fear or dread of speech —unconscious probably, but none the less potent.' (Boome, E.J., Baines, H.M.S., and Harries, D.G. *Abnormal Speech,* Sherwood Press, Cleveland, 1939)

Stuttering is seen in about 1 per cent

of the population and usually appears between the ages of two and six years. It occurs more frequently in males, in twins, and in those who are left-handed. It is rarely seen among diabetics and it is most uncommon among primitive peoples.

From the psychoanalytic point of view, stuttering is regarded as due in most instances to displacement of anal libido onto the throat and mouth and onto the act of word-forming. The anal-sadistic stutterer equates words with feces, and the expulsion or retention of words means the expulsion or retention of feces. Further, words acquire the same omnipotence they had in the infantile stage; 'words can kill' and the stutterer is constantly anxious about using so dangerous a weapon. While anal sadism forms the core of the problem, other component instincts typically contribute to the symptom. Phallic impulses, for example, often lead to an equation of speaking ability with potency and of disability with castration.

stygiophobia (sti-jē-ō-fō′bē-à) Fear of hell; hadephobia.

style, life See *constancy*.

subacute combined degeneration of the spinal cord See *sclerosis, posterolateral*.

subacute delirious state See *delirium, subacute*.

subclavian steal See *syndrome, subclavian steal*.

subconsciousness 1. Partial unconsciousness.
2. The state in which mental processes take place without conscious perception on the subject's part.

subcortical encephalopathy (sub-kor′ti-kal en-sef-a-lop′à-thi) See *sclerosis, diffuse*.

subdelirious state, subdelirium The prodromata of a full-blown delirium: restlessness, headache, oversensitiveness to auditory and visual stimuli, irritability, lability of emotions.

The term 'subacute delirious state' is applied to '. . . a syndrome in which incoherence of thought, speech and movement appear together with perplexity, in a setting of clouding of consciousness, fluctuating in degree. The state may fol-

low a typical delirium or appear independently. It may persist over a considerable period, weeks or months, outlasting the signs of the underlying physical illness, but always ending in recovery.' (Mayer-Gross, W., et al. *Clinical Psychiatry*, Williams & Wilkins, Baltimore, 1960)

subject homoerotic (hō-mō-e-rot′ik) See *homosexuality, male*.

subject-ill The subject-ill patient uses his own body to symbolize his emotions. This is achieved through somatization, which constitutes an organic language of the mind. See *somatization*.

In opposition to this type, Stekel calls object-ill the patient who is the victim of compulsions and expresses his emotions through symbolization of objects outside his body—usually a close member of the family.

The "subject-ill" makes efforts to extravert himself in order to adjust himself to the world; the "object-ill," however, is introverted and makes no attempts at extraversion.' (Stekel, W. *Compulsion and Doubt*, Liveright, New York, 1949)

subject-system See *complex, subject*.

subjective mentation *Autism* (q.v.).

sublimate (sub′li-māt) To externalize or objectivate instinctual impulses in ways that meet the situation. To sublimate is to refine, to purify instinctual manifestations. The instincts are not changed; their mode of expression is altered.

sublimation (sub-li-mā′shun) In psychoanalytic psychology, the process of modifying an instinctual impulse in such a way as to conform to the demands of society. Sublimation is a substitute activity which gives some measure of gratification to the infantile impulse which has been repudiated in its original form. Sublimation is an unconscious process and is a function of the normal ego. It is not technically a defense mechanism, for unlike the latter it does not lead to any restriction or inhibition of ego-functioning by requiring a constant counter-cathexis; rather, the impulse or wish is modified in such a way that gratification can be achieved without disapprobation or disapproval. Unlike the usual defenses, in sublimation the ego is not acting in opposition to the id; on the contrary, it is helping the id to gain external expression. Sublimation, in other words, does not involve repression. It is to be noted that the original impulse is never conscious in sublimation.

To put it another way, sublimation· is a form of *desexualization* (q.v.) in which the instinctive impulses, instead of requiring control by constant countercathexis, are deflected (by means of identification, displacement, and substitution) into acceptable channels. The aim or object (or both) of the drive is changed without blocking an adequate discharge. It seems likely that sublimation is intimately related to *identification* (q.v.), for both depend upon the presence of models and upon incentives supplied directly or indirectly by the environment.

E. Bergler (*Psychiatric Quarterly Supplement 23:* 313, 1949) considers acting a sublimation and he notes that, contrary to popular opinion, it is not exhibitionism which is the original id wish, for were this the case the original impulse would be conscious. Instead, according to him, it is voyeurism which is being sublimated. The id wish is: 'I want to look at mother (the breast) or father (the penis) or both (intercourse)'; but the superego vetoes this wish, and the ego defends itself against the reproach: 'I am not really interested in peeping; indeed, I do the opposite, I want to show off my own body.' But the exhibitionism is also forbidden, and the ego evades this second superego reproach by finding a socially approved and accepted outlet: 'I am neither aggressive in exhibitionism nor am I a voyeur. I am only socially minded and want to give pleasure to others.'

Interesting as this formulation is, it implies that reversal into the opposite or reaction-formation is necessary before sublimation can occur, a viewpoint to which not all would subscribe. See *reaction-formation.*

subliminal fringe (sub-lim′in-al) See *summation.*

submania Hypomania. See *mania.*

submissiveness, submission Passivity, acceptance, especially as contrasted with *ascendance* (q.v.) or dominance.

sub-psyche (sub′-sī′kē) A term intro-

duced by Bumke as synonymous with unconscious life.

sub-shock See *treatment, ambulatory insulin.*

substantia nigra (sub-stan-tē-à nē′grà) See *midbrain.*

substitute See *surrogate.*

substitute, displacement The affect, idea, object, etc., onto which the original affect or impulse is displaced. See *displacement.*

substitute-formation Symptom-formation; the tendency of repressed impulses to use any opportunity for indirect discharge. The energy of the warded-off instinct is displaced to any other impulse that is associatively connected with the repressed one, and the intensity of this substitute impulse is increased and often, in addition, the affect connected with it is changed in quality. Such substitute impulses are known as derivatives; most neurotic symptoms are derivatives.

substitute, regressive Displacing the unconscious sexual aim or object in the course of psychosexual development to a chronologically earlier one from which pleasure was derived.

In describing a patient with a phantasy of being beaten by the father, Freud states that 'it is not only the punishment for the forbidden genital relation [*incest*], but also the *regressive substitute* for it.' (Freud, S. *Collected Papers,* vol. 2, tr. by Riviere, J., Leonard and Virginia Woolf and The Institute of Psychoanalysis, London, 1924-25)

substitution neurosis *Obs.* Obsessional neurosis.

subthalamus (sub-tha-la′mus) That portion of the brain which is bounded by the dorsal thalamus anteriorly, the tegmentum of the midbrain posteriorly, the hypothalamus medially, and the internal capsule laterally. The subthalamus contains the rostral extensions of. the red nucleus and substantia nigra from the midbrain, the fields of Forel (which are probably a rostral extension of reticular nuclei), and the subthalamic nucleus (body of Luys). The last is functionally connected with the globus pallidus.

subwaking Being or held in a state inter-mediate between sleeping and waking; hypnoidal.

success, failure through A term used by Freud to describe the self-injuring con-duct of those who, on the verge of achiev-ing a long-desired aim, renounce it, obtain-ing gratification through its renunciation. Examples are 'the clinical assistant who for so long desired to become professor and renounced the position on his pre-decessor's sudden death,' or 'the girl who withdrew from the beloved man at the sudden death of his wife, her rival.' It is a moral veto. The fact is that at such a moment the force of conscience prevents the enjoyment, and even the acceptance, of success. The moral veto can enforce itself in different ways. 'A young man who has been dependent on an uncommonly thrifty, rich father, is suddenly notified that his father had died from apoplexy. He is the only heir. A few hours later he is so clumsy when driving his car that he perishes in an accident.' In a less spec-tacular reaction, this young man could have wasted his heritage, or he could have acquired a severe neurosis. It seems that this moral veto, with its reaction of renunciation, occurs only when it is pre-ceded by a period of phantasy which an-ticipates the misfortune or the death of the rival. (Reik, T. *Masochism in Modern Man*, Farrar and Rinehart, New York, 1941)

succinylcholine A muscle relaxant, usually administered intravenously; in psychia-try, used in association with electrocon-vulsive treatment to prevent or minimize the occurrence of bone fractures.

succubus (suk'u-bus) Demon or witch; specifically, a female demon who has sex-ual intercourse with men during their sleep. See *incubus*.

sucking, thumb The earliest and one of the most common manipulations of the body found in young children. In some children, it is observed at birth, to con-tinue on through infancy and early child-hood, when it becomes an undesirable habit and is classified as a neurotic trait. During the first months of life, thumb-sucking is a physiological and common, but not universal, characteristic of the in-fant. With the waning of the hand-to-mouth reaction phase, which takes place at about twelve months of age, according to Gesell, the habit ceases. Even past the age of twelve months and on through three and four years (two years according to Kanner) it is considered normal when recurring before nap, sleep, or at times of fatigue or emotional stress. Thumb-sucking is accompanied by movements and positions of the free hand, as well as the remaining fingers of the sucked thumb hand, which are characteristic of and constant for the individual child, the so-called accessory movements. (Levy, D.M. 'Finger Sucking and Accessory Move-ments in Early Infancy: An Etiologic Study,' *American Journal of Psychiatry* 7, 881-918, 1928) According to Levy, who has made an anamnestic and an experimental study of the subject, thumb-sucking occurs in children with insufficient lip movements or incompleteness of the sucking phase of earlier feeding, breast or other type.

The psychoanalytic school considers thumb-sucking an auto-erotic gratifica-tion, as an expression of infantile sexual cravings, the oral erogenic zone being in this case the level of stimulation and grati-fication.

suckling, eternal 'Perhaps Christoph Haitzmann was only a poor devil, one of those who never had any luck; perhaps he was too poorly gifted, too ineffective to make a living, and belonged to that well-known type, the "eternal suckling"—to those who are unable to tear themselves away from the joyous haven at the moth-er's breast, who hold fast all through their lives to their claim to be nourished by someone else.' (Freud, S. *Collected Papers*, vol. 4, tr. by Riviere, J., Leonard and Virginia Woolf and The Institute of Psychoanalysis, London, 1924-25)

suffocatio hysterica (soof-fô-kä'tē-ō hē-ste're̅-kà) Hysterical suffocation; hysteri-cal spasm of the muscles of the throat; often seen as part of the symptom picture in globus hystericus. Like the latter, suffo-catio hysterica is often based on the un-conscious rejection of incorporation phan-tasies of a sexual and/or aggressive nature.

suggestibility The state, quality, or ability of being influenced by *suggestion* (q.v.). *Negative suggestibility* is doing the oppo-site of what is suggested to the patient. See *schizophrenia, catatonic.*

suggestion The process of influencing a person to the point of uncritical acceptance of an idea, belief, or other cognitive process. Some would differentiate between heterosuggestion (when the source of the idea is someone outside the person) and autosuggestion (when the source of the idea is the subject himself, as when he keeps saying to himself that he is getting better and better every day, perhaps in hopes that he will one day come to believe his own statement).

While suggestion does not afford a complete explanation of hypnosis, it is obvious that it plays a large part in it, in that the subject comes to accept the hypnotist's repeated suggestions that he is becoming drowsy and soon finds that this is so. This is even more clear with post-hypnotic suggestion, when the subject will carry out some action which has been proposed to him during the trance-state.

The psychoanalytic method is a modification of hypnosis, and, like the latter, depends upon suggestion. '. . . we readily admit that the results of psycho-analysis rest upon a basis of suggestion; only by suggestion we must be understood to mean that which we, with Ferenczi, find that it consists of—influence on a person through and by means of the transference-manifestations of which he is capable.' (Freud, S. *Collected Papers,* vol. 2. tr. by Riviere, J., Leonard and Virginia Woolf and The Institute of Psychoanalysis, London, 1924-25) See *conditioning, operant.*

Prestige-suggestion is another form of psychotherapy; unlike psychoanalysis, however, it does not attempt to uncover or deal with the unconscious determinants of behavior. Its efficacy is chiefly dependent upon gratification of the patient's security needs; the patient submits to and identifies with the omnipotent authority (the therapist) and gives up his symptoms as part of his obedience to the therapist.

suggestion, affective See *hypotaxia.*

suggestion, post-hypnotic Suggestion given during the hypnotic stage to be acted upon after the hypnotic phase has passed.

suggestion, prestige A form of supportive psychotherapy in which the therapist, because he occupies a position of omnipotence in the eyes of the patient, is able to dictate the disappearance of symptoms. 'The motivation to comply is usually conditioned by a wish to gratify important security needs through archaic mechanisms of submission to and identification with an omnipotent authority.' (Wolberg, L.R. *The Technique of Psychotherapy.* Grune & Stratton, New York, 1954) Prestige-suggestion is probably the least successful of all treatment methods.

suggestion, verbal See *ideoplasty.*

suggestive In psychiatry this usually relates to hypnotic suggestion; thus, one speaks of hypnotic or suggestive therapeutics.

suicide The act of killing oneself. While it is believed by some that all suicides are psychotic, the more widely accepted view is that suicide can occur in any psychiatric disorder although the psychoses (depressions, including involutional psychoses, and the schizophrenias) account for the majority of cases. Alcoholics also contribute a disproportionately high number of suicides among the non-hospitalized population. Men outnumber women by three or four times when 'successful' suicides are considered; if attempted suicides are considered, however, the ratio is reversed. Suicide increases with increasing age, although particularly in females there is a large rise in incidence in the third decade and in both sexes there is another rise in the involutional period (40-55 years for females; 50-65 years for males). In the United States, suicide occurs less frequently in the Negro than in any other race. The larger the family, the smaller the risk of suicide; when classified by marital status and family constellation, suicides are seen to be most frequent among those who are divorced. While some series indicate that almost all suicides have had a relative or mate who committed suicide or otherwise met a violent, tragic, or dramatic death (the so-called 'death trend'), not all writers agree on the prognostic significance of the presence or absence of such loss of a loved one. Most suicides occur in the early morning hours (the time at which clinically depressed patients typically awake from their fitful, unrefreshing sleep), and more occur on Monday and Tuesday than on any other day of the week. The spring is the season with highest incidence of suicide. It is a common misconception that the patient who threatens suicide is not likely to commit suicide. The reverse is probably closer to the truth, for about 75 per cent of successful suicides had previously threatened or attempted it. Typically, the genuinely suicidal patient departs with a surge of hatred for the world and pejorative accusations of the self, leaving definite instructions and restrictions for those he has purposely deserted. Among the clinical depressions, those with prominent anxiety features, a feeling of losing ground, and/or a marked hypochondriacal trend are the most likely to make a suicide attempt. Ill-health is a prominent motive for suicide in both sexes, accounting for 40 per cent of the males and 20 per cent of the females, and such motives are likely to be associated with a high degree of success (50 per cent of the males and 25 per cent of the females). Other common motives include domestic difficulties, which account for 50 per cent of suicide attempts by women and 30 per cent of attempts by men; and unhappy love affairs (10 per cent of the women, 4 per cent of the men). Suicide often occurs when the patient seems to be recovering from an emotional crisis; approximately half occur within 90 days of such crisis.

The following table of suicide rates (per 100,000 adults) is adapted from the 1956 report of the World Health Organization:

	Total	Male	Female
U.S.A.	10.1	16.1	4.3
U.S.A. — whites	10.8	17.2	4.6
U.S.A. — non-whites	3.8	6.4	1.3
Scotland	5.9	8.3	3.7
Spain	5.9	9.1	2.9
Switzerland	22.6	33.9	12.0
Denmark	23.3	31.4	15.4
Japan	23.4	29.2	17.8

Psychodynamically, suicide or a suicide attempt is seen most frequently to be an aggressive attack directed against a loved one or against society in general; in others, it may be a misguided bid for attention or it may be conceived of as a means of effecting reunion with the ideal love-object or mother. That suicide is in one sense a means of release for aggressive impulses is supported by the change of wartime suicide rates. In World War II, for example, rates among the participating nations fell, sometimes by as much as 30 per cent; but in neutral countries, the rates remained the same.

In involutional depressions and in the depressed type of manic-depressive psychosis, the following dynamic elements are often clearly operative: the depressed patient loses the object which he depends upon for narcissistic supplies; in an attempt to force the object's return, he regresses to the oral stage and incorporates (swallows up) the object, thus regressively identifying with the object: the sadism which was originally directed against the deserting object is taken up by the patient's superego and is directed against the incorporated object, which now lodges within the ego; suicide occurs, not so much as an attempt on the ego's part to escape the inexorable demands of the superego, but rather as an enraged attack on the incorporated object in retaliation for its having deserted the patient in the first place.

suicide, psychic The killing of one's self without resorting to any physical agency; used in reference to those who make up their minds to die and actually do so. It is presumed that the same forces which lead a person to commit physical suicide are active in psychic suicide cases, but that, instead of operating overtly, these forces work endopsychically.

suicidogenic (sū-i-si-dō-jen'ik) Pertaining to suicidogenesis; causing suicide.

suigenderism (sū-i-jen'dēr-iz'm) The natural drift on a child's part to associate or group with others of his own *gender*. During latency the activities of boys are largely confined to boys, while those of girls are mainly limited to girls. For the manifestation of these natural, wholesome, unerotic relationships between members of one's own gender, the term *suigenderism* is recommended. When sex-feelings begin to crop up in suigenderism, it may become *homoerotism, homosexuality* or *homogenitality*, as the case may be.

Sullivan, Harry Stack (1892-1949) The chief proponent of the so-called dynamic-cultural school of psychoanalysis, which emphasizes sociologic rather than biologic events, present-day contacts with people rather than past experiences, current interpersonal relationships rather than infantile sexuality. Orthodox Freudians consider this a superficial approach that limits itself to a single facet of experience, the cultural.

summation 'The tendency to suppress our affections may accumulate; that is a *summation* of the *repressing* or *suppressing* egoistic wishes may occur, usually through the influence of puritanical associates.' (Kempf, E.J. *Psychopathology*, Mosby, St. Louis, 1921)

Freud uses the term *summation* in regard to the etiology of anxiety-neurosis. 'According to the disposition of the person concerned and the other burdens on his nervous system, a longer or shorter time will be required before the effect of this *summation* becomes evident. Those persons who tolerate coitus interruptus apparently without harmful results are in reality becoming thereby disposed to the disorder of anxiety neurosis, which may break out either at any time spontaneously or after an ordinary and otherwise insufficient trauma; just as the chronic alcoholic will in the end develop a cirrhosis or other illness as an effect of *summation*, or under the influence of a fever will go down with a delirium.' (Freud, S. *Collected Papers*, vol. 1, tr. by Riviere, J., Leonard and Virginia Woolf and The Institute of Psychoanalysis, London, 1924-25)

In neurophysiology, summation refers to a response obtained when two stimuli are applied, neither of which by itself is of sufficient intensity to elicit a response. In this sense, there are two types of summation, temporal and spatial. Temporal summation is seen when two successive stimuli, each of them too weak to elicit a response, are applied to the same nerve trunk within 0.1 to 0.5 millisecond of each other in which case a response will be evoked because of the enduring character of the local excitatory process. Spatial summation is seen when two different afferent nerves, which play upon the same reflex center, are stimulated either simultaneously or within a short interval (not more than 15 milliseconds); a response is evolved even though neither stimulus alone will elicit a response. Spatial summation is believed to be a result of additive excitatory alterations in the neurons involved. Sherrington and his associates refer to this excitatory al-

teration as the 'central excitatory state,' which is often abbreviated as c.e.s. The nerves affected are said to be in the 'subliminal fringe of excitation.'

summation, spatial See *summation*.

summation, temporal See *summation*.

superego In psychoanalytic psychology, there are three functional divisions of the psyche: the id, the ego, and the superego. The superego is the last of these to be differentiated. It is the representative of society within the psyche (i.e. conscience or morality) and also includes the ideal aspirations (ego-ideal). The superego is mainly unconscious; its functions include: (1) approval or disapproval of the ego's actions, i.e. judgment that an act is 'right' or 'wrong'; (2) critical self-observation; (3) self-punishment; (4) demands that the ego repent or make reparation for wrong-doing; (5) self-love or self-esteem as the ego reward for having done right. (Brenner, C. *An Elementary Textbook of Psychoanalysis*, International Universities Press, New York, 1955)

In general, the superego may be regarded as a split-off portion of the ego which arises on the basis of identification with certain aspects of the introjected parents. Since introjection and identification are among the earliest defense mechanisms to appear, it is obvious that the precursors of the superego are in evidence early in life, in the prephallic or pre-oedipal phase. Such precursors consist mainly of the various effects which the demands and prohibitions of the parents (and their surrogates) have on the child, and these are particularly evident in regard to bowel training (and thus Ferenczi's term, 'sphincter morality'). Yet until the oedipal phase, the superego does not make itself felt as a disturbance of the harmonious accord between the strivings of the ego and the strivings of the id. Morality in the young child, such as it is, is more a response to immediate external demands of the environment than obedience to an inner authority. It is only with the oedipal phase that the superego begins to take its final form as an internal authority which stands between ego and id, compelling the child on his own to renounce certain pleasures, and imposing punishment (loss of self-esteem, guilt-feelings, etc.) for violations of its orders.

The superego develops as a reaction to the Oedipus complex; as is often said, it is the *heir of the Oedipus complex*. It is a solution to the impulses of this period which have no prospect of succeeding in reality and which, if allowed to continue unchanged, would have been dangerous. These impulses, deriving from the id, are allowed access to the ego; the forbidden impulses (love for the mother, hatred of the father) are withdrawn from their objects and deposited in the ego, which thus becomes changed. The changed portion of the ego is the superego, and it contains the sadism which was originally directed against the father; so also does it contain the love originally felt for the mother, but the very process of introjecting the mother and changing the libido attached to the maternal object into ego libido has resulted ·in desexualizagion. Thus the love portion of the superego (the ego-ideal) is a non-sensual love.

What has happened, in short, is that the frustrations of the Oedipus complex have caused the ego to resort to primitive methods of defense; viz. introjection and identification. As a result, the oedipal objects are regressively replaced by identifications, and sexual longing for the maternal object has been replaced by an asexual alteration within the organization of the ego. These newly introjected objects, which replace the sexual and hostile impulses toward the parents, combine with the parental introjects from the prephallic period (internalized parental prohibitions), and the superego is formed.

In practice it is difficult to differentiate sharply between the superego, which is an image of the hated and feared objects, and the ego-ideal, which is an image of the loved objects in the libido. 'The ego ideal seems to contain more maternal libido, the superego, more of the paternal; in reality both are fused. Furthermore, just as there are some destructive elements to be found within the ego ideal because the libido is desexualized, there are also libidinal forces at work in the formation of the superego, since it develops through identification with the ambivalently loved father. The predominantly maternal ego ideal starts to develop as early as the pregenital stages, but the predominantly paternal superego is observed first in the genital stage. The impetus for the formation of the superego is the danger of castration, a danger which threatens the entire ego in consequence of its identification with the genitals. By taking the father into his ego, the boy not only escapes the danger of castration but also gains a protector in the image of the father absorbed by the ego.' (Nunberg, H. *Principles of Psychoanalysis*, International Universities Press, New York, 1955)

Melanie Klein and her followers believe that the superego begins to function much earlier than Freud (and most psychoanalysts since him) believed. 'Where I differ is in placing at birth the processes of introjection which are the basis of the superego. The superego precedes by some months the beginning of the Oedipus complex, a beginning which I date, together with that of the depressive position, in the second quarter of the first year. Thus the early introjection of the good and bad breast is the foundation of the superego and influences the development of the Oedipus complex. This conception of superego formation is in contrast to Freud's explicit statements that the identifications with the parents are the heir of the Oedipus complex and only succeed if the Oedipus complex is successfully overcome.' (*International Journal of Psychoanalysis 39: 84-90, 1958*)

superego, autonomous The normal superego, which demands that the ego behave in a 'good' way, in contrast to a heteronomous superego, which demands that the ego behave in accordance with what is expected. The heteronomous superego is a possible outcome of inconsistent handling of a child by his parents. The inconsistency makes it impossible for him to foresee what particular conduct might ensure continued affection from the parents; the child consequently renounces attempts to differentiate between good and bad, and instead responds only to the demand of the moment.

superego, double The double conscience sometimes seen in *psychic dualism*. The two consciences, or superegos, are usually antagonistic and regard each other vigilantly and belligerently. One conscience is usually considered masculine, the other feminine. Oberndorf cites the case of a male physician as an illustration of double superego. The patient's courtesy, conscientiousness,   and   consideration for others was often exaggerated to the point of masochistic subservience. The patient complained of depression secondary to the constant criticism which he underwent at the hands of his second superego. This second conscience, which never agreed with his masculine conscience, was traced to the story of the Dybbuk he had heard from his mother. In the story, the Dybbuk is the disembodied spirit of a wicked person which can reach heaven only after purification by entering the body of a young, virtuous girl. Thus the second conscience, which required almost absolute goodness, was viewed as feminine, and the patient's goodness became almost synonymous with femininity.

superego, group S.R. Slavson differentiates between the group superego and the infantile superego (*An Introduction to Group Therapy,* The Commonwealth Fund, Oxford University Press, New York, 1943). He considers that this superego is an outcome of the adaptations to and experiences with various groups of people beyond the relationship with parents.

superego, heteronomous (het'ĕr-on'ō-mus) See *autonomy-heteronomy.* A special type of superego which demands of the ego that it behave according to what is expected at the moment. A person with such a superego is irresolute and weak, for his behavior at any given moment is controlled by the desire to secure the approval of those about him; and he is likewise in constant fear of being criticized or punished—i.e. he has 'social anxiety.' This is in contrast to the normal type of superego, which demands only that the ego behave in a 'good way, according to a certain set of standards or ideals. Here the person goes by rule of thumb and is thus free of constant fear of criticism; he can come to decisions and carry out behavior independently of the approval or disapproval at the moment.

The heteronomous superego arose, for example, 'when the parents had shown so inconsistent a behavior that it became impossible for the child to foresee what conduct on his part would be most likely to ensure the continuance of their affection; whereupon, renouncing all attempts to distinguish between good and bad, he would take his bearings according to the

demand of the moment.' (Fenichel, O. *The Psychoanalytic Theory of Neurosis,* Norton, New York, 1945)

superego, parasites of the Ideals and values absorbed by the person 'which usurp the functions of the super-ego.' After one has entered the latency period, ideals usually continue to undergo modification. As the emotional ties to the family begin to loosen, becoming less intense, one's standards become more independent of the infantile models based upon the parents. Other persons or ideas begin to serve as models. These become part of the original superego which was formed at an earlier age from the parents' attitudes and activities. When the new ideals are only 'a slight modification of old ideals, the situation is not difficult . . . Sometimes, however, internal or external situations may create parasites of the superego which usurp the functions of the superego for a varying length of time.' Even though the later identifications with authorities other than the parent are usually superficial, they may be very influential. An example of a parasitic superego is the influence of mass suggestion. A person with a normal superego may, under mass suggestion, yield to impulses which would normally be suppressed and yet show no guilt-feelings: '. . . individuals acting as a group . . . (or mob) . . . are capable of instinctual outbreaks that would be entirely impossible for them as individuals.'

Another example of a parasitic superego occurs under hypnosis, when the hypnotist takes over the functions of the patient's superego. In the patient's psyche the hypnotist acts as a parasitic superego. 'As such he tries to undo the previous work of the super-ego that gave rise to the defensive struggle.' (Fenichel, O. *The Psychoanalytic Theory of Neurosis,* Norton, New York, 1945)

superego, parasitic A temporarily co-existing body of commands that conflict with the subject's own superego standards, such as internalizations of the leader's exhortation to kill during wartime.

superego, primitive A superego that exists apart from the parental superego and is older in origin than the force established by parents and teachers. The primitive superego is assumed to be hereditary and susceptible to the influence of hereditary factors in contrast to the parental super-ego which reflects tradition.

'For my part, I believe we must envisage, at least in theory, the existence of some sort of primitive super-ego having the function, according to us, as "organizer" of differentiating cells of the fetal organism, of assigning to them their places and functions in the physical framework, and of eliminating or destroying their tendencies to fulfill other functions. This organizer differentiates the activities of cells according to principles peculiar to each species.' (Laforgue, R. *The Relativity of Reality,* Nervous and Mental Disease Monographs No. 66, 1940, New York)

superfemale Metafemale; a female with a sex-chromosome pattern of XXX (instead of the normal XX). Rather than being more 'female' than the normal, however, such women are amenorrheic, sterile, and have underdeveloped female sexual characteristics. See *chromosome.*

supergene (su'pĕr-gēn) A type of variation of hereditary traits caused by chromosomal rearrangement; such a mutation affects an entire section of a chromosome but stimulates the single factor type of inheritance (which is produced by one major mutant gene).

superior paraplegia See *paraplegia.*

supermoron (sū-pĕr-mō'ron) A person slightly subnormal mentally, but in a grade above that of a moron.

super-ordinated See *ego* (Jung's definition of).

supersex (sū'pĕr-seks) A sexually abnormal type of sterile organisms, first observed by Bridges, which show intersexual features owing to the disturbed ratio of autosomes to heterosomes.

Supersexual individuals are either 'superfemales' characterized by three X chromosomes and two sets of autosomes or 'supermales' with one X chromosome and three sets of autosomes.

superstition An irrational belief in magic, chance, etc. or an exaggerated fear of the unknown. See *delusion.*

supervalent Referring to the excessive intensity of an idea that the subject cannot rid himself of; the intensity results from the multiple unconscious determinants of the idea, and/or from the need to keep the idea as a screen for a reverse or contrary thought. See *reaction-formation.*

supervision In psychiatry, the critical evaluation by an experienced therapist of the clinical work of a therapist in training.

support See *psychotherapy.*

suppression The act of consciously inhibiting an impulse, affect, or idea, as in the deliberate attempt to forget something and think no more about it. Suppression is thus to be differentiated from *repression* (q.v.), which is an unconscious process. It is probable that there is no sharp line of demarcation between suppression and repression, and it seems also likely that on occasion the unconscious defense of repression may be directed against material which the individual consciously suppresses. Nonetheless, it seems advisable in most instances to regard suppression and repression as distinctly different mechanisms.

suppression-neurosis See *neurosis, suppression.*

supra-individuals See *collective.*

suprarenalism (su-pra-ren'al-iz'm) Overactivity of the suprarenal glands.

surface-ego 'Freud conceives the ego as essentially a "surface-ego," that is to say, one which in its principal function is directed toward the outside world, whose stimuli it receives or wards off. It is therefore more readily able to assimilate a piece of knowledge presented to it from without than one which proceeds from within the psychic apparatus.' (Sachs, H. *International Journal of Psychoanalysis* VI, 7, 19, 1925)

surrender, schizophrenic (skiz-ō-fren'ik) A term used by C. MacFie Campbell to characterize the type of schizophrenia in which the mechanism is one of passive repression without initial anxiety or any conspicuous restitutional attempts.

The symptoms of schizophrenia can be

divided into two major groups: (1) the regressive symptoms and (2) the restitutional symptoms. The first category comprises those symptoms that are a direct expression of the regressive breakdown of the ego and an undoing of differentiations acquired through mental development. Some examples are phantasies of world destruction, feelings of depersonalization, delusions of grandeur, and physical sensations. In the second category are those symptoms that express the schizophrenic's attempt to regain the lost objective world; hallucinations, delusions of persecution, and some catatonic symptoms are in this category.

Hebephrenia is the purely regressive type of schizophrenia in which there are no restitutional or defensive attempts. The ego takes refuge in successively older and older types of adaptation, finally arriving at a vegetative existence and perhaps even intra-uterine' attitudes. The loss of the objective world and of any interest in it has become complete. The patient has undergone a 'schizophrenic surrender.' (Fenichel, O. *The Psychoanalytic Theory of Neurosis,* Norton, New York, 1945)

surrender, will to The psychic process through which the neurotic patient comes to the point of giving up his neurosis: it is a renunciating mental attitude through which the patient expresses his desire to submit to the analyst's aim of curing the illness. At the beginning of his psychotherapy, the patient's only aim seems to be a 'desire to protect and cherish his illness in defiance of the doctor's therapeutical endeavor.' It is only through the development of the will to surrender that the patient is ready to renounce his neurosis.

According to Stekel, a positive transference during analysis is a manifestation of this will to surrender. This desire is the opposite of the patient's 'will to power,' which is the expression of the patient's wish to master the analyst by love and attention, and defend his neurosis by so doing. (Stekel, W. *The Interpretation of Dreams,* Liveright, New York, 1943)

surrogate (sēr'ō-gāt) One who takes the place of another is a surrogate or substitute. From the standpoint of instinctual psychology, during growth, affective states originally expressed toward the parents are normally transferred from them to others who stand for them. Thus, a sister may be the first mother-surrogate, later a teacher, still later the mother of a friend, and finally a lover. With each new surrogate there is normally less and less resemblance to the original (mother). See *surrogate, mother.*

surrogate, father See *surrogate, mother.*

surrogate, mother One who takes the place of the mother. In normal growth youthful attachments to the mother should gradually be directed upon other women. The female schoolteacher, for instance, takes over part of the care of the child; she becomes a mother-surrogate; later, with the development of heterosexual interests, the adolescent substitutes other women for his mother. However, if strongly fixated upon the mother, the child may be unable to affect any substantial shift to another woman. He may select later love-objects more or less genuinely on a basis of the earlier fixations. From the standpoint of the (now grown-up) child, the qualities of the mother-surrogate may be essentially those of the mother.

The expression *mother-substitute* is synonymous with *mother-surrogate.*

The same concepts hold true with regard to the father: hence, the expressions *father-surrogate* and *father-substitute.*

survivor syndrome See *syndrome, survivor.*

suspenopsia (sus-pen-op'si-à) Literally, 'suspension of sight.' A tendency for the image arising in either eye to be entirely disregarded for a short period of time so that the individual is using one eye only for the time being.' (Orton, S.T. *Reading, Writing and Speech Problems in Children,* Norton, New York, 1937)

susto (sus'tō) An acute anxiety state seen in Peruvian children and adolescents, usually precipitated by an experience of violent fright. Susto, or magic fright, is characterized by an anxiety, excitability, dejection with considerable weight loss, and a belief that the patient's soul has been stolen from his body.

Sweetser, William (1797-1875) American psychiatrist who wrote the first American treatise on mental hygiene (1843).

swindler, epileptic See *epilepsy, affective.*

swindler, pathological (path-ō-log′i-kal) See *liar, pathological; imposter.*

Sydenham's chorea See *chorea, Sydenham's.*

syllable-stumbling A form of stuttering or stammering: the patient halts on syllables which he finds it difficult to enunciate.

symbiotic infantile psychosis See *psychosis, symbiotic infantile.*

symbol An object that stands for or represents something else. E. Jones ('The Theory of Symbolism,' *Papers on Psychoanalysis,* Baillière, Tindall & Cox, London, 1948) has pointed out that a symbol (1) is a representative or substitute of some other idea; (2) represents the primary element through having something in common with it; (3) is typically sensorial and concrete, whereas the idea represented may be relatively abstract and complex; (4) utilizes modes of thought which are more primitive, both ontogenetically and phylogenetically; (5) is a manifest expression of an idea that is more or less hidden, secret, or kept in reserve, and (6) is made spontaneously, automatically, and, in the broad sense of the word, unconsciously.

In psychoanalytic psychology, the symbol is a conscious representation or perception which replaces, and is a substitute for, unconscious mental content. The unconscious mental content is not recognized and its repression is maintained by the counter-cathexis of ego defenses; by the very fact that its meaning is unknown to the subject, the repressed psychic energy can, through the symbol, attain primary-process discharge, which would not be possible if the unconscious mental content were recognized as such. Symbols are the building stones for various other forms of indirect representation of unconscious content, viz. dreams, phantasies, hallucinations, symptoms, and even language.

Jones has this to say in regard to the extraordinary predominance of sexual symbols: 'A Swedish philologist, Sperber, has in a remarkable essay elaborated the theory, which has been several times suggested on other grounds by biologists, that sexual impulses have played the most important part in both the origin and later development of speech. According to this theory, which is supported by very weighty considerations, the earliest speech sounds were those that served the purpose of calling the mate (hence the sexual importance of the voice to this day), while the further development of speech roots accompanied the performance of work. . . . Words used during these common tasks thus had two meanings, denoting the sexual act and the equivalent work done respectively. In time the former meaning became detached and the word, now applying only to the work, thus "desexualized."
. . . The symbolic association is the relic of the old verbal identity; things that once had the same name as a genital organ can now appear in dreams, etc., as a symbol for it. Freud aptly likens symbolism to an ancient speech that has almost vanished, but of which relics still remain here and there.' (ibid)

As psychiatric symptoms, symbols may be expressed in any one or all of these general categories: (1) affects alone; thus, in anxiety-hysteria the symbol is intense anxiety without any relevant ideas; other symptoms (rapid pulse and breathing, feelings of impending collapse, etc.) are generally secondary symptoms; (2) affects with ideas, the latter being looked upon as thoroughly foreign and painful to the conscious ego. For example, a patient was 'tormented to death with the idea that I am slowly but certainly killing my children; that thought is furthest removed from my mind. I love them too dearly,' or (3) organic symptoms: the patients whose mental symptoms take an organic route of expression usually complain of a disease and not of symptoms; a woman, 35 years old, inordinately attached to her mother since early childhood, developed a deep sense of guilt when she left her invalid mother, who had a hemiplegia at the time. She repressed the guilt, replacing it with good intellectual reasoning, that is, with rationalization. The daughter later developed symptoms identical with those of her mother, and although these were not organically determined, the repressed guilt and its associated impulses returned to consciousness in the guise of a physical ailment.

Symbols may appear as delusions, hallucinations, morbid affects, compulsions, obsessions, conversions (i.e. hysterical), hypochondriasis, personalization of organs or organic systems, etc. Dreams form a special class of symbols.

symbol, memory A memory or idea that stands for, i.e. is substituted for, some other idea.

symbol, phallic (fal'ik) Anything which represents the penis. Many phallic symbols have been described: knife, spear, gun, and other similar weapons; tree, column, pillar, skyscraper, automobile, airplane, bird, snake, wild animals, cigar, cigarette, pen, pencil, key, screw, hammer, etc.

symbolamblyopia, congenital (sim-bol-am-blē-ō'pē-à) Claiborne's term (1906) for a type of reading disability. See *reading, disabilities of.*

symbolism The act or process of representing an object or idea by a substitute object, sign, or signal. In psychiatry, symbolism is of particular importance since it can serve as a defense mechanism of the ego, as where unconscious (and forbidden) aggressive or sexual impulses come to expression through symbolic representation and thus are able to avoid censorship. The symbolic expression of the unconscious impulse may then appear as the patient's symptom. In one of Freud's cases, for example, Dora's cough was a hysterical symptom which symbolized her unconscious phantasy of oral intercourse between her father and another woman, and this phantasy in turn covered her own erotic feelings for the other woman's husband. See *symbol.*

symbolism, anagogic (an-à-goj'ik) 'Pertaining to or arising from the striving of the inner psychic forms toward progressive ideals; pertaining to the interpretation and psychotherapy of dreams, symptoms, etc., with emphasis on such striving: as, *anagogic methods.*' (*Webster's New International Dictionary,* 2nd ed., Merriam, Springfield, Mass., 1948)

Silberer takes the symbol 'to be the expression of a striving for a high ethical ideal, one which fails to reach this ideal and halts at the symbol instead; the ultimate ideal, however, is supposed to be implicit in the symbol and to be symbo-

lized by it.' (Jones, E.J. *Papers on Psycho-Analysis,* Williams and Wilkins, Baltimore, 1949)

Therapists who embrace this concept of anagogic symbolism regularly make use. of it in their treatment of patients. Recognition and understanding of anagogic symbols is stressed and the striving for the achievement of the ideals expressed therein is encouraged.

symbolism, cryptogenic (krip-tō-jen'ik) Silberer uses the term *cryptogenic symbolism* for any form of pictorial representation or image formed in mental functioning. In other words, all functions of the mind, save the ideational, are represented by cryptogenic symbolism.

symbolism, cryptophoric (krip-tō-for'ik) See *symbolism, metaphoric.*

symbolism, functional Silberer subdivides symbolism into the first and second types; his first is called by Jones the 'material' type; his second, the 'functional' type. 'The first type is that which arises on the basis of an appreceptive insufficiency of purely intellectual origin, where the symbolized idea is not hindered by the influence of any affective complex; the second type arises, on the other hand, on the basis of an apperceptive insufficiency of affective origin.' (Jones, E. *Papers on Psycho-Analysis,* 4th ed., Wood, Baltimore, 1938)

Formerly Silberer used the expression *functional symbolism* with reference to the speed with which the mind was working, whether it was fast, slow, etc.

symbolism, material See *symbolism, functional.*

symbolism, metaphoric According to Jones, a form of indirect representation. It seems that he prefers the expression *indirect pictorial representation* to *symbolism,* or *metaphoric symbolism.* The latter may be defined, then, as a pictorial representation based on a metaphor.

Jones says that J.C. Flügel 'suggested to me that, as an alternative to my proposal, the term, "cryptophor" be used as a counterpart of "metaphor" so that one might speak of cryptophoric as contrasted with metaphoric symbolism, instead of, as I propose, speaking of symbolism as contrasted with metaphoric representation.' (Jones, E. *Papers on Psycho-Analysis,* 4th ed., Wood, Baltimore, 1938)

symbolism, threshold Silberer's term for symbolism occurring during the transition from one state of consciousness to, i.e. on the threshold of, another, for example, from sleep to wakefulness or *vice versa.* The term is the equivalent of *hypnagogic hallucination.* It is a subdivision of what Silberer calls *functional symbolism.*

symbolism, true 'The typical attributes of *true symbolism,* as modified from the description given by Rank and Sachs, are: (1) representation of unconscious material; (2) constant meaning, or very limited scope for variation in meaning; (3) non-dependence on individual factors only; (4) evolutionary basis, as regards both the individual and the race; (5) linguistic connections between the symbol and the idea symbolized; (6) phylogenetic parallels with the symbolism as found in the individual existing in myths, cults, religions, etc.' (Jones, E. *Papers on Psycho-Analysis,* 4th ed., Wood, Baltimore, 1938)

symbolization 'Symbolization according to psychoanalytic usage is an unconscious process built up on association and similarity whereby one object comes to represent or stand for (symbolize) another object, through some part, quality, or aspect which the two have in common. The resemblance is generally so slight or superficial that the conscious mind would overlook it.' (Healy, W., Bronner, A.F., and Bowers, A.M. *The Structure and Meaning of Psychoanalysis,* Knopf, New York, 1930). Other schools of psychiatric thought define symbolization in a similar way, though they may ascribe different reasons for the formation of symbols.

symbolophobia Fear of symbolism, i.e. of having a symbolical meaning attached to one's acts or words.

symmetrical See *complementary.*

sympathetic nervous system See *autonomic nervous system.*

sympathicotonia (sim-path-i-kō-tō′nē-à) Eppinger and Hess described a clinical syndrome in which there is increased tonus of the sympathetic nervous system with a marked tendency to vascular spasm and high blood pressure. This they named *sympathicotonia.* Here there is excessive functioning of the adrenals and a hypersensitivity to adrenalin.

sympathin (sim′pa-thin) See *epinephrine.*

sympathism Suggestibility.

sympathize To experience a feeling similar to that possessed by another. Usually reciprocal motivation is implied.

sympathomimetic See *mydriasis.*

sympathy In general, the existence of feeling identical with or resembling that which another experiences. According to Freud, identification may arise when there is no emotional attachment with the person imitated: for example, one person may copy the feelings and actions of another, because the imitator has an unconscious impulse set free upon hearing about or looking at the one copied. In *sympathy* the feelings of the imitator remain essentially within him. When one or both share similar feelings, based upon some common unconscious quality, the term *identification* is used. See *empathize.*

symptom A symptom is any sign, physical or mental, that stands for something else. In a medical sense the term *symptom* generally implies pathology, although in its broader meaning a symptom may reflect physiological action (as in hunger).

Before the advent of modern psychiatric knowledge, when almost all psychic manifestations were traced directly to cells of the body, the term *symptom* denoted a sign relating to mental and physical phenomena, that is to say, by tradition it carried with it thoughts of the soma or tissues. With the expansion of psychiatric understanding, the expression *symbol* has become identified with the realm of the psyche, i.e. a symptom of the psyche is a symbol. However, in this transitional period, many psychiatrists prefer symptom to symbol, particularly when there is any doubt concerning the origin of the symptom. But there is general agreement when a signal from the psyche is called a symbol. See *symbolism.*

symptom, accessory Bleuler differentiates

between fundamental symptoms and accessory symptoms of the schizophrenias. The accessory, secondary symptoms include hallucinations, illusions, delusions, certain memory disturbances (e.g. déjà vu, déjà fait), some of the disturbances of the person (e.g. speaking of one's self in the second or third person and other pronominal reversals), speech and writing disturbances (e.g. coprolalia, verbigeration, neologisms, metonymy, asyndesis, interpenetration), and physical symptoms such as headache, paresthesiae, 'will-of-the-wisp' gait, weight loss, and general signs of metabolic asthenia. See *symptom, fundamental.*

symptom, biphasic (bī-fāz'ik) A compulsive symptom or action that has two component parts, the second of which is the direct reverse of the first: e.g. the patient has the compulsion first to open the water tap and then to close it again. Obsessive thoughts or impulses may likewise have two parts, the second directly contradicting the first.

The first phase of the symptom represents an instinctual demand, whereas the second phase represents the *anti-instinctual force* or threat of the superego. 'The patient behaves alternately, as though he were a naughty child and a strict punitive disciplinarian.' (Fenichel, O. *The Psychoanalytic Theory of Neurosis,* Norton, New York, 1945) See *anticathexis.*

symptom, fundamental Bleuler differentiates between fundamental symptoms and accessory symptoms of the schizophrenias. The fundamental, primary, or principal symptoms are those that are characteristic of and pathognomonic of *schizophrenia* (q.v.). The accessory symptoms, on the other hand, while they may overshadow the fundamental symptoms in their intensity, are not the essential or basic elements of the schizophrenias since they are seen also in other diseases, and particularly in the organic brain syndromes. The fundamental symptoms include disturbances in the associations, in the affect, in the person, in the will, in attention, in activity and behavior, and also ambivalence (of affect, intellect and/or will), autism, and schizophrenic dementia.

symptom, gramophone Mayer-Gross' term

for a symptom seen often in *Pick's disease* (q.v.): the patient repeats ' . . . with correct expression and diction an elaborate anecdote, seeming himself to be highly amused by it, and could not be stopped until he had told the whole story. After a short interval he would repeat his anecdote as something quite new.' (Mayer-Gross, W., et al. *Clinical Psychiatry,* 2nd ed. Baltimore, Williams and Wilkins, 1960)

symptom, primary See *symptom, fundamental.*

symptom, primary defense A term used by Freud in describing the early development of obsessional neurosis. At the onset of sexual 'maturity,' self-reproach for the memories of pleasurable sexual activities in childhood is avoided by primary defense-symptoms, such as conscientiousness, shame, and self-distrust. These introduce the period of 'apparent health or better—that successful defense.' (Freud, S. *Collected Papers,* vol. 1, tr. by Riviere, J., Leonard and Virginia Woolf and The Institute of Psychoanalysis, London, 1924-25)

symptom, principal See *symptom, fundamental.*

symptom, secondary See *symptom, accessory.*

symptom, secondary defense The protective measures to which the ego resorts in obsessional neurosis, when the primary defense (against repressed memories and self-reproach) has failed. The secondary defense-symptoms include obsessive actions, obsessive speculating, obsessive thinking, the compulsion to test everything, *folie du doute;* 'secondary defense against the obsessional affects calls into being a still wider series of protective measures, which may be transformed into obsessive acts. These may be grouped according to their tendencies: *penitential* measures (burdensome ceremonials, the observation of numbers), *precautionary* measures (all kinds of phobias, superstitions, pedantry, exaggeration of the primary symptom of conscientiousness), *dread of betrayal* (collecting paper, misanthropia), *hebetude* (dipsomania).' (Freud, S. *Collected Papers,* vol. 1, tr. by Riviere, J., Leonard and Virginia Woolf and The Institute of Psychoanalysis, London, 1924 - 25)

symptom specificity See *specificity, symptom.*

symptomatic Having the nature or quality of a *symptom* (q.v.); indicative of underlying (organic) pathology. Thus, the symptomatic psychoses are secondary disturbances of psychic function dependent upon primary alterations in brain tissue function. Some reserve the term symptomatic psychoses for *acute brain disorders* (q.v.); the chronic brain disorders are then referred to as organic psychoses.

symptomatize In psychiatric usage, equivalent to *symbolize* (q.v.).

symptoms, compulsive The orderly and systematic behavior exhibited by the compulsion-neurotic in order to protect himself against dangerous anal-erotic instinctual demands. The compulsion-neurotic feels threatened by unconscious anal-sadistic drives. He is protecting himself against a rebellion of sensual and hostile demands (such as murder and incest) which through regression have become anal-erotic in nature. He accomplishes this by doing things in a compulsive systematic way, according to a prearranged plan, a routine. This protects him against the danger associated with spontaneity. He can be sure he is not committing a sin of which he is both unconscious and afraid. He knows beforehand what he will do and how he will do it and thus he overcomes his fear that his own excitement may induce him to do things he is afraid of. The systemization is especially noticeable with respect to money and time. 'Many compulsion neurotics have an exaggerated interest in all kinds of time-tables.'

The unconscious anal-sadistic drives, however, 'usually sabotage orderliness and clinging to a "system." They may reappear in the form of disorder or events that disturb the system . . .' Furthermore, the compulsion-neurotic never can feel that he has provided enough rules to govern all possibilities, that he knows all the rules sufficiently well, or that he is because the unconscious drives have actually permeated the systems themselves.

Frequently, people around the compulsion-neurotic are bidden to follow his systems in an effort to ensure their validity. The others' refusal to submit increases the patient's hostility as well as his attempts to compel those around him to conform, with the end result that the fear engendered by this show of hostility increases the patient's systematizing needs.

The systematization of the compulsion-neurotic often leads him to make false generalizations. All ideas are classified into certain mutually exclusive categories. Thus the likelihood of an unforeseen new event is excluded. The attitude is that the phenomenon or idea is already known — that is, has been classified — for unforeseen events are dangerous and are interpreted as temptations. (Fenichel, O. *The Psychoanalytic Theory of Neurosis,* Norton, New York, 1945) See *compulsion; obsession; obsessive-compulsive psychoneurosis.*

symptoms, phylogenetic (fī-lō-ge-net'ik) See *schizophrenia, hebephrenic.*

symptoms, withdrawal A term for the symptoms (restlessness, yawning, chills, characteristic pilomotor activity, excessive nasal secretion, lacrimation, sneezing, cramps in abdomen and lower extremities, vomiting and diarrhea, excessive perspiration, muscular twitching) experienced by addicts to morphine and heroin when the drug is suddenly withdrawn, that is, no longer taken.

synaptic delay See *facilitation.*

synchiria (sin-kī'rē-à) Perception of a stimulus to one side of the body as having been applied to both sides of the body.

synchronism The simultaneous occurrence of several developmental faults. In mongolism, for example, all organ systems of ectodermal, mesodermal, and entodermal origin which undergo specific development during the neofetal period are impaired; the particular synchronism of mongoloid symptoms points to the period between the sixth and twelfth weeks of fetal life as the time when the etiologic factors exert their greatest effect.

syncope (sing'kō-pē) Fainting; a swoon.

syncretism (sin'kre-tiz'm) See *thinking, physiognomonic.*

syndrome (sin'drōm; more rarely sin'drō-mē) Group or set of concurrent symptoms which together are indicative of a disease. 'A syndrome is fundamentally a statistical notion based on co-variation; it seems obvious that its derivation will be placed on more secure grounds when it is carried out (i) on the basis of a properly formulated model, (ii) with awareness of the statistical requirements and difficulties involved, (iii) on the firm foundation of quantitative measurement of objective test performance, (iv) in relation to properly selected samples of the population in question, (v) in accordance with the rules of significance widely accepted in biological statistics. It is not implied that the syndromes isolated by psychiatrists in the last hundred years or so are inevitably imaginary and to be discarded; it seems more likely that such consensus as there is points to important and fruitful dimensions which could be validated by proper statistical research, and perhaps improved and sharpened.' (Eysenck, H.J. *Handbook of Abnormal Psychology,* Basic Books, New York, 1960, p. 11)

syndrome, akinetic-abulic (a-kin-et'ik-a-bū'lik) A group of symptoms which frequently appear in the course of treatment with 'tranquilizers' or 'ataractics': pseudo-parkinsonism (tremor), bradykinesia, hypertonia, decreased mental drive, and lack of interest.

syndrome, apallic (à-pal'ik) Kretschmer's term for a prolonged state of disturbed consciousness, generally following closed head trauma, characterized by mutism, akinesia, primitive mass reflex, oral reflex, contractions, and extrapyramidal disturbances.

syndrome, Balint's Spatial agnosia due to opticomotor disturbances of cortical origin.

syndrome, battered child Physical injuries to children secondary to repeated, volitional, excessive beatings, usually by a parent. Other than the obvious immediate dangers to the child's life and adequate physical growth, it is possible that such cruelty and abuse may constitute a long-term hazard in that it predisposes to a psychic development along the lines of delinquency and violence.

syndrome, Behcet's A syndrome that may be allergic in nature consisting of recurrent iritis, aphthous lesions of the mouth, and ulcerations of the genitalia, all of which run a benign course. Some cases show neuro-psychiatric complications in addition, and these betoken a much more serious prognosis; they include episodic or progressive brain stem syndromes, meningo-encephalitic syndrome, and organic confusional syndrome.

R.N. De Jong (*Neurologia 9,* 61-66, 1964) has suggested that Behcet's syndrome is one of a group of related symptom complexes (rather than disease entities) and that multiple and diverse etiologies, such as virus or allergy, may be involved. The other syndromes that he includes in the grouping are:

(1) *Harada's syndrome:* uveitis, retino-choroidal detachment, cataract, and meningo-encephalitis;

(2) *Vogt-Koyanagi syndrome:* bilateral uveitis, vitiligo, alopecia, poliosis, dysacousia, often accompanied by meningo-encephalitis;

(3) *Fuch's syndrome:* headache, fever, cyanosis, swelling of the face, ulceration of the mucous membranes, and conjunctivitis;

(4) *Klauder's syndrome:* fever, vesicular eruption of hands and feet, and eruption of the mucous membranes and orifices;

(5) *Stevens-Johnson syndrome:* fever, severe and generalized maculopapular or vesicular or erythema multiforme-like eruptions of the orificial mucosa;

(6) Reiter's syndrome: arthritis, nonspecific urethritis, and conjunctivitis.

syndrome, Bing-Neel See *macroglobulinemia, Waldenstrom's.*

syndrome, Brown-Sequard (Charles Edouard Brown-Sequard, French physiologist, 1818-1894) This syndrome, which follows hemisection of the spinal cord, consists of lower motor neuron type paralysis and loss of touch sensation at the level of the lesion; ipsilateral upper motor neuron type paralysis and loss of proprioception and vibratory sense below the level of the lesion; and contralateral loss of pain and temperature sense below the level of the lesion.

syndrome, buffoonery 'The *buffoonery syndrome* is not always easily separated from catatonic states. In this syndrome the entire picture is taken up with playing demonstrative striking tricks, and with giving wrong answers; like the Ganser twilight state it probably only occurs as a reaction to a situation from which unconsciously one wants to escape through insanity.' (Bleuler, E. *Textbook of Psychiatry*, tr. by Brill, A.A., Macmillan, New York, 1930)

syndrome, Capgras' (kà-gràz´) A type of misidentification of people in one's environment seen most frequently in patients with paranoid schizophrenia; the patient affected asserts that one or more of the people around him are friends or relatives (the illusion of a positive double), or, less frequently, he claims that one or more persons around him have altered their appearance so that he will not recognize them (the illusion of a negative double; also known as *Fregoli's phenomenon*). Capgras' syndrome itself is also known as *illusions of doubles*, or *illusions of false recognition*.

syndrome, cat cry (31x.5) A cytogenetic abnormality consisting of deletion of the distal portion of the short arm of chromosome number 5; manifestations include a high, piercing, cat-like cry due to laryngomalacia *(cri-du-chat)*; mental retardation, microcephaly, moon-like facies, hypertelorism, bilateral epicanthus, low-set ears, tiny external genitalia, laryngeal abnormalities, and abnormal palmar dermatoglyphs. The syndrome was first described in 1963 by L. Lejeune.

syndrome, Dandy-Walker's Congenital atresia of the foramen of Magendie.

syndrome, de Lange (31x.9) A type of mental retardation with associated and highly variable minor physical manifestations, including low stature, mild microcephaly, low forehead, heavy confluent eyebrows, depressed bridge of the nose, flaring nostrils, small mandible, low-placed ears, micromelia and/or phocomelia, limitation of extension at the elbow joints, clinodactyly of the little fingers, low placed thumb, webbing of the second and third toe, and hypertrichosis. Cause is unknown; the syndrome was first described by Cornelia de Lange in 1933 and is sometimes known as the Amsterdam type of retardation.

syndrome, displaced child A form of separation phenomenon, often precipitated by the birth of another child; in DSM-II, coded 307.1 Symptoms include a mixture of irritability, discouragement, jealousy for his siblings, and feelings of rejection by other children.

syndrome, effort Neurocirculatory asthenia.

syndrome, Foster Kennedy (Foster Kennedy, American neurologist, 1884-1955) See *nerve, olfactory.*

syndrome, Freud's P. Janet coined this expression: 'The mania for repression . . . is still an interesting symptom; and it explains certain remarkable phenomena, such as monstrous and sacrilegious longings. It will continue to form a part of mental pathology under the name of "Freud's syndrome."' (Janet, P. *Psychological Healing*, vols. 1-2, tr. by Paul, E. and C., Macmillan, New York, 1925)

syndrome, Fuch's See *syndrome, Behcet's.*

syndrome, general adaptation The various changes in the body in response to and/or as defense against stress. Selye distinguishes three stages in this syndrome: the *alarm reaction*, in which adaptation is not yet acquired; the *stage of resistance*, in which adaptation is optimal; and the *stage of exhaustion*, in which the acquired adaptation is lost again. The hypophysis-adrenal interrelationships, which largely determine the various elements of the syndrome, are as follows: the stress agent, or stressor, acts not only upon the cells of the *target organ* but also acts (humoral or neural route?) upon the anterior pituitary and stimulates the latter to produce ACTH; in certain circumstances it may also induce a release of somatotrophic hormone (STH). ACTH, in turn, induces the adrenal cortex to produce glucocorticoids (such as cortisone). The latter exert primarily an inhibitory effect upon the various target organs —catabolism, diminution of granuloma formation and of allergic responses, etc. STH, on the other hand, by stimulating connective tissue, enhances defensive reactions in the target organs—anabolism, augmentation of granuloma formation and of allergic responses, etc. This action occurs by means of direct sensitization of the connective tissue elements to mineralo-corticoids (such as desoxycorticosterone) and also by stimulating the adrenal cortex to produce mineralo-corticoids. This latter corticotrophic effect, however, depends upon the simultaneous availability of ACTH. Thus the target organ response to stressors depends largely upon the balance between STH and the mineralo-corticoids on one hand, and ACTH and gluco-corticoids on the other.

syndrome, Gunn's See *synkinesis*.

syndrome, Harada's See *syndrome, Behcet's*.

syndrome, Horner's (Johann Friedrich Horner, Swiss ophthalmologist, 1831-86) Caused by paralysis of the cervical sympathetic, this condition has the following signs and symptoms: (1) miosis, (2) enophthalmos, (3) pseudoptosis, (4) occasionally ipsilateral vasodilatation and anhidrosis on the side of the face and neck.

syndrome, Horton's (Bayard T. Horton, contemporary American physician) See *histamine*.

syndrome, Hunt's Dyssynergia cerebellaris myocolonica, a syndrome characterized by myoclonic crises, cerebellar ataxia and dysarthria and, usually, epileptic seizures.

syndrome, hyperventilation Subjective symptoms (especially breathlessness, palpitation, dizziness or faintness, paresthesiae and excessive sweating) due to the progressive hypocapnia produced by overbreathing. The overbreathing is itself a form of reaction to anxiety ·or fear, but the importance of recognizing the syndrome lies in the fact that the subjective symptoms secondarily produced are of physiologic origin rather than specific symbolic representatives of the underlying neurotic conflict. See *spasmophilia*.

syndrome, intensive care (294.x, 309.x) Psychosis appearing in patients in postoperative recovery units or in intensive care units. Significant factors contributing to the development of such a complication include the following: (1) the physical conditions of the unit itself—often impersonal, highly mechanized, unfa-

miliar, isolated, windowless, and in certain ways a type of sensory deprivation experience; (2) the physical condition of the patient within the unit—he is usually immobilized to severe degree and in considerable discomfort; (3) the nature of the underlying pathology, including the medical-surgical complications and the age of the patient, and the effects these have on brain function; (4) the effects of medication and operative procedures on brain function; and (5) the premorbid level of functioning, including personality structure and genetic-constitutional factor.

syndrome, Kleine-Levin A syndrome consisting of episodes of hypersomnia, bulimia, and abnormal mental states such as clouded sensorium, partial or total amnesia for certain periods of the attack, and psychomotor retardation. The syndrome is distinct from narcolepsy, although it may be related to the latter. The Kleine-Levin syndrome appears to be a result of disturbance of function of the frontal lobe and/or the hypothalamus. Amphetamine drugs are often useful in treatment of the disorder. See *syndrome, pickwickian*.

syndrome, Klinefelter's (klīn′e-fel-tērs) A disease due to gross chromosome abnormality, consisting of 47 chromosomes (instead of the normal 46, there is an extra sex chromosome, giving an XXY pattern instead of the usual XX or XY). Affected subjects appear phenotypically to be males (indicating that the Y chromosome, far from being inert, is strongly determinant of maleness), but they show dysgenesis of the seminiferous tubules, gynecomastia, and eunuchoidism. The sex chromatin test is positive, as in the normal female. Known also as *primary microorchidism*.

syndrome, Klippel-Feil (klē-pel′ fāl′) (Maurice Klippel, 1858-1942, French neurologist; André Feil, contemporary French physician) A congenital anomaly characterized by absence and fusion of portions of the cervical spine, producing a shortness and stiffness of the neck. Compression of the cord may occur with motor and sensory changes. Mirror writing may occur in association with the syndrome.

syndrome, Klumpke-Déjérine (Mme. Auguste Déjérine-Klumpke, French neurologist, 1859-1927) A combination of paralysis of the cervical sympathetic with paralysis and atrophy of the small muscles of the hand.

syndrome, Klüver-Bucy A syndrome, described originally by Klüver and Bucy in monkeys who had been subjected to bilateral removal of the temporal lobes. In the human, symptoms include: (1) loss of recognition of people; (2) loss of fear and rage reactions; (3) increased sexual activity (especially masturbation and homosexuality); (4) bulimia; (5) hypermetamorphosis, and (6) memory defect. (Terzian, H., and Ore, G. Neurology 5: 373-80, 1955)

syndrome, Lauder's See syndrome, Behcet's.

syndrome, Laurence-Moon-Biedl (J.Z. Laurence, British ophthalmologist, 1830-74; Moon; A. Biedl, German physician, 1869-1933) A syndrome consisting of six cardinal signs in the following order of frequency: obesity, retinitis pigmentosa, mental deficiency (31x.4) genital dystrophy, familial occurrence, polydactyly. Also known as retinodiencephalic degeneration.

syndrome, Loeffler's An allergic reaction by sensitized lung tissue to various allergens, and especially drugs, consisting of pulmonary infiltration and eosinophilia. Loeffler's syndrome has been described in association with various psychotropic and psychedelic drugs. (W. Loeffler described it in Helv. Med. Acta 15, 223, 1948).

syndrome, Lowe's See syndrome, oculocerebro-renal.

syndrome, Main's The ability of a patient (usually a female psychotic who is a nurse or is otherwise closely related to the field of medicine, and part of whose productions include recounting long-continued incestuous relationships) to extort '. . . frantic sympathy and remarkable therapeutic privilege . . .' from her attendants, and to imbue '. . .doctor or nurse with a vivid sense of private significance for the patient, of being peculiarly attuned to her.' (Bourne, H. Archives of General

Psychiatry 2, 576, 1960) The syndrome was first described by T.F. Main in 1957.

syndrome, Marin Amat A syndrome described in 1918 consisting of closing of the eyelid on chewing or opening the mouth. Paralysis or spasm of the ipsilateral facial nerve usually precedes the appearance of the syndrome, which is probably due to a disturbance of intrinsic nuclear functions.

syndrome, Marinesco-Sjogren (31x.9) An hereditary disorder, transmitted through a polyphenous autosomal gene, consisting of congenital dementia, congenital cataract, and cerebellar ataxia.

syndrome, Mast (290.1, 309.6) A recessively inherited form of presenile dementia, named after the family in which it was first detected. The disorder begins in the late teens with intellectual deterioration, spasticity, and dysarthria; it progresses to complete incapacitation of the affected in their 30's or 40's. Early symptoms are blank facies, an unblinking stare, loss of initiative, short attention span, loss of remote memory, failure to understand verbal orders, difficulty in walking because of spasticity, and dysarthria. Extrapyramidal and cerebellar signs, if present at all, appear late in the course of the disorder. No specific treatment is applicable, and although no underlying metabolic disorder has been identified a specific enzyme defect, probably limited to the metabolism of nervous tissue, is suspected. (Cross, Harold and McKusick, Victor Archives of Neurology 16, 1-13, 1967)

syndrome, Melkersson-Rosenthal Recurrent, gradual, persistent swelling of the lips, clefts or folds in the tongue and facial paresis; the syndrome occurs in subjects with an unstable vegetative nervous system and is usually precipitated by stress or other psychic factors.

syndrome, Munchausen (300.13) A name suggested by Asher in 1951 to refer to patients who wander from hospital to hospital ('hospital hoboes'), feigning acute medical or surgical illness and giving false and fanciful information about their medical and social background. The underlying motivation for such behavior is not clearly understood, but apparently it does not include attempts to obtain drugs, avoid police, etc. Such patients would seem to be a particular form of *impostor* (q.v.).

syndrome, night-eating A syndrome seen in some obese patients consisting of nocturnal hyperphagia, insomnia, and morning anorexia. The syndrome tends to appear episodically, and during such periods weight control is especially difficult or even impossible for the patient.

A second type of eating pattern found in obese patients is *binge eating*—consumption at irregular intervals of large quantities of food in an orgiastic manner. A third pattern is *eating without saturation,* seen most frequently in patients with central nervous system disturbances, and characterized by overeating without relationship to stress situations and without regular periodicity.

syndrome, nonsense Popular synonym for *Ganser syndrome* (q.v.).

syndrome, oculo-cerebro-renal (31x.3) One of the diffuse demyelinating scleroses of genetic origin; also known as *Lowe's syndrome.* Symptoms include congenital cataract, progressive mental impairment, hypotonia, hyporeflexia, proteinuria, hyperaminoaciduria, and hyperchloremic acidosis. So far, the syndrome has been reported only in males; those affected usually die during childhood.

syndrome of approximate answers See *answers, syndrome of approximate.*

syndrome, organic The group of symptoms characteristic of the acute and chronic brain disorders. In any specific case, one or more of the characteristic symptoms may predominate. The basic syndrome consists of: (1) disturbances in orientation; (2) impairment of memory; (3) impairment in the maintenance of the level of consciousness and attention; (4) impairment of all intellectual functions (comprehension, calculation, knowledge, learning, etc.); (5) defective judgment; (6) lability, shallowness, and similar instabilities of the affect; and (7) overall changes in the personality, with the appearance of conduct which is foreign to the patient's natural or usual behavior. In the acute brain disorders, alteration in consciousness (with preoccupation, stu-

por, or coma) and defects in orientation and memory tend to predominate; the acute organic syndrome is sometimes called the *delirious reaction* In the chronic brain disorders (e.g. the Korsakov psychosis), intellectual defects are prominent (loss of general efficiency, inability to plan, judgment defects, disturbances in orientation and memory, confabulation), and disturbed affect and personality changes are also frequent. The term *dementia* is often used to refer to the irreversible intellectual defects of the patient with chronic brain disorder. See *abstract attitude; behavior, catastrophic; driveness, organic.*

syndrome, pedunculopontile (ped-ung-cū-lō-pon′tĭl) Weber's syndrome; see *hemiplegia alternans.*

syndrome, pickwickian Obesity associated with hypersomnolence, hypoventilation, and polycythemia, and often also with twitching movements, cyanosis, periodic respirations, congestive heart failure, arterial hypoxia and hypercapnia, and rightward axis deviation on electrocardiogram. The syndrome may sometimes be reversed by weight loss. Although the pathophysiology of the syndrome is but poorly understood, the drowsiness, sleep, and muscular twitching appear to be related to hypercapnia, while polycythemia (and cyanosis) appear to be related to arterial hypoxia. See *syndrome, Kleine-Levin.*

syndrome, Pierre Robin (31x.9) Also known as the *Robin triad,* this syndrome, presumably of genetic origin, consists of glossoptosis (which leads to severe respiratory disorders), microcephaly, and mental retardation.

syndrome, pontocerebellar angle (pon-to-ser-e-bel′ĕr) A group of symptoms caused by acoustic neuromas. Involvement of the acoustic nerve produces persistent tinnitus, progressive deafness, and vertigo. Involvement of the facial nerve produces homolateral facial anesthesia with loss of corneal and sneeze reflexes. Cerebellar involvement produces homolateral ataxia with staggering, and pontine involvement results in contralateral hemiplegia and slight hemianesthesia. In addition, there are general symptoms of brain tumor and increased intracranial pressure.

syndrome, Potzl's Pure alexia (i.e. symbol agnosia for written characters, although the writing is seen, and without any intrinsic disturbance of speech), combined with disturbances of color sense and defects of the visual field. Potzl's syndrome is generally seen in the presence of foci in the medullary layer of the lingual gyrus of the dominant hemisphere with damage of the corpus callosum.

syndrome, prisoner of war (POW) Psychopathologic manifestations occurring in prisoners of war, presumably a reaction to capture and imprisonment. Various types of reaction have been described, among them a syndrome of withdrawal, apathy, and sometimes death which has been likened to the anaclitic depression reported by Spitz in hospitalized or otherwise deprived children.

syndrome, Refsum's *Heredopathia atactica polyneuritiformis;* first described by the Norwegian neurologist Sigvald Refsum in 1946. Principal symptoms are: pigmentary retinitis, chronic polyneuritis, ataxia and other cerebellar disturbances, and albuminocytologic dissociation in cerebrospinal fluid. Other symptoms and signs are pupillary and skeletal anomalies, anosmia, deafness, ichthyosis, and changes in the electrocardiogram.

Onset is usually in childhood, although the disease may not appear until the third decade; most commonly the course is one of gradual progression. The disease is probably transmitted by an autosomal recessive gene that affects lipid metabolism.

syndrome, Reiter's See *syndrome, Behcet's.*

syndrome, restless legs *Tachyathetosis* (q.v.)

syndrome, Rubenstein-Taybi (31x.9) A type of mental retardation, first described in 1963, characterized by broad thumbs and great toes, facial abnormalities, and a cluster of congenital malformations. Etiology is unknown but is presumed to be genetic.

syndrome, silver cord A family constellation consisting of a passive or absent father and a dominating mother, believed by some to be significantly related to the subsequent development of schizophrenia. See *mother, schizophrenogenic.*

syndrome, Sjogren-Larsson Hereditary disorder first described in 1957 in Sweden by Sjogren and Larsson consisting of ichthyosis, mental retardation (31x.9), and spastic paralysis. Degenerative retinitis and speech disorders may occur in addition to the diagnostic triad of symptoms. Transmission of the disorder is of the autosomal recessive type.

syndrome, social breakdown The deterioration in social abilities, interpersonal relationships, and general behavior that frequently accompanies organic and functional psychoses (and especially the schizophrenias). The term emphasizes the belief that such personality distortions, rather than being an inherent part of the psychotic process, are instead a reaction to the patient's environment; the male patient who is isolated from women will no longer make attempts to be attractive to the opposite sex, the person who is deprived of all purposeful activity or removed from any meaningful occupation will have no reason to keep track of time, etc. The social breakdown syndrome occurs in many situations—mental hospitals, prisons, concentration camps, etc. See *psychiatry, community.*

syndrome, Stevens-Johnson See *syndrome, Behcet's.*

syndrome, Stewart-Morel Internal frontal hyperostosis with adiposity and mental disturbances.

syndrome, stiff-man A poorly understood syndrome, related to abnormal phosphorous metabolism, consisting of painful, iron-like spasms of muscle groups in various parts of the body. The spasms can be so severe as to cause fractures of the long bones, and most patients show secondary hypertrophy of affected muscles as well as varus deformity of the feet. Course is prolonged, and death may occur after a number of years during or shortly after a severe spasm.

syndrome, Strauss See *impulse-disorder, hyperkinetic.*

syndrome, striatal (strī'-tal Disease of the striatum or strio-pallidal system, characterized, in general, by the following: (1) rigidity (a general increase of muscle tonus); (2) tremor (abnormal involuntary movements); (3) hypokinesia (poverty of voluntary, especially spontaneous movements); (4) impairment of associated movements; (5) absence of sensory disturbances; (6) absence of 'true' paralysis, that is, absence of signs of involvement of pyramidal tracts.

syndrome, subclavian steal Symptoms of cerebral vascular insufficiency secondary to central stenosis or occlusion of the subclavian artery; blood is shunted past the occluded artery by reversal of blood flow in the vertebral artery, and blood is thereby 'stolen' from the cerebral circulation. Symptoms can sometimes be removed by reconstructive vascular surgery.

syndrome, survivor (300.x) Any number of symptoms, including depression, insomnia, anxiety, psychosomatic illnesses, nightmares, etc. that are believed to be based upon guilt feelings over being a sole—or nearly sole—survivor of a disaster in which others perished who were emotionally close, such as parents, siblings, spouse, or friends. The survivor syndrome is a type of traumatic neurosis. See *neurosis, traumatic.*

syndrome, Tapia's See *Tapia's syndrome.*

syndrome, thalamic (thal-a'mik) See *thalamus.*

syndrome, Vogt-Koyanagi See *syndrome, Behcet's.*

syndrome, vulnerable child Symptoms often noted in a child who, though he has survived an acute episode of severe illness, continues to be treated by his parents as if he were still in considerable danger to his life.

syndrome, Zieve's Transient hyperlipaemia, jaundice, and hemolytic anemia associated with alcoholic fatty liver and cirrhosis, probably due to specific damage to the alpha cells of the islets of Langerhans and to the liver; in most cases, upper abdominal pain is so severe that an operable condition is suspected. (Kessel, L. *American Journal of Medicine 32,* 747, 1962)

syndrome, acute Bleuler differentiated between the acute and chronic forms of schizophrenia. The acute syndromes are transitory states of various kinds that may occur as simple exacerbations of the chronic state or as reactive episodes, in response to emotionally charged experiences. The acute syndromes occur more frequently in the early years of the disease process; they may last for hours only, or they may persist for years. Subsequent memory for these episodes varies, but complete amnesia for them is unusual. Bleuler listed the following acute syndromes: melancholic conditions, manic conditions, catatonic states, delusions ('amentia' in the terms of the Viennese school), twilight-states, Benommenheit, confusional states, fits of anger, anniversary excitements, stupor, deliria, fugue-states, and dipsomania. See *schizophrenia.*

syneidesis (sīn-ī-dē'sis) This Greak work was proposed by Monakow to replace our English *conscience.* Monakow suggests that conscience is not a specifically human phenomenon and does not belong to the sphere of consciousness, but is a characteristic of all living beings in any stage of development. This concept is at variance with prevailing psychiatric opinion, which believes that conscience is a product of the interaction of the child with frustration-producing elements in the child's environment. See *conscience.*

synergism, sexual (sin'ēr-jiz'm) A sexual excitation that arises from a combination of various stimuli acting simultaneously. The manifold aspects of this combination range from pleasurable stimulation of the surface of the body to unpleasant, or even painful, processes within the organism. Freud considered that perhaps every important physical process contributes to the genesis of sexual excitement. Even the combination of the two opposed instinctual tendencies—love and hate—may arouse sexual excitement: sexual synergism can be aroused provided the intensity of discomfort and pain does not pass a certain limit. According to the individual sexual constitution, this synergism manifests itself in different ways. Reik asserts that sexual synergism 'constitutes the physiological basis for the psychic superstructure of masochism.' This peculiar sexual excitement is independent of the attitude of the subject toward the object: in many children mechanical concussions may produce this kind of sexual excitement, and, similarly, certain affective processes such as fright or horror may act as sexual stimuli, even in adults. In this respect one may cite the patients who distinguish between 'disagreeable' and 'interesting' pain. (Reik, T. *Masochism in Modern Man*, Farrar and Rinehart, New York, 1941)

synergy Co-ordination of muscular movements; co-operation in action, primarily a function of the cerebellum.

synesthesia (sin-es-thē'zē-à) See *sensation, secondary.*

syngamy (sing'gà-mē) *Fertilization,* the biological phenomenon which brings about the intermingling of paternal and maternal hereditary material.
'It is accomplished by a great variety of means in animals and plants. In the lowest groups the gametes may be equal in size and similar in structure (an *isogamous* condition), but in the great majority of all animals and plants they are unequal *(heterogamous)*, the male gamete being relatively small and consisting of little but a nucleus, and the female gamete (egg) being very much larger and possessing a considerable amount of cytoplasm in addition to its nucleus.' (Sinnott, E.W. and Dunn, L.C. *Principles of Genetics,* 3rd ed., McGraw-Hill, New York and London, 1939)

syngignoscism (sin-jig'nos-iz'm) Hypnotism; suggestion.

synkinesia, synkinesis An involuntary movement accompany a voluntary one; such as the movement (occurring in a paralyzed muscle) accompanying motion in another part. Any abnormal associated movement(s), indicative of neural injury or maldevelopment; they are brought out when the subject voluntarily contracts one muscle or muscle group, for then other unintended and unneeded movements appear.
Various forms of synkinesis have been described; Gunn, for example, described a palpebromandibular synkinesia, consisting of elevation of the upper lid during any movement of the lower jaw.

synnoetics (sin-oi-e'tiks) A term suggested by Fein for the science '. . . treating of the properties of composite systems . . . whose main attribute is that its ability to invent, to create, and to reason— its "mental" power—is usually greater than the "mental" power of its components.' Another term for synnoetics would be 'the computer-related sciences' which would include such subjects as cybernetics, computer science, bionics, etc. (Fein, L. *American Scientist 49;* 149, 1961)

synthesis The combination or grouping of parts or elements so as to form an integrated whole; the integration of the various factors making up the personality and, thus, the opposite of analysis. This term has been used with various shades of meaning by different writers. Morton Prince used it to refer to the ability to keep the component parts of the psyche together in close association; any weakening of synthesis tends to produce dissociation and, hence, neurosis, Synthesis has also been use to refer to maintenance of intactness of personality; in this sense, synthesis is the opposite of 'splitting' in Bleuler's sense. Gestalt psychologists use the term synthesis to refer to the tendency to perceive and appreciate situations as a whole. In psychoanalytic psychology, synthesis is considered to be a complex ego-function, probably a derivative of libido, which impels the person to harmonious unification and creativity in the broadest sense of the term. Synthesis includes a tendency to simplify, to generalize, and ultimately to understand—by assimilating external and internal elements, by reconciling conflicting ideas, by uniting contrasts, and by seeking for causality. See *psychosynthesis.*

synthesis, distributive In objective psychobiology, the 'synthesis of the various factors and strivings which will offer the patient security. . . . The material for such a synthesis is obtained by analysis of all the factors and situations which are of importance in the study of the human personality and more specifically in the pathologic reactions which bring a patient to the physician. . . . Every analysis should lead to synthesis and after each consultation physician and patient should be able to formulate what has been obtained from the analysis and how it can be used constructively.' (Diethelm, O. *Treatment in Psychiatry*, Macmillan, New York, 1936)

synthesis, syllabic (si-lab'ik) The combination of syllables of several words to form a new word or neologism. The process is common in the productions of schizophrenic patients and in dreams.

'The condensation-work of dreams becomes most palpable when it takes words and names as its objects. Generally speaking, words are often treated in dreams as things, and therefore undergo the same combinations as the ideas of things. The results of such dreams are comical and bizarre word-formations.' (Freud, S. *The Interpretation of Dreams*, 3rd ed., tr. by Brill, A.A., Macmillan, New York, 1933) See *neologism; condensation.*

syntone (sin'tōn) In psychiatry, one whose personality is in harmony with the environment. The term implies emotional rapport, in particular. Bleuler at times uses the expression interchangeably with *cyclothyme.*

'According to a more recent theory of these two groups of psychoses one observes *even in normal people* a syntonic ("cyclothymic") reaction type, in which the whole personality uniformly participates in a definite and relatively vivid affect, suitable for the situation of the moment, and the train of ideas follows substantially quite logical laws. . . .' (Bleuler, E. *Textbook of Psychiatry*, tr. by Brill, A.A., Macmillan, New York, 1930)

The term *syntone* implies normality, while usually *cyclothyme* describes a personality that is an exaggeration of the syntonic but is less intense than that observed in the manic-depressive reaction.

syntropy (sin'trō-pē) The state of wholesome association with others (Adolf Meyer).

syphilis (sif'i-lis) An infectious veneral disease caused by Treponema pallidum; lues.

syphilis, cerebral (ser'e-bral) (292.1 or 309.0) Meningo-vascular syphilis; interstitial syphilis. The term includes syphilitic leptomeningitis, vascular neurosyphilis, or luetic endarteritis and the gummatous subtype. The essential lesion in cerebral syphilis is vascular and perivas-

cular inflammation of varying degrees. Symptoms, which typically appear about three years after the primary infection, depend upon the site and extent of involvement. Thus there may be primarily a picture of acute or chronic leptomeningitis with signs of increased intracranial pressure and involvement of the cranial nerves (especially III, VI, and VII); or luetic endarteritis may lead to occlusion and thus to hemiplegia or convulsions; or development of a gumma may simulate the appearance of intracranial neoplasm. Superimposed on these neurological signs are mental symptoms such as intellectual dulling, emotional lability, stupor, fearful delirium and/or multiple somatic complaints. Cerebral syphilis often responds favorably to penicillin treatment.

syphilis, congenital See *neurosyphilis, congenital.*

syphilis, mesodermogenic (mes-ō-dĕr-mō-je'nik) Meningovascular syphilis; see *syphilis, cerebral.*

syphilomania *Rare.* Insanity resulting from syphilophobia.

syphilophobia Fear of syphilis.

syphilopsychosis (sif-i-lō-sī-ko'sis) Southard's term for psychosis associated with central nervous system syphilis.

syringobulbia (sir-in-gō-bul'bē-à) See *syringomyelia.*

syringomyelia (sir-in-go-mī-ē'lē-à) *Status dysraphicus;* a chronic disease, probably due to a developmental defect, consisting of central cavitation of the spinal cord or ventricle in the medulla (*syringobulbia*). Symptoms begin in the second and third decades; 70 per cent of those affected are male. Enlargement of the cavity affects, in order, the following structures: the anterior commissure, the anterior horn cells, and the pyramidal tracts. Pain and temperature sensation are impaired but touch and proprioception are intact; hand and finger movements become weak and awkward and a claw hand develops. Trophic disturbances are prominent, with thickened skin and various arthropathies (some would call this form *Morvan's disease*). In the bulbar form, symptoms referable to disturbances of the tenth, eighth, and fifth cranial nerves and of the medial lemniscus are seen. Affected patients usually live many years. Palliative X-ray irradiation of the affected region of the spinal cord or medulla is sometimes beneficial.

system The psychic apparatus, according to Freud, is 'a compound instrument, the component parts of which we shall call *instances,* or for the sake of clearness, *systems.* We shall then anticipate that these systems may perhaps maintain a constant spatial orientation to one another, very much as do the different and successive systems of lenses of a telescope. . . . For the sake of brevity, we shall henceforth speak of the component parts of the apparatus as "Ψ-systems."* (Freud, S. *The Interpretation of Dreams,* 3rd ed., tr. by Brill, A.A., Macmillan, New York, 1933)

There is what Freud calls the initial system which 'receives the stimuli of perception but retains nothing of them—that is, it has no memory: . . . behind it . . . lies a second system, which transforms the momentary excitation of the first into lasting traces.' The initial system is called the *P-system,* while the second is 'termed the *memory-system,* or *mem-system.* The latter is 'the basis of *association,*' that is, the linkage of one idea with another.' (ibid)

An element of the P-system is called a P-element and resides in consciousness; that of the mem-system is known as a mem-element. The latter is in the sphere of the unconscious; as Freud says, 'our memories, on the other hand, are unconscious in themselves; those that are most deeply impressed form no exception.' (ibid)

There is a motor end to the psychic apparatus and 'the last of the systems at the motor end we call the *pre-conscious (Pcs.)* to denote that the exciting processes in this system can reach consciousness without any further detention. . . .' (ibid) Behind the pre-conscious system is the *unconscious (Ucs.).*

Freud adds: 'The motive-power of the dream is funished by the *Uccs.,* and on account of this factor we shall assume the

*From Ψ *(psi),* the 23rd letter of the Greek alphabet, as the initial of the word *psyche (psy-chic apparatus),* analogously to Freud's use of the initials P., *Ucs., Pcs., Cs.,* for Percept, Unconscious, Preconscious Concsious, etc.

unconscious system as the starting-point for dream-formation.' (ibid)

system, action A bodily system which enables the organism to take action in response to a desire: a desire to keep one's feet dry will cause one to walk around and not through a puddle. The means by which this action is taken is produced by the integration of receptor, co-ordinative, effector systems into a functioning unit or action system.

The term action system was introduced by Kardiner in connection with his studies of the traumatic neuroses. Kardiner maintains that the traumatic neurosis presents a symptomatology and a psychodynamic structure which cannot be fully understood or adequately explained on the basis of instinct as an operational concept. Instead of using instinct as an operational concept in studying the traumatic neurosis, he takes as his operational concept the various action systems of the body by which instinct is put into action. The damaging of these action systems, with consequent impairment of their function, explains the traumatic neurosis and, indeed, *is* the traumatic neurosis. (Kardiner, A., and Spiegel, L. *War Stress and Neurotic Illness,* Hoeber, New York, 1947)

system, adviser A system introduced in various United States Service Units for the purpose of sustaining the 'morale' and preventing mental ailing or breakdowns through cadres of 'advisers' trained for that purpose.

Platoon cadres met in groups for lectures on the "practical psychology" of the men in their units. In additon, they were made conscious of the importance of: (1) explaining the thousand and one details which are accepted without question by the "old timer," but which seem meaningless to the new trainee (it is amazing how the "mind of the trainee" can be irritated by commands and demands which seem to be without reason); (2) taking a vital and personal interest in solving the emotional, domestic, and physical problems of the soldier; (3) providing the psychiatrist with an "army case history" of the soldier who is referred to the mental hygiene clinic; (4) assisting in the readjustment of the soldier as suggested by the psychiatrist through the encouragement of socialization and the proper assignment of tasks; and (5) bringing to the attention of his company commander any abuses and injustices present in the unit.

'This program was eminently successful not only in allaying psychoneurotic reactions in the unit; but the absence without leave (AWOL) decreased from 1.2 per cent in May, 1943, to 0.2 per cent in May, 1944. The program emphasized the vital importance of selecting and of training the sergeants if morale was to be high and neurotic and allied reactions low.' (Kraines, S.H. *The Therapy of the Neuroses and Psychoses,* Lea & Febiger, Philadelphia, 1948)

system, anabolic (an-à-bol'ik) In constitutional medicine two large systems are described—the anabolic and the catabolic, corresponding with the megalosplanchnic and the microsplanchnic habitus respectively.

system, boarding out A system under which psychotic patients are taken care of as boarders in private homes.

system, centrencephalic (sen-tren-se-fal'-ik) Penfield's term for a hypothesized central structure of neurones in the brain stem which is conceived of as the anatomical basis for the coherent unity of mental processes. In many respects, the centrencephalic system would appear to be identical with the reticular activating system. See *formation, reticular.*

system, chronological See *complex, subject.*

system, graphogenic (graf-ō-gen'ik) See *mechanism, homogenic.*

system, graphonomic (graf-ō-nom'ik) See *mechanism, homogenic.*

system, intralaminar (in-tra-lam'in-ēr) Morison and Dempsey's term for a diffuse, bilateral, nonspecific projection system of neurones in the thalamus. Also known as the *recruiting system,* the intralaminar system is associated with consciousness, sleep, and wakefulness and thus would appear to be identical with the *reticular activating system* in many respects. See *formation, reticular.*

system, perceptual-conscious That part of

the mental apparatus which absorbs perceptions from both the external world and the interior of the mind (the id). Early in the development of the human mind, one part of it becomes the recipient of stimuli. In this part of the mind the feeling of consciousness originates and, for this reason, it is named the perceptual conscious system.

As the mind develops, its new task is to protect the organism from the stimuli which are dangerous to the organism. The mind learns to retain a true picture of the external world by its memory of the perceptions which, through reality-testing, it keeps from being contaminated by instinctual demands. With this later function, anticipation, reason, and judgment become possible and take over the control of motility or action. The part of the mental apparatus which has developed the faculties of memory, reality-testing, reason, and judgment toward the end of controlling the instincts and thus protecting the organism is called the ego. But the earliest function which is decisive for the ego must be the perception of stimuli, since without this perception none of its more complex functions can be carried out. The ego thus originates in the perceptual-conscious system, 'the most superficial portion of the mental apparatus.' (Freud, S. *New Introductory Lectures on Psychoanalysis,* Norton, New York, 1933)

system, pride Horney's term for the sum total of the neurotically (over-)valued and the neurotically (over-)hated attributes of the self.

system, psychodynamic cerebral (si-kō-dī-nam'ik ser'e-bral) See *psychodynamics, adaptational.*

system, recruiting See *system, intralaminar.*

system, reticular (re-tik'ū-lēr) See *formation, reticular.*

system, rotation The method some group psychotherapists employ of treating individual patients in sequence in the presence of the group.

system, sign Schilder's term for the use of language as the main tool, or instrument, of psychotherapy. Through words, the psychiatrist gains access to and unveils the patient's hidden problems and inner personality. Words in the sign system are to the psychiatrist what knives and other instruments are to the surgeon. 'The psychotherapist has no immediate access to the body of the patient and to his gratifications. The influence he has on the patient is merely due to the words he speaks.' In a broader sense, every social relation between two persons speaking to each other includes the erotic. Man needs not only actual but also future gratification, 'and humanity has elaborated a system for such gratification,' language constituting the main though by no means the only element of this system. In the relationship between the sexes, words and sentences in themselves may become signs through which the individuals obtain their social and erotic gratifications. (Schilder, P. *Psychotherapy*, Norton, New York, 1938)

system, stereogenic (ste-rē-ō-jen'ik) See *constant, central; mechanism, orthogenic.*

system, stereonomic (ster-ē-ō-nom'ik) See *constant, central; mechanism, orthogenic.*

system, villa Boarding-out system.

T

T-group Sensitivity training group. An educational-psychotherapeutic technique in which a group of people meet regularly, usually with a specified leader, in order to learn about themselves, about interpersonal relationships, about group process, and about larger social systems. The T-group is experience-based learning (rather than a type of therapy for recognized emotional disturbance), and its major aims include increasing social effectiveness and interpersonal relatedness, and opening communication channels between the group member and others within his social system. The T-group is reality-oriented and focuses on connections between current reactions and universal psychologic concepts rather than on the individual genetic antecedents of those reactions. Used in industrial organizations, for example, the T-group tries to get its members to own up to their own feelings (including their feelings about each other), to become open to new ideas and experiment with new solutions to problems (i.e. to replace automaton conformity with a capacity for risk-taking), and thereby to generate effective decision-making within the organization. T-groups are sometimes also called human relations groups.

tabes (tā'bez) (L. 'a wasting, emaciation') Tabes (*tabes dorsalis, locomotor ataxia*) is a chronic, progressive disease of the nervous system occurring rather late in a comparatively small percentage of persons affected with syphilis. The main pathological process involves the posterior spinal ganglia in a mild inflammation. The roots between the ganglia and the spinal cord, and, to some extent, the meninges are also involved. There is a degeneration of the nerve fibers with a selective degeneration of the posterior columns of the cord. The cranial nerves, especially the optic and those supplying the ocular muscles, are particularly involved. The symptoms are ataxia, or muscular inco-ordination, neuralgia, anesthesia, visceral crises, lancinating pains, and muscular atrophy. Trophic disorders of the joints (arthropathies) are frequent, atrophy of the optic nerve occurs, and paralysis may be a late symptom. Mental symptoms are not usually prominent, although a severe depression may occur.

tabes, congenital See *neurosyphilis, congenital.*

tabes, juvenile Juvenile tabes presents an essentially identical pathologic process and clinical course as in the adult. The symptoms appear from about the age of ten onward, in children who have congenital syphilis or who acquired the disease in infancy or early childhood. Ataxia is rather infrequent while optic atrophy is very common in juvenile tabes. Mental symptoms and taboparesis occur frequently. The Wasserman blood reaction is often negative. The course is much more rapid than in the adult form, and the disease terminates fatally comparatively early.

tabetic curve (ta-bet'ik) See *Lange's colloidal gold reaction.*

table, frequency The number of subjects with a given character may be arrayed in order of size with respect to the amount of the character possessed by each individual in the series. If the entire range is divided into intervals, and if to each interval is assigned the number of cases falling within the limits of the class, the resulting distribution is called a frequency table.

Age Distribution of First Admissions
To New York Civil State Hospitals,
Year Ended June 30, 1938

Age (Years)	Number	Per cent
Under 15	176	1.4
15-19	527	4.2
20-24	841	6.7
25-29	940	7.4
30-34	1087	8.6
35-39	1165	9.2
40-44	1119	8.9
45-49	1084	8.6
50-54	1012	8.0
55-59	870	6.9
60-64	834	6.6
65-69	884	7.0
70 and over	2091	16.5
Unascertained	5	*
Total	12,635	100.0

*Less than 0.05.

table, life A life table is an instrument for determining the number of years that any person may, on the average, be expected to live after reaching a specified age. It also enables one to determine the chance of an individual dying within any specified number of years after reaching a given age.

Example. According to the life table for continental United States, 1929 to 1931, prepared by the U.S. Bureau of the Census, the expectation of life at birth for white males was 59.12 years. Again, according to this life table, of 100,000 males born alive, 81,457 will reach age 40. Therefore 18,543 will die before reaching age 40, and the chance of dying before reaching age 40 is 185.43 per 1,000. Those who reach age 40 will live, on the average 29.22 years, or they will die at an average age of 69.22 years.

table, statistical A summary of numerical data in accordance with logical criteria, showing the manner in which the variables included in the table are distributed with respect to their relative frequencies.

taboo, tabu 'For us the meaning of taboo branches off into two opposite directions. On the one hand it means to us, sacred, consecrated: but on the other hand it means uncanny, dangerous, forbidden and unclean. The opposite for taboo is designated in Polynesian by the word *noa* and signifies something ordinary and generally accessible. Thus something like the concept of reserve inheres in taboo; taboo expresses itself essentially in prohibitions and restrictions. Our combination of "hold dread" would often express the meaning of taboo.' (Freud, S. *The Basic Writings of Sigmund Freud,* tr. by Brill, A.A., Random House, New York, 1938)

taboparesis (tā-bō-par'ē-sis) A disease of the nervous system which combines the features of general paresis and tabes dorsalis. The mental and physical symptoms of general paresis are present together with spinal cord changes producing absent knee or ankle jerks, the Romberg sign, and bladder disturbances.

tachy- (tak-ē-) Combining form meaning fast, quick, speedy, from Gr. *tachýs,* quick, swift, fleet. Oppos. of *brady-*.

tachyathetosis Restless legs syndrome, probably an extrapyramidal hyperkinesis.

tachycardia, orthostatic (tak-ē-kär'dē-à, or-thō-stat'ik) Rapidity of pulse rate beyond the normal range occurring when one changes from the reclining to the standing position.

tachyglossa (-glos'à) See *tachylogia.*

tachyglossal Pertaining to or characterized by tachyglossa, or rapidity of speech.

tachylalia (-lā'lē-à) See *tachylogia; cluttering.*

tachylogia (-lō'jē-à) Rapid, pressured, voluble speech; also known as *logorrhea, verbomania.* Tachylogia is characteristic of the manic phase of manic-depressive disorder.

tachyphagia (-fāg'ē-à) Food-grabbing; extreme rapidity of eating. Tachyphagia is commonly seen in regressed, deteriorated schizophrenics, and often such patients will grab any object, edible or not, put it into the mouth, and swallow it.

tachyphemia (-fē'mē-à) See *tachylogia.*

tachyphrasia (-frā'zē-à) See *tachylogia.*

tachypnea, tachypnoea (tak-ip'nē-à) See *polypnoea.*

tachypragia (tak-ē-prā'jē-à) *Rare.* Psychomotor acceleration, as in the manic phase of manic-depressive disorder.

tachytrophism (-trō'fiz'm) Rapid or increased metabolism.

tactile sensation, double simultaneous The ability of the subject to perceive that he has been touched in two places at the same time. This is usually acquired by the age of six years and is considered an index of biological sentiency, level of organization, and discrimination of environmental changes. It is often late in developing or otherwise defective in childhood schizophrenics and in children with minimal brain dysfunction; it is often impaired also in patients with diffuse brain damage (e.g. cerebral arteriosclerosis). The *face-hand test* (of Fink-Green-Bender) is designed to measure such impairment. The patient is touched simultaneously on the cheek and the dorsum of the hand, and is asked to indicate where he was touched. Ten trials are given: eight face-hand (divided between four contralateral and four ipsilateral), and two interspersed combinations of face-face and hand-hand stimulation.

t(a)eniophobia (tē-nē-ō-fō′bē-à) Fear of tapeworms.

taint In genetics, the genotypical affection of an individual by a morbid factor inherited from, and manifested by, his ancestors, whether or not this factor is exhibited by the subject himself.

taint-carrier In a family survey, this genetic term is limited to the members who carry a particular genetic factor in their genotypes, but do not manifest it phenotypically. See *trait-carrier*.

talion Retaliation; see *dread, talion*.

tangentiality A type of association disturbance in which thought and speech diverge or digress from the topic of the moment so that they appear unrelated or irrelevant; if often repeated (and especially if the speaker does not return spontaneously to the topic), tangentiality is labelled 'loosening' or diffuseness of speech, and its end result is to destroy the value of speech as an effective means of communicating with others.

tantrum A child's dramatic outburst of crying, kicking, screaming, etc. in response to frustration. Such temper-tantrums are natural to the child of two or three and are an expression of aggression, anger, rage, and defiance. The child works himself rapidly, or gradually, into a rage—yells out, stamps his feet, throws his arms about, rolls on the floor, strikes everyone, throws every object within reach against the walls, curses, bites, or even bangs his head against the wall. The tantrum thus assumes uncontrolled and sweeping proportions in contrast to normal expressions of anger and rage.

Tantrums are seen almost routinely in the children of overindulgent, oversolicitous, and overprotective parents. Though originating in physical discomforts which increase the child's irritability, tantrums either are motivated by an attempt to obtain gratifications and dominate a family which allows itself to be controlled by these outbursts, or are a result of imitation of a parent or some other member of the household.

Treatment includes: (1) creation of an optimal environment which will afford conventional outlets for the expression of rage on the part of both parents and child; (2) correction of overindulgence, oversolicitousness, and overprotectiveness, when these are present; (3) attention to the acute or chronic discomforts, such as fatigue and hunger, which appear to precipitate the tantrums; (4) proper recreational and school adjustments; (5) correction of any existing jealousies within the family.

The tantrum should be treated calmly and without alarm. The child should be offered a change of scene or activity to allow him to drop the conflict without feeling complete defeat or loss of face. Under no conditions should there by any giving-in to the trantrum; the best procedure is to leave the child alone until he is calm—if tantrums gain too much for the child, they can readily become a recurrent behavior pattern.

taphephobia (taf-ē-fō′bē-à) Fear of being buried (alive).

taphophilia Morbid attraction to graves and cemeteries. A patient spent all his spare time either in cemeteries or in thoughts connected with them. Though highly intelligent, he was emotionally immature, having never resolved his childhood relationships with his parents. He was vividly anal-erotic, expressing among other things a strong coprophagic tendency. Another patient often carried out his impulse to defecate on graves, though, as he maintained, a grave was sacred to him. He endowed graves with unlimited magic power, to which he added his own power (feces). Still another patient saved most of his excrement, burying it from time to time in a neighboring cemetery.

Tapia's syndrome (Antonio Garcia Tapia, Spanish otolaryngologist, b. 1875) A bulbar syndrome due to involvement of the vagus and hypoglossal nerves, with homolateral paralysis and atrophy of the tongue, and homolateral paralysis of the pharynx and larynx.

tarantism (tar′an-tiz′m) 'An epidemic dancing mania prevalent in Italy in the sixteenth and seventeenth centuries, originating in fear of the bite of the tarantula, as a remedy for which the dance was adopted.' (*A Dictionary of Medicine,* edited by Quain, R.: D. Appleton, New York, 1899)

taraxein (tar-ak'sān) See *ceruloplasmin*.

target multiplicity See *multiplicity, target*.

target-organ See *syndrome, general adaptation*.

Tartarism *Mongolism* (q.v.).

TAT Thematic apperception test. See *test, thematic apperception*.

Tay-Sachs' disease (Warren Tay, English physician, 1843-1927; and Bernard Sachs, American neurologist, 1858-1944) *Amaurotic family idiocy* (q.v.).

technique, classical See *parameter*.

technique, play A psychotherapeutic method devised by Melanie Klein for special use in the treatment of children. By allowing the child to play with almost anything he wants, the therapist is, through this play, able to analyze and clarify the child's emotional problem. This technique is, in effect, a very useful substitute for the 'free-association' method, in view of the child's usual lack of verbal self-expression. Adult patients will, sooner or later, translate into words not only their problems but also the actions which may take place during the analysis. With children such verbalizations are next to impossible and the play technique is of paramount importance. 'Paper dolls, rag dolls, dolls which can be taken apart, wagons, tin toys of all kinds can be used. Little blocks of wood or stone are very often useful. The child should have a choice between many toys, but the situation generally becomes obscured if the variety of toys is too great. It is usually better to use toys which do not move by themselves but which have to be moved by the child. Frequently the child accompanies his play with short remarks which elucidate the situation. Sooner or later one will have to interpret to the child what is going on. One may participate in the play and accompany one's actions with appropriate gestures. If the child is not very young it will usually be difficult to bring it to an insight into the situation without words.' (Schilder, P. *Psychotherapy*, Norton, New York, 1938) See *therapy, play*.

tegmentum (teg-men'tum) See *midbrain*.

tele (tel'ē) (Gr. *tēle*, 'at a distance, far away, far off') 'A feeling process projected into space and time in which one, two, or more persons may participate is called a tele. It is an experience of some real factor in the other person and not a subjective fiction. It grows out of person-to-person and person-to-object contacts from the birth level on and gradually develops the sense for inter-personal relationships. The tele process is the chief factor in determining the position of an individual in the group.

'Positive tele occurs in any relationship between two or more persons which is produced by the affinity between some real factor in one person and some real factor in another person; negative tele, in any relationship between two or more persons involving repulsion based on some real factor in one person and some real factor in another person. If a person is attracted towards a certain person, and if this person is far from him in another group, the moving of this person towards him produces an experience which is therapeutic tele.

'The proof that a factor, tele, exists and operates within the social structure is demonstrated by the statistical and mathematical calculation of social configurations. This has been accomplished by comparing sociometric findings with a common reference base ascertained by chance calculation of choices. The Chi-Square Test was applied in comparing how much the computed chance values and the experimental chance values differ.

'The probability of mutual structures in actual configurations has been found to be 213 per cent greater than in mathematical and chance findings as well. This is an illustration of the validity of tele as an objective factor.' (Moreno, J.L. *Sociometry 1*, 351, 1938)

telemnemonike (tel-em-nē-mon'i-kē) Acquiring consciousness of matters held in the memory of another person.

telencephalon (tel-en-sef'ă-lon) That part of the *forebrain* (q.v.) or prosencephalon which forms the cerebral cortex, the striate bodies, the rhinencephalon, the lateral ventricles, and the anterior portion of the 3rd ventricle.

teleo-analysis See *teleological.*

teleological (tē-lē-ō-loj′i-kal) Goal directed, purposive; used particularly to refer to Adler's insistence on the holistic approach to personality and his belief that a person can best be understood by the goals he sets for himself, and not by any analysis or dissection of partial functions such as sexuality. The understanding of goals and the helping of patients to change their goals are so basic to Adlerian psychotherapy that Individual Psychology has sometimes been called *teleo-analysis.*

teleology (tē-lē-ol′ō-ji) The belief that natural processes are purposefully directed toward some end or goal. In psychiatry, the term is particularly used in reference to the psychologies of Jung and of Adler. Adler, for example, considers the present activity of the person as a preparation for his final state, for what he is going to be. Jung's analytical psychology is also teleological. Jung considers the mind as something much more than the result of past experiences: '. . . it is Becoming as well as Has Been, and therefore any analysis of it must include reference to its aims and to that which it is trying to realize within itself. In this connection the dream must therefore be regarded as partly determined by the future.' (Nicole, J. *Psychopathology,* Ballière, Tindall & Cox, London, 1948) Jung treats the symbols from the collective unconscious '. . . not only reductively as an expression of the past of the race, but synthetically also, as a sign that the unconscious is trying to exert a directive influence upon the individual's life-line. These symbols should be interpreted teleologically, as indicative of fundamental strivings that are aiming at guiding the personality along certain lines, certain necessary paths of development and fulfilment. It is only by thus giving these symbols a "final" or purposive value as well as a "causal" one, that we can adjust the unconscious to the conscious, the collective to the individual, the non-rational to the rational, without either principle doing violence to the other. This means that the physician's explanations must, of necessity, become educational and morally conditioned, thus performing a task that psycho-analysts refuse to undertake.' (ibid.)

teleophrenia (tē-lē-ō-frē′nē-à) Term coined by M. Nippe (*München. med. Wochenschr. 74,* 143, 1927) for a morbid mental condition that stands between traumatic neurosis and malingering; compensation neurosis.

telepathic (tel-e-path′ik) Pertaining to telepathy or characterized or communicated by thought-transference.

telepathy (te-lep′à-thē) See *perception, extra-sensory.*

telesthesia (tel-es-thē′zē-à) Telepathy.

telodendria See *neuron.*

telophase (tel′ō-fāz) In genetics, the final phase or stage of mitosis.

temper tantrum See *tantrum.*

temperament A constitutional tendency to react to one's environment in a certain way. Some people are more placid than others, some more vigorous, some more high-strung; it is likely that such differences are innate and recognizable from the moment of birth. Temperament is not identical with character, though often confused with it, especially in popular language. Temperament is probably instrumental in determining the particular type of character structure developed by a person in that it limits the potentialities for character development: it is unlikely that a constitutionally phlegmatic person would develop an anxious, rigid, and compulsive character structure. Character, on the other hand, is something in addition to temperament, as a component within the framework of the possibilities encompassed by the given temperament.

temperament, manic Kraepelin's designation for what is today known as one of the phases of cyclothymia. 'The intellectual endowment of the patients is for the most part mediocre, sometimes even fairly good, in isolated cases excellent. They acquire, however, as a rule, only scanty, and, in particular, very imperfect and unequal knowledge, because they show no perseverance in learning, do not like exerting themselves, are extraordinarily distractible, and seek to escape in every way from the constraint of a systematic mental training, and in place of that they pursue all possible side-occupations in variegated alternation.' (Kraepelin, E. *Manic-Depressive Inanity and Paranoia,* tr. by Barclay, R.M., Livingstone, Edinburgh, 1921.) He adds that the mood is 'permanently exalted, careless, confident' and that conduct is unsteady and restless.

temporal lobe seizure Psychomotor epilepsy. See *epilepsy.*

temporal summation See *summation.*

temptation, horrific One of Rado's subdivisions of obsessive attacks is called *fits of horrific temptation:* an idea or urge of compelling intensity to kill or harm someone (usually a close relative), an idea from which the patient shrinks back in horror.

tendency, anagogic (an-a-goj'ik) See *tendency, katagogic.*

tendency, final The ultimate goal or aim of the neurosis. Adler was the first to point out 'the presence of a final tendency in the structure of every neurosis.' In this respect he was guided by both Janet's theory of the *idée fixe* and Wernicke's concept of 'over-charged idea.' See *idea, overcharged.*
　　'The neurotic goals are not sheer strivings for power and recognition: they betoken a secret tendency toward future triumphs expressed in many forms that might even be antagonistic to each other. Nevertheless, it may be stated that every neurosis has a central idea around which the various *lay motives* group themselves.' The task of the analyst is to uncover as early as possible this central idea (the final tendency and ultimate goal of the neurosis) if success is to be expected in treatment. (Stekel, W. *Compulsion and Doubt,* Liveright, New York, 1949)

tendency, katagogic (kat-à-goj'ik) The 'downward-leading' restrictive psychic impulses that strive to prevent the person from achieving his positive and constructive aim in life. In fact, the katagogic tendency constitutes an inhibitory mechanism in opposition to what Stekel calls *anagogic tendency,* or 'upward-leading' impulses which are of a constructive nature. (Stekel, W. *The Interpretation of Dreams,* Liveright, New York, 1943)

tendency (of action) In objective psychobiology this expression designates the inclinations associated with action. 'One should always study the general behavior of a person while talking to him. Much can be learned from his way of entering the room, shaking hands, talking, and from his facial expression, gestures and posture.' . . . 'emotions are the regulative functions of our personality and are therefore closely related to the behavior of the person in action.' (Diethelm, O. *Treatment in Psychiatry,* Macmillan, New York, 1936)

tenesmus penis (te-nes'moos pā'nēs) (L. 'straining of the penis') *Priapism* (q.v.).

tension, instinctual The psychic and somatic manifestations of the need to gratify a primal trend or urge.

tension, mental The emotional charge with which components of the psyche are infused; *psychentonia.* The term *charge* is used here as it is in the field of electricity. When, as in certain senile states, the psyche is relatively void of activity or energy or charge, one speaks of low mental tension. The contrary state obtains, for example, in the manic phase of manic-depressive psychosis, in which condition psychical components are heavily charged with emotions, that is, there is high mental tension. See *cathexis.*

tension, need A tension that develops within the organism in connection with various 'needs' essential for survival, and demands contact with the outer world for its relief. 'Being born may be said to have already interfered with the equilibrium of the intra-uterine state, because stimuli are now registered upon the organism from within (hunger) and without (cold). To relieve these *need tensions* the infant must direct itself to the outer world, or show signs of the unpleasant effects created by these tensions.' (Kardiner, A., and Spiegel, H. *War Stress and Neurotic Illness,* Hoeber, New York, 1947)

tentigo venerea (ten-tē'gō ve-ne'rē-à) (L. 'venereal, sexual lust') Nymphomania.

tentigo veretri (ve-rā'trē) (L. 'tension or lust of the private parts') Satyriasis.

tentorium cerebelli (ten-tō-rē-oom kā-rā-bel'ē) See *meninges.*

TEPP See *psychotomimetic.*

teratophobia (ter-à-tō-fō'bē-à) Fear of bearing a monster.

terror, night or sleep Pavor nocturnus; a disorder allied to nightmare, occurring in children. The child awakes screaming with fright, the alarm persisting for a time during a state of semiconsciousness.

Night terrors are more serious than nightmares; they are not seen after puberty. 'In a night terror, the fear can only be inferred from the child's expression: staring eyes, agitation, screams for help, and clutching those around him. The child remains in a twilight state, cannot be wakened, and is not accessible to calming words of reassurance. He still sees whatever it is that terrifies him, and sweating and other physical evidence of fear continue, until of his own accord he falls into a deep and peaceful sleep. There is *complete amnesia* for the attack as well as for the dream content.' (Mayer-Gross, W., et al. *Clinical Psychiatry,* 2nd ed., Williams & Wilkins, Baltimore, 1960)

test, ability Any evaluation of presently existing potentiality or capacity to function; a test of maximal performance in any area.

test, ACE The American Council on Education intelligence test, designed for use with secondary school and college students.

test, achievement Any evaluation of what gains the subject has made in an area following training and instruction.

test, adrenalin-Mecholyl (a-dren'a-lin-mek-ō-lil) Funkenstein test; first described by Funkenstein, Greenblatt, and Solomon in 1952 as a test of prognostic significance in relation to electroshock treatment. The test consists of the administration, on two successive days and under comparable basal conditions, of intravenous epinephrine hydrochloride and intramuscular Mecholyl chloride. The blood pressure response to each drug is then recorded. Response to Mecholyl appears to be the more significant of the two measures, and it has been observed that patients with a hypotensive response: (1) are benefited by EST; (2) show a high rate of improvement when psychotherapy

is the sole method of treatment; (3) have good abstraction ability and good personality organization, and (4) appear clinically to maintain an appropriate and adequate level of affect. In general, patients with a hypertensive response to Mecholyl are not benefited by EST, show a relatively lower improvement rate with psychotherapy, have poor abstraction and inadequate or inappropriate affect, and give other evidence of personality disorganization.

test, Akerfeldt See *ceruloplasmin.*

test, analogies A test of ability to comprehend relationships, usually by asking the subject to name the fourth term which bears the same relation to the third as the second does to the first. Example: ship is to water as automobile is to what?

test, aptitude A test of the probable level of future performance that will be reached following further maturation and/or training.

Test, Army General Classification See AGCT.

test, Arthur Point Scale A nonverbal, performance measure of intellectual ability, consisting of 10 subtests which are mainly of the form-board variety. The test is most reliable within the 7-13 years age-range and is of particular value when the subject's verbal capacity is compromised by foreign language handicap, speech or hearing defect, or personal and cultural factors.

test, Bender Visual-Motor Gestalt A projective technique consisting of nine geometrical figures that are copied by the subject; devised by Lauretta Bender and first described by her in 1938. Its chief applications are to determine retardation, loss of function, and organic brain defects in children and adults, and in the study of personality deviations which show regressive phenomena. It is of limited usefulness in the study of psychoneuroses and psychosomatic disorders.

test, Bero (bā'rō) Behn-Rorschach test; a set of plates prepared by Behn with the assistance of Rorschach. Zullinger provided the norms for the Bero test.

test, beta A set of mental tests used in the U.S. Army in 1917-18, designed for illiterates. Instructions are given in signs and the material is pictorial in character, in contrast to alpha tests, which are carried out verbally.

test, block design A performance test in which the subject tries to match standard designs using colored blocks; used as a measure of intelligence and as an indicator of deterioration in brain damage and in the schizophrenias.

test, cancellation Any test in which the subject is instructed to strike out one or more specified symbols which are distributed irregularly within the test material. The symbols may be particular letters, numbers, words, or geometrical figures.

test, chi-square (kī-) A statistical test, developed originally by Karl Pearson, which measures the significance of differences occurring between groups. In a group of 500 cases of lobar pneumonia treated with penicillin, for example, the overall 'cure' rate was 94 per cent. But not all cases were treated with the same batch of penicillin. 100 cases were treated with batch A penicillin and 98 per cent were cured; 100 cases were treated with batch B and 89 per cent were cured; 100 cases with batch C and 95 per cent were cured; 100 cases with batch D and 92 per cent were cured; and 100 cases with batch E and 96 per cent were cured. In this imaginary example, the chi-square test could be applied to ascertain whether the different cure rates in different groups are due only to chance or whether, all other relevant factors being equal, the different results are due to different effectiveness of the individual batches of penicillin.

test, coin A test in which the subject is required to estimate the size of coins touched; an underestimation of the size has been believed to be indicative of a lesion of the pyramidal system, but mass examination of normal subjects reveals that approximately 70% of normals are unable to estimate coin size accurately, and that in 90% of the latter the size is underestimated.

test, comprehension See comprehension.

test, Cornell Word Form (CWF) A modi-fication of the word-association technique devised to distinguish 'normals' from subjects with neuropsychiatric and psychosomatic disorders in a way not apparent to the subject. The test is used primarily in industrial psychology. It consists of a list of stimulus words, each of which is followed by two response words. The subject is asked to encircle whichever of the two words seems to him to be most related to the stimulus word; e.g. mother—mine, woman.

test, draw-a-person A method of personality analysis based upon the interpretation of drawings of the human figure. Although figure drawings had been used by many workers in the field, it was Karen Machover who in 1949 outlined a system of interpretation which was correlated with clinical diagnostic categories.

test, drawing-of-a-man See test, Goodenough.

test, face-hand A test of diffuse cerebral dysfunction devised by Bender. The subject, whose eyes are closed, is touched simultaneously on the cheek and the dorsum of the hand; retesting is done with the eyes open. Results are considered positive if the subject fails consistently to identify both stimuli within 10 trials. By the age of seven, normal children respond with a negative test. Positive results are seen not only in cases of cerebral dysfunction in children and adults, but also in schizophrenic children. See tactile sensation, double simultaneous.

test, Fink-Green-Bender See tactile sensation, double simultaneous.

test, Funkenstein See test, adrenalin-Mecholyl.

test, Gesell developmental 'The Gesell Schedules consist of a series of 27 age-level recorded observations and reactions to standardized situations from birth through the first five years of life. At each age level an inventory of activities is divided into four categories of behavior: (1) Motor; (2) Adaptive, (3) Language; and (4) Personal-Social. Each of these categories of behavior is evaluated by observing the infant or child in a number of standardized situations.' (Masserman, J.H. The Practice of Dynamic Psychiatry, Saunders, Philadelphia, 1955) test, good and evil See *responsibility, criminal.*

test, Goodenough A test of a child's intellectual level of development based upon the subject's drawing of a human figure. The test was introduced in 1926 by Florence Goodenough, who standardized children's drawing of a man and thereby produced a simple and satisfactory test of intelligence.

test, heel-to-knee A test for ataxia; the patient in a recumbent position, with the eyes open or closed, is requested to raise the foot high, touch the knee with the opposite heel and carry the heel along the shin.

test, Holmgren (Alarik Fritniof Holmgren, Swedish physiologist, 1831-97) A test for color blindness which requires the subject to match skeins of different-colored yarn with standard skeins.

test, House-Tree-Person (HTP) A type of projective test in which the subject is asked to draw a house, tree, and a person.

test, Janet's (Pierre Marie Felix Janet, French physician, 1859-1947) A test for the determination of tactile sensibility; the patient answers 'yes' or 'no' when touched by the examiner's finger.

test, Kent EGY A series of 10 questions used for a quick estimate of intelligence.

test, Knox cube A performance test, of particular value when the subject suffers from a language handicap or barrier, in which the subject taps a series of four cubes in various prescribed sequences.

test, Kohnstamm The Kohnstamm maneuver is often used to demonstrate suggestibility to a subject being prepared for hypnotic trance induction. It is a normal neurophysiologic reaction, elicited by having the subject press his extended arm as strenuously as possible against a wall for approximately two minutes, after which the arm will rise automatically with or without a suggestion to that effect.

test, Kohs block-design An intelligence test in which the subject copies a design using small, multicolored cubes.

test, Lange See *Lange's colloidal gold reaction.*

test, Lichtheim's A means of determining the retention of inner language in patients with expressive aphasia or other severe speech disturbances: the patient is asked to indicate the number of syllables in words which he cannot utter.

test, Lowenfeld See *test, mosaic.*

test, Machover See *test, draw-a-person.*

test, Minnesota Multiphasic Personality Inventory Usually abbreviated *MMPI;* a personality questionnaire consisting of 550 statements concerning behavior, feelings, social attitudes, and frank symptoms of psychopathology. To each question, the subject must answer T (true), F (false), or ? (cannot say), and his answer sheet is then scored by various keys that have been standardized on different diagnostic groups and personality types. The MMPI was originally constructed by a psychiatrist, J.C. McKinley, and a psychologist, Starke Hathaway.

test, Mooney See *Mooney Problem Check List.*

test, mosaic A projective technique, introduced by Margaret Lowenfeld and further developed by Fredric Wertham, which employs a set of 300 colored pieces (black, blue, red, green, yellow, and off-white) in six shapes (squares, diamonds, oblongs, and 3 different-sized triangles). The subject is presented with the test objects on a tray and is asked to make anything he wants on the board. The designs made by adults and children have been correlated with diagnostic categories, and individual designs can be interpreted on the basis of these correlations.

test, myokinetic psychodiagnosis (mī-ō-kin-et'ik sī-kō-dī-ag-nō'sis) A test devised by Mira which consists of drawings of patterns with both the right and the left hands. The left hand drawings are believed to reveal genotypic reactions and the right hand drawings are said to express more superficial phenotypic reactions. Comparison of the drawings is made to diagnose various conditions and character traits.

test, organic integrity A modification of the Casagrandie test for color-dominance and form-dominance perception, described by H.C. Tien (*Archives of General Psychiatry* 3, 43, 1960). The *O.I.T.* is said to be a rapid test for organic brain disease; it is based on the theory that central nervous system damage will interfere with ability to perceive form.

test, Pandy (K. Pandy, Hungarian neurologist, b. 1808) A qualitative and quantitative test for protein (esp. globulin) in the cerebrospinal fluid. The fluid to be examined is mixed with carbolic acid and the degree of precipitation indicates the degree of protein content.

test-person The subject who is examined by the association method.

test, PMA A test of seven traits believed by Thurstone and Thurstone to account for most of the variance in primary mental abilities (PMA). These traits are: V (verbal comprehension), W (word fluency), N (number), S (space), M (associative memory), P (perceptual speed), and R (reasoning) or I (induction).

test, population The population test is a modification of the sociometric test. It is applied to people who anticipate moving into a new community. It is also applied to an already existing community which is in a state of disintegration.

In the population test, heads of families anticipating settling in a new community are called to a meeting in which they express whom they wish as neighbors in the new settlement. On the basis of their choices, a psychogeographical map is drawn and the assignment of homes is made on the basis of their sociometric positions.

In a community which has been functioning for some time, various changes may take place. Sometimes these changes are difficult to explain. Numerous people may move away for no apparent reason and frictions may develop among the groups remaining in the community. The population test is able to detect the underlying spontaneous structure of the community in repeated tests at various intervals and thus point out the causes of disintegration. The criteria used for the test may be established on the basis of visiting, borrowing, or exchanging work

relations.' (Moreno, J.L. *Who Shall Survive?* Nervous & Mental Disease Publishing Company, Washington, D.C., 1934)

test, progressive matrices An intelligence test in which the subject is asked to choose, from several alternatives, the one part which will complete the abstract design presented to him. The test is made up of 60 such designs.

test, projective A type of psychologic test in which the test material presented to the subject is such that any response will necessarily be determined by his own prevailing mood or underlying psychopathology. See *method, projective.*

test, psycholinguistic See *Illinois Test of Psycholinguistic Abilities.*

test, psychopenetration (sī-kō-pen-ē-trā'-shun) A psychodynamic test devised by Wilcox, who uses it in conjunction with carbon dioxide coma to serve as a guide for therapeutic procedures in different types of cases. It sorts reactions into five general classes, according to the degree of emotional flexibility or rigidity. The test consists of five questions, especially worded to elicit evidence of the degree of unconscious resistance to the concepts of attention, sex, killing, showing all feeling, and deceiving.

'Class I (flexibility plus mild CO_2 reaction) calls for electroconvulsive therapy in the presence of depression. Otherwise, Class I is the essentially normal pattern. Class II (flexibility plus tension CO_2 reactions) yields remarkably well to carbon dioxide comas and intensive psychotherapy. Improvement coincides with a shift to Class I. Class III (rigidity plus mild CO_2 reaction) in the presence of paranoid symptoms calls for subconvulsive electrocoma treatments. Improvement coincides with the development of flexibility and ultimately a Class I reaction. Class IV (rigidity plus tension CO_2 reactions) is a mixed group which requires trials of various types of shock-therapy to find the most effective one. Improvement is likely to be slow and the patient may follow a varying course of reactions until Class I pattern is achieved. Class V (rigidity plus paradoxical CO_2 reaction) is the profound catatonic and requires electroconvulsive therapy, spaced by periodic psychodynamic tests. As soon as the CO_2

reaction reverses, considerable gains occur by adding CO_2 comas to the treatment. Patients who have previously been considered to be schizophrenic, but who clearly react as Class II have quite different psychodynamic mechanisms than other schizophrenics.' (Spiegel, E.A. *Progress in Neurology and Psychiatry*, vol. 4, Grune and Stratton, 1949, p. 500)

test, right and wrong See *responsibility, criminal.*

test, Rorschach (Hermann Rorschach, Swiss psychiatrist, 1884-1922) A psychological test consisting of ten inkblots of varying designs and colors which are shown to the subject one at a time with the request to interpret them. Its purpose is to furnish a description of the dynamic forces of personality through an analysis of the formal aspects of the subject's interpretations. The test yields information as to the intellectual and emotional processes, the degree of personality integration, variability in mental functioning, and the degree to which the subject responds to environmental influences and to his inner promptings. The test not only is used to obtain a picture of the subject's personality, but also serves as an aid in problems of differential psychiatric diagnosis and prognosis.

test, Ross-Jones (Hugh Campbell Ross, English pathologist, 1875-1926). A test for excess of globulin in cerebrospinal fluid. Fluid is floated on top of an ammonium sulphate solution; excess globulin forms a grayish-white ring at the junction of the two fluids, and the width of the ring is a crude measure of the amount of globulin.

test, SHP The *Strongin-Hinsie-Peck test* for measurement of salivary secretion, average rate of which is decreased in depressions and increased in schizophrenias.

test, sociometric (sō-sē-ō-met'rik) 'The sociometric test is an instrument with which to measure the amount of the organization shown by social groups. It requires an individual to choose associates for any group of which he is or might become a member. The test reveals that the underlying attraction-repulsion pattern of a group differs widely from its visible structure and that groups tested upon the basis of different criteria tend toward diversity of structures. These structures have been revealed when the criteria of the test have been applied to home groups, work groups, and school groups.

The test is constructed in such a manner that it is in itself a motive, an incentive, or a purpose, primarily for the subject rather than for the tester. It is part of the procedure to put some of the choices of the subject into operation. The test can be repeated at any time without significant loss of interest to the subject.' (Moreno, J.L. *Who Shall Survive?* Nervous & Mental Disease Publishing Company, Washington, D.C., 1934)

test, spider's web A test of the biological effects of various body fluids (urine, serum, etc.) on the pattern of the spider's web. It has been found, for example, that schizophrenic urine gives different and more marked pattern changes than does non-schizophrenic urine.

test, spontaneity 'The spontaneity test proceeds by throwing the subject into standard life situations in which he improvises freely while acting opposite members of the group to whom he has been found emotionally related as revealed by the sociometric test, either through attraction or repulsion. The situations may express such emotions like anger, fear, sympathy, dominance or any other emotions. They may express roles such as father, mother, employer, or any other roles.

'The spontaneity test can be considered an intensification of the sociometric test, which does not reveal any factor beyond the attraction-repulsion pattern. The spontaneity test gives an additional insight into inter-personal relationships. In the course of the situations activated it reveals the specific emotions binding persons together the disturbances which they may have in the course of spontaneous performance, the range of words spoken and gestures shown during the acts, and the duration of the acts themselves.' (Moreno, J.L. *Who Shall Survive?* Nervous & Mental Disease Publishing Company, Washington, D.C., 1934; also Franz, J.G. *Sociometry 2*, No. 4)

test, Stanford-Binet 'The revised Stanford-Binet Intelligence Scale is the test most frequently used in the individual examination of children. It consists of 120 items, plus several alternative tests that are applicable to the age range between two years and adulthood. The tests have a variety of activities of graded difficulty, both verbal and performance, designed to tap a variety of intellectual functions such as memory, free association, orientation in time, language comprehension, knowledge of common objects, comparison of concepts, perception of contradictions, understanding of abstract terms, the ability to meet novel situations and the use of practical judgment. In addition to many other varieties of function, there are also tests of visual-motor coordination.' (Masserman, J.H. *The Practice of Dynamic Psychiatry*, Saunders, Philadelphia, 1955) The score is expressed in months of mental age, which figure is divided by the chronologic age and then multiplied by 100 to give the Intelligence Quotient.

test, Szondi A projective test, developed by Szondi in Switzerland in the 1940's, which consists of six sets of pictures, each set containing eight photographs. These eight photographs are of eight different types of mental patient—homosexual, sadist, epileptic, hysteric, catatonic schizophrenic, paranoid schizophrenic, manic-depressive depressed, manic-depressive manic. The subject chooses from each set the two pictures he likes most and the two he dislikes most. The eight different types of mental patient are presumed to be extreme pathological representatives of the eight basic emotional needs. The test is interpreted in terms of the degree of tension, and the subject's attitude to this tension, in each of these eight need-systems. The need-systems are as follows: the need for tender, feminine love ('h' factor); the need for aggression and masculinity ('s' factor); the mode of dealing with crude, aggressive emotions ('e' factor); the need to exhibit emotions ('hy' factor); narcissistic ego-needs ('k' factor); the expansive tendencies of the ego ('p' factor); the need for acquiring and mastering objects ('d' factor); and the need to cling to objects for enjoyment ('m' factor). Although the Szondi test can be used clinically, as a projective technique, without reference to the viewpoint which led to its development, the basis of the test is Szondi's theory of *genotropism* (q.v.).

test, Taschen's A test for nystagmus in which the subject is directed to turn five times around his axis within 10 seconds and must then fix his eyes on the upheld index finger of the examiner. Duration of nystagmus so provoked beyond 9 seconds is considered abnormal.

test, thematic apperception (T.A.T.) A projective technique, originally described by Morgan and Murray in 1935, which focuses primarily on the dynamics of interpersonal relationships. In its present form (the third set to be used since 1935), it consists of a series of 31 pictures which depict a number of social situations and interpersonal relations. In clinical practice, ten or twelve of the pictures are usually selected by the examiner on the basis of which of the total 31 are most likely to elicit information on the subject's problems. The selected pictures are then presented to the subject, who is asked to tell a story about what is going on in each picture. The stories are interpreted in terms of the subject's relationship to authority figures, to contemporaries of both sexes, and in terms of the compromises between and the needs of the id, the ego, and the superego. There are various methods of interpreting results; the one advocated by Murray is the need-press method (see *method, need-press*). Bellak recommends interpretation in terms of the following 14 categories: main theme, main hero, attitudes to parental figures, figures introduced, objects introduced, objects omitted, attribution of blame, significant conflicts, punishment for crime, attitude to hero, signs of inhibition (in aggression, sex, etc.), outcome, pattern of need gratification, and plot.

It is to be noted that the T.A.T. is only incidentally a diagnostic tool and is not primarily designed for nosologic classification.

test, T.P.I. Treponema Pallidum Immobilization test for syphilis. This test, developed ca. 1954, depends on antibody which develops as early as the reagin detected by serologic tests but is much more specific, dependable and persistent. It is of particular value in differentiating false serologic positives (which are often seen in the collagen diseases) from true positives due to latent syphilis.

test, visual distortion A test of subject's

reaction to the visual distortion produced by fitting subject with a set of + 6.00 sphD. or − 6.00 sphD. lenses for a period of 3-4 minutes; described by J. Ehrenwald (*Archives of General Psychiatry* 7, 30, 1962) who theorizes that it is a measure of ego strength in that it '. . . causes a temporary breakdown of the synthetic and integrative functions of the ego touched off by the dissociation of the visual and postural components of the patient's experiences of the body image and of the outside world.'

test, Wada dominance A method for determining the side of cerebral dominance by intracarotid injection of amobarbital, introduced by J. Wada in 1949 (*Medicine and Biology* 14, 221, 1949).

test, Wassermann (vàs′air-màn; popularly, wàs′er-mun) (August Paul von Wassermann, German bacteriologist, 1866-1925) A diagnostic test for syphilis, based upon complement fixation. The development and refinement of this test, in the years 1901 to 1907, made it possible to identify positively as syphilitic many neuropsychiatric conditions whose etiology had previously been only a matter of speculation. In general, it may be said that the blood Wasserman is positive in approximately 70% of cases with cerebral syphilis, 70% of tabetics, and almost 100% of paretics. The cerebrospinal fluid Wasserman is positive in approximately 60% with secondary syphilis, 100% with tertiary syphilis, and 100% with congenital syphilis.

test, Wechsler-Bellevue An intelligence test, the most widely used test in the average adult, consisting of five verbal tests, five performance tests, and an additional vocabulary test. The 11 subtests are as follows: general information, general comprehension, arithmetic, digit span, similarities, vocabulary, picture arrangement, picture completion, block design, object assembly and digit symbol. The subtests are scored on the basis of speed and accuracy, and results can be translated into standard scores which give the verbal I.Q., the performance I.Q., and the full-scale I.Q.

test, Word-in-Context A test of capacity for verbal reasoning in which the subject is asked to determine the meaning of a

given word by reading selected passages of prose.

test, Z See *test, Zulliger.*

test, Zulliger A brief Rorschach-type test of particular value for rapid screening of a group of patients; administration time averages ten minutes.

testing, reality See *reality-testing.*

tests, alpha A series of mental tests, first used in the United States military service (1917) to determine the relative mental ability of recruits. There are eight different types of test: for directions, arithmetical ability, practical judgment, synonyms and antonyms, correct arrangement of sentences, completion of series of digits, analogies, and information. The tests are designed particularly for group application and for rapid mechanical scoring.

tests, army mental Tests devised during the World War to determine the intellectual status of recruits examined for the United States Army.

tests, Binet-Simon (bē-nā′ sē-mawN′) (Alfred Binet, French psychologist, 1857-1911, and Th. Simon.) Tests of intellectual capacity, which is expressed as the Intelligence Quotient or I.Q., introduced in France in 1905 as a result of studies made to determine whether children could be educated as the new laws required. The Stanford revision of the tests for use with American children was made in 1916, although they had already been introduced into the United States by Goddard in 1910.

tests, Brunet (broo-nā′) A developmental scale designed for use with infants as young as one month.

tests, Buhler A developmental scale designed for use with infants from birth up to school age.

tests, sorting A method of psychological testing in which the subject is required to place objects into groups on the basis of similarity or some other abstract relationship. Such sorting or *Zuordnung* tests are particularly associated with the names of Kurt Goldstein, Vigotsky, Hanfmann, and Kasanin. Patients with cortical lesions, particularly, show impairment of abstract behavior as measured by these tests. Schizophrenics, too, do poorly on these tests; but performance is more varied than in ordinary brain damage cases, for the schizophrenic tends to project himself into the test objects and animate and embellish them.

tetanization (tet-à-ni-zā'shun) *Obs.* Fixation of attention.

'The spirit of exaltation, the tetanization of the attention, and the resulting psychic analgesia explain the deeds of many self-torturers, not only among those who are clearly insane, but in certain borderline cases—for instance, those of fanatics and many so-called martyrs.' (Paton, S. *Psychiatry*, Lippincott, Philadelphia and London, 1905)

tetraethylpyrophosphate (te-tra-e-thil-pī-rō-fos'fāt) See *psychotomimetic.*

tetraethylthiuram disulfide (te-tra-e-thil-thī'ū-ram dī-sul'fīd) See *Antabuse.*

tetrahydrocannabinol (te-tra-hī-drō-kannab'in-ol) See *psychotomimetic.*

tetraplegia (tet-rà-plē'jē-à) Quadriplegia; paralysis of the four extremities.

tetrasomy (tet'rà-sō-mē) The 'fourfoldness' in Jung's system of psychology. See *quaternity.*

thalamotomy (thal-à-mot'ō-mē) A psychosurgical procedure which produces a lesion in the thalamus by means of thermocoagulation. A stereotaxic apparatus is employed to position a wire or cannula into the desired subcortical area. Such a method results in minimal injury to superimposed cortex or white matter, and is a much less drastic procedure than are other methods, e.g. frontal lobectomy. The thalamotomy operation was devised by Spiegel and his coworkers, whose early reports indicate that small lesions of the dorsomedial nucleus of the thalamus (medial thalamotomy) relieve anxiety, emotional reactivity, and allied symptoms in psychoses and obsessive-compulsive states. This technique is obviously applicable to the production of lesions elsewhere in the brain.

thalamus (tha-la'mus) An ovoid-shaped constellation of nuclei lying between the mesencephalon and corpora striata, forming the lateral wall of the 3rd ventricle, and completely covered by the cerebral hemisphere. The prominent posterior portion is the pulvinar, lateral to which is the lateral geniculate body. The medial surface of the thalamus is connected to the thalamus of the opposite side by the massa intermedia.

Anatomically, six major nuclear masses are recognized (Walker's terminology): midline, anterior, medial, lateral, ventral, and posterior nuclei. The posterior nuclei include the pulvinar and the medial and lateral geniculate bodies.

The thalamus has somatic, special sense, and associative sensory functions. The ventral nuclei are concerned with somatic sensory functions, the lateroventral portion with unconscious proprioception, the posteroventral portion with conscious exteroception and proprioception, the posteroventral portion with conscious exteroception and proprioception, the lateral geniculate body with vision, the medial geniculate body with audition (? and equilibrium), and the pulvinar with auditory and visual association.

Thalamic lesions are commonly followed by various paresthesiae and hyperesthesiae which are believed to be due to release from intradiencephalic and corticothalamic projections. The 'thalamic syndrome' consists of a raising of the threshold (i.e. diminished sensitivity) to pinprick, heat and cold, but when sensation is felt it is disagreeable and unpleasant (thalamic hyperpathia).

thalassophobia (thà-las-ō-fō'bē-à) Fear of the sea.

thanatomania (than-à-tō-mā'nē-à) *Obs.* Suicidal mania.

thanatophobia Fear of death.

Thanatos According to Freud there are two sets of instincts. He terms one the life instinct or Eros, the other the death instinct or Thanatos. 'For the sake of clearness I will repeat in a sentence the three stages in the development of Freud's ideas concerning the duality of instincts. The first was the contrast between sexual and ego instincts; the second the contrast between object-love or allo-erotic libido, and self-love, narcissistic libido; and the third is the contrast between life and death instincts, between Eros and Thanatos.' (Jones, E. *Papers on Psycho-Analysis*, 4th ed., Wood, Baltimore, 1938) See *instinct, death*.

thanatotic (than-a-tot'ik) Pertaining to or manifesting the death instinct.

thaassophobia (thà-as-ō-fō'bē-à) Fear of sitting.

theatre, therapeutic 'An objective setting in which the subject and patient can act free from the anxieties and pressures of the outside world. In order to accomplish this, the total situation of the patient in the outside world has to be duplicated on a spontaneous level in the therapeutic theater, and even more than this, the invisible roles and invisible inter-personal relations he may have experienced must find a visible expression. This means that certain functions—a stage, lights, recording system, assistants, and psychiatrist or director—have to be introduced into its operation.' (Moreno, J.L. *Sociometry 1*, 16, 1937)

thelygonia (thē-li-gō'nē-à) 1. Procreation of female offspring. 2. *Obs.* Nymphomania.

theme, mythological 'The collective unconscious—so far as we can venture a judgment upon it—seems to consist of something of the nature of mythological themes or images. For this reason the myths of peoples are the real exponents of the collective unconscious. The whole of mythology could be taken as a kind of projection of the collective unconscious. (Jung, C.G. *Contributions to Analytical Psychology*, tr. by Baynes, H.G. and C.F., Kegan Paul, Trench, Trubner, London, 1928)

theomania (thē-ō-mā'nnē-à) *Obs.* Delusion that one is God.

theophobia Fear of God.

theory, Cannon's See *Cannon hypothalamic theory of emotions*.

theory, catastrophe The belief that the act of sexual intercourse is destructive to the penis. 'In the normal coitus of

individuals who are not neurotic, the inner tension seeking for discharge finally overcomes anxiety, although, as suggested in my ontogenetic and phylogenetic "catastrophe"-theory of coitus, some traces of anxiety may still persist.' (Ferenczi, S. *Further Contributions to the Theory and Technique of Psycho-Analysis*, tr. by Suttie, J., Leonard and Virginia Woolf and The Institute of Psychoanalysis, London, 1926)

theory, immanence The closed circle hypothesis of life that describes the function of each organ in terms of what it accomplishes for the rest of the organism. According to such a view, the life process would have the pattern of a logical vicious cycle. The part processes have the function of sustaining life; and life is an aggregation of these part processes. This theory is the opposite of *holism* (q.v.). (Angyal, A. *Foundations for a Science of Personality*, The Commonwealth Fund, Oxford University Press, New York, 1941)

theory, James-Lange-Sutherland 'The bodily changes follow directly the perception of the exciting fact, and our feeling of the same changes as they occur is the emotion. . . . The elements . . . of physiological processes, which comprise the emotion . . . are all organic changes, and each of them is the reflex effect of the exciting object.' (C.G. Lange and W. James. *The Emotions*, Williams and Wilkins, Baltimore, 1922) This theory admitted of no special brain centers for emotion and has been largely replaced by Papez' modification of the *Cannon hypothalamic theory of emotion* (q.v.).

theory, libido (li-bid'ō) Technically, the psychoanalytic hypothesis concerning the development and vicissitudes of the sexual drive or instinct. Often, however, libido is used to refer to all of the psychoanalytic hypotheses about the instincts in man. The confusion arises from the fact that until 1920 Freud did not fully develop his dual-instinct theory; before that time, all instinctual manifestation were considered to be a part of the sexual drive. Nowadays, however, the existence of two drives is assumed: sexual (libido) and aggressive.

therapeiology (ther-à-pā-ol'ō-jē) *Obs.* Therapeutics.

therapeutic (ther-a-pū'tik) Pertaining to or consisting of medical treatment; healing, curative.

therapeutic reaction, negative See *resistance, superego.*

therapy (ther'à-pē) Treatment of disease; therapeutics.

therapy, active The psychoanalytical method in which the psychiatrist does not confine himself to the interpretation of psychic material, but goes further to force the patient to actions that are hindered by his neurosis. The patient has to be forced precisely into the situations he fears, in order to accustom him to these situations and, consequently to enable him to overcome his fear. According to psychoanalytical theory, such actions bring forward and make available for interpretation the psychic material which otherwise might remain hidden. 'By the repetition of the act which he fears the patient will gain a better insight into his situation which, until then, he considered dangerous.' Through this forced action the patient is taught that there are no insurmountable difficulties in the situation. It is very important that the psychiatrist find out just what actions he can demand of a patient, in order to avoid asking too much and thereby throwing the individual into a panic. In cases of simple anxiety-neurosis, like that of a 'patient who does not dare to be far away from his home, he is ordered, at first, to walk two or three blocks.' After doing this three or four times, he is ordered to walk four or five blocks, and in this manner the therapy proceeds progressively. The only thing that should be asked of the patient is action; he should never be asked to exercise will-power, or suppress his thoughts: 'Such demands are useless and increase the sense of failure in the patient.' Very often it is difficult to find actions that are appropriate to the symptoms of the patient. According to Schilder, the principle of active therapy is 'probably also valid when thoughts which seem to be unacceptable to the patient are formulated again and again': the mere formulation of words seems to have an effect similar to the repetition of the act. (Schilder, P, *Psychotherapy,* Norton, New York, 1938)

therapy, activity group A special technique of applying psychotherapy through group activity. 'So that these [very shy] children might not feel threatened, a program of picnics and trips was arranged for them, and after some months of such therapy it was found that not only did they evidence gain in their social behavior, but that they had made general improvement in their personalities. From this inauspicious practice grew Slavson's activity group therapy.' (Klapman, J.W. *Group Psychotherapy,* Grune and Stratton, New York, 1946) See *psychotherapy, group.*

therapy, adjuvant (aj'oo-vant) Subsidiary therapy or curative means in the treatment of the psychoneuroses, in addition to psychotherapy, which they aid or assist. Adjuvant therapies consist primarily of drugs, suggestion, and hypnosis.

therapy, administrative Institutional treatment of psychologically disturbed people such as is employed in the therapeutic community, in contrast to mere custodial care. See *community, therapeutic.*

therapy, analytical (an-à-lit'i-kal) Therapeutic application of the principles of *analytic psychology* (q.v.). According to Jung the contents of consciousness are antithetic to those of the unconscious. One compensates for the others. 'In the normal condition the compensation is unconscious, i.e., it performs an unconscious regulation of conscious activity. In the neurotic state the unconscious appears in such strong contrast to the conscious that compensation is disturbed. The aim of analytical therapy, therefore, is to make the unconscious contents conscious in order that compensation may be established.' (Jung, C.G. *Psychological Types,* tr. by Baynes, H.G., Harcourt, Brace, New York and London, 1923) See *constructive; reductive.*

therapy, assignment 'Assignment therapy is the placement of the individual into a group in accord with his sociometric position in the community. It tries to give the individual the best opportunity for adjustment in the group and for the ascendance to such a position in it which expresses his spontaneous abilities. Such placements take into consideration the total picture of the group as well as its sexual, racial, and leadership cleavages.' (Moreno, J.L. *Who Shall Survive?* Nervous & Mental Disease Publishing Company, Washington, D.C., 1934)

therapy, atropine coma (a'trō-pēn) ACT; the use of atropine sulphate to induce coma in the treatment of psychoses, first reported by G.R. Forrer in 1950.

Greatest benefit has been reported in tense, anxious, and agitated psychotics.

therapy, attitude Originally, a process of treating children by working with the disturbed attitudes of their parents (David Levy. *American Journal of Orthopsychiatry 7:* 103-113, 1937) Nowadays, a type of re-educative psychotherapy which focuses on the current attitudes of the patient, their distortions, their origins, and their present purpose. In this type of therapy, the patient is helped to adopt attitudes that make for harmonious relationships as substitutes for his maladaptive attitudes.

therapy, aversion Negative conditioning, consisting of pairing the unwanted symptom or behavior (e.g. alcoholism, fetishism, homosexuality, enuresis, and psychopathic behavior) with painful or unpleasant stimuli until the undesirable behavior is suppressed. See *behavior theory.*

therapy, behavior See *behavior theory.*

therapy, brief stimulus A type of electroconvulsive therapy in which the current is modified so that the average electrical energy needed to produce a seizure is much less than with the usual method. It is claimed that BST gives as satisfactory clinical results as classical ECT, with the added advantage of reducing or even eliminating confusion. A disadvantage of BST is that patients are more fearful than with the classical method; this can be overcome by using pre-treatment barbiturates.

therapy, carbon dioxide inhalation A form of somatic treatment introduced by von Meduna (who also introduced Metrazol convulsive treatment for schizophrenia). In CO_2 inhalation therapy, the patient breathes from a cylinder containing a mixture of 30 per cent CO_2 and 70 per cent O_2 to the point of uncon-

sciousness. Treatments are given two or three times a week, sometimes to as many as 100 treatments. The method is of limited usefulness in the treatment of various psychoneuroses, and many workers feel that it may even retard or prevent recovery. Those who find it of some value feel that it is best suited to traumatic hysteria with dissociation, to conversion symptoms of recent origin, and to anxiety-hysteria.

therapy, child-guidance The treatment of emotional problems of children by the simultaneous therapy of the child and its parents, especially the mother.

therapy, client-centered *Non-directive therapy;* a type of therapeutic counseling associated with the name of Carl Rogers. Client-centered therapy is predicated on the belief that the patient possesses inherent potentialities for growth which need only to be released by the therapist. The patient is responsible for his own destiny and has the right of choice in the solution of his problems, and instead of imposing values on the patient the therapist must promote the free expression of feelings in the counseling relationship.

therapy, directed group See *psychotherapy, group.*

therapy, diversional In occupational therapy those simple occupations are regarded as diversional which are given primarily for the amusement and distraction of the patient from himself, 'in which simple processes are used to occupy the fingers and divert the mind of the patient from his or her condition, surroundings, etc.' Here it is largely a question of morale.' (Slagle, E.C. and Robeson, H.A. *Syllabus for Training of Nurses in Occupational Therapy,* State Hospitals Press, Utica, N.Y., 1933)

therapy, electric convulsion A form of somatic treatment for certain psychiatric conditions in which electrical current is applied to the brain through two electrodes placed on the temporal areas of the skull. Current is applied through a specially constructed machine, whose main features are a stop watch for time regulation to fractions of a second and a voltometer which regulates the voltage to be applied. The desired generalized convulsion is ordinarily obtained with voltage varying between 70 and 130 volts applied for 0.1 to 0.5 seconds. The convulsion usually occurs immediately with an initial tonic phase lasting about 10 seconds. The tonic phase slowly goes over into the clonic phase, which fades out after a total of 30 or 40 seconds for the whole seizure. The convulsion is accompanied by apnea. The seizure is followed by coma which lasts from 5 to 30 or more minutes.

Complications are rare, the most frequent one being bone fractures due to muscular contraction. Intravenous muscle relaxants, such as succinylcholine, are often used to prevent this complication. Respiratory and cardiovascular complications may occur; neurological complications are extremely rare. The probability of fatal incidents does not exceed 0.06 per cent of cases.

Electric convulsive therapy, or E.C.T., is indicated in mania, depressions, and certain cases of schizophrenia. Results are unsatisfactory in the psychoneuroses, except in psychoneurotic depression. All types of depression react favorably to E.C.T. after some four treatments. E.C.T. gives an 80 to 100 per cent remission rate in the depressive phase of manic-depressive psychosis, in involutional melancholia, and in agitated depressions, but it does not ward off episodic recurrences. The manic phase must usually be treated more intensively, with as many as two or three treatments a day. With such treatment the remission rate approaches that in the depressed phase. The paranoid type of involutional psychosis usually requires twenty treatments, in contrast to the ordinary maximum of ten treatments in the aforementioned groups, but, even so, the remission rate is less than 50 per cent. Schizophrenics also require a minimum of twenty treatments. About 65 per cent of schizophrenic cases of less than six months' duration respond favorably, some 40 per cent among those ill from six months to two years, and less than 10 per cent of those ill more than two years. In all cases, temporary remissions may be prolonged with E.C.T. maintenance therapy at weekly, fortnightly, even monthly intervals. (Kalinowsky, L.B., and Hoch, P.H. *Shock Treatments,* Grune and Stratton, New York, 1950)

Electric convulsive therapy was often used in combination with insulin therapy, particularly in schizophrenia. In these cases, E.C.T. was used to relieve the anxiety and apprehension components, insulin to clear the underlying thought disorder. Electric convulsive therapy does not afford insight to the patient; hence, in addition to somatic therapy, psychotherapy is usually indicated in order to bring more lasting benefit.

therapy, expressive A method of treatment in which the therapist's dominant aim is to encourage and help the patient to bring out, verbalize, act out, or emotionally express all ideas and feelings so that both the patient and the therapist come to know the dynamic emotional roots of the patient's symptoms and illness. Through encouragement and by bringing about a reversal of the *covering up* (or normal) defensive mechanism, expressive therapy endeavors to *uncover* the roots of mental and emotional illness. As epitomized in psychoanalysis, the main purpose of expressive therapy is, through a reversal of the repressive defensive mechanisms, to shift the material from the unconscious realm into the realm of conscious thought.

On the other hand, *suppressive therapy,* which is the opposite of expressive therapy, tends to cover up, to keep down, and strengthen the repressive, defensive forces of the personality. As such, suppressive therapy tries to build up the forces of concealment of the self toward hidden portions of itself, while expressive therapy brings about painful but valuable self-revelation. Suppressive therapy tends to maintain and continue the individual's comfortable and peaceful illusion of himself, while expressive therapy becomes painfully disillusioning and thus aims in the direction of self-realization and reality.

therapy, family group Treatment of the family as a unit rather than individual treatment of one or more members of the family. Among the first to undertake treatment of the family unit were John Bell and Nathan Ackerman. This type of treatment is an outgrowth of a shifting emphasis in recent years, from the view of the child as a victim of his family to a field-force concept, in which the family is viewed as a social unit whose operations can be understood only in terms of the reciprocal expectations of the family members.

therapy, inter-personal From the standpoint of psychodramatics, 'inter-personal therapy is a technique which is applied in such problems and mental disorders in which the treatment interrelates dynamically all the persons involved. An illustration of a situation demanding this approach is a "triangular neurosis." i.e. an inter-personal neurosis affecting three persons, for example, a husband, wife, and another individual.

'Inter-personal therapy is carried out in alternating sessions with each of the persons involved until the psychiatrist, the auxiliary ego, has returned to the subject with whom he began. The cycle can be repeated as often as necessary until catharsis is reached.' (Moreno, J.L. *Sociometry 1*, 3, 1937)

therapy, ludo Play therapy.

therapy, marriage A type of family therapy involving husband and wife and concerned primarily with their marital relationship. See *therapy, family group; counseling, marriage.*

therapy, mass A psychotherapeutic term that embraces various group techniques, particularly the didactic, recreational, and class methods used for large groups.

therapy, milieu Socio-environmental therapy, usually in a hospital setting. See *community, therapeutic; social therapy; total push treatment of schizophrenia.*

therapy, non-directive See *therapy, client-centered.*

therapy, occupational The American Occupational Therapy Association defined its functions in *Syllabus for Training of Nurses in Occupational Therapy* (Slagle, E.C. and Robeson, H.) as follows:

1. Occupational therapy is a method of treament for the sick or injured by means of purposeful occupation.
2. The goals are to arouse interest, courage and confidence; to exercise mind and body in healthy activity; to overcome disability; and to reestablish capacity for industrial and social usefulness.
3. In applying occupational therapy, system and precision are as important as in other forms of treatment.

4. The treatment should be prescribed and administered under constant medical advice and supervision and correlated with the other forms of treatment the patient is receiving.
5. The treatment should in each case be specifically directed to the individual patient's need.
6. Though some patients do best alone, employment in groups is usually advisable, because it provides exercise in social adaptation and the stimulating influence of example and comment.
7. The occupation selected should be within the patient's estimated interests and capability.
8. As the patient's strength and capability increase, the type and extent of occupation should be regulated and graded accordingly.
9. The only reliable measure of the treatment is the effect on the patient.
10. Inferior workmanship, or employment in an occupation which would be trivial for the healthy, may be attended with the greatest benefit to the sick or injured, but standards worthy of entirely normal people must be maintained for proper mental stimulation.
11. The production of well-made, useful and attractive articles or the accomplishment of useful tasks, requires healthy exercise of mind and body, gives the greatest satisfaction, and thus produces the most beneficial effects.
12. Novelty, variety, individuality, and utility of the product enhances the value of an occupation as a treatment measure.
13. Quality, quantity, salability of the products may prove beneficial by satisfying and stimulating the patient, but should never be permitted to obscure the main purpose.
14. Good craftsmanship and ability to instruct are essential qualifications in the occupational therapist; understanding, sincere interest in the patient, and an optimistic, cheerful outlook and manner are equally essential.
15. Physical exercises, games and music are useful forms of occupational therapy, and fall under two broad heads: (a) Gymnastics and calisthenics that are given for their value in a patient's

physical re-education, or in habit training in mental hospitals; (b) recreation and play activities, such as music, games, folk dancing, etc., which are provided because of their general and social value for the patients.

therapy, old-age See *geriatrics.*

therapy, physical Physiotherapy; the branch of physical medicine that makes use of physical and other effective properties of light, heat, cold, water, electricity, mechanical agents, and kinesitherapy (message, manipulation, therapeutic exercise, mechanical devices).

therapy, pineal Treatment with extracts of beef-pineal substance; such treatment has been reported to be of value in chronic schizophrenia. (M.D. Altschule,*New Engl. J. Med.* 257, 919-922, 1957)

therapy, play In child psychiatry, play therapy is a method of treatment which, in general, corresponds to the method of psychoanalysis in adult psychiatry, the difference being that the child expresses himself and reveals unconscious material to the therapist by means of play rather than by verbalization of thoughts, as the adult does in psychoanalysis. See *technique, play.*

The play of children, an essential part of their life, is self-expressive in its nature. If a playroom containing all manner of toys and games is set up for the child, much can be learned about the child by observing what game he chooses to play and the manner in which he plays it. For example, during a session in the play-therapy room, a nine-year-old boy took chalk of various colors and drew on the blackboard a charming picture of a house in the countryside. When the drawing had been finished the therapist warmly complimented the boy on his work, and then asked him to make up a story about the people living in that house. It was known that he was a child from a broken, poverty-stricken home in a tenement section of the city; he would not obey his mother, and allegedly had pushed his baby sister from a fire escape to her death. In play therapy he had created what he lacked, an attractive home in the country. In telling the story of the people who lived

in it, his feelings about his own home and his own family were drawn out. The therapist was able to help him face his insecurity, anxiety, and hostility and to learn better ways of dealing with them. Before this release through play therapy, the boy had been uncommunicative and inaccessible in several interviews with the therapist.

therapy, reconstructive See *psychotherapy.*

therapy, recreation See *recreation.*

therapy, re-educative See *psychotherapy.*

therapy, regressive electro-shock A form of electroconvulsive therapy in which several daily grand mal convulsions are produced for a number of days until the patient is out of contact and incontinent of urine and feces. In one study, four treatments were given each day for seven days; at the end of this time, in addition to the above symptoms, patients were underactive, did not talk spontaneously, lost their appetite and had to be spoon-fed, and movements were uncertain, slow and clumsy. These symptoms last for one or two weeks; recovery is gradual.

Regressive EST is ordinarily used only when the more usual methods fail and prognosis is poor, as in some forms of the schizophrenias.

therapy, relationship Therapy which emerges out of the totality of the relationship between patient and therapist during the entire course of treatment. Although Allen is a pioneer in relationship therapy with children, he considers the term misleading. In this connection, Kanner (*Child Psychiatry,* Thomas, Springfield, Ill., 1948) quotes Allen as follows: 'It [relationship therapy] seems to imply a special brand of psychological therapy. All therapy involves a relationship between patient and therapist.' However, 'here the therapeutic relationship is conceived as an immediate experience. The therapist begins where the patient is and seeks to help him draw on his own capacities toward a more creative acceptance and use of the self he has. While maintaining an interest in understanding what has been wrong, the therapeutic focus is on what the individual can begin to do about what was and, more important, still is wrong. Therapy emerges, then, from an experience in living, not in isolation but within a relationship with another from whom the patient can eventually differentiate himself as he comes to perceive and accept his own self as separate and distinct.'

therapy, release See *release.*

therapy, rhythmic sensory bombardment A form of treatment consisting of sonic, photic or tactile stimulation applied intermittently and rhythmically usually for a period of one hour. The affective psychoses, psychoneuroses, psychopathic personalities, and paranoid forms of schizophrenia are said to show favorable response.

therapy, shock A general term indicating the use of various somatic treatments which produce a 'shock' to the central nervous system, thus favorably influencing the course of a mental disease. The shock therapies include electroshock (EST) — also called electro-convulsive therapy (ECT) — insulin coma therapy, ambulatory insulin treatment (also called sub-shock or sub-coma insulin therapy), Metrazol convulsive treatment, brief stimulus electrotherapy, electrostimulation, electronarcosis, Indoclon inhalation therapy, atropine coma therapy, etc.

therapy, situational A term introduced by S.R. Slavson, in connection with his activity group psychotherapy, in which the social relationship and the physical environment themselves (i.e. the situation) have a therapeutic effect.

therapy, sleep-electroshock Electroshock treatment preceded by the administration of sufficient sedative or hypnotic drug to produce sleep. The method is of particular value in patients who develop a fear of electric shock and are unwilling to continue receiving such therapy. Pentothal sodium is commonly employed, administered intravenously as a 2.5 per cent solution. The electrodes are applied after sleep is induced. Many psychiatrists apply the current as soon as the patient spontaneously moves a limb during the waking process. The same amount of current is given as without the sleep-inducing drug. Other psychiatrists apply the current at a deeper stage of narcosis, as judged by the absence of spontaneous

movements and the presence of a corneal reflex. With the latter method a nonconvulsive or minor reaction is obtained, but the clinical effects as measured by the maintenance of the improved state are equally satisfactory.

therapy, supportive See *psychotherapy.*

therapy, suppressive See *therapy, expressive.*

therapy, will A form of psychotherapy associated with the name of Otto Rank and based upon his belief that birth trauma (the separation of the child from the mother at the moment of birth) is the central element in neurosis. The trauma of birth is believed to lead to two sets of strivings: (1) to return to the womb or (2) to re-enact separation and achieve independence. In will-therapy, separation reactions are studied as well as the struggle of will manifested in the patient's desire to continue therapy (and dependence) or to discontinue it (and become independent). The patient is actively encouraged to assert himself so as to develop and strengthen his will.

thermanesthesia, thermoanesthesia (thēr-man-es-thē′zē-à, thēr-mō-an-es-thē′-zē-à) Loss of the ability to distinguish between heat and cold; loss of the temperature sense; insensibility to heat or to temperature changes.

thermo- (thēr′mō-) combining form meaning heat from Gr. *thermós*, hot.

thermohyperesthesia (thēr-mō-hī-pēr-es-thē′zē-à) Extreme sensitiveness to heat stimuli.

thermohypesthesia (-hip-es-thē′zē-à) Diminished sensibility to heat stimuli.

thermoneurosis (-nū-rō′sis) *Obs.* An elevation of the temperature of the body due to neurosis as seen sometimes in hysteria.

theta rhythm or wave See *electroencephalogram.*

thinking, abstract See *thinking, physiognomonic.*

thinking, archaic-paralogical (är-kā′ik-par-à-loj′i-kal) Domarus classified thinking into: '(1) *prearchaic;* (2) *archaic-paralogical;* and (3) *paralogical-logical.* The latter two he considered to be typical of primitive savages, and common in schizophrenia, and the first as typical of man's anthropoid progenitors and of schizophrenic stupor.' In 1940, Osborne recommended changing the name of schizophrenia to palaeophrenia to emphasize the importance of regression to primitive subrational forms of thinking in the schizophrenic disorders.

Primitive thinking, primordial thinking, anthropoid thinking are all synonyms for archaic-paralogical thinking. They are all characterized by impairment or deficiency of abstraction and generalization, with a tendency toward 'concrete' rather than 'abstract' thinking. (Hunt, J.McV. *Personality and the Behavior Disorders,* vol. 2, Ronald Press, New York, 1944)

thinking-aside A disorder of associations seen in schizophrenic patients in which the patient loses himself in insignificant side association with the result that no unitary train of thought develops. Because of the paucity of genuinely casual links in such conversation or writing, thinking-aside would be considered a type of asyndesis.

thinking, associative Verbal catharsis that deals with immediate problems of patients in their everyday life rather than with traumatic problems originating in infancy. The latter sort of catharsis occurs through 'free-association.' Free association is regressive in its nature, which is not the case with associative thinking. Associative thinking is lateral in direction while free-association is vertical. (Slavson, S.R. *Analytic Group Psychotherapy,* Columbia University Press, New York, 1950, p. 189) See *presentation.*

thinking, autistic (aw-tis'tik) See *autism.*

thinking, categorical See *thinking, physiognomonic.*

thinking-compulsion See *brooding.*

thinking, concrete See *thinking, physiognomonic.*

thinking, concretistic (kon-krē-tis'tik) See *concretism.*

thinking, directed See *intellect.*

thinking-disorder See *association, disturbances of.*

thinking, double An infrequently used term with unclear definition; some authorities use the term synonymously with *thought-hearing.*

thinking, fragmentation of A disturbance in association, pathognomonic of schizophrenia, in which even such basic concepts as 'father' and 'mother' become vague and obscure and the thinking processes become so confused that they cannot result in a complete idea or action, but merely in vague movements. Bleuler calls this a 'primary symptom' of schizophrenia and believes that it is due to associations no longer following the logical pathways indicated by past experience. Instead, associations easily take new and seemingly illogical pathways, and thinking becomes bizarre. Thus two ideas, fortuitously encountered, are combined into one thought. Associations lack the concept of purpose. When the symptom is of mild degree, it may be noticed only that the patient gives generalized rather than precise answers. Thus one patient, asked to give the location of London, said 'Europe' rather than 'England.' (Bleuler, E. *Dementia Praecox or the Group of Schizophrenias,* International Universities Press, New York, 1950)

thinking, magical Archaic, primitive, prelogical thinking, such as is seen in the unconscious of neurotics, in small children, in normal persons under conditions of fatigue, as antecendents of thought in primitive man, and in schizophrenic thinking. The speech and thinking of the schizophrenic are frequently more concrete and active than normal, not yet capable of realistic abstractions, and more a symbolic equivalent of action. See *paleologic; process, primary.*

thinking, physiognomonic (fiz-i-og-nom'ō-nik) According to Kasanin, the first stage in the development of thought in the child. In this stage, the child animates objects and projects his ego into them, as when he plays with a stick and calls it a horse. Piaget calls this 'syncretic thinking.'

The second stage is concrete thinking,

characterized by literalness and lack of generalizations. In this stage, for example, the word 'table' refers not to tables in general but to the particular table in the subject's house.

The third stage is abstract or categoried thinking, characterized by use of abstractions and generalizations. This type of thinking appears relatively late, usually after adolescence and probably only after some degree of education.

thinking, prearchaic See *thinking, archaic-paralogical.*

thinking, preconscious One of the terms used by Fenichel to describe the preverbal, prelogical, pictorial phantasy thinking which precedes the development of logical thinking in small children.

Preconscious thinking is not in accordance with reality. All of its features are primitive and archaic. First, since it is ruled by the emotions and strives for the discharge of tensions, it is full of wishful or fear-laden misconceptions. Second, it is carried out through concrete pictorial images. Third, it is a magical type of thinking. 'The object and the idea of the object, the object and a picture or model of the object, the object and a part of the object are equated: similarities are not distinguished from identities; ego and nonego are not yet separated. What happens to objects might (by identification) be experienced as happening to the ego, and what happens to the ego causes the same thing to happen to the object . . .' Last the thinking is symbolic and thus vague, for the world is experienced and apperceived in symbolic forms. Stimuli that provoke the same emotional reactions are looked upon as identical. Thus if penis and snake provoke the same emotions they are apprehended by a common conception: they are one and the same thing. Although illogical and ineffective, this preconscious phantasy thinking is an attempt to master reality. It does postpone immediate discharge reactions and attempts to anticipate reality and bring about a more adequate discharge of tensions.

With the acquisition of words and the development of the faculty of speech, thinking becomes logical, and organized. Words can be linked to ideas. This is the decisive step in the final differentiation of conscious and unconscious and in the development of reality-testing. Now there can be precise anticipation of action through thinking, and instinctual excitations as well as the external world can be handled in a better way.

Preconscious thinking, however, recurs in the adult in several different ways. Before acquiring verbal formulation, all thoughts run through initial phases which resemble preconscious thinking. In dreams and in fatigue, words are retranslated into pictures. Conscious ideas may be symbols hiding objectionable unconscious ideas, and in dreams symbols appear not only in order to distort, but also as a characteristic of, archaic pictorial thinking visualizing abstract thoughts. In this way the fact that the symbol and the symbolized were once the same thing is utilized. Preconscious thinking may also appear as a substitute for unpleasant reality or a reality that cannot be influenced. This occurs, for example, in the magical daydreaming phantasies of the hysterical patient. In the compulsion-neurotic the magic power of concepts can be observed. Finally, psychotic thinking is identical with the preconscious thinking of small children, described above. (Fenichel, O. *The Psychoanalytic Theory of Neurosis,* Norton, New York, 1945)

thinking, syncretic (sin-kre′tik) See *thinking, physiognomonic.*

thinking, undirected See *intellect.*

third nervous system A system differentiated by Burrow on the basis of its specialization of function, not on the basis of anatomical demarcation. It involves the neural processes that govern man's symbolic interchange, and through its misuse is considered responsible for mans' disordered behavior.

thirteen, original The original thirteen were the founders (in 1844) of the Association of Medical Superintendents of America: William Awl, Luther Bell, Amariah Brigham, John Butler, Nehenich Cutter, Pliny Earle, John Galt, Thomas Kirkbride, Isaac Ray, Charles Stedman, Francis Stribling, Samuel White, and Samuel Woodward. In 1893 the name of the society was changed to the American Medicopsychological Association, which became the American Psychiatric Association in 1922.

thlasis depressio (thlä'sis dā-pres'sē-ō) *Obs.* Melancholia.

Thomism The philosophicotheological system of Thomas Aquinas.

'*Thomism* is an ideological system with the unrecognized premise that "father is always right" or "it is right because father said so." It is the ideological system which brooks no change and no investigation; and if it does (as it did even in the case of St. Thomas), scientific investigation is used only to prove again that "father was right." Such an ideological system cannot be proven either right or wrong. Its tenure depends entirely on its ability to serve as a vehicle to express ideas not incompatible with the needs of the individual. The failure of *Thomism* came when this obedience principle became an obstacle and the ideologies of the Reformation sought expression for the new investigative spirit which had already validated itself in practice. The old obedience dogma was not in harmony with it.' (Kardiner, A. *The Psychological Frontiers of Society*, Columbia University Press, New York, 1945)

Thompson, Clara (1893 - 1958) American psychoanalyst; associated with Harry Sullivan and his modifications of psychoanalysis (interpersonal relationships).

thought, archaic 'Schizophrenic thinking shows startling analogies to the thinking of primitive man. In other words it is *archaic* in character. A reasonably adequate discussion of schizophrreenic thinking would require that it be correlated with the principal historic features of the development of thought wherein it would be shown that it throws back to historically earlier ways of thinking in which feeling, perception and concreteness dominate, whille reasoning, differentiation, and abstraction are little in evidence.' (White, W.A. *Outlines of Psychiatry*, 12th ed., Nervous & Mental Disease Publishing Company, Washington, D.C., 1929)

thought, audible A type of auditory hallucination in which the voice is projected into the patient himself, as though he could hear his own thoughts. Such hallucinations with almost no sensory components are commonly designated as *inner voices*. Baillarger referred to them as *psychic hallucinations*. These are *hallucinations of conception* rather than of perception. Patients may use the term 'soundless voices' to refer to essentially the same phenomenon.

thought-blocking See *blocking*.

thought, constraint See *constraint of thought*.

thought-deprivation *Blocking* (q.v.).

thought-derailment See *derailment, thought*.

thought-disorder See *associations, disturbances of*.

thought-disorder, primary That type of schizophrenia in which there is striking involvement of intellectual functions with marked incoherence and irrelevance, tendency to neologisms, 'word-salads,' and peculiar syntactical speech formation.

thought-echoing Hearing one's own thoughts expressed in whispered or unbearably loud tones; *écho des pensées* (q.v.).

thought, emotional See *psychodynamics, adaptational*.

thought-hearing Some patients, notably those with schizophrenia, maintain that they hear their own thoughts; they may also believe that their thoughts are heard by others, too.

thought, imageless A thought completely devoid of optic pictures or representations.

thought, inelasticity of Reduction of the normal flow of thought, often observed in people of old age, when thoughts become more rigid, more static than in the years of youth.

thought, latent See *cerebration, unconscious*.

thought, multifocal Arieti's term for *asyndesis* (q.v.) and similar associational disturbances which he explains as being due to the fact that the patient's thought simultaneously focuses on many different planes and on different meanings with their different objective situations.

thought-nexus The union or linkage of thoughts. 'In obedience to the pain-principle, therefore, the first psi (Ψ) system is quite incapable of introducing anything unpleasant into the thought-nexus. The system cannot do anything but wish.' (Freud, S. *The Interpretation of Dreams*, 3rd ed., tr. by Brill, A.A., Macmillan, New York, 1933)

thought-omnipotence See *thinking, magical.*

thought-pressure This expression means that, as patients describe it, they have ideas that are forced into their mind. The patients assume little or no responsibility for developing the thoughts. This is particularly true in patients with schizophrenia, who may ascribe all their mental processes to the alleged pressure brought upon them by others.

The same phenomenon of thought-pressure may also appear in manic-depressive disorders, as well as in certain psychoneurotic states. In these diagnostic groups no external pressure is alleged; rather, the patients assert that the irresistible force arises within their own minds.

The condition is also known as *pressure of ideas.*

thought, reactive See *reinforcement, reactive.*

thought, re-enforced See *thought, supervalent.*

thought-rehearsal See *rehearsal, obsessional.*

thought, supervalent (sū-pĕr-vā′lent) 'A train of thought such as this may be described as exaggerated, or better *re-enforced*, or "supervalent" in Wernicke's sense of the word. It shows its pathological character, in spite of its apparently reasonable content, by the single peculiarity that no amount of conscious and voluntary effort of thought on the patient's part is able to dissipate or remove it.' (Freud, S. *Collected Papers*, Vol. 3, tr. by Strachey, A. and J., Leonard and Virginia Woolf, Hogarth Press, London, 1925)

thought-transference See *perception, extra-sensory.*

thought, unemotional See *psychodynamics, adaptational.*

thought-wit See *wit, thought.*

three-cornered therapy See *psychotherapy, multiple.*

threshold, sedation The amount of sodium amytal required, by intravenous injection, to produce slurring of speech and a concomitant inflection point in the 15-30 c.p.s. amplitude curve of the electroencephalogram. The EEG change occurs within 80 seconds of the time when slur is noted. Shagass has used this test to differentiate between psychotic and neurotic depressions; according to him, thresholds are low in psychotic depressions and high in neurotic depressions.

thromboangiitis obliterans, cerebral (throm-bō-an-jē-ī′tis ob-lit′ĕr-ans, ser′-e-bral) (293.1, 309.3) Thromboangiitis obliterans is far less common in the cerebral vessels than in the peripheral vessels, but when it does occur peripheral disease is often absent. The cerebral form is more common in males and usually begins in the fifth decade; heavy smoking may be of etiologic importance. Symptoms are very similar to those found with cerebral arteriosclerosis: a focal, neurological form or a generalized mental form. See *arteriosclerosis, cerebral.*

thrombosis, cerebral (throm-bō′sis, ser′e-bral) See *accident, cerebrovascular.*

thumb-sucking See *sucking, thumb.*

thymergasia (thīm-ĕr-gas′ē-à) Adolf Meyer's term for the psychiatric syndromes commonly known as affective psychoses or reaction-types. For example, the manic-depressive psychosis is a form of thymergasia.

-thymia (-thī′mē-à, -thim′ē-à) Combining form meaning state of mind and will, from Gr. *thymós*, soul, spirit, mind, temper.

thymo- (thī′mō-) Combining form meaning soul, spirit, temper, from Gr. *thymós*, soul, spirit, mind, temper.

thymoleptic Influencing or changing mood; this term is used to refer to drugs which ameliorate pathologic depressive states but which, in the absence of depression, do not act as central nervous system stimulants. See *psychotropics*.

thymopathic (thī-mō-path′ik) E. Bleuler uses this term with the meaning 'affectively disturbed.' The premorbid personality of the manic-depressive is characterized by lack of emotional poise, distractibility, feelings of inadequacy and frustration, irascibility, and periods of sadness. These personality characteristics are present from an early age and are presumed to be evidence of inherited predisposition. Such patients constitute the thymopathic type of personality.

thymopathy (thī-mop′ȧ-thē) A general term for morbidity of the affects.

thyroidism (thī′roid-iz′m) Excessive functioning of the thyroid gland.

thymopsyche (thī-mō-sī′kē) See *noopsyche*.

thyrotoxicosis Grave's disease; exophthalmic goiter. The usual personality pattern of patients with thyrotoxicosis is said to be a pseudo-self reliance to overcome security threats combined with an unconscious longing for dependence. Neurotic-like symptoms (309.5) are frequent and often lead to a mis-diagnosis of anxiety state or phobic reaction; if a psychosis develops, it is usually of the affective type, often with prominent manic symptoms (294.0).

tic Any brief, recurrent, inappropriate, irresistible movement involving a relatively small segment of the body; also known as habit spasm or habit contraction. While tics are frequently psychogenic, they are seen also in cases of chronic encephalitis, most commonly in association with disorders of respiration (e.g. yawning, sniffing, spasmodic cough, spitting). Other tics may be seen in the encephalitides, chiefly torticollis and complex co-ordinated rhythmical movements involving the jaw, lips, tongue, and palate.

When the tic is believed to have psychogenic relationship, it is often called habit tic. They comprise habitual repetition, such as grimacing, blinking, shrugging the shoulders, wry-neck, various movements of the head, etc.

Some use the expression local tic, when the movement is limited to some local region, e.g. the eye.

Mimic tic relates to involuntary twitching of the facial muscles.

Psychic tic is one that is induced by some unconscious process or impulse.

The French speak of *tic de pensée*, meaning the involuntary habit of giving expression to any idea that happens to be present in the mind.

Abraham considered the tic a conversion symptom at the anal-sadistic level, and most psychoanalytic writers have emphasized the well-defined anal character and, in addition, the markedly narcissistic makeup of the tiqueur.

'The repressed situations, whose motor intentions return in tic, are highly emotional ones representing again either instinctual temptations or punishments for warded-off impulses. In tics, a movement that was once the concomitant sign of an affect (sexual excitement, rage, anxiety, grief, triumph, embarrassment) has become an equivalent of this affect, and appears instead of the warded-off affect.

'This may occur in different ways: (1) The tic represents a part of the original affective syndrome, whose mental significance remains unconscious. (2) the tic represents a movement whose unconscious meaning is a defense against the intended affect. (3) The tic does not directly represent affect or defense against affect but, rather, other movements or motor impulses that once occurred during a repressed emotional excitement, either in the patient or in another person with whom the patient has made a hysterical identification.' (O. Fenichel. *The Psychoanalytic Theory of Neurosis*, Norton, New York, 1945)

tic, attitude Tonic rigidity in particular attitudes of the head of a limb, such as torticollis.

tic convulsif (tēk′kôN-vül-sēf′) (F. 'convulsive tic') Same as *tic*.

tic douloureux (tēk′ dōō-lōō-rē′) (F. 'painful tic; facial neuralgia') A chronic trigeminal neuralgia characterized by excruciating paroxysmal pain of short duration, flushing of the face, watering eyes, and rhinorrhea. The condition may affect either the second or the third division of the fifth cranial nerve, or both. The first division is rarely affected. The intermissions between paroxysms vary from weeks to as long as a year. With each succeeding attack seizures become more frequent and more severe. Many cases exhibit dolorogenetic or trigger zones on the face or mucous membranes, stimulation of which will evoke attacks. Tic douloureux is usually unilateral, is more common in adults over 40, and is more frequent among females. The cause is unknown, although the disease may be associated with dental or sinus pathology. There is probably some hereditary factor. Treatment is directed first toward remedying possible local causes. Trichlorethylene inhalations and alcohol injections into the peripheral branches of the nerve may be helpful, but the treatment of choice is retrogasserian neurectomy of the sensory root. Hyndman considers the cerebellar exposure superior to the subtemporal, even though the former requires greater care because of the risk of injury to the facial nerve. Partial section is adequate and does not give the widespread loss in sensation seen with total section. Tic douloureux is also known as trifacial neuralgia, prosopalgia, Fothergill's neuralgia, and chronic paroxysmal trigeminal neuralgia.

tic non-douloureux (nôN-doo-loo-rẽ') (F. 'non-painful tic') Charcot's term for a hysterical disorder of the face, usually unilateral, characterized by paroxysmal twitching of the facial muscles and anesthesia of the skin on the affected side of the face.

tic, psychic (sī'kik) A gesture of ejaculation made under the influence of an irresistible morbid impulse.

Tilney, Frederick (1876-1938), American neurologist; comparative anatomy.

time-agnosia (-ag-nō'sē-à) A condition in which the meaning of time is not comprehended, even though the patient may speak of time. There is disorientation in immediate time, the patient is unable to estimate short time-intervals, and long intervals of time are frequently shortened. Thus, one patient with time-agnosia stated that World War I had ended four years before, whereas actually it had ended ten years earlier. Patients with time-agnosia are able to relate events of the distant past and their interconnection with location, but cannot give the element of time of the event or time relations. Accompanying the time-agnosia, and probably a result of it, is an indifference to the past and future and a lack of concern about the condition itself. Time-agnosia follows trauma, such as head injury, especially of the temporal area, cerebrovascular accident, and alcoholic coma.

The trauma usually results in a mentally confused state of short duration. Then the patient regains orientation in space, but remains disoriented in time for the immediate present as well as for past events, to a varying degree. Time-agnosia often disappears gradually, depending on the extent and degree of permanency of the original lesion.

Davidson has described a syndrome of time-agnosia which includes post-traumatic muscular hypertonicity, vascular eye-ground changes (congested discs), and diminution of the acuity of sensibility in a generalized way. The prepsychotic personality of such patients includes a certain simplicity of make-up and a weakness of the sexual impulse. They have ordinarily led a colorless, drifting life wherein time has had no particular meaning to them. (Davidson, G.M. 'A Syndrome of Time-agnosia,' *Journal of Nervous and Mental Disease* 94, 337, 1941)

time, reaction See *reaction-time.*

tiqueur (tē-kẽr') One who suffers from a tic.

tocomania (tō-kō-mā'nē-à) Puerperal mania.

Todd's paralysis (Robert Bentley Todd, English psysician, 1809-1860) Temporary post-ictal extension of existing focal weakness following Jacksonian convulsion and/or temporary hemiparesis following any type of epileptic seizure.

toe-walking Walking on the toes rather than on the whole foot; toe-walking has been reported in approximately 20% of childhood schizophrenics.

togetherness Ackerman's term for the earliest stage in personality development, when the infant is in a state of primary psychic union with the mother, with little or no recognition of the self.

toilet training The process of teaching a child bowel and urine control. See *morality, sphincter; phase, anal; superego.*

tolerance Increasing resistance to the effects of a drug. Tolerance is an outstanding characteristic of the opiates and the amphetamines, and only somewhat less marked with the barbiturates. Although tolerance is not an essential for the development of drug dependence—the cocaine addict, for example, does not develop tolerance for his drug—it is an important consideration in any instance of drug dependence. For linked to tolerance is the need for increasing dosage to maintain or recapture the desired drug effect; and in general, the more saturated body cells become with any substance, the longer will be the period required to rid them of all traces of the drug. Tolerance of any marked degree also creates serious problems for the drug user in ensuring an adequate supply.

Closely allied to tolerance is *physical dependence,* the need to have some quantum of drug present within the body—or at least within some of its cellular elements or organ systems. Like tolerance, physical dependence is not essential to the development of drug dependence. The *abstinence syndrome* or *withdrawal syndrome* is the symptomatic expression of physical dependence—cells that have become accustomed to functioning under a mantle of drugs tend to fire or discharge or otherwise function in chaotic disorder when that mantle is suddenly removed. See *addiction; dependency, drug.*

tolerance, frustration The maximal point of tolerance of frustration at which the defenses of a person give way to the conflict and resentment that frustration sets up in him.

Tom o'Bedlam See *Abram man.*

tomomania (tō-mō-mā′nē-à) A morbid desire to be operated upon.

-tonia (-tō′nē-à) Combining form meaning (presence of) tonus or tension, from Gr. *tonos,* stretching, tension, tone.

tonicity State or condition of tone or tension, mental or physical. See *tension, mental.*

tonitrophobia (ton-it-rō-fō′bē-à) Fear of thunder; astrapophobia.

tonogenic (ton-ō-jen′ik) Giving rise to increased tension or tonus.

tonogeny (tō-noj′ē-ni) Tonogeny refers to any factor giving rise to increased tension or tonus. The vagus nerve is regarded as the tone-giving nerve of the stomach and intestines. The psyche may be the origin of tone-producing stimuli; for example, anxiety may be expressed in part through increased tension or tenseness. Extreme states of tension of long duration are common in the catatonic form of schizophrenia.

tonus (tō′nus) Tonicity.

TOP The association areas of the temporal, occipital, and parietal lobes of the cerebral hemisphere. The functions of TOP are imperfectly understood but presumably many of the highest psychic functions are dependent upon intactness of these regions. The TOP area and the prefrontal area are the last to develop phylogenetically.

topalgia (tō-pal′jē-à) Pain localized to one spot; the presence of a painful point or spot; a symptom occurring in hysteria or neurasthenia.

topectomy (tō-pek′tō-mē) A surgical operation for the excision (removal) of selected areas of the cerebral cortex (brain surface) in certain cases of mental illness; also known as the Columbia-Greystone operation since it was devised by that group. See *lobotomy, prefrontal.*

The following types of cases show the most favorable results: (1) Schizophrenic patients who, in spite of every kind of shock treatment, continue to manifest violent behavior, suicidal tendencies, homicidal tendencies, and destructiveness. . . (2) refractory obsessive-compulsive psychoneurotics who remain uninfluenced by prolonged psycho-analysis, direct interview psychotherapy, and electroshock treatment. . . (3) involutional melancholia which has failed to respond to shock therapy. . . (4) manic-depressive psychosis, with either a chronic depressed state or a chronic mania. . . (5) chronic depressions of old age, in patients over sixty who have failed to improve after electroshock treatment.' (Polatin, P. *How Psychiatry Helps*, Harper, New York, 1949)

topical flight Cameron's term for *flight of ideas* (q.v.).

topographic hypothesis See *id.*

topography, mental The mapping out of psychic structures is called mental topography or topographical psychology. It is a static representation of the components of the psyche, denoting their location. For example, the superego in the adult psyche is located in the realm of the unconscious; Jung's archetypes occupy one of the deeper layers of the unconscious.

Psychoanalysis differed from academic (descriptive) psychology mainly by reason of its dynamic conception of mental processes; now we have to add that it professes to consider mental topography also, and to indicate in respect of any given mental operation within what system or between what systems it runs its course. This attempt, too, has won it the name of "depth-psychology."' (Freud, S. *Collected Papers*, vol. 4, tr. by Riviere, J., Leonard and Virginia Woolf and The Institute of Psychoanalysis, London, 1924-25)

toponeurosis (top-ō-nū-rō'sis) A localized neurosis.

topophobia A general term meaning fear of place. For each patient the nature of the place is specific, although the word has come to be used as a synonym of agyiophobia, or fear of streets.

torpedoing The application of intense electrical currents to the bodily region involved in hysterical conversions.

torpillage (tor-pē-yàzh') (F. 'act of torpedoing') A form of treating cases of hysteria, particularly in wartime, by applying faradic currents to a shocking degree of pain — thus 'fighting fire with fire,' as it were.

'What it really consists in is giving authority to a medical officer to inflict pain on a patient up to the point at which the patient yields up his neurosis. Its unquestioned effectiveness . . . makes plain that under circumstances a military neurosis disappears under punishment.'

(Bailey, P. 'War Neuroses, Shell Shock and Nervousness in Soldiers,' *Journal of the American Medical Association 71*, 2148, 1918)

torpor (tor'pẽr) (L. 'numbness, stupefaction') When consciousness is so disordered that only very strong stimuli produce a reaction, the condition is known as *torpor*. See *coma; stupor.*

torsion dystonia See *dystonia, torsion.*

torsion-spasm A constant and irregular twisting and turning of the body, especially of the pelvis and neck muscles, with bizarre posturing of the body and limbs.

torticollis (tor-ti-kol'is) Wry neck. Torticollis is characterized by spasmodic contractions of the muscles of the neck, particularly those supplied by the spinal accessory nerve; the head is usually drawn to one side and rotated so that the chin points to the opposite side.

Torticollis is sometimes psychological in origin; Ferenczi regarded it as an attitude-tic.

'total-push' treatment of schizophrenia A method of treatment suggested by Myerson that includes physiotherapy, irradiation, exercise and games, diets, praise, blame, reward, punishment, regard for clothing and personal care. (Myerson, A. *American Journal of Psychiatry 95*, 1197-1204, 1939)

totem 'An animal, either edible or harmless, or dangerous and feared; more rarely the totem is a plant or a force of nature (rain, water) which stands in a peculiar relation to the whole clan. The totem is first of all the tribal ancestor of the clan, as well as its tutelary spirit and protector; it sends oracles and, though otherwise dangerous, the totem knows and spares its children. The members of a totem are therefore under a sacred obligation not to kill (destroy) their totem, to abstain from eating its meat or from any other enjoyment of it.' (Freud, S. *The Basic Writings of Sigmund Freud*, tr. by Brill, A.A., Random House, New York, 1938)

totemism The selection of animals, plants, and inanimate objects as representatives for the (primitive) individual and tribes.

Freud says that he divides 'the accepted theories of the derivation of totemism into three groups, (a) nominalistic, (b) sociological, (c) psychological.' Nominalistic totemism refers to that form of totemism which differentiates tribes by names. Freud, quoting from E. Durkheim, says that, as regards sociological totemism, 'the totem is the visible representative of the social religion of these [i.e. Australian] races. It embodies the community, which is the real object of veneration.' Psychological totemism, according to Frazer, was based upon the belief in an 'outward soul.' The totem was meant to represent a safe place of refuge where the soul is deposited in order to avoid the dangers which threaten it. (Freud, S. *The Basic Writings of Sigmund Freud*, tr. by Brill, A.A., Random House, New York, 1938)

touching A disturbance in association, peculiar to schizophrenia, in which the only recognizable association to external stimuli consists of feeling with the hands the contours of objects within reach. This process is similar to 'naming' except that a different motor activity is involved. See *naming*.

tower-head *Oxycephaly* (q.v.).

toxicomania (tok-si-kō-mā'nē-à) A craving for poison; drug dependency.

toxicophobia Fear of poison.

toxiphobia *Obs.* Toxicophobia.

toxiphrenia *Obs.* Schizophrenia associated with toxic, delirious reaction.

toxoplasmosis, congenital *In utero* infection with Toxoplasma, a protozoan-like organism, which may produce mental retardation (31x.0). Diagnosis is by serological testing of mother and infant.

T.P.I. Treponema Pallidum Immobilization. See *test, T.P.I.*

tract, pyramidal 'The pyramidal tracts are the means by which the nervous impulses which excite voluntary movements pass from the cerebral cortex to the lower motor neurones which arise in the brainstem and spinal cord. The pyramidal fibres or upper motor neurones are the axones of cells of the precentral convolution. Electrical excitation of these cells causes movements of the opposite side of the body. The movements thus excited are not simply contractions of isolated muscles, but always involve groups of muscles contracting harmoniously, so that an orderly movement results. The upper motor neurones therefore are organized in terms of movements, in contrast to the lower motor neurones, which are distributed to groups of muscle-fibres in individual muscles.' (Brain, W.R. *Diseases of the Nervous System*, Oxford University Press, London, 1951)

tractotomy, stereotactic A modification of psychosurgery consisting of implantation of radioactive yttrium Y90 seeds in the substantia innominata below the head of the caudate nucleus. Sometimes called *seed psychosurgery*, the procedure has been reported to be of benefit in intractable depression, anxiety, and obsessional states.

training, habit The acquisition (by the young child) of specific behavior patterns mainly related to the functions of eating, elimination, sleep, and dress. To the behaviorist, training is in the nature of conditioning. To the psychoanalyst, habit and habit training have a different meaning: 'A particular habit is for the child a defence against a particular unconscious fantasy or wish. His clinging to habit may be one of his main defences against the anxiety connected with aggressive impulses and fantasies in general.' (Isaacs, S. 'Habit,' Chapter V of *On the Bringing Up of Children*, ed. by J. Rickman. Kegan Paul, Trench, Trubner, London, 1936)

training, spontaneity 'Just as the spontaneity test is an intensification of the sociometric test, so the spontaneuty training process is an intensification of the assignment technique. New situations and new roles demand from some individuals spontaneous elements which are lacking. It is through graduated training of the personality in constructed situations and roles that such individuals learn how to act on the spur of the moment and how to integrate these roles into their personality without loss of spontaneity.' (Moreno, J.L. and Jennings, H. *Sociometric Review*, 1936, 17) trait In genetics, the characteristic symptomatology of a hereditary factor as it appears in the phenotypes of those who have inherited the predisposition to the given attribute.

trait-carrier In genetic family studies this means a tainted family member actually exhibiting the hereditary character under observation. These *trait-carriers* are distinguished from the *taint-carriers*.

traits, feminine, in male According to Adler, the following are feminine traits which the male neurotic perceives in himself either consciously or unconsciously: passive attitude, obedience, softness, cowardice, memory of defeat, ignorance, lack of capacity and tenderness. The person attempts to overcome these characteristics by developing hatred, defiance, cruelty, and egoism.

traits, neurotic (nū-rot'ik) See *behavior disorders*.

trance 1. hypnotism; 2. catalepsy; 3. ecstasy.

trance-coma The deep sleep following deep hypnotism.

trance, ecstatic See *ecstasy*.

tranquilizer Ataractic; the term tranquilizer or tranquilizing drug is currently used to refer to a group of phrenotropic compounds whose effects are exerted primarily at a subcortical level so that consciousness is not interfered with, in contrast to hypnotic and sedative drugs, which also have a calming effect. See *ergotropic; psychotropics*.
   Tranquilizer was used also by Dr. Benjamin Rush to refer to an invention of his designed to reduce blood flow to the head of the mental patient. It consisted of a chair to which the patient was strapped hand and foot so that he could not move.

transactional Relating to negotiating, conducting, performing, or carrying on, as an act or process; pertaining to an interplay. Grinker's transactional approach is an attempt to understand the interplay between therapist and patient— and ultimately between the patient and external reality—in terms of role theory.

'Activities within a transactional process, although they deal with current reality and start with well-defined explicit roles, expose the repetitive nature of the patient's unadaptive behavior and stimulates his recall of past experiences. . . . this transactional approach evokes implicit expressive or emotional roles and incites repetition of old transactions and illuminates the genetic source of the current behavior.' (Grinker, Roy R. in *Contemporary Psychotherapies*, edited by Stein, M.I., Glencoe, New York, 1961) See *role*.
   Interactional; referring to cross-communication and cross-influencing of each member in a relationship by the other member(s). In psychiatry, the term is generally used to refer to the dynamic, two-way interaction between therapist and patient. The earlier assumption that the psychoanalyst is totally objective and reflects none of his own values to his patient has undergone gradual modification in recent years. It is now recognized that in the psychoanalytic process, '. . . the therapist's personality, his value system, and his techniques of interaction, nonverbal as well as verbal, are . . . at least as important, and in many instances even more important than the uncovering of repressed content which has been the cornerstone of the traditional model of the psychoanalytic process. The increasing awareness of this among psychoanalysts has been reflected in recent years in the growing literature on the subject of "countertransference" attitudes in the analyst and their effect upon the analytic process.' (Marmor, J. *Archives of General Psychiatry 3*, 573, 1960)

transcultural psychiatry See *psychiatry, comparative*.

transfer In connection with institutional statistics, a transfer is a shift from one institution directly to another institution of the same class.

transfer RNA See *chromosome*.

transference In psychoanalytic therapy, the phenomenon of projection of feelings, thoughts, and wishes onto the analyst, who has come to represent an object from the patient's past. The analyst is reacted to as though he were someone from the patient's past; such reactions, while they may have been appropriate to the conditions that prevailed in the patient's previous life, are inappropriate and anachronistic when applied to an object (the analyst) in the present.

'During psychoanalytic treatment, the repressed unconscious material is revived, and since this material contains many infantile elements, the infantile strivings are reactivated and seek gratification in the transference. As the most important relationship of the child is that with his parents, the relationship between patient and analyst established in the transference becomes analogous to, or, at times, even similar to the patient's relationship with his parents in childhood. The patient endows the analyst with the same magic powers and omniscience which, in childhood, he attributed to his parents. The traits of submissiveness and rebellion, in transference, likewise reflect the attitude of the child to his parents. The patient behaves irrationally in the psychoanalytic situation; it often takes a long time to make him see the irrationality of his behavior, which is deeply rooted in his unconscious infantile life.' (H. Nunberg. *Principles of Psychoanalysis*, International Universities Press, New York, 1955)

Transference may be positive, as when the patient unrealistically overvalues or loves the analyst; or it may be negative, as when the patient dislikes or hates the analyst without due cause in reality. See *distortion, parataxic.*

It is to be noted that the term transference does not refer to reactions of the patient to the analyst that are based on reality factors in the therapeutic relationship; thus a patient may be angry with his therapist if the latter misses an appointment, but to call such a reaction a manifestation of transference is incorrect. It should also be recognized that transference can exist outside the analytic situation in relation to other people in the person's environment.

E. Krapf (*Psychoanalytic Quarterly 26:* 519-26, 1957) considers positive transference to be predominantly libidinal, negative transference as predominantly aggressive. He notes that there is a third type of transference, the transference of anxiety which always serves as a defense, while libidinal and aggressive transference are defensive in many instances but not in all. 'Thus we may list five types of transference: 1, libidinal; 2, aggressive; 3, libidinal-defensive;

4, aggressive-defensive; and 5, anxious-defensive.'

Jung stresses the question of transference, which he calls psychological rapport. He calls it 'the intensified tie to the physician which is a compensation symptom for the defective relationship to present reality.' He holds that 'the phenomenon of transference is inevitable in every fundamental analysis. . . . The patient must find a relationship to an object in the living present, for without it he can never adequately fulfill the demands that adaptation makes upon him.' (Jung, C.G. *Contributions to Analytical Psychology,* tr. by Baynes, H.G. and C.F., Kegan Paul, Trench, Trubner, London, 1928)

transference cure See *flight into health.*

transference, floating Also known as the floating positive; those generally positive and spontaneous attitudes and feelings that the patient has to the analyst and the analytic situation in the beginning of treatment. The floating transference is a preliminary sort of relationship and usually merges imperceptibly into the specific transference of affect brought about by the analytic situation and the fundamental rule.

transference, identification A term employed by S.R. Slavson to establish a differentiation from *libidinal* transference and *sibling* transference which occur in analytic group psychotherapy. It refers to the attitude and relations derived from identifying with other members of a therapy group of the desire to emulate or be like them. See *transference, libidinal; transference, sibling.*

transference, institutional Emotional dependence upon hospital, clinic, or similar establishment, rather than on a particular therapist or person within the institution; observed frequently in latent schizophrenics.

transference, libidinal (li-bid′i-nal) The transference derived from and charged with libidinal and other drives that the patient had felt toward his parents and now is re-directing upon the therapist. See *transference, identification; transference, sibling.*

transference, negative See *transference-resistance.*

transference-neurosis See *neurosis, transference.*

transference, positive See *transference.*

transference-resistance Transference may be positive (libidinal). It is so when the patient harmoniously transfers repressed material upon the physician. The material, however, may be rejected by the ego or super-ego, that is, there is resistance offered to the appearance of the material in consciousness, as a consequence of which it may be held in the unconscious; the patient gives an indirect clue by remaining silent on the topic in question. Or the material may be projected upon the physician, then appearing as something undesirable allegedly possessed by the physician. The repressed material may return to consciousness in one of the many known forms, but it is only when it constitutes a conflict between the patient and the physician that it is known as transference-resistance. The resistance gives rise to negative transference, an animosity or opposition to the physician. See *resistance, ego.*

transference, sibling Attitudes and feelings similar to those a patient has heretofore entertained toward the siblings of the family and now has toward other members of the group.

transformation See *affect, transformation of in dreams.*

transformation, affective Storch writes: 'There is a psychological law of "affective transformation," which says that emotionally toned and affectively emphasized values constantly strive to increase their dimensions. . . . This inclination to transformation on the part of the affects seems to play a very important role in primitive man. In drawings by children and primitives, the parts which are affectively toned are much enlarged.' (Storch, A. *The Primitive Archaic Forms in Schizophrenia,* tr. by Willard, C., Nervous and Mental Disease Publishing Company, New York and Washington, 1924) Affective transformation may be observed in all forms of psychiatric conditions; it is particularly noticeable in schizophrenia.

transformation of affect See *affect, transformation of.*

transfusion, exchange Total replacement of blood by transfusion. See *icterus gravis neonatorum.*

transient situational disturbances In the 1968 revision of psychiatric nomenclature (DSM-II), adjustment reactions of acute symptom-formation to an overwhelming situation; crisis reaction. Recession of symptoms occurs when the stress stimulus diminishes or disappears; persistence of symptoms indicates a more severe underlying disturbance. Included in the group are:

307.0 Adjustment reaction of infancy
307.1 Adjustment reaction of childhood
307.2 Adjustment reaction of adolescence
307.3 Adjustment reaction of adult life
307.4 Adjustment reaction of late life

transitivism (tran'si-ti-viz'm) One of the accessory or secondary changes in the person of the schizophrenic, consisting of detachment of a part of the personality from the patient with subsequent displacement of this part onto another person. In such cases, whatever the patient hallucinates or does is believed to be an experience of that other person.

transitivity (tran-si-tiv'i-tē) The character of passing over into something, a term applied principally to patients with schizophrenia. 'Transitivistic manifestations are nowhere so frequent as in schizophrenia. Very commonly, patients are convinced that those about them also hear their voices, sometimes even that they undergo the physical persecutions with them. A patient has holes in her hands and maintains that the nurse also has holes in her hands.' (Bleuler, E. *Textbook of Psychiatry,* tr. by Brill, A.A. Macmillan, New York, 1930)

transmissible That can be transmitted; formerly used synonymously with *inheritable.*

transmission Practically synonymous with *inheritance* (q.v.).

transposition of affect See *affect, transposition of.*

transsexualism See *transvestitism.*

transvestitism (trans-ves'ti-tiz'm) The morbid impulse to dress in the clothing of members of the opposite sex. A male patient, strongly homosexual, was completely dressed in delicate effeminate clothing underneath his masculine outer garments.

'Among the transvestites (personifiers) we find the most pronounced examples of masked homosexuality and stressed bisexuality.' (Stekel, W. *Bi-Sexual Love,* tr. by van Teslaar, J.S., Badger, Boston, 1922)

Some writers distinguish a rare form of intense transvestitism in which the patient feels he must be a woman in every respect and may seek castration or castrate himself (such behavior is termed *castrophilia*), and/or prefer suicide to living as a man. This severe form of transvestitism is sometimes called genuine transvestitism, eonism, psychic hermaphroditism, transsexualism, metatropism, or severe intersexuality. Constitutional and somatic factors, such as endocrinopathy, are sometimes demonstrable in such cases.

trauma (traw'mà) An injury, something hurtful. 'Freud with Breuer, published his viewpoint in 1895. Briefly, hysteria, for instance, is due to psychic trauma. Painful ideas, usually with sexual content and which for the particular individual are unacceptable to the conscious mind are not given an emotional outlet, but are relegated or forced or repressed into the subconscious mind and become buried complexes.' (Strecker, E.A. and Ebaugh, F.G. *Practical Clinical Psychiatry,* 4th ed., Blakiston, Philadelphia, 1935)

'Trauma may produce mental symptoms in one of two ways. Either it causes structural injury to the brain, or it causes emotional disturbances which in one form or another are prolonged for some time. . . . In the second [instance] the result is usually a psychoneurosis.' (Henderson, D.K. and Gillespie, R.D. *A Text-Book of Psychiatry,* 4th ed., Oxford University Press, London, 1936) See *anxiety.*

trauma, birth The trauma of birth is a topic extensively considered in psychiatry, particularly by psychoanalysts. The concept is described comprehensively by Otto Rank, who maintains that the circumstances of birth are deeply imprinted upon the psyche of the infant and often reappear in symbolic form in psychiatric patients.

It is said that intra-uterine existence is blissful, that it is free from all conflicts of a psychical nature. The act of being born is believed to mark a radical upheaval from both the psychical and physical points of view; it produces a psychic shock of great consequence, a trauma with which the person is never reconciled. Rank holds that certain people are always attempting to reconstruct the conditions of intra-uterine existence. In its most vivid and literal form intra-uterine life is reproduced by the patient showing the catatonic form of schizophrenia.

Freud says: 'The act of birth, moreover, is the first experience attended by anxiety, and is thus the source and model of the affect of anxiety.' (Freud, S. *The Basic Writings of Sigmund Freud,* tr. by Brill, A.A., Random House, New York, 1938) He believes that Rank overestimates the importance of birth upon the psyche of the infant. Freud says that 'we certainly may not presuppose that the fetus has any kind of knowledge that it is in danger of annihilation'; the fetus can only sense 'a wholesale disturbance in the economy of its narcistic libido.'

As an example of the symbolic representation of the birth act Rank refers to the phobia concerning animals entering and leaving holes.

Ferenczi states: 'The more I observe, the more I realize that none of the developments and changes which life brings finds the individual so well prepared as for birth.' (*Further Contributions to the Theory and Technique of Psycho-Analysis,* tr. by Suttie, J., Leonard and Virginia Woolf and the Institute of Psychoanalysis, London, 1926). He believes that birth is an agreeable and triumphant transition for the infant. What Rank calls birth phantasies Ferenczi says are coital phantasies.

Referring to the analysis of a dream, Jones says: 'Emergence, after great difficulty, from a dark chamber containing water, is a very usual way for unconscious thoughts about the birth act to be expressed. . . . In mythology the situation is often reversed by the hero being placed in an enclosing chamber and put *into,* or *onto,* water, such as with Moses in the bulrushes, Noah in the Ark, and so on. . . .' (Jones, E. *Papers on Psycho-Analysis,* 4th ed., Baltimore, 1938)

trauma, head See *compression, cerebral; concussion; contusion, brain.*

trauma, infantile The occurrence in infancy or childhood of a situation in which the psyche is bombarded by stimulation of such intensity that it can not be mastered or discharged. In such situations, anxiety develops automatically.

trauma, primal The original, supremely important, and most painful situation to which the person has been exposed early in life. Such a basic situation is necessarily of paramount importance and often constitutes the nucleus of the neurosis.

trauma, puberty The painful, disagreeable, or unacceptable experiences that occur during puberty. According to Stekel, such traumatic experiences during puberty are as important for the development of neurosis as the traumas suffered in childhood (see *trauma, infantile*), especially among girls, whose unpleasant sexual experiences can have fateful effects in their later lives. (Stekel, W. *The Interpretation of Dreams,* Liveright, New York, 1943) See *defloration; trauma, primal.*

traumasthenia (traw-mas-thē'nĭ-à) Nervous exhaustion following an injury; railway-spine; traumatic neurasthenia.

traumatic defect state (traw-ma'tik) See *psychosis, traumatic; neurosis, traumatic.*

traumatic neurosis See *neurosis, traumatic.*

traumatization (traw-ma-ti-zā'shun) See *libido, traumatization of the.*

traumatophilia (traw-mà-tō-fil'ē-à) Love of injury or the unconscious desire to be injured.

traumatophobia Fear of injury.

treatment Any measure designed to ameliorate or cure an abnormal or undesirable condition.
For specific treatments, see also listings under *therapy.*

treatment, ambulatory Such measures as may be carried out while the patient is up and about, or is not hospitalized.

treatment, ambulatory insulin 'A modification of the insulin coma treatment has been devised by Polatin and Spotnitz, for the purpose of relieving severe anxiety and tension states as well as the physical effects which may result from mental symptoms, such as loss of appetite and marked weight loss. These symptoms may occur in schizophrenia, in a patient whose head has suffered a severe blow, with resulting unconsciousness (postconcussional states), and in cases of hysterical vomiting or nervous dyspepsia as well as other psychoneuroses. The treatment is called "ambulatory," because the patients may walk about during the treatment period. They are not in a coma, as during the insulin shock treatment.
'In ambulatory insulin treatment the object is to induce, not coma, but hypoglycemia, which manifests itself by weakness, excessive perspiration and some drowsiness. The treatment consists of injecting intramuscularly relatively small doses of insulin, until the desired effect of hypoglycemia is reached.... Three hours after the injection of insulin, the hypoglycemia is, in all cases, terminated by a full meal rich in sugar and starches, which the patient can eat unassisted, since he is fully conscious. This treatment is given once daily, six days a week, usually for a course of one hundred treatments.' (Polatin, P., and Philtine, E. *How Psychiatry Helps,* Harper, New York, 1949) Also called *sub-shock* or *sub-coma insulin treatment.*

treatment, continuous sleep A symptomatic method of treatment in which the patient is sedated with any of a variety of drugs; the aim of treatment is to provide 20 hours of sleep per day, for periods up to 3 weeks in more agitated patients. Klaesi, in 1922, introduced continuous sleep treatment with barbiturates. The method has been superseded in large part by insulin coma, ambulatory insulin, electroconvulsive therapy, and treatment with the tranquilizing drugs; its chief uses at the present time are in manic excitements, agitated depressions, and acute anxiety neuroses.

treatment, insulin A form of treatment introduced into psychiatry by Sakel and used in certain psychiatric conditions. It consists in the production of coma, with or without convulsions, through the intramuscular administration of insulin.

treatment, malarial A form of treatment introduced by Wagner-Jauregg for syphilis of the central nervous system, especially general paralysis; blood containing tertian or quartan malaria parasites is injected into the patient, as a result of which he develops malarial fever.

treatment, Metrazol A form of treatment, introduced by von Meduna in 1934 in certain psychiatric conditions. It consists in the production of coma with or without convulsions, through the intravenous administration of Metrazol (cardiazol).

treatment, milieu (mēl-yü′) Treatment effected through the medium of the patient's surroundings and immediate environment, and specifically through the medium of the psychiatric hospital. See *community, therapeutic.*

treatment, prolonged sleep See *treatment, continuous sleep.*

treatment, psychiatric social 'Social treatment in psychiatric social work, as in other forms of social work, means the supervision of the patient in the community in such a way as to bring about a better social adjustment for him. In some cases all that is possible may be the modification of the environment so that a fairly satisfactory social adaptation may be made for him in spite of his mental handicap. Wherever the outlook for improvement is at all favorable, however, the aim of both the social and psychiatric treatment is to bring about a change in the attitude of the patient himself, to replace undesirable mental habits by wholesome ones, to modify his conduct by a training of his emotions, and to give him insight into his difficulties, so that he may eventually overcome his disabilities and be able to make a satisfactory adjustment in any environment.' ('Vocational Aspects of Psychiatric Social Work,' *Mental Hygiene,* 1925)

treatment, psycho-prophylactic (sī-kō-prō-fi-lak′tik, prof-i-) Mental hygiene.

treatment, shock A form of treating certain psychotic conditions by inducing coma (or convulsions) usually by electrical or chemical means, such as Metrazol, insulin, camphor, etc.

treatment, sub-coma insulin See *treatment, ambulatory insulin.*

treble safeguard, principle of See *principle, treble safeguard.*

tremophobia (trē-mō-fō′bē-à) Fear of trembling.

tremor Shaking or trembling. A disorder of muscular tone in which the usual, normal unappreciable tonic contractions of a muscle become exaggerated to the point of awareness.

In general, tremors can be classified into:
(1) coarse tremors, usually indicative of organic disease; included are—
  (a) passive tremor or rest tremor, a tremor that occurs while the affected area is at rest, as the pill-rolling tremor of Parkinsonism;
  (b) action tremor or intention tremor, which may be absent while the affected area is at rest and which is exaggerated by voluntary movement of the area, as the intention tremor of multiple sclerosis;
(2) fine tremors, often psychogenic although they may also be on a toxic basis (alcoholism, drug poisoning, hyperthyroidism, etc.);
(3) fasciculation, involuntary twitchings of a portion of a muscle; seen in fatigue, also in brain stem or anterior horn cell damage.

tremor, flapping *Asterixis* (q.v.). Rapid burst of flexion and extension in the wrist and metacarpo-phalangeal joints similar to the flapping of a bird's wings; such a tremor is indicative of hepatic failure.

tremor, hovering An early sign of Parkinson's disease which often precedes the full-blown condition by several years, consisting of a fine tremor of the hand and fingers with 3 - 6 beats per second which appears when subject is asked to salute without resting his hand against his temple.

trend, death See *suicide.*

trend, malignant The presence of components that ordinarily portend chronicity.

trend, pernicious Synonymous with *trend, malignant* (q.v.).

trend, statistical Uniform change in one direction as shown by statistics.

Over a long period of time natural and social phenomena tend to increase or decrease in a regular manner.

triad, anal The group of three prime or outstanding traits of the so-called *anal character:* (1) obstinacy; (2) parsimony; (3) pedantic orderliness. In everyday language the connection between miserliness and the retention of stool, both having in common the tendency to hold on to something, or holding something back, is often clearly manifested. The folk saying, 'he's so tight he couldn't pass a raspberry seed,' is an example of this symbolic and metaphorical ambiguous language. (Sterba, R. *Introduction to the Psychoanalytic Theory of the Libido,* Nervous and Mental DiseaseMonographs No. 68, New York, 1942) For further examples see *phase, anal.*

triad, Charcot (Jean Martin Charcot, French neurologist, 1825 - 93) See *sclerosis, multiple.*

triad, interdependent See *psychotherapy, family.*

triad, oral As defined by Lewin, this refers to the desires of the infant in the early oral phase—the wish to devour, the wish to be devoured, and the wish to go to sleep.

triad, Robin See *syndrome, Pierre Robin.*

triad, Sandler's See *Sandler's triad.*

triage (trē-àzh′, trī′àj) The process of choosing, selecting, sorting, or weeding out; in psychiatry, the immediate sorting out and classification of psychiatric casualties (as in disasters and crises) so that patients may be routed to and referred to appropriate treatment services.

tribade (trib′ad) A woman with an abnormally large clitoris, who plays the part of a male in homosexual practices. See *lesbianism; sapphism.*

tribute, virginal See *jus primae noctis.*

trichinophobia (trik-i-nō-fō′bē-à) Fear of trichinosis.

trichologia (tri-kō-lō′jē-à) Carphology.

trichopathophobia (-path-ō-fō′bē-à) Fear of hair.

trichophagy (tri-kof′à-jē) The tic of biting the hair.

trichophobia (tri-kō-fō′bē-à) Trichopathophobia.

trichotillomania (-til-ō-mā′nē-à) Morbid tendency to pull the hair. See *hair pulling.*

trifacial neuralgia (trī-fā′shal nū-ral′jē-à) See *tic douloureux.*

trigeminal cerebral angiomatosis See *angiomatosis, trigeminal cerebral.*

trigeminal neuralgia (trī-gem′in-al) See *tic douloureux.*

trihybrid (trī-hī′brid) Hybrid that differs in three hereditary characters. See *hybrid.*

triolist (trī′ol-ist) In triangular sex-relations one whose heterosexual partner is homosexual and, in addition, has a lover of the same sex. The origin of the term becomes more obvious when one bears in mind that commonly the conniving person's voyeur impulses are gratified by peeping at or watching the partner's intercourse with the third member of the sexual trinity.

triplet One of three children born at the same birth. See *birth, multiple.*

trisexuality (trī′sek-shoo-al′i-tē) The symbolic representation, especially in dreams, of the three currents or aspects—man, woman, and child—in which sexuality may be studied in a psychoanalytical sense. In other words, trisexuality may be considered as a kind of tripartition of the mind by which the subject may have at the same time the impulses of the three trends of sexuality. The patient will have simultaneously the desire to be a man, a woman, and a child, playing, at least symbolically, the three roles. (Stekel, W. *The Interpretation of Dreams,* Liveright, New York, 1943)

triskaidekaphobia (tris-kī'de-kà-fō'bē-à) Morbid fear of (the number) thirteen. Thirteen at table is viewed by many as an ill omen, and one more person is usually invited to join in the meal. The thirteenth day of the month is looked upon with dismay by those swayed by the superstition and, if it falls on a Friday, with double dismay—for Friday, long referred to as 'hangman's day,' was the usual day for hanging a criminal in the England of old. To prevent the possible loss of such fearsome clients (who would not live in a house No. 13) many office buildings in New York, and particularly hotels, have no thirteenth floor or rooms No. 13, or multifigured numbers ending with 13. Apparently the 'baker's dozen' (adding one roll for good measure, to avoid the severe penalties for short-counting) is an exception to this common fear of thirteen.

trisomy (trī'-sō-mē) A type of chromosomal abnormality in which three chromosomes appear in a position that normally is occupied by a chromosome pair. The most important known trisomy in psychiatry is 21-trisomy, or *Down's syndrome.* See *chromosome; mongolism.*

tristemania (trēst-ē-mā'nē-à) *Obs.* Melancholia.

tristitia (trē-stē'tē-à) *Obs.* Melancholy.

tromomania (trom-ō-mā'nē-à) Delirium tremens.

trophicity, neural This term refers to a concept, emphasized particularly by Russian neurophysiologists, which is an outgrowth of Pavlov's views of trophic functions of the nervous system. Pavlov believed that nervous impulses arising from one group of neurons do not only stimulate other neurons but also act upon the entire trophicity of those neurons: oxygen and nutrient supply, and assimilation and metabolism of these substances within those cells.

trophodermatoneurosis (trof-ō-der-mà-tō-nū-rō'sis) *Acrodynia* (q.v.).

trophoneurosis (trof-ō-nū-rō'sis) A nutritive disturbance, organically determined. It is believed that each organ of the body is supplied with nerves whose functions

are definitely identified with nutrition or trophism. When such nerves are disordered, nutrition of the organ suffers.

trophotropic (trō-fō-trō'pik) See *ergotropic.*

-trophy (-trō-fē) Combining form meaning nourishment, feeding, from Gr. *trophe*, nourishment, food, from *trephein*, to breed, rear, maintain, feed.

-tropy (-trō-pē) Combining form meaning turning, from Gr. *trope*, turn(ing), *trepein*, to turn.

trust, basic See *relatedness.*

truth-serum See *narcotherapy.*

TTR Type Token ratio. See *ratio, Type Token.*

tube, neural See *cephalogenesis.*

tubectomy (tū-bek'tō-mē) See *salpingectomy.*

tuberculomania (tū-bēr-kū-lō-mā'nē-à) An unfounded but unalterable conviction that one is suffering from tuberculosis; phthisiomania.

tuberculophobia Fear of tuberculosis or of associating in any way with a sufferer from that disease; phthisiophobia.

Tuke, Daniel Hack (1827 - 1895) British psychiatrist, editor of *Dictionary of Psychological Medicine.*

tumescence (tū-mes'ens) Swelling, engorgement; used particularly to refer to the swelling of genital tissues associated with sexual excitement.

tumor, brain See *tumor, intracranial.*

tumor, intracranial Any localized intracranial lesion, whether of neoplastic or of chronic inflammatory origin, which by occupying space within the skull tends to cause a rise in intracranial pressure. According to W.R. Brain (*Diseases of the Nervous System,* 4th ed., Oxford University Press, London, 1951): 'Over 1 per cent of all deaths are due to intracranial tumors which form about 17 per cent of all malignant neoplasms in man.' Symptoms of intracranial tumors are of two types: general symptoms, due to increased intracranial pressure, and focal symptoms, due to the local effects of the growth. The general symptoms of increased intracranial pressure include the classical triad of headache, papilledema, and vomiting. Other general symptoms are: epileptiform convulsions, aphasia, vertigo, disturbances of pulse-rate and blood pressure, and mental symptoms such as coma, confusion, disorientation, and progressive dementia.

tumultus sermonis (too-mool'toos ser-mō'-nēs) (L. 'confusion, disorder of speech') Tumultuous speech.

turbid Muddled, mentally confused.
'Naturally we often observe very mild twilight states and deliria, in which the thought process is only more or less unclear. These mild forms together with deliria and twilight states may provisionally be called *turbid states*.' (Bleuler, E. *Textbook of Psychiatry*, tr. by Brill, A.A., Macmillan, New York, 1930)

Turkish-bath method See *method, Turkish-bath.*

Turner's syndrome A chromosomal abnormality characterized by 45 chromosomes, rather than the usual number of 46; it is presumed that a Y chromosome is lacking. Symptoms and signs include retardation in physical growth, ovarian dysgenesis, and phenotypically the appearance of mainly female sex characteristics even though the sex chromatin test is negative (XO).

turrecephaly (tur-re-sef'à-lē) *Oxycephaly* (q.v.).

twilight-state Absence, a transitory disturbance of consciousness during which many acts, sometimes very complicated, may be performed without the subject's conscious volition and without retaining any remembrance of them.
Responsive as a rule only to some given complex, the subject acts in accordance with the demands of the complex, the rest of the personality being subordinated to or, as a rule, more or less completely submerged during the period of the twilight-state. For example, an epileptic patient, entirely unmindful of his natu-

ral surroundings, believed that he was walking around in Heaven; during the phase he was utterly unable to recall any part of his real life.
'During this period, if they [i.e. such patients] can be observed, they usually strike one as being abnormal; at times, however, they can use correctly ordinary means of intercourse, can associate with fellow travelers, and can even visit relatives, without betraying their condition.' (Bleuler, E. *Textbook of Psychiatry*, tr. by Brill, A.A., Macmillan, New York, 1930) See *fugue.*
The term twilight-state is also applied to one of the variations of delirium in which the patient passes abruptly into a state of severe clouding of consciousness combined with generally slow, monotonous movements but occasionally outbursts of rage and fear.

twilight-state, alcoholic A type of pathological drunkenness, characterized by 'sudden excitations or twilight states set free by alcohol, usually with a mistaking of the situation, often also with illusions and hallucinations, and excessive affects, mostly of anxiety and rage. In individual cases the entire morbid process can transpire in hardly a minute, but it usually lasts longer, up to several hours.' (Bleuler, E. *Textbook of Psychiatry*, tr. by Brill, A.A., Macmillan, New York, 1930) See *intoxication, alcoholic.*

twilight-state, clear See *equivalent, epileptic.*

twilight-state, post-epileptic Sometimes after an epileptic attack, a so-called twilight state exists for a variable period of time. During the twilight state the patient may carry out acts for which he is later amnesic.

twin One of two organisms born from a female that ordinarily brings forth only one offspring at a time.
In human beings there are two distinct types of twins, the *monozygotic* or *identical* twins, developed from a single egg, and the *dizygotic* or *fraternal* twins, developed from two eggs. Dizygotic twins are held to be as separate in their origin and biological development as are siblings in general. Monozygotic twins are like the right and the left halves of *one* organism; accordingly, they not only have the same

genotypical structure, but also exhibit frequently the phenomenon of *reversed asymmetry* (mirror-imaging) in handedness, hair whorl, dentition, palm patterns, and other asymmetrical characters, i.e. characters which are asymmetrical in one person. The presence of mirror-imaging is confirmatory evidence of monozygosity, but its absence does not refute it.

Of the two methods used for diagnosing twins with respect to their zygotic origin, the *similarity* method is now generally preferred to the *fetal-membrane* method, since it has been discovered that one-egg twins often have separate chorions and even separate placentae.

Twin studies are of great scientific significance in human genetics, because they throw light upon many fundamental aspects of the *nature-nurture* problem as well as of the *developmental* mechanism of the human organism throughout its life from the fertilization of the ovum to death. For these purposes a twin survey is usually based upon the particular technique of comparing the likenesses or differences between identical twins with the likenesses and differences between fraternal twins.

twin-study See *method, twin-study.*

twinned Born as a twin.

twinning The attribute of producing or state of being twins.

twins, Siamese (Chinese twins [Eng and Chang, born in Siam, 1811, died in North Carolina, 1874] whose bodies were joined by a band extending from umbilicus to the xiphoid cartilage)

Among various kinds of freak-twins, the variety of *Siamese twins* is characterized by an incomplete separation of the halves of the originally single embryo, from which the given set of monozygotic twins is developed. The division may be almost complete, so that the remaining link between the twins can be severed by operation, or it may be so incomplete as to result in twins with one body and two heads, or with one body and four legs and arms. See *birth, multiple.*

type See *type, constitutional.*

type, adenoid (ad'ē-noid) In constitutional medicine, a type in which the hyper-trophy of the pharyngeal tonsil is believed to be a sign of serious general constitutional anomaly. The more marked cases of this type are associated with such degenerative states as oxycephaly, deafmutism, cretinism, status thymicus, facial asymmetry and so forth. (Pende, N. *Constitutional Inadquacies,* tr. by Naccarati, S., Lea & Febiger, Philadelphia, 1928)

type, apoplectic (a-pō-plek'tik) See *habitus apoplecticus.*

type, asthenic (as-then'ik) Within the system of constitutional types described by Kretschmer, this term designates the type characterized by the general impression of a deficiency in volume combined with an average unlessened length, so that the subject appears taller than he really is (see *type, constitutional*).

The head of the asthenic rises like a bud upon a lean, long neck. In profile, the curve of the head is interrupted by sharp irregularities. The nose is a prominent feature and juts out from the long face, thus throwing back the forehead and chin. The line connecting the upper forehead, tip of nose, and chin tends to be angular on account of this disproportion between the long, sharp nose and the small mandible. In frontal outline the face is of short egg form. The middle face is long in proportion to the rest and the upper lip is short. The primary hair is strongly developed and has a tendency to grow down the neck and into the face, producing a fur cap appearance. When baldness occurs, it has an irregular outline.

The *chest* of the asthenic is long, narrow, and flat. The upper ribs fall inward and the xiphoid angle is acute. The prominence given to the clavicle is accentuated by the stooping attitude characteristic of the asthenic. The cavity of the abdomen is poorly developed, while the limbs appear long and thin, with lean muscles. The hips in the male are usually wider than the chest measurement accentuating the waist. The skin tends to be pale, dry, cold with scant subjacent fat.

As a *psychological* type, the asthenics are thought to be basically *schizothymic* (q.v.), thus constituting the bulk of the schizothymic group, although the athletic and dysplastic types also contribute to it. According to Kretschmer's theories, the asthenics may fall into any one of the three divisions accepted by him: namely, the *healthy* schizothymes (polite, sensitive types, world-hostile idealists, coldhearted egoists); the *schizoids* (the predominantly hyperesthetic temperaments including the cold, aristocratic types and pathetic idealists as well as the predominantly insensitive temperaments including despotic or passionate types and unsteady loafers); and the *schizophrenics* (q.v.).

When no attention is paid to particular modifications, it is appropriate to say that the *asthenic type* thus described corresponds fairly closely to the following types in other systems: the *habitus phthisicus* of Hippocrates, the *sensory, pneumatic, chlorotic, phthisic* and *lymphatic* constitutions of Carus, the *hypoplastic* type with a disposition to tuberculosis of Rokitansky-Benecke, the *first combination* of De Giovanni, the *macroskelic* type of Manouvrier, the *microsplanchnic* type of Viola, the *hypovegetative (dolichomorphic)* biotype of Pende, part of the *hypotonic* group of Tandler, the *asthenic habitus* of Bauer and Mills, the *narrow-chested* type of Brugsch, the *slender* biotype of Davenport and Aschner, the *linear* type of Stockard, the *T type* of Jaensch, the *regressive* type of Lewis, the *ectomorphic* type of Sheldon, the *sthenoplastic* type of Bounak, and the *hyperontomorphic* type of Beau.

type, athletic Robust, strong, vigorous, possessing a well-developed muscular system with resultant physical activity and prowess. Kretschmer's *athletic type* is characterized by a strong development of the locomotor apparatus, so that the bones and muscles stand out in plastic relief. The head shares in the overdevelopment of the skeleton, as is usually demonstrated by prognathous jaws and a marked occipital protuberance. A line connecting the upper forehead, tip of nose and chin forms a gentle curve. The frontal facial outline is steep egg-shaped. The head hair is abundant and tends to grow in a peak in the center of the forehead, receding in a bay-like manner on either side toward the temples.

The neck is strong and the shoulders are large. The trunk tapers down from the broad shoulder girdle, so that the trunk outline from the front appears inverted trapezoid. The limbs are relatively long, the hands and feet are large and the fingers are often blunt, thick and acromegaloid in character. The skin is thick, of good turgor, moderately tinted and medium as to sweat secretion.

As a psychological type, the athletics, too, are assumed by Kretschmer to be basically *schizothymic*, like the asthenics and the majority of the dysplastics. According to his theories, they constitute a considerable proportion of the total group of schizothymes, although a decidedly smaller one than do the asthenics, and they may also fall into any one of his three divisions of the schizothymic group, that is, the healthy schizothymes, the schizoids, and the schizophrenics (see *type, asthenic*).

The athletic type thus described corresponds approximately to the following types in other systems: the *muscular* type of Rostan, the *second (plethoric)* combination of De Giovanni, the *normosplanchnic* type of Viola, the *hypertonic* type of Tandler, the *sthenic* type of Mills, the *medium* biotype of Davenport, the *normal* type of Aschner, the *mesoskelic* type of Manouvrier, the *eumorphic* type of Pende, part of the *hypercompensatory* type of Lewis, and the *mesomorphic* type of Sheldon.

type, attitudinal One or the other of two types of introvert and extravert attitudes toward the world and oneself, in the Jungian system of psychology.

'The introvert turns in upon himself, is absorbed in his inner world, while the extravert turns outward to the world, and is much more concerned with what goes on there than with his own private experiences. Both of these types he [Jung] subdivides into thinking, feeling, intuition, and sensation types. That is, there may be a thinking introvert, a thinking extravert, a feeling introvert or extravert and so on.' (Thompson, C. *Psychoanalysis: Evolution and Development,* Hermitage House, New York, 1950) Introversion and extraversion are *attitudinal types;* thinking, feeling, intuition, and sensation are *functional types.* Jung believes that—probably by constitutional determination—every person is a combination of one or the other *attitudinal type plus one functional type of the four.* 'Whereas the functional type describes the way in which the empirical material is specifically grasped and formed, the attitudinal type introversion-extraversion characterizes the general psychological orientation, i.e. the direction of that general psychological energy which Jung conceives the libido to be . . . The functional type to which he belongs would be in itself an index to a man's psychological character. It alone, however, would not suffice. In addition, his general psychological attitude, i.e. his way of reacting to what meets him from without or within, must be determined. Jung distinguishes two such attitudes: extraversion and introversion. They represent orientations that essentially condition all psychic processes—the reaction habitus, namely, through which one's way of behaving, of subjectively experiencing, and even of compensating through the unconscious is given.' (Jacobi, J. *The Psychology of C.G. Jung*, Kegan Paul, Trench, Trubner, London, 1942)

type, B See *imagery, eidetic.*

type, belief Ferenczi holds that there are two fundamental types of personality, from the standpoint of belief. There are those who have a tendency to 'blind beliefs'; they accept statements without any question. He believes the tendency is derived at the time when the child is disillusioned about his own omnipotence and as a consequence he projects omnipotence upon others, originally upon his parents, later upon anyone in authority. There is the second type, constituting 'blind disbelief'; it is said also to stem from associations with the parents. It is a phase of disillusionment in the power of the parents or other superior people.

type, broad See *type, pyknic.*

type, C See *type, M.*

type, cerebral In the system of constitutional types described by Rostan and Sigaud, this type is distinguished from the *muscular, digestive* and *respiratory* types (qq.v.) by a predominance of the brain and nervous system over the other body systems. See *type, asthenic.*

type, choleric (kol'ĕr-ik) In constitutional medicine, this is one of the four classical temperamental and constitutional types of antiquity. Galen attributed the irritability of this type to the predominance of the yellow bile over the other three

humors (or fluids) of the human organism. See *type, pyknic.*

type, constitutional The constellations of traits, morphological, physiological and psychological, that are assumed to be associated with tendencies to certain diseases, physical and mental. Often used in a wider sense to include types of body and mind, even where no relation to any particular tendency to disease is postulated. See *constitution.*

The first typological system was developed by Hippocrates, who described a tendency to apoplexy, the *habitus apoplecticus* (q.v.), in persons of thickset, rounded appearance, and a tendency to pulmonary tuberculosis, the *habitus phthisicus* (q.v.), in persons of slender, angular appearance. This dichotomizing system was extended by Galen to four human types which were related to the four fluids or humors assumed to form the basis of the body. The *sanguine* type was thought to owe his enthusiasm to the 'strength of the blood,' the *melancholic* type was said to be sad because of the overproduction of the 'black bile,' the *choleric* type was irritable owing to the predominance of the 'yellow bile,' and the *phlegmatic* type was apathetic because of the predominance of the 'phlegm.' These four classical humors lived on as the explanation of temperamental and constitutional types for centuries, until Harvey's discovery of the circulation of the blood had the twofold effect of focusing attention on the blood as the important humor, and of emphasizing the role of the blood vessels. It was Haller who demonstrated the loose connection between the blood and the temperaments, and thereby paved the way for the modern typologists to describe their types in terms of anatomical systems instead of humors.

The discovery of the internal secretions and their effect on the morphology of body and mind led in all countries to a new humoral doctrine and, thus, to a classification of types on the basis of altered secretion of one of these glands. The prefixes hyper-, hypo-, and dys- were employed to indicate oversecretion, under-secretion, or qualitatively altered secretion. The main typological systems developed on the basis of these concepts were those of the modern French, Italian, German, and American typologists.

The ordinary system of the *French*

school has consisted, from the time of Rostan (1828), of the *digestive, respiratory, cerebral,* and *muscular* types (qq.v.). Other types accepted by Rostan's successors are the *reproductive* and the *atonic* types, corresponding to the old hypergenital and lymphatic types, and also the *round* and the *flat* types, explained by MacAuliffe in terms of colloidal chemistry.

The system of the *Italian* school dates from the work of De Giovanni (about 1890), who formulated the *law of under-deformation* (q.v.) and described three types of body build: the *first combination* or phthisic type, the *second combination* or plethoric type, and the *third combination.* Other tritypal classifications are based either on the form of the viscera, distinguishing *microsplanchnic, megalosplanchnic,* and *normosplanchnic* types (Viola), or on the total external characteristics, distinguishing *dolichomorphic, brachymorphic,* and *eumorphic* types. Pende modified this system by distinguishing a *hypervegetative* and a *hypovegetative* biotype, in addition to a number of *dysplastic* types.

The typological work of the modern *German* school was initiated by the phrenologist Gall at the end of the 18th century and continued by Beneke *(asthenic* or *hypoplastic* type, apoplectic or *hyperplastic* type, *normal* type); Carus *(athletic, phlegmatic, phthisic, cerebral, sterile* constitutions); Bauer *(status degenerativus, arthritic habitus, asthenic* type); and by E.R. and W. Jaensch *(integrated* and *disintegrated* types). In the field of psychiatry, the typological system of Kretschmer has certainly become the most influential one *(pyknic, asthenic, athletic,* and *dysplastic* types on the physical side; *cyclothymic* and *schizothymic* temperaments).

In the modern *American* school, the most systematic and effective work has been done by Draper *(panels of personality),* Davenport *(fleshy, slender, and medium* biotypes), Stockard *(lateral* and *linear* types), Lewis *(regressive, hypercompensatory,* and *normally compensating* types), and Sheldon *(ectomorphic, mesomorphic,* and *endomorphic* types).

Well-known *English* typologists are E. Miller, Spearman, and Cohen, and in the modern *Dutch* school Heymans and Wiersma are the outstanding workers.

type, degenerative See *status degenerativus.*

type, delicate See *type, cerebral.*

type, digestive In the system of constitutional types described by Rostan and Sigaud, this term is distinguished from the *muscular, respiratory,* and *cerebral* types by a predominance of the alimentary system of the body over the other systems. Persons of this type correspond to Kretschmer's *pyknic* type. See *type, pyknic.*

type, disintegrated In the system of constitutional types described by E.R. and W. Jaensch, this term refers to persons with an *disintegrated* psychological state, which is indicated by the *T type* of *eidetic imagery* and is further associated with particular physiological, biochemical, and clinical characteristics. See *imagery, eidetic.*

type, dysplastic (dis-plas′tik) In Kretschmer's system of constitutional types a form of physique which varies markedly from the average form of one of the main types called *asthenic, pyknic,* and *athletic* (qq.v.). Most dysplastic subjects are said to fall either into the category of elongated *eunuchoidism* with tower skull and, in the female, with masculinism, or into the groups of polyglandular *fat abnormalities* and *infantilism;* while their psychological make-up is held by Kretschmer to be basically *schizothymic* (q.v.).

The anomalies of the dysplastic type seem to be comparable to the *sterile, atrophic constitutions* described by Carus and to Bauer's *status degenerativus* (q.v.).

type, eidetic (ī-det′ik) Constitutional type characterized by a particular kind of *eidetic imagery* and by associated differences in other psychological qualities as well as in certain physiological, biochemical, and clinical features. There are two *eidetic* types, the *integrated* and the *disintegrated.* See *imagery, eidetic.*

type, extraverted When 'the state of extraversion becomes habitual,' Jung speaks of the person as possessing the extraverted type of personality. When introversion is habitual, the personality is of the introverted type.

'A type is a specimen, or example, which reproduces in a characteristic way the character of a species or general class. In the narrower meaning used in this particular work, a type is a characteristic model of a general attitude (see *type, general attitude*) occurring in many individual forms.

'Thus in both *general attitude* groups (the *extravert* and *introvert*) individuals with regard to *function* (i.e., reaction to a stimulus or event) may be either (1) *rational* (a) thinking, (b) feeling, or (2) *irrational* (c) intuitive, or (d) sensational. (Jung, C.G. *Psychological Types*, tr. by Baynes, H.G. Harcourt, Brace, New York and London, 1923). See *type, functional; extraversion.*

type, feeling The second of the four functional types of personality described by Jung. With his first (*thinking* type) it constitutes the *rational* class of *functional types.*

'When the total attitude of the individual is orientated by the function of feeling, we speak of a *feeling-type.*' (Jung, C.G. *Psychological Types*, tr. by Baynes, H.G., Harcourt, Brace, New York and London, 1923)

type, flaccid See *atonic.*

type, flat MacAuliffe's name for one of his two fundamental constitutional types evolved from considerations of colloidal chemistry. The *flat* type is believed to result from a slight craving of the tissues for water and is characterized by little surface tension, rapid metabolic processes, quick general reactions, economical energy expenditure and, on the psychological side, by an inherent general sobriety. It is distinguished from the *round* (q.v.) type by its marked cellular irritability and should not be confused with the type of a merely thin person.

type, fleshy See *type, pyknic.*

type, function This is a term used by Jung in analytical psychology. He first postulates two *general attitude* types—the introverted and extraverted. 'But, in addition, I shall also try to give a certain characterization of those special types whose particularity is due to the fact that his most differentiated function plays the principal role in an individual's adaptation or orientation to life. The former I would term *general attitude types*, since they are distinguished by the direction of general interest or libido movement, while the latter I would call *function-types.*' (Jung, C.G. *Psychological Types*, tr. by Baynes, H.G., Harcourt, Brace, New York and London, 1923)

type, functional This is an expression used by Jung (analytical psychology) to designate personality types from the standpoint of function. He postulates four functional classes, viz., thinking, feeling, intuitive, and sensational. 'In so far as such an attitude is *habitual*, thus lending a certain stamp to the character of the individual, I speak of a psychological type. These types, which are based upon the root-functions and which one can term the thinking, the feeling, the intuitive, and the sensational types, may be divided into two classes according to the quality of the respective basic function: viz., the *rational* and the *irrational*. The thinking and feeling types belong to the former. The intuitive and sensational to the latter. . . .' (Jung, C.G. *Psychological Types*, tr. by Baynes, H.G., Harcourt, Brace, New York and London, 1923)

But since *functioning* presupposes a static state or general attitude as the basis for the functioning, any one of the four functional types may occur in either of the two *general attitude* groups—the *extravert* or the *introvert;* i.e. there are: A. (1) thinking, (2) feeling, (3) intuitive, (4) sensational *extraverts,* and B. (1) thinking, (2) feeling, (3) intuitive, (4) sensational *introverts,* or *eight* varieties of psychological types in all. See *type, function.*

type, general attitude Jung's expression for the total mental cast or psychic make-up which (statically) determines a person's general attitude independently of or in advance of the external stimulus. This conception aggregates all human beings into two groups of *extraverts* and *introverts* (qq.v.).

With regard to the person's reaction (dynamically) to a life-stimulus, Jung classifies all mankind into *functional types* (see *type, functional*), also in two classes: (1) *rational* and (2) *irrational*.

type, heavy See *diathesis, arthritic.*

type, hyperaffective (hī-pĕr-a-fek'tiv) In the system of constitutional types described by Pende, a psychological type characterized by an abundance of emotional reactivity and roughly corresponding to the *cyclothymic* type.

type, hypercompensatory (hī-pĕr-kom-pen'sà-tō-ri) In the system of constitutional types described by Lewis, the type which on the physical side is characterized by *hyperplasia* of blood and lymph vessels, intestines, and ductless glands, and on the psychological side is inclined to *hypercompensatory* reactions taking the form of manic-depressive psychosis or paranoid reactions.

type, hypergenital (hī-pĕr-jen'i-tal) In constitutional medicine, a type distinguished by Pende as a sub-group of the *dolichomorphic* type and, in general, corresponding roughly to the *reproductive* type of Rostan.

The *male* type is characterized not only by an exaggerated and premature development of primary, secondary, and tertiary sexual characteristics, but also by a dolichomorphic form of trunk with a noticeable excess of thorax over abdomen, relative shortness of the extremities, large skull and heart, marked development of the skeletal muscles, and definite parasympathicotonia, and, on the psychological side, by a calm, stable, and energetic character and a strong development of artistic impulses.

In addition to an exuberant and premature development of the sexual system, especially of the pelvis, the female type is characterized by early menarche, a tendency to leucorrhoea in the intermenstrual periods, exaggerated local sensitiveness of the genital organs and breasts, megalosplanchnic proportions, great fecundity, and a stature which is somewhat below the average. 'When hypergenitalism is secondary or is combined with anomalies of the other endocrine glands, we observe as a rule marked dissociations in the sex-, ual development or a tendency to assume the characteristics of the opposite sex. Thus, women with hyperpituitary or hyperadrenal constitutions may present masculine characteristics, homosexual inclinations and an exaggerated libido.' (Pende, N. *Constitutional Inadequacies,* tr. by

Naccarati, S., Lea & Febiger, Philadelphia, 1928)

type, hypertonic (hī-pĕr-ton'ik) In the system of constitutional types described by Pende this term is used in connection with the *hypersthenic* type to designate a sub-group of both the *megalosplanchnic hypervegetative* constitution, where it stands in contrast to the *atonic* and *flaccid* sub-group, and of the *microsplanchnic hypovegetative* constitution where it stands in contrast to the *atonic* and *hyposthenic* sub-group.

The term hypertonic is also used in the constitutional system of Tandler to indicate a type characterized by a high degree of tonus of the voluntary muscles. This corresponds roughly to Kretschmer's *athletic* type.

type, hypervegetative (hī-pĕr-vej'e-tā-tiv) The hypervegetative biotype is contrasted with the hypovegetative biotype and corresponds exactly to the megalosplanchnic and brachymorphic types, and approximately to the equivalents of the pyknic type. See *hypovegetative.*

type, hypoaffective (hī-pō-a-fek'tiv) In Pende's system of constitutional types, a psychological type which in contrast to the *hyperaffective* type is characterized by a deficiency in emotional reactivity, corresponding roughly to the *schizothymic* type.

type, hypogenital (hī-pō-jen'i-tal) The *primary* hypogenital type is usually called *eunuchoid* and is characterized by exaggerated length of the lower extremities, a relatively hypoplastic state of trunk and head, and a deficient development of the genital organs and sexual characteristics. Various recent observations have suggested that this eunuchoid condition is inheritable as a sex-linked genetic factor. It seems to occur in women, too, although in a milder and less recognizable form.

In addition to the complete form of primary hypogenitalism, there is an attenuated type distinguished by Pende as the '*hypogenital temperament.*' (Pende, N. *Constitutional Inadequacies,* tr. by Naccarati, S., Lea & Febiger, Philadelphia, 1928)

type, integrated In their system of constitutional types E.R. and W. Jaensch denote by this term subjects with an *inte-grated* psychological state, of which the *B type* of *eidetic imagery* is an indicator.

type, inverted See *type, extraverted; extraversion.*

type, intuitive (in-tū′i-tiv) The third of Jung's four functional types of personality. With his fourth (*sensational* type) it constitutes the *irrational* class of *functional types.*
One who 'adapts himself by means of unconscious indications, which he receives through an especially fine and sharpened perception and interpretation of faintly conscious stimuli. How such a function appears is naturally hard to describe, on account of its irrational, and, so to speak, unconscious character.' The intuitive type 'raises unconscious perception to the level of a differentiated function, by which he also becomes adapted to the world.' (Jung, C.G. *Psychological Types,* tr. by Baynes, H.G., Harcourt, Brace, New York and London, 1923)

type, irrational See *type, rational.*

type, lateral See *type, pyknic.*

type, linear See *type, asthenic.*

type, lymphatic (lim-fa′tik) In the system of Carus, this corresponds to the asthenic type (Kretschmer) and the habitus phthisicus (Hippocrates). See *type, asthenic.*

type, M Rorschach differentiated two types of personality on the basis of the ratio between human movement ('M') responses and color ('C') responses. In the M type, M responses are more numerous than C responses; in the C type, the reverse is true. The M type shows a more imaginative and discriminating intelligence, more stability of emotions, and a more awkward and clumsy motility than the C type. In a general way, the M type corresponds to the obsessional type in Reich's description of character types, while the C type corresponds to the hysterical character.

type, medium See *type, athletic.*

type, megalosplanchnic (me-gal-ō-splangk′nik) In Viola's system, this corresponds to *type, pyknic* (q.v.).

type, microsplanchnic (mī-krō-splangk′-nik) In Viola's system, this corresponds to *type, asthenic* (q.v.).

type, muscular This type was first described in 1828 by Rostan of the French school. In contradistinction to the *digestive, respiratory,* and *cerebral* (qq.v.) this type is characterized by the predominance of the muscular and locomotor system over the other systems of the body and corresponds to Kretschmer's *athletic* (q.v.) type.

type, normal See *type, athletic.*

type, normally compensating In the system of constitutional types described by Lewis, this type is intermediate between his *hypercompensatory* and *regressive* types (qq.v.) and is characterized by an average intermediate degree of development of the viscera and, on the psychological side, by its capacity for compensatory reactions that are moderate and reversible and, therefore, usually of a temporary nature.

type, normosplanchnic (nor-mō-splangk′-nik) In Viola's system, this corresponds to *type, athletic* (q.v.).

type, organic reaction See *syndrome, organic.*

type, phlegmatic One of the four classical temperamental and constitutional types of antiquity. Galen attributed the torpor and apathy of this type to the predominance of the *phlegma* (mucus secreted in the air passages of the throat) over the other three humors (fluids) of the human body (see *type, pyknic*).

type, phthisic See *habitus phthisicus.*

type, plethoric (ple-thor′ik) See *type, pyknic; type, athletic.*

type, pneumatic See *type, asthenic.*

type, pyknic In Kretschmer's system of constitutional types, this is the type characterized by roundness of contour, amplitude of body cavities, and a plentiful endowment of fat.
The *head* of a pyknic is usually circular and smooth in profile, without any sharply prominent parts. The frontal facial out-

line is pentagonal or shield-shaped. The face is definitely broad and fleshy, particularly the nose. The neck is short and thick, with the head set a little forward on smoothly rounded shoulders. The line from the tip of the chin to the suprasternal notch is characteristic: inasmuch as it tends to be a smoothly sloping or even a straight line, but not an angle. The hair line borders the forehead in a regular, unindented curve. There is a tendency to baldness, the areas of which are regular in outline and have a smooth shiny surface.

The typically pyknic *trunk* is thickset and barrel-shaped, with the chest broadening to the lower part of the body. The abdomen is protruding and the xiphoid angle is wide. The limbs are well developed in thickness rather than in length, and the lower extremities, while not actually short, tend to appear short relative to the rest of the body because of their massiveness. The feet are broad, and well-covered, while the hands are square or broad, with podgy, fusiform fingers. The skin is warm and moist, with a well-developed fatty layer beneath it.

Pyknics may fall into any one of the three divisions of the *cyclothymes* as distinguished by Kretschmer: (1) the *healthy* cyclothymes (the gay chatterbox, the quiet humorist, the silent good-tempered man, the happy enjoyer of life, the energetic practical man); (2) the *cycloids* (the cheery hypomanic type, the quiet contented type, the melancholic type); and (3) the *manic-depressives.*

The *pyknic type* corresponds approximately to the following types in other leading systems: the *habitus apoplecticus* of Hippocrates, the *abdominal* and *digestive* types of the French school, the *phlegmatic, boeotic, plethoric venous, choleric* constitutions of Carus, the *hyperplastic* type with a disposition to carcinoma of Rokitansky-Beneke, the *third combination* of De Giovanni, the *brachyskelic (mikroskelic)* type of Manouvrier, the *megalosplanchnic* of Viola, the *hypervegetative (brachymorphic)* biotype of Pende, the *arthritic habitus* of Bauer, part of the *hypotonic* group of Tandler, the *hypersthenic* type of Mills, the *widechested* type of Brugsch, the *fleshy* type of Davenport, the *mesontomorph* of Beau, the *lateral* type of Stockard, the *broad* type of Aschner, the *B type* of Jaensch, the *euryplastic* type of Bounak, the *endomorphic* type of Sheldon, and part of the *hypercompensatory* type of Lewis.

type, rational According to Jung there are four basic psychological types, viz., the thinking, feeling, intuitive, and sensational, which form two groups: the first two he calls *rational* types 'because they are characterized by the supremacy of the reasoning and the judging functions. It is a general distinguishing mark of both types that their life is, to a large extent, subordinated to reasoning judgment.' The second two (intuitive, sensational) are termed *irrational* 'because their commissions and omissions are based not upon reasoned judgment but upon the absolute intensity of perception. Their perception is concerned with simple happenings, where no selection has been exercised by the judgment.' (Jung, C.G. *Psychological Types,* tr. by Baynes, H.G. Harcourt, Brace, New York and London, 1923)

type, reaction See *reaction-type.*

type, regressive In the system of constitutional types described by Lewis, this type is characterized on the physical side by *hypoplasia* of blood and lymph vessels, intestines and ductless glands and by its tendency to *tuberculosis.* Since on the psychological side this type is distinguished by its disposition to *schizophrenia,* the most severe of all regressive changes, persons of this type are comparable to the *asthenic* type in Kretschmer's system and its equivalents in other systems.

type, reproductive In Rostan's system of constitutional types this type was characterized by a predominance of the reproductive system over the other systems of the body. Although no major type of other systems is based on the degree of development of the reproductive system, this type of Rostan is comparable to the *hypergenital* type which is a sub-group of the *dolichomorphic* type (q.v.) in the system of Pende, and may best be contrasted with the sterile 'atrophic' constitution in the system of Carus.

type, respiratory In the system of Rostan and Sigaud, this type is distinguished from the *muscular, digestive* and *cerebral* types by a predominance of the circulatory and respiratory systems over the others. Many typologists classify such persons in the *asthenic* type, although they seem to be at the pole opposite to the asthenic with his flat underdeveloped chest, hypoplastic blood vessels, and poorly expanding lungs. See *type, asthenic.*

type, reversal Abraham and Jones use this expression for persons with a tendency to act in a way contrary to normal. They may express contrary opinions, though they know them to be illogical; they may dress 'out of style'; they may enumerate irrelevant items, etc.

type, round One of the two fundamental constitutional types evolved by MacAuliffe from considerations of colloidal chemistry (MacAuliffe: *Human Life*). In contradistinction to the *flat type* (q.v.), this type is characterized by an extremely *hydrophilic* tendency of the colloidal cells, great surface tension, increased osmotic pressure, and a considerable expenditure of energy with a corresponding dynamic sweep.

type, sanguine One of the four classical temperamental and constitutional types distinguished by Galen. He attributed the good humor and enthusiasm of this type to the predominance of the blood over the other three humors.

type, Séglas (ā-glà') (Jules Séglas, French physician, 1856-1939) The so-called psychomotor type of paranoia.

type, sensational The last of Jung's four functional types of personality. With his third (*intuitive* type) it constitutes the *irrational* class of functional types. 'Sensation, or sensing, is that psychological function which transmits a physical stimulus to perception. It is, therefore, identical with perception. . . . Primarily sensation is a *sense-perception,* i.e. perception transmitted *via* the sense organs and "bodily senses" (kinaesthetic, vasomotor, sensation, etc.).' (Jung, C.G. *Psychological Types,* tr. by Baynes, H.G., Harcourt, Brace, New York and London, 1923) Sensation 'always predominates over thinking and feeling, though not necessarily over intuition.' It is a conscious function, 'conscious perception,' as Jung says.

The sensational type of person shows 'little tendency either for reflection or commanding purpose. To sense the object, to have and if possible to enjoy sensations, is his constant motive. He is by no means unlovable; on the contrary, he frequently has a charming and lively

capacity for enjoyment; he is sometimes a jolly fellow and often a refined aesthete.' (ibid)

type, sensory See *type, asthenic.*

type, slender See *type, asthenic.*

type, social 'The role which a person assumes and to which he is assigned by society.' (Burgess, E.W., in Shaw, C.R. *The Jack-Roller,* University of Chicago Press, Chicago, 1930)

The social type consists of a set of attitudes on the part of the person toward himself and the group, and a corresponding set of attitudes of the group toward him, which all together determine the role of the person in his social milieu. (Wirth, L. 'Some Jewish Types of Personality,' in *The Urban Community,* edited by Burgess, E.W., University of Chicago Press, Chicago, 1926)

types, personality See *personality types.*

type, sthenic (sthen'ik) In constitutional medicine, this corresponds to Kretschmer's athletic type and its equivalents in other systems. See *type, athletic.*

In general psychology, the term sthenic indicates strength and vigor in different fields of emotional reactivity and adaptability. In accordance with this concept, the psycho-pathological behavior of the sthenic type has been described by Kretschmer as inclined to delusional reactions of a predominantly aggressive nature (paranoia, querulous ideas of reference), in contrast to the introspective tendency of paranoid or hypochondriac reactions in sensitive types.

type, T See *imagery, eidetic.*

type, Tartar Mongolian idiocy.

type, 'the exceptions' A character type first described by Freud; such persons, because of early frustrations, arrogate unto themselves the right to demand lifelong reimbursement from fate. This behavior is intensified if they are required to contradict a deep inner doubt as to their right to compensation.

type, thinking The first of the four functional types of personality described by Jung. With Jung's second (*feeling* type) it constitutes the *rational* class of *functional* types.

'It is a fact of experience that all the basic psychological functions seldom or never have the same strength or grade of development in one and the same individual. As a rule, one or another function predominates, in both strength and development. When *supremacy* among the psychological functions is given to thinking, i.e., when the life of an individual is mainly ruled by reflective thinking so that every important action proceeds from intellectually considered motives, or when there is at least a tendency to conform to such motives, we may fairly call this a *thinking type*. Such a type can be either introverted or extraverted.' (Jung, C.G. *Psychological Types*, tr. by Baynes, H.G., Harcourt, Brace, New York and London, 1923)

Type Token ratio See *ratio, Type Token*.

type, vital See *biotype*.

type, wide-chested See *type, pyknic*.

typhlomegaly (tif-lō-meg'à-lē) An unusually large size of the caecum. In Pende's system of constitutional types, this condition is frequently characteristic of the *ptotic habitus*.

typholexia, congenital (tēf-ō-lek'sē-à) A term used by Variot and Lecomte (1906) to refer to a type of *reading disability* (q.v.).

typical Pertaining to, or serving as, a type.

typology (tī-pol' o-jē) Study of *types*.

U

Ucs. abbreviation for *unconscious.*

ulcer, peptic (DSM-II, 305.5) A psychophysiologic disorder of the digestive tract consisting of circumscribed erosion of any of those areas exposed to acid-pepsin gastric juice, most commonly the lesser curvature of the stomach and the duodenal bulb. Etiology is uncertain, but even the most psychologically oriented theories assume the co-existence of somatic as well as emotional factors. Among the latter, Alexander has stressed conflict between repressed passive-receptive, oral-dependency needs and conscious desires for independence; oral needs are frustrated and the patient regresses to a desire to be fed. Gastric activity responds appropriately and the mucosa secretes as if preparing for actual feeding.

ultrasonic irradiation See *irradiation, ultrasonic.*

ululation (ūl-ū-lā′shun, ul-ū-) The inarticulate crying of hysterical or psychotic persons.

uncanny emotions See *not-me.*

uncertainy In information theory, *incongruity* (q.v.).

uncinate seizure (un′si-nāt) See *fit, uncinate.*

unconditioned response See *conditioning.*

unconscious The expression *unconscious* may be used as a noun or an adjective. In psychiatry it is used with two different and separate meanings. The first meaning has to do with the absence of participation of the conscious ego or the so-called perceptive-self. When the conscious part of the mind is not functioning, the subject is said to be unconscious. Unconsciousness is usually associated with absence of orientation and perception, particularly in its extreme expression.

The second meaning of *unconscious* (used as a noun) refers to a division of the psyche. One then speaks of *the unconscious* or of *unconsciousness.* In general it may be stated that all psychic material not in the immediate field of awareness is in the unconscious. When it is near enough to the former to be more or less easily accessible to it, it is said to be in the foreconscious or preconscious. See *id; ego.*

'Modern psychopathology has in its possession a wealth of observations regarding mental activities that are entirely analogous to conscious functions, and yet are unconscious. One can perceive, think, feel, remember, decide, and act, unconsciously. . . . How this is possible can best be seen if one imagines the mental functions and contents as resembling a night landscape over which the beam of a searchlight is playing. Whatever appears in this light of perception is conscious; what lies in the darkness beyond is unconscious, although none the less living and effective.' (Jung, C.G. *Contributions to Analytical Psychology,* tr. by Baynes, H.G. and C.F., Kegan Paul, Trench, Trubner, London, 1928)

'An appropriate and descriptive term to characterize that which is devoid of the attributes of consciousness.' '. . . unfortunately, however, the term has been also employed to characterize another and distinct class of facts, namely *Co-* [*or Sub-*] *conscious Ideas. . . .* It is sufficient to say here, that as conceived of, and as we have seen, there are very *definite states of coconsciousness—a coexisting dissociated consciousness or coconsciousness of which the personal consciousness is not aware.,* i.e., of which it is "unconscious." Hence they have been called "unconscious ideas". . . . But this is plainly using the term in a different sense—using it as a synonym for the longer phrase, "ideas we are unaware of," and not as a characterization of that which is physiological and nonpsychological.' (Prince, M. *The Unconscious.,* Macmillan, New York, 1916)

'"Unconscious ideas" in this sense (the equivalent of coconscious ideas) would include conscious states that we are not aware of simply because not in the focus of attention but in the fringe of the content of consciousness. The term would also include pathologically split-off and independently acting coconscious ideas or systems of ideas such as occur in hysteria, reaching their apogee in coconscious personalities and in automatic writings.' (ibid)

He further states that 'the unconscious is the great storehouse of neurograms which are the physiological records of our mental lives.' Abbreviated as *Ucs.*

unconscious, absolute Synonymous with collective unconscious. See *collective.*

unconscious, collective See *collective.*

unconscious, impersonal Collective unconscious. See *collective.*

unconscious, personal See *collective.*

unconscious, super-personal Synonymous with collective unconscious. See *collective.*

unconsciousness See *unconscious.*

underachiever A person who fails to produce or perform at the level for which he is qualified and capable; specifically, a student whose academic performance is below his known potential.

undercutting, cortical See *lobotomy, prefrontal.*

underload, informational See *deprivation, sensory.*

undoing One of the unconscious defense-mechanisms, consisting of a positive action which, actually or magically, is the opposite of something against which the ego must defend itself. Expiatory acts, counter-compulsions, and some forms of compulsive ceremonials and counting compulsions are among the more frequent expressions of undoing, which is characteristic of the obsessive-compulsive psychoneurosis.

unforthcomingness Impairment of motivation, and particularly that type of poor or disorganized motivation that has been observed in some children born of a stressful or complicated pregnancy. Some workers believe that minimal brain damage associated with stressful pregnancy may express itself behaviorally as unforthcomingness, and that the child so affected may be predisposed to delinquent breakdown.

unipolar double-bind See *bind, double.*

unit-character A single-gene trait transmitted in independently of other unit-characters, such as pigmentation vs. albinism.

unlust (un-lust', G. oon'loost) A German psychoanalytic term synonymous with the English terms 'ego pain,' 'unpleasure,' or 'anxiety.'

Unpleasure, or unlust, refers to the sensation of mild discomfort or frustration-tension that is felt in consciousness (by the ego) when instinctual trends, seeking gratification, are totally or partly opposed or blocked by the ego. This feeling of discomfort stands in marked contrast to the expected feeling of pleasurable relief from tension that usually results from the instinct's arousal following full gratification of the instinct.

The feeling of pain, unpleasure, frustration, tension, or discomfort is frequently mixed with, or associated with, anxiety. Unlust, or unpleasure, represents ego-suffering as an antithesis to pleasurable instinct satisfaction. It is this state of affairs that embodies the catalogue of all neurotic symptoms. (Sterba, R. *Introduction to the Psycho-analytic Theory of the Libido,* Nervous and Mental Disease Monographs No. 68, New York, 1942)

unpleasure See *unlust.*

unreality, feelings of See *depersonalization.*

unveiling A term used by Fritz Wittels to denote the uncovering or revelation of psychic components.

uranism (ū'rà-niz'm) *Obs.* A term used by Karl Heinrich Ulrichs in 1862 for homosexuality; the female homosexual he called *urinde,* the male *urning.*

The corresponding term for heterosexuality is *dionism* (from Dione, mother of Venus Pandemos).

uranomania *Obs.* The delusion that one is of divine or celestial origin.

uranophobia Fear of heaven.

urban crises See *social policy planning.*

Ur-defenses Masserman's term for what he considers the three fundamental psychologic maneuvers of man—the delusion of invulnerability and immortality, the delusion of the omnipotent servant (in the form of some abstract being or gnostic principle or system), and the conviction of man's kindness to man.

urethra (ū-rē'thra) The urethra, the canal leading from the urinary bladder to the outside of the body by way of the penis, gains importance in psychiatry because of the stress laid upon it by psychoanalysis. The urethra is regarded as an erogenous zone. Thus, psychoanalysts speak of urethral erotism and sadism.

'There were also indications present of *"urethral erotism."* As a child he often vied with other boys to see which could squirt his water highest in the air. As quite a little boy he had more than once let it fall into his mouth (Sadger's secondary auto-erotism).' (Jones, E. *Papers on Psycho-Analysis,* 4th ed., Wood, Baltimore, 1938)

urinam feminae dilectae in os proprium immitere To drink the contents of the urinary bladder directly from a beloved woman. Quoted from Stekel.

urninde (oor-nin'dē) *Obs.* Female homosexual.

urning (oor'ning) *Obs.* Male homosexual.

urningism Uranism.

urolagnia (ū-rō-lag'ni-à) (302.8) Pleasure

connected with urine. For example, some patients drink their own urine; others gain gratification in watching others urinate.

urophilia (ū-rō-fil'ē-à) (302.8) A pathologic love for, or interest in, urine; *urolagnia* (q.v.).

urorrhea Enuresis.

user A slang expression to describe a morphine or heroin addict who takes small doses daily for years to keep himself comfortable. See *hog.*

utero-mania *Obs.* Insanity associated with uterine disorder.

utilization technique Milton Erickson's term for one of his methods of handling resistance in hypnotic subjects and patients in brief psychotherapy: 'Erickson first asks the subject to do what he is already doing to resist him, and so do it under his direction. Then he begins to shift the patient's behavior into more co-operative activity until the patient is fully following his directions.' (Haley, J. *Archives of General Psychiatry 4,* 148, 1961)

uvula (ū'vū-là) See *cerebellum.*

uxoricide (uks-or'i-sīd) Killing of a wife by her husband.

V

vaccine, Salk See *poliomyelitis.*

vaccinophobia (vak-si-nō-fō′bē-à) A morbid fear or dread of being vaccinated.

vagina dentata A vagina with teeth; a phantasy, more often unconscious than conscious, in which the female genitalia are equated with a castrating, devouring mouth.

vaginismus (vaj-i-niz′mus) Painful spasm of the vagina. It generally takes place at some time during coitus or it may have its onset during the stage of preparation for the sexual act. Etiology is often psychic.

Typical cases develop spasms which make insertion of the penis impossible, and such spasms are responsible for the rare cases of penis captivus. Vaginismus usually represents inhibition of sexual excitement along with positive action to ensure maintenance of inhibition; in addition, it may be a conversion symptom expressing a wish to break off the penis and keep it.

vaginismus, psychic Painful spasm of the vagina preventing coitus; caused by repugnance to the sexual act.

vagotonia (vā-gō-tō′nē-à) Excessive excitability of the vagus nerve.

validation, consensual See *distortion, parataxic.*

validity The degree to which a test measures what it is supposed to measure; a valid intelligence test, for example, is truly a measure of general intelligence and not a test of rote memory. The degree of validity of a test depends upon the magnitude of the errors present in the measures obtained from it. Some indication of the validity of a given test is gained from a study of the correlations between scores on the given test and scores from other tests designed to measure the same factor.

value That which is esteemed, prized, or deemed worthwhile and desirable by a person or a culture. See *superego.*

vampirism Belief in bloodsucking ghosts (vampires); performing the actions of a vampire. While in neither sense is the term often used in clinical psychiatry, when it does appear in the literature it is generally in the second sense, as the act of drawing blood from an object with accompanying sexual pleasure. The blood may be drawn by cutting, biting, or similar means, and sometimes the drinking of the drawn blood is an important part of the action. Some writers regard the 'love-bite,' i.e. the biting of the sexual partner during sexual activity, as a form of vampirism. Psychodynamically, vampirism is usually interpreted as expressing conflicts in any or all of the following areas: oral sadism and incorporation, fear of castration, aggressive hostile wishes (including murder), and Oedipal strivings for the mother.

vampirism, parasitic Baynes uses the expression parasitic vampirism in a special sense, namely, that in a psychoneurotic patient compulsive mechanisms are present which are constantly driving the person. These drives have a demonic appetite—the more they have the more they demand. They know no reasonable bounds. Baynes believes that the neurotic symptoms, such as phobias, obsessions, and aggressions, are similar to a devouring monster which overpowers and possesses the patient in the manner of a blood-thirsty vampire. (Baynes, H.G. *Mythology of the Soul,* Williams and Wilkins, Baltimore, 1940)

vandalism, sexual An inordinate impulse to destroy the sexual zones represented in pictures, statuary, etc.

vapores uterini (và-pō′res oo-te-rē′nē) (L. 'uterine vapors') It was an ancient belief that vapors, originating in the uterus, passed into the brain, thus producing mental disorders.

vapors *Obs.* Hysteria; hypochondriasis.

variant, epileptic There are many clinical phenomena of the so-called epilepsies. Among them are the varieties listed by S.A. Kinnier Wilson in the *Journal of*

Neurology and Psychopathology, January 1928.

I. Motor Variants:
  1. Myoclonic or regional epilepsy
  2. Epilepsia partialis continua
  3. Tonic epilepsy
  4. Co-ordinated epilepsy
  5. Inhibitory or akinetic epilepsy
II. Sensory Variants:
  1. Reflex epilepsy
  2. Sensory epilepsy
  3. Affective epilepsy
III. Psychical Variants.
IV. Visceral Variants.

variation The varying phenotypical expressivity of hereditary characters, whose individual manifestations are *modifiable.* Since in a species originating through sexual reproduction no real hereditary homogeneity among its various individuals can be expected, the offspring of higher organisms are never exactly like the parents, but vary to a certain extent, each organism inheriting the entire characteristic modifiability of its kinship.

According to genetic theories, there are three possible mechanisms which can cause an organism to become different from its parents: *modification, combination,* and *mutation* (qq.v.).

The items in any frequency distribution differ from each other with respect to the amount of a given character which they all possess (e.g. height), and any frequency distribution may differ in a similar way from another frequency distribution describing the same character. Such differences constitute the phenomenon of variation.

vasectomy (vas-ek′tō-mi) A surgical and eugenic term; the *sterilizing* operation on men, of cutting and tying off the seminal ducts (vasa deferentia). Usually no unfavorable effect on the secondary sexual characters follows vasectomy, in contrast with the *castrating* operation of removing the testicles. See *sterilization.*

vasovagal attack of Gowers Gowers described a syndrome characterized by nausea and belching, precordial discomfort, respiratory difficulty, anxiety of impending death, and mild mental upset. The attack may last from a few minutes to an hour.

VDT Visual distortion test; see *test, visual distortion.*

vecordia (vē-kor′dē-à) *Obs.* Any mental affection.

vegative nervous system See *autonomic nervous system.*

ventricle puncture See *puncture, ventricle.*

ventriculogram (ven-trik′ū-lō-gram) An X-ray of the skull following replacement of cerebrospinal fluid by air by means of ventricular puncture. This drains the ventricular system but not the subarachnoid spaces and cisterns; the procedure is used when an expanding intracranial lesion is suspected, since ventriculography is considered safer than encephalography in such cases.

ventriculography (ven-trik-ū-log′rà-fē) Radiography of the brain-cavity. A means of determining the presence of structural changes in the intracranial contents, which are visualized by the X-ray, after the direct injection of air into the lateral ventricles.

Veraguth, fold of (Otto Veraguth, German neurologist, 1870-1940) Contraction upward and backward of the inner third of the upper lid, thus changing the arch of the upper lid into an angle. Veraguth described this change as a characteristic sign of the depressed type of manic-depressive psychosis.

verbalization In psychiatry, the state of being verbose or diffuse, commonly encountered in extreme degree in patients with the manic form of manic-depressive psychosis. In a more general sense, verbalization refers to the expression in words of thoughts, wishes, phantasies, or other psychic material which had previously been on a non-verbal level because of suppression or repression. 'Verbalize' is often used in a pseudoerudite way when 'talk about' is meant.

verbigerate (vēr-bij′ēr-āt) To repeat the same word, phrase or sentence over and over again.

verbigeration A manifestation of stereotypy, consisting of the morbid repetition of words, phrases or sentences; also called *cataphasia.* A patient with the catatonic form of schizophrenia kept repeating 'muscle, muscle, muscle,' in reply to all forms of questioning.

verbigeration, hallucinatory 'Many patients hear perpetually, in endless repetition or with slight changes, the same meaningless sentences, so that there is a kind of hallucinatory *verbigeration.*' (Kraepelin, E. *Dementia Praecox and Paraphrenia,* tr. by Barclay, R.M., Livingstone, Edinburgh, 1919)

verbochromia (vēr-bō-krō'mē-à) 'With some people certain words are accompanied by a sense of colour, varying with different words (verbochromia).' (Stoddart, W.H.B. *Mind and Its Disorders,* 5th ed., Lewis, London, 1926)

verbomania *Tachylogia* (q.v.).

verbose Overproductive in speech.

vermis (ver'mis) See *cerebellum.*

vertigo (vēr'ti-gō, L. ver-tē'gō) (L. 'a whirling of the head, dizziness') Dizziness; a feeling that the subject or the world around him is spinning or revolving.

vesania (vē-sā'nē-à) (L. 'madness') Insanity. Vesania is an old term, as well as an old concept, that meant insanity in general. It was used by Sauvages in his *Nosologia Methodica,* of 1763. The group termed *vesania* embraced psychiatric disorders not known to be associated with any organic disease or disorder.

vesania anomala (à-nō'mà-là) (L. 'irregular insanity') *Obs.* Mania transitoria.

vesania typica circularis (tē'pē-kà kēr-koo-lä'rēs) (L. 'typical circular insanity') In 1882 Kahlbaum used the term *cyclothymia* to designate the milder, recoverable forms of manic-depressive psychosis, and the expression *vesania typica circularis* for the chronic forms.

vestibular nerve (ves-tib'ū-lēr) See *nerve, acoustic.*

VF See *vigil, fatiguing.*

vice allemand (vēs'àl'mäN) (F. 'German vice') A term used by Hirschfeld synonymously with homosexuality. In the 18th century the French called homosexuality 'the German vice'; at an earlier period Europeans referred to homosexuality as 'the Oriental disease.' It seems that every nation disowns responsibility for originating homosexuality, and would like to shift it upon another's shoulders. But, as a matter of fact, homosexuality is recorded in classical literature.

vicissitudes, instinctual See *libido, plasticity of.*

vigil, fatiguing A type of sleep deprivation in which the experimental subject is required to perform mental work while he remains awake.

vigilambulism (vij-il-am'bū-liz'm) *Fugue* (q.v.). A condition of unconsciousness regarding one's surroundings, with automatism, resembling somnambulism, but occurring in the waking state.

vigilance The general alerting function or sentinel activity of the nervous system; in condition reflex experiments, each positive or negative conditioned stimulus causes a sharp spike of sudden alertness, termed stimulus-vigilance. Stimulus-vigilance is considered to be an emergency-reaction to a stress stimulus in a stressful situation. 'When an animal undergoing a regimen of difficult conditioning succumbs to an experimental neurosis we may suppose that its final traumatic reaction to the repeated stress situations of the conditioning laboratory was due to a gradual heightening of the vigilance level from day to day in consequence of the summation of the after-effects of stimulus-vigilance enduring for days, weeks, or months. Finally, an end point or breaking point is reached beyond which the animal's management of its emergency function becomes faulty as indicated by its neurotic manifestations. The intensity of the vigilance level of the day depends then not only upon the total stimulus load, i.e., upon the number, intensity, duration, and temporal spacing of the specific vigilance reactions aroused by the positive and negative conditioned stimuli of the experimental day, but also upon the lingering traces of stimulus-vigilance from previous conditioning sessions.' (H.S. Liddell, in *The Biology of Mental Health and Disease,* Hoeber, New York, 1952)

In 19th century writings, vigilance was equivalent to insomnia, agrypnia.

vigility of attention See *attention, vigility of.*

villa-system See *system, villa.*

V.I.P. Abbreviation for Very Important Person, and in clinical psychiatry applied to any patient who is able through personal influence or professional status to exert unusual pressure on the staff of a psychiatric hospital. A staff usually reacts adversely to such pressure with fear, anger, and withdrawal from the patient, and a vicious circle of increased patient pressure and further staff withdrawal is created. This has been termed the *VIP syndrome* and is of particular importance in that it generally ends in therapeutic failure, often in the form of suicide or discharge against medical advice. (W. Weintraub, *Journal of Nervous & Mental Disorders* 138, 181, 1964)

viraginity (vir-à-jin'i-tē) The adoption by women of male characteristics. It is an expression of homosexuality.

virium lapsus (vē'rē-oom làp'soos) (L. 'decay of energy') *Obs.* Lypothymia; melancholy.

visceral epilepsy See *epilepsy, visceral.*

viscerotonia (vis-er-ō-tō'nē-à) A personality type described by Sheldon which is correlated with the endomorph body type and which shows a love of food, comfort, and conviviality and a tendency to general relaxation.

viscosity of libido See *libido, viscosity of.*

vision See *lobe, occipital.*

vision, tubular (tū'bū-lēr) See *field defect.*

visionism (vizh'un-iz'm) Voyeurism.

visions, hypnagogic (hip-nà-goj'ik) The optic perceptions present in a state midway between sleep and waking. They are a phase of dream phenomena.

visual field See *field defect.*

visual-spatial agnosia See *agnosia, visual-spatial.*

vocational counseling See *counseling.*

Vogt, Oskar (1870 - 1959) (fôKt) German neuropathologist.

Vogt-Spielmeyer's disease See *amaurotic family idiocy; Spielmeyer-Vogt's disease.*

voice, soundless See *thought, audible.*

volition, derailment of See *derailment of volition.*

volubility (vol-ū-bil'i-tē) Overproductivity in speech.

vomiting, cyclic A disorder of children which is characterized by attacks of vomiting. The attacks begin suddenly, last several days, cease abruptly, and then recur in intervals or cycles of several weeks or months.

vomiting, nervous Functional vomiting of psychogenic emotional or neurotic origin, occurring most frequently in young women between the ages of 20 and 40. It usually expresses, in organ-language, symbolically and physically, the desire to reject a hated idea, or person, concerning whom there exist conscious and unconscious conflicts of an emotional nature; this is the only way out of the conflict left to these patients, because, in consciousness, they cannot stand their hostility and yet cannot express it verbally.

E. Weiss and O.S. English report the following case: 'A young white woman, with markedly repressed sexuality, developed frequent vomiting attacks after a marriage to which she had consented, in the main, because of her mother's urging. Her passive and dependent nature did not allow her to express hostility openly but instead her unconscious mental forces caused her to vomit as though to say: "I cannot stomach this situation."' (*Psychosomatic Medicine*, 2nd ed., Saunders, Philadelphia and London, 1949)

von Gierke's disease *Glucogenosis* (q.v.).

von Graefe's sign (Albrecht von Graefe, German ophthalmologist, 1828 - 70) Lag of the upper lid in following the downward movement of the eye, due to retraction of the upper lid such as occurs in exophthalmic goiter and in lesions in the upper part of the midbrain.

von Recklinghausen's disease (Friedrich Daniel von Recklinghausen, German pathologist, 1833 - 1910) *Neurofibromatosis* (q.v.).

voyeur (vwà-yēr') (F. 'onlooker, spectator, sexual pervert') Peeping Tom; scopophiliac (302.5). One who obtains sexual gratification by looking at the genitals of another. Any person with 'an exaggerated desire to see, by stealth, a member of the opposite sex in some stage of undress, in the sexual act or in the act of excretion, which is so intense that it surpasses in importance the normal sexual act.' (Yalom, I.D. *Archives of General Psychiatry 3*, 305, 1960)

voyeurism 'Peeping.' Sexual pleasure obtained by looking at the genitals of another or by witnessing others' sexual activity (302.5).

'Sublimation of the looking impulse can be brought about if the interest is turned from the genitals to the form of the body. This, Freud thinks, normally occurs as an intermediary sexual aim and makes possible the directing of a certain amount of the libido in artistic channels.' (Healy, W., Bronner, A.F., and Bowers, A.M. *The Structure and Meaning of Psychoanalysis,* Knopf, New York, 1930)

vulnerable child See *syndrome, vulnerable child.*

vulvismus (vul-viz'mus) Vaginismus.

W

W In Rorschach scoring, a whole response; i.e. a percept determined by the entire ink blot. According to Piotrowski, the W is primarily a measure of the tendency to organize and plan in the pursuit of external goals.

Wada test See *test, Wada dominance.*

Wagner von Jauregg, Julius (1857-1940) väg'nēr fôn you'reg) Austrian psychiatrist and neurologist; fever treatment of general paresis.

WAIS Wechsler Adult Intelligence Scale.

Wallenberg's syndrome (Adolf Wallenberg, German physician, b. 1862) The symptoms following occlusion of the posterior inferior cerebellar artery (which is known as 'the artery of thrombosis'): ipsilateral facial analgesia, ipsilateral Horner's syndrome, ipsilateral ataxia, and contralateral analgesia.

wanderlust Morbid impulse to roam or wander, believed to be associated with the Oedipus situation in the sense that the wanderer is incessantly seeking to establish affiliation with one or both parents as he had experienced it, or longed to experience it, when he was a young child.

war-neurosis See *shell-shock; neurosis, traumatic.*

Wassermann reaction See *test, Wassermann.*

Watson, John Broadus (1878-1958) American psychologist; behaviorism.

Watson-Crick model See *chromosome.*

waxy flexibility *Cerea flexibilitas.* See *catalepsy.*

weak-mindedness, hallucinatory *Obs.* By this expression, Kraepelin denoted one of the terminal states of schizophrenia.

Weber's syndrome (Sir Herman Weber, English physician, 1823-1918) Pedunculopontile syndrome; see *hemiplegia alternans.*

Weltmerism (after Sidney A. Weltmer, founder of the method and the Weltmer Institute at Nevada, Mo.) A system of therapeutics based on suggestion.

Wernicke, Carl (1848-1905) (vâr'ni-kē) German neurologist; aphasia.

Wernicke's encephalopathy (en-sef-a-lop'-á-thi) Polio-encephalitis hemorrhagica superior, described by Wernicke in 1881; in DSM-II, 291.5. A very severe disorder consisting of degeneration of nervous tissue especially marked in the midbrain. The syndrome occurs in a small percentage of chronic alcoholics and is probably due to a combination of nutritional deficiencies, especially a vitamin B deficiency. Onset is insidious, with vomiting, oculomotor palsies, ptosis, pupillary changes (such as Argyll-Robertson pupil), ataxia, insomnia, and a mental state consisting of an acute hallucinatory picture similar to delirium tremens except that there is no tremor and the delirium is dreamy and confused. Impaired consciousness may progress to stupor. The encephalopathy may terminate fatally, or there may be progression to a Korsakov syndrome. Thiamine chloride has been used successfully to reverse the ophthalmoplegia and has sometimes been of help in the mental state.

Westphal's sign See *sign, Westphal.*

Westphal-Strümpell's pseudosclerosis See *degeneration, hepatolenticular.*

wet-dream Popular term for seminal ejaculation during sleep.

Weygandt, Wilhelm (1870-1939) (vī'-gänt) German psychiatrist.

whiplash (309.3, 293.1) A syndrome following sudden hyperextension or hyperflexion of the neck consisting of rapid loss of memory of life experiences without loss of intellectually learned facts. The syndrome is based on bilateral vascular disturbances in the hippocampal gyri, consisting of thrombosis and embolism in the hippocampal branches of the posterior cerebral arteries.

whipping See *flagellation*.

whirling See *schizophrenia, childhood*.

White, Samuel (1777-1845) American psychiatrist; one of the 'original thirteen' founders of the Association of Medical Superintendents of America (forerunner of American Psychiatric Association).

White, William A. (1870-1937) American psychiatrist; psychodynamics, psychotherapy, forensic psychiatry.

Wihtiko psychosis A psychosis found in certain primitive people (Ojibwa or Chippewa, Eastern Cree) characterized by a morbid craving for human flesh and by a delusion of transformation into a Wiktiko, a supernatural being feared by this tribe.

Wilbur, Hervey Backus (1820-1883) American pioneer educator in the field of mental deficiency.

will, disturbances of the One of Bleuler's fundamental symptoms of the schizophrenias. Usually, the disturbance is in the direction of deficiency (hypobulia, hypoboulia) or lack (abulia, aboulia); such patients appear lazy, negligent of their duties, purposeless, and goalless, with no aims, ambitions or desires. *Platonization* (q.v.) is often seen and patients appear apathetic toward their environment and disinterested in the reality about them. At other times, because they have no real goals, they appear flighty, capricious, and undependable, adopting momentarily any goal which is thrust upon them. Or they may appear stubborn, robot-like, and wedded in a perseverative way to a particular activity which they cling to rather than have to make any decision or move toward purposeful change.

A few patients are hyperbulic and show a bizarre or inappropriate application and assiduity to unimportant and trivial occupations; these are the faddists, the shifters, persons who are forever brewing storms in teapots.

will therapy See *therapy, will*.

will-to-be-above Adler borrowed this term from Nietzsche to indicate the tendency of the neurotic female to identify herself with the male.

will-to-be-up Adler borrowed this term from Nietzsche to denote the neurotic's striving toward masculine aggression.

will-to-power This term, borrowed by Adler from Nietzsche, denotes the strivings of the neurotic towards masculinity, in order to escape the feeling of uncertainty and inferiority which connotes femininity.

Wilson's disease (Samuel A.K. Wilson, English neurologist, 1878-1936) See *degeneration, hepatolenticular*.

windigo See *Wihtiko*.

WISC Wechsler Intelligence Scale for Children.

wish An impulse, a purpose, a desire, a tendency, an urge, a striving, 'a course of action which some mechanism of the body is set to carry out, whether it actually does so or does not.' (Holt, E.B. *The Freudian Wish and Its Place in Ethics,* Holt, New York. 1915)

wish, child-penis The wish for a child with which, in her psychosexual development, the little girl replaces her wish for a penis. In the phallic stage of a woman's psychosexual development, the little girl obtains pleasurable sensations from her clitoris, which is the dominant erotogenic zone. As the psychosexual development proceeds, however, and the change to full womanhood occurs, 'the clitoris must give up to the vagina its sensitivity, and with it, its importance, either wholly or in part.' Moreover the little girl must change her love-object from the mother to the father. It is at this period in the development of the girl that the child-penis-wish emerges.

The little girl's first love-object is the mother, since it was she who provided the first satisfactions of life, nourishment, warmth, etc. The little girl's libidinal impulses to her first object, her mother, are manifold and express themselves through oral, anal, and phallic wishes, both active and passive. They are also completely ambivalent, being both tender and hostile. The phallic wishes are expressed by 'the desire to get the mother with child as well as the corresponding one, to have a child by the mother.' The mother contributed to these wishes in reality, since she aroused 'pleasurable sensations in the child's genitals in the ordinary course of attending to its bodily needs.' As the child develops, her strong attachment to her mother is replaced by an attachment to her father. This takes place in an atmosphere of hatred for the mother. Although there are many obvious sources for this hatred of the mother—the unavoidable necessity in the child's development of frustrating its insatiable desire for the breast; the birth of a sibling which deprives the little girl of the mother's exclusive attention; the frustration (with threat and disapproval from the mother) of the child's masturbatory activities, which the mother herself had unwittingly stimulated; the other necessary restrictions associated with education; and finally the strong ambivalence of the child's impulses toward her mother—Freud feels that in the girl's turning from her mother to her father the main and specific factor is her penis-envy, her wish for a penis. For when the girl first notices that the boy has something she has not—his male genitals—she feels at a great disadvantage. Now the little girl no longer enjoys her phallic sexuality. Her self-love is wounded 'by the unfavourable comparison with the boy who is so much better equipped,' and therefore she 'gives up the masturbatory satisfaction which she obtained from her clitoris . . . and . . . repudiates her love towards her mother.'

Having given up her love for her mother, who, too, is found to be castrated and, therefore, cannot satisfy her daughter's desire for a penis or the sexual phantasies associated with her masturbation, the little girl turns her love toward her father. She has not, however, relinquished her wish for a penis, which, in effect, her mother has refused her, and which she now expects from her father. Also, her passive instinctual impulses have gained the upper hand, since a certain amount of activity was surrendered along with the clitoric masturbation. Thus, the symbolic equation, child = penis, can come into effect and the wish for a penis is replaced by the wish for a child. The girl's strongest wish now is for a child by her father. 'With the transference of the child-penis-wish onto her father, the girl enters into the situation of the Oedipus complex.'

At an earlier age, before the development of her penis-envy, the little girl had expressed a wish for a child by playing with dolls. This wish for a child, however, was an expression of her active identification with her mother: she could do to the doll all that her mother used to do with her. It was not, however, associated with a wish for a penis. 'Only with the onset of the desire for a penis does the doll-child become a child by the father.' (Freud, S. *New Introductory Lectures on Psychoanalysis*, Norton, New York, 1933)

wish-dream, masochistic A dream which has to do with injury to the dreamer himself. 'From this last dream he awakens with the most unpleasant feelings; and yet it is a masochistic wish dream, which might be translated: It would serve me right if my brother were to make that sale against my interests. It would be my punishment for all the torments he has suffered at my hands.' '. . . even dreams with a painful content are to be analyzed as wish-fulfilments.' (Freud, S. *The Basic Writings of Sigmund Freud*, tr. by Brill, A.A., Random House, New York, 1938). See *dream, punishment.*

wish-fulfillment, asymptotic Gratification of an impulse or desire in a substitute or 'almost but not quite' way.

wish, id Instinctual urges having their source in the realm of the repressed, unconscious, primitive, and infantile regions of the personality (psyche or mind).

Id wishes, or instinctual urges, emanating from the unconscious are thought of in conflict with, and in juxtaposition to, wishes having their origin in the ego, on the one hand, and in the conscience, or superego, on the other. Wishes having their origin in the ego make for reality adjustment and control; while those having their origin in the conscience, or superego, make for the attainment of 'goodness' and 'approval.'

Id wishes are characterized by a driving urgency representative of their infantile and primordial biologic nature. They are mainly of a crudely aggressive and erotic nature.

wish, penis See *envy, penis; wish, child-penis.*

wishes, fundamental The concrete wishes of persons 'all fall under one or more of four types or patterns: (1) the desire for new experience; (2) the desire for security;

(3) the desire for response; and (4) the desire for recognition.' (Park, R.E. and Miller, H.A. *Old World Traits Transplanted*, Harper, New York, 1921)
'The organization of society has always a double character: it makes possible the gratification of the individual's wishes, and even the multiplication of them, but at the same time it requires that his wishes shall be gratified only in *usual* ways, that their expression shall be so regulated as not to interfere with the expression of the wishes of others.' (ibid)

wit The background of wit is fundamentally the same as the background of many other psychic phenomena, but wit is usually not a manifestation of morbidity, any more than are slips of the tongue or pen. There are no nosological disorders, nor syndromes, in which wit occupies the position of abnormality in the general sense of that term. To be sure, wit appears in certain clinical conditions, but its import to the total clinical picture is usually insignificant.
Freud regards wit 'as the most social of all those psychic functions whose aim is to gain pleasure. It often requires three persons, and the psychic process which it incites requires the participation of at least one other person. It must, therefore, bind itself to the condition of intelligibleness; it may employ distortion made practicable in the unconscious through condensation and displacement, to no greater extent than can be deciphered by the intelligence of the third person.'
Freud defines wit as 'a developed play' which 'seeks to draw a small amount of pleasure from the free and unencumbered activities of our psychic apparatus, and later to seize this pleasure as an incidental gain.'
The pleasure of wit originates 'from an *economy of expenditure in inhibition;* comic arises from an *economy of expenditure in thought;* while humor originates from an *economy of expenditure in feeling.'* (*The Basic Writings of Sigmund Freud,* tr. by Brill, A.A., Random House, New York, 1938)

wit, abstract See *wit, tendency.*

wit, allusion in Wit is often expressed through allusions, which Freud calls 'representation through "relationships and associations."'

'*Every fathom a queen,'* which is a modification of the familiar Shakespearean quotation, *'Every inch a king,'* and served as an allusion to a prominent woman who was unusually big physically. (Freud, S. *The Basic Writings of Sigmund Freud,* tr. by Brill, A.A., Random House, New York, 1938)
Freud says that *omission* is also a form of allusion. 'Once more we encounter the two Jews in front of the bathing establishment. *"Another year has passed by already,"* says one with a sigh.' (ibid)

wit, characterization Freud uses the expression *characterization-wit,* when the witticism serves, among other things, to emphasize certain traits of the principal character in the witticism. He cites the story of the Jewish marriage broker who 'assured the suitor that the father of the girl was no longer living. After the engagement had been announced, the news leaked out that the father was still living and serving a sentence in prison. The suitor reproached the agent for deceiving him. "Well," said the latter, "what did I tell you? Do you call that living?"' Freud adds that 'one might say that this joke is a "characterization-wit." It endeavors to illustrate by example the marriage agent's characteristic admixture of mendacious impudence and repartee.' (Freud, S. *The Basic Writings of Sigmund Freud,* tr. by Brill, A. A., Random House, New York, 1938)

wit, displacement When an object or a person in a joke is displaced by another, Freud speaks of *displacement-wit.*
'A begger implored the help of a wealthy baron for a trip to Ostend, where he asserted the physicians had ordered him to take sea baths for his health. "Very well, I shall assist you," said the rich baron, "but is it absolutely necessary for you to go to Ostend, which is the most expensive of all watering-places?" "Sir," was the reproving reply, "nothing is too expensive for my health."' (Freud, S. *The Basic Writings of Sigmund Freud,* tr. by Brill, A.A., Random House, New York, 1938)

wit, ellipsis A form of wit the humor of which is dependent on omitted connections. For example, in the question: 'Do you think ignorance is bliss?' and the answer: 'Well, you seem to be happy,' at least one thought, the intermediate link: ['You are ignorant —and'] 'well, you seem to be happy' is left out between the question and the answer. (Brill, A.A. *Basic Principles of Psychoanalysis,* Doubleday, New York, 1949)

wit, exaggeration in 'There are other ways to regain the feeling of nonsense in order to derive pleasure from it; *caricature, exaggeration, parody,* and *travesty* utilize the same and thus produce "comical nonsense."' (Freud, S. *The Basic Writings of Sigmund Freud,* tr. by Brill, A.A., Random House, New York, 1938)

wit, exhibition See *wit, obscene.*

wit, harmless See *wit, tendency.*

wit, indirect See *wit, allusion in.*

wit, naïve Freud says that 'the species of the comic that is most closely allied to wit is the *naïve.*

'Another little girl of four years heard her parents refer to a Jewish acquaintance as a Hebrew, and on later hearing the latter's wife referred to as Mrs. X, she corrected her mother, saying, "No, that is not her name; if her husband is a Hebrew she is a Shebrew."' (Freud, S. *The Basic Writings of Sigmund Freud,* tr. by Brill, A.A., Random House, New York, 1938)

wit, nonsense in 'Sense lurks in . . . witty nonsense and that this sense in nonsense transforms nonsense into wit.' (Freud, S. *The Basic Writings of Sigmund Freud,* tr. by Brill, A.A., Random House, New York, 1938)

'Never to be born would be best for mortal man.' 'But,' added the sages of the Fliegende Blatter, 'hardly one man in a hundred thousand has this luck.' (ibid)

wit, obscene 'Whenever wit is not a means to its end, i.e., harmless, it puts itself in the service of but two tendencies which may themselves be united under one viewpoint; it is either *hostile* wit serving as an aggression, satire, or defense, or it is *obscene* wit serving as a sexual exhibition.' (Freud, S. *The Basic Writings of Sigmund Freud,* tr. by Brill, A.A., Random House, New York, 1938)

wit, omission in See *wit, allusion in.*

wit, outdoing A form of wit, according to Freud, in which 'a contradiction takes the place of an exaggerated confirmation.'

'A Jew noticed remnants of food on the beard of another. "I can tell you what you ate yesterday," he remarked. "Well, let's hear it," said the other. "Beans," said the first one. "You are wrong," responded the other. "I had beans the day before yesterday." (Freud, S. *The Basic Writings of Sigmund Freud,* tr. by Brill, A.A., Random House, New York, 1938)

wit, parody in See *wit, exaggeration in.*

wit, recognition in Wit frequently exhibits what Freud calls *recognition,* that is, 'the discovery of the familiar where one expects to find something new instead. To discover the familiar is pleasurable and it is not difficult to recognize such pleasure as economy-pleasure and to refer it to the economy of psychic expenditure.' (Freud, S. *The Basic Writings of Sigmund Freud,* tr. by Brill, A.A., Random House, New York, 1938)

wit, tendency There are two major classifications of witty productions. 'Word- and thought-wit on the one hand, and abstract- and tendency-wit on the other hand, bear no relation of dependence to each other; they are two entirely independent classifications of witty productions.' (Freud, S. *The Basic Writings of Sigmund Freud,* tr. by Brill, A.A., Random House, New York, 1938)

When 'wit is wit for its own sake and serves no other particular purpose,' it is called *abstract* or *harmless* wit. Freud cites an example from Lichtenberg: '*They sent a small octavo to the University of Gottingen; and received back in body and soul a quarto*' (a fourth-form boy). (ibid)

Wit may serve some purpose; it may have deep meaning; it may be tendential; when such is the case, Freud speaks of *tendency-wit.* 'It makes possible the gratification of a craving (lewd or hostile) despite a hindrance which stands in the way; it eludes the hindrance and so derives pleasure from a source that has been inaccessible on account of the hindrance.' (ibid)

wit, thought Often it is not the word, but the thought in a witticism that bears significance. Freud speaks of such a form as *thought-wit,* which like *word-wit* may be *abstract* or *tendential.*

wit, travesty in See *wit, exaggeration in.*

wit, unification in Unification in wit 'is analogous to condensation by compression into similar words.' Freud cites an example from Lichtenberg: 'January is the month in which one extends good wishes to his friends, and the rest are months in which the good wishes are not fulfilled.' (Freud, S. *The Basic Writings of Sigmund Freud*, tr. by Brill, A.A., Random House, New York, 1938)

wit, word When the strength of wit lies in the word, Freud calls it *word-wit.* He cites the following example: 'Having been forsaken by *Dame Luck*, he degenerated into a *Lame Duck.* ' (Freud, S. *The Basic Writings of Sigmund Freud*, tr. by Brill, A.A., Random House, New York, 1938)

wit-work In the expression *wit-work* Freud uses the component element work in the same sense as he does in *dream-work*, namely, to denote the psychic processes operating to produce the witticism.

withdrawal The act of retracting, retiring, retreating, or going away from. Withdrawal is used in psychiatry to refer to (1) voluntary removal of the penis from the vagina in coitus interruptus; (2) abstaining from a drug on which the patient is dependent, and/or the symptoms associated with such abstinence; and (3) the turning away from objective, external reality that is seen so often as an expression of schizophrenic autism. In this third sense, withdrawal refers to the patient's retreat from society and interpersonal elationships into a world of his own. External stimuli are reduced, and if internal stimuli predominate one speaks of preoccupation which may progress to stupor or even to coma. The withdrawn person appears aloof, detached, disinterested, removed, and apart; he has difficulty in spontaneously initiating or planning with other people. He is unable to mingle freely and communication with others is an effort. He cannot share his experiences with others and even in a group appears to work independently rather than co-operatively. In its more extreme forms, withdrawal appears to be a regressive phenomenon in which the subject relinquishes his higher symbolic and social functions and falls back to the infantile level of shutting off the

perceptive system in order to avoid the anxiety aroused by interpersonal relationships.

Witzelsucht (vit'sel-zookt) Facetiousness; seen in lesions of the frontal lobe. See *lobe, frontal.*

Wolf-Man The patient reported on by Freud in his 1918 paper, 'From the History of an Infantile Neurosis.' The patient is so called because of a dream he had had at the age of four concerning six or seven white wolves sitting on a tree in front of the dreamer's window; he woke in terror, evidently of being eaten by the wolves. The interpretation of the dream extended over several years. Although the Wolf-Man responded well to psychoanalytic therapy, he suffered several relapses during which he showed increasingly severe paranoid symptoms.

Wollenberg, Robert (b. 1862) (vôl'enbĕrK) German neurologist and psychiatrist.

womb-phantasy See *phantasy, womb.*

women with penis See *penis, women with.*

Woodward, Samuel B. (1787-1850) First president of Association of Medical Superintendents of America (the forerunner of the American Psychiatric Association); treatment of alcoholism.

word-blindness Kussmaul's term (1877) for a type of *reading disability* (q.v.).

word-cathexis See *cathexis.*

word-deafness Auditory aphasia. See *aphasia, auditory.*

word-dumbness See *aphasia, motor.*

word-salad This is the type of speech, heard most frequently in advanced states of schizophrenia, characterized by a mixture of phrases that are meaningless to the listener and, as a rule, also to the patient producing them; also known as *jargon* or *paraphrasia.* A word-salad is a group of neologisms. They are meaningless until the patient discusses the neologisms at length, thus revealing their underlying significance. It is, so to speak, a coded language, not unlike dreams in principle;

the patient holds the table to the code and only he can provide meanings to the otherwise incomprehensible dialect.

words, microcosm of (mī'krō-koz'm) 'Words and worded concepts are shadows of things, constructed for the purpose of bringing order through trial acting into the chaos of real things.' Thus, words create a replica of the real world, a 'model world' or microcosm. 'The macrocosm of real things outside is reflected in the microcosm of things representative within.' The normal person uses this microcosm for calculating and acting out in advance, before real action is taken To him, then, words will have the characteristics of the things that they represent, but they will not have the reality or 'seriousness' which the things have. The normal person has mastered the words and, by using his words, will master the real things.

Such mastery of the real world through words is markedly disturbed in the compulsion-neurotic. Being afraid of emotions, he is afraid of the things that cause emotions. He therefore retreats from the macrocosm of things to the microcosm of words. He tries to repeat the process by which as an infant he learned to use words to master frightening aspects of the real world. However, 'under the pressure of his warded-off impulses' words have now acquired 'that emotional value which things have for other persons.' They have regained the magical quality they first had in infancy, when there was no clear differentiation between the microcosm and the macrocosm. That is, the words themselves now have the values and meanings they express. Unconsciously, words and thoughts are believed to have real effects. Therefore, the compulsion-neurotic handles words and thoughts very cautiously. This is the origin of compulsive thinking. (Fenichel, O. *The Psychoanalytic Theory of Neurosis*, Norton, New York, 1945)

work, case See *case-work, social.*

work-cure Treatment by occupation. See *therapy, occupational.*

work decrement Decrease in amount of work performed per unit time during a period of continuous practice; this phenomenon is probably a function of muscular

(peripheral) and central fatigue induced by continuous work. In most studies of the work curve, schizophrenics have been found to show more rapid work decrement than normals.

work, group See *group-work, social.*

work, social See *social work, psychiatric.*

worker, after-care Social worker.

worker, indigenous See *caregiver.*

working-over In psychoanalysis, an internal process of rearranging, adjusting, reconstituting, and remolding the excitations produced in the psyche and thereupon being able to direct them into other channels in order to prevent their harmful effect because of the impossibility or undesirability of discharging them outward.

'We have recognized our mental apparatus above all as a device for mastering excitations which would otherwise be felt as unpleasant or would have pathogenic effects. The "working-over" of stimuli in the mind accomplishes wonders for the internal discharge of excitations which are incapable of direct discharge outwards, or for which such a discharge is, for the moment, undesirable.' (Freud, S. *Collected Papers*, vol. 4, tr. by Riviere, J., Leonard and Virginia Woolf and The Institute of Psychoanalysis, London, 1924 -25)

working-through An ill-defined psychoanalytic concept no single definition of which has achieved general acceptance. Freud considered it a spontaneous psychic process that was the only effective means of countering id resistance. See *resistance, id.* On a descriptive level, working-through usually refers to a doldrum period, that is, a phase of relative inactivity on the part of the patient in psychoanalytic treatment, a period when the analyst's interpretations, no matter how extensive or intensive, seem to have no effect. Such a period is generally assumed to be due to an inability (perhaps constitutional) of the patient to be hurried through his analysis, and/or as due to the persistence of deep transference attitudes (such as hurt, suspicion, or ambivalence) which require prolonged periods of ventilation. 'It is easy to observe that after any crisis either in analysis or in ordinary life most individuals tend to "draw in their horns" until the situation has been stabilized. This process of spontaneous recuperation is best illustrated in the phenomena of normal grief; and it is of interest that this may vary in duration from a few weeks to a few years, indicating that the degree of "working through" varies normally within wide limits.' (Glover, E. *The Technique of Psycho-Analysis*, International Universities Press, New York, 1955)

Looked at in another way, working-through may be interpreted as the intrapsychic processes that must take place if insight in one area is to be amalgamated with other areas of the personality, if the patient is to be ennabled to experience new perceptions and conflict-free affects appropriate to those perceptions. Working-through involves the recognition and assimilation of newly learned truths, an alteration of balance among the defenses, neutralization of resistance, formation of new identifications, and reconstruction of the ego ideal. To a large extent, successful working-through depends upon the analyst, who is not only a mirror for the patient but must also be a teacher, a definer of reality, a non-judgmental object of drive-motivated behavior, a representative of the superego who influences by suggestion and even authority, and an idealized object who influences by example. Identification of the patient with the analyst is the basis for expansion and reconstruction of the ego ideal, which stimulates future attainment and is the source of realistic self-esteem. (Karush, A. *Psychoanalytic Quarterly 36*, 497-531, 1967)

It must also be recognized that the concept of working-through is sometimes used as a rationalization by the therapist for his failure to understand the origins of the patient's resistance at some point during psychoanalytic treatment.

working type See *assimilation*.

writing, automatic Writing without conscious volition, while in hypnotic trance. 'Automatic writing is a splendid means of gaining access to unconscious material that lies beyond the grasp of conscious recall. The portion of the cerebrum that controls the automatic writing seems to have access to material unavailable to centers that control speech. Consequently hypnotic verbalization of feelings and impulses may not yield information as vital as that brought up through automatic writing.' (Wolberg, L.R. *Hypnoanalysis*, Grune and Stratton, New York, 1945)

writing, mirror See *strephosymbolia*.

wryneck See *torticollis*.

WS In Rorschach scoring, a whole response (see *W*) that includes some white space as well as the entire blot.

X

X chromosome See *chromosome*.

xanthomatosis (zan-thō-ma-tō'sis) Schuller-Christian-Hand's syndrome; diabetic exophthalmic dysostosis. A rare disturbance of lipoid metabolism in which tissues are infiltrated by xanthomatous masses rich in cholesterol, this leading to diabetes insipidus, exophthalmos, and progressive erosion of the bones. Infiltration of the reticulo-endothelial cells with the lipoid material results in the characteristic foam-cell. Retardation of growth and mental development occurs in about half of the cases (31x.2). The disorder begins in childhood; males are three times as frequently affected as females.

xenoglossia (zen-ō-glos'ē-à) Speaking in a strange or foreign language; or distaste for or aversion to such speech.

xenophobia Fear of strangers.

XYY A chromosomal abnormality in which an extra Y (male) chromosome is present, bringing the total chromosomes to 47 (instead of the usual 46, with XY chromosomes in the normal male, and XX chromosomes in the normal female). The XYY pattern is uncommon in the general population; it is estimated to occur in from one in every 300 to one in every 2,000 men. But the pattern occurs much more frequently (perhaps in as many as 4%) in delinquents and criminals. Some of the adult XYY men studied to date showed a tendency toward tallness, thinness, myopia, disfiguring acne, mental dullness, and aggressive, sometimes even violent, behavior.

Y

Y chromosome See *chromosome*.

yen sleep See *sleep, yen*.

Yerkes, Robert Mearns 1876-1956) U.S. psychobiologist; behavior of primates.

ylophobia (ī-lō-fō'bē-à) Less correctly for *hylophobia*. Fear of the forest.

Z

zelophobia (zel-ō-fō'bē-à) Fear of jealousy.

zelotypia (-tip'ē-à) Excessive zeal, carried to the verge of insanity, in the advocacy of any cause.

Zieve's syndrome See *syndrome, Zieve's*.

Zilboorg, Gregory (1890-1959) Russian-born psychoanalyst; criminology, history of psychiatry, 'ambulatory' schizophrenia.

zoanthropy (zō-an'thrō-pē) Lycanthropia.

zoara (zōä'rà) *Obs.* Insomnia.

zone, erogenous (ē-roj'-e-nus) An organ or organ system that is invested with libidinal energy. Of the many erogenous zones, three are particularly important in psychoanalytic psychology: the oral, the anal, and the genital. See *anal-erotism; genitality; orality; ontogeny, psychic*.

zone, hypnogenic (hip-nō-jen'ik) Hypnogenic spot. See *spot, hypnogenic*.

zone, hysterogenic (his-tēr-ō-jen'ik) Any area of the body that precipitates an hysterical reaction when stimulated. See *spot, hypnogenic*.

zone, primacy Any dominating erotogenic area, by means of which more subordinated areas find instinctual discharge through displacement. The fashion in which the weaker or residual instinct sources are subordinated to the primacy zone has been termed 'libido organization.'

In the development of the libido, one primacy zone tends to succeed another in a typical and characteristic chronological order: (1) the oral; (2) the anal; (3) the phallic; (4) the genital.

zones, ultra-marginal 'Some of these marginal elements [see *fringe*] may be so distinctly within the field of awareness that we are conscious of them, but dimly so. Others, in particular cases at least, may be so far outside and hidden in the twilight obscurity that the subject is not even dimly aware of them. In more technical parlance, we may say, they are so far dissociated that they belong to *an ultra-marginal zone and are really subconscious.*' (Prince, M. *The Unconscious,* Macmillan, New York, 1916)

zoö- (zō'ō-) Combining form meaning animal, from Gr. *zöion,* living being, animal.

zoöerasty (zō-ō'ēr-as-ti) Krafft-Ebing's term for sexual intercourse with an animal. It is usually considered to be synonymous with *sodomy;* many psychiatrists prefer zooerasty, since etymologically it has a more definite meaning than sodomy.

zoölagnia (zō-ō-lag'nē-a) Sexual attraction to animals.

zoöphilia Sexual excitement caused by the stroking and fondling of animals; zoolagnia. It does not refer to sexual intercourse with animals, for which act Krafft-Ebing reserved the expression *zooerasty.*

zoöphilism, erotic (zō-of'i-liz'm) Erotic impulse to pat or stroke animals for sexual pleasure.

zoöphobia (zō-ō-fō'bē-à) Fear of animals.

zoöpsia (zō-op'sē-à) Act of 'seeing' insects, or any animal, as in the visual hallucinations of patients with delirium tremens.

zoösadism (zō-ō-sad'iz'm) The act of injuring animals for the morbid (as a rule, ultimately sexual) pleasure derived from it.

Zuordnungs (tsoo-ord'nungs) Sorting tests. See *tests, sorting.*

zwischenstufe (tsvish'en-shtoo-fē) Intermediary stage. Magnus Hirschfeld's term for an 'in-between' or homosexual.

zygote (zī'gōt, zig'ōt) A fertilized egg produced by the union of two cells to form one single cell in sexual reproduction. By an extension of meaning, however, the organisms themselves which develop from fertilized eggs are also called zygotes, in order to distinguish them from their germ cells, which are called *gametes.*

Zygotes are *diploid* with respect to their chromosomes and have two genes of each pair, while gametes are *haploid* and have only one gene of each pair. (Shull, F. *Heredity,* 3rd ed., McGraw-Hill, New York and London, 1938) See *chromosome.*

zygotic (zī-got'ik) Pertaining to a zygote. Referring either to a single cell produced by the union of two cells in reproduction or to the individual developing from such a fertilized egg.